WATER TREATMENT PLANT OPERATION

Third Edition
Volume II

A Field Study Training Program

prepared by

California State University, Sacramento
School of Engineering and Computer Science

in cooperation with the
National Environmental Training Association

★★

Kenneth D. Kerri, Project Director

★★

for the

California Department of Health Services
Sanitary Engineering Branch
Standard Agreement #80-64652

and

U.S. Environmental Protection Agency
Office of Drinking Water
Grant No. T-901361-01-0

1998

OPERATOR TRAINING MANUALS

OPERATOR TRAINING MANUALS IN THIS SERIES are available from Ken Kerri, California State University, Sacramento, 6000 J Street, Sacramento, CA 95819-6025, phone (916) 278-6142, e-mail: wateroffice@csus.edu or FAX (916) 278-5959.

1. *WATER TREATMENT PLANT OPERATION*, 2 Volumes,

2. *SMALL WATER SYSTEM OPERATION AND MAINTENANCE,*

3. *WATER DISTRIBUTION SYSTEM OPERATION AND MAINTENANCE,*

4. *UTILITY MANAGEMENT,*

5. *OPERATION OF WASTEWATER TREATMENT PLANTS*, 2 Volumes,

6. *ADVANCED WASTE TREATMENT,*

7. *INDUSTRIAL WASTE TREATMENT*, 2 Volumes,

8. *TREATMENT OF METAL WASTESTREAMS,*

9. *PRETREATMENT FACILITY INSPECTION,*

10. *OPERATION AND MAINTENANCE OF WASTEWATER COLLECTION SYSTEMS*, 2 Volumes,

11. *COLLECTION SYSTEMS: METHODS FOR EVALUATING AND IMPROVING PERFORMANCE,* and

12. *SMALL WASTEWATER SYSTEM OPERATION AND MAINTENANCE,* 2 Volumes (Volume II available 1999).

NOTICE

This manual is revised and updated before each printing based on comments from persons using the manual.

FIRST EDITION

First Printing, 1983	7,000
Second Printing, 1988	5,000
Third Printing, 1990	6,000
Fourth Printing, 1991	8,000

SECOND EDITION

First Printing, 1993	8,000
Second Printing, 1995	10,000

THIRD EDITION

First Printing, 1998	10,000

ISBN 1-884701-26-4 (Volume II)
ISBN 1-884701-27-2 (Volumes I and II)

PREFACE

VOLUME II

Volume II is a continuation of Volume I. In Volume I, the emphasis was on the knowledge and skills needed by operators of conventional surface water treatment plants. Volume II stresses information needed by those operators, but also includes information on specialized water treatment processes for iron and manganese control, fluoridation, softening, trihalomethanes, demineralization and the handling and disposal of process wastes. Topics of importance to the operators of all water treatment plants include maintenance, instrumentation, safety, advanced laboratory procedures, water quality regulations, administration, and how to solve water treatment plant arithmetic problems.

You may wish to concentrate your studies on those chapters that apply to your water treatment plant. Upon successful completion of this entire volume, you will have gained a broad and comprehensive knowledge of the entire water treatment field.

For information on:

1. Objectives of this manual,
2. Scope of this manual,
3. Uses of this manual,
4. Instructions to participants in the home-study course, and
5. Summary of procedure,

please refer to Volume I.

A short explanation of how our computer grades Objective Tests might be helpful to some students. True-False questions are considered as having only one possible answer so have a value of 1 point. Multiple Choice questions, however, are worth 5 points as there may be more than one correct answer and all correct answers must be filled in for full credit. For the Multiple Choice questions the computer deducts a point for each correct answer not filled in and each incorrect response filled in. For example, in a Multiple Choice question, if 1, 3 and 5 are the correct responses and you fill in 1 and 5, a point is deducted for failing to fill in 3. If you fill in 1, 3, 4 and 5, a point is deducted because 4 is filled in and should not be.

The Project Director is indebted to the many operators and other persons who contributed to this manual. Every effort was made to acknowledge material from the many excellent references in the water treatment field. Reviewers Leonard Ainsworth, Jack Rossum, and Joe Monscvitz deserve special recognition for their extremely thorough review and helpful suggestions. John Trax, Chet Pauls, and Ken Hay, Office of Drinking Water, U.S. Environmental Protection Agency, and John Gaston, Bill MacPherson, Bert Ellsworth, Clarence Young, Ted Bakker, and Beverlie Vandre, Sanitary Engineering Branch, California Department of Health Services, all performed outstanding jobs as resource persons, consultants and advisors. Larry Hannah served as Education Consultant. Illustrations were drawn by Martin Garrity. Charlene Arora helped type the field test and final manuscript for printing. Special thanks are well deserved by the Program Administrator, Gay Kornweibel, who typed, administered the field test, managed the office, administered the budget, and did everything else that had to be done to complete this project successfully.

KENNETH D. KERRI
PROJECT DIRECTOR

SAFE PROCEDURES ARE ALWAYS STRESSED

TECHNICAL CONSULTANTS

John Brady
Gerald Davidson
Larry Hannah

Jim Sequeira
Susuma Kawamura
Mike Young

NATIONAL ENVIRONMENTAL TRAINING ASSOCIATION REVIEWERS

George Kinias, Project Coordinator

E. E. "Skeet" Arasmith
Terry Engelhardt
Dempsey Hall
Jerry Higgins

Andrew Holtan
Deborah Horton
Kirk Laflin
Rich Metcalf

William Redman
Kenneth Walimaa
Anthony Zigment

PROJECT REVIEWERS

Leonard Ainsworth
Ted Bakker
Jo Boyd
Dean Chausee
Walter Cockrell
Fred Fahlen
David Fitch
Richard Haberman
Lee Harry
Jerry Hayes
Ed Henley
Charles Jeffs

Chet Latif
Frank Lewis
Perry Libby
D. Mackay
William Maguire
Nancy McTigue
Joe Monscvitz
Angela Moore
Harold Mowry
Theron Palmer
Eugene Parham
Catherine Perman

David Rexing
Jack Rossum
William Ruff
Gerald Samuel
Carl Schwing
David Sorenson
Russell Sutphen
Robert Wentzel
James Wright
Mike Yee
Clarence Young

WATER TREATMENT PLANT OPERATION, VOLUME I
COURSE OUTLINE

Page

1. The Water Treatment Plant Operator   1
   by Ken Kerri

2. Water Sources and Treatment   15
   by Bert Ellsworth

3. Reservoir Management and Intake Structures   39
   by Dick Barnett

4. Coagulation and Flocculation   91
   by Jim Beard

5. Sedimentation   147
   by Jim Beard

6. Filtration   199
   by Jim Beard

7. Disinfection   251
   by Tom Ikesaki

8. Corrosion Control   345
   by Jack Rossum

Page

9. Taste and Odor Control   391
   by Russ Bowen

10. Plant Operation   431
    by Jim Beard

11. Laboratory Procedures   475
    by Jim Sequeira

Appendix by Ken Kerri   555

     Final Examination and Suggested Answers   557

     How to Solve Water Treatment   569
     Plant Arithmetic Problems

     Water Abbreviations   622

     Water Words   623

     Subject Index   673

WATER TREATMENT PLANT OPERATION, VOLUME II
COURSE OUTLINE

Page

12. Iron and Manganese Control   1
    by Jack Rossum

13. Fluoridation   27
    by Harry Tracy

14. Softening   71
    by Don Gibson and Marty Reynolds

15. Trihalomethanes   125
    by Mike McGuire

16. Demineralization   145
    by Dave Argo

17. Handling and Disposal of Process Wastes   197
    by George Uyeno

18. Maintenance   225
    by Parker Robinson

19. Instrumentation   353
    by Leonard Ainsworth

Page

20. Safety   409
    by Joe Monscvitz

21. Advanced Laboratory Procedures   463
    by Jim Sequeira

22. Drinking Water Regulations   505
    by Tim Gannon

23. Administration   561
    by Tim Gannon

Appendix by Ken Kerri   641

     Final Examination and Suggested Answers   642

     How to Solve Water Treatment   661
     Plant Arithmetic Problems

     Water Abbreviations   697

     Water Words   699

     Subject Index   757

Other similar operator training programs that may be of interest to you are our courses and training manuals on the operation and maintenance of water distribution systems and small water systems.

WATER DISTRIBUTION SYSTEM OPERATION AND MAINTENANCE
COURSE OUTLINE

Page

1. The Water Distribution System Operator   1
   by Ken Kerri

2. Storage Facilities   15
   by Dan Saenz

3. Distribution System Facilities   53
   by Sam Kalichman and Nick Nichols

4. Water Quality Considerations in   159
   Distribution Systems
   by Sam Kalichman

5. Distribution System Operation and Maintenance   181
   by Sam Kalichman and Nick Nichols

6. Disinfection   291
   by Tom Ikesaki

Page

7. Safety   351
   by Dan Saenz

Appendix by Ken Kerri   425

   Final Examination and Suggested Answers   426

   How to Solve Water Distribution System   435
   Arithmetic Problems

   Water Abbreviations   475

   Water Words   477

   Subject Index   529

SMALL WATER SYSTEM OPERATION AND MAINTENANCE
(Wells, Small Treatment Plants, and Rates)
COURSE OUTLINE

Page

1. The Small Water System Operator   1
   by Ken Kerri

2. Water Sources and Treatment   15
   by Bert Ellsworth

3. Wells   39
   by Al Ward and John German

4. Small Water Treatment Plants   165
   by Jess Morehouse

5. Disinfection   259
   by Tom Ikesaki

6. Safety   319
   by Dan Saenz

Page

7. Laboratory Procedures   373
   by Jim Sequeira

8. Setting Water Rates for Small Water Utilities   449
   by Jim Beard

Appendix by Ken Kerri   471

   Final Examination and Suggested Answers   472

   How to Solve Small Water System   479
   Arithmetic Problems

   Water Abbreviations   514

   Water Words   515

   Subject Index   565

CHAPTER 12

IRON AND MANGANESE CONTROL

by

Jack Rossum

With a Special Section by

Gerald Davidson

TABLE OF CONTENTS

Chapter 12.   IRON AND MANGANESE CONTROL

		Page
OBJECTIVES		3
WORDS		4
12.0	NEED TO CONTROL IRON AND MANGANESE	6
12.1	MEASUREMENT OF IRON AND MANGANESE	6
	12.10 Occurrence of Iron and Manganese	6
	12.11 Collection of Iron and Manganese Samples	7
	12.12 Analysis for Iron and Manganese	7
12.2	REMEDIAL ACTION	7
	12.20 Alternate Source	9
	12.21 Phosphate Treatment	9
	12.22 Removal by Ion Exchange	11
	12.23 Oxidation by Aeration	12
	12.24 Oxidation With Chlorine	13
	12.25 Oxidation With Permanganate	13
	12.26 Operation of Filters	14
	12.27 Proprietary Processes	14
	by Bill Hoyer	
	12.28 Monitoring of Treated Water	15
	12.29 Summary	15
12.3	OPERATION OF AN IRON AND MANGANESE REMOVAL PLANT	17
	by Gerald Davidson	
	12.30 Description of Equipment and Process	17
	12.31 Regeneration of Manganese Greensand	19
	12.32 Troubleshooting	19
12.4	MAINTENANCE OF A CHEMICAL FEEDER	19
12.5	TROUBLESHOOTING RED WATER PROBLEMS	21
12.6	ARITHMETIC ASSIGNMENT	22
12.7	ADDITIONAL READING	22
12.8	ACKNOWLEDGMENT	22
DISCUSSION AND REVIEW QUESTIONS		22
SUGGESTED ANSWERS		23
OBJECTIVE TEST		24

OBJECTIVES

Chapter 12.   IRON AND MANGANESE CONTROL

Following completion of Chapter 12, you should be able to:

1. Identify and describe the various processes used to control iron and manganese,

2. Collect samples for analysis of iron and manganese,

3. Safely operate and maintain the following iron and manganese control processes:

   a. Phosphate treatment,
   b. Ion exchange,
   c. Oxidation by aeration,
   d. Oxidation with chlorine,
   e. Oxidation with permanganate,
   f. Greensand,
   g. Proprietary processes, and

4. Troubleshoot red water problems.

WORDS

Chapter 12.   IRON AND MANGANESE CONTROL

ACIDIFIED (uh-SID-uh-FIE-d)   ACIDIFIED

The addition of an acid (usually nitric or sulfuric) to a sample to lower the pH below 2.0. The purpose of acidification is to "fix" a sample so it won't change until it is analyzed.

AQUIFER (ACK-wi-fer)   AQUIFER

A natural underground layer of porous, water-bearing materials (sand, gravel) usually capable of yielding a large amount or supply of water.

BACKFLOW   BACKFLOW

A reverse flow condition, created by a difference in water pressures, which causes water to flow back into the distribution pipes of a potable water supply from any source or sources other than an intended source. Also see BACKSIPHONAGE.

BACKSIPHONAGE   BACKSIPHONAGE

A form of backflow caused by a negative or below atmospheric pressure within a water system. Also see BACKFLOW.

BENCH SCALE TESTS   BENCH SCALE TESTS

A method of studying different ways or chemical doses for treating water on a small scale in a laboratory.

BREAKPOINT CHLORINATION   BREAKPOINT CHLORINATION

Addition of chlorine to water until the chlorine demand has been satisfied. At this point, further additions of chlorine will result in a free chlorine residual that is directly proportional to the amount of chlorine added beyond the breakpoint.

CHELATION (key-LAY-shun)   CHELATION

A chemical complexing (forming or joining together) of metallic cations (such as copper) with certain organic compounds, such as EDTA (ethylene diamine tetracetic acid). Chelation is used to prevent the precipitation of metals (copper). Also see SEQUES-TRATION.

COLLOIDS (CALL-loids)   COLLOIDS

Very small, finely divided solids (particles that do not dissolve) that remain dispersed in a liquid for a long time due to their small size and electrical charge. When most of the particles in water have a negative electrical charge, they tend to repel each other. This repulsion prevents the particles from clumping together, becoming heavier, and settling out.

DIVALENT (die-VAY-lent)   DIVALENT

Having a valence of two, such as the ferrous ion, Fe^{2+}. Also called bivalent.

GREENSAND   GREENSAND

A mineral (glauconite) material that looks like ordinary filter sand except that it is green in color. Greensand is a natural ion exchange material which is capable of softening water. Greensand which has been treated with potassium permanganate ($KMnO_4$) is called manganese greensand; this product is used to remove iron, manganese and hydrogen sulfide from ground-waters.

INSOLUBLE (in-SAWL-you-bull)   INSOLUBLE

Something that cannot be dissolved.

ION EXCHANGE   ION EXCHANGE

A water treatment process involving the reversible interchange (switching) of ions between the water being treated and the solid resin. Undesirable ions in the water are switched with acceptable ions on the resin.

ION EXCHANGE RESINS

Insoluble polymers, used in water treatment, that are capable of exchanging (switching or giving) acceptable cations or anions to the water being treated for less desirable ions.

RESINS

See ION EXCHANGE RESINS.

SEQUESTRATION (SEE-kwes-TRAY-shun)

A chemical complexing (forming or joining together) of metallic cations (such as iron) with certain inorganic compounds, such as phosphate. Sequestration prevents the precipitation of the metals (iron). Also see CHELATION.

ZEOLITE

A type of ion exchange material used to soften water. Natural zeolites are siliceous compounds (made of silica) which remove calcium and magnesium from hard water and replace them with sodium. Synthetic or organic zeolites are ion exchange materials which remove calcium or magnesium and replace them with either sodium or hydrogen. Manganese zeolites are used to remove iron and manganese from water.

(SEE-kwes-TRAY-shun)

CHAPTER 12.   IRON AND MANGANESE CONTROL

12.0   NEED TO CONTROL IRON AND MANGANESE

Like the cities of Minneapolis and St. Paul, iron and manganese are referred to as a pair. They are, in fact, two distinct elements and are often found in water separately. Neither of them has any direct adverse health effects. Indeed, both are essential to the growth of many plants and animals, including humans; however, the iron and manganese found in drinking water have no nutrient value for humans. Even if they were available in beneficial amounts, the presence of iron and manganese in drinking water would still be objectionable.

Clothes laundered in water containing iron and manganese above certain levels come out stained. When bleach is added to remove the stains, they are only intensified and become fixed so that no amount of further washing with iron-free water will remove the stains. They can be removed by treatment with oxalic acid, but this is rather hard on fabrics, or by the use of commercial rust removers. Excessive amounts of iron and manganese are also objectionable because they stain plumbing fixtures, bathtubs, and sinks.

Perhaps the most troublesome consequence of iron and manganese in the water is that they promote the growth of a group of microorganisms known as iron bacteria. These organisms obtain energy for their growth from the chemical reaction that spontaneously occurs between iron and manganese and dissolved oxygen. These bacteria form thick slimes on the walls of the distribution system mains. Such slimes are rust colored from iron and black from manganese. Variations in flow cause these slimes to come loose and create dirty water (a big source of consumer complaints). Furthermore, these slimes will cause foul tastes and odors in the water.

The growth of iron bacteria is controlled by chlorination. However, when water containing iron is chlorinated, the iron is converted into rust particles, and manganese is converted into a jet black compound called manganese dioxide. These materials form a loosely adherent coating on the pipe walls. Pieces of this coating will break loose from the pipe walls when there are changes or reversals of flow in the distribution system.

Iron and manganese in water can be easily detected by observing the color of the inside walls of filters and the filter media. If the raw water is prechlorinated, there will be black stains on the walls below the water level and a black coating over the top portion of the sand filter bed. This black color will usually indicate a high level of manganese in the raw water while a brownish-black stain indicates the presence of both iron and manganese.

The generally acceptable limit for iron in drinking water is 0.3 mg/L and that for manganese is 0.05 mg/L. However, if the water contains more than 0.02 mg/L of manganese, the operator should initiate an effective flushing program to avoid complaints. By regularly flushing the water mains, the buildup of black manganese dioxide can be prevented.

QUESTIONS

Write your answers in a notebook and then compare your answers with those on page 23.

12.0A   What problems are caused by iron and manganese in drinking water?

12.0B   How can the growth of iron bacteria be controlled?

12.0C   What are the generally acceptable limits for iron and manganese in drinking water?

12.1   MEASUREMENT OF IRON AND MANGANESE

12.10   Occurrence of Iron and Manganese

Because both iron and manganese react with dissolved oxygen to form *INSOLUBLE COMPOUNDS*,[1] they are not found in high concentrations in waters containing dissolved oxygen except as *COLLOIDAL SUSPENSIONS*[2] of the oxides. Accordingly, surface waters are generally free from both iron and manganese. One exception to this rule is that manganese up to one mg/L or higher may be found in shallow reservoirs and may come and go several times a year.

---

[1] *Insoluble (in-SAWL-you-bull) Compounds.   Compounds that cannot be dissolved.*
[2] *Colloidal (CALL-loid-al) Suspensions.   Very small, finely divided solids (particles that do not dissolve) that remain dispersed in a liquid for a long time due to their small size and electrical charge. When most of the particles in water have a negative electrical charge, they tend to repel each other. This repulsion prevents the particles from clumping together, becoming heavier, and settling out.*

Iron or manganese is most frequently found in water systems supplied by wells and springs. Horizontal wells under rivers are notoriously prone to produce water containing iron. Bacteria will reduce iron oxides in soil to the soluble, *DIVALENT*[3] form of iron (Fe^{2+}) which will produce groundwater with a high iron content.

Iron bacteria can make use of the ferrous ion (Fe^{2+}). These bacteria will oxidize the iron and use the energy for reducing carbon dioxide to organic forms (slimes). The manganous ion (Mn^{2+}) is used in a similar fashion by certain bacteria. Very small concentrations of iron and manganese in water can cause problems because bacteria obtain the nutrients (iron and manganese) from water in order to grow, even when the concentrations are very low.

Iron bacteria are found nearly everywhere. They are frequently found in iron water pipes and everywhere else that a combination of dissolved oxygen and dissolved iron is usually or frequently present. Only one cell of iron bacteria is needed to start an infestation of iron bacteria in a well or a distribution system. Unfortunately it is almost impossible to drill a well and maintain sterile conditions to prevent the introduction of iron bacteria.

12.11 Collection of Iron and Manganese Samples

The best way to determine if there is an iron and manganese problem in a water supply is to look at the plumbing fixtures in a couple of houses. If the fixtures are stained, then there is a problem. Determination of the concentrations of iron and manganese in water is useful when evaluating well waters for use and treated waters for effectiveness of treatment processes.

The results of tests for iron and manganese are wrong more often than they are right. This is because samples for these substances are difficult to collect. Both iron and manganese form loosely adherent (not firmly attached) scales on pipe walls, including the sample lines. When the sample tap is opened, particles of scale may be dislodged and enter the sample bottle. If many of these particles enter the sample bottle, the error can become very large. Furthermore, unless the sample is acidified (enough nitric acid added to drop the pH to less than 2), both iron and manganese tend to form an adherent scale on the walls of the sample bottle in the few days that sometimes elapse before the analysis is started. When the sample is poured from the bottle for testing, most of the iron and manganese will then remain inside the sample bottle.

To avoid this situation, samples should be taken from a plastic sample line located as close to the well or other source as possible. Open the sampling tap slowly so that the flow rate is suitable for filling the sample bottle. Allow the sample water to flow for at least one minute for each 10 feet (3 m) of sample line before the sample is collected.

Samples for iron and manganese should be tested within 48 hours unless they have been acidified. If the sample contains any clay or if any particles of rust are picked up from a steel pipe or fitting, an acidified sample will dissolve the iron in these substances and the results will be too high. If clay or rust particles are observed in a sample, do not acidify and ask the lab to analyze the sample immediately. Furthermore, many laboratories fail to be sure that iron and manganese are in the divalent form (Fe^{2+} or Mn^{2+}) by adding enough nitric acid prior to the tests to lower the pH to less than 2, so laboratory errors may be even greater than sampling errors.

12.12 Analysis for Iron and Manganese

The preferred method of testing for iron and manganese is atomic absorption, but for the small plant the equipment is too

expensive. With careful attention to laboratory procedures, colorimetric methods (comparing colors of unknowns with known standards) can provide sufficient accuracy in most instances. Colorimetric methods use either a spectrophotometer, a filter photometer, or the less satisfactory set of matched Nessler tubes with standards. Good results have been obtained by the use of properly calibrated colorimeters (Figure 12.1). For detailed procedures on how to use a spectrophotometer to measure iron and manganese, see Chapter 21, "Advanced Laboratory Procedures."

QUESTIONS

Write your answers in a notebook and then compare your answers with those on page 23.

12.1A How do iron and manganese form insoluble compounds?

12.1B Why must iron and manganese samples be acidified when they are collected?

12.1C Where should a sample for iron and manganese testing be collected?

12.2 REMEDIAL ACTION

Several methods are available to control iron and manganese in water. This section discusses how to operate the most common treatment processes.

---

[3] *Divalent (die-VAY-lent).* *Having a valence of two, such as the ferrous ion, Fe^{2+}. Also called bivalent.*

Fig. 12.1   *Typical continuous on-line pump colorimeter analyzer*
for iron, manganese, or permanganate
(Permission of HACH)

12.20 Alternate Source

The construction of a plant to remove iron and manganese will cost as much as or more than a new well so it pays to investigate the possibility of obtaining an alternate supply of water that is free from iron and manganese. This investigation should include samples from nearby private wells, discussions with well drillers who have been active in the locality and discussions with engineers in the state agency responsible for the regulation of well drilling.

If the water produced by the well contains dissolved oxygen along with iron and manganese, this is an indication that water is being drawn from more than one *AQUIFER*.[4] One or more of the aquifers must be producing water containing dissolved oxygen but is free of iron and manganese since oxygen reacts with both elements to form insoluble compounds. Furthermore, it is highly probable that the iron- or manganese-bearing water is from deeper aquifers. It may be possible to cure the problem simply by sealing off these deeper aquifers.

12.21 Phosphate Treatment

If the water contains manganese up to 0.3 mg/L and less than 0.1 mg/L of iron, an inexpensive and reasonably effective control can be achieved by feeding the water with one of the three polyphosphates mentioned below. Chlorine usually must be fed along with the polyphosphate to prevent the growth of iron bacteria. The effect of the polyphosphate is to delay the precipitation of oxidized manganese for a few days so that the scale that builds up on the pipe walls is greatly reduced.

The chlorine dose for phosphate treatment should be sufficient to produce a free chlorine residual of approximately 0.25 mg/L after a five-minute contact time (a higher chlorine dose may be required with some water to maintain a free chlorine residual of at least 0.2 mg/L throughout the distribution system).

Any of the three polyphosphates (pyrophosphate, tripolyphosphate, and metaphosphate) can be used, but sodium metaphosphate is effective in lower concentrations than the others. The proper phosphate dose is determined by laboratory *BENCH SCALE TESTS*[5] in the following manner.

1. Treat a series of samples with a standard chlorine solution to determine the chlorine dose required to produce the desired chlorine residual.

2. Prepare a standard polyphosphate solution by dissolving 1.0 gram of polyphosphate in a liter of distilled water.

3. Treat another series of samples with varying amounts of polyphosphate solution. One mL of the standard polyphosphate solution (0.1% solution) in a liter sample is equivalent to 8.34 pounds of polyphosphate per million gallons (see Examples 2 and 3 on page 16). Stir to ensure that the polyphosphate has been well mixed, and continue stirring while adding the previously determined chlorine dose so as to minimize the creation of high concentrations of chlorine.

4. Observe the samples daily against a white background, noting the amount of discoloration. The proper polyphosphate dose is the lowest dose that delays noticeable discoloration for a period of four days.

Samples for the above bench test should be as fresh as possible and should be kept away from direct sunlight to avoid heating.

Polyphosphate treatment to control iron and manganese is usually most effective when the polyphosphate is added upstream from the chlorine, but satisfactory results may be obtained by feeding them together. The chlorine should never be fed ahead of the polyphosphate because the chlorine will oxidize the iron and manganese (cause insoluble precipitates to form too soon).

If you are able to install a one-half inch (12 mm) polyethylene hose in the well so that it discharges a few inches below the suction screen, you can construct a very satisfactory semiautomatic feed system. Use a gas-feed chlorinator whose water supply is obtained from the well discharge downstream from the check valve (Figure 12.2). In this way, the chlorinator operates only when the pump is running. The chlorine solution is fed down the polyethylene tube. Polyphosphate is fed down the same tube by means of a plastic tee. The phosphate is fed by means of an electrically operated solution feeder so connected as to run when the well pump runs.

The chlorine solution flowing through the polyethylene tube is extremely corrosive. If the tube does not discharge into flowing water, the corrosive effect of the solution on a metal surface can be disastrous. Wells have been destroyed by corrosion from this cause. The following simple test should be made at least once every three months.

---

[4] *Aquifer (ACK-wi-fer). A natural underground layer of porous, water-bearing materials (sand, gravel) usually capable of yielding a large amount or supply of water.*
[5] *Bench Scale Tests. A method of studying different ways or chemical doses for treating water on a small scale in a laboratory.*

Fig. 12.2   Polyphosphate and chlorine system

EXAMPLE 1

1. Calculate the time required for water to flow from the pump suction to the pump discharge.

   a. Record the following information:

      (1) Length of pump column from suction to discharge in feet, 324 ft.

      (2) Diameter of pump column in inches, 8 in.

      (3) Discharge rate from pump in gallons per minute, 423 GPM.

   b. Calculate the volume of the pump column in cubic inches.

$$\text{Volume, cu in} = (0.785)(\text{Diameter, in})^2(\text{Length, ft})(12\text{ in/ft})$$

$$= (0.785)(8\text{ in})^2(324\text{ ft})(12\text{ in/ft})$$

$$= 195{,}333\text{ cubic inches}$$

   c. Convert the pump column volume from cubic inches to gallons.

$$\text{Volume, gal} = \frac{\text{Volume, cu in}}{231\text{ cu in/gal}}$$

$$= \frac{195{,}333\text{ cu in}}{231\text{ cu in/gal}}$$

$$= 846\text{ gallons}$$

   d. Determine the time required for the water to flow from the pump suction to the pump discharge.

$$\text{Time, min} = \frac{\text{Volume, gallons}}{\text{Pump Discharge, GPM}}$$

$$= \frac{846\text{ gallons}}{423\text{ gal/min}}$$

$$= 2.0\text{ minutes}$$

2. Turn off the water supply to the chlorinator. Since some of the chlorine in the feed line will drain into the well, it may take several minutes for the chlorine residual to disappear. Check to be sure there is no chlorine residual in the water.

3. Turn the chlorinator back on, noting the exact time. Take samples for chlorine residual every 15 seconds. If the chlorine residual has reached its proper value within 30 seconds of the calculated time (two minutes in this example), you can be sure that the polyethylene tube is properly positioned below the suction screen.

Solutions of polyphosphate containing more than one-half pound per gallon (60 gm/L) may be very viscous (thick like molasses), depending upon which of the polyphosphates is used. Do not use a solution much over 48 hours old because the polyphosphates react slowly with water to form ortho-phosphates which are much less effective in preventing manganese deposits.

There are some reports in the literature of the successful use of tetrasodium pyrophosphate on iron-bearing waters, but many attempts to control iron have failed. The available information is not clear as to whether the process works only under special conditions or whether the reports of success are in error.

QUESTIONS

Write your answers in a notebook and then compare your answers with those on page 23.

12.2A   How could you find out if nearby wells produce water containing iron and manganese?

12.2B   If a well produces water containing dissolved oxygen as well as iron and manganese, how would you attempt to solve the iron and manganese problem?

12.2C   What are bench scale tests?

12.2D   Why should polyphosphate solutions over 48 hours old not be used?

12.22   Removal by Ion Exchange [6]

Iron and manganese ion exchange units are similar to a downflow pressure filter. The water to be treated enters the unit through an inlet distributor located in the top. The water is forced (usually by a pump) down through the ion exchange resin into an underdrain structure. From the underdrain structure, the treated water flows out of the unit to the next treatment process, to storage, or into the distribution system.

The actual location of the *ION EXCHANGE RESINS* [7] with respect to other water treatment processes will depend on the raw water quality and the design engineer. If the water to be treated contains no oxygen, both iron and manganese may be removed by ion exchange using the same resins that are used for water softening. If the water being treated contains any dissolved oxygen, the resin becomes fouled with iron rust or manganese dioxide. The resin can be cleaned but this is expensive and the capacity is reduced. Well water may contain no oxygen in normal operating conditions except immediately after the well is first turned on. If this is the case, provisions should be made to run the well to waste until the oxygen is no longer present.

In one Eastern city, an ion exchange plant had operated for seven years, reducing iron from 52 mg/L to 0.1 mg/L and manganese from 1.3 mg/L to zero. When a pump was repaired, a gasket on the suction side of the pump was

---

[6] *Ion Exchange. A water treatment process involving the reversible interchange (switching) of ions between the water being treated and the solid resin. Undesirable ions in the water are switched with acceptable ions on the resin.*

[7] *Ion Exchange Resins. Insoluble polymers, used in water treatment, that are capable of exchanging (switching or giving) acceptable cations or anions to the water being treated for less desirable ions.*

improperly installed, allowing air to enter the raw water. Within three months the resin was fouled by iron oxide.

The main advantage of ion exchange for iron and manganese removal is that the plant requires little attention. The disadvantages are the danger of fouling the ion exchange resin with oxides and high initial cost.

To operate an ion exchange unit, try to operate as close as possible to design flows. Monitor the treated water for iron and manganese on a daily basis. When iron and manganese start to appear in the treated water, the unit must be regenerated. Regenerate with a brine solution that is treated with 0.01 pound of sodium bisulfite per gallon (1.2 gm/L) of brine to remove oxygen present. After regeneration is complete, dispose of the brine in an approved manner.

See Chapter 14, "Softening," for procedures on how to calculate the frequency for regenerating the unit. Details are given in Chapter 17, "Handling and Disposal of Process Wastes," on how to properly dispose of brine solutions.

12.23   Oxidation by Aeration

Iron can be oxidized by aerating the water to form insoluble ferric hydroxide. As shown in Figure 12.3, this reaction is accelerated by an increase in pH. The rates indicated in Figure 12.3 were determined at 25°C (77°F) under laboratory conditions. If the water contains any organic substances, the rates will be significantly lower; reduced temperatures will also lower the rates. The oxidation of manganese by aeration is so slow that this process is not used on waters with high manganese concentrations.

Since pH is increased by the removal of carbon dioxide, it is important that the aeration (which removes carbon dioxide) be as efficient as possible. Lime is sometimes added to the water to increase the pH as well as remove carbon dioxide. The higher the pH, the shorter the time required for aeration, as shown in Figure 12.3.

Operation of the aeration process to remove iron and manganese requires careful control of the flow through the process. If the flow becomes too great, not enough time will be available for the reactions to occur. Flows are controlled by the use of variable speed pumps or the selection of the proper number or combinations of pumps. Carefully monitor the iron and manganese content of the treated water. If iron is detected, the flows may have to be reduced.

There are several methods of providing aeration. Either the water being treated is dispersed (scattered) into the air or air is bubbled through the water. Aeration may be achieved by the use of compressed air which passes through diffusers in the water. These diffusers produce many small bubbles which allow the transfer of oxygen in the air to dissolved oxygen in the water.

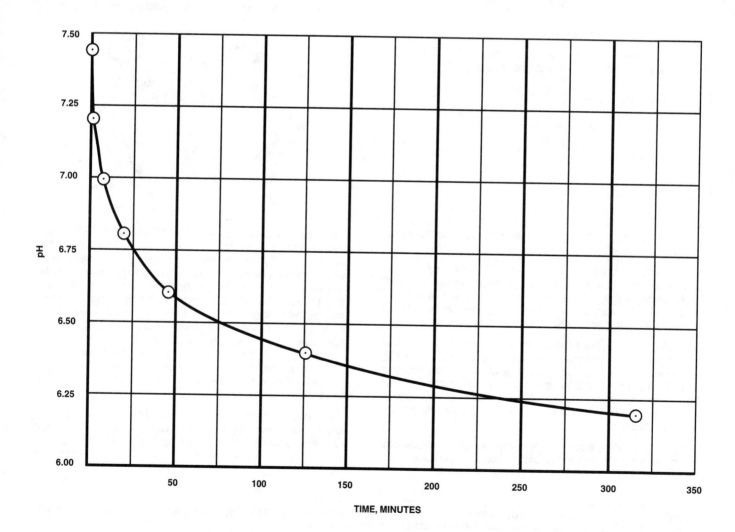

Fig. 12.3   pH vs. time to oxidize 99 percent iron

Other aeration techniques include forced draft, multiple trays, cascades, and sprays. These methods may develop slime growths on surfaces or coatings on media. Slime growths and coatings on media should be controlled to prevent the development of tastes and odors in the product water and the sloughing off of the slimes. Chlorination may be used to control slime growths and coatings. Regularly inspect aeration equipment for the development of anything unusual.

A reaction basin (sometimes called a collection or detention basin) follows the aeration process. The purpose of the reaction basin is to allow time for the oxidation reactions to take place. The aeration process should produce sufficient dissolved oxygen for the iron to be oxidized to insoluble ferric hydroxide. A minimum recommended detention time is 20 minutes with desirable detention times ranging from 30 to 60 minutes (see Example 4, page 16). As shown in Figure 12.3, the pH of the water strongly influences the time for the reaction to take place. Sometimes chlorine is added before the reaction basin.

The reaction basin may be a cylindrically (circular) shaped basin similar to a clarifier. Often the basin is baffled to prevent short-circuiting and the deposition of solids. Since there are no provisions for sludge removal, the basin must be drained and cleaned regularly. If the basins are not cleaned, slugs of deposits or sludge or also mosquito or fly larvae (young of any insect) could reach the filters in the next process and cause them to plug.

Operators of reaction basins must always be on the alert for potential sources of contamination. These basins should have covers and protective lids to keep out rain, storm water runoff, rodents, and insects. All vents must be properly screened. The outlet to the drain must not be connected directly to a sewer or storm water drain. There must be an air gap or some other protective device to prevent contamination from *BACKFLOW*.[8]

After the ferric hydroxide is formed, it is removed by sedimentation or by filtration alone. If only filtration is used, water from the reaction basin is usually pumped to pressure filters for filtration. The water may also be pumped or flow by gravity to rapid sand filters. For details on how to operate and maintain filters, see Chapter 6, "Filtration."

The main advantage of this method is that no chemicals are required; however, lime may be added to increase the pH. The major disadvantage is that small changes in raw surface water quality may affect the pH and soluble organics level and slow the oxidation rates to a point where the capacity of the plant is reduced.

12.24 Oxidation With Chlorine

Chlorine will oxidize manganese to the insoluble manganese dioxide and will oxidize iron to insoluble ferric hydroxide which can then be removed by filtration. The higher the chlorine residual, the faster this reaction occurs. Some very compact plants have been constructed by treating the water to a free chlorine residual of 5 to 10 mg/L, filtering, and dechlorinating to a residual suitable for domestic use. Do not use high doses of chlorine if the water contains a high level of organic color because excessive concentrations of total trihalomethanes (TTHMs) could develop. The water is dechlorinated by the use of reducing agents such as sulfur dioxide (SO_2), sodium bisulfite ($NaHSO_3$), and sodium sulfite (Na_2SO_3). Bisulfite is commonly used because it is cheaper and more stable than sulfite. When dechlorinating with reducing agents be very careful not to overdose because inadequate disinfection could result (no chlorine residual remains) and if the dissolved oxygen level in the water is depleted, fish kills could occur in home aquariums. Frequently, a reaction basin (as described in Section 12.23, "Oxidation by Aeration") is installed between the chlorination processes to allow time for the reactions to occur.

12.25 Oxidation With Permanganate

Potassium permanganate oxidizes iron and manganese to insoluble oxides, and can be used to remove these elements in the same way chlorine is used. The dose of potassium permanganate must be exact. Bench scale tests are required to determine the proper dosage. Too small a dose will not oxidize all the manganese in the water and too large a dose will allow permanganate to enter the system and may produce a pink color in the water. Actual observations of the water being treated will tell you if any adjustments of the chemical feeder are necessary. Most well waters have relatively consistent concentrations of iron and manganese. Therefore, once you set the chemical feeder, adjustments of the dosage usually aren't necessary.

Experience from many water treatment plants has shown that a regular filter bed (a rapid sand filter or a dual media filter bed) can remove manganese as long as iron and manganese concentrations are both less than one milligram per liter. These plants use either chlorine or permanganate to oxidize the iron and manganese before the water being treated flows through the filter bed.

Potassium permanganate is often used with manganese *ZEOLITE*[9] or manganese *GREENSAND*.[10] Greensand is a granular material. After the greensand has been treated with potassium permanganate it can oxidize both iron and manganese to their insoluble oxides. The greensand also acts as a filter and must be backwashed to remove the insoluble oxides.

---

[8] *Backflow.* A reverse flow condition, created by a difference in water pressures, which causes water to flow back into the distribution pipes of a potable water supply from any source or sources other than an intended source.

[9] *Zeolite.* A type of ion exchange material used to soften water. Natural zeolites are siliceous compounds (made of silica) which remove calcium and magnesium from hard water and replace them with sodium. Synthetic or organic zeolites are ion exchange materials which remove calcium or magnesium and replace them with either sodium or hydrogen. Manganese zeolites are used to remove iron and manganese from water.

[10] *Greensand.* A mineral (glauconite) material that looks like ordinary filter sand except that it is green in color. Greensand is a natural ion exchange material which is capable of softening water. Greensand which has been treated with potassium permanganate ($KMnO_4$) is called manganese greensand; this product is used to remove iron, manganese and hydrogen sulfide from groundwaters.

Manganese greensand filters can be operated in three modes: continuous regeneration (CR), intermittent regeneration (IR), and catalytic regeneration. The method used will depend on the concentrations of iron and manganese in the water and the pH of the water.

The manganese greensand continuous regeneration process can be used for waters containing iron concentrations as high as 15 mg/L or more, but with such high concentrations frequent backwashing will be necessary. Generally, waters having iron concentrations in the range of 0.5 to 3.0 mg/L can be treated with more acceptable run lengths of 18 to 36 hours before backwashing.

In the CR process, chlorine and potassium permanganate are typically added to the raw water ahead of the manganese greensand bed. Chlorine is added first to oxidize most of the iron and any sulfide. A slight excess of potassium permanganate is then added to oxidize the remaining iron and soluble manganese. This reaction produces insoluble oxides. When the raw water passes through the manganese greensand bed, two things occur: (1) the insoluble iron oxide particles are filtered out, and (2) any remaining permanganate is reduced to manganese oxides by the greensand. These manganese oxides attach to the grains of greensand, thereby continuously regenerating the manganese greensand. As the run progresses, the filter bed becomes clogged with insoluble oxides and the differential pressure increases. When head loss reaches a predetermined point or a certain number of gallons of water have been treated, the filter must be backwashed to remove the filtered particulates.

The intermittent regeneration (IR) process is suitable for raw water containing only manganese or mostly manganese with small amounts of iron. The raw water flows through a manganese greensand bed where oxidation of manganese occurs directly on the grains of greensand. Some iron will also be oxidized directly on the manganese greensand but if the iron concentrations are high, iron oxides will quickly coat or foul the media. To prevent fouling of the media, the iron is sometimes converted to its insoluble form before the water enters the greensand bed by adding chlorine ahead of the filter or aerating the water before it enters the greensand bed. After treating a certain number of gallons of water or when head loss reaches a predetermined point, the capacity of the greensand to oxidize manganese and iron is used up and the media must be backwashed and regenerated. Regeneration consists of the downflow passage of a dilute potassium permanganate solution through the bed using 1.5 ounces (43 milligrams) of $KMnO_4$ per cubic foot of media, followed by thorough rinsing of the media.

When the well water contains low concentrations of iron and manganese (less than 1.0 mg/L) and the pH is greater than 7.0, the catalytic regeneration mode of operation may be a suitable method for removing iron and manganese. In this process, sufficient chlorine is applied ahead of the filter to maintain a chlorine residual of 0.5 to 1.0 mg/L through a bed containing a specially refined grade of greensand. The chlorine keeps the greensand continuously regenerated. Manganese in the raw water can usually be oxidized directly by the manganese oxide coating on the greensand, provided that the pH is neutral and adequate detention time is provided. The advantages of catalytic oxidation are that the filter run lengths are longer than for other process modes, higher filtration rates can be used, the backwash waste suspended solids are low because the manganese is oxidized on the manganese greensand grains, and the chemical operating costs are minimal because only chlorine is required. For more information on the manganese greensand process, see Section 12.3, "Operation of an Iron and Manganese Removal Plant."

12.26   Operation of Filters

When iron and manganese are oxidized to insoluble forms by aeration, chlorination, or permanganate, the oxidation processes are usually followed by filters to remove the insoluble material. In addition to the procedures for operating and maintaining filters that were outlined in Chapter 6, "Filtration," the procedures discussed in this section apply to filters used to remove iron and manganese.

Iron tests should be made monthly on the water entering a filter to be sure the iron is in the ferric (Fe^{3+}) state. Collect a sample of the water and pass the water through a filter paper. Run an iron test on the water which has passed through the filter. If the iron is still in the soluble ferrous (Fe^{2+}) state, there will be iron in the water. If aeration is being used to oxidize the iron from the soluble ferrous to the insoluble ferric state and iron is still present in the soluble state in the water entering the filter, try adding chlorine or potassium permanganate. If chlorine or potassium permanganate is being used and soluble iron is in the water entering the filter, try increasing the chemical dose. If potassium permanganate is being used, the sand may be replaced by greensand to improve the efficiency of the process.

If oxidation is being accomplished by either aeration or chlorination, a free chlorine residual must be maintained in the effluent of the filter to prevent the insoluble ferric iron from returning to the soluble ferrous form and passing through the filter.

Most iron removal treatment plants are designed so that the filters are backwashed according to head loss. If iron breakthrough is a problem, filters should be backwashed when breakthrough occurs or just before breakthrough is expected. Accurate records can reveal when breakthrough occurs and also when breakthrough can be expected.

12.27   Proprietary Processes
by Bill Hoyer

Several patented processes are available for iron and manganese control. The best way to learn about the effectiveness and maintenance requirements of these processes is to contact someone who has one. Once you are operating one of these processes, the manufacturer is a good source of help when troubleshooting. Remember that various sources of raw water are different and what works for one operator may not work at your water treatment plant.

Electromedia iron and manganese removal systems are generally used on groundwater supplies at individual well sites because of their compactness and simplicity of treatment. The system uses reaction vessels where chemical reactions take place and an adsorptive media that requires no regeneration by special chemicals. Chlorine is used as the oxidizing chemical because of its cost and efficiency. (Any suitable oxidizing chemical can be used.) Almost 30 percent less chlorine, pound for pound, is required to perform the same amount of oxidation as potassium permanganate.

After oxidation with chlorine, a small dose of sulfur dioxide (0.25 to 0.50 mg/L) is introduced prior to the second reaction vessel. This dosage is factory set according to the general mineral analysis of the raw water. Dosage should not be altered. The sulfur dioxide is used to accelerate the oxidation of any sulfur compounds in the water to form compounds having no objectionable taste or odor.

The water is then sent to a filter operating at a preset rate of up to 15 gallons per minute per square foot (10 liters per second per square meter or 10 millimeters per second). In the filter vessel, the iron and manganese are adsorbed on the surface of the media until backwashing. The media can withstand a very high backwash rate (20 gallons per minute per square foot, 13.6 L/sec/sq m or 13.6 mm/sec) and requires only a four-minute backwash to obtain thorough cleaning.

The filter effluent can be sampled by a continuously monitoring analyzer that drives a 30-day strip chart recorder. The recorder may have a color-coded indicating strip to direct the operator in the proper chemical dosage. If the recorder trace falls out of the green, the operator increases the chlorine dosage. The dosage is adjusted by turning one knob and can be read immediately. The effect of the change can be seen on the chart trace in five minutes and will reach a steady state within 10 minutes. Thus the operator can quickly determine the proper dosage. With the chemical dosage set properly, a free chlorine residual exists in the filter effluent providing the required disinfection in the distribution system. Variations in water quality are quickly reflected in the chart tracing. Since no permanganate is used, there are no "black water" or "pink water" complaints from accidental underdosage or overdosage of chemicals.

The process uses BREAKPOINT CHLORINATION[11] and the very effective adsorptive qualities of the media. Each system is provided with an automatic control panel that permits adjustment of any of the filter cycles simply by rotating a timer knob. Status of the system is displayed on the front panel with pilot lights for easy viewing. The automatic control panel operates the manually set chemical feed system using gaseous chlorine and gaseous sulfur dioxide. Backwash is accomplished automatically by using a process signal and filtration timer with a differential pressure override.

Maintenance on the system is quite limited. Most systems are built with an automatic standby for the chemicals that will switch from an empty container to a full container. Table 12.1 lists the recommended maintenance.

Each application for iron and manganese removal is based on the general mineral analysis of the raw water. The required chemical treatment is provided for iron, manganese, and sulfide treatment. Additional equipment may be provided where corrosivity and/or chelating compounds are found to be present. Aeration may precede the process where methane extraction and/or carbon dioxide removal is required. Plant operators are directed to the operation and maintenance instructions provided with the equipment for additional details.

12.28 Monitoring of Treated Water

When controlling iron and manganese by aeration or with chemicals, the product water must be monitored closely. If lab

TABLE 12.1 RECOMMENDED MAINTENANCE FOR THE ELECTROMEDIA PROCESS

	Daily	Weekly	Monthly
1. Inspection of chart paper for proper chemical dosage	X		
2. Free chlorine residual test	X		
3. Total chlorine residual test	X		
4. Addition of buffer solution in the analyzer		X	
5. Colorimetric analysis of the influent and effluent for iron concentration		X	
6. Laboratory tests for analysis of influent and effluent for iron and manganese concentration			X
7. Changing of chart paper			X
8. Routine maintenance checks associated with valves, pipes, and pumps			X

facilities are available, the treated water can be analyzed for iron and manganese to be sure treatment is adequate. A quick way to monitor treated water is to collect a sample and add a dose of chlorine. If a brown- or rust-colored floc develops, then the treatment is inadequate. You will either have to increase the chemical doses or reduce the flows. If a pink color appears in the product water when using permanganate, then the dose is too high and must be reduced until the pink color is no longer visible.

12.29 Summary

Small iron and manganese water treatment plants can be very difficult to operate. If your plant is not operating as desired, talk to other operators in your area and see if they have any suggestions. If you have problems, you will have to try different chemical doses and procedures. Keep accurate records so you can evaluate the effectiveness of your efforts.

A lot of "iron complaints" in drinking water are caused by old steel or cast-iron water mains. A possible solution to this problem is to inject polyphosphates directly into the distribution mains. See Section 12.5, "Troubleshooting Red Water Problems," for additional ideas on how to solve problems.

---

[11] Breakpoint Chlorination. Addition of chlorine to water until the chlorine demand has been satisfied. At this point, further additions of chlorine will result in a free chlorine residual that is directly proportional to the amount of chlorine added beyond the breakpoint.

FORMULAS

A standard polyphosphate solution is prepared by mixing and dissolving a known amount of polyphosphate in a container and adding distilled water to the one-liter mark. To determine the settings on polyphosphate chemical feeders:

1. Prepare a series of samples and test with polyphosphate,

2. Select the optimum dosage in mg/L, and

3. Calculate the chemical feeder setting in pounds of polyphosphate per day.

$$\text{Stock Solution, mg/m}L = \frac{(\text{Polyphosphate, grams})(1{,}000 \text{ mg/gram})}{(\text{Solution, liter})(1{,}000 \text{ m}L/L)}$$

$$\text{Dose, mg/}L = \frac{(\text{Stock Solution, mg/m}L)(\text{Volume Added, m}L)}{\text{Sample Volume, }L}$$

$$\text{Dose, lbs/MG} = \frac{(\text{Dose, mg/}L)(3.785 \ L/\text{gal})(1{,}000{,}000/\text{Million})}{(1{,}000 \text{ mg/gm})(454 \text{ gm/lb})}$$

$$\text{Chemical Feeder, lbs/day} = (\text{Flow, MGD})(\text{Dose, mg/}L)(8.34 \text{ lbs/gal})$$

EXAMPLE 2

A standard polyphosphate solution is prepared by mixing and dissolving 1.0 gram of polyphosphate in a container and adding distilled water to the one-liter mark. Determine the concentration of the stock solution in milligrams per milliliter. If 5 milliliters of the stock solution are added to a one-liter sample, what is the polyphosphate dose in milligrams per liter and pounds per million gallons?

Known	Unknown
Polyphosphate, gm = 1.0 gm	1. Stock Solution, mg/mL
Solution, L = 1.0 L	2. Dose, mg/L
Stock Solution, mL = 5 mL	3. Dose, lbs/MG
Sample, L = 1 L	

1. Calculate the concentration of the stock solution in milligrams per milliliter.

$$\text{Stock Solution, mg/m}L = \frac{(\text{Polyphosphate, gm})(1{,}000 \text{ mg/gm})}{(\text{Solution, }L)(1{,}000 \text{ m}L/L)}$$

$$= \frac{(1.0 \text{ gm})(1{,}000 \text{ mg/gm})}{(1 \ L)(1{,}000 \text{ m}L/L)}$$

$$= 1.0 \text{ mg/m}L$$

2. Determine the polyphosphate dose in the sample in milligrams per liter.

$$\text{Dose, mg/}L = \frac{(\text{Stock Solution, mg/m}L)(\text{Vol Added, m}L)}{\text{Sample Volume, }L}$$

$$= \frac{(1.0 \text{ mg/m}L)(5 \text{ m}L)}{1 \ L}$$

$$= 5.0 \text{ mg/}L$$

3. Determine the polyphosphate dose in the sample in pounds of polyphosphate per million gallons.

$$\text{Dose, lbs/MG} = \frac{(\text{Dose, mg/}L)(3.785 \ L/\text{gal})(1{,}000{,}000/\text{Million})}{(1{,}000 \text{ mg/gm})(454 \text{ gm/lb})}$$

$$= \frac{(5.0 \text{ mg/}L)(3.785 \ L/\text{gal})(1{,}000{,}000/\text{Million})}{(1{,}000 \text{ mg/gm})(454 \text{ gm/lb})}$$

$$= 42 \text{ lbs/MG}$$

EXAMPLE 3

Determine the chemical feeder setting in pounds of polyphosphate per day if 0.4 MGD is treated with a dose of 5 mg/L.

Known	Unknown
Flow, MGD = 0.4 MGD	Chemical Feeder, lbs/day
Dose, mg/L = 5 mg/L	

Determine the chemical feeder setting in pounds per day.

$$\text{Chemical Feeder, lbs/day} = (\text{Flow, MGD})(\text{Dose, mg/}L)(8.34 \text{ lbs/gal})$$

$$= (0.4 \text{ MGD})(5 \text{ mg/}L)(8.34 \text{ lbs/gal})$$

$$= 17 \text{ lbs/day}$$

FORMULAS

To calculate the average detention time for a reaction basin:

1. Determine the dimensions of the basin, and

2. Measure and record the flow of water being treated.

$$\text{Basin Vol, cu ft} = (0.785)(\text{Diameter, ft})^2(\text{Depth, ft})$$

$$\text{Basin Vol, gal} = (\text{Basin Vol, cu ft})(7.48 \text{ gal/cu ft})$$

$$\text{Detention Time, min} = \frac{(\text{Basin Vol, gal})(24 \text{ hr/day})(60 \text{ min/hr})}{\text{Flow, gal/day}}$$

EXAMPLE 4

A reaction basin 12 feet in diameter and 5 feet deep treats a flow of 200,000 gallons per day. What is the average detention time in minutes?

Known	Unknown
Diameter, ft = 12 ft	Detention Time, min
Depth, ft = 5 ft	
Flow, GPD = 200,000 GPD	

1. Calculate the basin volume in cubic feet.

$$\text{Basin Vol, cu ft} = (0.785)(\text{Diameter, ft})^2(\text{Depth, ft})$$

$$= (0.785)(12 \text{ ft})^2(5 \text{ ft})$$

$$= 565 \text{ cu ft}$$

2. Convert the basin volume from cubic feet to gallons.

$$\text{Basin Vol, gal} = (\text{Basin Vol, cu ft})(7.48 \text{ gal/cu ft})$$

$$= (565 \text{ cu ft})(7.48 \text{ gal/cu ft})$$

$$= 4{,}226 \text{ gal}$$

3. Determine the average detention time in minutes for the reaction basin.

$$\text{Detention Time, min} = \frac{(\text{Basin Vol, gal})(24 \text{ hr/day})(60 \text{ min/hr})}{\text{Flow, gal/day}}$$

$$= \frac{(4,226 \text{ gal})(24 \text{ hr/day})(60 \text{ min/hr})}{200,000 \text{ gal/day}}$$

$$= 30 \text{ minutes}$$

QUESTIONS

Write your answers in a notebook and then compare your answers with those on page 23.

12.2E   What happens if water being treated for iron and manganese by ion exchange contains any dissolved oxygen?

12.2F   How does the pH of the water influence the rate of oxidation of iron to insoluble ferric hydroxide?

12.2G   What is the purpose of a reaction basin following the aeration process?

12.2H   After chlorine has been added to oxidize iron and manganese, how is the water dechlorinated?

12.2I   What are the three modes of operation for a manganese greensand process called?

12.3   OPERATION OF AN IRON AND MANGANESE REMOVAL PLANT
by Gerald Davidson

The very low recommended limits for iron (0.3 mg/L) and manganese (0.05 mg/L) in water make these contaminants difficult to treat and sometimes the processes are expensive. Because of this, operators should know how the processes work and what to check for when something goes wrong and the limits are exceeded. This section describes the operation of an iron and manganese removal plant using the continuously regenerated (CR) manganese greensand process.

12.30   Description of Equipment and Process

The filter is the most important piece of treatment equipment in an iron and manganese removal plant. Figure 12.4 illustrates a typical filter consisting of layers of gravel, manganese greensand, and anthracite coal. Some of the differences between greensand filters and conventional filters are: (1) the greensand is finer than filter sand; (2) the filtration rate is slower (2 to 5 GPM/sq ft (1.3 to 3.4 liters per sec/sq m or 1.3 to 3.4 mm/sec)); and (3) the backwash rate is lower (12 GPM/sq ft at 55°F versus 15 GPM/sq ft for sand/anthracite filters.

WATER TO BE TREATED

18 INCHES ANTHRACITE COAL
(0.6 - 0.8 mm Effective Size)

18 INCHES MANGANESE GREENSAND
(0.30 to 0.35 mm Effective Size)

12 INCHES GRADED GRAVEL
($^1/_8$" x $^1/_{16}$" to 1$^1/_2$" x $^3/_4$")

CONCRETE

TREATED WATER

Fig. 12.4   Multimedia manganese greensand filter (horizontal)

Figure 12.5 shows a typical flow diagram for a continuous regeneration (CR) manganese greensand plant. Treatment with manganese greensand can remove 95 percent of both iron and manganese. However, if the iron concentration is above 10 mg/L or manganese is above 5 mg/L, the efficiency of the greensand (or any other type of filter) drops very quickly as insoluble oxide particles accumulate on the grains of greensand and within the media bed. Pretreatment may be required to oxidize and remove a major portion of the iron and any sulfide present.

At the plant shown in Figure 12.5, raw water being pumped from a 50-foot (15-m) deep well contains 3.0 mg/L iron and 0.75 mg/L manganese (see Chapter 21 for test procedures) and it has a pH of 6.2. The pH of the water has a significant effect on iron removal. The oxidation potential of chlorine and potassium permanganate decreases as the pH increases, although the rate of reaction increases significantly with the increase in pH. Because the pH of the water in this example is 6.2, which is the minimum recommended pH for use of the CR process, the pH is adjusted to within the range of 6.5 to 6.8 by adding sodium carbonate or sodium hydroxide or by passing the water through a calcite neutralizing filter.

Next the water is injected with chlorine, flash mixed, and flocculated for a period of ten minutes in order to oxidize most of the iron. The chlorine dosage can be calculated using the following formula:

$$\text{Cl}_2 \text{ Required, mg/}L = 1 \times \text{Fe Conc, mg/}L$$

Therefore,

$$\text{Cl}_2 \text{ Required, mg/}L = 1 \times 3.0 \text{ mg/}L$$

$$= 3 \text{ mg/}L$$

After chlorination the water is injected with potassium permanganate (KMnO$_4$) to complete the oxidation of any

Fig. 12.5   Typical flow diagram of a continuous regeneration (CR) greensand process
(Permission of Hungerford & Terry, Inc.)

remaining iron and soluble manganese. Sodium hydroxide (30 mg/L)[12] may also be added if needed for corrosion control (pH correction, Figure 12.5). The KMnO$_4$ dosage can be calculated using the following formula:

KMnO$_4$ Required, mg/L = (0.2 x Fe Conc, mg/L) + (2 x Mn Conc, mg/L)

Therefore,

KMnO$_4$ Required, mg/L = (0.2 x 3.0 mg/L) + (2 x 0.75 mg/L)

$\doteq$ 2.1 mg/L

NOTE: The calculated 2.1 mg/L potassium permanganate dose is the minimum dose. This dose assumes there are no other oxidizable compounds in the raw water. However, typical oxidizable compounds usually found include organic color, bacteria, and even hydrogen sulfide (H$_2$S). Therefore, the actual dose may be higher. A bench scale test should be performed to determine the required dose.

To prepare a stock solution of potassium permanganate, mix 2 to 4 ounces (56 to 113 mg) of potassium permanganate chemical per gallon of water (15 to 30 mg/L) in a solution tank. Mix thoroughly to make sure the chemical dissolves completely. KMnO$_4$ is soluble up to 8.3 ounces (235 mg) per gallon (62 mg/L) of water at 68°F so you should have little trouble dissolving the chemical.

Problems will develop in the iron and manganese removal process using manganese greensand if you have too short a detention time for the chemicals to react. That is, it takes a little time for the chemicals to start working. If the plant you are operating does not allow sufficient detention time for the chemical reactions to take place, you should perform jar tests to see if a flash mix will improve performance. In some plants

the injection of the potassium permanganate solution in the volute of the pump will produce complete mixing of potassium permanganate.

The potassium permanganate feed system in our example plant consists of a 50-gallon (190-L) polyethylene solution vat, two $^1/_4$-HP mixers, liquid level switches, and a metering pump. The mixers do not have to run continuously because of the solubility of potassium permanganate in water.

The influent flow to the manganese greensand/anthracite filter is approximately 1,500 to 2,000 GPM. If the chemical dosage rate for KMnO$_4$ has been correctly calculated, the filter influent will have a slight pink/orange color due to the presence of a slight excess of permanganate. As the water is treated in the filter, this color will disappear because the permanganate will be reduced to manganese oxide by the manganese greensand. The manganese oxides will then precipitate on the grains, thus continuously regenerating the manganese greensand. It is important not to underfeed permanganate for an extended period of time. Without adequate permanganate, you will eventually exhaust the oxidative capacity of the media. If this happens, iron and manganese may pass through the filter into the distribution system and you will have to recharge the greensand (see Section 12.31).

As the filter run progresses and the amount of insoluble precipitates builds up in the media, the pressure drop across the filter will gradually increase. When the head loss reaches 10 psi, or after treating a predetermined number of gallons, the bed must be backwashed to remove the filtered particulates. Backwashing usually takes 10 to 15 minutes. Since the media is continuously regenerated during operation, there is no need to regenerate the greensand after backwashing. The used backwash water can be collected and reused after

---

[12] NOTE: Addition of 30 mg/L of sodium hydroxide (NaOH) will increase the sodium content of the water by 17 mg/L. If you are trying to keep the sodium level below 20 mg/L, then the sodium in the raw water must be below 3 mg/L.

allowing the precipitates to settle out. The settled precipitates may be disposed of in a sanitary sewer or sent to a drying bed.

In addition to backwashing, some plants use an air washing system to more thoroughly clean the manganese greensand grains on a weekly basis. Air wash is particularly useful for plants treating water that has a relatively high concentration of manganese. Manganese hydroxide oxidation products tend to be sticky or gummy and may cause the grains of greensand to stick together in clumps, especially in long filter runs. Backwashing alone may not always separate these grains and, over a period of time, "mudballs" may form. Agitating the greensand with an air wash (or better still an air-water wash) helps to keep the filter media in a free, loose, fluid condition. This will result in cleaner media and longer runs by minimizing cementation of the media bed.

Daily tests the operator should perform include iron, manganese, pH, and chlorine residual. The iron and manganese test tells the operator if the treatment plant is working and meeting state and federal water quality requirements. The pH test is also very important because of the relationship between pH and the corrosivity of water and because effective iron and manganese removal by the CR manganese greensand process requires a pH of 6.2 to 6.8.

12.31   Regeneration of Manganese Greensand

If the potassium permanganate charge is lost in the filter bed due to underdosing of potassium permanganate, the operator must regenerate the greensand. There are two ways to regenerate the bed:

1. Shut down and pour a saturated solution of potassium permanganate (about 5 percent) into the filters; let the saturated solution sit for approximately 24 hours. After 24 hours, backwash the filters at a normal rate to flush out the excess potassium permanganate; or

2. Recharge the greensand by increasing the potassium permanganate dosage until pink water flows out of the greensand media. Then decrease the potassium permanganate until you have a slight pink color before filtration. There should be no pink water after filtration when the water is being pumped into the distribution system. If there is still pink water after filtration, keep decreasing the potassium permanganate dose until no pink water is present in the water after filtration. The pink color is the best indication that the greensand is regenerated or recharged.

One problem with this method is that you might reduce the permanganate level too far and pass water with iron and manganese. This could cause red-colored water in the distribution system and stain clothes and/or bathroom fixtures. Because of the importance of the potassium per-

manganate in the greensand process, it is highly recommended that some type of fail-safe system be installed to prevent filtering water in the event the potassium permanganate solution vat reaches a low level. When a low level is reached, the plant should be automatically shut down. Typical fail-safe systems include low-level alarms in the vat or an automatic switchover system to another vat when the level drops too low in the vat in use.

Some operators find that method No. 1 is more effective. Since all treatment plants are unique in some respect, one method or the other or some modification may work best for your plant. Therefore, procedures and methods should be developed through actual experience. These methods should be adopted only if they provide the desired results without eliminating any concepts of design or of good operating practice.

12.32   Troubleshooting

See Table 12.2, "Troubleshooting Manganese Greensand Systems," for a listing of troubles, causes and remedies.

QUESTIONS

Write your answers in a notebook and then compare your answers with those on page 23.

12.3A   How does a water's pH affect the manganese greensand process?

12.3B   How can an operator quickly tell whether enough potassium permanganate is being fed in a continuous regeneration manganese greensand process?

12.3C   Why should a greensand plant be shut down when the permanganate solution level in the vat gets low?

12.4   MAINTENANCE OF A CHEMICAL FEEDER

In small water treatment plants that remove iron and manganese, a hypochlorite solution may be used to provide chlorine instead of using chlorine gas. Commercial sodium hypochlorite solutions (such as Clorox) contain an excess of caustic (sodium hydroxide, NaOH). When the solution is diluted with water containing carbonate alkalinity,[13] the resulting solution becomes supersaturated with calcium carbonate. This calcium carbonate tends to form a coating on the poppet valves in the solution feeder. The coated valves do not seal properly and the feeder fails to pump the hypochlorite solution properly.

---

[13] See Chapter 14, "Softening," for a discussion of carbonate alkalinity.

TABLE 12.2   TROUBLESHOOTING MANGANESE GREENSAND SYSTEMS

Trouble	Cause	Remedy
SYSTEM TYPE: CR/IR[a]		
1. Filter effluent clear, iron low, manganese higher than raw water.	Manganese being leached from greensand grains; bed is insufficiently regenerated.	Increase frequency of regeneration. Regenerate bed with sufficient $KMnO_4$ ($1^1/_2$ oz/cu ft) so heavy purple color comes through bed. Make sure proper influent chemicals (Cl_2 and/or $KMnO_4$) are being continuously fed.
2. Filter effluent turbid with yellow to brownish color. Iron and manganese high.	Too much alkali being fed ahead of filter.	Reduce alkali feed. Maintain correct pH prior to filter at 6.2-6.5. Post pH correct if higher pH required in system.
	Polyphosphate being fed ahead of filter.	Discontinue polyphosphate feed.
	Channeling through filters.	Check bed surface for mounds, pockets, and channeling. Backwash and air-scrub if possible.
	Iron organically bound: reactions with oxidizing agent produce a non-filterable colloid.	Feed alum or other coagulant prior to filter. Amount determined in field.
3. Excessive pressure drop across bed immediately after backwashing.	Accumulation of greensand fines at surface of bed.	Remove fines by scraping after backwashing. In severe cases bed replacement may be required.
		Check maximum pressure differential recommended and do not exceed 10 psi ΔP as additional fines may be formed.
	Backwash rate too low.	Increase backwash rate to 10-12 GPM/sq ft.
	Filter bed cemented as evidenced by mounding around periphery of vessel.	Break up cemented areas with air-water wash combination. Bed replacement may be necessary.
	Well throwing fine sand, silt, and colloidal clay.	Check well supply, especially immediately after pump start-up. Allow well to pump overboard at start of pumping cycle.
4. On multiple unit installations, water quality good on some units, bad on others.	Unequal distribution of pre-feed chemicals.	Inject chemical at a point where thorough mixing of chemicals with raw water occurs before diversion to the various filters.
SYSTEM TYPE: CR[a]		
5. Iron breakthrough before recommended maximum ΔP of 10 psi is reached.	Some iron waters filter in depth and do not build up head loss.	Backwash should be initiated by total number of gallons treated rather than by head loss. Use ΔP as a backup to prevent exceeding ΔP of 10 psi.
6. Faint pink color in filter effluent.	Permanganate feed rate is too high.	Operate filter for 1-2 hours with $KMnO_4$ feed off. Then reset feeder at slightly lower setting.
SYSTEM TYPE: IR[a]		
7. Low capacity.	Manganese oxide coating stripped from greensand grains due to insufficient regeneration. May be especially troublesome with high sulfide water.	Increase frequency of regeneration. Pre-feed Cl_2 with sulfide waters. Replace bed if required.
	Manganese greensand heavily iron-fouled.	Use CR method with dual-media anthracite/manganese greensand bed to prevent iron fouling.
	Excessive grain growth due to high manganese oxide buildup.	Increase frequency of regeneration. Bed replacement may eventually be required.

[a] CR — Continuous Regeneration
    IR — Intermittent Regeneration

(Reprinted with permission of Hungerford & Terry, Inc., Clayton, NJ)

Calcium carbonate scale can be removed from poppet valves by using the following procedure:

1. Fill a one-quart (946-mL) Mason jar half full of tap water.

2. Add one fluid ounce (44 mL) of 30- to 37-percent hydrochloric acid (HCl) to the Mason jar.

3. Finish filling the jar to the top with tap water.

4. Place the suction hose of the hypochlorinator in the jar and pump the entire contents of the jar through the system.

5. Return the suction hose to the solution tank and resume normal operation.

The hydrochloric acid (HCl), also called muriatic acid, can be obtained from stores selling swimming pool supplies.

One way to avoid the formation of calcium carbonate coatings is to obtain the dilution water for the hypochlorite from an ordinary home water softener.

For additional information on the operation and maintenance of various types of chemical feeders, see Chapter 13, "Fluoridation."

QUESTIONS

Write your answers in a notebook and then compare your answers with those on page 23.

12.4A What problems may develop in a chemical feeder pumping sodium hypochlorite?

12.4B How can the problems caused by calcium carbonate scale on a hypochlorinator's poppet valves be solved?

12.5 TROUBLESHOOTING RED WATER PROBLEMS

The first step when troubleshooting red or dirty water complaints is to be sure the iron and manganese treatment processes are working properly. If the iron and manganese are being removed by the treatment processes, investigate the distribution system for sources of the problem.

Red water or dirty water problems may be caused by corrosive water or iron bacteria in the distribution system. When an unstable or corrosive water (see Chapter 8, "Corrosion Control") is pumped into the distribution system, the water attacks cast-iron pipes and/or metal service lines, picks up iron, and causes red water complaints. All water treatment plants should run a Marble Test (see page 484 in Chapter 21). If the test indicates that the water is corrosive, the addition of caustic (sodium hydroxide, NaOH) to the water to increase

the pH will help. When the water becomes stable (according to the Marble Test), some of the red water complaints could be eliminated.

The growth of iron bacteria inside water mains causes one of the most troublesome and most difficult to eliminate red water problems. These bacteria are not harmful. They live and accumulate the iron in the water flowing through the distribution system. As the bacterial growths increase, slimes will build up in the mains and eventually slough off into the water. When these slimes come out a consumer's water tap, you can expect complaints of red water and slimes.

Slime growths can be controlled by maintaining a free chlorine residual throughout the distribution system. Sometimes the residual is very difficult to maintain. If bacterial growths have been in the distribution system for a long time and are flourishing, it is very difficult to maintain a free chlorine residual at the extremes or in dead ends of the system. Also if the water has a natural high chlorine demand, your chlorination equipment may not be capable of feeding enough chlorine to maintain a free chlorine residual. Remember that frequently when consumers complain about a strong chlorine taste or swimming pool-tasting water, the solution is to add more chlorine in order to get past the breakpoint.

One way to rid a distribution system of iron bacteria is to develop a flushing program.[14] Flushing should start at the location where the water enters the distribution system, such as an elevated tank. Flush the water mains by working toward the extremes or most distant points of the distribution system. Usually only one portion of the distribution system is flushed, followed by another portion until the entire system has been flushed.

A common practice is to open a hydrant at the extreme end of the system at the start of the flushing job to be sure the water being flushed will carry the sediment and insoluble precipitates in the desired direction and out of the system. Flushing is often done late at night when water demands are low so facilities won't be overworked and consumers will not be inconvenienced.

Valves will have to be opened and closed in the proper sequences to be sure the desired mains are being flushed and that no one will be without water. Hydrants that are opened to allow flushing must be of sufficient size to produce flushing velocities (2.5 up to 5.0 ft/sec preferred or 0.75 to 1.5 m/sec) in the mains. Also the mains providing the flushing flows must have sufficient capacity to deliver the desired flows.

When flushing a system, be sure the pressure in the distribution system does not drop below 20 psi (1.4 kg/sq cm or 138 kPa). If a four-inch (100-mm) water main is flushed using a six-inch (150-mm) hydrant, the water pressure in the main downstream from the hydrant could become dangerously low. When this happens, the distribution system could be subject to contamination by *BACKSIPHONAGE*.[15] *NEVER ALLOW A BACKSIPHON CONDITION TO DEVELOP IN A DISTRIBUTION SYSTEM.*

In summary, to minimize red water or dirty water problems and complaints, you must provide adequate treatment to control iron and manganese. This is necessary to ensure that the water pumped into the distribution system contains little or no iron and manganese. The water must be stable (noncorrosive)

---

[14] *See WATER DISTRIBUTION SYSTEM OPERATION AND MAINTENANCE in this series of manuals, Chapter 5, Section 5.706, "Pipe Flushing."*

[15] *Backsiphonage. A form of backflow caused by a negative or below atmospheric pressure within a water system.*

so that iron will not be picked up in the distribution system. Corrosion control treatment processes can produce a stable water. If bacterial growths are a problem, a free chlorine residual must be maintained in all water throughout the distribution system. If red or dirty water problems exist in a distribution system, a thorough flushing program can be very helpful.

12.6   ARITHMETIC ASSIGNMENT

Turn to the Appendix at the back of this manual and read Section A.30, "Iron and Manganese Control." Check all of the arithmetic in this section using an electronic calculator. You should be able to get the same answers. (Metric calculations can be found in Section A.50.)

12.7   ADDITIONAL READING

1. *NEW YORK MANUAL*, Chapter 13*, "Iron and Manganese."

2. *TEXAS MANUAL*, Chapter 11*, "Special Water Treatment (Iron and Manganese Removal)."

* Depends on edition.

NOTE: *A MANUAL OF INSTRUCTION FOR WATER TREAT-MENT PLANT OPERATORS*, also called *NEW YORK MANUAL*, is available from Health Education Services, Inc., P.O. Box 7126, Albany, NY 12224. Price, $19.00, includes cost of shipping and handling.

MANUAL OF WATER UTILITY OPERATIONS, also called *TEXAS MANUAL*, is available from Texas Water Utilities Association, 1106 Clayton Lane, Suite 101 East, Austin, TX 78723-1093. Price to members, $20.00; nonmembers, $32.00; plus $2.85 shipping and handling.

12.8   ACKNOWLEDGMENT

Portions of this chapter were revised by Raymond Ellis, Hungerford & Terry, Inc.

QUESTIONS

Write your answers in a notebook and then compare your answers with those on page 23.

12.5A   List the possible causes of red or dirty water complaints.

12.5B   How can slime growths be controlled in water distribution systems?

Please answer the discussion and review questions before continuing with the Objective Test.

DISCUSSION AND REVIEW QUESTIONS

Chapter 12.   IRON AND MANGANESE CONTROL

Write the answers to these questions in your notebook before continuing with the Objective Test on page 24. The purpose of these questions is to indicate to you how well you understand the material in the chapter.

1. Why should iron and manganese be controlled in drinking water?

2. Why are accurate results of tests for iron and manganese difficult to obtain?

3. Why is chlorine usually fed with polyphosphates when controlling iron and manganese?

4. How do polyphosphates control manganese?

5. How is the proper polyphosphate dose determined?

6. What happens when an ion exchange resin becomes fouled with iron rust or manganese dioxide?

7. When should iron and manganese ion exchange units be regenerated?

8. How would you determine whether or not to adjust the flows to an oxidation by aeration process to remove iron?

9. Why should reaction basins be drained and cleaned?

10. What are the advantages and disadvantages of the oxidation by aeration process to remove iron?

11. What happens if the dose of potassium permanganate to remove iron and manganese is not exact?

12. How does an operator decide when to backwash a manganese greensand filter?

13. What must you do if the potassium permanganate charge is lost in the filter bed?

14. How would you attempt to prevent red or dirty water complaints?

SUGGESTED ANSWERS

Chapter 12. IRON AND MANGANESE CONTROL

Answers to questions on page 6.

12.0A When clothes are washed in water containing iron and manganese, they will come out stained. Excessive iron and manganese in water can also stain plumbing fixtures. Iron bacteria will cause thick slimes to form on the walls of water mains. These slimes are rust colored from iron and black from manganese. Variations in flow cause these slimes to slough which results in dirty water. Furthermore, these slimes will impart foul tastes and odors to the water.

12.0B The growth of iron bacteria is easily controlled by chlorination. However, when water containing iron is chlorinated, the iron is converted into rust particles and manganese is converted into a jet black compound, manganese dioxide.

12.0C The generally accepted limit for iron is 0.3 mg/L and that for manganese is 0.05 mg/L.

Answers to questions on page 7.

12.1A Iron and manganese react with dissolved oxygen or chlorine to form insoluble compounds.

12.1B Iron and manganese samples are acidified when they are collected to prevent the formation of iron and manganese scales on the walls of the sample bottles.

12.1C Samples for iron and manganese testing should be collected as close to the well or source of water as possible.

Answers to questions on page 11.

12.2A To determine if nearby wells contain iron and manganese, samples could be collected and analyzed from nearby private wells. Also, discussions with well drillers who have been active in the locality and with engineers with the state agency responsible for the regulation of well drilling will be helpful.

12.2B If a well produces water containing dissolved oxygen as well as iron and manganese, the iron and manganese are probably coming from the lower aquifers. Try to seal off the lower aquifers.

12.2C Bench scale tests are a method of studying different ways or chemical doses for treating water on a small scale in a laboratory.

12.2D If polyphosphate solutions are much over 48 hours old, they will react slowly with water to form orthophosphates which are much less effective in preventing manganese deposits.

Answers to questions on page 17.

12.2E If water being treated for iron and manganese by ion exchange contains any dissolved oxygen, the resin becomes fouled with iron rust or insoluble manganese dioxide.

12.2F The higher the pH, the faster the rate of oxidation of iron to insoluble ferric hydroxide.

12.2G The purpose of the reaction basin is to allow time for the oxidation reactions to take place. The aeration process should produce sufficient dissolved oxygen for the iron to be oxidized to insoluble ferric hydroxide.

12.2H Water can be dechlorinated by the use of reducing agents such as sulfur dioxide (SO_2), sodium bisulfite ($NaHSO_3$), and sodium sulfite (Na_2SO_3). Bisulfite is commonly used because it is cheaper and more stable than sulfite.

12.2I The three process modes for manganese greensand are continuous regeneration, intermittent regeneration, and catalytic regeneration.

Answers to questions on page 19.

12.3A The oxidation potential of chlorine and potassium permanganate used in the manganese greensand process decreases as the pH increases. To operate efficiently, the CR manganese greensand process requires a pH range of 6.2 to 6.8.

12.3B When adequate potassium permanganate is being fed in a manganese greensand process, the filter influent will have a slight pink/orange color.

12.3C A greensand plant should be shut down when the permanganate solution level in the vat gets low because of the importance of the permanganate in the process. Without permanganate the greensand could lose its charge and iron and manganese will enter the distribution system.

Answers to questions on page 21.

12.4A When a chemical feeder pumps hypochlorite, calcium carbonate coatings may develop on the poppet valves if the dilution water contains carbonate alkalinity. Coated valves do not seal properly and the feeder fails to pump the hypochlorite solution properly.

12.4B The problems caused by calcium carbonate scale on a hypochlorinator's poppet valves can be solved in two ways:

1. A hydrochloric acid solution can be pumped through the system, or
2. The dilution water for the feeder can be obtained from an ordinary home water softener.

Answers to questions on page 22.

12.5A Red or dirty water complaints may be caused by:

1. Iron and/or manganese in the water,
2. Corrosive waters, and
3. Iron bacteria in the distribution system.

12.5B Slime growths in distribution systems can be controlled by maintaining a free chlorine residual throughout the distribution system and by a distribution system flushing program.

OBJECTIVE TEST

Chapter 12.   IRON AND MANGANESE CONTROL

Please write your name and mark the correct answers on the answer sheet, as directed at the end of Chapter 1 in Volume I. There may be more than one correct answer to each multiple-choice question.

True-False

1. Iron and manganese have direct adverse health effects.

   1. True
   2. False

2. Iron or manganese is most frequently found in water systems supplied by surface waters.

   1. True
   2. False

3. Sterile conditions are easily maintained when drilling a well to prevent the introduction of iron bacteria.

   1. True
   2. False

4. Water from a well containing iron and manganese and also dissolved oxygen comes from the same aquifer.

   1. True
   2. False

5. Chlorine can be used to prevent the growth of iron bacteria.

   1. True
   2. False

6. Iron and manganese ion exchange units are similar to an upflow pressure filter.

   1. True
   2. False

7. If the water to be treated contains no oxygen, both iron and manganese may be removed by ion exchange using the same resins that are used for water softening.

   1. True
   2. False

8. The dose of potassium permanganate to control iron and manganese must be exact.

   1. True
   2. False

9. Oxidized iron is in the soluble ferrous (Fe^{2+}) state.

   1. True
   2. False

10. Each application for iron and manganese removal is based on the general mineral analysis of the raw water.

    1. True
    2. False

11. A lot of "iron complaints" in drinking water are caused by old steel or cast-iron water mains.

    1. True
    2. False

12. Flushing water mains is often done late at night when water demands are low.

    1. True
    2. False

Best Answer (Select only the closest or best answer.)

13. Iron and manganese both are

    1. A cause of direct adverse health effects.
    2. A substitute for chlorine disinfection.
    3. Capable of enhancing the effectiveness of bleach.
    4. Essential to the growth of many plants and animals.

14. How can the growth of iron bacteria be controlled?

    1. Chlorination
    2. Coagulation
    3. Filtration
    4. Sedimentation

15. Why are the results of tests for iron and manganese frequently wrong? Because iron and manganese

    1. Are not uniformly mixed in raw water.
    2. Bacteria growth rates vary.
    3. May form nonuniform colloidal suspensions.
    4. Tend to form an adherent scale.

16. What should be done if clay or rust particles are observed in a sample to be analyzed for iron and manganese?

    1. Acidify sample on site
    2. Ask lab to analyze sample immediately
    3. Filter sample before analysis
    4. Shake sample vigorously

17. Why should chlorine never be fed ahead of the polyphosphate when controlling iron and manganese?

    1. Chlorine after polyphosphate lowers chlorine doses
    2. Chlorine after polyphosphate reduces THMs
    3. Chlorine will cause insoluble precipitates to form too soon
    4. Wrong, chlorine should be fed ahead to increase CT value

18. How is the proper phosphate dose determined to control iron and manganese?

    1. Field tests
    2. Laboratory bench scale tests
    3. Pilot plant tests
    4. Stoichiometric tests

19. Why can iron be controlled by oxidation? Oxidation

    1. Causes iron to remain in solution.
    2. Complexes iron so it won't adhere to surfaces.
    3. Converts iron to another valence state.
    4. Forms an insoluble precipitate which can be removed from water.

20. Following the addition of chlorine, how are insoluble manganese dioxide and insoluble ferric hydroxide removed from the water being treated?

    1. Coagulation
    2. Filtration
    3. Flocculation
    4. Precipitation

21. What problem will occur if too large a dose of potassium permanganate is used to control iron and manganese?

    1. Additional chlorine will be needed for disinfection
    2. Chemical feeder will be overloaded
    3. Oxidized iron will go back into solution
    4. Pink-colored water will enter the system

22. How can the greensand filter media be kept in a free, loose, fluid condition?

    1. Agitate media with an air wash or air-water wash
    2. Backwash with treated water
    3. Cleanse media with a detergent solution
    4. Reverse flows and use a chlorine wash

23. What problem is created on a hypochlorite chemical feeder when calcium carbonate is present?

    1. Alkalinity decreases and the insoluble iron will not flocculate
    2. Calcium increases the hardness of the water and the iron taste
    3. Carbonate neutralizes the chlorine and oxidation does not occur
    4. Poppet valves become coated and do not seal properly

24. How can red water problems caused by slime growths in distribution systems be controlled?

    1. Adjust pH to optimum level
    2. Control entry of slimes to system
    3. Filter slimes out of water
    4. Maintain a free chlorine residual

Multiple Choice (Select all correct answers.)

25. Which items can be stained by iron and manganese?

    1. Bathtubs
    2. Clothes
    3. Glass
    4. Plumbing fixtures
    5. Skin

26. How can iron and manganese be easily detected in water?

    1. Color of filter media
    2. Color of filter walls
    3. Color of raw water
    4. Odor of raw water
    5. Taste of raw water

27. What are the most common treatment processes used to control iron and manganese?

    1. Ion exchange
    2. Oxidation with chlorine
    3. Oxidation with permanganate
    4. Phosphate treatment
    5. Reduction by aeration

28. What factors can cause a lowering of the oxidation rates of iron using aeration?

    1. Addition of lime
    2. Organic substances
    3. Reducing flows
    4. Reducing pH
    5. Reducing temperature

29. How can aeration be provided to oxidize iron?

    1. Cascades
    2. Compressed air
    3. Multiple trays
    4. Sprays
    5. Trickling filters

30. What are potential sources of contamination of treated water in iron reaction basins?

    1. Air gaps
    2. Backwash water
    3. Rain
    4. Rodents
    5. Storm water runoff

31. How is fouling of greensand media prevented when controlling iron?

    1. Adjust water pH to optimum level
    2. Aerate water before it enters greensand bed
    3. Convert iron to insoluble form before water enters greensand bed
    4. Install sedimentation basin to remove precipitate
    5. Use ion exchange unit before greensand bed

32. What should be done if a dose of chlorine added to treated water produces a brown- or rust-colored floc?

    1. Adjust pH
    2. Decrease chemical dose
    3. Increase chemical dose
    4. Increase flows
    5. Reduce flows

33. Pretreatment may be required to remove what constituents in raw water before a manganese greensand process?

    1. Carbon dioxide
    2. Iron
    3. Manganese
    4. Nitrate
    5. Sulfide

34. What oxidizable compounds may be found in raw water that will require an increase in the dose of the oxidizing chemical?

    1. Bacteria
    2. Carbon dioxide
    3. Hardness
    4. Hydrogen sulfide
    5. Organic color

35. How can settled precipitates from backwash of a green-sand filter be disposed of?

1. Centrifuge
2. Drying bed
3. Filter press
4. Polymer flocculation
5. Sanitary sewer

36. What could be the cause of a turbid greensand filter effluent with a yellow to brownish color and both iron and manganese concentrations are high?

1. Backwash rate too low
2. Channeling through the filters
3. Iron organically bound
4. Polyphosphate being fed ahead of filter
5. Too much alkali being fed ahead of filter

37. What could be the cause of excessive pressure drop across a greensand filter bed immediately after backwashing?

1. Accumulation of greensand fines at surface of bed
2. Backwash rate too low
3. Channeling through filters
4. Filter bed cemented as evidenced by mounding around periphery of vessel
5. Well throwing fine sand, silt, and colloidal clay

38. What items should an operator consider when flushing a distribution system to control iron bacteria?

1. Flushing is scheduled during high-flow periods
2. Service valves remain closed until entire main is flushed
3. Water is delivered at flushing velocities
4. Water mains have sufficient capacity to carry flows
5. Water pressure does not exceed 20 psi

39. What is the setting on a potassium permanganate chemical feeder in pounds per day if the required chemical dose is 2.4 mg/L and the flow is 0.48 MGD?

1. 1.2 lbs/day
2. 4.0 lbs/day
3. 9.6 lbs/day
4. 13.5 lbs/day
5. 20.0 lbs/day

40. What is the setting on a potassium permanganate chemical feeder in pounds per million gallons if the chemical dose determined from a jar test is 3.7 mg/L?

1. 8 lbs/M Gal
2. 15 lbs/M Gal
3. 22 lbs/M Gal
4. 26 lbs/M Gal
5. 31 lbs/M Gal

41. A reaction basin 15 feet in diameter and 4 feet deep treats a flow of 390,000 gallons per day. What is the average detention time in minutes?

1. 10 minutes
2. 13 minutes
3. 20 minutes
4. 23 minutes
5. 29 minutes

End of Objective Test

CHAPTER 13

FLUORIDATION

by

Harry Tracy

TABLE OF CONTENTS

Chapter 13.   FLUORIDATION

		Page
OBJECTIVES		30
WORDS		31
13.0	IMPORTANCE OF FLUORIDATION	32
13.1	FLUORIDATION PROGRAMS	32
13.2	COMPOUNDS USED TO FURNISH FLUORIDE ION	32
13.3	FLUORIDATION SYSTEMS	33
	13.30 Chemical Feeders	33
	13.31 Saturators	41
	13.32 Downflow Saturators	41
	13.33 Upflow Saturators	41
	13.34 Large Hydrofluosilicic Acid Systems	45
13.4	FINAL CHECKUP OF EQUIPMENT	47
	13.40 Avoid Overfeeding	47
	13.41 Review of Designs and Specifications	47
13.5	CHEMICAL FEEDER START-UP	47
13.6	CHEMICAL FEEDER OPERATION	48
	13.60 Fine Tuning	48
	13.61 Preparation of Fluoride Solution	48
	13.62 Fluoridation Log Sheets	48
	13.620 Hydrofluosilicic Acid	48
	13.621 Sodium Silicofluoride	52
13.7	PREVENTION OF OVERFEEDING	55
13.8	UNDERFEEDING	55
13.9	SHUTTING DOWN CHEMICAL SYSTEMS	55
13.10	MAINTENANCE	57
13.11	SAFETY IN HANDLING FLUORIDE COMPOUNDS	57
	13.110 Avoid Overexposure	57
	13.111 Symptoms of Fluoride Poisoning	58
	13.112 Basic First Aid	58
	13.113 Protecting Yourself and Your Family	58
	13.114 Training	58
13.12	CALCULATING FLUORIDE DOSAGES	59

13.13 ARITHMETIC ASSIGNMENT 63

13.14 ADDITIONAL READING 63

13.15 ACKNOWLEDGMENTS 63

DISCUSSION AND REVIEW QUESTIONS 64

SUGGESTED ANSWERS 64

OBJECTIVE TEST 67

OBJECTIVES

Chapter 13.   FLUORIDATION

Following completion of Chapter 13, you should be able to:

1. Explain the reason for fluoridating drinking water,

2. Describe how fluoridation programs are implemented,

3. List the compounds used to furnish fluoride ion,

4. Review designs and specifications of fluoridation equipment,

5. Inspect fluoridation equipment,

6. Start up a chemical feeder,

7. Operate and maintain a chemical feeder,

8. Calculate fluoride dosages,

9. Prepare fluoride solutions,

10. Develop and keep accurate fluoride log sheets,

11. Prevent overfeeding of fluoride,

12. Shut down chemical feed systems, and

13. Safely handle fluoride compounds.

WORDS

Chapter 13.   FLUORIDATION

BATCH PROCESS   BATCH PROCESS

A treatment process in which a tank or reactor is filled, the water is treated or a chemical solution is prepared, and the tank is emptied. The tank may then be filled and the process repeated.

DAY TANK   DAY TANK

A tank used to store a chemical solution of known concentration for feed to a chemical feeder. A day tank usually stores sufficient chemical solution to properly treat the water being treated for at least one day. Also called an age tank.

ENDEMIC (en-DEM-ick)   ENDEMIC

Something peculiar to a particular people or locality, such as a disease which is always present in the population.

FLUORIDATION (FLOOR-uh-DAY-shun)   FLUORIDATION

The addition of a chemical to increase the concentration of fluoride ions in drinking water to a predetermined optimum limit to reduce the incidence (number) of dental caries (tooth decay) in children. Defluoridation is the removal of excess fluoride in drinking water to prevent the mottling (brown stains) of teeth.

GRAVIMETRIC FEEDER   GRAVIMETRIC FEEDER

A dry chemical feeder which delivers a measured weight of chemical during a specific time period.

POSITIVE DISPLACEMENT PUMP   POSITIVE DISPLACEMENT PUMP

A type of piston, diaphragm, gear or screw pump that delivers a constant volume with each stroke. Positive displacement pumps are used as chemical solution feeders.

SATURATOR (SAT-you-RAY-tore)   SATURATOR

A device which produces a fluoride solution for the fluoridation process. The device is usually a cylindrical container with granular sodium fluoride on the bottom. Water flows either upward or downward through the sodium fluoride to produce the fluoride solution.

VOLUMETRIC FEEDER   VOLUMETRIC FEEDER

A dry chemical feeder which delivers a measured volume of chemical during a specific time period.

FLOOR-uh-DAY-shun

CHAPTER 13. FLUORIDATION

13.0 IMPORTANCE OF FLUORIDATION

During the period 1902 to 1931 Dr. Frederick S. McKay, a dentist practicing in Colorado Springs, noted what seemed an *ENDEMIC* [1] brown stain on the teeth of his patients. McKay devoted much of his time researching the case of mottled (brown, chalky deposits) tooth enamel but it was not until 1931 that the cause was found to be excessive fluoride in the water supplies (2 to 13 mg/L). During this period McKay had also noted that the mottled teeth seemed to have fewer dental caries (decay or cavities).

The next logical step was to add fluoride to waters that were deficient in fluoride and to discover if children drinking water treated with fluoride had fewer cavities. In 1945 controlled fluoridation was started in the cities of Grand Rapids, Michigan, and Newburgh, New York, with control cities of Muskegon and Kingston.

Finally in 1955 the results were in and they showed a 60 percent reduction of caries in the children who drank fluoridated water compared to the children in the control cities.

The progress of fluoridation did not go smoothly. Antifluoridationists became increasingly vocal and were able to stop fluoridation in many cities through action in the political arena. Although dentists practicing in areas with naturally high fluoride waters noted that their patients had remarkably few cavities, there were still those disfiguring brown stains. Mottling of the teeth occurs when the fluoride level exceeds about 1.5 mg/L. Fluoride concentrations in excess of 1,000 mg/L have been found in waters from volcanic regions. Waters with fluoride concentrations more than 1.4 to 2.4 mg/L should be treated to reduce the level to approximately one milligram per liter. Recommended control limits for fluoride depend on the annual average of maximum daily air temperatures (Table 13.1). The maximum contaminant level (MCL) is 4.0 mg/L.

QUESTIONS

Write your answers in a notebook and then compare your answers with those on page 64.

13.0A What happens if a person drinks water with an excessive concentration of fluoride?

13.0B What happens if children drink a recommended dose of fluoride?

13.1 FLUORIDATION PROGRAMS

Generally speaking, fluoridation programs start with citizens' inquiries about fluoridation of their water supplies and encouragement of the local dental society. These requests for the addition of fluoride to prevent dental caries are passed along to appropriate governing agencies. The governing body will usually rely upon a vote of the people, or it may be forced into a vote by threat of a referendum. If the decision is made to fluoridate, the water department or water company will almost always make the final decisions as to types of chemical and feeding equipment to be used.

13.2 COMPOUNDS USED TO FURNISH FLUORIDE ION

The most commonly used compounds to fluoridate water systems are sodium fluoride, sodium silicofluoride and hydrofluosilicic (HI-dro-FLEW-oh-suh-LYS-ik) acid. There are also a few systems using such compounds as hydrofluoric acid and ammonium silicofluoride. All of these chemicals are refined from minerals found in nature and they yield fluoride ions identical to those found in natural waters. Hydrofluosilicic acid (also called fluorisilicic acid) is the compound most commonly used in several states (California, Florida, and Illinois).

TABLE 13.1 PRIMARY DRINKING WATER REGULATIONS FOR FLUORIDE AND RECOMMENDED LEVELS

	Annual Average Maximum Daily Temperatures[a]		Recommended Control Limits of Fluoride Levels, mg/L			Maximum Contaminant Level, mg/L
	°F	°C	Lower	Optimum	Upper	
a.	53.7 & Below	12.0 & Below	0.9	1.2	1.7	4.0
b.	53.8 to 58.3	12.1 to 14.6	0.8	1.1	1.5	4.0
c.	58.4 to 63.8	14.7 to 17.6	0.8	1.0	1.3	4.0
d.	63.9 to 70.6	17.7 to 21.4	0.7	0.9	1.2	4.0
e.	70.7 to 79.2	21.5 to 26.2	0.7	0.8	1.0	4.0
f.	79.3 to 90.5	26.3 to 32.5	0.6	0.7	0.8	4.0

[a] Contact your local Weather Service Office to determine the "Annual Average Maximum Daily Air Temperature" for your service area.

[1] *Endemic (en-DEM-ick). Something peculiar to a particular people or locality, such as a disease which is always present in the population.*

The American Water Works Association has developed standards for the purity and composition of the fluoride compounds most commonly used. In order for you to be confident of the fluoride compound you are using, insist that your supplier furnish only compounds meeting the appropriate AWWA specifications.

The plant should have as part of its records several copies of the appropriate AWWA standard for reference. Standards can be purchased from Customer Services, American Water Works Association, 6666 W. Quincy Avenue, Denver, CO 80235.

| Standard | Chemical | Price[a] | | Order No. |
		Members	Nonmembers	
B701-94	Sodium Fluoride	$18.00	$26.00	42701
B702-94	Sodium Silicofluoride	$13.00	$18.00	42702
B703-94	Hydrofluosilicic Acid	$18.00	$26.00	42703

[a] Price includes cost of shipping and handling.

Only the fluoride ion in these compounds is of any importance in the fluoridation of water; therefore, pound-for-pound, each compound will provide a different final fluoride level. If you switch from one type of fluoride compound to another, you will have to make separate calculations for each type. Table 13.2 summarizes the important properties of fluoride compounds.

When selecting a fluoridation chemical, several important factors must be considered. If powdered or crystal forms are used, solubility of the chemical in water will determine how readily it dissolves in water and how well it remains in solution. Operator safety and ease of handling must be given serious consideration. Storage and feeding requirements as well as costs must also be studied when selecting any chemical.

REMEMBER, All fluoridation chemicals are POISONOUS at HIGH LEVELS.

Hydrofluosilicic acid is usually the easiest fluoridation chemical to feed. However, hydrofluosilicic acid produces poisonous fumes that must be vented and is very irritating to your skin. Sodium fluoride is easier to feed than the other powdered fluoridation chemicals because it is more soluble in water.

Operators can receive instructions from the manufacturer on how to make up the chemical solutions and how much solution to meter per million gallons. See Section 13.61, "Preparation of Fluoride Solution," for calculations and procedure details.

Prior to fluoridation, the water should be checked for its natural fluoride level. If there is natural fluoride in the water, it is only necessary to add enough to bring the total to the desired level recommended by the local health authorities.

TABLE 13.2 FLUORIDE COMPOUNDS

		Sodium Silico-fluoride Na_2SiF_6	Sodium Fluoride NaF	Hydrofluo-silicic Acid H_2SiF_6
1.	Form	Powder	Powder or Crystal	Liquid
2.	Molecular Weight	188.1	42.0	144.1
3.	Commercial Purity, %	98-99	95-98	22-30 by Weight
4.	Fluoride Ion, % (Purity, %)	60.7 (100%) 59.8 (98.5%)	45.3 (100%) 43.4 (96%)	79.2 (100%) 23.8 (30%)
5.	Density	55-72 lb/cu ft	65-90 lb/cu ft	10.5 (30%) lb/gal
6.	Solubility in Water, % (gram/100 mL water at 77°F or 25°C)	0.76	4.05	100[a]
7.	pH of Saturated Solution	3.5	7.6	1.2 (1% Solution)

[a] Infinite because we are dealing with a liquid.

QUESTIONS

Write your answers in a notebook and then compare your answers with those on page 64.

13.1A   Who makes the final decisions as to types of fluoride chemicals and feeding equipment to be used?

13.2A   List the three compounds most commonly used to fluoridate water.

13.3 FLUORIDATION SYSTEMS

Drinking waters may come to contain fluoride ions by three different types of situations. First, the raw water source may have adequate or excessive fluoride ions naturally present. Second, sometimes two water sources are blended together to produce an acceptable level of fluoride ions. This can occur when one source has a higher than acceptable level of fluoride ions and the other is below the desired level. This chapter is mainly concerned with the third situation in which fluoride ions must be added to the water to achieve an acceptable level of fluoride ions.

13.30 Chemical Feeders

Fluoride ions are added to water by either chemical solution feeders or dry feeders. Solution feeders are *POSITIVE DISPLACEMENT*[2] diaphragm pumps (Figure 13.1), peristaltic pumps (Figure 13.2), or electronic pumps (Figure 13.3),

[2] *Positive Displacement Pump. A type of piston, diaphragm, gear or screw pump that delivers a constant volume with each stroke. Positive displacement pumps are used as chemical solution feeders.*

Fig. 13.1   *Positive displacement diaphragm pumps*
(Permission of Wallace & Tiernan, Inc.)

that deliver a fixed amount of liquid fluoridation chemical with each stroke or pulse. The dry feeders are either *VOLUMETRIC* [3] or *GRAVIMETRIC* [4] types of chemical feeders. Volumetric feeders (Figures 13.4 and 13.5) are usually simpler, less expensive, less accurate and feed smaller amounts of chemicals than gravimetric feeders. Gravimetric feeders (Figure 13.6) are usually more accurate than volumetric feeders; however, they are more expensive and require more space for installation. The amount fed is measured on the basis of the weight of chemical to be fed to the system. Fluoride chemical feeders must be very accurate.

Whatever the type of feeding system or chemical used, the design should be planned by an engineer experienced in developing feeding systems (Figure 13.7). The design must incorporate means to prevent both overfeeding and back-siphonage along with a means to monitor the amount of chemical used. It is also desirable to incorporate some means of feeding fluoride which is adjusted (paced) according to the plant flow rate. Also a means to continuously measure the finished water's fluoride ion content with an adjustable "high" fluoride alarm is desirable. Fluoride doses must never be metered against a negative or suction head.

---

[3] *Volumetric Feeder.   A dry chemical feeder which delivers a measured volume of chemical during a specific time period.*
[4] *Gravimetric Feeder.   A dry chemical feeder which delivers a measured weight of chemical during a specific time period.*

THREE-QUARTER VIEW

END VIEW

ROLLER

PUMPING TUBE

out

in

DETAIL OF
PLASTIC TUBE
HOUSING

SIDE VIEW

GEAR MOTOR

MECHANICAL
FEED RATE
CONTROL

PLASTIC
TUBE
HOUSING

Fig. 13.2   Peristaltic feeder

(Reproduced from *WATER FLUORIDATION*, A Training Course Manual for Engineers
and Technicians, by permission of the Dental Disease Prevention Activity,
U.S. Public Health Service)

Fig. 13.3   Electronic feeder
(Permission of Wallace & Tiernan, Inc.)

FLOAT

HOPPER

FLUORIDE
CHEMICAL

GUIDE
VANES

MOTOR

FEED
SLIDE

FEED
ROLLS

WATER
SPRAY
INLET

SOLUTION
TANK

WATER LEVEL
LINE

DISCHARGE
LINE

OVERFLOW
LINE & DRAIN

Fig. 13.4   Volumetric feeder, roll-type

(Reproduced from *WATER FLUORIDATION*, A Training Course Manual for Engineers
and Technicians, by permission of the Dental Disease Prevention Activity,
U.S. Public Health Service)

Fig. 13.5   Volumetric feeder, screw-type

(Reproduced from WATER FLUORIDATION, A Training Course Manual for Engineers
and Technicians, by permission of the Dental Disease Prevention Activity,
U.S. Public Health Service)

VERTICAL
GATE

FLUORIDE
CHEMICAL

HOPPER

SMALL SCALES

ROLLER

MOTOR

WEIGH BELT

SOLUTION
TANK

WATER INLET
CONTROLS

MIXER

WATER SUPPLY

CLEARWELL

Fig. 13.6 Gravimetric feeder, belt-type

(Reproduced from *WATER FLUORIDATION,* A Training Course Manual for Engineers
and Technicians, by permission of the Dental Disease Prevention Activity,
U.S. Public Health Service)

Direct Acid Feed System

Diluted Acid Feed System

Volumetric Feeder — Solution Tank System

Manual Batch System With Dry Chemicals

Fig. 13.7 *Typical fluoridation systems*
(Permission of Wallace & Tiernan, Inc.)

13.31 Saturators[5]

The saturator (Figure 13.8) is a special application of a solution feeder. A small pump delivers a saturated solution of sodium fluoride into the water system. The principle of a saturator is that a saturated solution will result if water is allowed to trickle through a bed containing sodium fluoride.

Although saturated solutions of sodium fluoride can be manually prepared, generally the easiest and best way is an automatic feed device. Only crystal-grade (20 to 60 mesh) sodium fluoride should be fed with a saturator. Sodium fluoride has a nearly constant solubility at normal temperature ranges and thus produces a fluoride solution of uniform strength. Sodium silicofluoride is not recommended to feed through the saturator because of its very low solubility in water (see Table 13.2). Maintain a depth of six to ten inches (150 to 250 mm) in the sodium fluoride bed of the saturator. Saturators should be stirred every day to prevent fluoride solids from building up on the bottom. The use of powdered sodium fluoride is not recommended because this chemical will clog the saturator.

Many dry chemical feed systems include a mixer, dissolving tank, and *DAY TANK*[6] (Figure 13.9). The mixer mixes a known amount of chemicals with a measured amount of water in a dissolving tank or solution chamber. This is a "batch mixed" process because the chemicals are mixed with a specified amount of water, rather than being mixed in flowing water. The dissolving tank allows the chemicals to become dissolved in water. The solution is then either continuously applied to the water being treated or is stored in a day tank or storage tank. The day tank usually stores enough chemical solution to properly treat the plant flow for at least one day. The chemical solution is fed from the day tank to the water being treated by a chemical feeder (feed pump) whose feed rate continuously adjusts to the flow being treated (flow-paced).

When working with fluoridation systems using a sodium fluoride solution, the hardness of the water is very important.

Hard water can produce problems in systems using saturators and dissolving tanks through the formation of low solubility calcium and magnesium fluoride compounds. If the dilution water has a hardness of less than 10 mg/L hardness as $CaCO_3$, there will be no problem. If the hardness range is above 10 mg/L and below 75 mg/L, scaling will continue to occur and the cost of ongoing cleaning and maintenance must be considered. Above a hardness of 75 mg/L, a softened water must be used for the water to prepare a fluoride solution in order to prevent severe scaling in the equipment.

Water can be softened prior to use with fluoridation equipment by the use of zeolite ion exchangers. As an alternative to the zeolite water softener, polyphosphates (at 7 to 15 mg/L) may be used to prevent plugging by scale in the feed system. The polyphosphates are added to the day tank to prevent scale deposits. If neither a zeolite softener nor polyphosphates are used, plugging may occur at any point in the feed system, including valves, saturator bed, and injection point. Remove these hardness deposits by flushing the system with vinegar or a five-percent solution of hydrochloric acid (muriatic acid). The saturator beds also may require the removal of water hardness deposits.

13.32 Downflow Saturators (Figure 13.10)

There are two kinds of saturators, the upflow saturator and the downflow saturator. In the downflow saturator, the solid sodium fluoride is held in a plastic drum or barrel and is isolated from the prepared solution by a plastic cone or a pipe manifold. A filtration barrier is provided by layers of sand and gravel to prevent particles of undissolved sodium fluoride from infiltrating the solution area under the cone or within the pipe manifold. The feeder pump draws the solution from within the cone or manifold at the bottom of the plastic drum. Downflow saturators require clean gravel and sand. In some systems the gravel and sand must be cleaned every day or two.

13.33 Upflow Saturators (Figure 13.11)

In an upflow saturator, undissolved sodium fluoride forms its own bed below which water is forced upward under pressure. No barrier is used since the water comes up through the bed of sodium fluoride and the specific gravity of the solid material keeps it from rising into the area of the clear solution above. A spider-type water distributor located at the bottom of the tank contains hundreds of very small slits. Water, forced under pressure through these slits, flows upward through the sodium fluoride bed at a controlled rate to ensure the desired four-percent solution. The feeder pump intake line floats on

---

[5] *Saturator (SAT-you-RAY-tore).   A device which produces a fluoride solution for the fluoridation process. The device is usually a cylindrical container with granular sodium fluoride on the bottom. Water flows either upward or downward through the sodium fluoride to produce the fluoride solution.*

[6] *Day Tank.   A tank used to store a chemical solution of known concentration for feed to a chemical feeder. A day tank usually stores sufficient chemical solution to properly treat the water being treated for at least one day. Also called an age tank.*

Fig. 13.8   Fluoride saturator
(Permission of Wallace & Tiernan, Inc.)

OPTIONAL

MIXING
FUNNEL

ADD A MEASURED AMOUNT OF CHEMICAL

WATER METER

MECHANICAL MIXER

MEASURED
AMOUNT OF
WATER

DISSOLVING TANK
(BATCH MIXED)

DAY TANK OR
STORAGE TANK

KNOWN
CONCENTRATION
OF SOLUTION

CHEMICAL
FEEDER
(FLOW-
PACED)

TO WATER
BEING
TREATED

Fig. 13.9   Dry chemical dissolver, day tank, and feeder

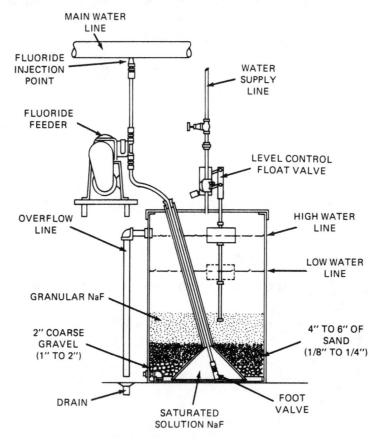

Fig. 13.10   Downflow saturator

(Reproduced from WATER FLUORIDATION, A Training Course Manual for Engineers
and Technicians, by permission of the Dental Disease Prevention Activity,
U.S. Public Health Service)

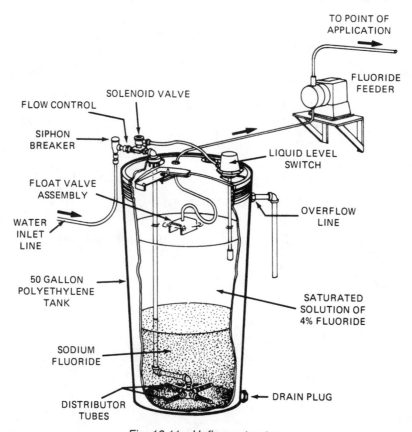

Fig. 13.11   Upflow saturator

(Reproduced from WATER FLUORIDATION, A Training Course Manual for Engineers
and Technicians, by permission of the Dental Disease Prevention Activity,
U.S. Public Health Service)

top of the solution in order to avoid withdrawal of undissolved sodium fluoride. The water pressure requirements are 20 psi (138 kPa) minimum to 125 psi (862 kPa) maximum and the flow is regulated at 4 GPM (0.25 L/sec). Since introduction of water to the bottom of the saturator constitutes a definite cross connection, *A MECHANICAL SIPHON-BREAKER MUST BE INCORPORATED INTO THE WATER LINE*; or better still, the saturator can be factory modified to include an air gap and a water feed pump.

Figures 13.8 and 13.11 show two configurations of upflow-type saturators which feed and prepare constant strength fluoride solution from granular sodium fluoride. The upflow type is the preferred type over the downflow saturator, as it is much easier to clean and maintain. Under normal conditions, it should need cleaning only once a year. For these reasons the construction and use of an upflow saturator is discussed in some detail.

To prepare an upflow saturator for use, the following steps should be taken.

1. With the distributor tubes in place, and the floating suction device removed, add 200 to 300 pounds (91 to 136 kg) of sodium fluoride directly to the tank. Any type of sodium fluoride can be used, from coarse crystal to fine crystal, but fine crystal will dissolve better than coarse material. If crystal is not available, powder can be used, but it is not as desirable as a crystal form of sodium fluoride.

2. Connect the solenoid water valve to an electric outlet and turn on the water supply. The water level should be slightly below the overflow; if it is not, the liquid level switch should be adjusted.

3. Replace the intake float and connect it to the feeder intake line. The saturator is now ready to use.

4. By looking through the translucent wall of the saturator tank, you should be able to see the level of undissolved sodium fluoride. Whenever the level is low enough, add another 100 pounds (45 kg) of fluoride.

5. The water distributor slits are supposed to be essentially self-cleaning. The accumulation of insolubles and precipitates is not as serious a problem as it is in a downflow saturator; however, a periodic cleaning is still required. Frequency of cleaning is dictated by the severity of use and the rate of accumulation of debris.

6. Because of the thicker bed of sodium fluoride attainable in an upflow saturator, higher withdrawal rates are possible. With 300 pounds (136 kg) of sodium fluoride in the saturator tank, more than 15 gallons per hour (58 L/hr) of saturated solution can be fed. This rate is sufficient to treat about 5,000 gallons per minute (135 L/sec) of water to a fluoride level of 1.0 mg/L.

7. The fixed water inlet rate of 4 GPM (0.25 L/sec) should register satisfactorily on a ⅝-inch (16-mm) meter.

From a financial point of view, many water agencies will want to design their fluoridation plants for unattended operation. In such cases, the system design will include provisions for automatic shutdown and an alarm system. For the sake of the operator who has to respond at all hours, alarm lights should be wired to indicate reasons for plant shutdown. For example, alarms could be set to indicate low water flow in the main pipeline, high fluoride flow, high or low fluoride levels, low injection water pressure, power outage, and a running time meter to indicate "down" time. These warning systems are particularly helpful in large systems.

13.34 Large Hydrofluosilicic Acid Systems
(Figure 13.12)

A more complicated system for fluoridation is a closed-loop control feeding system using hydrofluosilicic acid. This system finds use in large installations where the hydrofluosilicic acid can be delivered by tanker truck of around 4,000 gallons (15,140 L), although, of course, smaller amounts can be purchased. The installation depicted in Figure 13.12 can treat up to 285 million gallons per day (1,079 ML/day). The advantages in this system are the elimination of dust hazards and minimal labor requirements.

The storage tanks are made of filament-wound fiberglass. The interior lining is Dera Kane 411-45 Resixl with a final barrier of Nexus Veil (which has replaced Dynel). Steel tanks lined with at least ³/₃₂ inch (2.34 mm) polyvinyl chloride sheet or neoprene sheet secured to the metal surface with adhesive can also be used. Hydrofluosilicic acid storage tanks constructed of plastic should be housed in enclosures to protect the tanks from vandalism. Leaks could be dangerous to passersby and will kill surrounding vegetation. The tanks must be vented to the outside as the fumes from the acid are highly corrosive.

Inspection of internal conditions of the hydrofluosilicic tanks should be made on two-year intervals as some lining deterioration can be expected over a period of time. Should small leaks occur in the PVC piping, repairs should be made at once; they will only become worse and any acid dripping on concrete surfaces will dissolve the surface fairly quickly.

The use of a closed-loop control system in an unattended plant utilizing a fluoride analyzer as one of the controls is not recommended. The problem is that if the analyzer goes haywire and incorrectly indicates low fluoride levels, the system will try to correct itself and increase the addition of fluoride chemical. The net result will be to actually over-fluoridate the water supply.

QUESTIONS

Write your answers in a notebook and then compare your answers with those on page 64.

13.3A List the three different types of situations whereby drinking waters may contain fluoride ions.

13.3B List three important design features of fluoridation systems.

13.3C What problems can be created by hard water in systems using saturators and dissolving tanks?

13.3D What is a saturator?

Fig. 13.12 Large automatic hydrofluosilicic system

13.4 FINAL CHECKUP OF EQUIPMENT

13.40 Avoid Overfeeding

The operator must be certain that there will be no overfeed of fluoride ions. A gross overfeed can cause illness and bad public relations. Of all the chemicals used in the water treatment plant, fluoride concentrations probably require the closest attention to maximum dosages.

13.41 Review of Designs and Specifications

When reviewing fluoride feeding system designs and specifications, the operator should check the items listed below.

1. Review the results of pre-design tests to determine the fluoride rate for both the present and future. The fluoridator should be sized to handle the full range of chemical doses or provisions should be made for future expansion.

2. Determine if sampling points are provided to measure chemical feeder output.

3. Examine plans for valving to allow flushing the system with water before removing from service.

4. Be sure corrosion-resistant drip pans and drains are provided to prevent chemical leaks from reaching the floor, for example, drips from pump packing.

5. Check that all piping, valves, and fittings are made of corrosion-resistant materials such as PVC or Stainless Steel Type 316.

6. Determine the amount of maintenance required. The system should require a minimum of maintenance. Equipment should be standard, with replacement parts readily available.

7. Consider the effect of changing head conditions (both feeder suction and discharge head conditions) on the chemical feeder output. Changing head conditions will not affect the output if the proper chemical feeder has been specified and installed.

8. Determine whether locations for monitoring readouts and dosage controls are convenient to the operation center and easy to read and record.

9. Any switches that throw the equipment from automatic into a hand or manual mode should be equipped with a color-coded red warning light to indicate that the equipment is on "hand" or "manual." This can easily be accomplished by a double-throw, double-pole toggle switch.

Lights with different colors can be used to indicate normal or automatic operation as well as ON or OFF in order to avoid confusion.

10. The location where fluoride is added to the water should be where there will be the least possible removal of fluoride by other chemicals added to the water (after filtration and before the clear well).

11. Be sure the chemical hoppers are located where there is plenty of room so they can be conveniently and safely filled with the fluoride chemical.

12. Dust exhaust systems should be installed where substantial amounts of dry chemicals are handled.

13. In any fluoridation system, except the sodium fluoride saturator, scales are necessary for weighing the quantity of chemical (including solution) fed per day.

14. Alarms are important to signal and prevent both the loss of feed and overfeeding.

15. Any potable water line connected to a chemical feeder unit must be provided with a vacuum breaker or an air gap to prevent a cross connection.

13.5 CHEMICAL FEEDER START-UP

After the chemical feed system has been purchased and installed, carefully check the system out before start-up. Even if the contractor who installed the system is responsible for ensuring that the equipment operates as designed, the operation by plant personnel, the functioning of the equipment, and the results from the process are the responsibility of the chief operator. Therefore, before start-up, check the items listed below.

1. Inspect the electrical system for proper voltage, for properly sized overload protection, for proper operation of control lights on the control panel, for proper safety lockout switches and operation, and for proper equipment rotation.

2. Confirm that the manufacturer's lubrication and start-up procedures are being followed. Equipment may be damaged in minutes if it is run without lubrication.

3. Examine all fittings, inspection plates, and drains to ensure that they will not leak when placed into service.

4. Determine the proper positions for all valves. A positive displacement pump will damage itself or rupture lines in seconds if allowed to run against a closed valve or system.

5. Be sure that the type of fluoride to be fed is available and in the hopper or feeder. A progressive cavity pump will be damaged in minutes if it is allowed to run dry.

6. Inspect all equipment for binding or rubbing.

7. Confirm that safety guards are in place.

8. Examine the operation of all auxiliary equipment including the dust collectors, fans, cooling water, mixing water, and safety equipment.

9. Check the operation of alarms and safety shutoffs. If it is possible, operate these devices by manually tripping each one. Examples of these devices are alarms and shutoffs for high water, low water, high temperature, high pressure, and high chemical levels.

10. Be sure that safety equipment such as eyewash, drench showers, dust masks, face shields, gloves, and vent fans are in place and functional.

11. Record all important nameplate data and place it in the plant files for future reference.

QUESTIONS

Write your answers in a notebook and then compare your answers with those on pages 64 and 65.

13.4A   Why must overfeeding of fluoridation chemicals be prevented?

13.4B   What should be the capacity or size of the fluoridator?

13.5A   What items should be considered when inspecting the fluoridation electrical system?

13.5B   List the safety equipment that should be available near a fluoridation system.

13.6   CHEMICAL FEEDER OPERATION

13.60   Fine Tuning

Once the chemical feed equipment is in operation and the major "bugs" are worked out, the feeder will need to be "fine tuned." To aid in fine tuning and build confidence in the entire chemical feed system, the operator must maintain accurate records (see Section 13.62, "Fluoridation Log Sheets").

A comment or remarks section should be used to note abnormal conditions, such as a feeder plugged for a short time, related equipment that malfunctions, and other problems. Daily logs should be summarized into a form that operators can use as a future reference.

13.61   Preparation of Fluoride Solution

To learn how to make up a fluoride solution, let's assume a hypothetical case using the following data:

1. Flow to be treated is 10 million gallons per day,

2. Hydrofluosilicic acid 20% is the chemical to be used,

3. The unfluoridated water contains 0.05 mg/L (ppm) fluoride ion (F⁻), and

4. The desired fluoride concentration in the treated water is 1.0 mg/L.

What should the feed rate be?

See "Treatment Chart I, Hydrofluosilicic Acid," located on the next page.

Locate the 10 MGD flow on the left-hand scale of the graph and follow that line to the right until it intersects the *20 PERCENT* diagonal line. Project this point down vertically to the intersection of bottom line indicating gallons per day (or gallons per hour) required to produce a one-mg/L (ppm) dose of fluoride (F). The answer is *50 GALLONS PER DAY* or a little less than 2.1 GPH (gallons per hour). Multiply the 50 by (1.00 − 0.05) to give the needed treatment of 47.5 gallons per day or 2 GPH. The 1.00 is the desired dose of 1.00 mg/L and the 0.05 is the actual fluoride concentration of 0.05 mg/L in the untreated water.

In some cases it might be desirable to use a weaker acid solution to avoid feed rates below the minimum capacity of the metering pump. Dilution then is in order. The concentration may be reduced by volumetric proportions, for example one gallon of 20-percent acid plus one gallon of water results in two gallons of 10-percent acid. If possible try to avoid having to dilute acid because of potential errors and problems, especially with hard water. Peristaltic and electronic feeder pumps (Figures 13.2 and 13.3) may be used when the feed rates are low.

See Section 13.12, "Calculating Fluoride Dosages," for eleven example problems.

13.62   Fluoridation Log Sheets

You will probably want to design your own log sheets so they will be consistent with the installation features at your plant. Sample log sheets are shown on Figures 13.13, 13.14 and 13.15 (see pages 51, 53, and 55).

13.620   Hydrofluosilicic Acid

Figure 13.13 shows a typical log sheet from a hydrofluosilicic acid station. An explanation of the various columns is given below.

1. "Date" refers to calendar date when readings were logged or the date a shipment of fluoride was received.

2. "Time" refers to time event happened.

3. "Tank" that is supplying the feeder is circled. "Gals." refers to the gage reading of the amount of acid in the tank.

4. "% & Sp. Gr." Each delivery is accompanied by a vendor's laboratory analysis. The specific gravity is not measured until the tank is ready to be placed in service. When mixing acids of varying strengths, the end percentage must be calculated and entered in the proper column. See Example 10 in Section 13.12, "Calculating Fluoride Dosages."

5. For each tank follow the directions given in Step 4.

6. "Tank Loss Gals." refers to the amount of feed during the reporting period. In the sample 2,930 − 2,600 = 330 gallons. The feeding equipment should be equipped with an acid totalizer readout.

TREATMENT CHART I
Hydrofluosilicic Acid

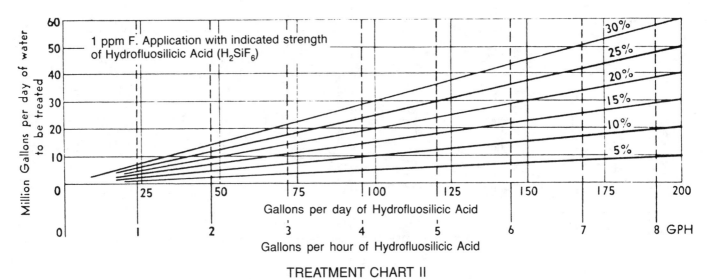

TREATMENT CHART II
Hydrofluosilicic Acid

(Permission of Wallace & Tiernan, Inc.)

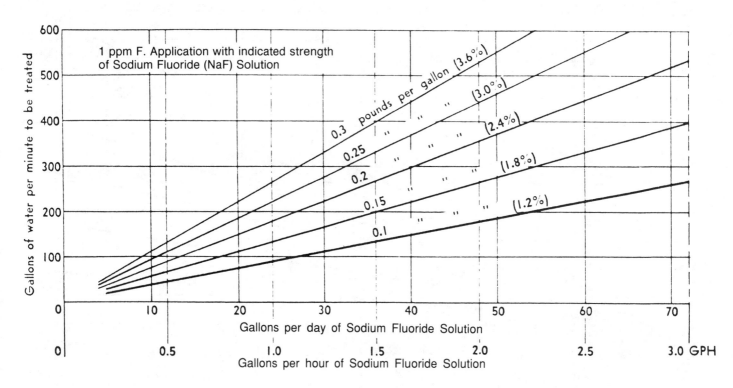

TREATMENT CHART III
Sodium Fluoride

TREATMENT CHART IV
Sodium Fluoride

(Permission of Wallace & Tiernan, Inc.)

BYPASS TUNNEL FLUORIDE STATION

Week Ending _December 11, 1995_

DATE	TIME	ACID STORAGE TANK 1 GALS.	TANK 1 % & SP. GR.	TANK 2 GALS.	TANK 2 % & SP. GR.	TANK 3 GALS.	TANK 3 % & SP. GR.	TANK 4 GALS.	TANK 4 % & SP. GR.	TANK LOSS GALS.	RATIO	H₂SIF₆ TOTALIZER	H₂SIF₆ GALS.	WATER METER TOTALIZER	WATER M/GALS.	ACID GAL/MG	F RESID. PPM	DOWN TIME	OBS. BY
END OF PREVIOUS WEEK		2930	1.226 / 22.9	7370	23.0	120	23.9	2315	23.1		0.88	884676.08		191.01			0.98		
12/5	11:00A	2600								330	0.88	885005.50	329.42	268.00	76.99	4.28	0.97		TMcK

FLOW — BIF METER — F & P METER

REMARKS:

7. The "ratio" column indicates the feed setting computed using the acid strength, specific gravity, and required dosage. The following steps illustrate how to calculate the feed setting for a specific piece of equipment.

   (a) (Sp. Gr.)(lbs/gal water)(% H_2SiF_6)(% F^- (in H_2SiF_6)) = lbs F^-/gal.

   (b) Substituting figures in the above formula.

   (c) $(1.226)(8.34)(0.229)(0.791) = 1.85$ lbs F^-/gal.

   (d) Dosage: $8.34 \div 1.85 = 4.51$ gallons acid/MG water.

   (e) In order to compensate for the .05 mg/L F^- in the raw water supply, the above figure of 4.51 should be reduced by 5% which is the relationship of the desired level of say 1 mg/L F^- to the raw water level of .05 mg/L F^-.

   (f) $4.51 - (.05 \times 4.51) = 4.51 - .23 = 4.28$ gal/MG.

   (g) Ratio setting therefore is $4.28 \div 4.80$ or 0.89.

   (h) The flow capacity of the pipeline water meter at 100% is 300 MGD.

   (i) The flow capacity of the acid feed pump is 1,440 gallons of H_2SiF_6/day.

      The ratio of the above two 100% capacities is $1,440 \div 300$ or 4.8 gal/MG.

      Note the difference of the setting of 0.88 and the calculated figure of 0.89. This adjustment is made in order that the fluoride dosage will agree with the laboratory results. In all instances, the laboratory results should determine the feed settings.

      The small difference in calculated setting and actual setting can also result from accumulated errors in the control equipment, that is, flow transmitter, square root ($\sqrt{}$) extractor, and ratio controller.

8. The H_2SiF_6 column records the totalizer values.

9. "H_2SiF_6 Gals." is the actual amount of acid fed into the system and is derived as follows:

   $885,005.50 - 884,676.08 = 329.42$ gallons

   This figure should be fairly close to the reading obtained at Step 6. If it is not, look for errors in readings, leaks, or equipment malfunctioning.

10. "Water Meter Totalizer" is the cumulative total of the amount of water being treated measured by a Venturi or some other type of primary water meter.

11. "Water M/Gals." is the actual amount of water passing through the water meter for the time period involved and again is derived by simple subtraction:

   $268.00 - 191.01 = 76.99$ Million Gallons.

12. "Acid Gal/MG" is the rate of treatment for hydrofluosilicic acid and is obtained by dividing the figures from Step 9 by the figure from Step 11.

   $329.42 \div 76.99 = 4.28$

13. "F Resid. PPM" is actual fluoride content in the treated water as read by continuous flow fluoride ion analyzer.

14. "Down Time." The equipment should be equipped with a running time meter reading in seconds that begins to operate any time the plant shuts down. This will give reasons for low feed as indicated by the readings in Step 12. The operator should know why this deviation occurred.

15. "Obs. By." This will be the operator's initials.

13.621 Sodium Silicofluoride

1. Figure 13.14 is a typical log sheet for a gravimetric feeder feeding powdered sodium silicofluoride.

2. "Date" and "Time" are entered in the first two columns.

3. "Totalizer Reading (lbs.)." This reading indicates a cumulative reading of the amount of silicofluoride that has been fed by the machine.

4. "Weight Loss per 24 hrs. (lbs.)" is the amount of silicofluoride actually fed during the time frame and is determined from the readings observed in Step 3 as follows:

   $44,165.5 - 43,276.9 = 888.6$.

5. "Mach. Feed Setting" is the feed rate being used. This rate may vary from machine to machine depending upon gear ratios and other devices used to control the rate of chemical feed. If the laboratory tests indicate low or high fluoride ion level, the adjustment is made with this setting on a percentage basis. If the laboratory fluoride ion level is 10 percent low, then this setting should be raised 10 percent.

6. "Chem. Added to Bin (lbs.)" is the amount of chemical taken from storage and dumped into the feeder hopper.

7. "Chemical Left in Storage (lbs.)" is the amount of fluoride in the bulk storage. This is useful in programming supply orders and in checking the accuracy of the feeder over a period of time. To check accuracy, compare this amount with the amount indicated in Step 4 over a six-month or one-year period.

8. "Pump Operating" is useful if several pumps are available to inject the dissolved sodium silicofluoride into the water main.

9. "Water Meter Reading (m.g.)" is the reading from the main line water meter.

10. "Water Treated (m.g.)" is the amount of water actually treated and is derived from Step 9 data as follows:

   $39,829.73 - 39,762.41 = 67.32$.

FLUORIDE STATION REPORT

Station _Sunset Supply Line_

Week Ending _December 14, 1995_

Date	Time	Totalizer Reading (lbs.)	Weight Loss per 24 hrs. (lbs.)	Mach. Feed Setting	Chem. Added to Bin (lbs.)	Chemical Left in Storage (lbs.)	Pump Operating	Water Meter Reading (m.g.)	Water Treated (m.g.)	Dosage (lbs. per m.g.)	Plant Down Time (Hrs.)	Feeder Time Lapse (sec.)	Observ.
END OF PREVIOUS WEEK		43276.9		52.8		42000	1A	39762.41		13.2			
12/5	10:20A	44165.5	888.6	52.8	400	41600	1A	39829.73	67.32	13.7		12735	

Fig. 13.14 Log sheet for fluoride station reports

11. "Dosage (lbs. per m.g.)" represents the actual dosage of fluoride in the water. This figure should be constant, barring down time, changes in machine feed setting, Step 5 or equipment malfunctioning. The value is derived from the weight loss (Step 4) divided by the water treated (Step 10) as follows:

$$888.6 \div 67.32 = 13.2.$$

12. "Plant Down Time (Hrs.)" is the period of time fluoride was not being fed and the plant was shut down because of power failure or automatic shutdown. The installation should be equipped with a resettable running time meter reading hours and tenths.

13. Figure 13.15 is a typical small plant log sheet used in plants utilizing sodium silicofluoride. This log sheet is provided through the courtesy of the City of Palo Alto, California.

QUESTIONS

Write your answers in a notebook and then compare your answers with those on page 65.

13.6A What should be the feed rate in gallons per day for treating 6 MGD with hydrofluosilicic acid 20 percent if the desired fluoride ion concentration is 1.2 mg/L? Assume the raw water does not contain any fluoride ion.

13.6B What could be the causes of differences between the recorded volume of acid used from a storage tank and the volume of acid fed into the system as measured by a flowmeter?

13.7 PREVENTION OF OVERFEEDING

1. Operators must ensure that no overfeeding occurs because no additional benefits result from overfeeding and there is a waste of chemicals and money. Excessive overfeeding could be harmful to consumers. Overfeeding can be prevented by proper operation and continuous monitoring of the product water.

2. If the size of the installation warrants, a continuous fluoride ion analyzer should be installed in the treated water line located downstream a sufficient distance so that adequate mixing is ensured.

3. In a large plant involving shift operation, grab samples can be analyzed for the fluoride level during each shift; otherwise, once-a-day checks will suffice.

4. If the plant uses one of the solid fluoride compounds and the operator questions whether there is total solubility, the fluoride feeder can be shut down and the lack of fluoride traced out in the distribution system. There should be a

sudden drop to zero fluoride or to the background level if total solubility is not being achieved (the undissolved solid fluoride compound will settle out).

5. All liquid systems should be checked for positive protection against backsiphonage from fluoride storage tanks.

6. Shut down the plant if there is any significant overfeeding. Start flushing the affected mains and notify the local and state health departments. The water department and the health departments will then decide if public notification should be undertaken.

13.8 UNDERFEEDING

In contrast to the chlorination process where continuous operation must be ensured, fluoridation does not have to be continuous. Shutdowns for cleaning, adjustments, or due to safety controls can be tolerated for short time periods. This does not mean that sloppy operation and maintenance is desirable. Every attempt should be made to maintain constant feeding. For example, the installation of standby electrical generating equipment just to maintain fluoridation equipment in operation would not be warranted. If the standby generator had to be purchased for other reasons, then the emergency circuit may also include the fluoride feeding equipment. Underfeeding should not be allowed because this results in a very significant reduction of the benefits of fluoridation.

Daily inspection of the fluoridation equipment, fluoride tests on the treated water, and calculation of the dosage from water treatment and chemical use data can greatly minimize the possibility of both overfeeding and underfeeding.

QUESTIONS

Write your answers in a notebook and then compare your answers with those on page 65.

13.7A Why should overfeeding be prevented?

13.7B What should be done if significant overfeeding occurs?

13.8A Why might a fluoridation operation be shut down?

13.9 SHUTTING DOWN CHEMICAL SYSTEMS

If the fluoridation equipment is going to be shut down for an extended length of time, it should be cleaned out to prevent corrosion and/or the solidifying of the chemical. Lines and equipment could be damaged when restarted if chemicals left in them solidify. Operators could be seriously injured if they open a chemical line that has not been properly flushed out.

The following items should be included in your checklist for shutting down the chemical system:

1. Flush out the chemical supply with water,

2. Run dry chemicals completely out of the equipment and clean equipment by using a vacuum cleaner,

3. Flush out all the solution lines with water until the lines are clean,

4. Shut off the electrical power,

5. Shut off the water supply and *PROTECT FROM FREEZING*,

6. Drain and clean the mix and feed tanks, and

7. Padlock (lock out) the main electric switch box to the fluoride equipment.

Fig. 13.15 Weekly water production and treatment log

WATER FLUORIDATION EQUIPMENT CHECK PROCEDURES[a]

Start

Yes — Does Fluoridator Operate? — No

Make minor adjustments for optimum fluoride level.

Turn off water well pump using manual control.

Close all fluoridator valves.

Disconnect the high and low pressure sides of the Venturi or orifice plate.

CAUTION
Fluoridator tanks are pressurized. Bleed off pressure slowly at disconnection points.

Disassemble and clean ball and check valves. Assemble and reinstall valves in closed position.

Turn off water well pump using manual control. Open all fluoridator valves, starting at the high pressure side of Venturi/orifice plate. Follow flow through fluoridator employing the following method:

1. Open valve on high pressure side at Venturi/orifice plate.
2. Open brass pressure release valve on salt vat. Check for water flow through valve.
3. Open three-way valve below flowmeter/needle valve. Check for water flow through flowmeter/needle valve.
4. Open three-way valve leaving the fluoride saturator tank. Open this valve to waste and check for water flow.
5. Open ball valve at low pressure side of Venturi/orifice plate.

No — Water Flows? — Yes

Make minor adjustments to provide optimum fluoride level.

Close all fluoridator valves.
Release pressure in salt vat, zeolite tank and fluoride tank by opening three-way valves capable to drain to waste.

Disconnect the salt vat, clean, reassemble and connect.

Disconnect the flowmeter/needle valve, disassemble, clean, reassemble and reinstall.

Disconnect the three-way valve, clean, reassemble and reinstall.

Connect all parts then start well water pump and open fluoridator valves.

No — Water Flows? — Yes

1. Release pressure.
2. Disassemble drop-pipes. Clean and reassemble.
3. Water jet drop-pipes into zeolite and sodium fluoride.
4. Fill all tanks with system water, cap tanks.
5. Open fluoridator valves.

The system should operate with good efficiency.
Take water samples and test for fluoride concentration. Adjust needle valve until several samples show 1.1 to 1.2 mg/L fluoride concentrations.

[a]   Reproduced with permission from *OPERATOR'S DRUMBEAT*, Volume 1, Number 6, March-April 1989. Albuquerque Area Indian Health Service, J.R. Olguin, Publisher.

13.10 MAINTENANCE

Maintenance should follow the same routine as with any similar chemical feeder, including regular cleanup and painting of the equipment and appurtenant metal piping and conduits. In order to give the plant a fresher look and hold down on painting, consider using all plastic piping even though it is needed only for the water supply. Conduit and fittings should also be plastic for the same reason. Vacuum any gears and other similar parts to remove fluoride dust.

Since fluoride solutions are extremely corrosive, be constantly on the lookout for drips or leaks and any other evidence of corrosion. Repair these conditions as quickly as possible. Also look for the buildup of insoluble deposits in feedlines and equipment. Schedule the removal of insoluble deposits on a regular basis to prevent buildups from creating any problems.

All containers of fluoride chemicals must be disposed of in an acceptable manner. Thoroughly rinse all containers with water to remove all traces of chemicals before allowing containers to leave your plant. You may burn the containers if a nuisance will not be created. Remember that fluoride fumes can kill vegetation and are harmful to people.

You don't need to be too concerned about checking the feed rate by catching a given amount of fluoride over a time period. The log will show long-period discrepancies and the daily laboratory tests will indicate any drifting from the desired fluoride concentration in the treated water.

Either you or the laboratory personnel must analyze the fluoridated water daily. Check the results for any deviations from the norm and take corrective action. Hand-held colorimeters are available for measuring fluoride in water. See Chapter 21, "Advanced Laboratory Procedures," for details on how to analyze samples for the fluoride ion.

An important part of your maintenance program is the prevention of any sanitary defects that could adversely affect the safety or quality of your treated drinking water. Sanitary defects that could develop in fluoridation systems include:

1. Lack of or inadequate start-stop controls,
2. Inadequate feed rate control equipment,
3. No analyzer to measure fluoride ion levels in treated water,
4. Lack of or inadequate backflow safeguards,
5. Fluoridation chemical not meeting AWWA specifications, and
6. Inadequate free chlorine residual in treated water.

13.11 SAFETY IN HANDLING FLUORIDE COMPOUNDS[7]

From the operator's viewpoint, fluoride chemicals have one thing in common with all other chemicals found in treatment plants: *FLUORIDE CHEMICALS* can seriously injure or kill the careless or untrained operator. Safety should be of special concern to *YOU* because it is your own health that is at stake.

13.110 Avoid Overexposure

One of the major causes of overexposure is the inhalation of fluoride dust. This usually occurs while a dry feeder or saturator is being loaded. Even with the use of dust collector systems, dust will circulate in the air. Always use approved respirators equipped with cartridges for organic dusts and vapors, protective coveralls, and gloves when emptying sacks or cleaning up equipment and plant surfaces.

When loading a saturator, dust will be minimized if crystalline sodium fluoride is fed instead of powdered sodium fluoride. When loading a dry feeder, you should wear a mask, apron, and rubber gloves to minimize exposure.

When the protection gear is removed, the remaining small traces of chemical should also be removed from your body. Some large water plants have dust collection systems that use a partial vacuum to draw dust from your body and vent it to the outside air after filtering.

Care should be taken when emptying bags of chemicals into a feeder hopper. The bags should be opened carefully at the top and the contents poured gently to minimize dust. Care should also be taken during storage of the bags. Bags should be stored in a dry place, preferably off the floor. If bags are stacked too high there is the possibility of them falling and breaking open.

If a saturator is used, you should be cautious about allowing the solution to come in contact with skin and clothing. If this does happen, the affected area should be washed immediately with water. This also applies to other fluoride solutions (such as the dissolving water used in a dry feeder).

If a fluoride acid is being fed, extra precaution must be taken. Fluoride acid is probably the most corrosive chemical found in a water plant. The pH of fluoride acid is approximately 1.2 and it will eat through glass faster than chlorine. Special care should be taken to keep fumes to a minimum. If the acid does come in contact with your skin, you may not be able to wash it off fast enough to prevent a burn. If this happens, standard first aid should be administered as soon as possible.

A good pair of safety goggles should be worn at all times when working around fluoridation equipment where there is any possibility of splashing fluoride solutions. Be especially cautious around the fluoride acids as the concentrated acid can dissolve the whites of one's eyes in addition to the usual burns associated with acids. Another "must" is a safety shower. This must be located within easy access to both the unloading operation and points of liquid usage.

Another safety precaution that should be followed is the labeling of all feeders and solution tanks. Proper labeling will help prevent placement of chemicals in the wrong feeder. If possible, fluoride chemical should be tinted blue to differentiate it from other water treatment chemicals.

13.111   Symptoms of Fluoride Poisoning

In the event that someone is poisoned, it is vitally important to recognize the early symptoms.

Some of the obvious signs of poisoning are vomiting, stomach cramps, and diarrhea. Usually, the person will become very weak, have trouble speaking, be very thirsty, and have poor color vision. In cases of extreme poisoning, there are strong, jerky muscle contractions in the arms and legs leading to convulsions. If poisoning is not treated immediately, the person may die. Fatal doses range from 4 to 5 gm, or about a tablespoon. This equals about 2,000 times the amount of fluoride swallowed by a person from a water supply.

If a person is poisoned by inhaling fluoride, the first symptoms will be a sharp, biting pain in the nose followed by a runny nose or nosebleed. It is doubtful that a person could inhale enough fluoride to produce the same effects as encountered from drinking a large amount of fluoride. However, the sudden presence of bad stomach cramps and pains in the nose and eyes should not be ignored.

The victim should see a doctor immediately, and the water treatment practices should be checked to determine the source of the fluoride poisoning. It is probably a good idea to check out treatment practices occasionally.

The importance of quick treatment for fluoride poisoning cannot be overemphasized. In such cases a doctor should be called immediately, and if the poisoning is severe, an ambulance should be called.

13.112   Basic First Aid

Once it is established that fluoride is the cause of the poisoning, first aid should be started while waiting for medical help. The following are recommended first-aid procedures:

1. Move the person away from any contact with fluoride and keep warm,

2. Inhalation: Remove exposed person to an uncontaminated area immediately. If breathing has stopped, start artificial respiration at once. Oxygen should be provided for an exposed person having difficulty breathing (but only by an authorized person) until exposed person is able to breathe easily unassisted. Exposed person should be examined by a physician.

3. Eye Contact: Flush eyes for at least 15 minutes with large amounts of water. Eyelids should be held apart during the flushing to ensure contact of water with all accessible tissue of the eyes and lids. Medical attention should be given as soon as possible.

4. Skin Contact: Exposed person should be removed to an uncontaminated area and subjected immediately to a drenching shower of water for a minimum of 15 to 20 minutes. Remove all contaminated clothing while under shower. Medical attention should be given as soon as possible for all burns, regardless of how minor they seem.

5. Ingestion: If conscious, give the exposed person large quantities of water immediately to dilute the acid. *DO NOT* induce vomiting. Milk may be given for its soothing effect. A physician should be contacted immediately.

6. Take the person to the hospital as soon as possible.

If common sense and good safety practice are used, the hazard to the water plant operator should be as small as the hazard to the water consumer.

Fluoridation chemicals are poisonous. Protect yourself from these toxic chemicals.

13.113   Protecting Yourself and Your Family

Avoid swallowing fluoridation chemicals. Don't eat, drink or smoke in or around chemical storage or feed areas. Do not inhale chemical dusts or vapors. Wear a respirator. Be sure exhaust fans and dust collectors are operating properly. Prevent hydrofluosilicic acid from coming in contact with your skin or eyes because hydrofluosilicic acid is very corrosive. If any hydrofluosilicic acid touches you, flood the contact area with plenty of water. If you are acutely poisoned by a fluoride chemical, you may be thirsty, vomit, and have stomach cramps, diarrhea, difficulty in speaking, and disturbed color vision. If any of these symptoms occur, consult a physician immediately.

When leaving the fluoride plant, wash your hands and change coveralls so that fluoride dust is not carried home.

13.114   Training

Special safety training must be given to all operators who will handle fluoride compounds. Training must include how to safely receive compounds from supplier, store until needed, prepare solutions, load feeders, and dose water being treated.

QUESTIONS

Write your answers in a notebook and then compare your answers with those on page 66.

13.9A   Why should fluoridation equipment be cleaned out if the equipment is going to be shut down for an extended length of time?

13.10A   How can fluoride dust be removed from gears?

13.10B   How would you determine if your fluoridation equipment was providing the desired dosage?

13.11A   What are the symptoms of acute fluoride poisoning?

13.12 CALCULATING FLUORIDE DOSAGES

FORMULAS

1. Charts can be used to determine feed rates. The feed rate is usually based on a dose of one mg/L; therefore actual feed rates must be adjusted.

$$\text{Actual Feed Rate, GPD} = \frac{(\text{Chart Feed Rate, GPD})(\text{Actual Dose, mg/}L)}{1 \text{ mg/}L}$$

2. Feed rates may be calculated on the basis of pounds per day or gallons per day. Consideration must be given to the pounds of fluoride ion per pound of commercial chemical.

$$\text{Feed Rate,} \atop \text{lbs/day} = \frac{(\text{Flow, MGD})(\text{Dose, mg/}L)(8.34 \text{ lbs/gal})(100\%)}{\text{Solution, \% F}}$$

or $$\text{Feed Rate,} \atop \text{lbs/day} = \frac{\text{Feed Rate, lbs F/day}}{\text{lbs F/lb Commercial Chemical}}$$

or $$\text{Feed Rate,} \atop \text{gal/day} = \frac{\text{Feed Rate, lbs/day}}{\text{Chemical Solution, lbs/gal}}$$

3. If the water being treated contains some fluoride ion, but not sufficient, then a feed dose must be calculated.

$$\text{Feed Dose, mg/}L = \text{Desired Dose, mg/}L - \text{Actual Concentration, mg/}L$$

4. Commercial chemicals usually are not 100 percent pure. Also, the chemical only contains a portion of the ion of concern (fluoride ion in this chapter).

$$\text{Portion F} = \frac{(\text{Commercial Purity, \%})(\text{Fluoride Ion, \%})}{(100\%)(100\%)}$$

The portion F is the pounds of F per pound of commercial chemical. For example, 0.6 pound F per one pound of commercial sodium silicofluoride.

5. To calculate the fluoride dosage or any chemical dosage, you need to know the pounds of chemical and volume of water in million gallons.

$$\text{Dosage, mg/}L = \frac{\text{Chemical, lbs}}{(\text{Water, M Gal})(8.34 \text{ lbs/gal})}$$

$$= \frac{\text{lbs Chemical}}{\text{Million lbs Water}}$$

If we substitute milligrams for pounds, we get

$$= \frac{\text{mg Chemical}}{\text{Million mg Water}}$$

One million milligrams of water occupy a volume of one liter.

$$= \frac{\text{mg Chemical}}{\text{Liter of Water}}$$

$$= \text{mg/}L$$

6. To determine the amount of feed solution in either gallons or gallons per day to treat a water, you need to know the amount of water to be treated in gallons or gallons per day, the feed dose in milligrams per liter and the feed solution in milligrams per liter.

$$\text{Feed Solution,} \atop \text{gal} = \frac{(\text{Flow, gal})(\text{Feed Dose, mg/}L)}{\text{Feed Solution, mg/}L}$$

NOTE: If the "Feed Solution" is in gallons per day instead of gallons, then the "Flow" must be in gallons per day also instead of gallons.

7. When mixing the same two acids or chemicals, but of different strengths, the volumes or flows of the chemicals and their strengths must be known.

$$\text{Mixture} \atop \text{Strength,} \atop \% = \frac{(\text{Volume 1, gal})(\text{Strength 1, \%}) + (\text{Volume 2, gal})(\text{Strength 2, \%})}{\text{Volume 1, gal} + \text{Volume 2, gal}}$$

NOTE: The "Volumes" may be in gallons or treated as flows in GPD or MGD. The "Strengths" may be in percentages or concentrations such as mg/L.

8. When using chemicals for fluoridation, we need to know the percentage fluoride ion purity. This information will allow us to convert the pounds of chemical dosage to pounds of fluoride ion available.

$$\text{Fluoride Ion} \atop \text{Purity, \%} = \frac{(\text{Molecular Weight of Fluoride})(100\%)}{\text{Molecular Weight of Chemical}}$$

EXAMPLE 1

A flow of 4 MGD is to be treated with a 20-percent solution of hydrofluosilicic acid (H_2SiF_6). The water to be treated contains no fluoride and the desired fluoride concentration is 1.8 mg/L. What should be the feed rate of hydrofluosilicic acid? Use the treatment charts.

Known		Unknown
Flow, MGD	= 4 MGD	1. Feed Rate, gal/day
Acid Solution, %	= 20%	2. Feed Rate, gal/hr
Desired F, mg/L	= 1.8 mg/L	

1. Use Treatment Chart I on page 49 because we are treating a relatively small flow (4 MGD).

2. Start on the left side at the 4 MGD value and move horizontally to the right to the 20 percent diagonal line.

3. At this point drop vertically downward to the bottom lines and read the feed rates for one mg/L (ppm).

   a. Feed Rate, gallons per day = 19 gal/day
   b. Feed Rate, gallons per hour = 0.8 gal/hr

4. Calculate the feed rate to produce the desired fluoride concentration of 1.8 mg/L.

   a. $$\text{Feed Rate, GPD} = \frac{(\text{Feed Rate, GPD})(\text{Desired F, mg/}L)}{1 \text{ mg/}L}$$

   $$= \frac{(19 \text{ GPD})(1.8 \text{ mg/}L)}{1 \text{ mg/}L}$$

   $$= 34.2 \text{ gal/day}$$

   b. $$\text{Feed Rate,} \atop \text{gal/hr} = \frac{(\text{Feed Rate, gal/hr})(\text{Desired F, mg/}L)}{1 \text{ mg/}L}$$

   $$= \frac{(0.8 \text{ gal/hr})(1.8 \text{ mg/}L)}{1 \text{ mg/}L}$$

   $$= 1.44 \text{ gal/hr}$$

EXAMPLE 2

A flow of 4 MGD is to be treated with a 20-percent solution of hydrofluosilicic acid (H_2SiF_6) which contains a fluoride purity of 79.2%. The water to be treated contains no fluoride and the desired fluoride concentration is 1.8 mg/L. Assume the hydrofluosilicic acid weighs 9.8 pounds per gallon. What should be the feed rate of hydrofluosilicic acid? Calculate the feed rate.

Known		**Unknown**
Flow, MGD	= 4 MGD	1. Feed Rate, gal/day
Acid Solution, %	= 20%	2. Feed Rate, gal/hr
Acid, lbs/gal	= 9.8 lbs/gal	
Purity, %	= 79.2%	
Desired F, mg/L	= 1.8 mg/L	

1. Calculate the hydrofluosilicic acid feed rate in pounds per day.

$$\text{Feed Rate, lbs/day} = \frac{(\text{Flow, MGD})(\text{Desired F, mg/}L)(8.34 \text{ lbs/gal})(100\%)(100\%)}{(\text{Acid Solution, \%})(\text{Purity, \%})}$$

$$= \frac{(4 \text{ MGD})(1.8 \text{ mg/}L)(8.34 \text{ lbs/gal})(100\%)(100\%)}{(20\%)(79.2\%)}$$

$$= 379 \text{ lbs acid/day}$$

2. Determine the feed rate of the acid in gallons per day.

$$\text{Feed Rate, gal/day} = \frac{\text{Feed Rate, lbs/day}}{\text{Acid, lbs/gal}}$$

$$= \frac{379 \text{ lbs acid/day}}{9.8 \text{ lbs acid/gal}}$$

$$= 39 \text{ gal acid/day}$$

NOTE: We obtained a feed rate of 34 gallons of acid per day from Treatment Chart I. The differences result from the problems of drawing and reading the chart accurately.

3. Calculate the feed rate in gallons of acid per hour.

$$\text{Feed Rate, gal/hr} = \frac{\text{Feed Rate, gal/day}}{24 \text{ hr/day}}$$

$$= \frac{39 \text{ gal acid/day}}{24 \text{ hr/day}}$$

$$= 1.6 \text{ gal acid/hr}$$

EXAMPLE 3

A flow of 200 GPM is to be treated with a 2.4-percent (0.2 lbs/gallon) solution of sodium fluoride (NaF). The water to be treated contains 0.7 mg/L of fluoride ion and the desired fluoride ion concentration is 1.6 mg/L. What should be the feed rate of sodium fluoride? Use the treatment charts.

Known		**Unknown**
Flow, GPM	= 200 GPM	1. Feed Rate, gal/day
NaF Solution, %	= 2.4%	2. Feed Rate, gal/hr
Desired F, mg/L	= 1.6 mg/L	
Actual F, mg/L	= 0.7 mg/L	

1. Use Treatment Chart III on page 50 because we are treating 200 GPM.

2. Start at the left side at the 200 GPM value and move horizontally to the right to the 2.4 percent diagonal line.

3. At this point drop vertically downward to the bottom lines and read the feed rates for one mg/L (ppm).

   a. Feed Rate, gallons per day = 26.5 gal/day
   b. Feed Rate, gallons per hour = 1.1 gal/hr

4. Calculate the feed rate to produce the desired fluoride concentration of 1.6 mg/L.

$$\text{Feed Dose, mg/}L = \text{Desired Dose, mg/}L - \text{Actual Conc, mg/}L$$

$$= 1.6 \text{ mg/}L - 0.7 \text{ mg/}L$$

$$= 0.9 \text{ mg/}L$$

$$\text{Feed Rate, GPD} = \frac{(\text{Feed Rate, GPD})(\text{Feed Dose, mg/}L)}{1 \text{ mg/}L}$$

$$= \frac{(26.5 \text{ gal/day})(0.9 \text{ mg/}L)}{1 \text{ mg/}L}$$

$$= 23.8 \text{ GPD}$$

$$\text{Feed Rate, gal/hr} = \frac{(\text{Feed Rate, gal/hr})(\text{Feed Dose, mg/}L)}{1 \text{ mg/}L}$$

$$= \frac{(1.1 \text{ gal/hr})(0.9 \text{ mg/}L)}{1 \text{ mg/}L}$$

$$= 0.99 \text{ gal/hr or 1 gal/hr}$$

EXAMPLE 4

A flow of 200 GPM is to be treated with a 2.4-percent (0.2 pounds per gallon) solution of sodium fluoride (NaF). The water to be treated contains 0.7 mg/L of fluoride ion and the desired fluoride ion concentration is 1.6 mg/L. What should be the feed rate of sodium fluoride? Calculate the feed rate. Assume the sodium fluoride has a fluoride ion purity of 45.3 percent.

Known		**Unknown**
Flow, GPM	= 200 GPM	1. Feed Rate, gal/day
NaF Solution, %	= 2.4%	2. Feed Rate, gal/hr
NaF Solution, lbs/gal	= 0.2 lb/gal	
Desired F, mg/L	= 1.6 mg/L	
Actual F, mg/L	= 0.7 mg/L	
Purity, %	= 45.3%	

1. Convert flow from gallons per minute to million gallons per day.

$$\text{Flow, MGD} = \frac{(\text{Flow, gal/min})(60 \text{ min/hr})(24 \text{ hr/day})}{1,000,000/\text{Million}}$$

$$= \frac{(200 \text{ gal/min})(60 \text{ min/hr})(24 \text{ hr/day})}{1,000,000/\text{Million}}$$

$$= 0.288 \text{ MGD}$$

2. Determine the fluoride feed dose in milligrams per liter.

$$\text{Feed Dose, mg/}L = \text{Desired Dose, mg/}L - \text{Actual Conc, mg/}L$$

$$= 1.6 \text{ mg/}L - 0.7 \text{ mg/}L$$

$$= 0.9 \text{ mg/}L$$

3. Calculate the feed rate in pounds of fluoride ion per day.

$$\text{Feed Rate, lbs F/day} = \text{(Flow, MGD)(Feed Dose, mg/L)(8.34 lbs/gal)}$$

$$= \text{(0.288 MGD)(0.9 mg/L)(8.34 lbs/gal)}$$

$$= 2.16 \text{ lbs F/day}$$

4. Convert the feed rate from pounds of fluoride per day to gallons of sodium fluoride solution per day.

$$\text{Feed Rate, gal/day} = \frac{\text{(Feed Rate, lbs F/day)(100\%)}}{\text{NaF Solution, lbs F/gallon)(Purity, \%)}}$$

$$= \frac{\text{(2.16 lbs F/day)(100\%)}}{\text{(0.2 lb F/gal)(45.3\%)}}$$

$$= 23.8 \text{ gal/day}$$

NOTE: We obtained a feed rate of 23.8 gal/day in both Examples 3 and 4. Sometimes you may get slightly different results using these two methods of calculating the feed rate. The differences could result from inaccurately preparing and reading the treatment chart as well as the assumed purity of fluoride ion in the sodium fluoride.

5. Convert the feed rate from gallons per day to gallons per hour.

$$\text{Feed Rate, gal/hr} = \frac{\text{Feed Rate, gal/day}}{24 \text{ hr/day}}$$

$$= \frac{23.8 \text{ gal/day}}{24 \text{ hr/day}}$$

$$= 1.0 \text{ gal/hr}$$

EXAMPLE 5

A flow of 1 MGD is treated with sodium silicofluoride (Na_2SiF_6) to provide a fluoride ion dose of 1.4 mg/L. What is the feed rate in pounds per day? Commercial sodium silicofluoride has a purity of 98.5 percent and the fluoride ion purity of sodium silicofluoride is 60.7 percent.

Known		Unknown
Flow, MGD	= 1 MGD	1. Feed Rate, lbs/day
Dose, mg/L	= 1.4 mg/L	
Na_2SiF_6 Purity, %	= 98.5%	
Fluoride Ion Purity, %	= 60.7%	

1. Calculate the portion of fluoride ion in the commercial sodium silicofluoride.

$$\text{Portion F} = \frac{\text{(Na_2SiF_6 Purity, \%)(Fluoride Ion Purity, \%)}}{\text{(100\%)(100\%)}}$$

$$= \frac{\text{(98.5\%)(60.7\%)}}{\text{(100\%)(100\%)}}$$

$$= 0.598 \text{ lb F/lb Commercial } Na_2SiF_6$$

This says that there is 0.598 pound of fluoride ion in a pound of commercial sodium silicofluoride.

2. Calculate the pounds of fluoride required per day.

$$\text{Fluoride, lbs/day} = \text{(Flow, MGD)(Dose, mg/L)(8.34 lbs/gal)}$$

$$= \text{(1 MGD)(1.4 mg/L)(8.34 lbs/gal)}$$

$$= 11.7 \text{ lbs F/day}$$

3. Determine the chemical feed rate for the commercial sodium silicofluoride in pounds per day.

$$\text{Feed Rate, lbs/day} = \frac{\text{Fluoride, lbs/day}}{\text{Fluoride, lbs/lb Commercial } Na_2SiF_6}$$

$$= \frac{11.7 \text{ lbs F/day}}{0.598 \text{ lb F/lb Commercial } Na_2SiF_6}$$

$$= 19.6 \text{ lbs/day Commercial } Na_2SiF_6$$

EXAMPLE 6

A flow of 1.4 MGD is treated with sodium silicofluoride. The raw water contains 0.4 mg/L of fluoride ion and the desired fluoride ion concentration is 1.6 mg/L. What should be the chemical feed rate in pounds per day? Assume each pound of commercial sodium silicofluoride (Na_2SiF_6) contains 0.6 pound of fluoride ion.

Known		Unknown
Flow, MGD	= 1.4 MGD	1. Feed Rate, lbs/day
Raw Water F, mg/L	= 0.4 mg/L	
Desired F, mg/L	= 1.6 mg/L	
Chemical, lbs F/lb	= 0.6 lb F/lb	

1. Determine the fluoride feed dose in milligrams per liter.

$$\text{Feed Dose, mg/L} = \text{Desired Dose, mg/L} - \text{Actual Conc, mg/L}$$

$$= 1.6 \text{ mg/L} - 0.4 \text{ mg/L}$$

$$= 1.2 \text{ mg/L}$$

2. Calculate the fluoride feed rate in pounds per day.

$$\text{Feed Rate, lbs F/day} = \text{(Flow, MGD)(Feed Dose, mg/L)(8.34 lbs/gal)}$$

$$= \text{(1.4 MGD)(1.2 mg/L)(8.34 lbs/gal)}$$

$$= 14.0 \text{ lbs F/day}$$

3. Determine the chemical feed rate in pounds of commercial sodium silicofluoride per day.

$$\text{Feed Rate,} \atop \text{lbs/day} = \frac{\text{Feed Rate, lbs F/day}}{\text{lbs F/lb Commercial Na}_2\text{SiF}_6}$$

$$= \frac{14.0 \text{ lbs F/day}}{0.6 \text{ lb F/lb Commercial Na}_2\text{SiF}_6}$$

$$= 23.3 \text{ lbs/day Commercial Na}_2\text{SiF}_6$$

EXAMPLE 7

The totalizer for a water treatment plant indicated that a total of 100,000 gallons of water had been treated with three pounds of 98 percent pure sodium fluoride (NaF). The fluoride ion purity for sodium fluoride is 45.3 percent. What was the added fluoride ion dosage in milligrams per liter?

Known	Unknown
Water Treated, MG = 0.1 M Gal	Fluoride Dosage, mg/L
NaF, lbs = 3 lbs	
NaF Purity, % = 98%	
F Ion Purity, % = 45.3%	

1. Calculate the portion of fluoride ion in the commercial sodium fluoride.

$$\text{Portion F} = \frac{(\text{NaF Purity, \%})(\text{Fluoride Ion Purity, \%})}{(100\%)(100\%)}$$

$$= \frac{(98\%)(45.3\%)}{(100\%)(100\%)}$$

$$= 0.444$$

or $= 0.444$ lb F/lb commercial NaF

2. Calculate the pounds of fluoride used.

$$\text{Fluoride,} \atop \text{lbs} = (\text{Commercial NaF, lb})(0.444 \text{ lb F/lb Comm. NaF})$$

$$= (3 \text{ lbs Comm. NaF})(0.444 \text{ lb F/lb Comm. NaF})$$

$$= 1.33 \text{ lbs F}$$

3. Calculate the fluoride dosage in milligrams per liter.

$$\text{Fluoride} \atop \text{Dosage,} \atop \text{mg/L} = \frac{\text{Fluoride, lbs F}}{(\text{Water Treated, M Gal})(8.34 \text{ lbs/gal})}$$

$$= \frac{1.33 \text{ lbs F}}{(0.1 \text{ M Gal})(8.34 \text{ lbs/gal})}$$

$$= \frac{1.33 \text{ lbs F}}{0.834 \text{ Million lbs Water}}$$

$$= \frac{1.6 \text{ lbs F}}{1 \text{ M lbs Water}}$$

$$= 1.6 \text{ mg/L}$$

EXAMPLE 8

Determine the percentage of fluoride ion in the feed solution from a saturator. The saturator contains 95 percent pure sodium fluoride, the maximum water solubility for sodium fluoride is four percent, and sodium fluoride is 45.3 percent fluoride ion.

Known	Unknown
Commercial NaF Purity, % = 95%	Solution, % F
NaF Solubility, % = 4%	
F Ion Purity, % = 45.3%	

Calculate the percentage of fluoride ion in the feed solution.

$$\text{Solution, \% F} = \frac{(\text{NaF Solubility, \%})(\text{F Ion Purity, \%})}{100\%}$$

$$= \frac{(4\%)(45.3\%)}{100\%}$$

$$= 1.8\%$$

NOTE: In a saturator, the commercial NaF purity of 95 percent does not enter into the calculations because the four percent solubility is all NaF.

EXAMPLE 9

The feed solution from a saturator containing 1.8 percent fluoride ion is used to treat a total flow of 400,000 gallons of water. The raw water has a fluoride ion content of 0.5 mg/L and the desired fluoride in the finished water is 1.8 mg/L. How many gallons of feed solution are needed?

Known	Unknown
Flow Vol, gal = 400,000 gal	Feed Solution, gallons
Raw Water F, mg/L = 0.5 mg/L	
Desired F, mg/L = 1.8 mg/L	
Feed Solution, % F = 1.8% F	

1. Convert the feed solution from a percentage fluoride ion to milligrams fluoride ion per liter of water.

1.0% F = 10,000 mg F/L

$$\text{Feed Solution, mg/L} = \frac{(\text{Feed Solution, \%})(10,000 \text{ mg/L})}{1\%}$$

$$= \frac{(1.8\%)(10,000 \text{ mg/L})}{1\%}$$

$$= 18,000 \text{ mg/L}$$

2. Determine the fluoride feed dose in milligrams per liter.

Feed Dose, mg/L = Desired Dose, mg/L − Raw Water F, mg/L

$$= 1.8 \text{ mg/L} - 0.5 \text{ mg/L}$$

$$= 1.3 \text{ mg/L}$$

3. Calculate the gallons of feed solution needed.

$$\text{Feed Solution, gal} = \frac{(\text{Flow Vol, gal})(\text{Feed Dose, mg/}L)}{\text{Feed Solution, mg/}L}$$

$$= \frac{(400{,}000 \text{ gal})(1.3 \text{ mg/}L)}{18{,}000 \text{ mg/}L}$$

$$= 28.9 \text{ gallons}$$

EXAMPLE 10

A hydrofluosilicic acid (H_2SiF_6) tank contains 300 gallons of acid with a strength of 18 percent. A commercial vendor delivers 2,000 gallons of acid with a strength of 20 percent to the tank. What is the resulting strength of the mixture as a percentage?

Known		Unknown
Tank Contents, gal	= 300 gal	Mixture Strength, %
Tank Strength, %	= 18%	
Vendor, gal	= 2,000 gal	
Vendor Strength, %	= 20%	

Calculate the strength of the mixture as a percentage.

$$\text{Mixture Strength, \%} = \frac{(\text{Tank, gal})(\text{Tank, \%}) + (\text{Vendor, gal})(\text{Vendor, \%})}{\text{Tank, gal} + \text{Vendor, gal}}$$

$$= \frac{(300 \text{ gal})(18\%) + (2{,}000 \text{ gal})(20\%)}{300 \text{ gal} + 2{,}000 \text{ gal}}$$

$$= \frac{5{,}400 + 40{,}000}{2{,}300}$$

$$= \frac{45{,}400}{2{,}300}$$

$$= 19.7\%$$

EXAMPLE 11

Sodium silicofluoride (Na_2SiF_6) is used as the chemical to fluoridate a water supply. What is the fluoride ion purity as a percentage?

Known		Unknown
Atomic Weights		Fluoride Ion Purity, %
Na	= 22.99	
Si	= 28.09	
F	= 19.00	

1. Determine the molecular weight of the fluoridation chemical, sodium silicofluoride, Na_2SiF_6.

Symbol	No. Atoms	x Atomic Wt.[a]	= Molecular Wt.
Na_2	2	x 22.99	= 45.98
Si	1	x 28.09	= 28.09
F_6	6	x 19.00	= 114.00
	Molecular Wt of Chemical		= 188.07

---
[a] Atomic weight values can be obtained from a chemistry book.

2. Calculate the fluoride ion purity as a percentage.

$$\text{Fluoride Ion Purity, \%} = \frac{(\text{Molecular Weight of Fluoride})(100\%)}{\text{Molecular Weight of Chemical}}$$

$$= \frac{(114.00)(100\%)}{188.07}$$

$$= 60.62\%$$

This means that there is 0.6062 pound of fluoride ion in every pound of sodium silicofluoride.

13.13 ARITHMETIC ASSIGNMENT

Turn to the Arithmetic Appendix at the back of this manual. In Section A.3, "Typical Water Treatment Plant Problems," read and work the problems in Section A.31, "Fluoridation." Section A.51 contains similar problems using metric units.

13.14 ADDITIONAL READING

1. *NEW YORK MANUAL*, Chapter 16*, "Fluoridation."

2. *TEXAS MANUAL*, Chapter 11*, "Special Water Treatment (Fluoridation)."

3. *WATER FLUORIDATION PRINCIPLES AND PRACTICES*, 1995 (M4). Available from Customer Services, American Water Works Association, 6666 W. Quincy Avenue, Denver, CO 80235. Order No. 30004. Price to members, $28.00; nonmembers, $44.00; price includes cost of shipping and handling.

4. *WATER FLUORIDATION*, A Manual for Engineers and Technicians. Available from Centers for Disease Control, Division of Oral Health, Mail Stop F10, 1600 Clifton Road, Atlanta, GA 30333. No charge.

* Depends on edition.

13.15 ACKNOWLEDGMENTS

The author wishes to acknowledge the assistance graciously given by Robert A. Hewitt, Assistant Water Quality Engineer, San Francisco Water Department, San Francisco, California, and Tom Reeves, Centers for Disease Control, Center for Prevention Services, Dental Disease Prevention Activity, Atlanta, Georgia.

Please answer the discussion and review questions before continuing with the Objective Test.

DISCUSSION AND REVIEW QUESTIONS

Chapter 13.   FLUORIDATION

Write the answers to these questions in your notebook before continuing with the Objective Test on page 67. The purpose of these questions is to indicate to you how well you understand the material in the chapter.

1. Why are drinking waters fluoridated?

2. What factors would you consider when selecting a fluoridation chemical?

3. Why should the finished water's fluoride ion content be automatically monitored on a continuous basis?

4. How can water be softened prior to use with fluoridation equipment?

5. What items should be considered when reviewing plans and specifications for the location of fluoride chemical hoppers?

6. How can overfeeding be prevented?

7. What should be done if significant overfeeding occurs?

8. What should be done when fluoridation equipment is going to be shut down for an extended length of time?

9. How would you dispose of fluoride chemical containers?

10. How would you protect yourself from the dusts of dry fluoride compounds?

SUGGESTED ANSWERS

Chapter 13.   FLUORIDATION

Answers to questions on page 32.

13.0A   If a person drinks water with an excessive amount of fluoride, the teeth become mottled (brown, chalky deposits).

13.0B   Children who drink a recommended dose of fluoride have fewer dental caries (decay or cavities).

Answers to questions on page 33.

13.1A   The water department or water company makes the final decisions as to types of fluoride chemicals and feeding equipment to be used.

13.2A   The three compounds most commonly used to fluoridate water are hydrofluosilicic acid, sodium fluoride and sodium silicofluoride.

Answers to questions on page 45.

13.3A   Drinking waters may contain fluoride ions by three different types of situations:

1. Raw water source may have adequate or excessive fluoride ions naturally present,

2. Two water sources may be blended together (one higher and one lower than acceptable level) to produce an acceptable level, and

3. Fluoride ions must be added to the water to achieve an acceptable level.

13.3B   Fluoridation systems must incorporate means to prevent both overfeeding and backsiphonage along with means to monitor the amount of chemical used.

13.3C   Hard water can produce problems in systems using saturators and dissolving tanks through the formation of low solubility deposits of calcium and magnesium fluoride compounds.

13.3D   A saturator is a device which produces a fluoride solution for the fluoridation process. The device is usually a cylindrical container with granular sodium fluoride on the bottom. Water flows either upward or downward through the sodium fluoride to produce the fluoride solution.

Answers to questions on page 48.

13.4A   Overfeeding of fluoridation chemicals must be prevented to avoid illness and bad public relations.

13.4B   The fluoridator should be sized to handle the full range of both present and future doses or provisions should be made for future expansion.

13.5A   When inspecting the fluoridation electrical system, inspect the system for (1) proper voltage, (2) properly sized overload protection, (3) proper operation of control lights on control panel, (4) proper safety lockout switches and operation, and (5) proper equipment rotation.

13.5B Safety equipment that should be available near a fluoridation system include an eyewash, drench showers, dust masks, face shields, gloves, and vent fans.

Answers to questions on page 54.

13.6A

	Known	Unknown
Flow, MGD	= 6 MGD	Feed Rate, gal/day
Conc Fluoride, mg/L	= 1.2 mg/L	
Hydrofluosilicic Acid, %	= 20%	

1. Use Treatment Chart I, Hydrofluosilicic Acid. Start at the left side with 6 MGD and move horizontally to the right to the intersection of the 20% diagonal line.

2. Drop down vertically to the chemical feed rate of *30 GALLONS PER DAY*, for 1 mg/L fluoride application.

3. Adjust the flow rate for a dose of 1.2 mg/L.

$$\text{Flow Rate, gal/day} = \frac{(\text{Flow Rate from Chart, gal/day})(\text{Desired Dose, mg/L})}{1\ mg/L}$$

$$= \frac{(30\ gal/day)(1.2\ mg/L)}{1\ mg/L}$$

$$= 36\ gal/day$$

13.6B Differences between the volume of acid used from a storage tank and the volume actually fed into the system could be caused by errors in readings, leaks, or equipment malfunctions.

Answers to questions on page 54.

13.7A Overfeeding should be prevented because no additional benefits result from overfeeding and there is a waste of chemicals and money. Excessive overfeeding could be harmful to consumers.

13.7B If significant overfeeding occurs, the plant should be shut down. The affected mains should be flushed and the local and state health departments notified.

13.8A A fluoridation operation could be shut down for cleaning, adjustments, or due to safety controls.

Answers to questions on page 58.

13.9A If fluoridation equipment is going to be shut down for an extended length of time, it should be cleaned out to prevent corrosion and/or the solidifying of the chemical. Lines and equipment could be damaged when restarted if chemicals left in them solidify.

13.10A Fluoride dust can be removed from gears by the use of a vacuum cleaner.

13.10B To determine if the fluoridation equipment is providing the desired dosage, monitor the fluoride ion concentration in the treated water.

13.11A If you are acutely poisoned by a fluoride chemical, you may be thirsty, vomit, and have stomach cramps, diarrhea, difficulty in speaking, and disturbed color vision.

NOTES

OBJECTIVE TEST

Chapter 13. FLUORIDATION

Please write your name and mark the correct answers on the answer sheet, as directed at the end of Chapter 1. There may be more than one correct answer to each multiple-choice question.

True-False

1. Hydrofluosilicic acid is easier to feed than other powdered fluoridation chemicals because it is more soluble in water.

    1. True
    2. False

2. Fluoride chemical feeders must be very accurate.

    1. True
    2. False

3. Coarse fluoride crystals will dissolve better than fine material.

    1. True
    2. False

4. Of all the chemicals used in the water treatment plant, fluoride concentrations probably require the most attention to maximum dosages.

    1. True
    2. False

5. Fluoridation system alarms are important to signal both the loss of feed and overfeeding.

    1. True
    2. False

6. The most commonly used compounds to fluoridate water systems are chemically engineered compounds made from synthetic materials.

    1. True
    2. False

7. Both volumetric and gravimetric feeders measure volume of chemical delivered during a specific time period.

    1. True
    2. False

8. Fluoridation must be a continuous operation.

    1. True
    2. False

9. Fluoride solutions are extremely corrosive.

    1. True
    2. False

10. If a person is poisoned by inhaling fluoride, the first symptom will be a sharp, biting pain in the nose followed by a runny nose or nosebleed.

    1. True
    2. False

Best Answer (Select only the closest or best answer.)

11. Dry fluoride chemical feeders are what type of chemical feeder?

    1. Diaphragm
    2. Electronic
    3. Peristaltic
    4. Volumetric

12. Fluoride chemical doses must never be metered against what type of head?

    1. Discharge
    2. Neutral
    3. Positive
    4. Suction

13. What problems are caused by hard water in systems using saturators?

    1. Excessive fluoride doses
    2. Irregular fluoride doses
    3. pH fluctuations
    4. Scaling

14. Why should a saturator include an air gap? To

    1. Avoid a cross connection.
    2. Ensure uniform flow through the saturator.
    3. Minimize cost of fluoride production.
    4. Produce a constant fluoride concentration.

15. What problem can be caused by a gross overfeed of fluoride ions?

    1. Illness
    2. Increase in dental cavities
    3. Oversupply of fluoride chemicals
    4. Too long a storage time of chemicals

16. Why should fluoridation systems be provided with corrosion-resistant drip pans and drains? To prevent

    1. Accidents.
    2. Chemicals from reaching the floor.
    3. Evaporation of toxic gases.
    4. Loss of valuable fluoride chemicals.

17. Where should fluoride be added to drinking water?

    1. After addition of coagulant chemical
    2. At intake to maximize contact time
    3. Before filtration
    4. Where least possible removal of fluoride occurs

18. Why must any potable water line connected to a chemical feeder unit be provided with a vacuum breaker or an air gap? To prevent

    1. Cross connection.
    2. Overfeeding.
    3. Suction of chemicals.
    4. Water hammer.

19. Why should continuous underfeeding of fluoride not be allowed?

    1. Fluoride chemicals will clog chemical feeders
    2. Insufficient fluoride storage space will be a problem
    3. Severe illness could occur
    4. Significant reduction in benefits from fluoridation results

20. Why should consideration be given for all piping to be plastic?

    1. Allow use of heavier pipe
    2. Avoid replacement costs
    3. Provide rigid pipe
    4. Reduce painting costs.

Multiple Choice (Select all correct answers.)

21. Which chemicals are commonly used to fluoridate water?

    1. Hydrofluosilicic acid
    2. Potassium fluoride
    3. Potassium silicofluoride
    4. Sodium fluoride
    5. Sodium silicofluoride

22. What types of pumps are used to add fluoride ions to water?

    1. Centrifugal pumps
    2. Diaphragm pumps
    3. Electronic pumps
    4. Peristaltic pumps
    5. Propeller pumps

23. Why are upflow saturators preferred over downflow saturators?

    1. Easier to clean
    2. Easier to feed chemical
    3. Easier to fluoridate water
    4. Easier to maintain
    5. Easier to mix solution

24. Which of the following items must be considered when selecting a fluoridation chemical?

    1. Costs
    2. Ease of handling
    3. Operator safety
    4. Solubility of chemical in water
    5. Storage requirements

25. The design of a fluoride chemical feeding system should incorporate means to perform which of the following tasks?

    1. Continuously measure the finished water's fluoride ion content
    2. Feed fluoride which is adjusted according to the plant flow rate
    3. Meter fluoride doses against a negative or suction head
    4. Prevent backsiphonage
    5. Prevent overfeeding

26. What should an operator do if significant overfeeding of fluoride occurs?

    1. Check for positive protection against backsiphonage
    2. Determine if there is total solubility of the fluoride compounds
    3. Notify local and state health departments
    4. Shut down the plant
    5. Start flushing the affected mains

27. What items should be included in a checklist for shutting down a fluoride chemical system?

    1. Drain and clean the mix and feed tanks
    2. Flush out the chemical supply lines with water
    3. Flush out the solution lines with water
    4. Leave the water supply to the chemical system on
    5. Shut off and lock out the electrical power

28. What safety hazards can be caused by fluoride fumes?

    1. Can kill vegetation
    2. Cause tastes in drinking water
    3. Deplete ozone
    4. Harmful to people
    5. Produce undesirable odors

29. What sanitary defects could develop in a fluoridation system?

    1. Fluoridation chemical not meeting AWWA specifications
    2. Inadequate feed rate control equipment
    3. Inadequate free chlorine residual in treated water
    4. Lack of backflow safeguards
    5. No analyzer to measure fluoride ion levels in treated water

30. How can an operator become exposed to fluoride?

    1. Eye contact
    2. Ingestion
    3. Inhalation
    4. Skin contact
    5. Washing

31. Safety procedures that should be observed while handling or storing fluoride include

    1. Empty bags of chemicals into feeder hopper quickly from the bottom to minimize operator exposure.
    2. In case of eye contact, flush eyes for at least 15 minutes with large amounts of water.
    3. In case of ingestion, do not induce vomiting; if conscious, give person large quantities of water.
    4. Label all feeders and solution tanks.
    5. Store bags of chemicals in a cool place, preferably on the floor.

32. A flow of 1.2 MGD is to be treated with an 18-percent solution of hydrofluosilicic acid (H_2SiF_6). The water to be treated contains no fluoride and the desired fluoride concentration is 1.4 mg/L. Assume the hydrofluosilicic acid weighs 9.5 pounds per gallon and 79.2 percent fluoride purity of the acid. Calculate the hydrofluosilicic acid feed rate in gallons per day. Select the closest answer.

    1. 5.8 GPD
    2. 10.3 GPD
    3. 11.6 GPD
    4. 12.9 GPD
    5. 14.5 GPD

33. A flow of 180 GPM is to be treated with a 2.4-percent (0.2 pound per gallon) solution of sodium fluoride (NaF). The water to be treated contains 0.3 mg/L of fluoride ion and the desired fluoride ion concentration is 1.4 mg/L. Calculate the sodium fluoride feed rate in gallons per day. Assume the sodium fluoride has a fluoride purity of 43.4 percent. Select the closest answer.

    1. 2.4 gal/day
    2. 3.3 gal/day
    3. 14 gal/day
    4. 23 gal/day
    5. 28 gal/day

34. A flow of 0.9 MGD is treated with sodium silicofluoride (Na_2SiF_6) to provide a fluoride ion dose of 1.3 mg/L. What is the feed rate in pounds per day? Commercial sodium silicofluoride has a purity of 98.5 percent and the fluoride ion purity of sodium silicofluoride is 60.7 percent. Select the closest answer.

   1. 7.8 lbs/day
   2. 16.3 lbs/day
   3. 18.1 lbs/day
   4. 21.7 lbs/day
   5. 23.6 lbs/day

35. The feed solution from a saturator containing 1.8 percent fluoride ion is used to treat a flow of 550,000 gallons per day. The desired dose is 1.3 mg/L of fluoride ion and the raw water does not have any fluoride. Calculate the feed rate of the saturator solution in gallons per day. Select the closest answer.

   1. 27.8 gal/day
   2. 39.7 gal/day
   3. 46.9 gal/day
   4. 65.0 gal/day
   5. 84.4 gal/day

End of
Objective Test

CHAPTER 14

SOFTENING

by

Don Gibson

and

Marty Reynolds

TABLE OF CONTENTS

Chapter 14.   SOFTENING

Page

OBJECTIVES 74

WORDS 75

LIME-SODA ASH SOFTENING by Don Gibson

LESSON 1

14.0   WHAT MAKES WATER HARD? 78

14.1   WHY SOFTEN WATER? 79

14.2   CHEMISTRY OF SOFTENING 80

    14.20   Hardness 80

    14.21   pH 81

    14.22   Alkalinity 81

14.3   HOW WATER IS SOFTENED 83

    14.30   Basic Methods of Softening 83

    14.31   Chemical Reactions 84

        14.310   Lime 84

        14.311   Removal of Carbon Dioxide 84

        14.312   Removal of Carbonate Hardness 84

        14.313   Removal of Noncarbonate Hardness 85

        14.314   Stability 85

        14.315   Caustic Soda Softening 85

        14.316   Calculation of Chemical Dosages 86

    14.32   Lime Softening 87

    14.33   Split Treatment 87

    14.34   Lime-Soda Ash Softening 88

    14.35   Caustic Soda Softening 88

    14.36   Handling, Application, and Storage of Lime 90

14.4   INTERACTIONS WITH COAGULANTS 91

14.5   STABILITY 91

14.6   SAFETY 92

14.7   SLUDGE RECIRCULATION AND DISPOSAL 93

14.8   RECORDS 93

14.9 JAR TESTS 94

    14.90   Typical Procedures 94

    14.91   Examples 94

    14.92   Calculation of Chemical Feeder Settings 98

DISCUSSION AND REVIEW QUESTIONS 100

ION EXCHANGE SOFTENING by Marty Reynolds

LESSON 2

14.10   DESCRIPTION OF ION EXCHANGE SOFTENING PROCESS 101

14.11   OPERATIONS 104

    14.110   Service 104

    14.111   Backwash 106

    14.112   Brine 106

    14.113   Rinse 106

14.12   CONTROL TESTING OF ION EXCHANGE SOFTENERS 107

14.13   LIMITATIONS CAUSED BY IRON AND MANGANESE 107

14.14   DISPOSAL OF SPENT BRINE 107

14.15   MAINTENANCE 108

14.16   TROUBLESHOOTING 109

    14.160   Test Units 109

    14.161   Service Stage 109

    14.162   Backwash Stage 109

    14.163   Brine Injection Stage 109

    14.164   Rinse Stage 110

14.17   START-UP AND SHUTDOWN OF UNIT 110

14.18   ION EXCHANGE ARITHMETIC 112

14.19   BLENDING 114

14.20   RECORDKEEPING 116

14.21   ARITHMETIC ASSIGNMENT 116

14.22   ADDITIONAL READING 116

14.23   ACKNOWLEDGMENTS 116

DISCUSSION AND REVIEW QUESTIONS 116

SUGGESTED ANSWERS 117

OBJECTIVE TEST 121

OBJECTIVES

Chapter 14.   SOFTENING

Following completion of Chapter 14, you should be able to:

1. Explain what makes water hard and the advantages of softening,

2. Describe the processes used to soften water,

3. Prepare chemical doses to soften water with considerations given to coagulants and stability,

4. Safely handle softening chemicals,

5. Dispose of process sludges and brines,

6. Keep neat and accurate softening records,

7. Perform jar tests and apply results,

8. Operate and maintain chemical precipitation and ion exchange softening processes,

9. Start up and shut down water softening units, and

10. Blend softened waters with unsoftened waters (split treatment) for delivery to consumers.

WORDS

Chapter 14. SOFTENING

ALKALINITY (AL-ka-LIN-it-tee)

The capacity of water to neutralize acids. This capacity is caused by the water's content of carbonate, bicarbonate, hydroxide, and occasionally borate, silicate, and phosphate. Alkalinity is expressed in milligrams per liter of equivalent calcium carbonate. Alkalinity is not the same as pH because water does not have to be strongly basic (high pH) to have a high alkalinity. Alkalinity is a measure of how much acid must be added to a liquid to lower the pH to 4.5.

ANION (AN-EYE-en)

A negatively charged ion in an electrolyte solution, attracted to the anode under the influence of a difference in electrical potential. Chloride ion (Cl^-) is an anion.

CALCIUM CARBONATE EQUILIBRIUM

A water is considered stable when it is just saturated with calcium carbonate. In this condition the water will neither dissolve nor deposit calcium carbonate. Thus, in this water the calcium carbonate is in equilibrium with the hydrogen ion concentration.

CALCIUM CARBONATE ($CaCO_3$) EQUIVALENT

An expression of the concentration of specified constituents in water in terms of their equivalent value to calcium carbonate. For example, the hardness in water which is caused by calcium, magnesium and other ions is usually described as calcium carbonate equivalent. Alkalinity test results are usually reported as mg/L $CaCO_3$ equivalents. To convert chloride to $CaCO_3$ equivalents, multiply the concentration of chloride ions in mg/L by 1.41, and for sulfate, multiply by 1.04.

CATION (CAT-EYE-en)

A positively charged ion in an electrolyte solution, attracted to the cathode under the influence of a difference in electrical potential. Sodium ion (Na^+) is a cation.

DIVALENT (die-VAY-lent)

Having a valence of two, such as the ferrous ion, Fe^{2+}. Also called bivalent.

EQUIVALENT WEIGHT

That weight which will react with, displace or is equivalent to one gram atom of hydrogen.

GREENSAND

A mineral (glauconite) material that looks like ordinary filter sand except that it is green in color. Greensand is a natural ion exchange material which is capable of softening water. Greensand which has been treated with potassium permanganate ($KMnO_4$) is called manganese greensand; this product is used to remove iron, manganese and hydrogen sulfide from groundwaters.

HARD WATER

Water having a high concentration of calcium and magnesium ions. A water may be considered hard if it has a hardness greater than the typical hardness of water from the region. Some textbooks define hard water as water with a hardness of more than 100 mg/L as calcium carbonate.

HARDNESS, WATER

A characteristic of water caused mainly by the salts of calcium and magnesium, such as bicarbonate, carbonate, sulfate, chloride and nitrate. Excessive hardness in water is undesirable because it causes the formation of soap curds, increased use of soap, deposition of scale in boilers, damage in some industrial processes, and sometimes causes objectionable tastes in drinking water.

HYDRATED LIME

Limestone that has been "burned" and treated with water under controlled conditions until the calcium oxide portion has been converted to calcium hydroxide ($Ca(OH)_2$). Hydrated lime is quicklime combined with water. $CaO + H_2O \rightarrow Ca(OH)_2$. Also called slaked lime. Also see QUICKLIME.

INSOLUBLE (in-SAWL-you-bull)   INSOLUBLE

Something that cannot be dissolved.

ION   ION

An electrically charged atom, radical (such as SO_4^{2-}), or molecule formed by the loss or gain of one or more electrons.

ION EXCHANGE   ION EXCHANGE

A water treatment process involving the reversible interchange (switching) of ions between the water being treated and the solid resin. Undesirable ions in the water are switched with acceptable ions on the resin.

ION EXCHANGE RESINS   ION EXCHANGE RESINS

Insoluble polymers, used in water treatment, that are capable of exchanging (switching or giving) acceptable cations or anions to the water being treated for less desirable ions.

METHYL ORANGE ALKALINITY   METHYL ORANGE ALKALINITY

A measure of the total alkalinity in a water sample. The alkalinity is measured by the amount of standard sulfuric acid required to lower the pH of the water to a pH level of 4.5, as indicated by the change in color of methyl orange from orange to pink. Methyl orange alkalinity is expressed as milligrams per liter equivalent calcium carbonate.

NPDES PERMIT   NPDES PERMIT

National Pollutant Discharge Elimination System permit is the regulatory agency document issued by either a federal or state agency which is designed to control all discharges of pollutants from point sources and storm water runoff into U.S. waterways. NPDES permits regulate discharges into navigable waters from all point sources of pollution, including industries, municipal wastewater treatment plants, sanitary landfills, large agricultural feedlots and return irrigation flows.

PHENOLPHTHALEIN (FEE-nol-THAY-leen) ALKALINITY   PHENOLPHTHALEIN ALKALINITY

The alkalinity in a water sample measured by the amount of standard acid required to lower the pH to a level of 8.3, as indicated by the change in color of phenolphthalein from pink to clear. Phenolphthalein alkalinity is expressed as milligrams per liter of equivalent calcium carbonate.

PRECIPITATE (pre-SIP-uh-TATE)   PRECIPITATE

(1) An insoluble, finely divided substance which is a product of a chemical reaction within a liquid.

(2) The separation from solution of an insoluble substance.

QUICKLIME   QUICKLIME

A material that is mostly calcium oxide (CaO) or calcium oxide in natural association with a lesser amount of magnesium oxide. Quicklime is capable of combining with water, that is, becoming slaked. Also see HYDRATED LIME.

RECARBONATION (re-CAR-bun-NAY-shun)   RECARBONATION

A process in which carbon dioxide is bubbled into the water being treated to lower the pH. The pH may also be lowered by the addition of acid. Recarbonation is the final stage in the lime-soda ash softening process. This process converts carbonate ions to bicarbonate ions and stabilizes the solution against the precipitation of carbonate compounds.

RESINS

See ION EXCHANGE RESINS.

SATURATION

The condition of a liquid (water) when it has taken into solution the maximum possible quantity of a given substance at a given temperature and pressure.

SLAKE

To mix with water so that a true chemical combination (hydration) takes place, such as in the slaking of lime.

SLAKED LIME

See HYDRATED LIME.

SUPERSATURATED

An unstable condition of a solution (water) in which the solution contains a substance at a concentration greater than the saturation concentration for the substance.

TITRATE (TIE-trate)

To *TITRATE* a sample, a chemical solution of known strength is added drop by drop until a certain color change, precipitate, or pH change in the sample is observed (end point). Titration is the process of adding the chemical reagent in increments until completion of the reaction, as signaled by the end point.

CHAPTER 14.   SOFTENING

Lime-Soda Ash Softening by Don Gibson

(Lesson 1 of 2 Lessons)

14.0   WHAT MAKES WATER HARD?[1]

Water hardness is a measure of the soap- or detergent-consuming power of water. Technically hardness is caused by *DIVALENT*[2] metallic cations which are capable of reacting (1) with soap (detergent) to form precipitates, and (2) with certain anions present in water to form scale.

Cations Causing Hardness	Most Common Anions
Calcium, Ca^{2+}	Bicarbonate, HCO_3^-
Magnesium, Mg^{2+}	Sulfate, SO_4^{2-}
Strontium, Sr^{2+}	Chloride, Cl^-
Iron, Fe^{2+}	Nitrate, NO_3^-
Manganese, Mn^{2+}	Silicate, SiO_3^{2-}

Calcium and magnesium are usually the only cations that are present in significant concentrations. Therefore, hardness is generally considered to be an expression of the total concentration of the calcium and magnesium ions that are present in the water. However, if any of the other cations listed are present in significant amounts, they should be included in the hardness determination.

Table 14.1 describes various levels of hardness. Different textbooks will use similar classifications. Hardness levels in source waters, local conditions, and local usage will influence consumers' attitudes towards the hardness of their water.

TABLE 14.1   DESCRIPTION OF VARIOUS LEVELS OF HARDNESS[3]

Description	Hardness in Terms of mg/L as Calcium Carbonate
1. Extremely soft to soft	0-45
2. Soft to moderately hard	46-90
3. Moderately hard to hard	91-130
4. Hard to very hard	131-170
5. Very hard to excessively hard	171-250
6. Too hard for ordinary domestic use	OVER 250

To help you understand this chapter on water softening, some of the terms used are defined below.

HARD WATER is a water having a high concentration of calcium and magnesium ions. A water may be considered hard if it has a hardness greater than the typical hardness of water from the region. Some textbooks define hard water as a water with a hardness of more than 100 mg/L as calcium carbonate.

HARDNESS is a characteristic of water caused mainly by the salts of calcium and magnesium, such as bicarbonate, carbonate, sulfate, chloride, and nitrate. Excessive hardness in water is undesirable because it causes the formation of soap curds, increased use of soap, deposition of scale in boilers, damage in some industrial processes, and it sometimes causes objectionable tastes in drinking water.

CALCIUM HARDNESS is caused by calcium ions (Ca^{2+}).

MAGNESIUM HARDNESS is caused by magnesium ions (Mg^{2+}).

TOTAL HARDNESS is the sum of the hardness caused by both calcium and magnesium ions.

CARBONATE HARDNESS is caused by the alkalinity present in water up to the total hardness. This value is usually less than the total hardness.

NONCARBONATE HARDNESS is that portion of the total hardness in excess of the alkalinity.

---

[1] *Portions of the material covered in the first three sections of this chapter were provided by Don Gibson, Marty Reynolds, Susumu Kawamura, Terry Engelhardt, Jack Rossum, and Mike Curry.*
[2] *Divalent (die-VAY-lent).   Having a valence of two, such as the ferrous ion, Fe^{2+}. Also called bivalent.*
[3] *Lipe, L.A. and M.D. Curry, "Ion Exchange Water Softening," a discussion for water treatment plant operators, 1974-75 seminar series sponsored by Illinois Environmental Protection Agency.*

ALKALINITY (AL-ka-LIN-it-tee) is the capacity of water to neutralize acids. This capacity is caused by the water's content of carbonate, bicarbonate, hydroxide, and occasionally borate, silicate, and phosphate. Alkalinity is expressed in milligrams per liter of equivalent calcium carbonate. Alkalinity is a measure of how much acid must be added to a liquid to lower the pH to 4.5.

CALCIUM CARBONATE (CaCO₃) EQUIVALENT is an expression of the concentration of specified constituents in water in terms of their equivalent value to calcium carbonate. For example, the hardness in water which is caused by calcium, magnesium, and other ions is usually described as calcium carbonate equivalent. Alkalinity test results are usually reported as mg/*L* CaCO₃ equivalents. To convert chloride to CaCO₃ equivalents, multiply the concentration of chloride ions in mg/*L* by 1.41, and for sulfate, multiply by 1.04.

14.1 WHY SOFTEN WATER?

The dissolved minerals (calcium and magnesium ions) in water cause difficulties in doing the laundry and in dishwashing in the household. These ions also cause a coating to form inside the hot water heater similar to that in a tea kettle after repeated use.

Hardness, in addition to inhibiting the cleaning action of soaps, will tend to shorten the life of fabrics that are washed in hard water. The scum or curds may become lodged in the fibers of the fabric and cause them to lose their softness and elasticity.

In industry hardness can cause even greater problems. Many processes are affected by the hardness content of the water used. Industrial plants using boilers for processing steam or heat must remove the hardness from their makeup water, even beyond what a water treatment plant would do. The reason for this is that the minerals will plate out on the boiler tubes and form a scale. This scale forms an insulation barrier which prevents proper heat transfer, thus causing excessive energy requirements to fire the boilers. The problems associated with process water softening are too numerous to go into; however, everything from food processing to intricate manufacturing processes is affected by the hardness of water.

In addition to the removal of hardness from water, some other benefits of softening include:

1. Removal of iron and manganese,

2. Control of corrosion when proper stabilization of water is achieved,

3. Disinfection due to high pH values when using lime (especially the excess lime softening process),

4. Sometimes a reduction in tastes and odors,

5. Reduction of some total solids content by the lime treatment process, and

6. Removal of radioactivity.

Possible limitations of softening might include:

1. Free chlorine residual is predominantly hypochlorite at pH levels above 7.5 and is a less powerful disinfectant.

2. Costs and benefits must be carefully weighed to justify softening.

3. Ultimate disposal of process wastes.

4. At the pH levels associated with softening chemical precipitation, the trihalomethane fraction in the treated water may increase (depends on several other factors).

5. Production of an "aggressive" water which would tend to corrode metal ions from the distribution system piping. Hard waters usually do not corrode pipe. However, excessively hard water can cause scaling on the inside of pipes and thereby restrict flow.

In many cases, the decision to soften the water is left up to each community as softening is done mostly as a customer service. Hard water does not have an adverse effect on health, but can create several unwanted side effects, some of which are:

1. Over a period of time, the detergent-consuming power of hard water can be very costly,

2. Scale problems on fixtures will be more noticeable, and

3. The life cycle of several types of clothing will be reduced with repeated washing in hard water. Also, a residue can be left in clothing, creating a dirty appearance.

Once the decision is made to soften, a method must be selected. The two most common methods used to soften water are chemical precipitation (lime-soda ash) and *ION EXCHANGE*.[4] Ion exchange softening can best be applied to waters high in noncarbonate hardness and where the total hardness does not exceed 350 mg/*L*. This method of softening can produce a water of zero hardness, as opposed to lime softening where zero hardness cannot be reached.

Ion exchange softening will also remove noncarbonate hardness without the addition of soda ash which is required with lime softening. Ion exchange is a nonselective method of softening. This means it will remove total hardness (the sum of carbonate and noncarbonate hardness) making it a very desirable means of water softening.

Limitations of the ion exchange softening process include an increase in the sodium content of the softened water if the ion exchanger is regenerated with sodium hydroxide. The sodium level should not exceed 20 mg/*L* in treated water because of the potentially harmful effect on persons susceptible to hypertension. Also the ultimate disposal of spent brine and rinse waters from softeners can be a major problem for many installations.

---

[4] *Ion Exchange. A water treatment process involving the reversible interchange (switching) of ions between the water being treated and the solid resin. Undesirable ions in the water are switched with acceptable ions on the resin.*

QUESTIONS

Write your answers in a notebook and then compare your answers with those on page 117.

14.0A What causes hardness in water?

14.0B Why is excessive hardness undesirable in a domestic water supply?

14.1A What are some of the limitations of the ion exchange softening process?

14.2 CHEMISTRY OF SOFTENING

To understand how water hardness is described and also how hardness is removed from water by softening processes, operators need to have an idea of the chemical reactions that take place in water. In this section hardness, pH, and alkalinity reactions in water will be discussed.

14.20 Hardness

Hardness is due to the presence of divalent metallic cations in water, but the Nineteenth Edition of STANDARD METH-ODS[5] identifies only calcium and magnesium as hardness constituents. Hardness is commonly measured by TITRA-TION[6] as described in Volume I (see Chapter 11, Section 11.3, 5. "Hardness"). Individual divalent cations may be measured in the laboratory using an atomic absorption (AA) spectrophotometer for very accurate work.

Hardness is usually reported as CALCIUM CARBONATE (CaCO_3) EQUIVALENT.[7] This procedure allows us to combine or add up the hardness caused by both calcium and magnesium and report the results as total hardness.

$$\text{Calcium Hardness, mg/L as } CaCO_3 = (\text{Calcium, mg/L})\left(\frac{\text{Equivalent Weight of } CaCO_3}{\text{Equivalent Weight of Calcium}}\right)$$

$$= (\text{Ca, mg/L})\left(\frac{50}{20}\right)$$

$$= 2.50(\text{Ca, mg/L})$$

This equation indicates that if the calcium concentration in milligrams per liter is multiplied by 2.50, the result is the calcium hardness in milligrams per liter as calcium carbonate. The EQUIVALENT WEIGHT[8] of most elements or chemical radicals (SO_4^{2-} is a radical) can be obtained by dividing the molecular weight by the valence.

$$\frac{\text{Equivalent Weight}}{\text{of Calcium}} = \frac{\text{Atomic Weight}}{\text{Valence}}$$

$$= \frac{40}{2}$$

$$= 20$$

To express the magnesium hardness of water as calcium carbonate equivalent use the following formula.

$$\text{Magnesium Hardness, mg/L as } CaCO_3 = (\text{Magnesium, mg/L})\left(\frac{\text{Equivalent Weight of } CaCO_3}{\text{Equivalent Weight of Magnesium}}\right)$$

$$= (\text{Mg, mg/L})\left(\frac{50}{12.15}\right)$$

$$= 4.12 (\text{Mg, mg/L})$$

The total hardness of water is the sum of the calcium and magnesium hardness as $CaCO_3$.

$$\text{Total Hardness, mg/L as } CaCO_3 = \text{Calcium Hardness, mg/L as } CaCO_3 + \text{Magnesium Hardness, mg/L as } CaCO_3$$

EXAMPLE 1

Determine the total hardness as $CaCO_3$ for a sample of water with a calcium content of 30 mg/L and a magnesium content of 20 mg/L.

Known	**Unknown**
Calcium, mg/L = 30 mg/L	Total Hardness,
Magnesium, mg/L = 20 mg/L	mg/L as $CaCO_3$

Calculate the total hardness as milligrams per liter of calcium carbonate equivalent.

$$\text{Total Hardness, mg/L as } CaCO_3 = \text{Calcium Hardness, mg/L as } CaCO_3 + \text{Magnesium Hardness, mg/L as } CaCO_3$$

$$= 2.50(\text{Ca, mg/L}) + 4.12(\text{Mg, mg/L})$$

$$= 2.50(30 \text{ mg/L}) + 4.12(20 \text{ mg/L})$$

$$= 75 \text{ mg/L} + 82.4 \text{ mg/L}$$

$$= 157.4 \text{ mg/L as } CaCO_3$$

---

[5] *STANDARD METHODS FOR THE EXAMINATION OF WATER AND WASTEWATER, 19th Edition, 1995, Order No. 10071. Available from Customer Services, American Water Works Association, 6666 W. Quincy Avenue, Denver, CO 80235. Price to members, $147.00; nonmembers, $188.00; price includes cost of shipping and handling.*

[6] *Titrate (TIE-trate). To TITRATE a sample, a chemical solution of known strength is added drop by drop until a certain color change, precipitate, or pH change in the sample is observed (end point). Titration is the process of adding the chemical reagent in increments until completion of the reaction, as signaled by the end point.*

[7] *Calcium Carbonate (CaCO_3) Equivalent. An expression of the concentration of specified constituents in water in terms of their equivalent value to calcium carbonate. For example, the hardness in water which is caused by calcium, magnesium and other ions is usually described as calcium carbonate equivalent. Alkalinity test results are usually reported as mg/L CaCO_3 equivalents. To convert chloride to CaCO_3 equivalents, multiply the concentration of chloride ions in mg/L by 1.41, and for sulfate, multiply by 1.04.*

[8] *Equivalent Weight. That weight which will react with, displace or is equivalent to one gram atom of hydrogen. The equivalent weight of an element (such as Ca^{2+}) is equal to the atomic weight divided by the valence.*

$$\text{Equivalent Weight of } CaCO_3 = \frac{\text{Molecular Weight}}{\text{Number of Equivalents}}$$

$$= \frac{100}{2}$$

$$= 50$$

Total hardness is also described as the sum of the carbonate hardness (temporary hardness) and noncarbonate hardness (permanent hardness).

$$\text{Total Hardness,} \atop \text{mg/}L \text{ as CaCO}_3 = {\text{Carbonate Hardness,} \atop \text{mg/}L \text{ as CaCO}_3} + {\text{Noncarbonate Hardness,} \atop \text{mg/}L \text{ as CaCO}_3}$$

The amount of carbonate and noncarbonate hardness depends on the alkalinity of the water. This relationship can be described as follows.

1. When the alkalinity (expressed as calcium carbonate equivalent) is greater than the total hardness, all the hardness is in the carbonate form.

$$\text{Carbonate Hardness,} \atop \text{mg/}L \text{ as CaCO}_3 = {\text{Total Hardness,} \atop \text{mg/}L \text{ as CaCO}_3}$$

2. When the total hardness is greater than the alkalinity, the alkalinity is carbonate hardness, and noncarbonate hardness is the difference between total hardness and alkalinity.

$$\text{Carbonate Hardness,} \atop \text{mg/}L \text{ as CaCO}_3 = {\text{Alkalinity,} \atop \text{mg/}L \text{ as CaCO}_3}$$

$$\text{Noncarbonate Hardness,} \atop \text{mg/}L \text{ as CaCO}_3 = {\text{Total Hardness,} \atop \text{mg/}L \text{ as CaCO}_3} - {\text{Alkalinity,} \atop \text{mg/}L \text{ as CaCO}_3}$$

14.21 pH

pH is an expression of the intensity of the basic or acidic condition of a liquid. Mathematically, pH is the logarithm (base 10) of the reciprocal of the hydrogen ion activity.

$$pH = \text{Log} \frac{1}{[H^+]}$$

The pH may range from 0 to 14, where 0 is most acidic, 14 most basic, and 7 neutral. Natural waters usually have a pH between 6.5 and 8.5.

Table 14.2 shows the relationship between pH and hydrogen and hydroxide ions.

TABLE 14.2 RELATIONSHIP BETWEEN pH AND HYDROGEN AND HYDROXIDE IONS

pH	Hydrogen Ion (H⁺), Moles/Liter	Hydroxide Ion (OH⁻), Moles/Liter
0	1.0	0.000 000 000 000 01
1	0.1	0.000 000 000 000 1
2	0.01	0.000 000 000 001
3	0.001	0.000 000 000 01
4	0.000 1	0.000 000 000 1
5	0.000 01	0.000 000 001
6	0.000 001	0.000 000 01
7	0.000 000 1	0.000 000 1
8	0.000 000 01	0.000 001
9	0.000 000 001	0.000 01
10	0.000 000 000 1	0.000 1
11	0.000 000 000 01	0.001
12	0.000 000 000 001	0.01
13	0.000 000 000 000 1	0.1
14	0.000 000 000 000 01	1.0

When treating waters, the pH is very important. The pH of water may be increased or decreased by the addition of certain chemicals used to treat water (Table 14.3). In many instances, the effect on pH of adding one chemical is neutralized by the addition of another chemical. When softening water by chemical precipitation processes (lime-soda softening for example), the pH must be raised to 11 for the desired

TABLE 14.3 INFLUENCE OF WATER TREATMENT CHEMICALS ON pH

Lowers pH	Increases pH
Aluminum Sulfate (Alum), $Al_2(SO_4)_3 \cdot 18H_2O$	Calcium Hypochlorite, $Ca(OCl)_2$
Carbon Dioxide, CO_2	Caustic Soda, NaOH
Chlorine, Cl_2	Hydrated Lime, $Ca(OH)_2$
Ferric Chloride, $FeCl_3$	Soda Ash, Na_2CO_3
Hydrofluosilicic Acid, H_2SiF_6	Sodium Aluminate, $NaAlO_2$
Sulfuric Acid, H_2SO_4	Sodium Hydrochlorite, NaOCl

chemical reactions to occur. The levels of carbon dioxide, bicarbonate ion, and carbonate ion in waters are very sensitive to pH.

The stability of treated water is determined by measuring the pH and calculating the Langelier Index (see Volume I, Chapter 8, Section 8.322, "Calcium Carbonate Saturation"). This index reflects the equilibrium pH of a water with respect to calcium and alkalinity.

$$\text{Langelier Index (L.I.)} = pH - pH_S$$

where pH = actual pH of the water, and

pH_S = pH at which water having the same alkalinity and calcium content is just saturated with calcium carbonate.

A negative Langelier Index indicates that the water is corrosive and a positive index indicates that the water is scale-forming. After water has been softened, the treated water distributed to consumers must be stable (neither corrosive nor scale-forming).

14.22 Alkalinity

Alkalinity is the capacity of water to neutralize acids. This capacity is caused by the water's content of carbonate, bicarbonate, hydroxide, and occasionally borate, silicate, and phosphate. Alkalinity is expressed in milligrams per liter of equivalent calcium carbonate. Alkalinity is not the same as pH because water does not have to be strongly basic (high pH) to have a high alkalinity. Alkalinity is a measure of how much acid must be added to a liquid to lower the pH to 4.5.

Alkalinity is measured in the laboratory by the addition of color indicator solutions and the alkalinity is then determined by the amount of acid required to reach a titration end point (specific color change) (see Chapter 11, "Laboratory Procedures," Section 11.3, 1. "Alkalinity"). The P (phenolphthalein) end point is at pH 8.3. When the pH is below 8.3, there is no P alkalinity present. When the pH is above 8.3, P alkalinity is present. No carbon dioxide is present when the pH is above 8.3, so there is no carbon dioxide in the water when P alkalinity is present. Also, hydroxide and carbonate alkalinity are not present when pH is below 8.3.

The relationship between the various alkalinity constituents (bicarbonate (HCO_3^-), carbonate (CO_3^{2-}), and hydroxide (OH^-)) can be based on the P (phenolphthalein) and T (total or methyl orange) alkalinity as shown in Table 14.4 and Figure 14.1.

TABLE 14.4   ALKALINITY CONSTITUENTS

Alkalinity, mg/L as $CaCO_3$			
Titration Result	**Bicarbonate**	**Carbonate**	**Hydroxide**
P = 0	T	0	0
P is less than ½T	T-2P	2P	0
P = ½T	0	2P	0
P is greater than ½T	0	2T-2P	2P-T
P = T	0	0	T

where P = phenolphthalein alkalinity
      T = total alkalinity

When the pH is less than 8.3, all alkalinity is in the bicarbonate form and is commonly referred to as natural alkalinity. When the pH is above 8.3, the alkalinity may consist of bicarbonate, carbonate, and hydroxide. As the pH increases, the alkalinity progressively shifts to carbonate and hydroxide forms.

Total alkalinity is the sum of the bicarbonate, carbonate, and hydroxide. Each of these values can be determined by measuring the P and T alkalinity in the laboratory and referring to Table 14.4. Alkalinity is expressed in milligrams per liter as calcium carbonate equivalents. Alkalinity is influenced by chemicals used to treat water as shown in Table 14.5.

TABLE 14.5   INFLUENCE OF WATER TREATMENT CHEMICALS ON ALKALINITY

Lowers Alkalinity	Increases Alkalinity
Aluminum Sulfate (Alum), $Al_2(SO_4)_3 \cdot 18H_2O$	Calcium Hypochlorite, $Ca(OCl)_2$
Carbon Dioxide, CO_2	Caustic Soda, NaOH
Chlorine Gas, Cl_2	Hydrated Lime, $Ca(OH)_2$
Ferric Chloride, $FeCl_3$	Soda Ash, Na_2CO_3
Ferric Sulfate, $Fe_2(SO_4)_3$	Sodium Aluminate, $NaAlO_2$
Sulfuric Acid, H_2SO_4	

EXAMPLE 2

Results from alkalinity titrations on a raw water sample were as follows:

Known

Sample Size, mL	= 100 mL
mL Titrant Used to pH 8.3, A	= 0 mL
Total mL of Titrant Used, B	= 8.2 mL
Acid Normality, N	= 0.02 N H_2SO_4

Unknown

1. Total Alkalinity, mg/L as $CaCO_3$
2. Bicarbonate Alkalinity, mg/L as $CaCO_3$
3. Carbonate Alkalinity, mg/L as $CaCO_3$
4. Hydroxide Alkalinity, mg/L as $CaCO_3$

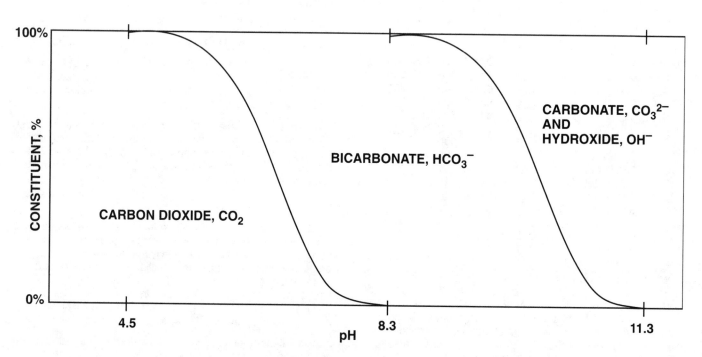

Fig. 14.1   *Relationship between pH and alkalinity constituents (CO_2, HCO_3^-, CO_3^{2-}, and OH^-)*

See Chapter 11, "Laboratory Procedures," Section 11.3, 1. "Alkalinity" for details and formulas.

1. Calculate the phenolphthalein alkalinity in mg/L as $CaCO_3$.

$$\text{Phenolphthalein Alkalinity, mg/L as } CaCO_3 = \frac{A \times N \times 50,000}{mL \text{ of sample}}$$

$$= \frac{(0 \text{ mL}) \times (0.02 \text{ } N) \times (50,000)}{100 \text{ mL}}$$

$$= 0 \text{ mg/L}$$

2. Calculate the total alkalinity in mg/L as $CaCO_3$.

$$\text{Total Alkalinity, mg/L as } CaCO_3 = \frac{B \times N \times 50,000}{mL \text{ of sample}}$$

$$= \frac{(8.2 \text{ mL}) \times (0.02 \text{ } N) \times (50,000)}{100 \text{ mL}}$$

$$= 82 \text{ mg/L}$$

3. Refer to Table 14.4 for alkalinity constituents. The first row indicates that since P = 0, the total alkalinity is equal to the bicarbonate alkalinity.

$$\text{Bicarbonate Alkalinity, mg/L as } CaCO_3 = \text{Total Alkalinity, mg/L as } CaCO_3$$

$$= 82 \text{ mg/L}$$

The first row also indicates that since P = 0, the carbonate and hydroxide alkalinities are also zero.

$$\text{Carbonate Alkalinity, mg/L as } CaCO_3 = 0 \text{ mg/L}$$

$$\text{Hydroxide Alkalinity, mg/L as } CaCO_3 = 0 \text{ mg/L}$$

QUESTIONS

Write your answers in a notebook and then compare your answers with those on page 117.

14.2A What laboratory procedures are used to measure hardness?

14.2B Determine the total hardness as $CaCO_3$ for a sample of water with a calcium content of 25 mg/L and a magnesium content of 14 mg/L.

14.2C Which water treatment chemicals lower the pH when added to water?

14.2D Results from alkalinity titrations on a sample of water were as follows: sample size, 100 mL; mL titrant used to pH 8.3, 1.2 mL; total mL of titrant used, 5.6 mL; and the acid normality was 0.02 N H_2SO_4. Calculate the total, bicarbonate, carbonate and hydroxide alkalinity as $CaCO_3$.

14.3 HOW WATER IS SOFTENED

14.30 Basic Methods of Softening

The two basic methods of softening a municipal water supply are chemical precipitation and ion exchange. Ion exchange will be discussed in the second portion of this chapter in Sections 14.10 through 14.21. We'll begin here with the chemical precipitation methods, mainly lime-soda ash softening and variations of this process.

Hardness is not completely removed by the chemical precipitation methods used in water treatment plants. That is, hardness is not reduced to zero. Water having a hardness of 150 mg/L as $CaCO_3$ or more is usually treated to reduce the hardness to 80 to 90 mg/L when softening is chosen as a water treatment option.

The minimum hardness that can be achieved by the lime-soda ash process is around 30 to 40 mg/L as $CaCO_3$. The effluent from an ion exchange softener could contain almost zero hardness. Regardless of the method used to soften water, consumers usually receive a blended water with a hardness of around 80 to 90 mg/L as $CaCO_3$ when softening is used in water treatment plants.

Lime-soda softening may produce benefits in addition to the softening of water. These advantages include:

1. Removal of iron and manganese,

2. Reduction of solids,

3. Removal and inactivation of bacteria and viruses due to high pH,

4. Control of corrosion and scale formation with proper stabilization of treated water, and

5. Removal of excess fluoride.

Limitations of the lime-soda softening process include:

1. Unable to remove all hardness,

2. A high degree of operator control must be exercised for maximum efficiency in cost, hardness removal, and water stability,

3. Color removal may be complicated by the softening process due to high pH levels, and

4. Large quantities of sludge are created which must be handled and disposed of in an acceptable manner.

QUESTIONS

Write your answers in a notebook and then compare your answers with those on page 117.

14.3A   What is the minimum hardness that can be achieved by the lime-soda ash process?

14.3B   List some of the benefits that could result from the lime-soda softening process in addition to softening the water.

14.31   Chemical Reactions

In the chemical precipitation process, the hardness-causing ions are converted from soluble to insoluble forms. Calcium and magnesium become less soluble as the pH increases. Therefore, calcium and magnesium can be removed from water as insoluble precipitates at high pH levels.

Addition of lime to water increases the hydroxide concentrations, thus increasing the pH. Addition of lime to water also converts alkalinity from the bicarbonate form to the carbonate form which causes the calcium to be precipitated as calcium carbonate ($CaCO_3$). As additional lime is added to the water, the phenolphthalein (P) alkalinity increases to a level where hydroxide becomes present (excess causticity) allowing magnesium to precipitate as magnesium hydroxide.

Following the chemical softening process, the pH is high and the water is *SUPERSATURATED*[9] with excess caustic alkalinity in either the hydroxide or carbonate form. Carbon dioxide can be used to decrease the causticity and scale-forming tendencies of the water prior to filtration.

The chemical reactions which take place in water during the chemical precipitation process are described in the remainder of this section. The procedures for softening water depend on whether the hardness to be removed is carbonate or noncarbonate hardness. Carbonate hardness (also called "temporary hardness") can be removed by the use of lime only. Removal of noncarbonate hardness (also called "permanent hardness") requires both lime and soda.

14.310   Lime

The lime used in the chemical precipitation softening process may be from either *HYDRATED LIME*[10] ($Ca(OH)_2$, calcium hydroxide, or "slaked" lime) or calcium oxide (CaO, *QUICKLIME*[11] or "unslaked" lime). The hydrated lime may be used directly. The calcium oxide or quicklime must first be *SLAKED*.[12] This involves adding the calcium oxide (CaO) pellets to water and heating to cause "slaking" (the formation of calcium hydroxide ($Ca(OH)_2$)) before use. Small facilities commonly use hydrated lime ($Ca(OH)_2$). Large facilities may find it more economical to use quicklime (CaO) and slake it on site.

14.311   Removal of Carbon Dioxide

The application of lime for the removal of carbonate hardness also removes carbon dioxide. Carbon dioxide does not contribute to hardness and therefore does not need to be removed. However, carbon dioxide will consume a portion of the lime to be used and therefore must be considered. Equation (1) describes the reaction of carbon dioxide with lime.

(1) Carbon Dioxide + Lime → Calcium Carbonate ↓ + Water

$$CO_2 + Ca(OH)_2 \rightarrow CaCO_3 \downarrow + H_2O$$

14.312   Removal of Carbonate Hardness

The equations below describe the removal of carbonate hardness.

(2) Calcium Bicarbonate + Lime → Calcium Carbonate ↓ + Water

$$Ca(HCO_3)_2 + Ca(OH)_2 \rightarrow 2\,CaCO_3 \downarrow + 2\,H_2O$$

(3) Magnesium Bicarbonate + Lime → Calcium Carbonate ↓ + Magnesium Carbonate + Water

$$Mg(HCO_3)_2 + Ca(OH)_2 \rightarrow CaCO_3 \downarrow + MgCO_3 + 2\,H_2O$$

(4) Magnesium Carbonate + Lime → Calcium Carbonate ↓ + Magnesium Hydroxide ↓

$$MgCO_3 + Ca(OH)_2 \rightarrow CaCO_3 \downarrow + Mg(OH)_2 \downarrow$$

---

[9] *Supersaturated.   An unstable condition of a solution (water) in which the solution contains a substance at a concentration greater than the saturation concentration for the substance.*

[10] *Hydrated Lime.   Limestone that has been "burned" and treated with water under controlled conditions until the calcium oxide portion has been converted to calcium hydroxide ($Ca(OH)_2$). Hydrated lime is quicklime combined with water. $CaO + H_2O \rightarrow Ca(OH)_2$. Also called slaked lime. Also see QUICKLIME.*

[11] *Quicklime.   A material that is mostly calcium oxide (CaO) or calcium oxide in natural association with a lesser amount of magnesium oxide. Quicklime is capable of combining with water, that is, becoming slaked. Also see HYDRATED LIME.*

[12] *Slake.   To mix with water so that a true chemical combination (hydration) takes place, such as in the slaking of lime.*

When lime is added to water, any carbon dioxide present is converted to calcium carbonate if enough lime is added (Equation 1). With the addition of more lime the calcium bicarbonate will be precipitated as calcium carbonate. To remove both the calcium and magnesium bicarbonate, an excess of lime must be used.

14.313 Removal of Noncarbonate Hardness

Magnesium noncarbonate hardness requires the addition of both lime and soda ash (sodium carbonate, Na_2CO_3).

(5) Magnesium Sulfate + Lime → Magnesium Hydroxide↓ + Calcium Sulfate

$$MgSO_4 + Ca(OH)_2 \rightarrow \qquad Mg(OH)_2\downarrow + CaSO_4$$

(6) Calcium Sulfate + Soda Ash → Calcium Carbonate↓ + Sodium Sulfate

$$CaSO_4 + Na_2CO_3 \rightarrow \qquad CaCO_3\downarrow + Na_2SO_4$$

Equation (6) is also one of the equations for the removal of calcium noncarbonate hardness. Similar equations can be written for the removal of noncarbonate hardness caused by calcium and magnesium chloride.

14.314 Stability

The main chemical reaction products from the lime-soda softening process are $CaCO_3\downarrow$ and $Mg(OH)_2\downarrow$. The water thus treated has been chemically changed and is no longer stable because of pH and alkalinity changes. Lime-soda softened water is usually supersaturated with calcium carbonate ($CaCO_3$). The degree of instability and excess calcium carbonate depends on the degree to which the water is softened. Calcium carbonate hardness is removed at a lower pH than magnesium carbonate hardness. If maximum carbonate hardness removal is practiced (thus requiring a high pH to remove the magnesium carbonate hardness), the water will be supersaturated with calcium carbonate and magnesium hydroxide. Under these conditions deposition of precipitates will occur in filters and pipelines.

Excess lime addition to remove magnesium carbonate hardness results in supersaturated conditions and a residual of lime which will produce a pH of about 10.9. The excess lime is called caustic alkalinity since it raises the pH. If the pH is then lowered, better precipitation of calcium carbonate and magnesium hydroxide will occur. Alkalinity will be lowered also. This is usually accomplished by pumping carbon dioxide (CO_2) gas into the water. This addition of carbon dioxide to the treated water is called RECARBONATION.[13]

Recarbonation may be carried out in two steps. The first addition of carbon dioxide would follow excess lime addition to lower the pH to about 10.4 and encourage the precipitation of calcium carbonate and magnesium hydroxide. A second addition of carbon dioxide after treatment removes noncarbonate hardness. This would again lower the pH to about 9.8 and would encourage precipitation. By carrying out recarbonation prior to filtration, the buildup of excess lime and also calcium carbonate and magnesium hydroxide precipitates in the filters will be prevented or minimized. The recarbonation reaction for excess lime removal is shown below.

(7) Calcium Hydroxide + Carbon Dioxide → Calcium Carbonate↓ + Water

$$Ca(OH)_2 + CO_2 \rightarrow CaCO_3\downarrow + H_2O$$

Care must be exercised when using recarbonation. Feeding excess carbon dioxide may result in no lowering of the hardness by causing calcium carbonate precipitates to go back into solution and cause carbonate hardness.

(8) Calcium Carbonate + Carbon Dioxide + Water → Calcium Bicarbonate

$$CaCO_3 + CO_2 + H_2O \rightarrow Ca(HCO_3)_2$$

14.315 Caustic Soda Softening

An alternative method in the lime-soda softening process is the use of sodium hydroxide (NaOH, often called caustic soda) in place of soda ash. The chemical reactions of sodium hydroxide with carbonate and noncarbonate hardness are listed below.

(9) Carbon Dioxide + Sodium Hydroxide → Sodium Carbonate + Water

$$CO_2 + 2 NaOH \rightarrow Na_2CO_3 + H_2O$$

(10) Calcium Bicarbonate + Sodium Hydroxide → Calcium Carbonate↓ + Sodium Carbonate + Water

$$Ca(HCO_3)_2 + 2 NaOH \rightarrow CaCO_3\downarrow + Na_2CO_3 + 2 H_2O$$

(11) Magnesium Bicarbonate + Sodium Hydroxide → Magnesium Hydroxide↓ + Sodium Carbonate + Water

$$Mg(HCO_3)_2 + 4 NaOH \rightarrow Mg(OH)_2\downarrow + 2 Na_2CO_3 + 2 H_2O$$

(12) Magnesium Sulfate + Sodium Hydroxide → Magnesium Hydroxide↓ + Sodium Sulfate

$$MgSO_4 + 2 NaOH \rightarrow Mg(OH)_2\downarrow + Na_2SO_4$$

These chemical reactions show that in removing carbon dioxide and carbonate hardness, sodium carbonate (Na_2CO_3, soda ash) is formed which will react to remove the noncarbonate hardness. Not only will sodium hydroxide substitute for soda ash, but it may replace all or part of the lime ($Ca(OH)_2$) requirement for removal of the carbonate hardness. The use of caustic soda (usually as a 50-percent solution) may have several advantages:

1. Stability in storage,

2. Less sludge is formed, and

3. Ease of handling and storage.

Safe handling procedures for caustic soda must be used at all times. A 50-percent caustic solution is very dangerous. Caustic soda is a strong base and will attack fabrics and leather and cause severe burns to the skin. Rubber gloves, respirator, safety goggles, and a rubber apron must be worn when handling caustic soda. A safety shower and an emergency eye wash must be readily available at all times.

---

[13] Recarbonation (re-CAR-bun-NAY-shun). A process in which carbon dioxide is bubbled into the water being treated to lower the pH. The pH may also be lowered by the addition of acid. Recarbonation is the final stage in the lime-soda ash softening process. This process converts carbonate ions to bicarbonate ions and stabilizes the solution against the precipitation of carbonate compounds.

The decision to use caustic soda rather than soda ash depends on the quality of the source water and the delivered costs of the various chemicals.

QUESTIONS

Write your answers in a notebook and then compare your answers with those on page 118.

14.3C   What causes the pH to increase during the lime-soda softening process?

14.3D   Why is the pH increased during the lime-soda softening process?

14.3E   How are the scale-forming tendencies reduced in water after the chemical softening process?

14.3F   What is recarbonation?

14.3G   Under what conditions might caustic soda softening be used?

14.316   Calculation of Chemical Dosages

There are several different approaches to calculating chemical doses for the lime-soda softening process. This section illustrates one step-by-step procedure. To use this procedure you need to obtain a chemical analysis of the water you are softening. From this analysis obtain the known values for your water similar to the "Knowns" listed in Example 3. Then calculate the dosages of chemicals for your water by following the steps in the example.

To help you understand where some of the numbers come from in the formulas, we have listed the molecular weights of the major chemical components involved in the chemical precipitation softening process.

Quicklime, CaO	= 56
Hydrated Lime, $Ca(OH)_2$	= 74
Magnesium, Mg^{2+}	= 24.3
Carbon Dioxide, CO_2	= 44
Magnesium Hydroxide, $Mg(OH)_2$	= 58.3
Soda Ash, Na_2CO_3	= 106
Alkalinity, as $CaCO_3$	= 100
Hardness, as $CaCO_3$	= 100

FORMULAS

1. The lime dosage for softening can be estimated by using the following formula:

$$\text{Quicklime (CaO) Feed, mg/}L = \frac{(A + B + C + D)1.15}{\text{Purity of Lime, as a decimal}}$$

Where A = CO_2 in source water
(mg/L as CO_2)(56/44)

B = Bicarbonate alkalinity removed in softening
(mg/L as $CaCO_3$)(56/100)

C = Hydroxide alkalinity in softener effluent
(mg/L as $CaCO_3$)(56/100)

D = Magnesium removed in softening
(mg/L as Mg^{2+})(56/24.3)

1.15 = Excess lime dosage
(using a 15 percent excess)

NOTE: If hydrated lime ($Ca(OH)_2$) is used instead of quicklime, substitute, 74 for 56 in A, B, C, and D.

2. The soda ash dosage to remove noncarbonate hardness can be estimated by using the formula below.

$$\text{Soda Ash } (Na_2CO_3) \text{ Feed, mg/}L = (\text{Noncarbonate Hardness, mg/}L \text{ as } CaCO_3)(106/100)$$

3. The dosage of carbon dioxide required for recarbonation can be estimated using the formula below.

$$\text{Total } CO_2 \text{ Feed, mg/}L = (Ca(OH)_2 \text{ excess, mg/}L)(44/74)$$
$$+ (Mg(OH)_2 \text{ residual, mg/}L)(44/58.3)$$

EXAMPLE 3

Calculate the hydrated lime ($Ca(OH)_2$) with 90 percent purity, soda ash, and carbon dioxide dose requirements in milligrams per liter for the water shown below.

Known

Constituents	Source Water	Softened Water After Recarbonation and Filtration
CO_2, mg/L	= 6 mg/L	= 0 mg/L
Total Alkalinity, mg/L	= 170 mg/L as $CaCO_3$	= 30 mg/L as $CaCO_3$
Total Hardness, mg/L	= 280 mg/L as $CaCO_3$	= 70 mg/L as $CaCO_3$
Mg^{2+}, mg/L	= 21 mg/L	= 3 mg/L
pH	= 7.5	= 8.8
Lime Purity, %	= 90%	

Unknown

1. Hydrated Lime, mg/L
2. Soda Ash, mg/L
3. Carbon Dioxide, mg/L

1. Calculate the hydrated lime ($Ca(OH)_2$) required in milligrams per liter.

   A = (CO_2, mg/L)(74/44)

   = (6 mg/L)(74/44)

   = 10 mg/L

   B = (Alkalinity, mg/L)(74/100)

   = (170 mg/L − 30 mg/L)(74/100)

   = 104 mg/L

   C = 0   Hydroxide Alkalinity = 0

   D = (Mg^{2+}, mg/L)(74/24.3)

   = (21 mg/L − 3 mg/L)(74/24.3)

   = 55 mg/L

$$\text{Hydrated Lime } (Ca(OH)_2) \text{ Feed, mg}/L = \frac{(A + B + C + D)1.15}{\text{Purity of Lime, as a decimal}}$$

$$= \frac{(10 \text{ mg}/L + 104 \text{ mg}/L + 0 + 55 \text{ mg}/L)1.15}{0.90}$$

$$= \frac{(169 \text{ mg}/L)(1.15)}{0.90}$$

$$= 216 \text{ mg}/L$$

2. Calculate the soda ash required in milligrams per liter.

$$\text{Total Hardness Removed, mg}/L \text{ as } CaCO_3 = \text{Total Hardness, mg}/L \text{ as } CaCO_3 - \text{Total Hardness Remaining, mg}/L \text{ as } CaCO_3$$

$$= 280 \text{ mg}/L - 70 \text{ mg}/L$$

$$= 210 \text{ mg}/L \text{ as } CaCO_3$$

$$\text{Noncarbonate Hardness, mg}/L \text{ as } CaCO_3 = \text{Total Hardness Removed, mg}/L \text{ as } CaCO_3 - \text{Carbonate Hardness, mg}/L \text{ as } CaCO_3$$

$$= 210 \text{ mg}/L - 170 \text{ mg}/L$$

$$= 40 \text{ mg}/L \text{ as } CaCO_3$$

$$\text{Soda Ash } (Na_2CO_3) \text{ Feed, mg}/L = \left(\text{Noncarbonate Hardness, mg}/L \text{ as } CaCO_3 \right)(106/100)$$

$$= (40 \text{ mg}/L)(106/100)$$

$$= 42 \text{ mg}/L$$

3. Calculate the dosage of carbon dioxide required for recarbonation.

$$\text{Excess Lime, mg}/L = (A + B + C + D)(0.15)$$

$$= (10 \text{ mg}/L + 104 \text{ mg}/L + 0 + 55 \text{ mg}/L)(0.15)$$

$$= (169 \text{ mg}/L)(0.15)$$

$$= 25 \text{ mg}/L$$

$$\text{Total } CO_2 \text{ Feed, mg}/L = (Ca(OH)_2 \text{ excess, mg}/L)(44/74) + (Mg^{2+} \text{ residual, mg}/L)(44/24.3)$$

$$= (25 \text{ mg}/L)(44/74) + (3 \text{ mg}/L)(44/24.3)$$

$$= 15 \text{ mg}/L + 6 \text{ mg}/L$$

$$= 21 \text{ mg}/L$$

QUESTION

Write your answer in a notebook and then compare your answer with the one on page 118.

14.3H Calculate the hydrated lime ($Ca(OH)_2$) with 90 percent purity, soda ash, and carbon dioxide dose requirements in milligrams per liter for the water shown below.

Constituents	Source Water	Softened Water After Recarbonation and Filtration
CO_2, mg/L	= 5 mg/L	= 0 mg/L
Total Alkalinity, mg/L	= 150 mg/L as $CaCO_3$	= 20 mg/L as $CaCO_3$
Total Hardness, mg/L	= 240 mg/L as $CaCO_3$	= 50 mg/L as $CaCO_3$
Mg^{2+}, mg/L	= 16 mg/L	= 2 mg/L
pH	= 7.4	= 8.8
Lime Purity, %	= 90%	

14.32 Lime Softening (Figure 14.2)

Water having hardness caused by calcium and magnesium bicarbonate (carbonate hardness) can usually be softened to an acceptable level using only lime. The lime reacts with the bicarbonate to form calcium carbonate which will precipitate and settle out (convert from soluble to insoluble form) at a pH above 10 and magnesium carbonate which will remain in solution. The magnesium carbonate reacts with additional lime at a pH above 11 to form magnesium hydroxide which will precipitate.

In practice, if enough hardness can be removed by reacting lime with the calcium bicarbonate, softening can be accomplished at less expense. This procedure is sometimes called partial lime softening (no magnesium removal). On the other hand, if some of the magnesium is to be removed, additional lime will be required.

Figure 14.2 is a flow diagram of a typical straight lime softening treatment plant. Settling should be provided after the addition of carbon dioxide (recarbonation) to ease the load on the filters. Recarbonation is used to lower the pH of the water. When properly recarbonated the water is still supersaturated with calcium carbonate ($CaCO_3$). If the pH is much above 9, the water will usually cause scale to form. By recarbonation the pH can be lowered to a range between 8.8 and 8.4 and the Langelier Index will still be positive; therefore there will be little or no corrosion. A polyphosphate is sometimes added to the water to prevent excessively heavy calcium carbonate scale deposits from forming. A polyphosphate may not be necessary if recarbonation is properly controlled. Addition of acid will *NOT* accomplish the same things as recarbonation and the addition of a polyphosphate; however, adding acid will lower the pH.

14.33 Split Treatment

The amount of calcium and magnesium in source waters may vary. When the water contains a high level of magnesium, a method known as split treatment may be used (Figure 14.3). Split treatment can be used in lime treatment only or lime-soda ash treatment. In split treatment a portion of the water (say 80 percent) is treated with an excess amount of lime to remove the magnesium at a pH of over 11. Then

Fig. 14.2   Straight lime treatment

Fig. 14.3   Split lime treatment

source water (the other 20 percent) is added in the next basin to neutralize (lower the pH) the excess-lime-treated portion. The percentages will vary depending upon the water hardness, treatment layout, and desired results.

Split treatment softening can eliminate the need for recarbonation as well as offer a significant savings in lime feed. Since the fraction of the water that is treated has a high lime dose, magnesium is almost completely removed from this portion. When this water is mixed with the unsoftened water, the carbon dioxide and bicarbonate in the unsoftened fraction of the water tend to recarbonate in the final blend or mix of the treated water (effluent).

If the water shown in Figure 14.4 was treated by conventional treatment (not split treatment), it would require a lime dose of 400 mg/L as $CaCO_3$ (which is 25 percent higher) and a carbon dioxide dose of 145 mg/L as $CaCO_3$ to produce a water having a hardness of 61 mg/L as $CaCO_3$ and a pH of 8.63.

While split treatment may be used in the lime-soda process, it is often advantageous to use a lime-ion exchange process (see Section 14.10). The salt used to remove noncarbonate hardness in the ion exchange process is much less expensive than the soda ash required in the lime-soda ash process.

The curves shown in Figure 14.4 assume that carbonate equilibrium has been achieved. In practice, it is not possible to attain equilibrium, but if the reactions take place in solids contact units the results are very close to carbonate equilibrium.

The proper fraction of water to bypass is rather critically dependent on the lime dose and chemical composition of the unsoftened water. The proper fraction may be calculated, but the calculations are very complex. An experienced water chemist can perform the calculations.

QUESTIONS

Write your answers in a notebook and then compare your answers with those on page 118.

14.3I   What compounds are formed when calcium and magnesium are precipitated out of water in the lime softening process?

14.3J   What hardness is removed by partial lime softening (no magnesium removal)?

14.3K   What is split lime treatment?

14.34   Lime-Soda Ash Softening

Let's look now at hardness requiring lime-soda ash treatment for removal (Figure 14.5).

When water cannot be softened to the desired level with lime only, it no doubt contains noncarbonate hardness. Noncarbonate hardness requires the addition of a compound which increases carbonate concentration, usually soda ash (sodium carbonate).

A water could contain only calcium hardness, yet require both lime and soda ash treatment. This would occur if the hardness were only calcium bicarbonate, sulfate and/or chloride. In other words, all of the hardness is calcium carbonate and calcium noncarbonate hardness. This would not require split treatment (Figure 14.6).

14.35   Caustic Soda Softening

An alternative to the lime-soda ash process is the use of caustic soda (sodium hydroxide, NaOH) instead of soda ash.

The reactions of caustic soda with the carbonate and noncarbonate hardness are given in Section 14.315. Recall that

UNSOFTENED WATER

TEMPERATURE	=	25°C		Ca	=	150 mg/L as $CaCO_3$
TDS	=	400 mg/L		Mg	=	100 mg/L as $CaCO_3$
pH	=	7.2		Alk	=	250 mg/L as $CaCO_3$

DOSAGE

LIME = 320 mg/L as $CaCO_3$

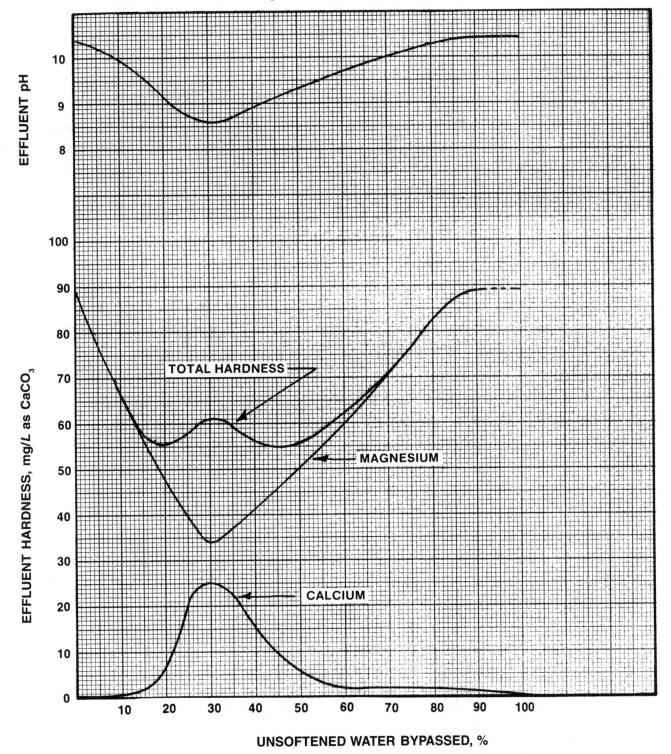

Fig. 14.4   Split treatment softening

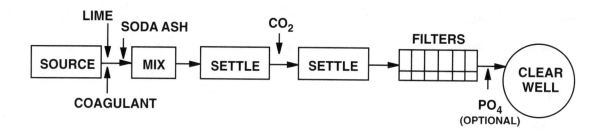

Fig. 14.5 Lime-soda ash treatment

Fig. 14.6 Lime-soda ash split treatment

caustic soda reacts with the carbonate hardness to form soda ash (sodium carbonate) which will react with calcium sulfate to form calcium carbonate ($CaCO_3$) as shown previously.

The advantages of using liquid caustic soda include ease of handling and feeding, lack of deterioration in storage, and less calcium carbonate sludge to handle and dispose of. Caustic soda is capable of removing both carbonate and noncarbonate hardness. Therefore, caustic soda may be used instead of soda ash, but also in place of part or all of the lime requirement. The use of caustic soda depends on a comparison of the costs of caustic soda, lime, and soda ash, and the characteristics of the source water.

Two points to observe are that sodium does not contribute to hardness, thus all the reactions having sodium compounds as an end product are non-hardness-producing compounds. However, sodium levels in drinking water should be less than 20 mg/L. The second point is that the precipitated compounds ($CaCO_3\downarrow$ and $Mg(OH)_2\downarrow$) are the desired end products whether lime or lime-soda ash or caustic soda treatment is used.

QUESTIONS

Write your answers in a notebook and then compare your answers with those on page 118.

14.3L   Under what conditions would lime-soda ash softening be used?

14.3M   What chemical is used to remove noncarbonate hardness in the chemical precipitation softening process?

14.36 Handling, Application, and Storage of Lime

Where the daily requirements for lime are small, lime is usually delivered to the water treatment plant in bags. At larger treatment plants either quicklime (CaO) or hydrated lime ($Ca(OH)_2$) is delivered in bulk quantities. Truck loads of lime are commonly transferred to weathertight bins or silos by mechanical or pneumatic conveying systems.

Storage areas for bagged lime must be covered to prevent rain from wetting the bags. Bagged quicklime (CaO or calcium oxide) should never be stored close to combustible materials because considerable heat will be generated if the lime accidentally gets wet. Quicklime may be stored as long as six months, but in general should not be stored over three months. Hydrated lime should not be stored for more than three months before use.

Lime may be applied by dry feeding techniques using volumetric or gravimetric feeders. Lime is too insoluble to make "solution feeding" by pump feeders practical because of the accumulation of carbonate precipitation. See Chapter 13, "Fluoridation," for additional details and pictures of the various types of chemical feeders.

Operator safety must be considered before attempting to work with lime. A properly designed lime feeding system can minimize or eliminate lime dust problems. If lime dust is a problem, operators must wear protective clothing to avoid burns from contact with lime. Protective clothing includes long-sleeved shirt with sleeves and collar buttoned, trousers with legs down over tops of shoes or boots, head protection, and gloves. Clothing should not fit too tightly around your neck, wrists or ankles. A protective cream should be applied to exposed parts of the body, especially your neck, face and wrists. You should wear a lightweight filter mask and tight-fitting safety glasses with side shields to protect yourself from the lime dust.

If lime comes in contact with your skin or eyes, immediately flush the affected areas with water and consult a physician if necessary. Do not rub your eyes if they are irritated with lime dust because rubbing will make the irritation worse. Keep any lime burns covered with a bandage during healing to prevent infection.

After handling lime, you should take a shower. If your clothes are covered with dust, or splattered with a lime slurry, take them off and have them washed. If possible, wear clean clothes on every shift.

For additional information regarding lime, contact the National Lime Association, 200 N. Glebe Road, Suite 800, Arlington, VA 22203, and request a copy of their publication, *LIME HANDLING, APPLICATION, AND STORAGE IN TREATMENT PROCESSES*, 7th Edition, 1995. Price, $19.95, plus $3.00 shipping and handling. Lime, as well as other water treatment chemicals, should comply with the Standards of the American Water Works Association.

QUESTIONS

Write your answers in a notebook and then compare your answers with those on page 118.

14.3N   How is lime delivered to plants where the daily requirements are small?

14.3O   Why should quicklime be kept dry?

14.3P   What types of chemical feeders are used to apply dry lime?

14.4   INTERACTIONS WITH COAGULANTS

Coagulation is discussed in detail in Chapter 4, "Coagulation and Flocculation." However, the interactions of lime and soda ash with metallic coagulants such as alum, iron salts (ferric chloride, ferric sulfate, and ferrous sulfate), sodium aluminate, and many polymers are important.

Alum and iron salts are acidic and react with the alkalinity in water to cause a demand the same way that free carbon dioxide will. Therefore, this acidic condition must be met before softening can occur. In other words, extra lime will be required as the alum or iron feed rate goes up and therefore less lime will be required as the alum or iron feed rate is reduced.

Cationic polymers are not very pH sensitive and are often used as coagulant aids in softening plants rather than alum or iron salts. On the other hand, when sodium aluminate (a basic rather than an acidic compound) is the coagulant, the lime required to achieve a specific hardness reduction will be less, and will vary the opposite of alum or iron salts. The proportion of lime required in either instance is directly related to the coagulant dosage as well as the hardness removal desired. Approximate relationships can be calculated; however, experimentation is in order since plant equipment and source water variations are primary factors in the efficiencies of each waterworks. Jar tests are discussed later in Section 14.9.

If you are treating highly colored waters, these waters must be coagulated for color removal at low pH values. Alum is a good coagulant under these conditions. Ozone, permanganate, and chlorine may be tried along with alum to oxidize color. The high pH values required during softening tend to "set" the color which then becomes very difficult to remove.

QUESTIONS

Write your answers in a notebook and then compare your answers with those on page 119.

14.4A   What happens to the lime dose when the alum dose is increased for coagulation?

14.4B   How can color be removed from water?

14.5   STABILITY

In nature, most waters are more or less stable. That is, they are in chemical balance. When lime is added, the chemical balance is changed. The calcium carbonate ($CaCO_3$) formed in lime treatment is scale forming unless the exact chemical balance is achieved, which is seldom the case.

Under most conditions, a slight excess of lime is fed to cause a caustic condition to ensure complete reactions and achieve the desired results. In order to prevent scale formation on the filter sand, distribution mains, and household plumbing, the excess caustic and unprecipitated carbonate ions (pin floc) must be converted to soluble forms. Recarbonation is the most common way to do this. Again, as with all chemical treatment, recarbonation must be controlled to achieve the desired results.

Recarbonation lowers the pH to about 8.8 and thus converts some of the carbonate (CO_3^{2-}) back to the original bicarbonate (HCO_3^-) that existed in the source water. Recarbonation can be accomplished, to a degree, by using the source water in the split treatment mode discussed earlier. Usually this is not adequate so further recarbonation is required. One reason for using source water as a neutralizing agent is that the recarbonation process is much less costly than if a high caustic water (high pH) is neutralized by chemical addition.

Use of carbon dioxide gas is the most common method of recarbonation. The reactions are:

1. $Ca(OH)_2 + CO_2 + H_2O \rightarrow Ca(HCO_3)_2$ and

2. $CaCO_3 + CO_2 + H_2O \rightarrow Ca(HCO_3)_2$.

These reactions may be looked at as lime softening in reverse and will increase the hardness slightly. In these reactions you are producing bicarbonate ions which were removed in softening as carbonate hardness. This process tends to move the water back toward its original state, thus rendering it more stable.

The use of acids such as sulfuric or hydrochloric instead of recarbonation with carbon dioxide (CO_2) does not produce the same results. When carbon dioxide is added to a water containing calcium ions (Ca^{2+}) and hydroxide ions (OH^-), a calcium carbonate ($CaCO_3$) precipitate will form and the water will be saturated (or supersaturated) with calcium carbonate. If a strong acid is added to neutralize the softened water which is highly basic, these reactions will not take place.

The marble test is the simplest method of measuring stability in the laboratory. Run the marble test [14] as outlined below:

1. Collect a sample of tap water that has been softened and stopper the sample bottle (avoid splashing into the flask).

2. To an identical sample, add one gram of powdered calcium carbonate. Mix and let stand for an hour or so.

3. Filter both samples (so they are both exposed to the same conditions).

4. Run pH and alkalinity tests on both samples.

5. The goal is to have the sample of softened tap water as nearly matched to the softened sample treated with calcium carbonate as possible. The plant treatment must be controlled to permit this condition to exist. If the pH and alkalinity in the softened sample are higher than in the softened sample treated with calcium carbonate, you are probably overtreating your supply and have scale-forming water. But, if the pH and alkalinity in your untreated softened sample are lower than in the treated one (calcium carbonate added), you are undertreating your supply. If they are similar, then stability is near.

Another way to check your water is to suspend a couple of nails on strings in your filter. Observe the nails occasionally to see if they are rusting or scaling up. To further protect the distribution system as well as prevent scale formation in the filter bed, 0.7 to 1.0 mg/L polyphosphate could be fed far enough ahead of the filters to allow mixing before the water reaches the filters. Addition of polyphosphate can *PREVENT THE FORMATION OF SCALE* on filter media and in distribution system mains, but polyphosphate does *NOT* prevent corrosion. The Langelier Index (see Section 8.322 in Chapter 8, Volume I) is another approach to determining the corrosivity of water.

Caution should be exercised when using polyphosphate compounds. If they are converted to the orthophosphate form, they will lose their effectiveness. With the addition of phosphorus to water, there could be an increase in bacterial growths in the distribution system. Also some wastewater treatment plants have phosphorus discharge limitations and polyphosphates added to drinking water can cause wastewater treatment plants to violate their discharge requirements.

QUESTIONS

Write your answers in a notebook and then compare your answers with those on page 119.

14.5A   What problems are sometimes created when a slight excess of lime is fed during softening to cause a caustic condition to ensure complete reactions?

14.5B   How can excess caustic and unprecipitated carbonate ions (pin floc) be removed from softened water?

14.5C   How can nails be used to determine if a water is stable?

14.5D   What test is used to determine if a water is stable?

14.6 SAFETY

When quicklime reacts with water in the slaking process (Figure 14.7), it gets hot enough to cause serious burns. Also, being caustic in nature, it can harm your eyes and skin. *ALWAYS* wear goggles or a face shield when working with lime that has been or is in the process of slaking. Flush with water if exposed to lime. Seek medical attention if it gets in your eyes. As for hands or face burns, immediately wash the affected areas and consult a physician if the burns appear serious.

Feeding equipment has moving parts. All moving machinery is a potential safety hazard. A paste-type slaker is particularly dangerous. This type of slaker will "eat you alive." Never put your hand in or near the slaker paddles while the slaker is running. Use wooden paddles as cleaning tools on any slaker in operation. A metal tool will damage the slaker and could even injure the operator if dropped by accident. However, a wooden paddle is less likely to damage the equipment or the operator.

Types of equipment vary greatly. Usually the operator has little or no input in this area. Engineers usually design a plant and specify the type of chemical feed equipment.

Equipment suppliers are usually quite cooperative in advising any operator in the use and care of their equipment in your treatment plant. Detailed start-up, shutdown, and maintenance procedures are available in the equipment manuals supplied by the manufacturer of the equipment.

Another important safety precaution is to avoid using the same conveyor or bin for alternately handling both quicklime and one of the coagulants containing water, such as alum, ferric sulfate, or copperas. This water may be withdrawn by the quicklime and could generate enough heat to cause a fire. Explosions have been reported to have been caused by lime-alum mixtures in enclosed bins. Therefore, always clean facilities before switching from one chemical to another.

---

[14] *For additional information on the marble test, see Chapter 21, "Advanced Laboratory Procedures," Test Procedure 9, "Marble Test."*

Fig. 14.7 Lime-slaking system
(Permission of Wallace & Tiernan, Inc.)

QUESTIONS

Write your answers in a notebook and then compare your answers with those on page 119.

14.6A Why should wooden paddles be used as cleaning tools on any slaker in operation?

14.6B Where would you look for information on how to safely maintain equipment?

14.7 SLUDGE RECIRCULATION AND DISPOSAL

Considerable sludge may be produced by the lime and lime-soda softening processes. When calcium and magnesium hardness are converted from soluble forms to insoluble precipitates (calcium carbonate and magnesium hydroxide), these precipitates form sludge. This sludge is removed from the bottom of settling basins and may be recirculated or must be disposed of by an acceptable procedure.

In some instances, sludge is recirculated back into the primary mix area of conventional plants to help "seed" the process. The advantages are (1) recirculation speeds up the precipitation process, and (2) some reduction of chemical requirements may result. One disadvantage is that an increase in magnesium could result. Only trial and error will really determine if sludge recirculation will serve a useful purpose in your plant.

Sludge disposal is a problem everywhere. Perhaps the most common method is landfill disposal. This is accomplished by dewatering the sludge (drying beds or mechanical means) and then hauling the sludge to landfill sites developed solely for sludge disposal or sanitary landfills. Generally, a sludge with a Ca:Mg ratio of less than 2:1 will be difficult to dewater, whereas a sludge with a Ca:Mg ratio of greater than 5:1 will dewater relatively easily. The less water in the sludge, the less volume to transport to the disposal site and the less space required in the landfill.

To a lesser degree, sanitary sewer disposal is sometimes used. This only moves the sludge to another location for someone else to deal with. Some work has also been done with land application as a substitute for agricultural lime to increase the pH of highly acidic soils. The lime sludge is applied at a rate which will produce the optimum soil pH for the crops to be planted. For additional information on sludge disposal, see Chapter 17, "Handling and Disposal of Process Wastes."

14.8 RECORDS

Records should be kept on the amounts of chemicals ordered and the amounts fed. Laboratory results should be recorded in a permanent lab book. See Chapter 18, "Maintenance," for details on how to keep equipment maintenance schedules and records. Again, every plant is different, but accurate records will help a good operator be a better operator.

QUESTIONS

Write your answers in a notebook and then compare your answers with those on page 119.

14.7A   What is a disadvantage of recirculating sludge back to the primary mix area?

14.7B   How could you determine if sludge recirculation will serve a useful purpose in your plant?

14.8A   What types of records should be kept regarding treatment plant chemicals?

14.9   JAR TESTS

14.90   Typical Procedures

Approximate amounts of chemicals required can be calculated (see Section 14.316, "Calculation of Chemical Dosages"); however, the best method of determining the proper dosages is by the use of the jar test. See Chapter 11, "Laboratory Procedures," for details on the equipment and procedures required to run jar tests.

Chemical reagents may be made up by adding one gram of reagent to a liter of water.[15] This will produce a 0.1-percent chemical solution. When 1.0 gram/liter of lime, soda ash or coagulant is made up as the stock solution, one mL of the stock solution in a one-liter sample of water equals one-mg/L dosage. If large doses of lime are required, add 10 grams of lime per liter. With this stock solution, one mL of stock solution in a one-liter sample of water equals ten-mg/L dosage.

Set up 6 samples and estimate the dosage required by adding varying amounts to each sample. Trial and error will put you in the "ball park." To refine the dosage, pick the best looking sample from the settling properties of the floc to establish the optimum lime dose. Then do the same with varying amounts of soda ash, leaving the lime dosage constant. By running pH, alkalinity, and hardness tests you can find the optimum dosages that give the desired softened water results.

The exact procedures used to soften water by chemical precipitation using the lime-soda ash process depend on the hardness and other chemical characteristics of the water being treated. A series of jar tests are commonly used to determine optimum dosages. In many cases, the feed rates determined by jar tests do not produce the exact same results in an actual plant. This is because of differences in water temperature, size and shape of jars as compared with plant basins, mixing equipment, and influence of coagulant (a heavy alum feed will neutralize more of the lime). You must remember that jar test results are a starting point. You may have to make additional adjustments to the chemical feeders in your plant based on actual analyses of the treated water.

Convert the jar test results to plant feed rates. Always feed enough chemical to achieve the desired results, but don't overfeed. Overtreating is a waste of money and quality control will suffer.

14.91   Examples

Let's set up some jar tests to determine the optimum dosages for lime or lime-soda treatment to remove hardness from a municipal water supply. To get started, add 10.0 grams of hydrated lime to a one-liter graduated cylinder or flask and fill to the one-liter mark with tap water. Thoroughly mix this stock solution in order to thoroughly suspend all of the lime. One mL of this solution (which has been thoroughly mixed) in a liter of water is the same as a lime dose of ten mg/L, or 0.5 mL in 500 mL is still the same as a ten-mg/L lime dose.

Set up a series of hardness tests by adding 5.0 mL, 10.0 mL, 15.0 mL, 20.0 mL, 25.0 mL, 30.0 mL, 35.0 mL and 40.0 mL to one-liter (1,000-mL) beakers or jars. Fill the beakers to the 1,000-mL mark with the water being tested. Mix thoroughly for as long as normal mixing will occur in your plant. Allow the precipitate to settle (20 minutes if this is the settling time in your plant) and measure the hardness remaining in the water above the precipitate. A plot of the hardness remaining against the lime dosage will reveal the optimum dosage. Examination of Figures 14.8, 14.9, and 14.10[16] reveals that the water of all three cities responded differently to the increasing lime dosage. City 1 (Figure 14.8) should be providing a lime dose of 100 mg/L. The cost of increasing the dosage to 150 mg/L is not worth the slight reduction in hardness from 110 to 100 mg/L as $CaCO_3$. Note that an overfeed of lime will actually increase the hardness.

City 2 (Figure 14.9) should be providing a lime dose of 200 mg/L. A dose of 300 mg/L will reduce hardness, but the increase in lime costs is too great. City 3 (Figure 14.10) should be dosing lime between 200 and 250 mg/L. Note that the greater the lime dose, the less the hardness, but the greater the quantities of sludge that must be handled and disposed of.

---

[15] *Some operators add 10 grams of reagent to a liter of water. This will produce a one-percent solution. One mL of the stock solution in one liter will produce a ten-mg/L dosage.*

[16] *These figures were adapted from an article titled, "Use of Softening Curve for Lime Dosage Control," by Michael D. Curry, P.E., which appeared in THE DIGESTER/OVER THE SPILLWAY, published by the Illinois Environmental Protection Agency.*

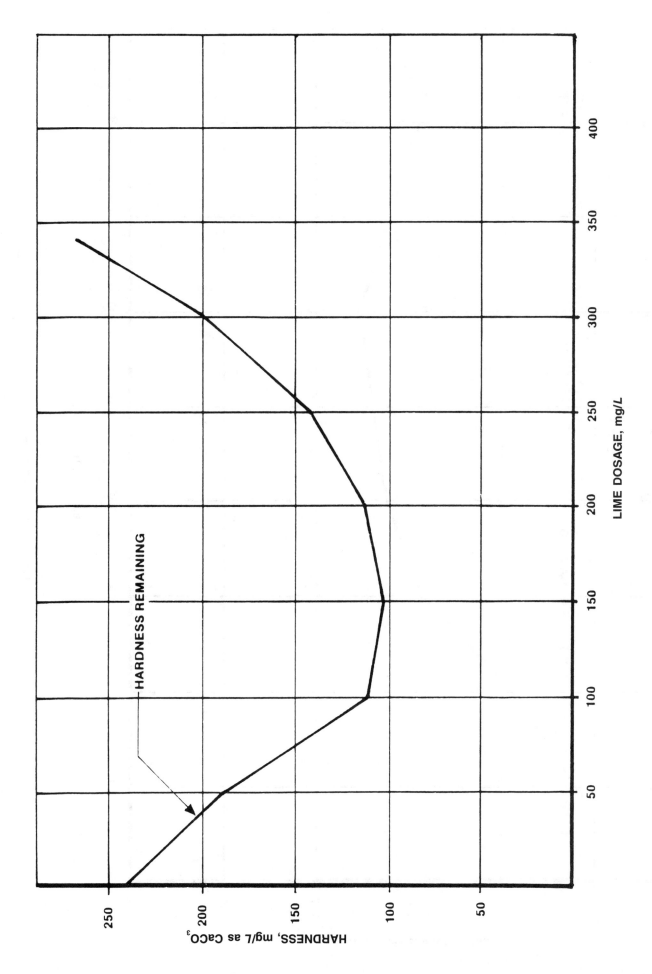

Fig. 14.8   Softening curve for City 1

Fig. 14.9   Softening curve for City 2

Fig. 14.10 Softening curve for City 3

If lime added to the water does not remove sufficient hardness, select the optimum lime dose and then add varying amounts of soda ash. From Figure 14.9 we found that the optimum lime dose was 200 mg/L (300 mg/L would have reduced the hardness slightly). Let's take six one-liter containers and add 20 mL of our lime stock solution (a dosage of 200 mg/L). Prepare a stock solution of soda ash similar to our lime solution by adding 10 grams of soda ash to a one-liter container, fill with distilled water and mix thoroughly. Add zero, 2.5 mL (25-mg/L dose), 5 mL, 7.5 mL, 10 mL, and 12.5 mL to the one-liter containers. Mix thoroughly, allow the precipitate to settle, and measure the hardness remaining in the water above the precipitate. A plot of hardness remaining against the soda ash dosage will reveal the desired dosage. We would like the final hardness to be in the 80- to 90-mg/L as $CaCO_3$ range in this example.

To select the optimum doses of lime and soda ash, consider the items discussed below.

1. Optimum dosage of lime was based on increments of 50 mg/L. You should refine this test by trying at least two 10-mg/L increments above and below the optimum dose. From Figure 14.8 we found that 100 mg/L was the optimum dose. Try lime doses of 80, 90, 100, 110, and 120 mg/L.

2. Optimum dosage of soda ash can be refined by trying smaller increments also.

3. Try slightly increasing the actual lime dose in your plant to see if there is any decrease in the remaining hardness. Is the decrease in hardness worth the increase in lime costs?

4. Try slightly increasing and decreasing both lime and soda ash dosages at your plant one at a time, and evaluate the results.

5. If you are treating well water or a water of constant quality, all you have to do to maintain proper treatment is to make minor adjustments to keep the system fine tuned.

6. If you are treating water from a lake or a river and the water quality (including temperature) changes, you'll have to repeat these procedures whenever the raw water quality changes. Water quality changes of concern include raw water hardness, alkalinity, pH, turbidity and temperature.

7. *REMEMBER*, you do not want to produce water of zero hardness. If you can get the hardness down to around 80 to 90 mg/L, that usually will be low enough for most domestic consumers. When selecting a target hardness level for your plant, consider the uses of your softened water and the cost of softening.

QUESTIONS

Write your answers in a notebook and then compare your answers with those on page 119.

14.9A   If lime added to water does not reduce the hardness of a water sufficiently, what would you do?

14.9B   What items should be considered when determining the hardness of the treated water from a water softening plant?

14.92   Calculation of Chemical Feeder Settings

After chemical doses have been calculated or determined from jar tests, convert the results to plant chemical feed rates. Depending on the type of chemical feeder, you may have to calculate the feed rates in pounds per day, pounds per hour or pounds per minute. Always feed enough chemical to achieve the desired results, but don't overfeed. Overtreating is a waste of money and quality control will suffer.

EXAMPLE 4

The optimum lime dosage from the jar tests is 230 mg/L. If the flow to be treated is 6 MGD, what is the feeder setting in pounds per day and the feed rate in pounds per minute?

Known	Unknown
Lime Dose, mg/L = 230 mg/L	1. Feeder Setting, lbs/day
Flow, MGD = 6 MGD	2. Feed Rate, lbs/min

1. Calculate the feeder setting in pounds per day.

$$\text{Feeder Setting, lbs/day} = (\text{Flow, MGD})(\text{Lime, mg/L})(8.34 \text{ lbs/gal})$$

$$= (6 \text{ MGD})(230 \text{ mg/L})(8.34 \text{ lbs/gal})$$

$$= 11,509 \text{ lbs/day}$$

2. Calculate the feed rate in pounds per minute.

$$\text{Feed Rate, lbs/min} = \frac{\text{Feeder Setting, lbs/day}}{(60 \text{ min/hr})(24 \text{ hr/day})}$$

$$= \frac{11,509 \text{ lbs/day}}{(60 \text{ min/hr})(24 \text{ hr/day})}$$

$$= 8.0 \text{ lbs/min}$$

When the calculated feed rate of eight pounds of lime per minute is put into the plant process, observations and tests will determine if optimum levels are met. In many instances, jar tests and actual plant feed rates do not agree exactly. This is because of temperature, size and shape of jars vs. size and shape of plant facilities, mixing time, and influence of the coagulant (a heavy alum feed would neutralize more of the lime). Jar tests are merely indicators or a point at which to begin.

If underfeeding results, reactions will not be complete and the results will be undertreated water having a hardness higher than desired.

If overfeeding results, chemicals are being wasted. Also, it is quite possible to have excessive calcium in the water. This results in unstable conditions which cause buildup on filter media sand grains and the interior of the water mains. This is where the stability test enters the picture (refer to Section 14.5, "Stability").

The above discussion has dealt with establishing the proper lime feed. The same process would be used to determine the soda ash requirements if you are removing noncarbonate hardness. Set up the lime feed jar tests as discussed. Pick the optimum dosage. Then set up another series of jars using the same lime feed rate in all jars. Now, vary the soda ash feed rate.

EXAMPLE 5

How much soda ash is required (pounds per day and pounds per minute) to remove 50 mg/L noncarbonate hardness as $CaCO_3$ from a flow of 6 MGD?

Known	**Unknown**
Noncarbonate Hardness Removed, mg/L as $CaCO_3$ = 50 mg/L	1. Feeder Setting, lbs/day
	2. Feed Rate, lbs/min
Flow, MGD = 6 MGD	

1. Calculate the soda ash dose in milligrams per liter. (See Section 14.316, "Calculation of Chemical Dosages" for an explanation of the following formula.)

$$\text{Soda Ash,} \atop \text{mg/}L = \left(\begin{array}{c}\text{Noncarbonate Hardness,} \\ \text{mg/}L \text{ as CaCO}_3\end{array}\right)(106/100)$$

$$= (50 \text{ mg/}L)(106/100)$$

$$= 53 \text{ mg/}L$$

2. Determine the feeder setting in pounds per day.

$$\text{Feeder Setting,} \atop \text{lbs/day} = (\text{Flow, MGD})(\text{Soda Ash, mg/}L)(8.34 \text{ lbs/gal})$$

$$= (6 \text{ MGD})(53 \text{ mg/}L)(8.34 \text{ lbs/gal})$$

$$= 2,652 \text{ lbs/day}$$

3. Calculate the soda ash feed rate in pounds per minute.

$$\text{Feed Rate,} \atop \text{lbs/min} = \frac{\text{Feeder Setting, lbs/day}}{(60 \text{ min/hr})(24 \text{ hr/day})}$$

$$= \frac{2,652 \text{ lbs/day}}{(60 \text{ min/hr})(24 \text{ hr/day})}$$

$$= 1.8 \text{ lbs/min}$$

After you determine the proper feed rates and implement them, if you are treating well water or other water of constant quality, all you have to do to maintain proper treatment is make minor adjustments to keep the system fine tuned.

On the other hand, if you treat a river or lake supply subject to constant or frequent changes in water quality, it's an entirely different set of circumstances. Until you learn from experience to judge the chemical changes necessary by the fluctuations in raw water hardness, alkalinity, and turbidity, you almost have to check yourself daily by the jar test method.

When your treatment process does not work properly, the first thing to check is whether or not the feeder is feeding properly. If it is, the next step is to check your source water quality. Generally, one of these two will be the cause of your problem.

QUESTIONS

Write your answers in a notebook and then compare your answers with those on page 119.

14.9C Why should the overfeeding of chemicals be avoided?

14.9D What should be the lime feeder setting in pounds per day to treat a flow of 2 MGD when the optimum lime dose is 160 mg/L?

14.9E How much soda ash is required in pounds per day to remove 40 mg/L of noncarbonate hardness from a flow of 2 MGD?

End of Lesson 1 of 2 Lessons on
SOFTENING

Please answer the discussion and review questions next.

DISCUSSION AND REVIEW QUESTIONS

Chapter 14.   SOFTENING

(Lesson 1 of 2 Lessons)

At the end of each lesson in this chapter you will find some discussion and review questions. The purpose of these questions is to indicate to you how well you understand the material in the lesson. Write the answers to these questions in your notebook before continuing.

1. Why should water be softened?

2. What are the benefits of softening water in addition to hardness removal?

3. Why is settled water recarbonated after the precipitation of calcium carbonate?

4. What are the advantages of using liquid caustic soda to soften water?

5. Why should quicklime never be stored close to combustible material?

6. How can operators protect themselves from lime?

7. Why is the stability of a water important?

8. Why is a paste-type slaker dangerous?

9. Why should you avoid using the same conveyor or bin for alternately handling both quicklime and one of the coagulants containing water, such as alum?

10. Why is sludge sometimes recirculated back into the primary mix area of conventional plants?

11. When running jar tests, how would you determine the optimum dosage for a coagulant, lime, and soda ash?

12. When your lime-soda ash softening plant does not perform properly, what is the first thing you should check?

CHAPTER 14.   SOFTENING

Ion Exchange Softening by Marty Reynolds

(Lesson 2 of 2 Lessons)

14.10   DESCRIPTION OF ION EXCHANGE SOFTENING PROCESS

The term "Zeolite" is most often associated with sodium ion exchangers and should be considered to mean the same as the term ion exchange. Most ion exchange units in use today use sulfonated polystyrene resins as the exchange media. Ion exchange softening can be defined as exchanging hardness-causing ions (calcium and magnesium) for the sodium ions that are attached to the ion exchange resins to create a soft water.

The treatment plant operator should be aware of the three basic types of softeners on the market.

1. An upflow unit in which the water enters from the bottom and flows up through the ion exchange bed and out the top.

2. A unit which is constructed and operated like a gravity rapid sand filter. The water enters the top, flows down through the ion exchange bed and out the bottom.

3. The pressure downflow ion exchange softener, which is the most common, will be discussed in this chapter. See Figures 14.11 and 14.12. Pressure filters may be either horizontal or vertical units. Vertical units are preferred because there is less chance of short-circuiting.

To help explain the construction and activity that occurs in an ion exchanger, let's compare it to a pressure filter. The water enters the unit through an inlet distributor located in the top; it is forced (usually pumped) down through a bed of some type of media into an underdrain structure. From the underdrain structure, the treated water flows out of the unit and into storage or into the distribution system.

The flow pattern through a filter and softener are similar, the key difference being the action that takes place in the media or bed of each unit. The filter bed may be considered an adsorption and mechanical straining device used to remove suspended solids from the water. The bed usually consists of sand, anthracite (crushed coal) or a combination of both. Once the bed becomes saturated with the insoluble material (usually clay, suspended solids and iron, manganese hydroxide), the filter is taken out of service, backwashed and returned to service. This pressure filter will continue to operate until the condition reoccurs and the procedure is repeated.

The bed, media, or resin in an ion exchange softener, however, is much more complex. This resin serves as a medium in which an ion exchange takes place. As hard water is passed through the resin, the sodium ions on the resin are exchanged for the calcium and magnesium ions (in the case of sodium exchange resins). The sodium ions are released from the exchange resin and remain in the water which flows out of the softener. The calcium and magnesium ions, however, are retained by the resin. The softener effluent is free from calcium and magnesium ions and therefore is softened (Figure 14.13).

Once a softener has exchanged all of its sodium ions and the resin is saturated with calcium and magnesium, it will no longer produce soft water. At this time the unit must be taken out of service and the calcium and magnesium must be removed from the resin by exchange with sodium ions. This process is referred to as a regeneration cycle.

In a regeneration cycle, the calcium and magnesium ions that have been retained by the resin must be removed and the sodium ions restored. In order for the exchange to take place, the resin must hold all ions loosely. If the calcium and magnesium ions cannot be removed, the resin will not accept the addition of new sodium ions that are necessary for additional softening.

Salt in the form of a concentrated brine solution is used to regenerate (recharge) the ion exchange resin. When salt is added to water it changes into or ionizes to form sodium cation (Na^+) and chloride anions (Cl^-). When the brine solution is fed into the resin, the sodium cations are exchanged for calcium and magnesium cations. As the brine solution travels down through the resin, the sodium cations are attached to the resin while the calcium, magnesium, and chloride (from the salt) ions flow to waste. After the regeneration has taken place, the bed is ready to be placed in service again to remove calcium and magnesium by ion exchange.

VERTICAL SOFTENER TANK

_____" DIAMETER

_____" SIDE SHELL HEIGHT

_____ P.S.I. W.P.

AIR RELEASE LINE

BAFFLE

FREEBOARD

_____" ZEOLITE =
_____ CU. FT.

_____" FILTER SAND, SIZE ___ TO ___ MM.
_____" GRADED GRAVEL, SIZE 1/4" x *10
_____" GRADED GRAVEL, SIZE 1/2" x 1/4"
_____" GRADED GRAVEL, SIZE 3/4" x 1/2"
_____" GRADED GRAVEL, SIZE 1 1/2" x 3/4"

GRAVEL BED

UNDERDRAIN

STANDARD SOFTENER

UNDERDRAIN:-
    RIGIDLY SUPPORTED PLATE OVER 100 %
    FILTER AREA WITH STAINLESS STEEL
    BAFFLE ASSEMBLIES.

ZEOLITE:- _____ CUBIC FEET.

SUPPORTING GRAVEL:- _____" GRADED.

STAINLESS STEEL
BAFFLE ASSEMBLY

Fig. 14.11   _Pressure downflow ion exchange softener_
(Permission of General Filter Company)

Fig. 14.12   Semiautomatic controls for ion exchanger
(Permission of General Filter Company)

[1]
EXCHANGE RESIN
PRIOR TO SOFTENING
(AFTER REGENERATION)

[2]
Na⁺ AND SOFT WATER EXCHANGE
RESIN AFTER START OF SOFTENING CYCLE

PLUG FLOW-PISTON EFFECT
HARDNESS APPLIED
Ca⁺⁺ Mg⁺⁺

[3]
Na⁺ AND SOFT WATER EXCHANGE
RESIN DURING SOFTENING CYCLE

[4]
EXCHANGE RESIN EXHAUSTED
(ALL SOFTENING CAPACITY LOST-
READY TO REGENERATE, SEE [1])

Fig. 14.13   Ion exchange resin condition during softening cycle

QUESTIONS

Write your answers in a notebook and then compare your answers with those on page 119.

14.10A   List the three basic types of softeners on the market.

14.10B   What happens during the regeneration cycle of an ion exchange softener?

14.11   OPERATIONS

Many factors influence the procedures used to operate an ion exchange unit and the efficiency of the softening process. These factors include:

1. Characteristics of the ion exchange resin,

2. Quality of the source water,

3. Rate of flow applied to the softener,

4. Salt dosage during regeneration,

5. Brine concentration, and

6. Brine contact time.

Each ion exchange softener, regardless of manufacturer, will have at least four common stages of operation. These stages are listed below and will be explained as each occurs in the softener operation (see Figure 14.14).

1. Service,

2. Backwash,

3. Brine, and

4. Rinse.

14.110   Service

The service stage of each unit is where the actual softening of the water occurs. Hard water is forced into the top of the unit and allowed to flow down through the exchange resin. As this takes place, the calcium and magnesium ions exchange with sodium on the resin. The sodium ions are released into the water and the exchange capacity of the unit is slowly exhausted.

The length of each service stage is dependent on several factors; source water hardness is a main consideration. The harder the water, the more calcium and magnesium must be removed to reach a level of zero hardness. Simply stated, the harder the water, the less water you can treat before the resin becomes exhausted. As long as the design flow for the ion exchange unit is not exceeded, changes in the hardness of the source water may be automatically adjusted for in the ion exchange unit. The effluent from the unit usually will have zero

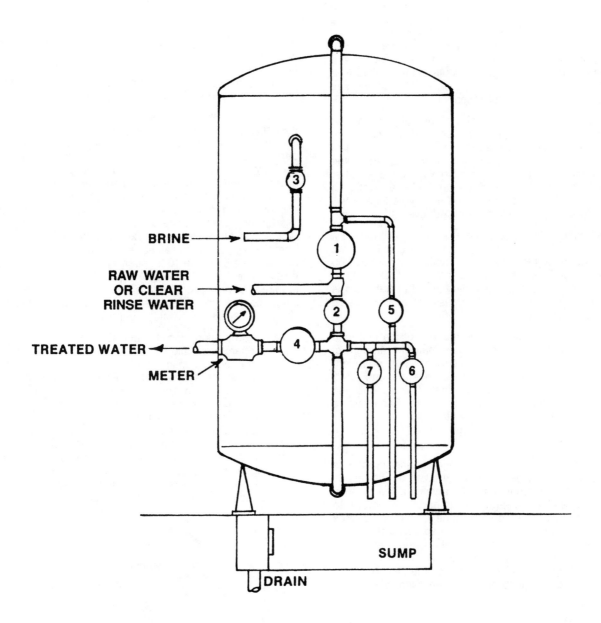

BRINE

RAW WATER
OR CLEAR
RINSE WATER

TREATED WATER

METER

SUMP

DRAIN

OPERATION	VALVE NUMBER						
	1	2	3	4	5	6	7
SERVICE	OPEN	CLOSE	CLOSE	OPEN	CLOSE	CLOSE	CLOSE
BACK WASH	CLOSE	OPEN	CLOSE	CLOSE	OPEN	CLOSE	CLOSE
BRINE	CLOSE	CLOSE	OPEN	CLOSE	CLOSE	OPEN	CLOSE
RINSE	OPEN	CLOSE	CLOSE	CLOSE	CLOSE	CLOSE	OPEN

Fig. 14.14   Valve positions for each stage
of ion exchange softener operation
(Permission of General Filter Company)

hardness until the unit needs regeneration. If the total dissolved solids (TDS) in the water supply is fairly high (above 500 mg/L), there may be some leakage. If a high TDS water has a high sodium content, the sodium may hinder the process by causing a local exchange on the media of calcium and magnesium (hardness leakage) for some of the sodium. The amount of hardness leakage depends on the TDS and the salt dosage (percent salt) used for regeneration.

Other factors involved are the size of the softener and the exchange capacity of the resin. Softeners can vary in size from a few cubic feet to several hundred cubic feet. The size of the unit will generally be consistent with regard to the overall treatment plant design. In other words, the softener should be capable of producing enough softened water so that the mix or blend of softened and unsoftened water will produce a treated water with the desired level of hardness.

The exchange resin will also vary in its removal capacity. There are many types of strong acid cation exchange resins on the market today. Most will range in capacity from 20,000 to 30,000 grains of hardness removal per cubic foot (0.011 to 0.016 kg/cu m) of resin. The removal ability of the resin is usually expressed in grains of hardness removal per cubic foot of material or resin.

The source water hardness, and the size of the unit, and removal capacity of the resin will determine the amount of water that can be treated before the softener must be regenerated. With a few simple calculations, an operator can determine the softening capacity of the units. Calculations and examples will be given at the end of the chapter. See Example 8 in Section 14.18, "Ion Exchange Arithmetic."

14.111   Backwash

The second stage of the ion exchange softener process is the backwash. In this stage, the unit is taken out of service and the flow pattern through the unit is reversed. The purpose of this is to expand and clean the resin particles and also to free any material such as iron, manganese, and particulates that might have been removed during the softening stage. The backwash water entering the softener at the beginning of this stage should be applied at a slow steady rate. If the water enters the unit too quickly, it could create a surge in the resin and wash it out of the unit with the water going to waste.

Ideal bed expansion during the softener backwash should be 75 to 100-percent. In other words, when the unit is backwashed, the resin should expand to occupy a volume from 75 to 100 percent greater than when in normal service. An example of this would be an ion exchange softener with 24 inches (60 cm) of resin while in service. When the unit is backwashed, the resin should expand to 48 inches (120 cm) for a 100-percent expansion of the bed. As the bed expands a shearing action due to the backwash water and some scrubbing action will free any material that might have formed on the resin particles during the softening stage.

During the backwash a small amount of resin could be lost. This amount, however, should be minimal and you should check the backwash effluent at different intervals to ensure that the resin is not being lost. A glass beaker can be used to catch a sample of the effluent while the unit is backwashing. A trace amount of resin should cause no alarm, but a steady loss of resin could indicate a problem in the unit and the cause should be located and corrected as soon as possible. Too much loss of resin may be caused by an improper freeboard on the tank or wash troughs. The backwash duration and flow rate will vary depending on the manufacturer, the type and size of resin used, and the water temperature.

14.112   Brine

The third stage is most often termed the regeneration or brine stage. At this point, the sodium ion concentration of the resin is recharged by pumping a concentrated brine solution onto the resin. The solution is allowed to circulate through the unit and displace all water from the resin in order to provide full contact between the brine solution and the resin.

Most treatment plants use a brine solution to regenerate their softening units. The optimum brine concentration coming in contact with the ion exchange resin is around 10- to 14-percent sodium chloride solution. Concentrated brine is only used when the water within the softener tank serves as the dilution water. A 26-percent brine solution (fully concentrated or saturated) causes too great of an osmotic shock on the ion exchange resin and can cause it to break up. The salt dosage used to prepare the brine solution is one of the most important factors affecting the ion exchange capacity and ranges from 5 to 15 pounds of salt per cubic foot (80 to 240 kg/cu m) of resin. See Example 10 on page 114 for procedures on how to calculate the salt dosage and gallons of brine solution required. Brine concentrations less than saturated require longer contact time and more solution must be applied to the unit to achieve a successful regeneration.

The regeneration stage of the softener is very important and the operator should be certain it is properly carried out. In the regeneration stage, the sodium ions present in the brine solution are exchanged with the calcium and magnesium ions on the resin. The ions on the resin were exchanged during the service or softening stage. The regeneration rate is usually one to two GPM per cubic foot (2.2 to 4.4 liters per second per cubic meter) of resin for the first 55 minutes and then three to five GPM per cubic foot (6.6 to 11 liters per second per cubic meter) for the last five minutes of fast drain. If the regeneration process is performed correctly, the result is a bed that is completely recharged with sodium ions and will again soften water when the unit is returned to service.

14.113   Rinse

The fourth and final stage of softener operations is the rinse stage. After adequate contact time has been allowed between the brine solution and resin, a clear rinse is applied from the top of the unit to remove the waste products and excess brine solution from the softener. The flow pattern is very similar to the service stage except that the softener effluent goes to waste instead of storage. The waste discharge contains high concentrations of calcium and magnesium chloride. Most rinse stages will last between 20 and 40 minutes, depending on the size of the unit and the manufacturer. See Section

14.14, "Disposal of Spent Brine," for procedures on how to dispose of the waste discharge.

Again, the operator should pay close attention to the softener while it rinses. The rinse must be long enough to remove the heavy concentration of waste from the unit. If the rinse is not of the correct length and the unit returns to service, a salty taste will be very noticeable in the softener effluent. Taste the waste effluent near the end of the rinse stage to determine if the majority of chloride ions have been removed. The chloride ion concentration may also be measured by titration as outlined in Chapter 21, "Advanced Laboratory Procedures," or by measuring the conductivity of the water. If the water still has a strong salty taste or excessive chloride ions are present, check the rinse rate and timer settings. The unit may need adjustment to increase the duration of the rinse stage.

QUESTIONS

Write your answers in a notebook and then compare your answers with those on page 120.

14.11A What is the main consideration in determining the length of the service stage of an ion exchange softener?

14.11B What is the purpose of the backwash stage of an ion exchange softener?

14.11C How are ion exchange softeners regenerated?

14.11D Where does the softener effluent go during the rinse stage?

14.12 CONTROL TESTING OF ION EXCHANGE SOFTENERS

In most small treatment plants, the operator has to perform many jobs and may not always have time to monitor the softening units as they should be monitored. If a few simple test procedures are learned and carried out on a regular basis, the operator can feel confident the ion exchange units are operating properly. Control tests the operator should perform are listed in this section.

1. Softener Influent

Be aware of the iron and manganese levels entering the softener. These levels should be kept to a minimum to prevent fouling of the media bed as the unit will remove a certain amount of iron and manganese before becoming plugged. Insoluble particles of iron and manganese will plug the filter media. Soluble ionic iron (Fe^{2+}) and manganese (Mn^{2+}) will exchange onto the media and will not be fully removed by regeneration. If the source water entering the plant is high in iron and manganese, proper oxidation and filtration of the water *BEFORE* the softener should reduce the levels and prevent problems from developing in the softeners.

Monitor source water hardness on a routine basis. Generally, hardness will not vary, but if it changes, you will need to adjust the amount of water treated by each softener before the media becomes exhausted and the unit must be regenerated.

2. Softener Effluent

At the end of a regeneration stage, as the unit goes back into service, check the effluent for hardness. This one test will tell you if the regeneration of the softener has been properly conducted. Allow a few minutes to ensure that all of the rinse water in the unit has been purged (removed).

Run a hardness test on the effluent side of the unit. The results should indicate a water of zero hardness. Several test kits are available on the market today that are fairly quick and simple to use to measure water hardness.

14.13 LIMITATIONS CAUSED BY IRON AND MANGANESE

Ion exchange units are very versatile. The primary purpose of the unit is to remove calcium and magnesium from the water thus making the water soft. Ion exchange softeners, however, will also remove iron and manganese in either the soluble or precipitated form. If this occurs, the iron and manganese will seriously affect the life of the exchange capacity of the resin. If water high in iron and manganese is applied to the ion exchange resin for very long, iron fouling or the loss of exchange capacity will result.

When the softeners remove iron in the ferrous (soluble) or ferric (solid) form, the two problems discussed below could result.

1. If water with iron in the ferrous form is applied to the softener, the resin will remove the iron from the water. The iron can be retained on the surface of the resin or is sometimes captured deep inside the resin itself. As this happens, the resin or bed will develop an orange or rusty appearance. If the resin becomes iron coated, the efficiency of the softener will be reduced greatly.

2. The second problem associated with high iron levels is a plugging or clogging of the resin bed. When water containing iron in the ferric form (solid) is applied to the unit, it will act like a filter and strain the iron from the water, leaving the iron trapped in the bed. If high iron loadings continue, the upper layer of the bed could become plugged, forcing the water to channel or short-circuit through the bed. The result is incomplete contact between the water and media thus creating hardness leakage and loss of softening efficiency.

IRON AND MANGANESE MUST BE REDUCED TO THEIR LOWEST POSSIBLE LIMITS BEFORE APPLYING WATER TO THE SOFTENER. Oxidation of iron and manganese (see Chapter 12, "Iron and Manganese Control") *BEFORE* applying water to ion exchange units is very helpful. You should also be aware of the chlorine levels applied to the softening units. Normal chlorine dosages will not present a problem, but high residuals could damage the resin and reduce its life span.

14.14 DISPOSAL OF SPENT BRINE

One of the largest problems associated with the design and operation of ion exchange softening plants is the disposal of the softener waste.

The waste discharge from softeners consists mostly of calcium, magnesium, and sodium chlorides. These by-products are corrosive to material they contact and possess varying toxic levels in relationship to the environment.

Many water treatment plants discharge spent brine into nearby sewers. This procedure may be approved if the downstream wastewater treatment plant and receiving waters can handle the brine. Usually the water treatment plant must have some type of holding tank to store the spent brine. The brine is slowly discharged into the sewer at a rate which will not upset (or be toxic to) the biological treatment processes at the wastewater treatment plant. Also the salt level in the effluent from the wastewater treatment plant must not adversely impact the aquatic life in the receiving waters or cause a violation of the wastewater treatment plant's *NPDES PERMIT*.[17]

Some water treatment plants may be issued an NPDES Permit to discharge spent brine into receiving waters. This could happen only if the flow in the receiving waters was very high (plenty of dilution) and the flow of spent brine was very low. A holding tank would be needed for the spent brine and the brine could be discharged very slowly. The receiving waters would have to be monitored to be sure that the discharge of brine will not cause a significant increase in the level of brine.

Sanitary landfills also may be an acceptable means of disposing of spent brine. See Chapter 17, "Handling and Disposal of Process Wastes," for additional information.

Each ion exchange treatment plant probably has only one approved method of waste disposal. Very few options are available to plants discharging this type of waste. Alternate waste disposal methods available for spent brine are discussed in Chapter 17, "Handling and Disposal of Process Wastes."

The operator needs to be aware of the seriousness involved with softener waste. If a problem develops at the treatment plant, the operator should be working with the agency in the area that governs waste disposal as several considerations must be studied when changing a disposal method.

QUESTIONS

Write your answers in a notebook and then compare your answers with those on page 120.

14.12A Which water quality indicators should be monitored in the effluent of an ion exchange softener?

14.13A What happens when high chlorine residual levels are applied to the softening units?

14.14A Why is the disposal of spent brine a problem?

14.15 MAINTENANCE

Most of the ion exchange water softening equipment on the market today is fully automated (Figure 14.12). The reason for most of this automation is to reduce the time an operator must spend with each unit. Automation is fine for operational control, but it does not mean a unit is maintenance free. Systems like this have a tendency to lead operators astray. A small routine maintenance item can go unnoticed until it becomes a full-scale problem if the operator does not run a regular maintenance schedule on the equipment. For example, most valves on ion exchange units are pneumatic or are equipped with some type of self-operating device (valve actuators). This does not mean, however, the valve will operate each time it is required to do so without a regular examination and overhaul. The operator must check the equipment to ensure it is always in proper working order. One valve that fails to open or to close during a regeneration stage could mean trouble (a storage tank full of salty water or no brine at all).

The components of an ion exchange softening system that should receive constant attention are the brine pumps and piping. A saturated brine solution is very corrosive and will attack any unprotected metallic surface it comes in contact with. Try to keep the system as tight as possible. An uncontained brine leak will only get worse.

If you must change the pipe work in the brine system, give serious consideration to installing PVC pipe. The material is much cheaper than bronze and will outlast steel or galvanized pipe when properly installed and supported. Future repairs are also much easier to make if PVC pipe is used.

The pump on the brine system is most often made of brass which offers some additional protection from the brine solution. The impeller should be bronze and the shaft stainless steel. A strainer or screen device should be installed ahead of the pump on the suction side.

Most treatment plants buy salt in bulk to make their brine solution. Regardless of the salt supplier, a certain amount of insoluble material will accompany each bulk delivery. This insoluble material will consist of rocks, coal, sand, and other particles that can clog or destroy an impeller if they reach the pump. Check the strainer assembly on the brine pumps quite often and keep spare parts on hand in case replacement is required.

The use of packing on the pumps is recommended over mechanical seals. Regardless of how well the strainers perform, a small amount of sand will usually end up in the pump. The combination of sand and mechanical seals will most often result in high repair and maintenance costs. Packing is cheaper and easier to install and maintain than mechanical seals and packing will usually outlast mechanical seals in this type of installation.

The brine pump motor should have a "heavy-duty" rating and a body made of cast iron is preferable. Aluminum or mild steel motor housings do not hold up as well as cast iron when subjected to the corrosive environment around the brine pumping station.

An area most often neglected until problems arise is the bulk brine storage area of the treatment plant. Most storage areas are underground pits equipped with rock or gravel strainers above some type of underdrain collection system. Over a period of time, the strainers will silt in with sand and impurities received with salt deliveries. The best way to prevent this from occurring is to regularly shut down, drain, and replace the strainer systems in the pit. This is a great deal of work, but it is a necessity if the brine system is to stay in operation.

---

[17] *NPDES Permit.* **N**ational **P**ollutant **D**ischarge **E**limination **S**ystem permit is the regulatory agency document issued by either a federal or state agency which is designed to control all discharges of pollutants from point sources and storm water runoff into U.S. waterways. NPDES permits regulate discharges into navigable waters from all point sources of pollution, including industries, municipal wastewater treatment plants, sanitary landfills, large agricultural feedlots and return irrigation flows.

Some brine storage areas have become so clogged that the brine solution could not penetrate the strainer media and reach the underdrain system. Like the head loss on a filter, the strainers can become so clogged that the solution cannot seep through to the underdrain system. If this happens and the system cannot be shut down for cleaning, a pipe can be driven down through the sand and impurities into the gravel layers. If enough holes are driven through the zones of impurities, the solution will eventually seep into the underdrains and can be pumped into the softeners. This is a temporary repair measure only and the storage area should be cleaned as soon as possible.

Inspect the brine solution makeup water line while the storage area is shut down. This line must be kept in good working order because it provides potable water to the salt supply. This water makes the saturated brine solution that is used to regenerate the softener. PVC pipe would provide excellent service in a corrosive environment such as a storage area.

Wet salt brine storage tanks are another location at a water treatment plant where sanitary defects may develop. The makeup water line must have a free fall or air gap someplace in the system to prevent the backflow of a brine solution into the potable water supply. The brine tanks must be protected from contamination just like any other water storage facility. The cover and access hatches must be of the raised-lip, overlapping-cover type. All vents must be properly screened to keep out insects, birds, and rodents.

Not every area of maintenance in an ion exchange softening plant can be covered here because each plant will differ with the type of equipment used and its method of operation. Set up a maintenance routine that is appropriate for your treatment plant. The objective of the maintenance routine must be to keep the plant operating and hold repair costs to a minimum.

QUESTIONS

Write your answers in a notebook and then compare your answers with those on page 120.

14.15A What could happen if a valve fails to open or close during a regeneration stage?

14.15B Why should the brine pumps and piping receive constant attention?

14.15C Why is packing on brine pumps recommended over mechanical seals?

14.16 TROUBLESHOOTING

14.160 Test Units

Ion exchange softeners, if properly operated and maintained, will usually provide years of trouble-free service. If problems arise, however, the operator should be able to identify and correct the situation without a great deal of difficulty.

The best way to ensure that a softener will continue to operate properly is to occasionally test the unit during various stages of operation. Learn to recognize minor problems as they develop and make the necessary repairs before a full-scale problem exists.

Items an operator should check on in each stage are discussed in this section.

14.161 Service Stage

In the service stage, while the unit is producing soft water, hardness tests should be run on the softener effluent to ensure the water has a hardness of zero. One grain hardness per gallon of water (17.1 mg/L) showing up in the effluent should not cause alarm, but concentrations of hardness higher than one grain hardness per gallon signal the need to investigate the softener's operation more closely.

14.162 Backwash Stage

Check the backwash stage for adequate flow rates and full extent of the time required to complete the stage. Unless the rate is high enough to remove trapped turbidity particles and other insoluble material that is trapped in the resin, a loss of softener efficiency could result.

Check the timer on the backwash stage to make sure the unit is washed for the required length of time.

If high iron concentrations have been applied to the softener, check the condition of the resin by visually inspecting the top layer of the bed. Color is a key factor to watch for in units beginning to show signs of an iron-fouled resin. The resin will be an orange, rusty color, while the backwash effluent will appear a light orange at the end of the backwash stage. Also, the head loss on the unit will run higher than normal as the bed becomes plugged with iron.

If iron fouling appears to be a problem, the length of the backwash stage should be increased to wash as much of the particulate matter from the resin as possible. A means of surface washing the resin must be provided for this procedure to be effective. Avoid exceeding recommended manufacturer's flow rates to prevent washing resin from the unit.

A chemical cleaner can be used to remove heavy iron coatings from the resin itself. These cleaners are mostly sodium hydrosulfite and can be mixed in solution form and poured into the softener. The hydrosulfite could also be added to the resin during the regeneration stage by dumping a concentrated powder form in with the brine solution. Consult the resin supplier or manufacturer before using any cleaner on the resin.

14.163 Brine Injection Stage

The brine injection stage of the softener sequence must be correctly applied or the unit will not perform satisfactorily when it returns to service. If the resin is not regenerated during this stage, there will be no sodium ions to exchange with the hardness ions in the water when the water is applied to the unit.

The brine storage area should always contain enough salt to provide a brine solution when makeup water is added.

Also check the amount of salt solution that is pumped into the softener. This is usually done with a meter that is preset to deliver the exact amount of brine solution required to regenerate the softener. If a brine solution is less than saturated, longer contact time is required between the media and the solution.

The required amount of solution must be delivered consistently to achieve a successful regeneration of the unit. If hardness leakage appears early in the service or softening stage, check the amount and saturation of brine solution in the brine system since these are the main reasons for hardness leakage.

If hardness leakage is excessive immediately following a regeneration stage, shut the unit down and check the media level. The bed could be disrupted from excessive backwash or rinse rates. Iron fouling could also cause a channeling condition to occur and cause the water to short-circuit through the media without contacting the complete bed volume.

14.164   Rinse Stage

The rinse stage of the softener should be checked when tests indicate problems are developing. The rinse rate is a key factor in keeping the softener functioning properly. If the rinse starts too soon, the brine solution could be forced out of the unit before adequate contact time has elapsed. If the rinse rate is too low, all the waste material might not be removed from the unit before it goes into the service stage.

The rate settings on the unit should be compared, on all stages, against the actual manufacturer's recommended settings. As equipment ages, it wears. Over a period of time, valves might need adjustment to keep the unit operating within the manufacturer's guidelines.

QUESTIONS

Write your answers in a notebook and then compare your answers with those on page 120.

14.16A   What is the maximum hardness level expected in the effluent of a properly operating ion exchange softener before the operator should investigate the operation?

14.16B   What is the purpose of the backwash stage of an ion exchange softener operation?

14.16C   What would you do if hardness leakage is excessive immediately following a regeneration stage?

14.16D   What problems may occur if the rinse stage starts too soon or the rinse rate is too slow?

14.17   START-UP AND SHUTDOWN OF UNIT

At times it becomes necessary to shut a unit down and take it out of service for repairs or inspection. If the operator will follow common sense guidelines, no problems should arise from unit shutdowns.

When dealing with these units, drain and fill them slowly. This will prevent surging of the media which will either wash it out of the unit or disrupt it, thus making the media uneven and creating channeling problems. If you suspect problems with a unit, the last thing you want to do is make the situation worse by rapidly backfilling or backwashing the softener.

Most units are equipped with automatic air release valves (Figure 14.15). Be certain these valves are operating properly, because the venting of trapped air is an important step in filling a unit after it has been shut down.

During unit shutdown, make a complete visual inspection. Now is the time to detect and correct minor problems that might otherwise develop into bigger ones. Check the brine inlet distributors while the unit is down. They should be visible from the top hatch on most softeners.

Make sure the pipe work is level and the nozzles or openings are not clogged. The distributors play an important role in the regeneration stage by applying the brine solution evenly to the top of the resin bed. If the pipe work is deteriorating from the brine solution, PVC pipe should be used as a replacement.

If the resin and gravel support material are removed from the softener, check the underdrain structures in the unit and repair any problems you discover. In filling the unit with gravel and resin, each zone of the bed should be leveled and sized according to manufacturer's specifications.

The procedure for filling a unit with water after a total shutdown is very important. The flow into the unit should be from the bottom at a slow, controlled rate. This is done by putting the unit in the backwash position, running water into the unit from the bottom and out the backwash effluent valve. The purpose of this procedure is to fill the unit with water and purge the air that was trapped in the resin and softener during the replacement process.

After the unit is filled the backwash rate should be increased to normal and continued until the effluent is clear. Again, care should be taken when bringing the rates up to the manufacturer's recommendations to prevent disrupting or displacing resin from the bed.

Once the unit has been satisfactorily backwashed, the bed should be regenerated. This can be accomplished by running the softener through a normal brine and rinse procedure before it is returned to service. Run a hardness test on the effluent to ensure all stages have performed correctly and the unit is softening water.

AIR RELEASE ASSEMBLY

Pressure aeration and pressure filtration type filter plants require an automatic air release assembly to prevent accumulation of an excessive volume of air in the pressure filter tanks. This air release assembly consists of an automatic air release valve, and necessary pipe, valves and fittings to install on filter tank. The air release valve is a float operated type and must be installed with center line of valve level with or above top of filter tank. Air from top of filter enters air release valve at top connection and water from filter inlet pipe enters valve at bottom connection. Excessive air from filter fills valve body with air forcing water level down and thereby allowing float to drop. Downward movement of float allows excessive air to escape through the needle valve until an air-water pressure balance is restored.

In normal operation valves 1 and 3 are open and valve 2 is closed. To flush air release valve close valve 1 and open valve 2 which allows water from top of filter to flush down through the valve to the drain. Valve 3 is left open at all times unless it is necessary to remove air release valve.

Fig. 14.15   Air release assembly
(Permission of General Filter Company)

QUESTIONS

Write your answers in a notebook and then compare your answers with those on page 120.

14.17A Why must ion exchange softeners be drained and filled slowly during start-up and shutdown?

14.17B What should be done if the pipe work in an ion exchange softener is deteriorating from the brine solution?

14.18 ION EXCHANGE ARITHMETIC

Hardness is usually expressed as mg/L of $CaCO_3$. In ion exchange softening, however, hardness is most often expressed in terms of grains per gallon or grains of hardness removed from the water being treated.

The exchange capacity of most softeners is expressed as kilograins (1,000 grains) of hardness removed per cubic foot of resin.

Salt in solution form is used to regenerate ion exchange softeners. The theoretical salt requirement is 0.17 pound of salt for 1,000 grains of hardness removed. Most regenerations, however, require 0.3 to 0.5 pound of salt per 1,000 grains of hardness removal.

In this section you will learn how to calculate the volume of the brine solution required to regenerate the softening unit as well as the pounds of salt required for regeneration. The concentration of brine solution used at each treatment plant may vary. Table 14.6 lists the pounds of salt present in the percentage of brine solution being used.

TABLE 14.6   SALT SOLUTION CHARACTERISTICS

Percent NaCl or grams per 100 grams of solution	Specific Gravity at 15°C or 59°F	Salameter Degree	Lbs NaCl per U.S. Gal	Lbs NaCl per Cu Ft
1.0	1.0073	4	0.084	0.63
2.0	1.0145	8	0.169	1.27
3.0	1.0217	11	0.255	1.91
4.0	1.0290	15	0.343	2.57
5.0	1.0362	19	0.432	3.23
6.0	1.0437	23	0.522	3.90
7.0	1.0511	27	0.612	4.59
8.0	1.0585	30	0.705	5.28
9.0	1.0659	34	0.799	5.98
10.0	1.0734	38	0.874	6.69
11.0	1.0810	42	0.990	7.41
12.0	1.0885	45	1.09	8.14
13.0	1.0962	49	1.19	8.83
14.0	1.1038	53	1.29	9.63
15.0	1.1115	67	1.39	10.4
16.0	1.1194	60	1.49	11.2
17.0	1.1273	65	1.60	12.0
18.0	1.1352	68	1.70	12.7
19.0	1.1432	72	1.81	13.5
20.0	1.1511	76	1.92	14.4
21.0	1.1593	80	2.03	15.2
22.0	1.1676	84	2.14	16.0
23.0	1.1758	87	2.25	16.9
24.0	1.1840	91	2.37	17.7
25.0	1.1923	95	2.48	18.6
26.0	1.2010	99	2.60	19.5
26.4	1.2040	100	2.65	19.8

FORMULAS AND CONVERSION FACTORS

Hardness is usually expressed as milligrams of hardness per liter of water as $CaCO_3$.

Treatment for hardness is often discussed as grains of hardness per gallon of water.

1 grain per gallon = 17.1 milligrams per liter

or   1 gpg = 17.1 mg/L

7,000 grains = 1 pound

To convert grains per gallon to milligrams per liter,

$$\text{Hardness, mg/L} = \frac{(\text{Hardness, grains/gallon})(17.1\ \text{mg/L})}{1\ \text{gpg}}$$

To convert milligrams per liter to grains per gallon,

$$\text{Hardness, grains/gallon} = \frac{(\text{Hardness, mg/L})(1\ \text{gpg})}{17.1\ \text{mg/L}}$$

To find the exchange capacity (removal capacity) of a softener, you need to know the removal capacity of the softener in grains per cubic foot of resin or in kilograins per cubic foot of resin and the volume of the resin in cubic feet.

$$\text{Exchange Capacity, kilograins} = (\text{Removal Capacity, kilograins/cu ft})(\text{Media Vol, cu ft})$$

$$\text{Water Treated, gal} = \frac{\text{Exchange Capacity, kilograins}}{\text{Hardness Removed, kilograins/gal}}$$

$$\text{Operating Time, hr (At a Given Flow Rate Before Regeneration)} = \frac{(\text{Water Treated, gal})(24\ \text{hr/day})}{\text{Avg Daily Flow, gal/day}}$$

To determine the amount of salt required for regeneration, you need to know the pounds of salt per 1,000 grains required for regeneration. To calculate the gallons of brine required for regeneration, you need to know the percent brine solution or the pounds of salt per gallon of brine.

$$\text{Salt Needed, lbs} = (\text{Salt Required, lbs/1,000 gr})(\text{Hardness Removed, gr})$$

$$\text{Brine, gallons} = \frac{\text{Salt Needed, lbs}}{\text{Salt Solution, lbs salt/gallon of brine}}$$

EXAMPLE 6

How many milligrams of hardness per liter are there in a water with 16 grains of hardness per gallon of water?

Known	**Unknown**
Hardness, gpg = 16 gpg	Hardness, mg/L

1. Calculate the hardness of the water in milligrams per liter.

$$\text{Hardness, mg/L} = \frac{(\text{Hardness, grains/gallon})(17.1\ \text{mg/L})}{1\ \text{grain/gallon}}$$

$$= \frac{(16\ \text{grains/gallon})(17.1\ \text{mg/L})}{1\ \text{grain/gallon}}$$

$$= 274\ \text{mg/L}$$

EXAMPLE 7

Convert the hardness of a water at 290 mg/L to grains per gallon.

Known	Unknown
Hardness, mg/L = 290 mg/L	Hardness, grains/gallon

1. Convert the hardness from milligrams per liter to grains per gallon.

$$\text{Hardness, grains/gallon} = \frac{(\text{Hardness, mg/}L)(1 \text{ grain/gallon})}{17.1 \text{ mg/}L}$$

$$= \frac{(290 \text{ mg/}L)(1 \text{ grain/gallon})}{17.1 \text{ mg/}L}$$

$$= 17 \text{ grains/gallon}$$

EXAMPLE 8

An ion exchange softener contains 50 cubic feet of resin with a hardness removal capacity of 20 kilograins per cubic foot of resin. The water being treated has a hardness of 300 mg/L as $CaCO_3$. How many gallons of water can be softened before the softener will require regeneration?

Known	Unknown
Resin Volume, cu ft = 50 cu ft	Water Treated, gal
Removal Capacity, gr/cu ft = 20,000 grains/cu ft	
Hardness, mg/L = 300 mg/L	

1. Convert the hardness from mg/L to grains per gallon.

$$\text{Hardness, grains/gallon} = \frac{(\text{Hardness, mg/}L)(1 \text{ grain/gallon})}{17.1 \text{ mg/}L}$$

$$= \frac{(300 \text{ mg/}L)(1 \text{ grain/gallon})}{17.1 \text{ mg/}L}$$

$$= 17.5 \text{ grains/gallon}$$

2. Calculate the exchange capacity of the softener in grains.

$$\text{Exchange Capacity, grains} = (\text{Resin Vol, cu ft})(\text{Removal Capacity, grains/cu ft})$$

$$= (50 \text{ cu ft})(20,000 \text{ grains/cu ft})$$

$$= 1,000,000 \text{ grains of removal capacity}$$

3. Calculate the volume of water in gallons that may be treated before regeneration.

$$\text{Water Treated, gal} = \frac{\text{Exchange Capacity, grains}}{\text{Hardness, grains/gallon}}$$

$$= \frac{1,000,000 \text{ grains}}{17.5 \text{ grains/gallon}}$$

$$= 57,143 \text{ gallons}$$

Therefore, 57,000 gallons of water with 17.5 grains of hardness per gallon of water can be treated before the resin becomes exhausted.

EXAMPLE 9

An ion exchange softening plant has two softeners that are eight feet in diameter and the units have a resin depth of six feet. The resin has a 20 kilograin removal ability. How many gallons of water can be treated if the hardness is 14 grains per gallon? If the flow rate to the softeners is 500 gallons per minute, how long will they operate before regeneration is required?

Known	Unknown
Number of Softeners = 2 Softeners	1. Water Treated, gal
Diameter, ft = 8 ft	2. Operating Time, hr
Resin Depth, ft = 6 ft	
Removal Capacity, gr/cu ft = 20,000 grains/cu ft	
Hardness, grains/gallon = 14 grains/gallon	
Flow, gallons/min = 500 gallons/min	

1. Calculate the total volume of softener media.

$$\text{Resin Vol, cu ft} = (0.785)(\text{Diameter, ft})^2(\text{Depth, ft})(\text{No. Softeners})$$

$$= (0.785)(8 \text{ ft})^2(6 \text{ ft})(2 \text{ Softeners})$$

$$= 603 \text{ cu ft}$$

2. Calculate the total exchange capacity of the two softeners in grains.

$$\text{Exchange Capacity, grains} = (\text{Resin Vol, cu ft})(\text{Removal Capacity, grains/cu ft})$$

$$= (603 \text{ cu ft})(20,000 \text{ grains/cu ft})$$

$$= 12,060,000 \text{ grains of removal capacity of the beds}$$

3. Calculate the volume of water in gallons that may be treated before the resin is exhausted.

$$\text{Water Treated, gal} = \frac{\text{Exchange Capacity, grains}}{\text{Hardness, grains/gallon}}$$

$$= \frac{12,060,000 \text{ grains}}{14 \text{ grains/gallon}}$$

$$= 861,429 \text{ gallons can be treated before resin is exhausted}$$

4. Find the length of time the softeners can run before requiring regeneration.

$$\text{Operating Time, hr} = \frac{\text{Water Treated, gal}}{(\text{Avg Daily Flow, gal/min})(60 \text{ min/hr})}$$

$$= \frac{861,429 \text{ gal}}{(500 \text{ gal/min})(60 \text{ min/hr})}$$

$$= 28.7 \text{ hours of operation before regeneration is required}$$

EXAMPLE 10

An ion exchange softener will remove 1,000,000 grains of hardness before the resin becomes exhausted. If 0.3 pound of salt is required per 1,000 grains of hardness, how many pounds of salt are needed? If a 15-percent salt solution is used to regenerate the unit, how many gallons of brine are required? Table 14.6 indicates that 1.39 pounds of salt is present in each gallon of 15-percent brine solution.

Known		Unknown
Hardness Removal, grains	= 1,000,000 grains	1. Salt Needed, lbs
Salt Required, lbs/1,000 gr	= 0.3 lbs/1,000 gr	2. Brine, gal
Salt Solution, lbs/gal	= 1.39 lbs/gal	

1. Determine the pounds of salt needed for regeneration.

$$\text{Salt Needed, lbs} = (\text{Salt Required, lbs/1,000 gr})(\text{Hardness Removed, gr})$$

$$= \frac{(0.3 \text{ lbs Salt})(1,000,000 \text{ grains})}{(1,000 \text{ grains})}$$

$$= 300 \text{ lbs of salt}$$

2. Find the gallons of brine solution required.

$$\text{Brine, gal} = \frac{\text{Salt Needed, lbs}}{\text{Salt Solution, lbs/gallon of brine}}$$

$$= \frac{300 \text{ lbs of Salt}}{1.39 \text{ lbs of salt/gallon of brine}}$$

$$= 216 \text{ gallons of brine} \quad (15\text{-percent salt solution})$$

EXAMPLE 11

Use the same information as in Example 10, except use a 12-percent brine solution. Table 14.6 indicates that 1.09 pounds of salt are present in each gallon of 12-percent brine solution. Three hundred pounds of salt are needed for regeneration. How many gallons of 12-percent brine solution are required?

Known		Unknown
Salt Needed, lbs	= 300 lbs	Brine, gal
Salt Solution, lbs/gal	= 1.09 lbs/gal	

1. Find the gallons of brine solution required.

$$\text{Brine, gal} = \frac{\text{Salt Needed, lbs}}{\text{Salt Solution, lbs/gal of brine}}$$

$$= \frac{300 \text{ lbs}}{1.09 \text{ lbs/gal}}$$

$$= 275 \text{ gallons of 12-percent brine solution}$$

NOTE: More gallons of brine solution are required when using a 12-percent brine solution than when using a 15-percent solution. The weaker concentration requires more gallons to achieve the same results.

QUESTIONS

Write your answers in a notebook and then compare your answers with those on pages 120 and 121.

14.18A A source water has a hardness of 150 mg/L as $CaCO_3$. What is the hardness in grains per gallon?

14.18B An ion exchange softener contains 60 cubic feet of resin with a hardness removal capacity of 25 kilograins per cubic foot of resin. The water being treated has a hardness of 250 mg/L as $CaCO_3$. How many gallons of water can be softened before the softener will require regeneration?

14.19 BLENDING

Ion exchange softeners will produce a water with zero hardness. Water with zero hardness must not be sent into a distribution system. Water with zero hardness is very corrosive and over a period of time will attack steel pipes in the system and create red water problems. Also, providing a water supply with zero hardness water would be very expensive.

At most softening plants, the zero hardness effluent from the softeners is mixed with filtered water having a known hardness concentration. In other words, a certain amount of water the treatment plant produces will bypass the softening units (split treatment). This water has a known hardness concentration and is mixed in various proportions with the softener effluent to arrive at a desired level of hardness in the finished water (Figure 14.16).

An example would be a treatment plant that has a filtered water hardness of 16 grains/gallon. If the desired plant effluent hardness is 8 grains/gallon, fifty percent of the plant influent must be softened and the other fifty percent would be filtered water mixed together with the softener effluent. The result would be water that has a hardness of 8 grains per gallon.

The blending of water is very simple and is usually controlled by a valve and meter. The operator adjusts the exact gallons per minute bypassing the softener to produce the desired hardness.

FORMULAS

To calculate the bypass flow in gallons per day to blend water, determine the total flow, the source water hardness, and the desired effluent hardness.

Fig. 14.16 *Automatic softener bypass*
(Permission of General Filter Company)

The softener capacity in gallons and both the softener and bypass flows in gallons per day are needed to determine the volume of bypass water.

The total flow produced by the plant before regeneration is the sum of the flows through the softener and the bypass flow.

Bypass Flow, GPD = $\dfrac{\text{(Total Flow, GPD)(Plant Effl Hardness, gpg)}}{\text{Source Water Hardness, gpg}}$

Bypass Water, gal = $\dfrac{\text{(Softener Capacity, gal)(Bypass Flow, GPD)}}{\text{Softener Flow, GPD}}$

Total Flow, gal = Softener Capacity, gal + Bypass Water, gal

EXAMPLE 12

A softener plant treats 120,000 gallons per day. The source water has a hardness of 15 grains per gallon (256 mg/L) and the desired hardness in the plant effluent is 5 grains per gallon (86 mg/L). How much water in gallons per day must bypass the softener to produce the desired level of hardness?

Known		Unknown
Total Flow, GPD	= 120,000 GPD	Bypass Flow, GPD
Source Hardness, gpg	= 15 gpg	
Effl Hardness, gpg	= 5 gpg	

1. Calculate the bypass flow in gallons per day.

Bypass Flow, GPD = $\dfrac{\text{(Total Flow, GPD)(Plant Effl Hardness, gpg)}}{\text{Source Water Hardness, gpg}}$

= $\dfrac{(120,00 \text{ GPD})(5 \text{ gpg})}{15 \text{ gpg}}$

= 40,000 GPD

EXAMPLE 13

Using the information in Example 12, how many gallons of water will be bypassed before the softener requires regeneration? The softener has the capacity to treat 105,000 gallons. From Example 12 the bypass flow is 40,000 GPD and the total flow is 120,000 GPD. Therefore the softener flow is 80,000 GPD (120,000 GPD − 40,000 GPD). What is the total flow produced by the plant per regeneration?

Known		Unknown
Softener Capacity, gal	= 105,000 gal	1. Bypass Water, gal
Softener Flow, GPD	= 80,000 GPD	2. Total Flow, gal
Bypass Flow, GPD	= 40,000 GPD	

1. Calculate the gallons of water that will be bypassed before the softener requires regeneration.

Bypass Water, gal = $\dfrac{\text{(Softener Capacity, gal)(Bypass Flow, GPD)}}{\text{Softener Flow, GPD}}$

= $\dfrac{(105,000 \text{ gal})(40,000 \text{ GPD})}{80,000 \text{ GPD}}$

= 52,500 gallons

2. Determine the total flow produced by the plant per regeneration.

Total Flow, gal = Softener Capacity, gal + Bypass Water, gal

= 105,000 gal + 52,500 gal

= 157,500 gallons

14.20   RECORDKEEPING

Keeping correct and up-to-date records is as important as performing scheduled maintenance on a regular routine. The recordkeeping system should be set up to record data on a daily basis. Record the total flow through the softener each day, along with the blend rates and gallons that have bypassed the unit. The total gallons of brine used each day, along with the pounds of salt used to keep the ion exchange softener in good working order should be recorded. Records of the tests performed on the softeners should be kept up to date in order to warn the operator of any problems that might be developing with the softening unit. Good records are an important part of a successful treatment plant operation. Many problems can be avoided or solved with an adequate recordkeeping system if you review your daily records and compare them with the normal records to determine operating problems.

QUESTIONS

Write your answers in a notebook and then compare your answers with those on page 121.

14.19A   Why is source water blended with the effluent from an ion exchange softener?

14.20A   What records should be kept by the operator of an ion exchange softening plant?

14.21   ARITHMETIC ASSIGNMENT

Turn to the Appendix at the back of this manual on "How to Solve Water Treatment Plant Arithmetic Problems." In Section A.32, "Softening," read the material, work the example problems and check the arithmetic using your calculator.

14.22   ADDITIONAL READING

1. *NEW YORK MANUAL*, Chapter 11*, "Softening."

2. *TEXAS MANUAL*, Chapter 11*, "Special Water Treatment (Softening and Ion Exchange)."

3. *NOTES ON WATER CHEMISTRY*, prepared for "Advanced Water Works Operations," by Michael D. Curry. Available from Environmental Resources Training Center, Campus Box 1075, SIUE, Edwardsville, IL 62026-1075. Price, $3.00, includes cost of shipping and handling.

* Depends on edition.

14.23   ACKNOWLEDGMENTS

Portions of the material discussed on ion exchange softening came from the following sources:

1. Bowers, Eugene, "Ion Exchange Softening" in *WATER QUALITY AND TREATMENT*, 4th Ed., Customer Services, American Water Works Association, 6666 W. Quincy Avenue, Denver, CO 80235. Order No. 10053. Price to members, $103.75; nonmembers, $157.00; price includes cost of shipping and handling.

2. Lipe, L.A. and M.D. Curry, "Ion Exchange Water Softening," a discussion for water treatment plant operators, 1974-75 seminar series sponsored by Illinois Environmental Protection Agency, and

3. Riehl, Merrill L., *WATER SUPPLY AND TREATMENT*, National Lime Association, 200 N. Glebe Road, Suite 800, Arlington, VA 22203. Price, $39.95, plus $4.00 shipping and handling.

End of Lesson 2 of 2 Lessons on SOFTENING

Please answer the discussion and review questions before continuing with the Objective Test.

DISCUSSION AND REVIEW QUESTIONS

Chapter 14.   SOFTENING

(Lesson 2 of 2 Lessons)

Write the answers to these questions in your notebook before continuing with the Objective Test on page 121. The question numbering continues from Lesson 1.

13. What happens in the resin or media in an ion exchange softener during the softening stage?

14. How would you ensure that large amounts of resin are not being lost during the backwash stage?

15. How would you determine if an ion exchange softener rinse stage has been successful?

16. What happens if an ion exchange softener removes iron in the ferrous (soluble) or ferric (solid) form?

17. What types of insoluble material may be found in salt? What problems can be caused by this material and how can these problems be prevented?

18. How would you prevent the strainers under the bulk brine storage area from silting in with sand and impurities?

19. How would you determine if iron has fouled the resin of an ion exchange softener?

20. How are ion exchange units filled with water after total shutdown?

21. Why is water with zero hardness not delivered to consumers?

SUGGESTED ANSWERS

Chapter 14. SOFTENING

ANSWERS TO QUESTIONS IN LESSON 1

Answers to questions on page 80.

14.0A Hardness is caused mainly by the calcium and magnesium ions in water.

14.0B Excessive hardness is undesirable because it causes the formation of soap curds, increased use of soap, deposition of scale in boilers, damage in some industrial processes, and it sometimes causes objectionable tastes in drinking water.

14.1A Limitations of the ion exchange softening process include (1) an increase in the sodium content of the softened water and (2) ultimate disposal of spent brine and rinse waters.

Answers to questions on page 83.

14.2A Hardness is commonly measured by titration. Individual divalent cations may be measured by using an atomic absorption (AA) spectrophotometer.

14.2B Determine the total hardness as $CaCO_3$ for a sample of water with a calcium content of 25 mg/L and a magnesium content of 14 mg/L.

Known	Unknown
Calcium, mg/L = 25 mg/L	Total Hardness,
Magnesium, mg/L = 14 mg/L	mg/L as $CaCO_3$

Calculate the total hardness as milligrams per liter of calcium carbonate equivalent.

$$\text{Total Hardness, mg/}L \text{ as } CaCO_3 = \text{Calcium Hardness, mg/}L \text{ as } CaCO_3 + \text{Magnesium Hardness, mg/}L \text{ as } CaCO_3$$

$$= 2.50(\text{Ca, mg/}L) + 4.12(\text{Mg, mg/}L)$$

$$= 2.50(25 \text{ mg/}L) + 4.12(14 \text{ mg/}L)$$

$$= 62.5 \text{ mg/}L + 57.7 \text{ mg/}L$$

$$= 120.2 \text{ mg/}L \text{ as } CaCO_3$$

14.2C Water treatment chemicals which lower the pH when added to water include alum, carbon dioxide, chlorine (Cl_2), ferric chloride, hydrofluosilicic acid, and sulfuric acid.

14.2D Results from alkalinity titrations on a sample of water were as follows:

Known

Sample Size, mL	= 100 mL
mL Titrant Used to pH 8.3, A	= 1.2 mL
Total mL of Titrant Used, B	= 5.6 mL
Acid Normality, N	= 0.02 N H_2SO_4

Unknown

1. Total Alkalinity, mg/L as $CaCO_3$
2. Bicarbonate Alkalinity, mg/L as $CaCO_3$
3. Carbonate Alkalinity, mg/L as $CaCO_3$
4. Hydroxide Alkalinity, mg/L as $CaCO_3$

1. Calculate the phenolphthalein alkalinity in mg/L as $CaCO_3$.

$$\text{Phenolphthalein Alkalinity, mg/}L \text{ as } CaCO_3 = \frac{A \times N \times 50{,}000}{\text{m}L \text{ of sample}}$$

$$= \frac{(1.2 \text{ m}L) \times (0.02 \text{ }N) \times 50{,}000}{100 \text{ m}L}$$

$$= 12 \text{ mg/}L \text{ as } CaCO_3$$

2. Calculate the total alkalinity in mg/L as $CaCO_3$.

$$\text{Total Alkalinity, mg/}L \text{ as } CaCO_3 = \frac{B \times N \times 50{,}000}{\text{m}L \text{ of sample}}$$

$$= \frac{(5.6 \text{ m}L) \times (0.02 \text{ }N) \times (50{,}000)}{100 \text{ m}L}$$

$$= 56 \text{ mg/}L \text{ as } CaCO_3$$

3. Refer to Table 14.4 for alkalinity constituents.

From Table 14.4 we want the second row because P = 12 mg/L which is less than $\frac{1}{2}$T[($\frac{1}{2}$)(56 mg/L) = 28 mg/L]. Therefore,

a. Bicarbonate Alkalinity = T – 2P

$$= 56 \text{ mg/}L – 2(12 \text{ mg/}L)$$

$$= 32 \text{ mg/}L \text{ as } CaCO_3$$

b. Carbonate Alkalinity = 2P

$$= 2(12 \text{ mg/}L)$$

$$= 24 \text{ mg/}L \text{ as } CaCO_3$$

c. Hydroxide Alkalinity = 0 mg/L as $CaCO_3$

Answers to questions on page 84.

14.3A The minimum hardness that can be achieved by the lime-soda ash process is around 30 to 40 mg/L as $CaCO_3$.

14.3B Benefits that could result from the lime-soda softening process in addition to softening include:

1. Removal of iron and manganese,
2. Reduction of solids,
3. Removal and inactivation of bacteria and viruses due to high pH,
4. Control of corrosion and scale formation with proper stabilization of treated water, and
5. Removal of excess fluoride.

Answers to questions on page 86.

14.3C The pH is increased because calcium and magnesium become less soluble as the pH increases. Therefore, calcium and magnesium can be removed from water as insoluble precipitates at high pH levels.

14.3D The addition of lime to water increases the hydroxide concentration, thus increasing the pH.

14.3E After the chemical softening process, the scale-forming tendencies of water are reduced by bubbling carbon dioxide (recarbonation) through the water.

14.3F Recarbonation is a process in which carbon dioxide is bubbled into the water being treated to convert carbonate ions to bicarbonate ions to stabilize the solution against the precipitation of carbonate compounds. The pH may also be lowered by the addition of acid.

14.3G Caustic soda softening might be used in place of soda ash. The decision to use caustic soda rather than soda ash depends on the quality of the source water and the delivered costs of various chemicals.

Answer to question on page 87.

14.3H Calculate the hydrated lime ($Ca(OH)_2$) with 90 percent purity, soda ash, and carbon dioxide dose requirements in milligrams per liter for the water shown below.

Known

Constituents	Source Water	Softened Water After Recarbonation and Filtration
CO_2, mg/L	= 5 mg/L	= 0 mg/L
Total Alkalinity, mg/L	= 150 mg/L as $CaCO_3$	= 20 mg/L as $CaCO_3$
Total Hardness, mg/L	= 240 mg/L as $CaCO_3$	= 50 mg/L as $CaCO_3$
Mg^{2+}, mg/L	= 16 mg/L	= 2 mg/L
pH	= 7.4	= 8.8
Lime Purity, %	= 90%	

Unknown

1. Hydrated Lime, mg/L
2. Soda Ash, mg/L
3. Carbon Dioxide, mg/L

1. Calculate the hydrated lime ($Ca(OH)_2$) required in milligrams per liter.

$A = (CO_2 \text{ mg/}L)(74/44)$

$= (5 \text{ mg/}L)(74/44)$

$= 8 \text{ mg/}L$

$B = (\text{Alkalinity, mg/}L)(74/100)$

$= (150 \text{ mg/}L - 20 \text{ mg/}L)(74/100)$

$= 96 \text{ mg/}L$

$C = 0 \quad$ Hydroxide Alkalinity = 0

$D = (Mg^{2+}, \text{ mg/}L)(74/24.3)$

$= (16 \text{ mg/}L - 2 \text{ mg/}L)(74/24.3)$

$= 43 \text{ mg/}L$

$$\text{Hydrated Lime } (Ca(OH)_2) \text{ Feed, mg/}L = \frac{(A + B + C + D)1.15}{\text{Purity of Lime, as a decimal}}$$

$$= \frac{(8 \text{ mg/}L + 96 \text{ mg/}L + 0 + 43 \text{ mg/}L)1.15}{0.90}$$

$$= \frac{(147 \text{ mg/}L)(1.15)}{0.90}$$

$$= 188 \text{ mg/}L$$

2. Calculate the soda ash required in milligrams per liter.

$$\text{Total Hardness Removed, mg/}L \text{ as } CaCO_3 = \text{Total Hardness, mg/}L \text{ as } CaCO_3 - \text{Total Hardness Remaining, mg/}L \text{ as } CaCO_3$$

$$= 240 \text{ mg/}L - 50 \text{ mg/}L$$

$$= 190 \text{ mg/}L \text{ as } CaCO_3$$

$$\text{Noncarbonate Hardness, mg/}L \text{ as } CaCO_3 = \text{Total Hardness Removed, mg/}L \text{ as } CaCO_3 - \text{Carbonate Hardness, mg/}L \text{ as } CaCO_3$$

$$= 190 \text{ mg/}L - 150 \text{ mg/}L$$

$$= 40 \text{ mg/}L \text{ as } CaCO_3$$

$$\text{Soda Ash } (Na_2CO_3) \text{ Feed, mg/}L = \left(\frac{\text{Noncarbonate Hardness,}}{\text{mg/}L \text{ as } CaCO_3}\right)(106/100)$$

$$= (40 \text{ mg/}L)(106/100)$$

$$= 42.4 \text{ mg/}L$$

3. Calculate the dosage of carbon dioxide required for recarbonation.

$$\text{Excess Lime, mg/}L = (A + B + C + D)(0.15)$$

$$= (8 \text{ mg/}L + 96 \text{ mg/}L + 0 + 43 \text{ mg/}L)(0.15)$$

$$= (147 \text{ mg/}L)(0.15)$$

$$= 22 \text{ mg/}L$$

$$\text{Total } CO_2 \text{ Feed, mg/}L = (Ca(OH)_2 \text{ excess, mg/}L)(44/74) + (Mg^{2+} \text{ residual, mg/}L)(44/24.3)$$

$$= (22 \text{ mg/}L)(44/74) + (2 \text{ mg/}L)(44/24.3)$$

$$= 13 \text{ mg/}L + 4 \text{ mg/}L$$

$$= 15 \text{ mg/}L$$

Answers to questions on page 88.

14.3I In the lime softening process, calcium is precipitated out as calcium carbonate and magnesium as magnesium hydroxide.

14.3J Partial lime softening (no magnesium removal) removes hardness caused by calcium ions. This may be referred to as calcium hardness.

14.3K In split lime treatment, a portion of the water is treated with excess lime to remove the magnesium at a high pH. Then source water (the remaining portion) is added in the next basin to neutralize (lower the pH) the excess-lime-treated portion.

Answers to questions on page 90.

14.3L Lime-soda ash softening is used when lime alone will not remove enough hardness.

14.3M Noncarbonate hardness is removed by the addition of soda ash in the chemical precipitation softening process.

Answers to questions on page 91.

14.3N Where the daily requirements for lime are small, lime is usually delivered to the water treatment plant in bags.

14.3O Considerable heat is generated if quicklime accidentally gets wet.

14.3P Lime may be applied by dry feeding techniques using volumetric or gravimetric feeders.

Answers to questions on page 91.

14.4A   When the alum dose increases for coagulation, the lime dose must be increased also.

14.4B   Color can be removed from water by coagulation with alum at low pH values. The high pH values required during softening tend to "set" the color which then becomes very difficult to remove.

Answers to questions on page 92.

14.5A   A slight excess of lime can cause a scale to form on the filter sand, distribution mains, and household plumbing.

14.5B   Excess caustic and unprecipitated carbonate ions (pin floc) can be removed from softened water by recarbonation. Recarbonation is the bubbling of carbon dioxide through the water being treated to lower the pH. Recarbonation can be accomplished, to a degree, by using source water in the split treatment mode.

14.5C   Suspending a couple of nails on strings in a filter can indicate if the water is stable. If the nails are rusting, the water is corrosive. If a scale forms on the nails, then scale is forming on your filter media and in your distribution system.

14.5D   The marble test is used to determine if a water is stable. The Langelier Index is also used to determine the corrosivity of water.

Answers to questions on page 93.

14.6A   Wooden paddles should be used as cleaning tools on any slaker in operation. A metal tool will damage the slaker and could even injure the operator if dropped by accident. However, a wooden paddle will likely be broken up with no damage to the equipment or operator.

14.6B   Information on how to safely maintain equipment may be found in equipment manuals provided by equipment suppliers and manufacturers.

Answers to questions on page 94.

14.7A   A disadvantage of recirculating sludge back to the primary mix area is that an increase in magnesium could result.

14.7B   Only trial and error will really determine if sludge recirculation will serve a useful purpose in your plant.

14.8A   Records should be kept on the amounts of treatment plant chemicals ordered and the amounts fed.

Answers to questions on page 98.

14.9A   If lime added to water does not reduce the hardness of a water sufficiently, use the optimum lime dose and run jar tests with varying soda ash doses. Select the soda ash dose that will produce a water with a hardness of around 80 to 90 mg/L.

14.9B   When selecting the target hardness for a water softening plant, consider the uses of the softened water and the cost of softening.

Answers to questions on page 99.

14.9C   The overfeeding of chemicals is a waste of money and quality control will suffer.

14.9D   What should be the lime feeder setting in pounds per day to treat a flow of 2 MGD when the optimum lime dose is 160 mg/L?

Known		Unknown
Flow, MGD	= 2 MGD	Feeder Setting, lbs/day
Lime Dose, mg/L	= 160 mg/L	

Calculate the lime feeder setting in pounds per day.

$$\text{Feeder Setting, lbs/day} = (\text{Flow, MGD})(\text{Lime, mg/L})(8.34 \text{ lbs/gal})$$
$$= (2 \text{ MGD})(160 \text{ mg/L})(8.34 \text{ lbs/gal})$$
$$= 2,669 \text{ lbs/day}$$

14.9E   How much soda ash is required in pounds per day to remove 40 mg/L noncarbonate hardness from a flow of 2 MGD?

Known		Unknown
Flow, MGD	= 2 MGD	Feeder Setting, lbs/day
Hardness Removed, mg/L	= 40 mg/L	

1. Calculate the soda ash dose in milligrams per liter.

$$\text{Soda Ash, mg/L} = (1.1)(\text{Hardness Removed, mg/L})$$
$$= (1.1)(40 \text{ mg/L})$$
$$= 44 \text{ mg/L}$$

2. Determine the soda ash feeder setting in pounds per day.

$$\text{Feeder Setting, lbs/day} = (\text{Flow, MGD})(\text{Soda Ash, mg/L})(8.34 \text{ lbs/gal})$$
$$= (2 \text{ MGD})(44 \text{ mg/L})(8.34 \text{ lbs/gal})$$
$$= 734 \text{ lbs/day}$$

ANSWERS TO QUESTIONS IN LESSON 2

Answers to questions on page 104.

14.10A   The three basic types of softeners on the market are:

1. An upflow unit,
2. A gravity flow unit, and
3. A pressure downflow unit (the most common).

14.10B   During the regeneration cycle the softener is taken out of service. Salt in the form of a concentrated brine solution is used to regenerate (recharge) the ion exchange media. When the brine solution is fed into the media, the sodium cations are exchanged for calcium and magnesium cations. As the brine solution travels down through the media, the sodium cations are attached to the media while the calcium, magnesium, and chloride (from the salt) ions flow to waste. After the regeneration has taken place, the bed is ready to be placed in service again to remove calcium and magnesium by ion exchange.

Answers to questions on page 107.

14.11A   The source water hardness is the main consideration in determining the length of the service stage of an ion exchange softener.

14.11B   The purpose of the backwash stage is to expand and clean the media or resin particles and also to free any material such as iron and manganese that might have been removed during the softening stage.

14.11C   Ion exchange softeners are regenerated by the use of a concentrated brine solution.

14.11D   During the rinse stage the softener effluent goes to waste.

Answers to questions on page 108.

14.12A   Hardness should be monitored in the effluent from an ion exchange softener.

14.13A   High chlorine residual levels applied to softening units could damage the resin and reduce its life span.

14.14A   The disposal of spent brine is a problem because the brine is very corrosive and toxic to many living things in the environment.

Answers to questions on page 109.

14.15A   One valve that fails to open or close during a regeneration stage could mean a storage tank full of salty water or no brine.

14.15B   Brine pumps and piping must receive constant attention because a saturated brine solution is very corrosive. An uncontained brine leak will only get worse.

14.15C   Packing is recommended over mechanical seals on brine pumps because sand in mechanical seals will result in high repair and maintenance costs.

Answers to questions on page 110.

14.16A   The maximum expected hardness level in the effluent from an ion exchange softener should not exceed one grain hardness per gallon (17.1 mg/L).

14.16B   The purpose of the backwash stage is to remove trapped turbidity particles and other insoluble material that is trapped in the resin.

14.16C   If hardness leakage is excessive immediately following a regeneration stage, shut the unit down and check the media level. The bed could be disrupted from excessive backwash or rinse rates. Iron fouling could also cause a channeling condition to occur and cause the water to short-circuit through the media without contacting the complete bed area.

14.16D   If the rinse stage starts too soon, the brine solution could be forced out of the unit before adequate contact time has elapsed. If the rinse rate is too low, all the waste material might not be removed from the unit before it goes into the service stage.

Answers to questions on page 112.

14.17A   Ion exchange softeners must be drained and filled slowly during start-up and shutdown to prevent surging of the media which will either wash it out of the unit or disrupt it, thus making the media uneven and creating a channeling problem.

14.17B   If the pipe work is deteriorating from the brine solution, PVC pipe should be used as a replacement.

Answers to questions on page 114.

14.18A   A source water has a hardness of 150 mg/L as $CaCO_3$. What is the hardness in grains per gallon?

Known	Unknown
Hardness, mg/L = 150 mg/L	Hardness, grains/gallon

Calculate the source water hardness in grains per gallon.

$$\text{Hardness, grains/gallon} = \frac{(\text{Hardness, mg}/L)(1 \text{ gpg})}{17.1 \text{ mg}/L}$$

$$= \frac{(150 \text{ mg}/L)(1 \text{ gpg})}{17.1 \text{ mg}/L}$$

$$= 8.8 \text{ grains/gal}$$

14.18B   An ion exchange softener contains 60 cubic feet of resin with a hardness removal capacity of 25 kilograins per cubic foot of resin. The water being treated has a hardness of 250 mg/L as $CaCO_3$. How many gallons of water can be softened before the softener will require regeneration?

Resin Vol, cu ft   = 60 cu ft   Water Treated, gal

Removal Capacity, gr/cu ft   = 25,000 gr/cu ft

Hardness, mg/L   = 250 mg/L

1. Convert the hardness from mg/L to grains per gallon.

$$\text{Hardness, grains/gallon} = \frac{(\text{Hardness, mg}/L)(1 \text{ grain/gal})}{17.1 \text{ mg}/L}$$

$$= \frac{(250 \text{ mg}/L)(1 \text{ grain/gal})}{17.1 \text{ mg}/L}$$

$$= 14.6 \text{ grains/gal}$$

2. Calculate the exchange capacity of the softener in grains.

$$\text{Exchange Capacity, grains} = (\text{Resin Vol, cu ft})(\text{Removal Capacity, gr/cu ft})$$

$$= (60 \text{ cu ft})(25,000 \text{ grains/cu ft})$$

$$= 1,500,000 \text{ grains of hardness removal capacity}$$

3. Calculate the volume of water in gallons that may be treated before regeneration.

$$\text{Water Treated,} \atop \text{gal} = \frac{\text{Exchange Capacity, grains}}{\text{Hardness, grains/gal}}$$

$$= \frac{1,500,000 \text{ grains}}{14.6 \text{ grains/gal}}$$

$$= 102,700 \text{ gal}$$

Therefore, 102,700 gallons of water with 14.6 grains of hardness per gallon of water can be treated before the resin becomes exhausted.

Answers to questions on page 116.

14.19A Source water is blended with the effluent from an ion exchange softener so the consumers will receive water with an acceptable hardness. Delivering water with zero hardness is very expensive and the water is very corrosive.

14.20A Records that should be kept by the operator of an ion exchange softening plant include:

1. Total daily flow through unit,
2. Blend rates,
3. Total daily gallons that have bypassed unit,
4. Gallons of brine used each day,
5. Pounds of salt used each day, and
6. Results of tests performed on source water, softener effluent, and blended water.

OBJECTIVE TEST

Chapter 14.   SOFTENING

Please write your name and mark the correct answers on the answer sheet, as directed at the end of Chapter 1. There may be more than one correct answer to each multiple-choice question.

True-False

1. Local usage will influence consumers' attitudes toward the hardness of their water.

   1. True
   2. False

2. Hardness in water will tend to increase the life of fabrics that are washed in hard water.

   1. True
   2. False

3. pH is an expression of the intensity of the basic or acidic condition of a liquid.

   1. True
   2. False

4. A positive Langelier Index indicates that water is corrosive.

   1. True
   2. False

5. Alkalinity is the capacity of water to neutralize bases.

   1. True
   2. False

6. Hardness is completely removed by chemical precipitation methods used in water treatment plants.

   1. True
   2. False

7. Calcium and magnesium become more soluble as the pH increases.

   1. True
   2. False

8. Carbonate hardness can be removed by soda only.

   1. True
   2. False

9. Calcium carbonate hardness is removed at a higher pH than magnesium carbonate hardness.

   1. True
   2. False

10. When water is supersaturated with calcium carbonate and magnesium hydroxide, deposition of precipitates will occur in filters and pipelines.

    1. True
    2. False

11. Cationic polymers are very pH sensitive.

    1. True
    2. False

12. When treating highly colored waters, these waters must be coagulated for color removal at low pH values.

    1. True
    2. False

13. Always wear goggles or a face shield when working with lime that has been or is in the process of slaking.

    1. True
    2. False

14. A saturated ion exchange brine solution is very corrosive.

    1. True
    2. False

15. The use of packing on brine pumps is recommended over mechanical seals.

    1. True
    2. False

Best Answer (Select only the closest or best answer.)

16. What does water hardness measure?

    1. Concentration of anions in water
    2. Concentration of cations in water
    3. Incompressibility of water
    4. Soap- and detergent-consuming power of water

17. After water has been softened, what must be the condition of the water distributed to consumers?

    1. Cool
    2. Corrosive
    3. Scale-forming
    4. Stable

18. What is a limitation of the lime-soda softening process?

    1. Color removal may be complicated
    2. Inactivation of bacteria
    3. Removal of excess fluoride
    4. Removal of iron and manganese

19. How can carbon dioxide be used in the chemical softening process?

    1. To decrease the need for lime to improve softening
    2. To decrease the scale-forming tendencies prior to filtration
    3. To increase the alkalinity prior to alum addition
    4. To increase the causticity to reduce corrosion

20. What is the addition of carbon dioxide to water called?

    1. Carbon dioxide gasification
    2. First-stage carbonation
    3. Meeting carbonaceous demand
    4. Recarbonation

21. What happens if quicklime accidentally gets wet?

    1. Considerable heat will be generated
    2. Hardness will not be removed
    3. Quicklime will not dissolve in water
    4. Storage time will be increased

22. Why should the use of the same conveyor or bin for both quicklime and one of the coagulants containing water be avoided?

    1. Chemical feeders become plugged
    2. Cost savings are insufficient
    3. Enough heat could be generated to cause a fire
    4. Mixing the chemicals increases hardness

23. What is the most common method of chemical softening sludge disposal?

    1. Land application
    2. Landfill
    3. Recirculation
    4. Sanitary sewer

24. What is ion exchange softening?

    1. Exchanging hard water for soft water
    2. Exchanging hardness-causing ions for alkalinity ions
    3. Exchanging hardness-causing ions for sodium ions
    4. Exchanging softening chemicals for resins

25. How is an ion exchange resin regenerated?

    1. Calcium chloride solution
    2. Concentrated brine solution
    3. Heat treatment
    4. Reverse flow

26. What happens when a fully concentrated or saturated brine solution is used to regenerate an ion exchange softening unit?

    1. Causes ion exchange resin to break up
    2. Minimizes dilution water needs
    3. Reduces contact time for regeneration
    4. Shortens required rinse time

27. What problem can develop if water high in iron and manganese is applied to the ion exchange resin for very long?

    1. Iron and manganese will need to be removed from resin effluent
    2. Iron will pass through the resin
    3. Loss of exchange capacity will result
    4. Manganese will pass through the resin

28. What can be done if iron fouling is a problem?

    1. Color removal will be required
    2. Exchange resin should be replaced
    3. Iron should be removed from effluent
    4. Length of backwash stage should be increased

29. What is the main reason for hardness leakage early in the service stage?

    1. Backwash stage too short
    2. Improper amount and saturation of brine solution
    3. Iron fouling
    4. Rinse stage started too soon

30. Why should an ion exchange softening unit be filled from the bottom at a slow, controlled rate?

    1. Control iron fouling
    2. Purge air trapped in resin
    3. Redistribute resin evenly
    4. Remove hardness

Multiple Choice (Select all correct answers.)

31. Technically, hardness is caused by divalent metallic cations which are capable of reacting with what?

    1. Certain anions to form scale
    2. Hydroxides to form precipitates
    3. Iron and manganese to form stains
    4. Organics to form tastes and odors
    5. Soap (detergent) to form precipitates

32. Why is excessive hardness in water undesirable?

    1. Deposition of scale in boilers
    2. Formation of soap curds
    3. Increased use of soap
    4. Iron and manganese stains
    5. Objectionable tastes

33. What are some of the benefits of softening in addition to the removal of hardness?

    1. Control of corrosion with proper stabilization
    2. Lack of process wastes for ultimate disposal
    3. Removal of iron and manganese
    4. Removal of radioactivity
    5. Sometimes a reduction in tastes and odors

34. Which water treatment chemical(s) lowers the pH of the water being treated?

    1. Aluminum sulfate (alum)
    2. Caustic soda
    3. Hydrated lime
    4. Soda ash
    5. Sodium hypochlorite

35. What benefits are produced from lime-soda softening in addition to softening water?

    1. Minimum quantities of sludge created
    2. Reduction of solids
    3. Removal and inactivation of bacteria and viruses
    4. Removal of all hardness
    5. Removal of iron and manganese

36. What are the advantages of using caustic soda instead of soda ash for softening?

    1. Ease of handling and storage
    2. Less safety hazard
    3. Less sludge is formed
    4. Protective clothing need not be worn when handling
    5. Stability in storage

37. What should be done if lime comes in contact with your skin or eyes?

    1. Consult a physician if necessary
    2. Flush affected areas with water
    3. Keep burns covered with a bandage
    4. Put on head protection
    5. Rub your eyes if irritated

38. Why is the stability of water important?

    1. To control corrosion
    2. To control scaling
    3. To disinfect drinking water
    4. To reduce chemical costs
    5. To reduce hardness

39. Why do the feed rates determined by jar tests not always produce the exact same results in an actual plant? This is because of differences in

    1. Methods of calculation.
    2. Mixing equipment.
    3. Size and shape of jars as compared with plant basins.
    4. Source water.
    5. Water temperature.

40. What are the common stages of operation of an ion exchange softener?

    1. Backwash
    2. Brine
    3. Maintenance
    4. Rinse
    5. Service

41. The backwash duration and flow rate of an ion exchange softener will vary depending on which factors?

    1. Amount of alkalinity being removed
    2. Amount of hardness being removed
    3. Manufacturer
    4. Temperature of the water
    5. Type of resin used

42. Which water quality indicators should be monitored in the influent to an ion exchange softener?

    1. Alkalinity
    2. Hardness
    3. Iron and manganese
    4. pH
    5. Temperature

43. What can an operator do if iron fouling appears to be a problem on an ion exchange softener?

    1. Apply a chemical cleaner such as sodium hydrosulfite
    2. Decrease the strength of the brine used in the regeneration stage
    3. Increase backwash flow rates
    4. Increase duration of backwash stage
    5. Increase duration of service stage

44. How many gallons of water with a hardness of 16 grains per gallon may be treated with an ion exchange softener with an exchange capacity of 12,000 kilograins?

    1. 0.31 M gal
    2. 0.53 M gal
    3. 0.58 M gal
    4. 0.64 M gal
    5. 0.75 M gal

45. How many hours will an ion exchange softening unit operate when treating an average flow of 375 GPM? The unit is capable of softening 400,000 gallons of water before requiring regeneration.

    1. 18 hours
    2. 27 hours
    3. 31 hours
    4. 45 hours
    5. 93 hours

End of Objective Test

CHAPTER 15

TRIHALOMETHANES

by

Mike McGuire

TABLE OF CONTENTS

Chapter 15.   TRIHALOMETHANES

Page

OBJECTIVES 127

WORDS 128

15.0   THE TRIHALOMETHANE (THM) PROBLEM 129

15.1   FEASIBILITY ANALYSIS PROCESS 131

15.2   PROBLEM DEFINITION 131

    15.20   Sampling 131

    15.21   THM Calculations 132

    15.22   Chemistry of THM Formation 133

15.3   CONTROL STRATEGIES 134

15.4   EXISTING TREATMENT PROCESSES 134

15.5   TREATMENT PROCESS RESEARCH STUDY RESULTS 135

    15.50   Consider Options 135

    15.51   Remove THMs After They Are Formed 135

    15.52   Remove THM Precursors 137

    15.53   Alternative Disinfectants 138

15.6   SELECTION AND IMPLEMENTATION OF A COST-EFFECTIVE ALTERNATIVE 138

15.7   REGULATORY UPDATE 139

15.8   SUMMARY AND CONCLUSIONS 139

15.9   ARITHMETIC ASSIGNMENT 140

15.10   ADDITIONAL READING 140

DISCUSSION AND REVIEW QUESTIONS 140

SUGGESTED ANSWERS 141

OBJECTIVE TEST 142

OBJECTIVES

Chapter 15. TRIHALOMETHANES

Following completion of Chapter 15, you should be able to:

1. Describe how trihalomethanes are formed,

2. Explain why trihalomethanes are a problem in drinking water,

3. Collect samples for trihalomethane analysis,

4. Identify control strategies for trihalomethanes,

5. Describe treatment processes capable of controlling tri-halomethanes, and

6. Select and implement a cost-effective means of controlling tri-halomethanes.

WORDS

Chapter 15.   TRIHALOMETHANES

CARCINOGEN (CAR-sin-o-JEN)   CARCINOGEN

Any substance which tends to produce cancer in an organism.

MCL   MCL

Maximum **C**ontaminant **L**evel. The largest allowable amount. MCLs for various water quality indicators are specified in the National Primary Drinking Water Regulations (NPDWR).

NONVOLATILE MATTER   NONVOLATILE MATTER

Material such as sand, salt, iron, calcium, and other mineral materials which are only slightly affected by the actions of organisms and are not lost on ignition of the dry solids at 550°C. Volatile materials are chemical substances usually of animal or plant origin.

PRECURSOR, THM (pre-CURSE-or)   PRECURSOR, THM

Natural organic compounds found in all surface and groundwaters. These compounds *MAY* react with halogens (such as chlorine) to form trihalomethanes (tri-HAL-o-METH-hanes) (THMs); they *MUST* be present in order for THMs to form.

REPRESENTATIVE SAMPLE   REPRESENTATIVE SAMPLE

A sample portion of material or water that is as nearly identical in content and consistency as possible to that in the larger body of material or water being sampled.

TRIHALOMETHANES (THMs) (tri-HAL-o-METH-hanes)   TRIHALOMETHANES (THMs)

Derivatives of methane, CH_4, in which three halogen atoms (chlorine or bromine) are substituted for three of the hydrogen atoms. Often formed during chlorination by reactions with natural organic materials in the water. The resulting compounds (THMs) are suspected of causing cancer.

VOLATILE (VOL-uh-tull)   VOLATILE

(1) A volatile substance is one that is capable of being evaporated or changed to a vapor at relatively low temperatures. Volatile substances also can be partially removed by air stripping.

(2) In terms of solids analysis, volatile refers to materials lost (including most organic matter) upon ignition in a muffle furnace for 60 minutes at 550°C. Natural volatile materials are chemical substances usually of animal or plant origin. Manufactured or synthetic volatile materials such as ether, acetone, and carbon tetrachloride are highly volatile and not of plant or animal origin. Also see NONVOLATILE MATTER.

CHAPTER 15. TRIHALOMETHANES

15.0 THE TRIHALOMETHANE (THM) PROBLEM

For the past few decades water utilities have been concerned about the presence of organic compounds in drinking water. The analytical methods for detecting inorganic compounds such as calcium, magnesium, and iron have been known for many decades. However, the ability to analyze for organic compounds in water has been developed only recently. What are organic compounds? Organic compounds are defined as those compounds that contain a carbon atom. Carbon is one of the basic chemical elements. Examples of organic compounds include: proteins, carbohydrates, fats, vitamins, and a wide variety of compounds that modern technology has created.

In 1974, researchers with the U.S. Environmental Protection Agency (EPA) and in the Netherlands published their findings that trihalomethanes are formed in drinking water when free chlorine comes in contact with naturally occurring organic compounds (*THM PRECURSORS*[1]). Trihalomethanes are a class of organic compounds in which there has been a replacement of the three hydrogen atoms in the methane molecule with three halogen atoms (chlorine or bromine). The four most commonly found THMs are chloroform, bromodichloromethane, dibromochloromethane, and bromoform (Figure 15.1). While it is theoretically possible to form iodine-substituted THMs, they are rarely found in treated water and they are not regulated at this time. In general, methane is not involved in the THM reaction. The production of THMs can generally be shown as:

EQUATION 1

$$\begin{array}{c} \text{Free} \\ \text{Chlorine} \end{array} + \begin{array}{c} \text{Natural} \\ \text{Organics} \\ \text{(precursor)} \end{array} + \text{Bromide} \rightarrow \text{THMs} + \begin{array}{c} \text{Other} \\ \text{Products} \end{array}$$

Free chlorine is added to drinking water as a disinfectant. The naturally occurring organics get into water when the water partially dissolves organic materials from algae, leaves, bark, wood, soil, and other similar materials. This dissolving action is similar to what happens when a teabag is placed in hot water; the water dissolves those parts of the tea leaves which are soluble organic and inorganic compounds. While it is possible to form THMs by reactions between chlorine and industrial organic chemicals, the overwhelming bulk of THM precursors in water are from natural organic compounds.

One source of bromide is seawater. Water agencies whose supplies are subject to seawater intrusion can expect THMs in their treated water to have high levels of bromide. Bromide reaction products can be found in most surface waters, even where bromide concentrations are low. The "other products" formed in this reaction are very poorly understood and are not regulated at this time.

After THMs were discovered in drinking waters around the country, several studies were made of the possible health effects of THMs in general and chloroform (a THM) in particular. The results of these tests indicated that chloroform caused cancer in laboratory animals (rats and mice) and was suspected of causing cancer in humans. Further studies comparing people who used different sources of drinking water suggested that there may be a link between the presence of manmade organic compounds like THMs and increased levels of cancer. Animal feeding experiments and population studies are not definite proof that THMs in drinking water cause cancer. Under the Safe Drinking Water Act, EPA may pass a regulation for any contaminant which MAY HAVE any adverse health effect.

On November 29, 1979, the THM regulations were published in the *FEDERAL REGISTER*. These regulations were amended on February 28, 1983 (see Section 15.7, "Regulatory Update"). The general aspects of the regulation are outlined below:

MAXIMUM CONTAMINANT LEVEL: 0.10 mg/*L* total trihalomethanes (TTHMs) — sum of the concentrations of chloroform, bromodichloromethane, dibromochloromethane, and bromoform.

APPLIES TO: All community water systems that add a disinfectant to their water supply and serve a population greater than 10,000 persons.

MONITORING REQUIREMENTS: Monitoring compliance based on an annual running TTHM (total trihalomethane) average of four quarters of data. Schedule, locations, and numbers of samples depend on system size and to be worked out with state or EPA.

---

[1] *Precursor, THM (pre-CURSE-or). Natural organic compounds found in all surface and groundwaters. These compounds MAY react with halogens (such as chlorine) to form trihalomethanes (tri-HAL-o-METH-hanes) (THMs); they MUST be present in order for THMs to form.*

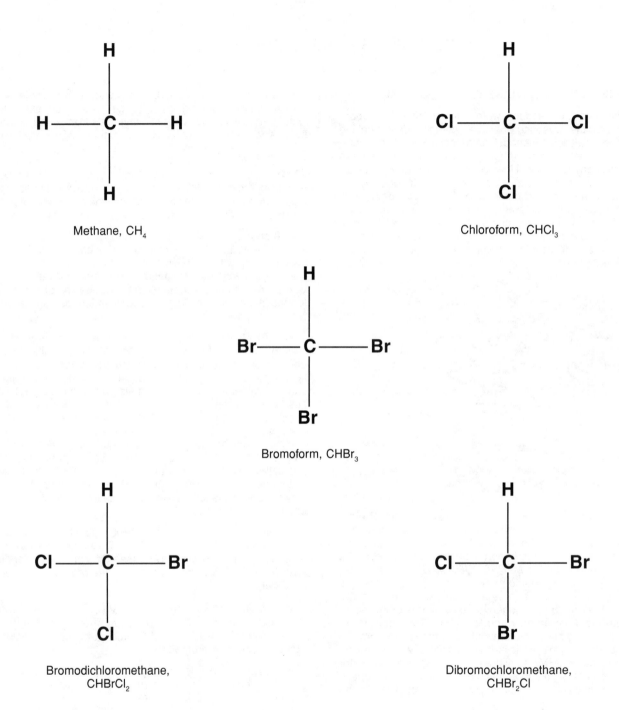

Methane, CH$_4$

Chloroform, CHCl$_3$

Bromoform, CHBr$_3$

Bromodichloromethane,
CHBrCl$_2$

Dibromochloromethane,
CHBr$_2$Cl

Fig. 15.1   Methane and THMs

ENSURING MICROBIOLOGICAL QUALITY: State or EPA must be notified of significant modifications to treatment processes to remove TTHMs in order to ensure microbiological quality of the treated water.

The MCL for TTHMs was not established on the basis of the health-effects data, but was set as a feasible level for compliance. The supporting material for the regulation states very clearly that the MCL may be lowered in the future to 0.025 mg/L or perhaps as low as 0.010 mg/L.

The rest of this chapter is devoted to a discussion of how to collect samples for THM analysis and how a utility can evaluate the many alternatives available to control THMs in its system. This discussion is presented in outline form. A much more detailed treatment of control techniques for THMs is presented in an EPA publication entitled *TREATMENT TECHNIQUES FOR CONTROLLING TRIHALOMETHANES IN DRINKING WATER*, by J. M. Symons, et al., September 1981.[2] A large part of this chapter is a summary of material from that source.

QUESTIONS

Write your answers in a notebook and then compare your answers with those on page 141.

15.0A   How are trihalomethanes formed?

15.0B   What are THM precursors?

15.0C   Why is free chlorine added to drinking water?

15.0D   What is one source for bromide in drinking water?

15.1 FEASIBILITY ANALYSIS PROCESS

In any problem-solving process, it is useful to follow a series of prescribed steps that will lead you to the most cost-effective solution. Table 15.1 lists the stages of a feasibility analysis process that has been used to solve a water utility's THM problem. However, the process outlined in Table 15.1 is very general and can also be applied to solving other treatment or operational problems.

TABLE 15.1 FEASIBILITY ANALYSIS PROCESS

1. Determine extent of THM problem
   a. Monitor THM levels
   b. THM chemistry (time of formation)
2. Evaluate control strategies
   a. Change sources of supply
   b. Treatment options
      (1) Remove THMs
      (2) Remove precursors
      (3) Adjust or modify the chlorine application points
      (4) Use alternative disinfectants
3. Evaluate existing treatment processes
4. Examine studies of proposed treatment processes (Bench-, pilot- and full-scale)
5. Select a cost-effective option
6. Implement the chosen option

15.2 PROBLEM DEFINITION

In order to determine the extent of a THM problem in a system, a reliable analytical technique must be used. THM analytical services may be developed by the utility or may be purchased from a contract laboratory. A discussion of the THM analytical methods will not be made here; rather, the reader is referred to the *FEDERAL REGISTER* publication of the regulation or to the EPA document prepared by J. M. Symons which was previously discussed.

15.20 Sampling

To determine the extent of the THM problem, collect *REPRESENTATIVE SAMPLES*[3] from the distribution system of the water utility and analyze them according to an approved method to determine if the utility is in compliance with the THM regulation. Of course, four quarters of data are needed to make a definite judgment on the MCL. However, even one quarter of data can show how close the system will be to complying with the MCL. See Section 15.21, "THM Calculations," Examples 1 and 2, for procedures on how to calculate quarterly average TTHM levels and annual TTHM running averages.

To collect samples to determine THM levels, use the following procedures:

1. A minimum of four samples per quarter (every three months) must be taken on the same day for each treatment plant in the distribution system.

2. Twenty-five percent of these samples must be collected from the extremities of the distribution system (the points farthest from each treatment plant), and

3. Seventy-five percent of all the four samples must be representative of the population served by the distribution system.

---

[2] *Available from Order Department, National Technical Information Service, 5285 Port Royal Road, Springfield, VA 22161. Order No. PB82-163197. Price, $61.50, plus, $4.00 shipping and handling.*

[3] *Representative Sample. A sample portion of material or water that is as nearly identical in content and consistency as possible to that in the larger body of material or water being sampled.*

Do not collect samples from swivel faucets, faucets with aerators, or faucets with hoses because of the possibility of contaminating the sample or loss of THMs.

To collect samples for THM analysis, use a narrow-mouth, screw-cap, glass sample bottle that can hold at least 25 mL of water. Use a polytetrafluoroethylene (PTFE)-faced silicon-septia bottle-cap liner to provide an airtight seal over the sample bottle. The bottle caps must screw tightly on the sample bottles.

Some sample bottles will contain a small amount of a chemical reducing agent (usually sodium thiosulfate or sodium sulfite). The reducing agent will stop the chemical reaction that occurs between chlorine and the THM precursors (humic and fluvic acids). By stopping this chemical reaction, THMs will not continue to form in the sample after it has been collected from the distribution system. When using sample bottles that contain a reducing agent, do not rinse out the reducing agent before collecting the sample.

Some sample bottles will not contain a reducing agent. Water samples from these bottles will be tested for the maximum concentration of TTHMs that can form over an extended period of time. These tests cannot be performed if a reducing agent has been added to the sample. When using sample bottles that do not contain a reducing agent, do not add any chemicals to the bottles.

When collecting water samples for THM analysis, use the following procedures:

1. Turn on the sampling tap,

2. Allow sufficient time (about five minutes) for the water temperature to become constant,

3. Fill the sample bottle until it begins to overflow,

4. Set the bottle on a level surface and place the bottle-cap liner on top of the bottle,

5. Screw the bottle cap tightly on the bottle and turn the bottle upside down,

6. The sample is properly sealed if no air bubbles are present, and

7. If air bubbles are present, remove the bottle cap and bottle-cap liner, turn on the sampling tap and add a small amount of water to the sample in the bottle. Repeat steps 4 through 6.

A good practice is to collect two samples at each location. This procedure allows the laboratory to double-check test results and, if a sample bottle is broken, there will be another sample available for testing.

Each sample bottle must include a label on which important information is recorded. Be sure to write on the label the sample location, date, and name of person collecting the sample.

Samples should be sent to the laboratory immediately after they are collected and should be analyzed within 14 days. When sending samples to the lab, be sure to include the complete name and address of the person to whom the test results are to be returned. Samples do not have to be refrigerated during storage. Do not use dry ice when shipping or storing samples because the water in the bottles may freeze and break the sample bottles.

15.21 THM Calculations

FORMULAS

In order to calculate the average of a group of measurements, sum up the measurements and divide the total by the number of measurements.

$$\text{Average} = \frac{\text{Sum of Measurements}}{\text{Number of Measurements}}$$

To calculate the running annual average, sum up the average measurements for each quarter and divide the total by the number of quarters.

$$\text{Running Average} = \frac{\text{Sum of Averages for Each Quarter}}{\text{Number of Quarters}}$$

Whenever data for a new quarter become available, the newest quarterly average replaces the oldest quarterly average and the running annual average is recalculated.

EXAMPLE 1

A water utility collected and analyzed eight samples from a water distribution system on the same day for TTHMs. The results are shown below.

Sample No.	1	2	3	4	5	6	7	8
TTHM, µg/L	80	50	70	110	90	120	80	90

What was the average TTHM for the day?

Known	**Unknown**
Results from analyses of 8 TTHM samples	Average TTHM level for the day

Calculate the average TTHM level in micrograms per liter.

$$\text{Avg TTHM, µg/L} = \frac{\text{Sum of Measurements, µg/L}}{\text{Number of Measurements}}$$

$$= \frac{\begin{array}{c} 80 \text{ µg/L} + 50 \text{ µg/L} + 70 \text{ µg/L} + 110 \text{ µg/L} \\ + 90 \text{ µg/L} + 120 \text{ µg/L} + 80 \text{ µg/L} + 90 \text{ µg/L} \end{array}}{8 \text{ Measurements}}$$

$$= \frac{690 \text{ µg/L}}{8}$$

$$= 86 \text{ µg/L}$$

EXAMPLE 2

The results of the quarterly average TTHM measurements for two years are given below. Calculate the running annual average of the four quarterly measurements in micrograms per liter.

Quarter	1	2	3	4	1	2	3	4
Avg Quarterly TTHM, µg/L	87	72	99	82	62	111	138	89

Known	**Unknown**
Results from analyses of 2 years of TTHM samples	Running annual average of quarterly TTHM measurements

Calculate the running annual average of the quarterly TTHM measurements.

$$\text{Annual Running TTHM Average, µg/L} = \frac{\text{Sum of Avg TTHM for Four Quarters}}{\text{Number of Quarters}}$$

Quarters 1, 2, 3, and 4

$$\text{Annual Running TTHM Average, µg/L} = \frac{87 \text{ µg/L} + 72 \text{ µg/L} + 99 \text{ µg/L} + 82 \text{ µg/L}}{4}$$

$$= \frac{340 \text{ µg/L}}{4}$$

$$= 85 \text{ µg/L}$$

Quarters 2, 3, 4, and 1

$$\text{Annual Running TTHM Average, µg/L} = \frac{72 \text{ µg/L} + 99 \text{ µg/L} + 82 \text{ µg/L} + 62 \text{ µg/L}}{4}$$

$$= \frac{315 \text{ µg/L}}{4}$$

$$= 79 \text{ µg/L}$$

Quarters 3, 4, 1, and 2

$$\text{Annual Running TTHM Average, µg/L} = \frac{99 \text{ µg/L} + 82 \text{ µg/L} + 62 \text{ µg/L} + 111 \text{ µg/L}}{4}$$

$$= \frac{354 \text{ µg/L}}{4}$$

$$= 89 \text{ µg/L}$$

Quarters 4, 1, 2, and 3

$$\text{Annual Running TTHM Average, µg/L} = \frac{82 \text{ µg/L} + 62 \text{ µg/L} + 111 \text{ µg/L} + 138 \text{ µg/L}}{4}$$

$$= \frac{393 \text{ µg/L}}{4}$$

$$= 98 \text{ µg/L}$$

Quarters 1, 2, 3, and 4

$$\text{Annual Running TTHM Average, µg/L} = \frac{62 \text{ µg/L} + 111 \text{ µg/L} + 138 \text{ µg/L} + 89 \text{ µg/L}}{4}$$

$$= \frac{400 \text{ µg/L}}{4}$$

$$= 100 \text{ µg/L}$$

SUMMARY OF RESULTS

Quarter	1	2	3	4	1	2	3	4
Avg Quarterly TTHM, µg/L	87	72	99	82	62	111	138	89
Annual Running TTHM Avg, µg/L					85	79	89	98	100

15.22 Chemistry of THM Formation

An understanding of the chemistry of THM formation is crucial if a water utility is to solve a THM problem. Equation 1 shown in Section 15.0, "The Trihalomethane (THM) Problem," describes the overall mechanism. Very little is known about the specific reactions that free chlorine and natural organics (precursors) undergo. In general, the effects of time, temperature, pH, and concentrations of the chemicals on the production of THMs have been studied by various investigators and are fairly well understood.

Depending on the type of natural organics present in the water, the time it takes for 0.10 mg/L (100 µg/L) of THMs to form may range from minutes to days. Set up a THM monitoring program on the source water(s) of the utility to measure the production of THMs over an appropriate time period (time from when chlorine is first added to water until water is consumed). A plot of the THMs produced against time will give you an idea of the TTHM (Total Trihalomethanes) formation potential (TTHMFP) of each source water. For many systems, a large part of the production of THMs will take place after the water leaves the treatment plant.

The higher the temperature, the faster the THMs will be produced. As might be expected, a dependence on temperature will probably show up as a seasonal effect — higher THM levels in the summer than in the winter. Temperature may not be the only controlling factor, however; higher THM levels may show up in the winter, as they have in California.

The higher the pH of the water, the faster the production of THMs. For most water utilities this will not be a concern; however, utilities raising the pH of treated water by caustic soda or by lime for corrosion control (Langelier Index) or using lime softening should be aware that free chlorine in contact with natural organics at a pH of 10.5 or higher will produce THMs much faster than if the pH was near 7.0.

The higher the concentrations of free chlorine and natural organics in the water, the more THMs will be produced. In the past, the amount of free chlorine that utilities used was only limited by economics and possible taste and odor complaints from consumers. Careful use of chlorine may help a utility to lower the THMs in its system. However, because of the danger of using too little chlorine (inadequate disinfection) in a system, the THM regulation specifically requires state or EPA approval of major treatment changes to meet the regulation.

The concentration of precursors in water is as important as the types of precursors that are found in water. Some naturally occurring organic compounds can produce 10 or 100 times more THMs on an equivalent basis than organics from another source. Also, some types of precursors will produce THMs faster than others. For these reasons it is important to evaluate the TTHMFP of each source of supply as a possible THM control measure.

The effect of higher bromide concentrations on THM production is not as clear as the effects of temperature and pH.

The more bromide present, the more bromide-containing THMs will be formed. Free chlorine selectively attacks the bromide ion and changes it to bromine, which reacts quickly with precursors to form bromoform, dibromochloromethane, and bromodichloromethane. The usual result of high bromide levels is higher THM levels because the higher molecular weights of these compounds mean more molecules are available for these chemical reactions.

Now that some of the basics of THM chemistry are understood and a THM problem can be properly defined, it is time to look at some of the possible control strategies.

QUESTIONS

Write your answers in a notebook and then compare your answers with those on page 141.

15.1A   List the major steps that a water utility could take to solve a THM problem.

15.1B   List the possible control strategies that could be evaluated to control a THM problem.

15.2A   What important factors influence the production of trihalomethanes?

15.2B   How does lime used for softening influence the production of THMs?

15.3   CONTROL STRATEGIES

Assuming that a utility discovers a THM problem in its system, there are two ways to control it: change the source of supply or provide some type of treatment. Changing the source of supply can consist of an entire range of alternatives such as shifting between wells of different water quality, drawing water from different levels in a reservoir, or abandoning a surface water supply altogether during part of the year. Since most utilities do not have the flexibility to abandon a source of supply, this alternative will have limited application.

The three treatment options available to control THMs are as follows:

1. Remove THMs after they are formed,

2. Remove THM precursors before chlorine is added, and

3. Use a disinfectant other than free chlorine.

A later section will examine each of these options and the processes associated with them. At this point it is useful to discuss overall treatment strategies. The general equation for forming THMs illustrates how each of the three options can work.

EQUATION 1

$$\text{Free Chlorine} + \begin{array}{c}\text{Natural}\\\text{Organics}\\\text{(precursor)}\end{array} + \text{Bromide} \rightarrow \text{THMs} + \begin{array}{c}\text{Other}\\\text{Products}\end{array}$$

Removing THMs after they are formed is generally not the strategy of choice unless there is a particular circumstance at the utility that warrants its evaluation. Since precursors are not necessarily removed when THMs are removed, there is the problem of continued THM formation, especially in the distribution system.

Removing precursors before free chlorine is added has some major advantages, particularly if the precursors can be removed by a fairly inexpensive process. Also, removing precursors allows the continued use of free chlorine as a disinfectant, which has been proven to be an effective barrier against disease for many decades. As Equation 1 shows, fewer precursors also means the formation of fewer "other products." These other products consist of high-molecular-weight organic compounds that contain chlorine and bromine. The health significance of these other products is not known, but concern has been raised by regulatory agencies.

Using a disinfectant other than free chlorine has a number of advantages and disadvantages that must be evaluated case by case. Abandoning free chlorine is a serious move in view of its superior performance as a disinfectant. However, if any of the alternative disinfectants are lower cost alternatives, they must be given careful consideration.

15.4   EXISTING TREATMENT PROCESSES

Before beginning a complex, expensive research program, it is valuable to examine how well existing treatment processes can control the formation of THMs. The following sections cover the potential of individual processes for THM control; however, some generalizations can be made with regard to existing unit processes. Aeration unit processes are sometimes available in water treatment plants to control tastes and odors. The same process may show measurable removals of THMs after they are formed. Oxidation of tastes and odors with chlorine dioxide (ClO_2) and potassium permanganate are common unit processes available in water treatment plants. Chlorine dioxide does not form THMs. Permanganate sometimes can be used to oxidize THM precursors if they are affected by this kind of treatment.

Coagulation/sedimentation/filtration and softening processes can remove THM precursors depending on the types that are present in the water supply. Studies at many water treatment plants have revealed that a significant reduction of total organic carbon (TOC) in source water by chemical coagulation often shows very little effect on total trihalomethane (TTHM) formation (which is a disappointment). Powdered activated carbon and granular activated carbon used for taste and odor control can have a limited impact on the removal of both THMs and THM precursors.

QUESTIONS

Write your answers in a notebook and then compare your answers with those on page 141.

15.3A   If a utility discovers a THM problem, what are two ways to control the problem?

15.3B   Why is abandoning the use of free chlorine considered a serious move?

15.4A   List the water treatment processes that can be used to control THMs.

15.5 TREATMENT PROCESS RESEARCH STUDY RESULTS

15.50 Consider Options

There is a long list of treatment options that can be investigated for the control of THMs. Since a large number of them have already been studied and reported on, it is not necessary for every utility to repeat this work. A careful evaluation of the results published by the US EPA will help a utility focus on the treatment processes that should be looked at on a bench-, pilot-, or full-scale basis.

Most feasible treatment options include the removal of precursor materials prior to the formation of a THM, the avoidance of generation of a THM by use of an alternate disinfectant, or the actual removal of a THM by means of aeration or carbon adsorption. Also the geographic and climatological conditions can have a very important influence on the choice of the most desirable process. For example, aeration is not a desirable method of treatment where severe cold weather is common.

15.51 Remove THMs After They Are Formed

There are three treatment processes available to remove THMs after they have been formed:

1. Oxidation

    a. Ozone

    b. Chlorine dioxide

    c. Ozone/ultraviolet light

2. Aeration

    a. Open storage

    b. Diffused air

    c. Towers

3. Adsorption

    a. Powdered activated carbon

    b. Synthetic resins

OXIDATION. Oxidation of THMs using any one of the three oxidants listed above has not been very successful. The combination of ozone/ultraviolet light showed some promise; however, the cost-effectiveness of the process has yet to be demonstrated.

AERATION. In contrast, aeration is an effective process for removing THMs from water, although the individual THMs are removed at different efficiencies. THM removal efficiencies by

aeration, ranging from the easiest to most difficult, are from chloroform to bromodichloromethane to dibromochloromethane and to bromoform. Allowing water containing THMs to stand uncovered will ultimately result in the THMs leaving the water, since they are *VOLATILE*[4] compounds that are poorly soluble in water. In other words, THMs have a natural tendency to migrate from water into the atmosphere if given the chance. Because of this tendency, THM reductions may be noticeable in effluents from uncovered finished water reservoirs after a significant detention time (days).

More efficient removal of THMs can be accomplished if energy is put into the aeration process. A convenient way to put energy into aeration is by bubbling air into water. Many water treatment plants currently have an aeration process of some kind to help control tastes and odors in the source water. The efficiencies of these existing processes would not be expected to be very great for THM removal.

Operators should realize that aeration of treated water can cause a significant amount of contamination. Air in many areas may contain large amounts of dust, dirt, bacteria, and other pollutants which can contaminate treated water and also lead to operation and maintenance problems.

In the research results that are currently available, countercurrent tower aeration (Figure 15.2) has produced the highest removals of THMs with air-to-water ratios (the ratio of the volume of air added to the volume of water treated) in the 20 to 1 to 50 to 1 range. Treatment efficiencies greater than 90 percent removal have been demonstrated with some aeration towers on some types of water.

Countercurrent aeration towers are designed so that the water and air pass over a packing material countercurrent to each other (in opposite directions). A significant amount of theoretical work has been done on the possible tower designs for any given set of treatment conditions. Pilot-scale testing is usually recommended before a full-scale plant is constructed.

Aeration is most effective on the more volatile chemicals. Chloroform is the most volatile of the THMs and is generally the most easily removed by aeration. Bromoform, on the other hand, is the least volatile THM and consequently is the hardest to remove by aeration. If the TTHM content of the water contains a significant amount of bromoform, aeration may not be the most desirable technique to investigate.

ADSORPTION. THMs can be removed by a wide variety of activated carbons and synthetic resins. The adsorption process involves the individual THM compounds leaving the water and becoming attached to the surface of the carbon or resin. THMs are generally considered difficult to adsorb on any surface. The efficiency by adsorption from easiest to most difficult is bromoform, dibromochloromethane, bromodichloromethane, and chloroform.

Powdered activated carbon (PAC) is usually added as a treatment chemical in the rapid-mix process or in the sedimentation basin effluent. PAC is normally used in water treatment for taste and odor control at dosages of less than 20 mg/L. Studies have shown that PAC dosages of 100 mg/L or more

---

[4] *Volatile (VOL-uh-tull). (1) A volatile substance is one that is capable of being evaporated or changed to a vapor at relatively low temperatures. Volatile substances also can be partially removed by air stripping. (2) In terms of solids analysis, volatile refers to materials lost (including most organic matter) upon ignition in a muffle furnace for 60 minutes at 550°C. Natural volatile materials are chemical substances usually of animal or plant origin. Manufactured or synthetic volatile materials such as ether, acetone, and carbon tetrachloride are highly volatile and not of plant or animal origin.*

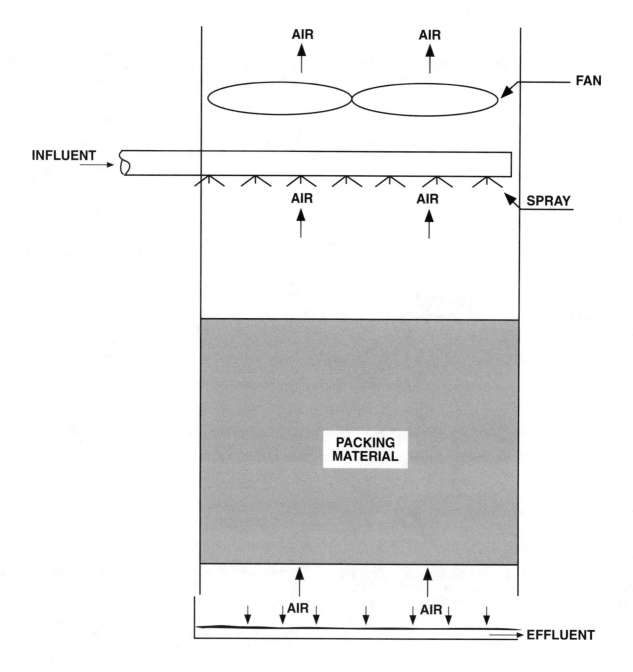

Fig. 15.2   Countercurrent aeration tower

are necessary to get significant removals of THMs. Chloroform is particularly difficult to remove with PAC.

Synthetic resins such as XE-340 have been demonstrated to be effective in removing THMs from water; however, economics must be taken into consideration, since the cost of the resins is high in comparison with other alternatives. Regeneration of the resins has not been worked out satisfactorily. Pilot-scale studies show some promise, but full-scale applications are not available.

QUESTIONS

Write your answers in a notebook and then compare your answers with those on page 141.

15.5A Which is the better process for removing THMs after they are formed, oxidation or aeration?

15.5B How does the storage of water in uncovered reservoirs affect THM levels?

15.5C How does the adsorption process work?

15.52 Remove THM Precursors

A variety of treatment processes have been investigated to remove THM precursors before they come in contact with chlorine. These include:

1. Aeration

2. Oxidation

    a. Ozone

    b. Chlorine dioxide

    c. Permanganate

    d. Ozone/ultraviolet light

    e. Hydrogen peroxide

3. Clarification

    a. Coagulation/sedimentation/filtration

    b. Softening

4. Adsorption

    a. Powdered activated carbon

    b. Granular activated carbon

    c. Synthetic resins

5. Ion Exchange

AERATION. Since THM precursors are not volatile compounds, it is not surprising that aeration is ineffective in removing them from water.

OXIDATION. All of the oxidants listed above have some effect on removing or modifying THM precursors. Since THM precursors vary so much between locations, it is difficult to generalize on the effectiveness of any of the oxidants. In fact, some studies have demonstrated that the formation potential for THMs can *INCREASE* with the application of certain dosages of ozone and potassium permanganate. In general, it is necessary to perform bench- and/or pilot-scale studies on the water in question before the usefulness of any of these oxidants can be considered. The US EPA is also concerned with the production of potentially harmful by-products that could result from the use of any of these oxidants. Once again, studies on the water to be treated are necessary to determine whether or not this is a problem.

In the southeastern United States and in other locations, water supplies are relatively warm and contain high levels of organic matter. Under these conditions, controlled oxidation with small doses of ozone can actually coagulate organic material and make conventional sedimentation more effective. Too much ozone can break the organics down and make them more reactive with chlorine. However, small controlled doses of ozone may be an effective microflocculant and may be added to conventional water treatment plants to improve the physical removal of THM precursors to the point that prechlorination disinfection is possible.

CLARIFICATION. The clarification process used in water treatment plants has the potential for removing significant amounts of THM precursors. Dozens of studies by the US EPA have demonstrated widely varying removal efficiencies (0 to 100 percent) because of the highly variable nature of THM precursors from place to place. The use of this process, which is available in most water treatment plants, to remove THM precursors holds great promise for an economical solution to any THM problem. Moving the addition of free chlorine to a point following the clarification process is the key to success for this approach. Many water utilities have adopted this approach to solve their problem.

ADSORPTION. The use of powdered activated carbon (PAC) and granular activated carbon (GAC) are effective in removing THM precursors; however, the economics of these processes must be carefully evaluated. Dozens of studies have reported a wide variety of THM precursor removal efficiencies. Because of the high cost of PAC and GAC, their use as THM control methods will be restricted to those cases where no other alternatives are available. Synthetic resins showed limited removal potential for THM precursors. Effective regeneration of the resins for additional precursor removal has not been demonstrated.

ION EXCHANGE. Anion exchange resins can be effective for removing THM precursors, which generally have a negative charge. Both strong-base and weak-base anion exchange resins have been investigated. As with the activated carbons discussed above, anion exchange resins will only find a role in controlling THMs if the economics of the treatment process for a particular site are favorable. Disposal of the spent regenerant liquid may be a problem.

QUESTIONS

Write your answers in a notebook and then compare your answers with those on page 141.

15.5D List the major treatment processes that have been investigated to remove THM precursors before they come in contact with chlorine.

15.5E What is the key to the success of using clarification to remove THM precursors from the water being treated?

15.53 Alternative Disinfectants

Removing free chlorine from the chlorine/bromide/precursor reaction will stop the formation of any significant amount of THMs. However, free chlorine has been an effective barrier between people and disease-causing bacteria since the beginning of this century, and abandoning its use is a very serious step. There are other disinfectants that can be used instead of free chlorine, but the advantages and disadvantages of each alternative must be carefully evaluated.

The most commonly considered alternative disinfectants are ozone, chlorine dioxide, and chloramines. Ozone is a gas that is produced by passing oxygen through an electrical discharge. While ozone is a highly effective disinfectant, it is very expensive, it must be generated on site, and it does not leave a residual in the treated water. Chlorine dioxide is a gas produced by the reaction of free chlorine and sodium chlorite. Chlorine dioxide is a very effective disinfectant which does leave a residual in the treated water; however, there are some concerns regarding the health implications of the inorganic breakdown products, chlorite and chlorate. The THM regulation recommended a 0.5 mg/L limit for the total concentration of chlorine dioxide, chlorite, and chlorate in water after chlorine-dioxide treatment.

Chloramines are produced in water by the reaction between free chlorine and ammonia. Chloramines are weaker disinfectants than free chlorine, ozone, or chlorine dioxide, but the residuals remain much longer than free chlorine and they have been used successfully by dozens of water utilities. For example, the City of Denver has used chloramines for many years. The effectiveness of monochloramines as a disinfectant depends on water temperature, pH, and biological quality, as well as the proper ratio of ammonia to chlorine.

The use of chloramines can also cause problems in a utility's system unless proper precautions are taken. Chloramines must be removed from the water before it is used in kidney dialysis machines. Chloramines in water can pass through kidney dialysis machines and into a patient's blood where the ammonia will decrease the oxygen-carrying capacity of the blood. In addition, chloramines are toxic to fish in home aquariums, and they must be removed from water before it comes in contact with fish. Dechlorination of water with activated carbon, ascorbic acid, or sodium thiosulfate will prevent any of these problems if the removal of chloramines is properly controlled. Any oxidants that are present in drinking water can cause problems with kidney dialysis machines and fish in home aquariums. However, chloramines are somewhat more difficult to remove than the other alternative disinfectants.

Before an alternative disinfectant is applied to any system, the source of the water supply, water quality, and treatment effectiveness for bacteriological control must be evaluated. For example, the use of a weaker disinfectant such as chloramines may not be appropriate for a surface water supply that is highly contaminated with discharges from municipal and industrial wastewater treatment plants unless an extra high dosage and a long contact time are provided. Also, many of the conventional water treatment processes are capable of removing bacteria, viruses, and protozoa from the water (for example, softening and coagulation/sedimentation/filtration). These conventional processes may help to provide the required disinfection barrier between a contaminated supply and the population served, which could allow the use of a less potent disinfectant in the distribution system.

Upgraded monitoring of the distribution system before and after a disinfectant change must be provided by the utility. The THM regulation specifies guidelines that the states must use in establishing such a monitoring program. Guidelines describing coliforms, standard plate count, turbidity, and nutrients are included in the suggested monitoring list. With "before and after" monitoring by the water utility, it will be possible to determine if there is any significant degradation of the bacteriological quality in the distribution system. Control of THMs must not be accomplished at the expense of a higher risk of bacterial and viral diseases among the population that is being served. Therefore, a decision to use a disinfectant other than free chlorine must be based on a carefully considered plan. A utility that rushes into the use of an alternative disinfectant without the required studies is likely to experience many problems that are easily avoided with proper planning.

QUESTIONS

Write your answers in a notebook and then compare your answers with those on page 141.

15.5F   What items must be considered before an alternative disinfectant is applied to any system?

15.5G   What type of distribution system monitoring must be provided by a utility before and after a disinfectant change?

15.5H   What water quality indicators should be monitored before and after a disinfectant change?

15.6 SELECTION AND IMPLEMENTATION OF A COST-EFFECTIVE ALTERNATIVE

A detailed evaluation of the comparative economics of the many treatment processes described above is outside the scope of this chapter. In many cases, a utility will commission a special cost-effectiveness study that will be accomplished in-house or by an outside consultant. The US EPA THM treatment manual presents a detailed look at cost estimates for various alternatives with equivalent THM control levels. However, these data are not current and should be updated to reflect current economic conditions whenever cost studies are conducted.

If existing processes are not capable of solving a utility's THM problem, the least-cost solution will probably be an alternative disinfectant. While no statistics are currently available, evidence from discussions with consultants and utility managers suggests that alternative disinfectants, especially chloramines, are the overwhelming least-cost solution for water utilities with a THM problem. However, the use of chloramines may cause problems for persons using kidney dialysis machines.

Implementation of a THM control strategy requires a number of well-defined steps:

1. Full-scale design,

2. Construction,

3. Start-up, and

4. Operation.

The length of time required to complete these steps will depend on the complexity of the control strategy chosen and the availability of engineering services to complete the assigned tasks. Throughout the implementation phase, it is important that the bench-, pilot-, and full-scale tests initiated in the feasibility analysis phase be continued so that the chosen strategy can be refined and optimized. For example, a pilot plant can be used to train treatment plant operators to use the new technology that will soon be on line.

QUESTIONS

Write your answers in a notebook and then compare your answers with those on pages 141 and 142.

15.6A   If existing water treatment processes are not capable of solving a THM problem, what is the most likely least-cost solution?

15.6B   What appears to be the most popular alternative disinfectant?

15.7 REGULATORY UPDATE

On February 28, 1983, the US EPA published in the *FEDERAL REGISTER* (page 8406) an amendment to the THM regulation originally published on November 29, 1979. The amendment specifies the treatment alternatives that a utility must consider or investigate in detail before it can apply for and receive a variance from meeting the MCL as defined under the regulation. The U.S. Environmental Protection Agency or the state may require a community water system to use a "generally available" technology before granting a variance. "Generally available" (or Group 1) treatment techniques are:

1. Use of chloramines or chlorine dioxide as an alternative or supplement to chlorine for oxidation and disinfection,

2. Use of chloramines, chlorine dioxide, or potassium permanganate as an alternative to chlorine for preoxidation,

3. Moving the point of chlorination in order to reduce THM formation,

4. Improvement of existing clarification, and

5. Use of powdered activated carbon (PAC), intermittently as necessary, to reduce TTHM or THM precursors. The dosage of PAC is not to exceed an annual average of 10 mg/L.

Any of these technologies may be required in the variance unless the regulatory agency, US EPA, or the state determines that "such treatment method ... is not available and

effective for TTHM control for the system." The rule allows exemption from the use of a technique if the method would not be technically appropriate and technically feasible for the system or if the method would result in only a marginal reduction in TTHM.

The rule also allows the regulator to require the study of Group 2 technologies by water systems where Group 1 technologies are not appropriate or sufficient in meeting the MCL. If a Group 2 technology would be technically feasible and economically reasonable and result in significant TTHM reductions in line with the cost of treatment, then the regulator can require the use of a Group 2 technology.

The listed Group 2 technologies are introduction of off-line water storage, aeration, introduction of clarification, alternative sources of raw water, and the use of ozone as an alternative or supplement to chlorine for disinfection or oxidation.

The February 28, 1983, amendment to the THM regulations does not mention granular activated carbon (GAC) or biological activated carbon (BAC) as treatment alternatives that must be considered. These two treatment methods were judged to be too expensive and are not widely enough used in the U.S. to warrant their evaluation for THM control. In general, the amendment is designed to reduce the economic impact of the THM regulation on those utilities that have THM problems and limited resources to drastically modify their treatment procedures.

EPA is expected to further regulate not only THMs but also other disinfection by-products. These products might include halonitriles, halogenated acids, alcohols, aldehydes, and ketones. EPA intends to limit the disinfectant residual concentration as well as the levels of disinfection by-products. The goal is a balance between projected microbiological and chemical risks. Interim regulations are expected by November, 1998.

Utilities that may be affected by THM regulations are advised to follow future developments in the *FEDERAL REGISTER*. Also, see Chapter 22, Section 22.24, "Information Collection Rule (ICR)."

15.8 SUMMARY AND CONCLUSIONS

1. Trihalomethanes are produced when free chlorine, which is added as a disinfectant, reacts with naturally occurring bromide and organic compounds.

2. A trihalomethane regulation is now in effect which has established a 0.10 mg/L maximum contaminant level and monitoring requirements.

3. A feasibility analysis process is a series of logical steps to arrive at a cost-effective solution to a THM problem:

   1. Determine the extent of THM problem

      a. Monitor

      b. Examine THM chemistry

2. Evaluate control strategies

   a. Change sources of supply

   b. Treatment options

     (1) Remove THMs

     (2) Remove precursors

     (3) Use alternative disinfectants

3. Evaluate existing treatment processes

4. Research studies of treatment processes

   a. Bench-, pilot-, and full-scale

5. Select a cost-effective option

6. Implement chosen option

4. There are three treatment options available to control THMs:

  1. Remove THMs after they are formed,

  2. Remove THM precursors before chlorine is added, and

  3. Use a disinfectant other than free chlorine.

5. A water utility must not create a possible health problem by ignoring bacteriological safeguards in an attempt to solve a THM problem.

6. An amendment to the THM regulation specifies treatment techniques that must be evaluated before a utility may receive a variance. Since this amendment affects a utility's feasibility analysis procedure, the steps outlined in the amendment should be followed.

QUESTIONS

Write your answers in a notebook and then compare your answers with those on page 142.

15.7A   What treatment processes must utilities evaluate before applying for and receiving a variance?

15.7B   If treatment processes are not technically feasible nor economically reasonable, then what should utilities consider?

15.9   ARITHMETIC ASSIGNMENT

Turn to the Appendix at the back of this manual and read Section A.33, "Trihalomethanes." Work all of the problems on your pocket calculator. You should be able to get the same answers.

15.10   ADDITIONAL READING

1. *TREATMENT TECHNIQUES FOR CONTROLLING TRIHALOMETHANES IN DRINKING WATER* by James M. Symons, Alan S. Stevens, Robert M. Clark, Edwin E. Geldreich, O. Thomas Love, Jr., and Jack DeMarco. Drinking Water Research Division, Municipal Environmental Research Laboratory, Office of Research and Development, U.S. Environmental Protection Agency, Cincinnati, OH 45268. EPA-600/2-81-156, September 1981. Available from Order Department, National Technical Information Service, 5285 Port Royal Road, Springfield, VA 22161. Order No. PB82-163197. Price, $61.50, plus $4.00 shipping and handling.

Please answer the discussion and review questions before continuing with the Objective Test.

DISCUSSION AND REVIEW QUESTIONS

Chapter 15.   TRIHALOMETHANES

Write the answers to these questions in your notebook before continuing with the Objective Test on page 142. The purpose of these questions is to indicate to you how well you understand the material in the chapter.

1. How are trihalomethanes formed in drinking water?

2. On what basis was the Maximum Contaminant Level (MCL) for total trihalomethanes (TTHMs) established?

3. What is the influence of higher temperatures and pH on the production of trihalomethanes (THMs)?

4. What are some of the options if a water utility decides to investigate changing the source of the water supply?

5. What are the advantages of removing precursors before free chlorine is added?

6. Why might ozone be used prior to clarification and filtration?

7. List the three alternative disinfectants to free chlorine and the advantages and limitations to each one.

8. What items must be considered before an alternative disinfectant is applied to any system?

9. What are the advantages of using a pilot plant in the implementation of a THM control strategy?

SUGGESTED ANSWERS

Chapter 15. TRIHALOMETHANES

Answers to questions on page 131.

15.0A Trihalomethanes are formed by the reactions of natural organic compounds with halogens (such as chlorine).

15.0B THM precursors are defined as natural organic compounds found in all surface and groundwaters. These compounds *MAY* react with halogens (such as chlorine) to form trihalomethanes (THMs); they *MUST* be present in order for THMs to form.

15.0C Free chlorine is added to drinking water as a disinfectant.

15.0D One source of bromide is seawater.

Answers to questions on page 134.

15.1A The major steps that a water utility could take to solve a THM problem include

1. Determine extent of THM problem,
2. Evaluate control strategies,
3. Evaluate existing treatment processes,
4. Examine research studies of treatment processes,
5. Select most cost-effective option, and
6. Implement selected option.

15.1B Control strategies that could be evaluated to control a THM problem include:

1. Change sources of supply, and
2. Treatment options
   (a) Remove THMs,
   (b) Remove precursors,
   (c) Adjust or modify the chlorine application points, and
   (d) Use alternative disinfectants.

15.2A Important factors that influence the production of trihalomethanes include the effects of time, temperature, pH, and the types and concentrations of chemicals.

15.2B Those utilities that use lime softening should be aware that free chlorine in contact with natural organics at a pH of 10.5 or higher will produce THMs faster than if the pH was near 7.0.

Answers to questions on page 134.

15.3A The two methods of controlling a THM problem are (1) change the source of supply or (2) provide some type of treatment.

15.3B Abandoning the use of free chlorine is a serious move in view of its superior performance as a disinfectant.

15.4A Water treatment processes that can be used to control THMs include:

1. Aeration,
2. Oxidation with chlorine dioxide and/or potassium permanganate,
3. Coagulation, sedimentation, and filtration,
4. Softening processes, and
5. Powdered activated carbon applications.

Answers to questions on page 137.

15.5A Aeration is a much more effective process than oxidation for removing THMs after they have been formed.

15.5B THM concentrations should be reduced in waters which have been stored in uncovered reservoirs because of loss to the atmosphere.

15.5C The adsorption process involves the individual THM compounds leaving the water and becoming attached to the surface of the carbon or resin.

Answers to questions on page 137.

15.5D The major treatment processes that have been investigated to remove THM precursors before they come in contact with chlorine include:

1. Aeration,
2. Oxidation (including ozone oxidation prior to coagulation and clarification),
3. Clarification,
4. Adsorption, and
5. Ion exchange.

15.5E Moving the addition of free chlorine to a point following the clarification process is the key to success when using clarification to remove THM precursors.

Answers to questions on page 138.

15.5F Before an alternative disinfectant is applied to any system, the source of the water supply, water quality, and treatment effectiveness for bacteriological control must be evaluated.

15.5G Upgraded monitoring (more samples and tests) of the distribution system before and after a disinfectant change must be provided by a utility.

15.5H Before and after a disinfectant change, the distribution system monitoring program should include coliforms, standard plate count, turbidity, and nutrients.

Answers to questions on page 139.

15.6A If existing water treatment processes are not capable of solving a THM problem, the least-cost solution will probably be an alternative disinfectant.

15.6B   Apparently the most popular alternative disinfectant is chloramines.

Answers to questions on page 140.

15.7A   Before applying for and receiving a variance, utilities must evaluate the following treatment processes:

1. Use of chloramines or chlorine dioxide as an alternative or supplement to chlorine for oxidation and disinfection,
2. Use of chloramines, chlorine dioxide, or potassium permanganate as an alternative to chlorine for preoxidation,
3. Moving the point of chlorination in order to reduce THM formation,

4. Improvement of existing clarification, and
5. Use of powdered activated carbon (PAC), intermittently as necessary, to reduce TTHM or THM precursors. The dosage of PAC is not to exceed an annual average of 10 mg/L.

15.7B   If treatment processes are not technically feasible or not economically reasonable, then utilities must consider:

1. Off-line storage for precursor reduction,
2. Aeration where appropriate,
3. Introduction of clarification where not practiced,
4. Alternative sources of raw water, and
5. Use of ozone as an alternative or supplement to chlorine for disinfection or oxidation.

OBJECTIVE TEST

Chapter 15.   TRIHALOMETHANES

Please write your name and mark the correct answers on the answer sheet, as directed at the end of Chapter 1. There may be more than one correct answer to each multiple-choice question.

True-False

1. Animal feeding experiments and population studies are definite proof that THMs in drinking water cause cancer.
   1. True
   2. False

2. The MCL for TTHMs was established on the basis of the health effects data.
   1. True
   2. False

3. Samples to be analyzed for THMs must be refrigerated during storage.
   1. True
   2. False

4. For many systems, a large part of the production of THMs will take place after the water leaves the treatment plant.
   1. True
   2. False

5. Chlorine dioxide forms THMs.
   1. True
   2. False

6. Cation exchange resins can be effective for removing THM precursors, which generally have a negative charge.
   1. True
   2. False

7. Removing free chlorine from the chlorine/bromide/precursor reaction will stop the formation of any significant amount of THMs.
   1. True
   2. False

8. A water utility must not create a possible health problem by ignoring bacteriological safeguards in an attempt to solve a THM problem.
   1. True
   2. False

9. The concentration of precursors in water is as important as the types of precursors that are found in water for the production of THMs.
   1. True
   2. False

10. Using oxidants to remove THMs after they are formed has been very successful.

    1. True
    2. False

Best Answer (Select only the closest or best answer.)

11. Trihalomethanes (THMs) are formed in drinking water when free chlorine comes in contact with what kinds of compounds?

    1. Naturally occurring inorganic compounds
    2. Naturally occurring organic compounds
    3. Synthetic organic compounds
    4. Synthetic volatile organic compounds (VOCs)

12. What are THM precursors?

    1. Natural inorganic compounds that may react with halogens (such as chlorine)
    2. Natural organic compounds that may react with halogens
    3. Synthetic inorganic compounds that may react with halogens
    4. Synthetic organic compounds that may react with halogens

13. Where should representative samples be collected to determine the extent of a THM problem?

    1. Clear well of treatment plant
    2. Distribution system
    3. Intake of treatment plant
    4. Source watershed

14. Why is a reducing agent added to THM sample bottles?

    1. Maintain a constant chlorine residual in the sample bottle
    2. Provide an airtight seal over the sample bottle
    3. Reduce natural organics in sample
    4. Stop formation of THMs after sample is collected

15. Why is removing THMs after they are formed NOT a strategy of choice?

    1. Effectiveness of disinfecting chemical will be reduced
    2. Removal of high concentrations of THMs cannot be achieved
    3. Strategy will allow for a continued chlorine demand
    4. THMs will continue to form in distribution systems

16. What must be evaluated before any disinfectant is applied to any system?

    1. Availability of chemical disinfectant
    2. Effectiveness for bacteriological control
    3. Log removal level of disinfectant
    4. Solubility of the disinfectant

Multiple Choice (Select all correct answers.)

17. What sources of organic materials dissolve in water to produce naturally occurring organics in water?

    1. Algae
    2. Bark
    3. Leaves
    4. Soil
    5. Wood

18. Where should samples be collected for THMs?

    1. Faucets with aerators
    2. Faucets with hoses
    3. Hose bibs
    4. Sampling taps
    5. Swivel faucets

19. What important factors influence the production of trihalomethanes?

    1. Concentration of chemicals
    2. Location of chlorine application
    3. pH of water
    4. Temperature of water
    5. Type of pipe material

20. How can a utility attempt to control a THM problem?

    1. Change source of supply
    2. Initiate a public education program
    3. Issue a boil water order
    4. Provide some type of treatment
    5. Suggest bottled water be used for drinking

21. What types of treatment processes are available to remove THMs after they are formed?

    1. Adsorption
    2. Aeration
    3. Clarification
    4. Filtration
    5. Oxidation

22. What treatment processes can be used to remove THM precursors?

    1. Adsorption
    2. Aeration
    3. Clarification
    4. Ion exchange
    5. Oxidation

23. What contaminants in air used for aeration cause contamination of treated water?

    1. Bacteria
    2. Chlorine
    3. Dirt
    4. Dust
    5. Ozone

24. What are the most commonly considered alternative disinfectants to free chlorine?

    1. Chloramines
    2. Chlorine dioxide
    3. Ozone
    4. Polyphosphate
    5. Potassium permanganate

25. Chloramines are a weaker disinfectant than what other disinfectants?

    1. Chlorine dioxide
    2. Free chlorine
    3. Ozone
    4. Permanganate
    5. Sodium chloride

26. How can water containing chloramines be dechlorinated?

    1. Activated carbon
    2. Ascorbic acid
    3. Hydrochloric acid
    4. Sodium chloride
    5. Sodium thiosulfate

27. What are the proper sampling procedures for analysis of THM levels?

    1. Collect at least four quarterly samples
    2. Refrigerate samples and analyze within 14 days
    3. Rinse sample bottles before use
    4. Seal bottles tightly with no air bubbles
    5. Use glass sample bottles

28. Which clarification process used in many water treatment plants can be an effective way to remove THM precursors?

    1. Dissolved air flotation
    2. Free chlorine is added before chlorination
    3. Hydroxide precipitation thickening
    4. Polyphosphates are used as a filter aid
    5. The addition of free chlorine following clarification

29. Which water quality indicators should be monitored in the distribution system before and after a disinfectant change?

    1. Chloride
    2. Coliforms
    3. Nutrients
    4. Standard plate count
    5. Turbidity

30. Results of the quarterly average TTHM measurements for five quarters are given below. What is the running annual average of quarterly TTHM measurements at the end of the period?

Quarter	1	2	3	4	5
Avg Quarterly TTHM, $\mu g/L$	70	61	87	58	74

    1. 56 $\mu g/L$
    2. 70 $\mu g/L$
    3. 71 $\mu g/L$
    4. 89 $\mu g/L$
    5. 95 $\mu g/L$

End of Objective Test

CHAPTER 16

DEMINERALIZATION

by

Dave Argo

Revised by

Warren Casey

TABLE OF CONTENTS

Chapter 16.   DEMINERALIZATION

(Removal of Dissolved Minerals by Membrane Processes)

Page

OBJECTIVES 148

WORDS 149

LESSON 1

16.0   SOURCES OF MINERALIZED WATERS 151

16.1   DEMINERALIZING PROCESSES 152

16.2   REVERSE OSMOSIS 152

    16.20   What Is Reverse Osmosis? 152

    16.21   Reverse Osmosis Membrane Structure and Composition 155

    16.22   Membrane Performance and Properties 155

    16.23   Definition of Flux 156

    16.24   Mineral Rejection 157

    16.25   Effects of Feedwater Temperature and pH on Membrane Performance 159

    16.26   Recovery 159

DISCUSSION AND REVIEW QUESTIONS 166

LESSON 2

16.3   COMPONENTS OF A REVERSE OSMOSIS UNIT 166

    16.30   Pressurization Pump 166

    16.31   Piping 166

    16.32   Pressure Vessel Housings 169

    16.33   Concentrate Control Valve 169

    16.34   Sample Valves 169

    16.35   Flush Connections 169

    16.36   Cleaning Connections 169

    16.37   Permeate Rinse 169

    16.38   Permeate Drawback Tank 169

    16.39   Energy Recovery Devices 169

    16.310   Membranes 169

16.4   OPERATION 172

    16.40   Pretreatment 172

    16.41   Removal of Turbidity and Suspended Solids 173

16.42   pH and Temperature Control 173

16.43   Other Potential Scalants 173

16.44   Microbiological Organisms 173

16.45   RO Plant Operation 174

16.46   Typical RO Plant Operations Checklist 174

16.47   Membrane Cleaning 178

16.48   Safety 179

    16.480   Use of Proper Procedures 179

    16.481   Chemical Safety 179

    16.482   Hydraulic Safety 179

    16.483   Electrical Safety 179

DISCUSSION AND REVIEW QUESTIONS 179

LESSON 3

16.5   ELECTRODIALYSIS 180

16.6   PRINCIPLES OF ELECTRODIALYSIS 181

16.60   Anions and Cations in Water 181

16.61   Effect of Direct Current (D.C.) Potential on Ions 181

16.62   Anion and Cation Membranes and Three-Cell Unit 181

16.63   Multi-Compartment Unit 183

16.7   PARTS OF AN ELECTRODIALYSIS UNIT 183

16.70   Flow Diagram 183

16.71   Pretreatment 183

16.72   Pumping Equipment and Piping 183

16.73   D.C. Power Supply 183

16.74   Membrane Stack 187

16.75   Chemical Flush System 187

16.8   ROUTINE OPERATING PROCEDURES 187

16.80   Design Specifications for Feedwater 187

16.81   Detailed Operating Procedures 187

16.9   SAFETY PRECAUTIONS 189

16.10   ARITHMETIC ASSIGNMENT 190

16.11   ADDITIONAL READING 190

DISCUSSION AND REVIEW QUESTIONS 190

SUGGESTED ANSWERS 191

OBJECTIVE TEST 193

OBJECTIVES

Chapter 16.   DEMINERALIZATION

Following completion of Chapter 16, you should be able to:

1. Describe the various demineralizing processes,

2. Explain how the reverse osmosis process works,

3. Operate and maintain a reverse osmosis demineralization plant,

4. Explain the principles of electrodialysis,

5. Identify and describe the parts of an electrodialysis plant,

6. Operate and maintain an electrodialysis plant, and

7. Safely perform your duties around reverse osmosis and electrodialysis plants.

DEE-MIN-er-al-uh-ZAY-shun

WORDS

Chapter 16. DEMINERALIZATION

atm   atm

The abbreviation for atmosphere. One atmosphere is equal to 14.7 psi or 100 kPa.

ANGSTROM (ANG-strem)   ANGSTROM

A unit of length equal to one-tenth of a nanometer or one-tenbillionth of a meter (1 Angstrom = 0.000 000 000 1 meter). One Angstrom is the approximate diameter of an atom.

CHELATION (key-LAY-shun)   CHELATION

A chemical complexing (forming or joining together) of metallic cations (such as copper) with certain organic compounds, such as EDTA (ethylene diamine tetracetic acid). Chelation is used to prevent the precipitation of metals (copper). Also see SEQUESTRATION.

COLLOIDS (CALL-loids)   COLLOIDS

Very small, finely divided solids (particles that do not dissolve) that remain dispersed in a liquid for a long time due to their small size and electrical charge. When most of the particles in water have a negative electrical charge, they tend to repel each other. This repulsion prevents the particles from clumping together, becoming heavier, and settling out.

CONCENTRATION POLARIZATION   CONCENTRATION POLARIZATION

(1) A buildup of retained particles on the membrane surface due to dewatering of the feed closest to the membrane. The thickness of the concentration polarization layer is controlled by the flow velocity across the membrane.

(2) Used in corrosion studies to indicate a depletion of ions near an electrode.

(3) The basis for chemical analysis by a polarograph.

CONDUCTANCE   CONDUCTANCE

A rapid method of estimating the dissolved solids content of a water supply. The measurement indicates the capacity of a sample of water to carry an electric current, which is related to the concentration of ionized substances in the water. Also call SPECIFIC CONDUCTANCE.

DEMINERALIZATION (DEE-MIN-er-al-uh-ZAY-shun)   DEMINERALIZATION

A treatment process which removes dissolved minerals (salts) from water.

ENZYMES (EN-zimes)   ENZYMES

Organic substances (produced by living organisms) which cause or speed up chemical reactions. Organic catalysts and/or bio-chemical catalysts.

FEEDWATER   FEEDWATER

The water that is fed to a treatment process; the water that is going to be treated.

FLUX   FLUX

A flowing or flow.

HYDROLYSIS (hi-DROLL-uh-sis)   HYDROLYSIS

(1) A chemical reaction in which a compound is converted into another compound by taking up water.

(2) Usually a chemical degradation of organic matter.

OSMOSIS (oz-MOE-sis)   OSMOSIS

The passage of a liquid from a weak solution to a more concentrated solution across a semipermeable membrane. The membrane allows the passage of the water (solvent) but not the dissolved solids (solutes). This process tends to equalize the conditions on either side of the membrane.

PERMEATE (PURR-me-ate)   PERMEATE

(1) To penetrate and pass through, as water penetrates and passes through soil and other porous materials.

(2) The liquid (demineralized water) produced from the reverse osmosis process that contains a *LOW* concentration of dissolved solids.

REVERSE OSMOSIS (oz-MOE-sis)   REVERSE OSMOSIS

The application of pressure to a concentrated solution which causes the passage of a liquid from the concentrated solution to a weaker solution across a semipermeable membrane. The membrane allows the passage of the water (solvent) but not the dissolved solids (solutes). The liquid produced is a demineralized water. Also see OSMOSIS.

SALINITY   SALINITY

(1) The relative concentration of dissolved salts, usually sodium chloride, in a given water.

(2) A measure of the concentration of dissolved mineral substances in water.

SEQUESTRATION (SEE-kwes-TRAY-shun)   SEQUESTRATION

A chemical complexing (forming or joining together) of metallic cations (such as iron) with certain inorganic compounds, such as phosphate. Sequestration prevents the precipitation of the metals (iron). Also see CHELATION.

SPECIFIC CONDUCTANCE   SPECIFIC CONDUCTANCE

A rapid method of estimating the dissolved solids content of a water supply. The measurement indicates the capacity of a sample of water to carry an electric current, which is related to the concentration of ionized substances in the water. Also called CONDUCTANCE.

TOTAL DISSOLVED SOLIDS (TDS)   TOTAL DISSOLVED SOLIDS (TDS)

All of the dissolved solids in a water. TDS is measured on a sample of water that has passed through a very fine mesh filter to remove suspended solids. The water passing through the filter is evaporated and the residue represents the dissolved solids. Also see SPECIFIC CONDUCTANCE.

CHAPTER 16. DEMINERALIZATION

(Removal of Dissolved Minerals by Membrane Processes)

(Lesson 1 of 3 Lessons)

16.0 SOURCES OF MINERALIZED WATERS

As our country's population continues to grow, so does our demand for more water resources. Traditionally, water supplies have been obtained from "fresh water" sources. This constantly increasing need for water has started to deplete the available fresh water supplies in some areas of the country.

Faced with potential shortages, water planners must now consider new treatment technologies which until recently were not considered to be economically feasible. Since most of the earth's water supplies are saline (the ocean is high in dissolved minerals) rather than fresh, these impurities must be removed. One process receiving considerable attention is demineralization. Demineralization is the process that removes dissolved minerals (salts) from water.

All available water supplies can be classified according to their mineral quality. All waters contain various amounts of *TOTAL DISSOLVED SOLIDS (TDS)*,[1] including fresh water. A majority of the dissolved materials are inorganic minerals (salts). Minerals are compounds commonly found in nature that consist of positive metallic ions (such as calcium, sodium) bonded to negative ions (such as chloride, sulfate, carbonate). Many of these compounds are soluble in water and come from the weathering and erosion of the earth's surface.

Fresh water supplies, which have been the major sources of water developed in the past, usually contain less than 1,000 mg/L of total dissolved solids. Secondary drinking water standards recommend 500 mg/L TDS as the limit. Waters containing slightly higher concentrations can be used without adverse effects.

Brackish water contains from 1,000 to 10,000 mg/L TDS (seawater has 35,000 mg/L TDS). Most brackish water is found in groundwater. Figure 16.1 shows that over one half of the United States overlays groundwater containing TDS levels ranging from 1,000 to 3,000 mg/L. To date, brackish water has not been widely used for municipal drinking water supplies

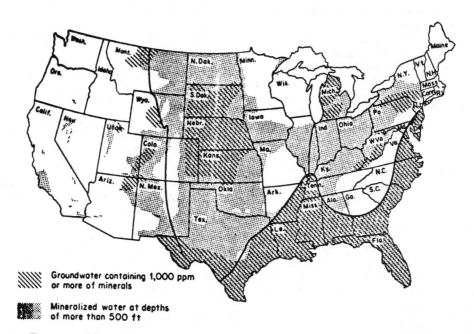

Groundwater containing 1,000 ppm or more of minerals

Mineralized water at depths of more than 500 ft

Fig. 16.1   Map of the conterminous United States showing depth to and quality of shallowest groundwater containing more than 1,000 mg/L dissolved solids

(from paper by Bill Katz, "Treating Brackish Water for Community Supplies," published in Proceedings in "Role of Desalting Technology," a series of Technology Transfer Workshops presented by the Office of Water Research and Technology)

---

[1] *Total Dissolved Solids (TDS).   All of the dissolved solids in a water. TDS is measured on a sample of water that has passed through a very fine mesh filter to remove suspended solids. The water passing through the filter is evaporated and the residue represents the dissolved solids.*

because of its highly mineralized taste and associated problems such as scaling in pipes. With the advent of new treatment technologies, however, demineralization of brackish waters (including reuse of wastewater) has great potential for further development.

The largest available source of water in terms of quantity is classified as seawater, which usually contains more than 35,000 mg/L TDS. While seawater may be an important future water resource because of its seemingly unlimited availability in coastal areas, it is more expensive to treat than brackish water because of its greater TDS concentration.

The purpose of this chapter is to introduce and familiarize the water treatment plant operator with the newer treatment processes which have been developed to remove the dissolved minerals (TDS) from water. The development of the membrane demineralization processes has significantly reduced the cost of demineralization. This savings, combined with diminished fresh water supplies, will increase the use of demineralization treatment processes. The large quantities of mineralized groundwater and the increased SALINITY[2] of many rivers and lakes due to waste discharges, agricultural runoff, and other uses will increase the need for demineralization.

Some areas of the United States, such as the Florida Gulf Coast, are already turning to demineralization. The worldwide capacity of brackish water demineralization plants is increasing every year. Thus, it is important that the water treatment plant operator become more knowledgeable concerning the methods used to demineralize water.

QUESTIONS

Write your answers in a notebook and then compare your answers with those on page 191.

16.0A   What is demineralization?

16.0B   Why is seawater more expensive to treat than brackish water?

16.1 DEMINERALIZING PROCESSES

Methods of removing minerals from water can be divided into two classes: (1) those that use a phase change such as freezing or distillation, and (2) non-phase change methods such as reverse osmosis, electrodialysis, and ion exchange.

Demineralizing processes have primarily been used to remove dissolved inorganic material (TDS) from industrial water and wastewater, municipal water and wastewater, and seawater. However, some processes will also remove suspended material, organic material, bacteria, and viruses. Application

of the various demineralizing processes is partially dependent upon the total dissolved solids (TDS) concentration of the water to be treated. Figure 16.2 illustrates the approximate TDS range for use of two phase change processes (distillation and freezing) and three non-phase change processes (reverse osmosis, electrodialysis, and ion exchange).

The selection of a demineralizing process for a particular application depends on several factors including:

1. Mineral concentration in FEEDWATER[3] (brackish water supply),
2. Product water quality required,
3. Brine disposal facilities,
4. Pretreatment required,
5. Need to remove other material such as bacteria and viruses,
6. Availability of energy and chemicals required for the process, and
7. Cost.

The basic system is similar for all demineralizing processes and includes the processes shown in Figure 16.3.

Since freezing and distillation apply primarily to seawater demineralization and their widespread use seems unlikely, these processes will not be discussed. Neither will ion exchange because of its limited use for brackish water (1,000 to 3,000 mg/L TDS). Currently, activity within the water industry is focused primarily on the membrane demineralizing processes known as reverse osmosis and electrodialysis.

QUESTIONS

Write your answers in a notebook and then compare your answers with those on page 191.

16.1A   List the two classes of methods of removing minerals from water.

16.1B   List the common membrane demineralizing processes.

16.2 REVERSE OSMOSIS

16.20 What Is Reverse Osmosis?

Osmosis can be defined as the passage of a liquid from a weak solution to a more concentrated solution across a semipermeable membrane. The membrane allows the passage of the water (solvent) but not the dissolved solids (solutes).

Osmosis plays a vital role in many biological processes. Nutrient and waste minerals are transported by osmosis through the cells of animal tissues, which show varying degrees of permeability to different dissolved solids. A striking example of a natural osmotic process is the behavior of blood cells placed in pure water. Water passes through the cell walls to dilute the solution inside the cell. The cell swells and eventually bursts, releasing its red pigment. If the blood cells are placed in a concentrated sugar solution, the reverse process occurs; the cells shrink and shrivel up as water moves out into the sugar solution.

The bottom half of Figure 16.4 illustrates osmosis. The transfer of the water (solvent) from the fresh side of the membrane continues until the level (shown in shaded area)

---

[2] Salinity.   (1) The relative concentration of dissolved salts, usually sodium chloride, in a given water. (2) A measure of the concentration of dissolved mineral substances in water.

[3] Feedwater.   The water that is fed to a treatment process; the water that is going to be treated.

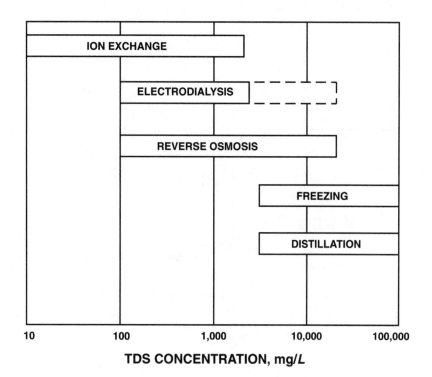

TDS CONCENTRATION, mg/L

NOTE: The dashed lines indicate a feasible range of operation, but not typical range.

Fig. 16.2   Demineralization processes versus feedwater TDS concentrations

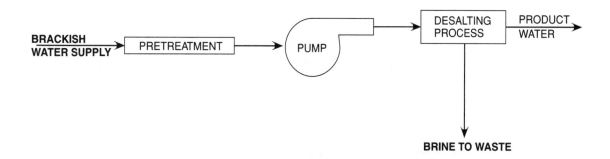

Fig. 16.3   Basic system for demineralizing processes

REVERSE OSMOSIS — FLOW REVERSED BY APPLICATION OF PRESSURE TO HIGH CONCENTRATION SOLUTION

OSMOSIS — NORMAL FLOW FROM LOW TO HIGH CONCENTRATION

Fig. 16.4   Flows through a semipermeable membrane

rises and the head or pressure is large enough to prevent any net transfer of the solvent (water) to the more concentrated solution. At equilibrium, the quantity of water passing in either direction is equal; the difference in water level between the two sides of the membrane is defined as the osmotic pressure of the solution.

If a piston is placed on the more-concentrated solution side of the semipermeable membrane (Figure 16.4) and a pressure, P, is applied which is greater than the osmotic pressure, water flows from the more concentrated solution to the "fresh" water side of the membrane. This condition illustrates the process of reverse osmosis.

16.21 Reverse Osmosis Membrane Structure and Composition

The two types of semipermeable membranes that are used most often for demineralization are cellulose acetate and thin film composites. Cellulose acetate, the first commercially available membrane (since the mid-1960s) is made by casting a cellulose acetate/solvent solution onto a porous support material. After quenching and annealing operations, the cellulose acetate membrane, often referred to as CA, exhibits the structure shown in Figure 16.5. The cellulose acetate membrane is asymmetric, meaning that one side is different from the other. The total cellulose acetate layer is 50 to 100 microns thick; however, a thin, dense layer approximately 0.2 micron thick exists at the surface. This thin, dense layer serves as the rejecting barrier of the membrane. The characteristics of a CA membrane are given in Table 16.1.

Fig. 16.5   Cellulose acetate membrane cross section

TABLE 16.1   CELLULOSE ACETATE MEMBRANE TYPICAL CHARACTERISTICS

Net Driving Pressure:	400 psi
NaCl Rejection:	92 – 97%
Flux Rate at 400 psi, 77°F:	25 GFD[a]
Operating pH range:	4.0 – 6.0
Cleaning pH range:	3.0 – 6.0
Cost relative to thin film composite membrane:	lower
Allowable feedwater chlorine concentration:	1.0 mg/L
Maximum operating temperature:	104°F (40°C)

Subject to biological attack
Subject to hydrolysis
Salt passage rate typically doubles after three years
Most suitable for treatment of municipal wastes and some heavily pretreated surface supplies (due to lower fouling rate vs. thin film)

---

[a] gallons of flux per square foot per day

During the 1970s, researchers realized the need for a membrane with better *FLUX*[4] and rejection characteristics than those of cellulose acetate. The basic approach to developing

a better membrane was to improve the efficiencies of the thin rejecting layer and the porous substrate by casting each layer separately during the manufacturing process, hence the term "thin film composite." A typical thin film composite membrane is shown in Figure 16.6. The first step in preparing a thin film composite membrane is the casting of the porous support, usually a polysulfone solution, onto the support fabric. The next step is to contact the composite support with the polymers that will actually form the semipermeable thin film rejecting barrier. The thin film rejecting barrier is formed *in situ*, or in position, by interfacial polymerization. It is the ability to form the semipermeable membrane separate from the support layers that has enabled membrane manufacturers to select polymers that will produce membranes with optimum dissolved solids rejection and water flux rates. The characteristics of thin film composite membranes are given in Table 16.2.

Fig. 16.6   Thin film composite membrane cross section

TABLE 16.2   THIN FILM COMPOSITE MEMBRANE TYPICAL CHARACTERISTICS

Net Driving Pressure:	200 psi
NaCl Rejection:	98 – 99%
Flux Rate at 200 psi, 77°F:	25 – 30 GFD[a]
Operating pH range:	3.0 – 10.0
Cleaning pH range:	2.0 – 12.0
Cost relative to cellulose acetate membrane:	higher
Allowable feedwater chlorine concentration:	none
Maximum operating temperature:	113°F (45°C)
Salt passage increase after three years:	≤30%

Not subject to biological attack, hydrolysis, or compaction
Higher rejection and flux rates than cellulose acetate membrane
Higher fouling rates than cellulose acetate on certain waste and surface water supplies
Sensitive to oxidants in feedwater

---

[a] gallons of flux per square foot per day

16.22   Membrane Performance and Properties

The basic behavior of semipermeable cellulose acetate reverse osmosis membranes can be described by two equations. The product water flow through a semipermeable membrane can be expressed as shown in Equation 1.

EQUATION 1

$$F_w = A(\Delta P - \Delta \pi)$$

Where

F_w = Water flux (gm/sq cm-sec),

A = Water permeability constant (gm/sq cm-sec atm[5]),

ΔP = Pressure differential applied across the membrane (atm),

$\Delta \pi$ = Osmotic pressure differential across the membrane (atm).

---

[4] *Flux.   A flowing or flow.*
[5] *atm.   The abbreviation for atmosphere. One atmosphere is equal to 14.7 psi or 100 kPa.*

Note that the water flux is the flow of water in grams per second through a membrane area of one square centimeter. Think of this as similar to the flow through a rapid sand filter in gallons per minute through a filter area of one square foot (GPM/sq ft).

The mineral (salt) flux (mineral passage) through the membrane can be expressed as shown in Equation 2.

EQUATION 2

$F_s = B(C_1 - C_2)$

Where

F_s = Mineral flux (gm/sq cm-sec),

B = Mineral permeability constant (cm/sec),

$C_1 - C_2$ = Concentration gradient across the membrane (gm/cu cm).

The water permeability (A) and mineral permeability (B) constants are characteristics of the particular membrane that is used and the processing it has received.

An examination of Equations 1 and 2 shows that the water flux (the rate of water flow through the membrane) is dependent on the applied pressure, *WHILE THE MINERAL FLUX IS NOT DEPENDENT ON PRESSURE*. As the pressure of the feedwater is increased, the flow of water through the membrane increases while the flow of minerals remains essentially constant. Therefore, both the quantity and the quality of the purified product (the *PERMEATE* [6]) should increase with increased pressure. This occurs because there is more water to dilute the same amount of mineral.

The water flux (F_w) *DECREASES* as the mineral content of the feed increases because the osmotic pressure contribution ($\Delta\pi$) increases with increasing mineral content. In other words, since $\Delta\pi$ increases, the term ($\Delta P - \Delta\pi$) decreases which results in a decrease in F_w, the water flux. Further, as more and more feedwater passes through the membrane, the mineral content of the feedwater becomes higher and higher (more concentrated). The osmotic pressure contribution ($\Delta\pi$) of the concentrate increases, resulting in a lower water flux.

Finally, since the membrane rejects a constant percentage of mineral, product water quality decreases with increased feedwater concentration. Also note that Equation 2 reveals that the greater the concentration gradient ($C_1 - C_2$) across the membrane, the greater the mineral flux (mineral flow). Therefore, the greater the feed concentration, the greater the mineral flux and also mineral concentration in the product water.

Water treatment plant operators must have a basic understanding of these mathematical relationships which describe RO (reverse osmosis) membrane performance. To help develop a better understanding of the interrelationships of flux, rejection, time, temperature, pH, and recovery, further explanation of these variables continues in the next section.

EXAMPLE 1

Convert a water flux of 5×10^{-4} gm/sq cm-sec[7] to gallons per day per square foot.

Known	Unknown
Water Flux, gm/sq cm-sec = 5×10^{-4} gm/sq cm-sec	Flow, GPD/sq ft

Convert the water flux from gm/sq cm-sec to flow in GPD/sq ft.

$$\text{Flow, GPD/sq ft} = \frac{\left(\begin{array}{c}\text{Water Flux,}\\ \text{gm/sq cm-sec}\end{array}\right)(2.54\ cm/in)^2(12\ in/ft)^2(60\ sec/min)(60\ min/hr)(24\ hr/day)}{(1,000\ gm/L)(3.785\ L/gal)}$$

$$= \frac{(0.0005\ gm/sq\ cm\text{-}sec)(2.54\ cm/in)^2(12\ in/ft)^2(60\ sec/min)(60\ min/hr)(24\ hr/day)}{(1,000\ gm/L)(3.785\ L/gal)}$$

$$= 10.6\ \text{GPD/sq ft}$$

QUESTIONS

Write your answers in a notebook and then compare your answers with those on page 191.

16.2A   What is the osmotic pressure of a solution?

16.2B   What type of semipermeable membrane is commonly used today?

16.2C   What is the meaning of water flux and of mineral flux? What units are used to express measurement of these quantities?

16.2D   When additional pressure is applied to the side of a membrane with a concentrated solution, what happens?

16.2E   When higher mineral concentrations occur in the feedwater, what happens to the permeate or product water?

16.23   Definition of Flux

The term flux is the expression used to describe the rate of water flow through the semipermeable membrane. Flux is usually expressed in gallons per day per square foot of membrane surface or in grams per second per square centimeter.

---

[6] *Permeate (PURR-me-ate).   (1) To penetrate and pass through, as water penetrates and passes through soil and other porous materials. (2) The liquid (demineralized water) produced from the reverse osmosis process that contains a LOW concentration of dissolved solids.*
[7] *5×10^{-4} is the same as 0.0005.*

The average membrane flux rate of a reverse osmosis system is an important operating guideline. In practice, most reverse osmosis systems will require periodic cleaning. It has been demonstrated that the cleaning frequency can be dependent on the average membrane flux rate of the system. Too high a flux rate may result in excessive fouling rates requiring frequent cleaning. Some general industry guidelines for acceptable flux rates are:

Feedwater Source	Flux Rate, GFD
Industrial/Municipal Waste	8-12
Surface (river, lake, ocean)	8-14
Well	14-20

EXAMPLE 2

The permeate flow through an arrangement (or array) of RO membrane pressure vessels is 1,330,000 gallons per day (GPD). Feedwater first flows to 33 vessels operating in parallel. The concentrate from the 33 first-pass vessels is combined and sent to a set of 11 second-pass vessels. Each vessel (or tube) contains six membrane elements. Each element is 8 inches in diameter and 40 inches long, thus providing 325 square feet of membrane surface area per element. Calculate the average membrane flux rate for the system in gallons per day per square foot (GFD).

Known	Unknown
Permeate Flow, GPD = 1,330,000 GPD	Average Flux Rate, GFD
No. of Vessels = 44 (33 + 11)	
No. of Elements per Vessel = 6	
Membrane Area per Element, sq ft = 325 sq ft	

1. Determine the total membrane area in the system.

$$\text{Membrane Area, sq ft} = (\text{No. Vessels})(\text{No. Elements/vessel})(\text{Surface Area/element})$$

$$= (44 \text{ vessels})(6 \text{ elements/vessel})(325 \text{ sq ft/element})$$

$$= 85,800 \text{ sq ft}$$

2. Calculate the average membrane flux rate for the system.

$$\text{Average Flux Rate, GFD} = \frac{\text{Permeate Flow, GPD}}{\text{Membrane Area, sq ft}}$$

$$= \frac{1,330,000 \text{ GPD}}{85,800 \text{ sq ft}}$$

$$= 15.5 \text{ GFD}$$

Even under ideal conditions (pure feedwater and no fouling of the membrane surface), there is a decline in water flux with time. This decrease in flux is due to membrane compaction. This phenomenon is considered comparable to "creep" observed in other plastics or even metals when subjected to compressing stresses (pressure).

The term "flux decline" is used to describe the loss of water flow through the membrane due to compaction plus fouling. In the real world, feedwaters are never "pure" and contain suspended solids, dissolved organics and inorganics, bacteria, algae, and other potential foulants. These impurities can be deposited or grow on the membrane surface, thus hindering the flow of water through the membrane.

16.24 Mineral Rejection

The purpose of demineralization is to separate minerals from water; the ability of the membrane to reject minerals is called the mineral rejection. Mineral rejection is defined as:

EQUATION 3

$$\text{Rejection, \%} = \left(1 - \frac{\text{Product Concentration}}{\text{Feedwater Concentration}}\right) \times 100\%$$

Mineral rejections can be determined by measuring the TDS and using Equation 3. Rejections also may be calculated for individual constituents in the solution by using their concentrations.

The basic equations which describe the performance of a reverse osmosis membrane indicate that rejection decreases as feedwater mineral concentration increases. Remember, this is because the higher mineral concentration increases the osmotic pressure. Figure 16.7 illustrates the rejection performance for a typical RO (reverse osmosis) membrane operating on three different feedwater solutions. This figure shows that as feed mineral concentration increases (TDS in mg/L), rejection decreases at a given feed pressure. Notice also that rejection improves as feed pressure increases.

Typical rejection for most commonly encountered dissolved inorganics is usually between 92 and 99 percent. Divalent ions like calcium and sulfate are better rejected than monovalent ions such as sodium or chloride. Table 16.3 lists the typical rejection of an RO membrane operating on a brackish feedwater.

TABLE 16.3 TYPICAL REVERSE OSMOSIS REJECTIONS OF COMMON CONSTITUENTS FOUND IN BRACKISH WATER

Contaminant	Units	Feedwater Concentration	Percent Removal
EC[a]	μmhos	1,400	92
TDS[a]	mg/L	900	92
Calcium	mg/L	100	99
Chloride	mg/L	120	92
Sulfate	mg/L	338	99
Sodium	mg/L	158	92
Ammonia	mg/L	22.5	94
Nitrate	mg/L	2.9	55
COD[a]	mg/L	12.5	95
TOC[a]	mg/L	6.0	88
Silver	μg/L	1.2	88
Arsenic	μg/L	<5.0	—
Aluminum	μg/L	71.0	93
Barium	μg/L	24.0	96
Beryllium	μg/L	<1.0	—
Cadmium	μg/L	3.4	98
Cobalt	μg/L	4.6	>90
Chromium	μg/L	3.6	80
Copper	μg/L	12.7	63
Iron	μg/L	24.0	91
Mercury	μg/L	0.8	41
Manganese	μg/L	1.0	85
Nickel	μg/L	2.5	88
Lead	μg/L	<1.0	—
Selenium	μg/L	<5.0	—
Zinc	μg/L	<100.0	—

[a] EC, Electrical Conductivity; TDS, Total Dissolved Solids; COD, Chemical Oxygen Demand; and TOC, Total Organic Carbon.

MINERAL REJECTION, %

SODIUM CHLORIDE REJECTION
VS
APPLIED PRESSURE
STANDARD FLUX MODULE

1,000
5,000
10,000

FEED PRESSURE, psi

Fig. 16.7   Typical RO rejection for three different feedwater concentrations of TDS in mg/L
(Source: *REVERSE OSMOSIS PRINCIPLES AND APPLICATIONS*, by Fluids Systems, Division of UOP, October 1970)

EXAMPLE 3

Estimate the ability of a reverse osmosis plant to reject minerals by calculating the mineral rejection as a percent. The feedwater contains 1,500 mg/L TDS and the product water TDS is 150 mg/L.

Known	Unknown
Feedwater TDS, mg/L = 1,500 mg/L	Mineral Rejection, %
Product Water TDS, mg/L = 150 mg/L	

Calculate the mineral rejection as a percent.

$$\text{Mineral Rejection, \%} = \left(1 - \frac{\text{Product TDS, mg/L}}{\text{Feed TDS, mg/L}}\right)(100\%)$$

$$= \left(1 - \frac{150 \text{ mg/L}}{1,500 \text{ mg/L}}\right)(100\%)$$

$$= (1 - 0.1)(100\%)$$

$$= 90\%$$

While most demineralization applications require the use of a membrane with high rejection rates (greater than 95 percent), some applications can use a membrane with lower rejection rates (80 percent) and lower operating pressures (less than 150 psi). The membranes that fit this classification are commonly referred to as softening or nanofiltration membranes. These membranes produce the same quantity of water as standard RO membranes but at lower operating pressures. A comparison of standard and softening RO membranes is given below:

	Standard	Softening (Nanofiltration)
Flux	25 – 30 GFD	25 – 30 GFD
Applied Pressure	225 psi	150 psi
Minimum Salt Rejection	97 – 98%	75 – 80%
Hardness Rejection	>99%	>95%

Softening or nanofiltration membranes are seeing widespread use for demineralization of municipal water supplies that require high rejection rates for hardness and THM formation potential, and moderate TDS rejection.

Reverse osmosis membrane manufacturers provide computer software to project the permeate water quality of a reverse osmosis system. Figures 16.8 and 16.9 are examples of computer printouts of permeate projections showing the expected initial performance of a thin film composite membrane (Figure 16.8) and a cellulose acetate membrane (Figure 16.9). The same feedwater was used for both projections.

QUESTIONS

Write your answers in a notebook and then compare your answers with those on page 191.

16.2F   Water flux is usually expressed in what units?

16.2G   What is "flux decline"?

16.2H   How is mineral rejection measured?

16.2I   What are the two major differences between standard RO membranes and softening membranes?

16.25   Effects of Feedwater Temperature and pH on Membrane Performance

In reverse osmosis operation, feedwater temperature has a significant effect on membrane performance and must therefore be taken into account in system design and operation. Essentially, the value of the water permeation constant is only constant for a given temperature. As the temperature of the feedwater increases, flux increases. Usually, flux is reported at some standard temperature reference condition, such as 25°C. Figure 16.10 illustrates the increase in flux for a standard RO module over a range of operating temperatures when 400 psi (2,758 kPa or 28 kg/sq cm) net operating pressure is applied.

Cellulose acetate membrane is subject to long-term *HYDROLYSIS*.[8] Hydrolysis results in a lessening of mineral rejection capability. The rate of hydrolysis is accelerated by increased temperature, and is also a function of feed pH (Figure 16.11). Slightly acidic pH values (5 to 6) ensure a lower hydrolysis rate, as do cooler temperatures. Therefore, to ensure the longest possible lifetime of the cellulose acetate membrane and to slow hydrolysis, acid is added as a pretreatment step before demineralization. Table 16.4 indicates the relative time for mineral passage to increase 200 percent at different feedwater pH levels. Thin film composite membranes are not subject to hydrolysis but pH adjustment of the feedwater may be required for scale control.

TABLE 16.4   TIME REQUIRED TO ACHIEVE A 200 PERCENT INCREASE IN MINERAL PASSAGE AT 23°C AT VARIOUS pH LEVELS

pH 5.0	6 years
6.0	3.8 years
7.0	1 year
8.0	0.14 year = 51 days
9.0	0.01 year = 3.6 days

16.26   Recovery

Recovery is defined as the percentage of feed flow which is recovered as product water. Expressed mathematically, recovery can be determined by Equation 4.

EQUATION 4

$$\text{Recovery, \%} = \left(\frac{\text{Product Flow}}{\text{Feed Flow}}\right)(100\%)$$

The recovery rate is usually determined or limited by two considerations. The first is the desired product water quality. Since the amount of mineral passing through the membrane is influenced by the concentration differential between the brine and product, there is a possibility of exceeding product quality criteria with excessive recovery. The second consideration concerns the solubility limits of minerals in the brine. One should not concentrate the brine to a degree that would precipitate minerals on the membrane. This effect is commonly referred to as *CONCENTRATION POLARIZATION*.[9]

---

[8] *Hydrolysis (hi-DROLL-uh-sis).* (1) A chemical reaction in which a compound is converted into another compound by taking up water. (2) Usually a chemical degradation of organic matter.

[9] *Concentration Polarization.* A buildup of retained particles on the membrane surface due to dewatering of the feed closest to the membrane. The thickness of the concentration polarization layer is controlled by the flow velocity across the membrane.

```
HYDRANAUTICS DESIGN PROGRAM -  VERSION 4.01 (1991)          05-26-97
Calculation was made by: CWC

Project name : SANTA ANA WATERSHED              Permeate flow :   1330000 GPD

Feedwater temperature :     21.0 C     Recovery :     77.0%
Raw water pH :               7.20      Element age :    0.0 years
Acid dosage, ppm(100%):     32.7 H2SO4 Flux decline coefficient :        -0.025
Acidified feed CO2,ppm :    66.7       3-yr salt passage increase factor :1.2


Feed Pressure : 157.4 psi                 Concentrate Pressure : 118.1 psi
```

Pass	Feed Flow Total gpm	Feed Flow Vessel gpm	Conc. Flow Total gpm	Conc. Flow Vessel gpm	Beta	Conc. Press. psi	Element Type	Element No.	Array
1	1199.5	36.3	454.7	13.8	1.22	142.7	8040-LSY-CPA2	198	33x6
2	454.7	41.3	275.9	25.1	1.08	118.1	8040-LSY-CPA2	66	11x6

Ion	Raw water mg/l	Raw water ppm*	Feed water mg/l	Feed water ppm*	Permeate mg/l	Permeate ppm*	Concentrate mg/l	Concentrate ppm*
Ca	140.0	349.1	140.0	349.1	1.8	4.6	602.5	1502.5
Mg	42.0	172.8	42.0	172.8	0.6	2.3	180.8	743.8
Na	168.0	365.2	168.0	365.2	10.5	22.8	695.4	1511.7
K	3.8	4.9	3.8	4.9	0.3	0.4	15.5	19.9
NH4	0.0	0.0	0.0	0.0	0.0	0.0	0.0	0.0
Ba	0.0	0.0	0.0	0.0	0.0	0.0	0.0	0.0
Sr	0.0	0.0	0.0	0.0	0.0	0.0	0.0	0.0
CO3	0.3	0.5	0.1	0.2	0.0	0.0	2.1	3.5
HCO3	367.0	300.8	326.6	267.7	18.8	15.4	1357.2	1112.5
SO4	243.0	253.1	275.1	286.5	2.3	2.3	1188.4	1237.9
Cl	162.0	228.5	162.0	228.5	5.2	7.4	686.8	968.7
F	0.4	1.1	0.4	1.1	0.0	0.1	1.7	4.4
NO3	93.0	75.0	93.0	75.0	5.9	4.8	384.5	310.1
SiO2	40.0		40.0		0.7		171.7	
TDS	1259.5		1251.0		46.1		5286.5	
pH	7.2		6.9		5.7		7.5	

```
Notes: *ppm as CaCO3.     Calculated concentrations are accurate to  +/- 10%
```

	Raw water	Feed water	Concentrate
CaSO4/Ksp*100,%	7.9	8.8	55.2
SrSO4/Ksp*100,%	0.0	0.0	0.0
BaSO4/Ksp*100,%	0.0	0.0	0.0
SiO2 sat.,%	34.2	34.2	146.8
Langelier ind.	0.21	-0.14	1.69
Stiff & Davis ind.	0.20	-0.15	1.44
Ionic strength	0.03	0.03	0.11
Osmotic press.,psi	9.2	9.1	38.5

Fig. 16.8   Computer printout of permeate projections for a thin film composite membrane
(Source: Hydranautics)

```
HYDRANAUTICS DESIGN PROGRAM -   VERSION 4.01 (1991)          05-26-97
Calculation was made by: CWC

Project name : SANTA ANA WATERSHED          Permeate flow :   1330000 GPD

Feedwater temperature :     21.0 C    Recovery :     77.0%
Raw water pH :              7.20      Element age :   0.0 years
Acid dosage, ppm(100%):     0.0 H2SO4 Flux decline coefficient :      -0.035
Acidified feed CO2,ppm :    37.9      3-yr salt passage increase factor :2.0


Feed Pressure : 297.9 psi                Concentrate Pressure : 257.5 psi

Pass    Feed Flow     Conc. Flow     Beta    Conc.    Element     Element  Array
     Total  Vessel  Total  Vessel            Press.    Type        No.
      gpm    gpm     gpm    gpm                psi

 1   1199.5  36.3   480.9   14.6     1.21    282.8  8040-MSY-CAB1   198     33x6
 2    480.9  43.7   275.9   25.1     1.11    257.5  8040-MSY-CAB1    66     11x6
```

Ion	Raw water mg/l	Raw water ppm*	Feed water mg/l	Feed water ppm*	Permeate mg/l	Permeate ppm*	Concentrate mg/l	Concentrate ppm*
Ca	140.0	349.1	140.0	349.1	2.5	6.2	600.4	1497.3
Mg	42.0	172.8	42.0	172.8	0.7	3.1	180.1	741.2
Na	168.0	365.2	168.0	365.2	27.9	60.6	637.2	1385.1
K	3.8	4.9	3.8	4.9	0.8	1.0	13.8	17.7
NH4	0.0	0.0	0.0	0.0	0.0	0.0	0.0	0.0
Ba	0.0	0.0	0.0	0.0	0.0	0.0	0.0	0.0
Sr	0.0	0.0	0.0	0.0	0.0	0.0	0.0	0.0
CO3	0.3	0.5	0.3	0.5	0.0	0.0	4.6	7.7
HCO3	367.0	300.8	367.0	300.8	21.3	17.5	1524.3	1249.4
SO4	243.0	253.1	243.0	253.1	1.8	1.9	1050.5	1094.2
Cl	162.0	228.5	162.0	228.5	22.6	31.8	628.8	886.9
F	0.4	1.1	0.4	1.1	0.0	0.1	1.6	4.3
NO3	93.0	75.0	93.0	75.0	24.3	19.6	323.1	260.6
SiO2	40.0		40.0		10.4		139.0	
TDS	1259.5		1259.5		112.3		5103.5	
pH	7.2		7.2		6.0		7.8	

```
Notes: *ppm as CaCO3.    Calculated concentrations are accurate to  +/- 10%
```

	Raw water	Feed water	Concentrate
CaSO4/Ksp*100,%	7.9	7.9	50.1
SrSO4/Ksp*100,%	0.0	0.0	0.0
BaSO4/Ksp*100,%	0.0	0.0	0.0
SiO2 sat.,%	34.2	34.2	118.8
Langelier ind.	0.21	0.21	2.04
Stiff & Davis ind.	0.20	0.20	1.79
Ionic strength	0.03	0.03	0.11
Osmotic press.,psi	9.2	9.2	37.0

Fig. 16.9 Computer printout of permeate projections for a cellulose acetate membrane
(Source: Hydranautics)

Fig. 16.10　Effect of temperature on water flux rate, cellulose acetate
membrane operating pressure at 400 psi (2,758 kPa or 28 kg/sq cm) net
(Source: REVERSE OSMOSIS PRINCIPLES AND APPLICATIONS, by Fluids Systems, Division of UOP, October 1970)

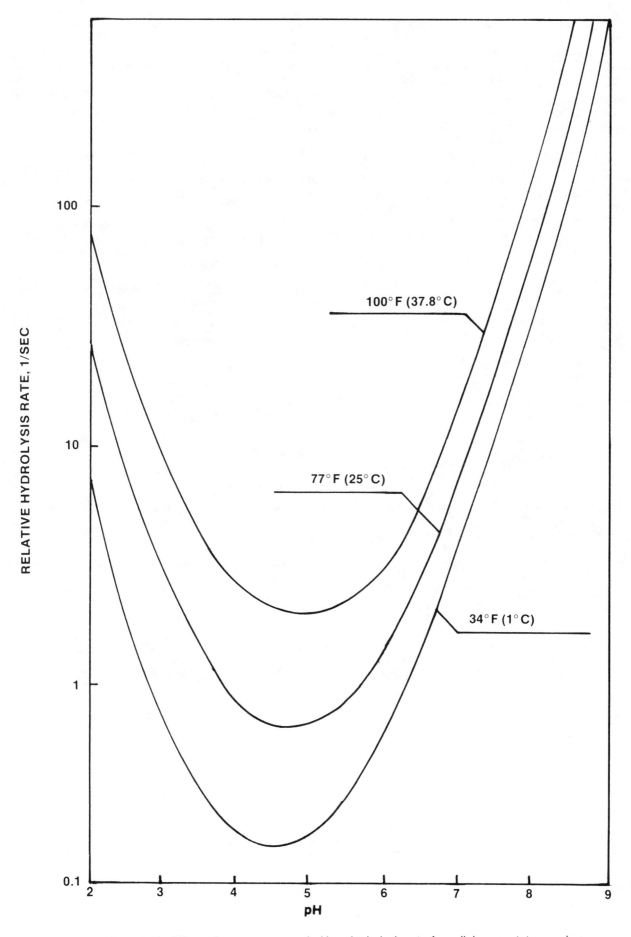

Fig. 16.11   Effect of temperature and pH on hydrolysis rate for cellulose acetate membrane

THE MOST COMMON AND SERIOUS PROBLEM RE-SULTING FROM CONCENTRATION POLARIZATION IS THE INCREASING TENDENCY FOR PRECIPITATION OF SPAR-INGLY SOLUBLE SALTS AND THE DEPOSITION OF PAR-TICULATE MATTER ON THE MEMBRANE SURFACE.

In any flowing hydraulic system, the fluid near a solid surface travels more slowly than the main stream of the fluid. In other words, there is a liquid boundary layer at the solid surface. This is also true at the surface of the membrane in a spiral-wound element or in any other membrane packaging configuration. Since water is transmitted through the membrane at a much more rapid rate than minerals, the concentration of the minerals builds up in the boundary layer (concentration polarization) and it is necessary for the minerals to diffuse back into the flowing stream. Polarization will reduce both the flux and rejection of a reverse osmosis system. Since it is impractical to totally eliminate the polarization effect, it is necessary to minimize it by good design and operation.

The boundary layer effect can be minimized by increased water flow velocity and by promoting turbulence within the RO elements. Brine flow rates can be kept high as product water is removed by staging (reducing) the module pressure vessels. This is popularly referred to as a "Christmas Tree" arrangement. Typical flow arrangements such as 4 units - 2 units - 1 unit (85 percent recovery) or 2 units - 1 unit (75 percent recovery) are used most often (Figure 16.12).

These configurations consist of feeding water to a series of pressure vessels in parallel where about 50 percent of the water is separated by the membrane as product water and 50 percent of the water is rejected. The reject is then fed to half as many vessels in parallel where again about 50 percent is product water and 50 percent rejected. This reject becomes

the feed for the next set of vessels. By arranging the pressure vessels in the 4-2-1 arrangement, it is possible to recover over 85 percent of the feedwater as product water and to maintain adequate flow rates across the membrane surface to minimize polarization. For example, a system consisting of a total of 35 vessels would have a 20-10-5 pressure vessel arrangement for an 85 percent recovery.

EXAMPLE 4

Estimate the percent recovery of a reverse osmosis unit with a 4-2-1 arrangement if the feed flow is 5.88 MGD and the product flow is 5.0 MGD.

Known	**Unknown**
Product Flow, MGD = 5.0 MGD	Recovery, %
Feed Flow, MGD = 5.88 MGD	

Calculate the recovery as a percent.

$$\text{Recovery, \%} = \frac{(\text{Product Flow, MGD})(100\%)}{\text{Feed Flow, MGD}}$$

$$= \frac{(5.0 \text{ MGD})(100\%)}{5.88 \text{ MGD}}$$

$$= 85\%$$

QUESTIONS

Write your answers in a notebook and then compare your answers with those on page 191.

16.2J   How will an increase in feedwater temperature influence the water flux?

16.2K   How does hydrolysis influence the mineral rejection capability of a membrane?

16.2L   How is recovery defined?

16.2M   Recovery rate is usually limited by what two considerations?

16.2N   Define concentration polarization.

End of Lesson 1 of 3 Lessons on DEMINERALIZATION

Please answer the discussion and review questions next.

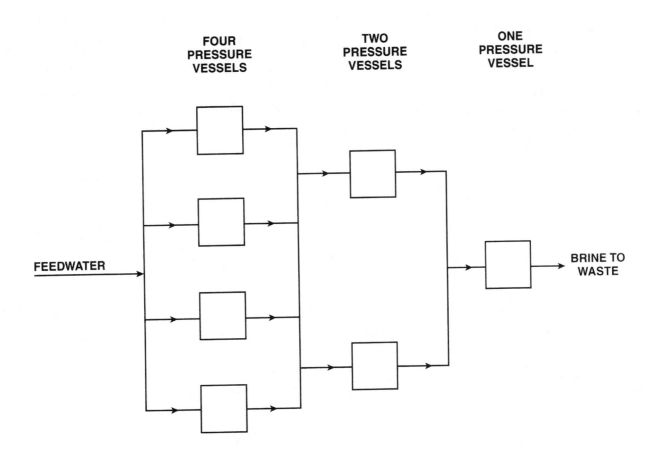

FOUR
PRESSURE
VESSELS

TWO
PRESSURE
VESSELS

ONE
PRESSURE
VESSEL

FEEDWATER

BRINE TO
WASTE

NOTES: 1. BRINE FLOWS OUT OF PRESSURE
VESSELS TO NEXT VESSEL.

2. PRODUCT WATER IS NOT SHOWN.
PRODUCT WATER FLOWS OUT OF EACH
VESSEL INTO A COMMON HEADER.

Fig. 16.12 Typical 4-2-1 "Christmas Tree" arrangement

DISCUSSION AND REVIEW QUESTIONS

Chapter 16.   DEMINERALIZATION

(Lesson 1 of 3 Lessons)

At the end of each lesson in this chapter you will find some discussion and review questions. The purpose of these questions is to indicate to you how well you understand the material in the lesson. Write the answers to these questions in your notebook before continuing.

1. Why has brackish water not been widely used for municipal drinking water supplies?

2. What is reverse osmosis?

3. Indicate what will happen to both the water flux and mineral flux when:

   a. Pressure differential applied across the membrane (ΔP) increases,

   b. Osmotic pressure differential across the membrane ($\Delta \pi$) increases, and

   c. Concentration gradient across the membrane ($C_1 - C_2$) increases.

4. What usually happens to water flux with time? Explain.

5. How does fouling develop on membranes?

6. What factors influence the rate of hydrolysis of a membrane? Explain.

7. What is the most common and serious problem resulting from concentration polarization?

8. Why do demineralization plants use a pressure vessel Christmas Tree configuration?

CHAPTER 16.   DEMINERALIZATION

(Lesson 2 of 3 Lessons)

16.3   COMPONENTS OF A REVERSE OSMOSIS UNIT

A reverse osmosis unit is shown in Figure 16.13. Several RO units, along with the necessary auxiliary equipment for a large reverse osmosis demineralization plant, are shown in Figure 16.14. The major components are shown in the schematic, Figure 16.15.

16.30   Pressurization Pump

The pressures required for reverse osmosis can range from 100 to 1,200 psi. Typically, the pressure ranges can be broken down as follows:

Application	Pressure Range (psi)
Softening	100 – 200
Brackish	200 – 500
Brackish/Seawater Mixture, Industrial Concentrating	500 – 800
Seawater	800 – 1,200

Two basic types of pumps are used for pressurizing the feedwater: centrifugal and positive displacement. Important characteristics of each type of pump relating to its use in RO applications are listed below.

Centrifugal Pumps

1. Typically used for applications less than 500 psi.

2. Most cost effective for applications below 500 psi.

3. Single impellers geared to operate higher than motor speed create excessive noise.

4. Multistage centrifugal pumps are more costly than single-stage but more efficient.

Positive Displacement Pumps

1. Typically used for applications greater than 500 psi.

2. Very efficient for seawater (800 to 1,200 psi).

3. Flow pulsations require use of pulsation dampener for velocities greater than 2 FPS (feet per second).

The output of a centrifugal pump may be throttled by use of a multi-turn throttling valve. This is often done for new systems, or after a successful membrane cleaning.

The output of a positive displacement pump may not be throttled. The pump discharge line should contain a pressure relief mechanism. Optional items would be a bypass valve to control flow to the membrane section and a pulsation dampener.

16.31   Piping

Selection of piping material depends on the water salinity and/or pressure. Seawater reverse osmosis requires the use of high-grade stainless steels for high-pressure lines. The most common types of materials used to date are 316L and 317L. These have been chosen for the high-molybdenum content. Brackish water plants typically use 304 and 316 stainless steel.

Low-pressure piping is typically polyvinyl chloride (PVC) or fiber-reinforced plastic (FRP). Some exotic materials such as 316SS and polyvinylidene fluoride (PVDF) are used in high-purity applications such as for semiconductor rinse water.

Fig. 16.13   Reverse osmosis unit

Fig. 16.14   RO units with necessary auxiliary equipment

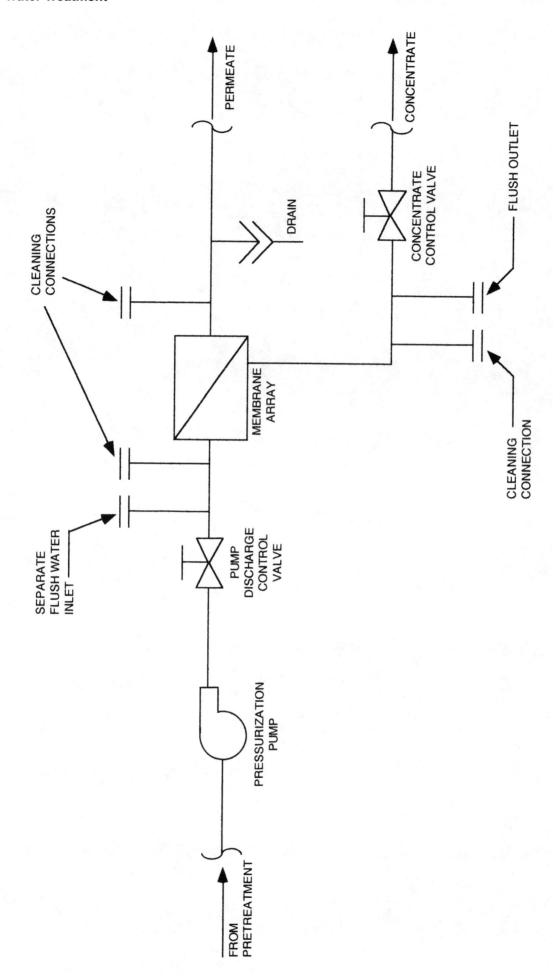

Fig. 16.15   Schematic of reverse osmosis unit

16.32   Pressure Vessel Housings

Several spiral-wound membrane elements (described later in Section 16.310) are connected in series and contained in pressure vessels. For most applications, a maximum of six 40-inch long spiral-wound elements are contained in a single vessel. Due to recent improvements in the hydraulics of the spiral-wound design, seven 40-inch long elements have been placed in one vessel. The standard material of construction is fiber reinforced polyester (FRP). The pressure vessels are available in 200, 400, 600, 1,000, and 1,200 psi ratings. Some manufacturers can provide vessels constructed and stamped according to ASME Code — Section X.

Hollow fiber bundles (described later in Section 16.310) are packaged in individual fiberglass housings. For seawater desalination, these housings can be rated up to 1,200 psi.

16.33   Concentrate Control Valve

A regulating valve located in the concentrate line provides a means of applying a back pressure to the membrane. Positioning this valve in conjunction with the pump discharge valve (bypass valve for positive displacement pumps) will set the concentrate and permeate flow rates.

16.34   Sample Valves

Sample valves should be located on the feed, permeate, and concentrate lines. Locations should be such that samples can be taken during all modes of operation such as servicing, flushing, cleaning, and rinsing. Sample valves should also be located in the permeate line of each permeator or pressure vessel.

16.35   Flush Connections

Provisions should be made for flushing the unit for certain applications. Examples would be seawater or brackish waters with high organic content. The flush water could be acidified feed or permeate. If permeate is used a separate inlet would be required. For all units that require flushing, a separate outlet in the concentrate line upstream of the concentrate control valve should be provided. The concentrate control valve would restrict flush flow which is usually greater than the design concentrate flow.

16.36   Cleaning Connections

All units should have cleaning connections for each bank of permeators or pressure vessels connected in parallel. Isolation valves for each bank would allow for one bank to soak while the upstream or downstream bank is being cleaned. On large systems with many vessels or permeators connected in parallel, the cleaning system is sized for economic reasons to clean only a portion of the bank. In this case valves are required to isolate the specific amount of vessels that can be cleaned at one time.

16.37   Permeate Rinse

It is useful to have provisions for sending the permeate from one bank or unit to drain. Some processes require that the permeate achieve quality by rinsing to drain after a shutdown period. Also for certain troubleshooting procedures, poor quality permeate can be directed to drain while individual vessels are checked for poor quality.

16.38   Permeate Drawback Tank

For seawater applications a permeate drawback tank may be provided. The purpose of the drawback tank is to provide a supply of water for an off-line unit that is subject to osmosis.

Upon shutdown with removal of applied pressure, reverse osmosis ceases and osmosis begins. During osmosis, flow will occur from permeate to the feed-concentrate side of the membrane. Flushing the feed-concentrate channels with permeate after shutdown should prevent natural osmosis, but as a precaution, drawback banks may be provided to prevent dehydration of the membrane.

16.39   Energy Recovery Devices

Energy recovery devices installed in the high pressure concentrate line are used in some seawater reverse osmosis plants. The basic principle of operation is the conversion of the potential energy of the high pressure concentrate into kinetic energy. A nozzle directs the concentrate flow toward a rotor with dished vanes. The flow strikes the vanes and turns the rotor. The shaft of the rotor is connected to a pump which pre-pressurizes the seawater feed. Due to lack of cost effectiveness, corrosion problems, and size restrictions, energy recovery turbines of this type have seen limited use.

16.310   Membranes

Operating plants use the RO principle in several different membrane configurations. Three types of commercially available membrane configurations which have been used in operating plants include:

1. Spiral wound,

2. Hollow fine fiber, and

3. Tubular.

The spiral-wound RO module was developed by Gulf Environmental Systems Company (now Fluids Systems Division, UOP) under contract to the U.S. Office of Saline Water. This RO unit was conceived as a method of obtaining a relatively high ratio of membrane area to pressure vessel volume. The membrane is supported on both sides of a backing material and sealed with glue on three of the four edges of the laminate. The laminate is also sealed to a central tube which has been drilled to allow the demineralized water to enter. The membrane surfaces are separated by a screen material which acts as a brine spacer. The entire package is then rolled into a spiral configuration and wrapped in a cylindrical form. The membrane modules are loaded, end to end, into a pressure vessel as shown in Figure 16.16. Feed flow is parallel to the central tube while permeate flows through the membrane toward the central tube. Plants using this type of system include the brackish water demineralizing plants at Key Largo, Florida, and Kashima, Japan; the wastewater demineralizing plants in California; and the seawater demineralizing plant at Jeddah in Saudi Arabia. Spiral-wound membrane elements are pictured in Figure 16.16.

The hollow fiber type of membrane was developed by DuPont and Dow Chemical. The membranes manufactured by DuPont are made of aromatic polyamide fibers about the size of a human hair with an inside diameter of about 0.0016 inch (0.04 mm). In these very small diameters, fibers can withstand high pressures. In an operating process the fibers are placed in a pressure vessel; one end of each fiber is sealed and the other end protrudes outside the vessel. The brackish water is under pressure on the outside of the fibers and product water flows inside of the fiber to the open end. A DuPont module is illustrated in Figure 16.17. For operating plants, the membrane modules are assembled in a configuration similar to the spiral-wound unit. Municipal demineralizing plants (manufactured by DuPont) in Greenfield, Iowa, and in Florida and seawater demineralizing plants in the Middle East use this type of membrane.

ROLL TO
ASSEMBLE

FEED SIDE
SPACER

FEED FLOW

PERMEATE
OUT

PERMEATE SIDE BACKING

(MATERIAL WITH MEMBRANE ON
EACH SIDE AND GLUED AROUND
EDGES AND TO CENTER TUBE)

PERMEATE FLOW

(AFTER PASSAGE
THROUGH MEMBRANE)

SPIRAL-WOUND REVERSE OSMOSIS MODULE

PRODUCT WATER
OUTLET

FEED CONNECTION

CONCENTRATE
OUTLET

HYDRAULIC
TUBE

SEAL

MODULE

PRESSURE VESSEL ASSEMBLY

Fig. 16.16   Spiral-wound reverse osmosis module (as manufactured by UOP)

(From paper by Mack Wesner, "Desalting Process and Pretreatment," published in Proceedings on "Role of Desalting Technology,"
a series of Technology Transfer Workshops presented by the Office of Water Research and Technology)

FIBER CROSS SECTION

OPEN ENDS
OF FIBERS

42 μ
(0.0016 inch)

85 μ
(0.0033 inch)

POROUS

THIN SKIN
0.1–1 μ THICK

SNAP RING

CONCENTRATE
OUTLET

POROUS
BACK-UP DISC

'O' RING
SEAL

FLOW SCREEN

EPOXY
TUBE SHEET

FEED

PERMEATE

END PLATE

FIBER

SHELL

FIBER

END PLATE

'O' RING SEAL/
SNAP RING

POROUS FEED
DISTRIBUTION TUBE

Fig. 16.17   Hollow fiber reverse osmosis module (as manufactured by DuPont)

(From paper by Mack Wesner, "Desalting Process and Pretreatment," published in Proceedings on "Role of Desalting Technology,"
a series of Technology Transfer Workshops presented by the Office of Water Research and Technology)

Tubular membrane processes operate on much the same principle as the hollow fine fiber except that the tubes are much larger in diameter, on the order of 0.5 inch (12 mm). Use of this type of membrane system is usually limited to special situations such as for wastewater with a high suspended solids concentration. The tubular membrane process is not economically competitive with other available systems for treatment of most waters.

QUESTIONS

Write your answers in a notebook and then compare your answers with those on page 191.

16.3A   List the three types of commercially available membrane configurations which have been used in operating plants.

16.3B   What type of membrane process is used to treat wastewater with a high suspended solids concentration?

16.4   OPERATION

16.40   Pretreatment

Water to be demineralized always contains impurities which should be removed by pretreatment to protect the membrane and to ensure maximum efficiency of the reverse osmosis process. Depending on the water to be demineralized, it is usually necessary to treat the feedwater to remove materials and conditions potentially harmful to the RO process such as:

1. Remove turbidity/suspended solids,

2. Adjust pH and temperature,

3. Remove materials to prevent scaling or fouling, and

4. Disinfect to prevent biological growth.

Table 16.5 provides a summary of pretreatment requirements for various feedwater constituents.

TABLE 16.5   RO PRETREATMENT REQUIREMENTS

Constituent	Problem	Treatment
Fine suspended solids (that is, causing turbidity)	Fouling. Collects on face of element and on the feed concentrate mesh spacer.	Clarification and/or coagulant addition followed by media filtration.
Gross suspended solids and particulates (that is, sand, debris)	Blockage of lead element face and entrapment within feed/concentrate channels.	Media filtration and/or cartridge filtration. Cartridge filters usually required to protect high pressure pumps as well.
Oil and Grease	Fouls membrane surface. Difficult to remove by cleaning.	Ultrafiltration. Batch separators, skimmers.
Microbiological matter	Fouling of the feed/concentrate mesh spacer. Adheres to some membrane surfaces.	Addition of oxidizing agent. In limited cases, ultraviolet sterilization.
Oxidizing agents (that is, chlorine)	Causes membrane degradation for some types of membranes.	Activated carbon and/or addition of reducing agents (sodium bisulfite).
Carbonates (CO_3, HCO_3)	Scaling. Combines with excess calcium to form calcium carbonate scale on membranes' surfaces.	Acid addition to convert alkalinity to carbon dioxide. Softening to remove calcium. Scale inhibitor in some cases.
Sulfate (SO_4)	Scaling. Combines with calcium, barium, strontium, or aluminum to form scale on membranes' surfaces.	Scale inhibitor addition. Softening to remove cations that could combine with sulfate. Reduce recovery of RO unit.
Silica	Scaling. Forms insoluble gel on membrane surface when supersaturated.	Lime softening. Reduce recovery of RO unit.
Iron (Ferric, +3)	Scaling and fouling. Forms iron oxides. Iron in the ferrous (+2) form is acceptable.	For groundwaters, no aeration or addition of oxidizing agents prior to RO unit. Greensand filters for removal of all forms of iron prior to RO unit.
Hydrogen Sulfide (H_2S)	Scaling and fouling (due to formation of elemental sulfur) when H_2S is aerated or oxidized prior to RO unit.	Best treatment technique is to avoid aeration or oxidation prior to RO unit and to remove H_2S from permeate by degasification.

16.41   Removal of Turbidity and Suspended Solids

In general, the feedwater should be filtered to protect the reverse osmosis system and its accessory equipment. When the water source is a groundwater or previously treated municipal or industrial supply, this may be accomplished by a simple screening procedure. However, such a procedure may not be adequate when the source is an untreated surface water. The amount of suspended matter in surface waters may vary by several orders of magnitude and may change radically in character and composition in a very short time. In such cases, in addition to the mechanical action of the filter, the operator may have to introduce chemicals for coagulation and flocculation and use filtration equipment in which the media can be washed or renewed at low cost. Pressure and gravity sand filters and diatomaceous earth filters may be required, particularly for large installations. When the particulates approach or are *COLLOIDAL*,[10] chemical treatment and filtration are almost essential.

Cartridge filters function as a particle safeguard and not as a primary particle removal device. In general, the influent turbidity to a cartridge filter should be less than one TU. Typical cartridge filter sizes range from 5 to 20 microns and loading rates vary from 2 to 4 GPM/sq ft (1.4 to 2.8 mm/sec).

16.42   pH and Temperature Control

As previously discussed, an important limiting factor in the life of cellulose acetate membranes in reverse osmosis is the rate of membrane hydrolysis. Cellulose acetate will break down (hydrolyze) to cellulose and acetic acid. The rate at which this hydrolysis occurs is a function of feedwater or source water pH and temperature. As the membrane hydrolyzes, both the amount of water and the amount of solute that permeate the membrane increase and the quality of the product water deteriorates. The rate of hydrolysis is at a minimum at a pH of about 4.7, and it increases with both increasing and decreasing pH. Thus it is standard practice to inject acid, usually sulfuric acid, to adjust feedwater pH to 5.5. Not only does pH adjustment minimize the effect of hydrolysis, but it is also essential in controlling precipitation of scale-forming or membrane-fouling minerals.

Calcium carbonate and calcium sulfate are probably the most common scaling salts encountered in natural waters and are certainly the most common cause of scale in reverse osmosis systems. The addition of a small amount of acid can reduce the pH to a point where the alkalinity is reduced; this shifts the equilibrium to the point where calcium bicarbonate, which is much more soluble, is present at all points within the reverse osmosis loop. Neutralization of 75 percent of the total alkalinity usually provides sufficient pH adjustment to achieve calcium carbonate scale control and bring the membrane into a reasonable part of the hydrolysis curve. The pH reached by 75-percent neutralization is about 5.7. Calcium carbonate precipitation is also inhibited by the control procedure used for calcium sulfate.

Calcium sulfate is relatively soluble in water in comparison to calcium carbonate. Again, however, as "pure" or product water is removed from a feed solution containing calcium and sulfate, these chemicals become further concentrated in the feedwater. When the limits of saturation are eventually exceeded, precipitation of calcium sulfate will occur. Since calcium sulfate solubility occurs over a wide pH range, the scale control method used to inhibit calcium sulfate precipitation is a threshold treatment[11] with sodium hexametaphosphate (SHMP). This precipitation inhibitor represses both calcium carbonate and calcium sulfate by interfering with the crystal formation process. Other polyphosphates may also be used but are not as effective as the hexametaphosphate. Generally 2 to 5 mg/L of SHMP are added to the feedwater to decrease precipitation of calcium sulfate.

16.43   Other Potential Scalants

The oxides or hydroxides most commonly found in water are those of iron, manganese, and silica. The oxidized and precipitated forms of iron, manganese, and silica can be a serious problem to any demineralization scheme because they can coat the reverse osmosis membrane with a tenacious (difficult to remove) film which will affect performance. The scale inhibitor most frequently used is sodium hexametaphosphate.

16.44   Microbiological Organisms

Reverse osmosis modules provide a large surface area for the attachment and growth of bacterial slimes and molds. These organisms may cause membrane fouling or even module plugging. There is also some evidence that occasionally the enzyme systems of some organisms will attack the cellulose acetate membrane. The continuous application of chlorine to produce a 1 to 2 mg/L chlorine residual will help inhibit or retard the growth of most of the organisms encountered. However, caution must be exercised since continuous exposure of the membrane to higher chlorine residuals will impair membrane efficiency. Shock concentrations of up to 10 mg/L of chlorine are applied from time to time. When an oxidant-intolerant polyamide-type membrane is used, chlorination must be followed with dechlorination. One of the dechlorination agents, sodium bisulfite, is also known to be a disinfectant. Another disinfection option is the use of ultraviolet disinfection which leaves no oxidant residual in the water.

---

[10] *Colloids (CALL-loids).   Very small, finely divided solids (particles that do not dissolve) that remain dispersed in a liquid for a long time due to their small size and electrical charge. When most of the particles in water have a negative electrical charge, they tend to repel each other. This repulsion prevents the particles from clumping together, becoming heavier, and settling out.*

[11] *Threshold treatment refers to the practice of using the least amount of chemical to produce the desired effect.*

QUESTIONS

Write your answers in a notebook and then compare your answers with those on page 191.

16.4A   How are turbidity and suspended solids removed from feedwater to the reverse osmosis system?

16.4B   How are colloidal particulates removed from feedwater to the reverse osmosis system?

16.4C   What happens to the product water as an acetate membrane hydrolyzes?

16.4D   How is the precipitation of calcium sulfate prevented?

16.4E   How is biological fouling on membranes controlled?

16.45   RO Plant Operation

Following proper pretreatment, the water to be demineralized is pressurized by high pressure feed pumps and delivered to the RO pressure vessel membrane assemblies. An example of a typical RO plant layout is given in Figure 16.18. The membrane assemblies consist of a series of pressure vessels (usually fiber-reinforced plastic) arranged in the "Christmas Tree" layout depending on the desired recovery. Typical operating pressure for brackish water demineralizing varies from 150 to 400 psi (1,050 to 2,760 kPa or 10.5 to 28 kg/sq cm). A control valve on the influent manifold regulates the operating pressure. The volumes of feed flow and of product water are also monitored. The demineralized water is usually called permeate, and the reject, concentrate (brine). The recovery rate is controlled by increasing feed flow (increase operating pressure) and controlling the concentrate (brine) or reject with a preset brine control valve.

The operator must properly maintain and control all flows and recovery rates to avoid possible damage to the membranes from scaling.

You must remember that the

BRINE FLOW VALVES ARE NEVER TO BE FULLY CLOSED.

Should they be accidentally closed during operation, 100 percent recovery will result in almost certain damage to the membranes due to precipitation of inorganic salts (CaSO$_4$). Product or permeate flow is not regulated and varies as feedwater pressure and temperature change as previously discussed.

Most RO systems are designed to operate automatically and require a minimum of operator attention. However, the continuous monitoring of system performance is an important aspect of operation. An example of a typical operation log for monitoring the Orange County Water District's 5 MGD (19 MLD) RO plant is given in Figure 16.19.

QUESTIONS

Write your answers in a notebook and then compare your answers with those on pages 191 and 192.

16.4F   How is the operating pressure on a reverse osmosis unit regulated?

16.4G   The demineralized water is usually called _____ , the reject, _____ .

16.4H   How does the product or permeate flow vary or change?

16.46   Typical RO Plant Operations Checklist

1. Check cartridge filters. Properly installed filters ensure additional removal of suspended solids that could damage either the high pressure feed pumps or foul the membrane elements. Cartridge filters should be replaced whenever head loss exceeds manufacturer's recommendations or effluent turbidity exceeds one TU.

2. Start up and check scale inhibitor feeding equipment and adjust feed rate to desired dose (2 to 5 mg/L). Most RO systems should not be operated without the addition of a scale inhibitor to protect membranes from precipitation of calcium sulfate or other inorganics. The scale inhibitor most frequently used is sodium hexametaphosphate.

3. If chlorine is used to prevent biological fouling, start chlorine feed and adjust dose to produce a chlorine residual of between 1 and 2 mg/L.

4. Start up and adjust acid feed system to correct feedwater pH to a level between 5.0 and 6.0 to protect membranes from possible damage due to hydrolysis. Note, feedwater should always be bypassed until the pH is properly adjusted.

5. Most RO systems are designed with automatic controls and various shutdown alarms. These alarms prevent start-up or running of the unit until proper operating conditions are reached. After satisfying these conditions, high pressure feed pumps can be started and water delivered to the RO units. A control valve is used to regulate feedwater pressure. Typical operating pressures vary from 150 to 400 psi (1,050 to 2,760 kPa or 10.5 to 28 kg/sq cm).

6. Adjust permeate and concentrate flow to establish the desired recovery rate.

7. Once flow has been established, check the differential pressure (ΔP) across the RO unit (ΔP = feed pressure − concentrate pressure) which is usually indicated by a meter and recorded. The importance of ΔP relates to cleaning. When the elements become fouled, ΔP usually increases, thus indicating the need for cleaning. The ΔP should not exceed 60 psi per 6-element pressure vessel (414 kPa or 4.1 kg/sq cm) because of possible damage to the RO modules.

8. With the system on line, monitor the performance. Rely on flow measurements, product water quality, and various pressure indications. A sample of a typical log sheet is shown in Figure 16.19.

Fig. 16.18   RO flow diagram

Pretreatment

TIME	Cl mg/l	Cartridge Filters #1 psig	#2 psig	#3 psig	#4 psig	Turb NTU	Temp °F	Feed Cond µmhos/cm	pH	Pump-2 Disch. A psig	B psig	C psig
0400												
1200												
2000												

RO Unit 1 / RO Unit 2 / Total Brine / Total Product

TIME	RO Unit 1 Feed psig	Feed Flow MGD	Product Cond. (µ)	RO Unit 2 Feed psig	Feed Flow MGD	Product Cond. (µ)	Total Brine Flow MGD	pH	Conductivity µmhos/cm	Total Product KWH Ton	pH	Conductivity µmhos/cm	Flow MGD
0400													
1200													
2000													

RO Unit 1

TIME	Section 1A-Product EC Feed psig	ΔP 1st	2nd	3rd	Product gpm	Brine MGD	Section 1B-Product EC Feed psig	ΔP 1st	2nd	3rd	Product gpm	Brine MGD	Section 1C-Product EC Feed psig	ΔP 1st	2nd	3rd	Product gpm	Brine MGD
0400																		
1200																		
2000																		

RO Unit 2

TIME	Section 2A-Product EC Feed psig	ΔP 1st	2nd	3rd	Product gpm	Brine MGD	Section 2B-Product EC Feed psig	ΔP 1st	2nd	3rd	Product gpm	Brine MGD	Section 2C-Product EC Feed psig	ΔP 1st	2nd	3rd	Product gpm	Brine MGD
0400																		
1200																		
2000																		

Fig. 16.19   Data sheet, Orange County Water District 5.0 MGD (19 MLD) reverse osmosis system

Shift	Operator

Date

24 Hour Totalizer				
TIME	Feed Flow MGD	Bypass Flow MGD	Total Product MGD	Total Brine MGD
(A)2400 (II)				
(B)2400 (I)				

Cl$_2$	SHMP	ACID	ELAPSED TIME		POWER
			RO #1	RO #2	
2400 (11)					2400 (11)
2400 (1)	lbs	gal			2400 (1)

REMARKS: _____

_____

_____

_____

_____

_____

_____

_____

_____

_____

_____

_____

_____

_____

_____

_____

_____

_____

Fig. 16.19 Data sheet, Orange County Water District
5.0 MGD (19 MLD) reverse osmosis system (continued)

16.47   Membrane Cleaning

Periodically the performance of the RO system will decline. This is usually observed when either the product water flow rate (flux) decreases, or salt removal (rejection) decreases. Table 16.6 summarizes common causes of membrane damage or loss of performance. Note that in Cases III and IV the corrective action requires cleaning of the element. Provisions for the periodic cleaning of the reverse osmosis elements are usually included in the system design. This makes it possible to clean impurities off the membrane surfaces and restore normal flow rates without removing the elements from the pressure vessels. Element cleaning should be performed at regular intervals to ensure as low an operating pressure as practical. The elements should be cleaned when the pressure required to maintain the rated capacity has either been increased by 15-percent (or a 15-percent decrease in product water flow has occurred at constant pressure), or a rise of 15 percent in the system differential pressure has been observed.

Most RO systems are provided with in-place cleaning systems. This includes tanks, pumps, valves, and piping for mixing and pumping cleaning solutions through the membrane elements. For cleaning, the unit is shut down and cleaning solutions are pumped through the vessels in a manner similar to feedwater. Typically, cleaning solutions are passed through the pressure vessels at low pressure and at flow rates where the ΔP does not exceed 60 psi (414 kPa or 4.1 kg/sq cm) to avoid damaging the elements. The cleaning solutions are returned to clean tanks at the end of a cleaning cycle, which usually lasts about one hour. Different cleaning solutions are available for use depending upon the type of fouling. Membranes are typically cleaned for approximately 45 minutes after which the cleaning solution is spent.

To remove inorganic precipitates, use an acid flush of citric acid. For biological or organic fouling, various solutions of detergents, sequestrants, chelating agents, bactericides, and

enzymes are available. Examples include sodium tripolyphosphate, B13, Triton X-100, and EDTA.

To improve the long-term performance of an RO system, the membranes should be flushed with flush water during periods of shutdown to remove raw feed water and concentrate. If raw water is allowed to remain in the unit, precipitation may occur. Flushing is also done after cleaning to remove the cleaning solution prior to system start-up. In some cases, where the system is shut down for long periods of time, formaldehyde may be added to the flush water to inhibit biological growth.

QUESTIONS

Write your answers in a notebook and then compare your answers with those on page 192.

16.4I   Why is chlorine added to the feedwater to a reverse osmosis unit?

16.4J   Why must the operator check the differential pressure (ΔP) across the RO unit?

16.4K   When should the reverse osmosis elements be cleaned?

TABLE 16.6   SUMMARY OF COMMON CAUSES OF MEMBRANE DAMAGE

Symptom	Cause	Restoration Procedure
Case I[a] 1. Lower product water flow rate 2. Higher salt rejection	Membrane compaction[b] accelerated by operating pressure greater than 500 psi (3,450 kPa or 35 kg/sq cm).	None. Requires element replacement when product water flow rate reaches an unacceptable level.
Case II[a] 1. Higher product level flow rate 2. Lower salt rejection	Membrane hydrolysis 1. pH outside operating limits 2. Bacterial degradation 3. Temperature outside operating limits.	Injection of colloid 189 (size) or element replacement.
Case III[c] 1. Lower product water flow rate and/or 2. Lower salt rejection	Membrane fouling.	Element cleaning.
Case IV[c] 1. Lower product water flow rate 2. High ΔP	Membrane fouling.	Element cleaning.

[a] CA-cellulose acetate membranes.
[b] Membrane Compaction. Product water flow rate declines with operational time in addition to fouling of the membrane surface due to other factors. Water flow rate plotted versus time on log-log paper will yield a straight line (flow rate decline).
[c] All types of membranes.

16.48 Safety

16.480 Use of Proper Procedures

As in any water treatment plant, there are forces and chemicals used in a reverse osmosis plant which must be handled properly to ensure the safety and protection of personnel. Safety needs for demineralization plants can be divided into three general groups consisting of chemicals, electrical, and hydraulics.

16.481 Chemical Safety

Operation of an RO plant requires the use of a wide variety of chemicals. Whenever you must handle chemicals, follow the proper procedures for each chemical. The manufacturer's recommendations for use of each chemical must be observed. A list of the commonly used chemicals requiring special handling found in an RO plant operation include:

1. Acid,

2. Chlorine,

3. Sodium hexametaphosphate,

4. Formaldehyde,

5. Citric acid, and

6. Numerous cleaning agents.

See Chapter 20, "Safety," for more detailed procedures on the safe use of hazardous chemicals.

16.482 Hydraulic Safety

For the reverse osmosis process to function properly, hydraulic pressure in excess of the solution's average osmotic pressure (π) is required. Within the plant, therefore, most of the pipes, tubing, vessels, and their associated equipment, along with the substances inside these items, operate under varying levels of hydraulic pressure (150 to 400 psi (1,050 to 2,760 kPa or 10.5 to 28 kg/sq cm)). Therefore, prior to ANY repairs, modifications, or work of any kind, NO MATTER HOW MINOR, know the substances contained, isolate the piece of equipment, and equalize pressure levels to atmospheric pressure.

After being repaired, any piece of equipment should be purged of ALL foreign substances BEFORE being restarted. When bringing a piece or pieces of equipment on line, increase the hydraulic pressures slowly. Keep all personnel in a safe area to maximize their personal safety.

16.483 Electrical Safety

An RO plant consists of a series of electrically powered pumps and mechanical equipment. Electric shocks due to the use of electrical equipment occur without warning and are usually serious. The average individual thinks of the hazards of electric shock in terms of high voltage and does not always realize that it is primarily the current that kills, not the voltage. Consequently, persons who work around low voltage equipment do not always have the same healthy respect for current as they do for high voltage. Whenever working around electrically operated equipment, strictly observe all applicable rules of the 1997 National Electrical Safety Code.[12]

QUESTIONS

Write your answers in a notebook and then compare your answers with those on page 192.

16.4L   List the three general groups of safety needs for a demineralization plant.

16.4M   What type of electrical equipment is used around reverse osmosis plants?

End of Lesson 2 of 3 Lessons on DEMINERALIZATION

Please answer the discussion and review questions next.

DISCUSSION AND REVIEW QUESTIONS

Chapter 16. DEMINERALIZATION

(Lesson 2 of 3 Lessons)

Write the answers to these questions in your notebook before continuing. The question numbering continues from Lesson 1.

9. Why does water to be demineralized require pretreatment?

10. What problems are created for demineralization processes by the oxidized and precipitated forms of iron, manganese, and silica?

11. How does the operator of a reverse osmosis plant avoid possible damage to the membrane from scaling?

12. What will happen in a reverse osmosis plant if the brine flow valves are accidentally closed during operation?

13. What is the purpose of cartridge filters and when should they be replaced?

14. How can the operator determine if the performance of the RO system is declining?

15. What does hydraulic safety consist of around a reverse osmosis process?

[12] 1997 NATIONAL ELECTRICAL SAFETY CODE. Available from Institute of Electrical and Electronic Engineers, Inc., IEEE Service Center, PO Box 1331, 445 Hoes Lane, Piscataway, NJ 08855-1331. Order No. SH94406. Price to members, $44.10 plus $4.00 shipping; nonmembers, $63.00, plus $5.00 shipping and handling charges.

CHAPTER 16. DEMINERALIZATION

(Lesson 3 of 3 Lessons)

16.5 ELECTRODIALYSIS

Electrodialysis (ED) is a well-developed process with a history of many years of operation on brackish well water supplies. A 650,000 GPD (2.5 MLD) ED plant, manufactured by Ionics, Inc., Watertown, Massachusetts, began operation on well water at Buckeye, Arizona, in September 1972 and has been in continuous operation to date. ED plants are also in operation demineralizing municipal water supplies in Siesta Key, Florida; Sanibel Island, Florida; Sorrento Shores, Florida; and at the Foss Reservoir in Oklahoma. The process is also used for industrial water demineralizing.

Typical removals of inorganic salts from brackish water by ED range from 25 to 40 percent of dissolved solids per stage of treatment. Higher removals require treatment by multiple stages in series. Less than 20 percent of the organics remaining in activated carbon-treated secondary effluent are removed by electrodialysis. Energy required for ED is about 0.2 to 0.4 kilowatt-hour per 1,000 gallons (kWh/1,000 gal) for each 100 mg/L dissolved solids removed, plus 2 to 3 kWh/1,000 gal for pumping feedwater and brine. Advantages of the ED process include: (1) well-developed technology, including equipment and membranes; (2) efficient removal of most inorganic constituents; and (3) waste brine contains only salts removed plus a small amount of acid used for pH control in some ED applications.

In the ED process brackish water flows between alternating cation-permeable and anion-permeable membranes as illustrated in Figure 16.20. A direct electric current provides the motive force to cause ions to migrate through the membranes. Many alternating cation and anion membranes, each separated by a plastic spacer, are assembled into membrane

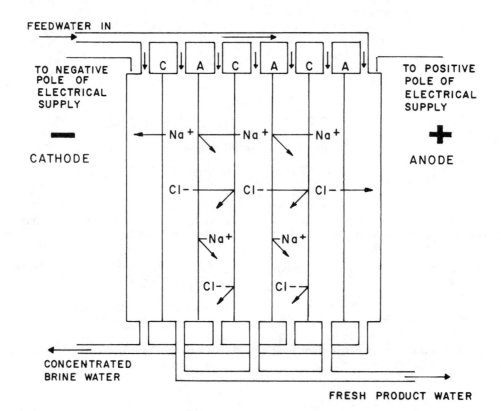

C   CATION—PERMEABLE MEMBRANE

A   ANION—PERMEABLE MEMBRANE

Fig. 16.20 Electrodialysis demineralization process

(From *STANDARD OPERATION INSTRUCTION PLAN FOR ELECTRODIALYSIS*, prepared by Ionics, Inc.)

stacks. The spacers (about 0.04-inch (1-mm) thick) contain the water streams within the stack and direct the flow of water through a tortuous path across the exposed faces of the membranes. Membrane thicknesses generally range between 0.005 and 0.025 inch (0.125 and 0.625 mm).

Physically, the equipment takes the form of a plate-and-frame assembly similar to that of a filter press. The spacers determine the thickness of the solution compartments and also define the flow paths of the water over the membrane surface. Several hundred membranes and their separating spacers are usually assembled between a single set of electrodes to form a membrane stack. End plates and tie rods complete the assembly. When a membrane is placed between two salt solutions and subjected to the passage of a direct electric current, most of the current will be carried through the membrane by ions, hence the membrane is said to be ion selective. Typical selectivities are greater than 90 percent. When the passage of current is continued for a sufficient length of time, the solution on the side of the membrane that is furnishing the ions becomes partially desalted, and the solution adjacent to the other side of the membrane becomes more concentrated. These desalting and concentrating phenomena occur in thin layers of solution immediately adjacent to the membrane resulting in the desalting of the bulk of the solution.

Passage of water between the membranes of a single stack, or stage, usually requires 10 to 20 seconds, during which time the entering minerals in the feedwater are removed. The actual percentage removal that is achieved varies with water temperature, type and amounts of ions present, flow rate of the water, and stack design. Typical removals per stage range from 25 to 40 percent and systems use one to six stages. An ED system will operate at temperatures up to 110 degrees Fahrenheit (110°F (43°C)) and the removal efficiency increases with increasing temperature. Ion-selective membranes in commercial electrodialysis equipment are commonly guaranteed for as long as 5 years and experience has demonstrated an effective life of over 10 years.

The most commonly encountered problem in ED operation is scaling (or fouling) of the membranes by both organic and inorganic materials. Alkaline scales are troublesome in the concentrating compartments when the diffusion of ions to the surface of the anion membrane in the diluting cell is insufficient to carry the current. Water is then electrolyzed and hydroxide ions pass through the membrane and raise the pH in the cell. This increase is often sufficient to cause precipitation of materials such as magnesium hydroxide or calcium carbonate. The accumulation of particulate matter increases the electrical resistance of the membrane; this may damage or destroy the membranes. This condition can be offset by feeding acid to the concentrate water stream to maintain a negative Langelier Index to ensure scale-free operation.

Ionics, Inc., has developed a type of ED unit which does not require the addition of acid or other chemicals for scale control. This system reverses the D.C. current direction and the flow path of the dilution and concentrating streams every 15 minutes. The electrodes reverse by switching the polarity of the cathodes and anodes. The stream flow paths also exchange their source every 15 minutes. Motor-operated valves controlled by timers switch the streams so that the flow path that was previously the diluting stream becomes the concentrating stream and the flow path that was previously the concentrating stream becomes the diluting stream. This reversing polarity system is commonly referred to as electrodialysis polarity reversal (EDR).

QUESTIONS

Write your answers in a notebook and then compare your answers with those on page 192.

16.5A   What are the typical removals of inorganic salts from brackish water by electrodialysis (ED) per stage of treatment?

16.5B   What is a membrane stack in an electrodialysis unit?

16.5C   What is the most commonly encountered problem in ED operation?

16.6   PRINCIPLES OF ELECTRODIALYSIS

16.60   Anions and Cations in Water

When most common salts, minerals, acids, and alkalis are dissolved in water, each molecule splits into two oppositely charged particles called "ions." All positively charged ions are known as "cations" and all negatively charged ions, as "anions." For instance, when common table salt (sodium chloride or NaCl) is dissolved in water, it separates into positive sodium ions (Na^+) and negative chloride ions (Cl^-). The following ions are found in seawater or brackish water in appreciable quantities.

Cations		Anions	
Sodium	Na^+	Chloride	Cl^-
Calcium	Ca^{2+}	Bicarbonate	HCO_3^-
Magnesium	Mg^{2+}	Sulfate	SO_4^{2-}

16.61   Effect of Direct Current (D.C.) Potential on Ions

If a D.C. potential is applied across a solution of salt in water by means of insertion of two electrodes in the solution, the cations will move toward a negative electrode, which is known as the "cathode," and the anions will move toward the positive electrode, which is known as the "anode." In Figure 16.21 (A) we have a solution of sodium chloride in water. The cations (Na^+) and anions (Cl^-) are moving about at random. In Figure 16.21 (B) a D.C. potential has been introduced in the solution and the anions move toward the positive electrode and the cations move toward the negative electrode.

16.62   Anion and Cation Membranes and Three-Cell Unit

Advantage could be taken of this movement of ions if proper barriers were available to isolate the purified zone in Figure 16.21 (B) so as to prevent remixing. There are two types of membranes which can be used as such barriers:

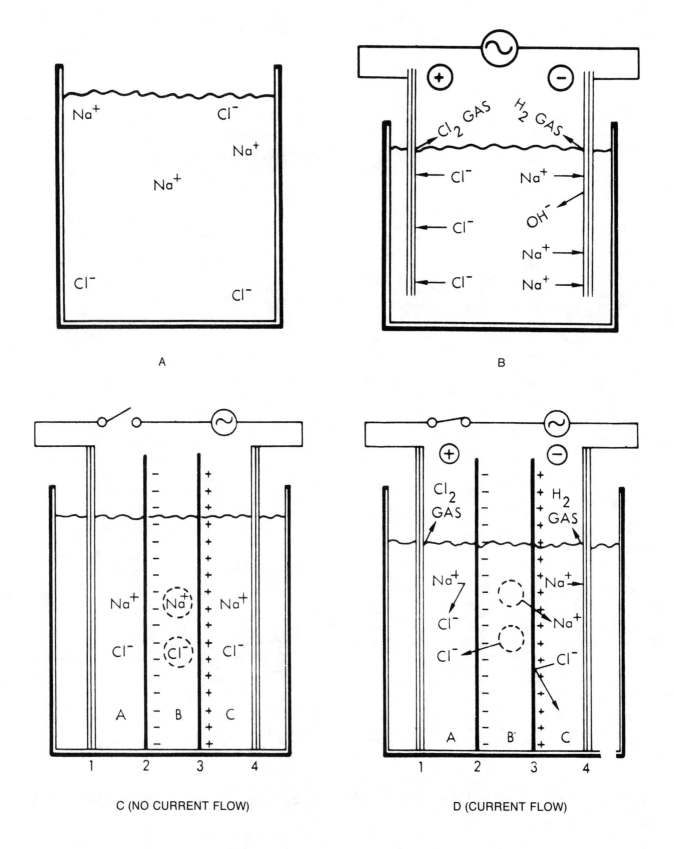

Fig. 16.21   Influence of current flow

(From *STANDARD OPERATION INSTRUCTION PLAN FOR ELECTRODIALYSIS*, prepared by Ionics, Inc.)

1. Cation Membranes — Permit only the passage of cations (positively charged ions); and

2. Anion Membranes — Permit only the passage of anions (negatively charged ions).

Introduction of a cation membrane and anion membrane into a salt solution to form three watertight compartments (Figure 16.21 (C)) followed by a direct electric current into the water (Figure 16.21 (D)) will result in the demineralization of the central compartment.

In the three-cell unit shown in Figure 16.21 (C) and (D), "1" is the anode (positive electrode), "2" is the anion membrane, "3" is the cation membrane, and "4" is the cathode (negative electrode). In Figure 16.21 (C) there is no electric flow so the ions move at random in their respective compartments. In Figure 16.21 (D) the introduction of a D.C. potential gives these ions direction: the cations (Na^+) move toward the cathode and the anions (Cl^-) toward the anode. The following occurs:

1. Na^+ from compartment A cannot pass through anion membrane (2) into compartment B,

2. Cl^- from compartment A reacts at the anode (1) to give off chlorine gas,

3. Na^+ from compartment B passes through cation membrane (3) into compartment C,

4. Cl^- from compartment B passes through anion membrane (2) into compartment A,

5. Na^+ from compartment C reacts at the cathode to give off hydrogen gas and hydroxyl ions (OH^-), and

6. Cl^- from compartment C cannot pass through cation membrane (3) into compartment B.

This description indicates how the overall effect has produced a demineralization of the central compartment.

16.63   Multi-Compartment Unit

Figure 16.22 presents a multi-compartment unit similar in principle to a stack. Letter "A" designates the anion membranes; letter "C," the cation membranes; the "+" sign, the anode; the "−" sign, the cathode. A salt solution of Na^+ and Cl^- ions flows between the membranes. On application of the D.C. potential, the overall effect will be as shown, a movement of ions from the compartments bounded by an anion membrane on the left and a cation membrane on the right into the adjacent compartments. The compartments losing salt are labeled "dilute" and those receiving the transferred salt are labeled "brine." Two electrode compartments are also found in the drawing. Each is bordered by a cation membrane and the electrode. At the anode, a reaction takes place evolving chlorine and oxygen gases; at the cathode, hydrogen gas is produced and hydroxyl ions (OH^-) are left in the solution. Hydroxyl ions are alkaline.

QUESTIONS

Write your answers in a notebook and then compare your answers with those on page 192.

16.6A   What happens if a D.C. potential is applied across a solution of salt in water by means of insertion of two electrodes in the solution?

16.6B   What type of ions can pass through cation membranes?

16.6C   In a multi-compartment ED unit, the compartments losing salt are labeled _____ and those receiving the transferred salt, _____ .

16.7   PARTS OF AN ELECTRODIALYSIS UNIT

16.70   Flow Diagram

The basic electrodialysis unit consists of:

1. Pretreatment equipment,

2. Pumping equipment (feed, brine, and recirculation),

3. D.C. power supply,

4. Membrane stack and electrodes, and

5. In-place cleaning system.

Figure 16.23 shows a typical flow diagram and Figure 16.24 a photo of an electrodialysis unit.

16.71   Pretreatment

A certain degree of pretreatment of the feedwater supply is necessary in order to prepare it for demineralization in the stacks. Pretreatment depends on the specific water being treated, but it usually includes the removal of suspended or dissolved solids which could adversely affect the surface of the membranes or mechanically block the narrow passageways in the individual cells. Cartridge filters are used as a particle safeguard before the ED unit. Before development of the electrodialysis polarity reversal (EDR) unit, acid addition to prevent carbonate scaling was always practiced. With the electrodialysis reversal process, the requirement for acid addition is reduced or eliminated. Removal of specific materials such as iron, manganese, or chlorine residual if required is included in pretreatment.

16.72   Pumping Equipment and Piping

In the electrodialysis process the water pump(s) is used only for circulation of the water through the stack. The head loss for this circulation varies with the construction of the stacks, number of stages, stacks, and piping, but generally a pumping pressure of only about 50 to 75 psi (345 to 517 kPa or 3.5 to 5.2 kg/sq cm) is needed.

Since only low operating pressures compared to RO are required, ED systems are constructed with common materials found in most water treatment applications. This has allowed the use of a great deal of standard plastic pipe and fittings. The use of plastic pipe produces benefits including lower cost (compared to stainless steel), high resistance to corrosion in a saline environment, and ease of construction.

16.73   D.C. Power Supply

The rectifier provides the D.C. power to the membrane stack assembly. The input (alternating current (A.C.)) is converted by the rectifier to direct current which is applied to the electrodes on each side of the membrane stack to remove the

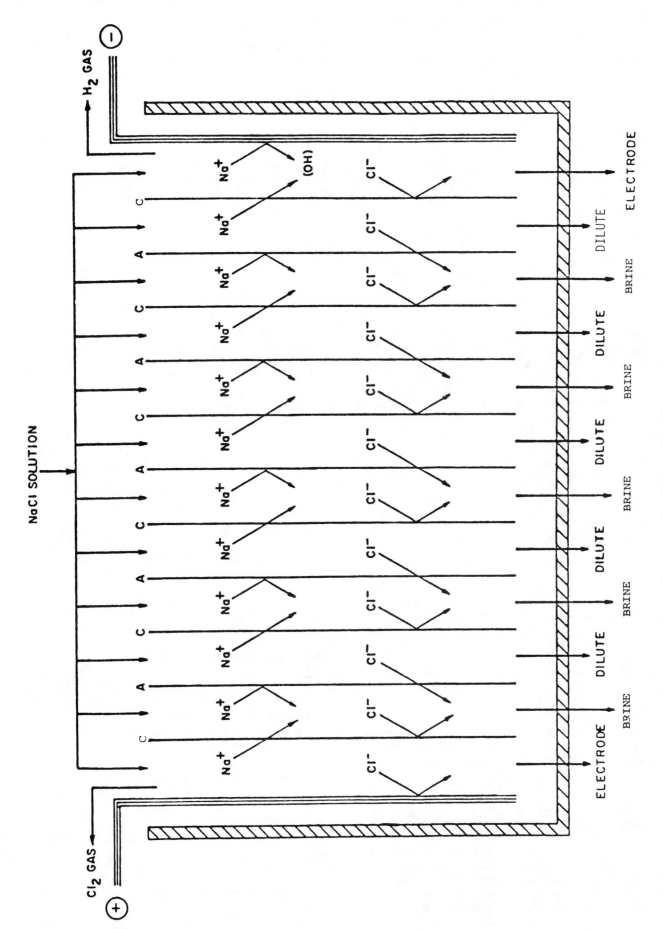

Fig. 16.22 Multi-compartment ED stack
(From STANDARD INSTRUCTION PLAN FOR ELECTRODIALYSIS, prepared by Ionics, Inc.)

Fig. 16.23   Typical electrodialysis flow diagram

MEMBRANE STACKS

ELECTRODES

ELECTRICAL PANEL

HYDRAULIC CONTROL PANELS

D.C. POWER SUPPLY (RECTIFIER)

CIRCULATION PUMP

PRETREATMENT (FEEDWATER FILTERS)

Fig. 16.24   Basic parts of an electrodialysis unit

(Courtesy of Ionics, Inc.)

ions from the feed stream. This equipment also includes a control module for periodic reversal of the current every 15 to 30 minutes on all new electrodialysis polarity reversal (EDR) models.

16.74 Membrane Stack

The membrane "stack" is so called because it is composed of a large number of stacked pieces, like a deck of cards. Half of these pieces are spacers and half are membranes which alternate from the bottom to the top of the stack. In other words, in examining any portion of the stack, you will find a membrane above and below every spacer (except at the electrodes) and a spacer above and below every membrane. Two membranes or two spacers should never occur together.

Each membrane stack constitutes one stage of demineralization and is a separate hydraulic and electrical stage. The total number of stacks in the unit will be arranged in either one line or two lines running in parallel (each with an equal number of stacks). Since all the stacks in a line are connected in a series, the number of stacks per line will equal the number of stages of demineralization.

The membranes and spacers in the main section of the stack make up the number of cell pairs noted in the stack specifications. A cell pair consists of one anion membrane, one cation membrane, and two inter-membrane spacers and is the basic demineralizing element. The metal electrodes located at the ends of the stack apply the D.C. electric power required for demineralization.

16.75 Chemical Flush System

ED units are equipped with a Clean-In-Place (CIP) flush system to allow periodic flushing of the membrane stacks and associated piping with acid solutions down to pH 1 or with brine solutions up to 10 percent sodium chloride.

The two chemical solutions which are used most often for stack cleaning are a five-percent solution of hydrochloric acid (for removal of scale and normal cleaning), and a five-percent salt solution which has caustic soda added to adjust the pH to between 12 and 13 (for removal of organic fouling or slime).

QUESTIONS

Write your answers in a notebook and then compare your answers with those on page 192.

16.7A What must be removed by pretreatment of the feedwater supply to the electrodialysis unit?

16.7B What is the purpose of the rectifier in an electrodialysis unit?

16.8 ROUTINE OPERATING PROCEDURES

16.80 Design Specifications for Feedwater

The electrodialysis desalting unit will produce demineralized water at a rate dependent on water temperature and mineral composition of feedwater. The quality of the feedwater and its ionic composition are extremely important and the design of the ED unit is based on these conditions.

The ions most often encountered in feedwater are:

Cations	Anions
1. Calcium	1. Bicarbonate
2. Iron	2. Chloride
3. Magnesium	3. Sulfate
4. Silica	
5. Sodium	

An excessive concentration of any of these constituents could lead to chemical fouling due to scaling. Iron in the feedwater will cause certain process problems; above 0.1 mg/L certain precautions have to be taken. One of the effects of excess iron in feedwater is the deposit of an orange film onto the membrane surface which increases the electrical resistance of the membrane stack. Concentrations of iron in excess of 0.3 mg/L should be removed by pretreatment.

There are other important considerations regarding feedwater quality. These include pH, biological quality, and bacteriological quality of the feed. To prevent biological fouling of the cation and anion membranes, the feedwater should be free of bacteria. Proper control of feedwater pH is also important, particularly in terms of corrosion control in piping and plumbing equipment. Because chlorine attacks the ED membrane, the feedwater cannot contain any chlorine residual. If prechlorination is practiced, the feedwater must be dechlorinated before entering the ED unit. Generally the unit should *NOT* be operated when the feedwater contains any of the following:

1. Chlorine residual of any concentration,

2. Hydrogen sulfide of any concentration,

3. Calgon or other hexametaphosphates in excess of 10 mg/L,

4. Manganese in excess of 0.1 mg/L, and

5. Iron in excess of 0.3 mg/L.

16.81 Detailed Operating Procedures

Detailed operating procedures vary from one system to the next. Most ED or EDR units come designed with fully automatic control systems. A typical operating log used to monitor an ED system is given in Figure 16.25.

Date									
Polarity									
Feed Temp (°F)									
Feed TDS (mg/L)									
Product TDS (mg/L)									
Product Conductivity									
Dilute Flowrate (GPM)									
Brine Make-up (GPM)									
PRESSURES	Stack Inlet								
	Stack Outlet								
	Differential In								
	Differential Out								
	Before Filter								
	After Filter								
	Electrode Inlet								
Stage 1 Volts	Line 1								
	Line 2								
Stage 1 Amps	Line 1								
	Line 2								
Stage 2 Volts	Line 1								
	Line 2								
Stage 2 Amps	Line 1								
	Line 2								
Stage 3 Volts	Line 1								
	Line 2								
Stage 3 Amps	Line 1								
	Line 2								
Stage 4 Volts	Line 1								
	Line 2								
Stage 4 Amps	Line 1								
	Line 2								
Stage 5 Volts	Line 1								
	Line 2								
Stage 5 Amps	Line 1								
	Line 2								
Stage 6 Volts	Line 1								
	Line 2								
Stage 6 Amps	Line 1								
	Line 2								

Fig. 16.25   Typical operating log sheet for ED unit

The detailed specifications for any plant will give the proper settings for the various controls on the unit. These control settings should be checked and recorded at least once every 24 hours using the sample log sheet given in Figure 16.25. Any action needed to keep the plant running according to the specifications should be taken immediately.

In addition to checking the specifications, the routine maintenance schedule outlined below should be followed closely in order to reduce the risk of lengthy and expensive downtimes. Any process problems discovered must be acted upon immediately.

Daily

1. Fill out log sheet,

2. Verify that electrodes are bumping and flowing properly,

3. Inspect stacks for excess external leakage (greater than 10 gallons per hour or 38 liters per hour per stack), and

4. Check the pressure drop across the cartridge filter and change the cartridges whenever the pressure drop reaches 10 psi (69 kPa or 0.7 kg/sq cm).

Weekly

1. Voltage probe the membrane stacks,

2. Check the oil level on pumps fitted with automatic oilers,

3. Inspect all piping and skid components for leaks, and

4. Twice per week, measure all electrode waste flows.

QUESTIONS

Write your answers in a notebook and then compare your answers with those on page 192.

16.8A List the ions most often encountered in the feedwater to an electrodialysis unit.

16.8B What items must be considered to prevent biological fouling of the cation and anion membranes?

16.8C Generally the electrodialysis unit should *NOT* be operated when the feedwater contains _____. (List the appropriate water quality constituents.)

16.8D List the recommended daily activities for the operator of an electrodialysis unit.

16.9 SAFETY PRECAUTIONS

1. Grounding. The entire unit, including the stacks, must be connected to an electrical ground of each potential. *AT THE TIME OF INSTALLATION IT IS NECESSARY TO GROUND THE SKID OR THE CONTROL PANEL CABINET, EITHER BY A METAL CONDUIT OR A SEPARATE GROUNDING WIRE.*

   Each time the unit is moved or dismantled, check the ground connections before turning on the power. The skid, power supply cabinet, and stack(s) must always be firmly connected to the building ground or other suitable ground.

2. Check the *ELECTRODE TAB* connecting bolts and be sure these are tight and there is no corrosion. Loose connections at these points will cause overheating which could result in serious damage to the membrane stack.

3. Do not touch wet stack sides or electrode tabs when the D.C. power is on.

4. Always wear rubber gloves when voltage probing the membrane stack.

5. When washing down the area, never direct a hose on the membrane stack when the D.C. power is on.

6. Never operate a dry centrifugal pump, even when checking rotation.

7. Never apply D.C. voltage to the membrane stack without water flowing through the stack.

8. Expect the D.C. amperage to *DROP* when the feedwater temperature *DROPS*. Never increase the D.C. stack voltage as the water temperature drops in an attempt to raise currents to those recorded at the higher temperatures unless you have received specific instructions to do so from the manufacturer.

9. Expect the D.C. amperage to *RISE* when the feedwater temperature *RISES*. As this happens, the D.C. stack voltages must be lowered until the D.C. amperage returns to the normal setting. This conserves power and prevents damage to the stack.

10. Never allow oil, organic solutions, solvents, detergents, wastewater, chlorine, nitric acid, strong bleach, or other oxidizing agents to come in contact with the membranes and spacers unless directed to do so by the manufacturer. Membranes can be damaged by a feedwater containing even 0.1 mg/L free chlorine.

11. Always keep the membranes wet. Store in the membrane tube supplied or in the original plastic bags provided the seals are not broken.

12. Do not smoke or use exposed flames or sparks in the gas separator tank area due to the presence of potentially explosive gases.

13. Do not service the gas separator tank when the unit is in operation. Especially avoid the vent lines where toxic and explosive gases can be present. If it is necessary to service the tank, operate the unit for 30 minutes without D.C. power, then wait an additional hour before beginning work or ventilate with fans to ensure complete dispersion of dangerous gases.

14. If it is necessary to troubleshoot any of the electric panels, be extremely careful of the live panel voltages. This maintenance should be done only by someone familiar with the circuits and wiring. The unit should never be operated with the panel doors open, except for maintenance purposes, and only by experienced personnel.

15. Should shorting occur from a metal end plate across the plastic end block to the electrode, *IMMEDIATELY* turn off the rectifier. Try to eliminate the cause of the shorting by wiping excess moisture off the block. Also, be sure to completely remove the black carbon that has formed at the point of shorting. If this is not effectively done, the shorting will recur when the rectifier is turned back on.

16. Feedwater containing Calgon or other hexametaphosphates will cause high membrane stack resistance. Avoid operation when these are present.

17. Red warning lamps are mounted on the wire way for the stack power connections. The lamps are lit when the D.C. power is applied to the stacks.

18. When the plant is on automatic, the plant is controlled by the product water tank's level switch. Therefore, when working on the equipment, the plant should be switched to manual operation and locked out, thus avoiding the possibility of an unexpected start-up.

19. Use of the "STOP" switch or "STOP/START" switch activates an automatic flushing cycle and therefore does *NOT* immediately stop operation of all components of the unit. If the operation of the entire unit must be stopped immediately, the *MAIN BREAKER* should be switched off.

QUESTIONS

Write your answers in a notebook and then compare your answers with those on page 192.

16.9A What problems can be created by loose connections at the electrode tab connecting bolts?

16.9B What happens to the D.C. amperage when the feedwater temperature drops?

16.9C How can shorting be prevented from the metal end plate across the plastic end block to the electrode?

16.9D How can the operation of the entire electrodialysis unit be stopped immediately?

16.10 ARITHMETIC ASSIGNMENT

Turn to the Appendix at the back of this manual. Read and work the problems in Section A.34, "Demineralization." You should be able to get the same answers on your pocket calculator.

16.11 ADDITIONAL READING

1. *TEXAS MANUAL*, Chapter 11*, "Special Water Treatment (Desalting)."

* Depends on edition.

End of Lesson 3 of 3 Lessons on DEMINERALIZATION

Please answer the discussion and review questions before continuing with the Objective Test.

DISCUSSION AND REVIEW QUESTIONS

Chapter 16. DEMINERALIZATION

(Lesson 3 of 3 Lessons)

Write the answers to these questions in your notebook before continuing with the Objective Test on page 193. The question numbering continues from Lesson 2.

16. How does an electrodialysis unit demineralize brackish water?

17. What are the parts of a basic electrodialysis unit?

18. What are the benefits of using plastic pipe in an electrodialysis plant?

19. What is the purpose of the chemical flush system in an electrodialysis unit?

20. An excessive concentration of any specific ion in the feedwater to an electrodialysis unit can cause what problem?

21. When should you check to be sure that an electrodialysis unit is properly grounded?

SUGGESTED ANSWERS

Chapter 16.   DEMINERALIZATION

ANSWERS TO QUESTIONS IN LESSON 1

Answers to questions on page 152.

16.0A   Demineralization is the process that removes dissolved minerals (salts) from water.

16.0B   Seawater is more expensive to treat than brackish water because of its much higher TDS concentration.

Answers to questions on page 152.

16.1A   Methods of removing minerals from water can be divided into two classes:

1. Those that use a phase change such as freezing or distillation, and
2. Non-phase change methods such as reverse osmosis, electrodialysis, and ion exchange.

16.1B   The common membrane demineralizing processes are reverse osmosis and electrodialysis.

Answers to questions on page 156.

16.2A   The osmotic pressure of a solution is the difference in water level on both sides of a membrane.

16.2B   The modified cellulose acetate membrane is commonly used today.

16.2C   The water flux is the flow of water in grams per second through a membrane area of one square centimeter (or gallons per day per square foot) while the mineral flux is the flow of minerals in grams per second through a membrane area of one square centimeter.

16.2D   When additional pressure is applied to the side of a membrane with a concentrated solution, the water flux (rate of water flow through the membrane) will increase, but the mineral flux (rate of flow of minerals) will remain constant.

16.2E   When higher mineral concentrations occur in the feedwater, the mineral concentrations will increase in the permeate (or product water).

Answers to questions on page 159.

16.2F   Water flux is usually expressed in gallons per day per square foot (or grams per second per square centimeter) of membrane surface.

16.2G   The term "flux decline" is used to describe the loss of water flow through the membrane due to compaction plus fouling.

16.2H   Mineral rejection is defined as

$$\text{Rejection, \%} = \left(1 - \frac{\text{Product Concentration}}{\text{Feedwater Concentration}}\right)(100\%)$$

Mineral rejection can be determined by measuring the TDS and using the above equation. Rejections also may be calculated for individual constituents in the solution by using their concentrations.

16.2I   Softening membranes operate at lower pressures and lower rejection rates than standard reverse osmosis membranes.

Answers to questions on page 164.

16.2J   An increase in feedwater temperature will increase the water flux.

16.2K   Hydrolysis of a membrane results in a lessening of mineral rejection capability.

16.2L   Recovery is defined as the percentage of feed flow which is recovered as product water.

$$\text{Recovery, \%} = \frac{(\text{Product Flow})(100\%)}{\text{Feed Flow}}$$

16.2M   Recovery rate is usually limited by (1) desired product water quality and (2) the solubility limits of minerals in the brine.

16.2N   Concentration polarization is a buildup of retained particles on the membrane surface due to dewatering of the feed closest to the membrane. The thickness of the concentration polarization layer is controlled by the flow velocity across the membrane.

ANSWERS TO QUESTIONS IN LESSON 2

Answers to questions on page 172.

16.3A   The three types of commercially available membrane configurations which have been used in operating plants are (1) spiral wound, (2) hollow fine fiber, and (3) tubular.

16.3B   The tubular membrane process is used to treat wastewater with a high suspended solids concentration.

Answers to questions on page 174.

16.4A   To protect the reverse osmosis system and its accessory equipment, the feedwater should be filtered. When the water source is a groundwater or a previously treated municipal or industrial supply, filtration may be accomplished by a simple screening procedure. An untreated surface water will probably require coagulation, flocculation, sedimentation, and filtration.

16.4B   Colloidal particulates are removed from feedwater by chemical treatment and filtration.

16.4C   As an acetate membrane hydrolyzes, both the amount of water and the amount of solute that permeate the membrane increase and the quality of the product water deteriorates.

16.4D   The scale control method which is used to inhibit calcium sulfate precipitation is a threshold treatment with 2 to 5 mg/L of sodium hexametaphosphate (SHMP).

16.4E   A 1 to 2 mg/L chlorine residual is maintained to control biological fouling.

Answers to questions on page 174.

16.4F   Operating pressure on a reverse osmosis unit is regulated by a control valve on the influent manifold.

16.4G   The demineralized water is usually called *PERMEATE*, the reject, *CONCENTRATE*.

16.4H   Product or permeate flow is not regulated and varies as feedwater pressure and temperature change.

Answers to questions on page 178.

16.4I   Chlorine is added to the feedwater to prevent biological fouling.

16.4J   The operator must check the differential pressure across the RO unit to know when to clean the elements. When the elements become fouled, ΔP usually increases, thus indicating the need for cleaning.

16.4K   The reverse osmosis elements should be cleaned when the operator observes (1) lower product water flow rate, (2) lower salt rejection, (3) higher differential pressure (ΔP), and (4) higher operating pressure.

Answers to questions on page 179.

16.4L   Safety needs for demineralization plants can be divided into three general groups consisting of chemicals, electrical, and hydraulics.

16.4M   Electrical equipment used around reverse osmosis plants consists of a series of electrically powered pumps.

ANSWERS TO QUESTIONS IN LESSON 3

Answers to questions on page 181.

16.5A   Typical removals of inorganic salts from brackish water by ED range from 25 to 40 percent of dissolved solids per stage of treatment.

16.5B   A membrane stack in an electrodialysis unit consists of several hundred membranes and their separating spacers assembled between a single set of electrodes. End plates and tie rods complete the assembly.

16.5C   The most commonly encountered problem in ED operation is scaling (or fouling) of the membranes by both organic and inorganic materials. Alkaline scales are troublesome in the concentrating compartments when the diffusion of ions to the surface of the anion membrane in the diluting cell is insufficient to carry the current.

Answers to questions on page 183.

16.6A   If a D.C. potential is applied across a solution of salt in water by means of insertion of two electrodes in the solution, the cations will move toward a negative electrode, which is known as the "cathode," and the anions will move toward the positive electrode, which is known as the "anode."

16.6B   Only cations (positively charged ions) can pass through cation membranes.

16.6C   In a multi-compartment ED unit, the compartments losing salt are labeled "dilute" and those receiving the transferred salt, "brine."

Answers to questions on page 187.

16.7A   Iron, manganese, and chlorine residual must be removed from the feedwater supply to the electrodialysis unit.

16.7B   The rectifier provides the D.C. power to the membrane stack assembly. The input (alternating current (A.C.)) is converted by the rectifier to D.C. which is applied to the electrodes on each side of the membrane stack to remove the ions from the feed stream.

Answers to questions on page 189.

16.8A   The ions most often encountered in the feedwater to an electrodialysis unit include:

Cations	**Anions**
1. Calcium	1. Bicarbonate
2. Iron	2. Chloride
3. Magnesium	3. Sulfate
4. Silica	
5. Sodium	

16.8B   To prevent biological fouling of the cation and anion membranes, the operator must control feedwater pH, biological quality, and bacteriological quality.

16.8C   Generally the electrodialysis unit should *NOT* be operated when the feedwater contains any of the following:

1. Chlorine residual of any concentration,
2. Hydrogen sulfide of any concentration,
3. Calgon or other hexametaphosphates in excess of 10 mg/*L*,
4. Manganese in excess of 0.1 mg/*L*, and
5. Iron in excess of 0.3 mg/*L*.

16.8D   The recommended daily activities for the operator of an electrodialysis unit include:

1. Fill out log sheet,
2. Verify that electrodes are bumping and flowing properly,
3. Inspect stacks for excess external leakage, and
4. Check the pressure drop across the cartridge filter and change the cartridges whenever the pressure drop reaches 10 psi.

Answers to questions on page 190.

16.9A   Loose connections at the electrode tab connecting bolts will cause overheating which could result in serious damage to the membrane stack.

16.9B   Expect the D.C. amperage to *DROP* when the feedwater temperature *DROPS*.

16.9C   Should shorting occur from a metal end plate across the plastic end block to the electrode, *IMMEDIATELY* turn off the rectifier. Try to eliminate the cause of the shorting by wiping excess moisture off the block. Also, be sure to completely remove the black carbon that has formed at the point of shorting.

16.9D   If the operation of the entire unit must be stopped immediately, the *MAIN BREAKER* should be switched off.

OBJECTIVE TEST

Chapter 16. DEMINERALIZATION

Please write your name and mark the correct answers on the answer sheet, as directed at the end of Chapter 1. There may be more than one correct answer to each multiple-choice question.

True-False

1. Demineralization is the process which removes dissolved minerals (salts) from water.

   1. True
   2. False

2. Seawater is less expensive to treat than brackish water.

   1. True
   2. False

3. The mineral flux through a membrane depends on pressure.

   1. True
   2. False

4. The cleaning frequency of a membrane depends on the average membrane flux rate of the system.

   1. True
   2. False

5. All reverse osmosis units should have cleaning connections for each bank of permeators or pressure vessels connected in parallel.

   1. True
   2. False

6. Oxidizing agents, such as chlorine, should be removed by pretreatment before RO units to prevent membrane degradation.

   1. True
   2. False

7. As the membrane hydrolyzes, both the amount of water and the amount of solute which permeate the membrane increase and the quality of the product water deteriorates.

   1. True
   2. False

8. Other polyphosphates are more effective than hexametaphosphate in decreasing precipitation of calcium sulfate.

   1. True
   2. False

9. When an oxidant-intolerant membrane is used, feedwater chlorination must be followed by dechlorination.

   1. True
   2. False

10. Brine flow valves are never to be fully closed.

    1. True
    2. False

11. When operating a reverse osmosis plant, operators adjust permeate and concentrate flow to establish the desired recovery rate.

    1. True
    2. False

12. Cations move toward the positive electrode known as the cathode.

    1. True
    2. False

13. Cation membranes prevent the passage of cations.

    1. True
    2. False

14. Never apply D.C. voltage to the membrane stack without water flowing through the stack.

    1. True
    2. False

15. Always keep the electrodialysis membranes wet.

    1. True
    2. False

Best Answer (Select only the closest or best answer.)

16. The development of which demineralization process has significantly reduced the cost of demineralization?

    1. Distillation
    2. Freezing
    3. Ion exchange
    4. Membrane

17. What is a limitation of thin film composite membranes?

    1. Sensitive to oxidants in feedwater
    2. Subject to biological attack
    3. Subject to compaction
    4. Subject to hydrolysis

18. What happens to the water flux through the membrane as the mineral content of the feed decreases?

    1. Decreases
    2. Fluctuates
    3. Increases
    4. Stays constant

19. As more and more feedwater passes through the membrane, what happens to the mineral content of the feedwater?

    1. Fluctuates
    2. Higher and higher
    3. Lower and lower
    4. Stays constant

20. How does an increase in feedwater temperature affect membrane performance?

    1. Flux decreases
    2. Flux increases
    3. Mineral rejection capacity increases
    4. Rate of hydrolysis is decreased

21. What is the most common and serious problem resulting from concentration polarization?

    1. Compaction of membrane surface
    2. Cracks on membrane surface
    3. Deposition of particulate matter on membrane surface
    4. Deterioration of membrane surface

22. What is the function of cartridge filters for reverse osmosis (RO) pretreatment?

    1. Particle safeguard
    2. Primary particle removal device
    3. Removal of colloids
    4. Treatment of suspended solids

23. What is a disinfection option other than chlorination for a reverse osmosis (RO) process?

    1. Brine solution
    2. Permanganate
    3. pH adjustment
    4. Ultraviolet

24. How can inorganic precipitates be removed from membranes?

    1. Chelating agents
    2. Citric acid flush
    3. Detergent solutions
    4. Sequestrants

25. What is the most commonly encountered problem in electrodialysis operation?

    1. Electrode fouling
    2. Membrane compaction
    3. Membrane fouling
    4. Membrane hydrolysis

26. What is the purpose of the electrodialysis polarity reversal (EDR) system?

    1. Control scale
    2. Decrease electrical power requirements
    3. Increase percent mineral removal
    4. Reduce electrical safety hazards

Multiple Choice (Select all correct answers.)

27. What types of semipermeable membranes are used most often for demineralization?

    1. Cellulose acetate
    2. Geosynthetics
    3. Permeable rubber
    4. Porous plastic
    5. Thin film composites

28. What impurities in feedwater can cause membrane fouling?

    1. Algae
    2. Bacteria
    3. Dissolved inorganics
    4. Dissolved organics
    5. Suspended solids

29. Why are nanofiltration membranes being used?

    1. Corrosion control
    2. Hardness rejection
    3. Iron and manganese removal
    4. Remove THM formation potential
    5. TDS rejection

30. What factors influence the piping material used for reverse osmosis units?

    1. Water compressibility
    2. Water flow rate
    3. Water pressure
    4. Water salinity
    5. Water temperature

31. Where should sample valves be located?

    1. Chemical feed line
    2. Concentrate line
    3. Feedwater line
    4. Permeate line
    5. Sludge line

32. Why should feedwater be pretreated before the reverse osmosis process?

    1. Adjust pH
    2. Adjust temperature
    3. Disinfect to prevent biological growth
    4. Remove materials to prevent fouling
    5. Remove turbidity

33. What constituents in feedwater can cause scaling or fouling problems on RO membranes?

    1. Carbonates
    2. Ferric iron
    3. Hydrogen sulfide
    4. Oxidizing agents
    5. Silica

34. What factors influence the rate of hydrolysis of cellulose acetate?

    1. Microbiological matter in feedwater
    2. Oil and grease in feedwater
    3. Oxidizing agents in feedwater
    4. pH of feedwater
    5. Temperature of feedwater

35. What is the purpose of pH adjustment pretreatment prior to the RO process?

    1. Control membrane-fouling minerals
    2. Control scale-forming minerals
    3. Disinfect microbiological matter
    4. Minimize effect of hydrolysis
    5. Remove oil and grease

36. What are the symptoms of membrane fouling?

    1. High pressure difference
    2. Higher product water flow rate
    3. Higher salt rejection
    4. Lower product water flow rate
    5. Lower salt rejection

37. How can biological or organic fouling be removed from membranes?

    1. Bactericides
    2. Chelating agents
    3. Citric acid flush
    4. Detergent solution
    5. Enzymes

38. Which of the following chemicals require special handling by the operators of a reverse osmosis plant?

    1. Chlorine
    2. Citric acid
    3. Formaldehyde
    4. Sodium hexametaphosphate
    5. Sulfuric acid

39. What are the advantages of the electrodialysis process for demineralization?

    1. Efficient removal of most inorganic constituents
    2. Low cost of operation
    3. Minimal operator knowledge required
    4. Waste brine contains only salts removed
    5. Well-developed technology

40. What factors influence the actual percentage removal of minerals by an electrodialysis unit?

    1. Amount of ions present
    2. Flow rate of water
    3. Pressure differential
    4. Type of ions present
    5. Water temperature

41. Pretreatment of feedwater to an electrodialysis stack includes which treatment processes? Removal of

    1. Chlorine residual
    2. Iron
    3. Manganese
    4. Sodium
    5. Suspended solids

42. What chemical solutions are used in electrodialysis cleaning?

    1. Caustic soda
    2. Chelating agents
    3. Citric acid
    4. Detergents
    5. Hydrochloric acid

43. Which of the following items is/are acceptable in the feedwater to an electrodialysis unit?

    1. Chlorine residual
    2. Hydrogen sulfide
    3. Iron
    4. Manganese
    5. Sodium

44. Which of the following tasks should be performed daily by the operator of an electrodialysis unit?

    1. Check the oil level on pumps fitted with automatic oilers.
    2. Fill out log sheet.
    3. Inspect stacks for excess external leakage.
    4. Verify that electrodes are bumping and flowing properly.
    5. Voltage probe the membrane stacks.

45. Estimate the ability of a reverse osmosis plant to reject minerals by calculating the mineral rejection as a percent. The feedwater contains 1,800 mg/L TDS and the product water TDS is 130 mg/L.

    1. 88%
    2. 90%
    3. 92%
    4. 93%
    5. 94%

46. Estimate the percent recovery of a reverse osmosis unit with a 4-2-1 arrangement if the feed flow is 4.1 MGD and the product flow is 3.8 MGD.

    1. 85%
    2. 87%
    3. 89%
    4. 91%
    5. 93%

End of Objective Test

CHAPTER 17

HANDLING AND DISPOSAL OF PROCESS WASTES

by

George Uyeno

TABLE OF CONTENTS

Chapter 17.   HANDLING AND DISPOSAL OF PROCESS WASTES

Page

OBJECTIVES 199

WORDS 200

17.0   NEED FOR HANDLING AND DISPOSAL OF PROCESS WASTES 201

17.1   SOURCES OF TREATMENT PROCESS WASTES 201

17.2   PROCESS SLUDGE VOLUMES 202

17.3   METHODS OF HANDLING AND DISPOSING OF PROCESS WASTES 203

17.4   DRAINING AND CLEANING OF TANKS 203

17.5   BACKWASH RECOVERY PONDS (SOLAR LAGOONS) 205

17.6   SLUDGE DEWATERING PROCESSES 208

        17.60   Solar Drying Lagoons 208

        17.61   Sand Drying Beds 208

        17.62   Belt Filter Presses 209

        17.63   Centrifuges 209

        17.64   Filter Presses 213

        17.65   Vacuum Filters 213

17.7   DISCHARGE INTO COLLECTION SYSTEMS (SEWERS) 213

17.8   DISPOSAL OF SLUDGE 213

17.9   EQUIPMENT 218

        17.90   Vacuum Trucks 218

        17.91   Sludge Pumps 220

17.10   PLANT DRAINAGE WATERS 220

17.11   MONITORING AND REPORTING 220

17.12   ADDITIONAL READING 220

DISCUSSION AND REVIEW QUESTIONS 221

SUGGESTED ANSWERS 221

OBJECTIVE TEST 223

OBJECTIVES

Chapter 17. HANDLING AND DISPOSAL OF PROCESS WASTES

Following completion of Chapter 17, you should be able to:

1. Explain why the operators of water treatment plants should be concerned about the handling and disposal of process wastes,

2. Identify the sources of water treatment plant wastes,

3. Drain and clean sedimentation tanks,

4. Discharge process wastes to collection systems (sewers),

5. Operate and maintain backwash recovery ponds (lagoons) and sludge drying beds,

6. Dispose of process wastes,

7. Safely operate and maintain sludge handling and disposal equipment, and

8. Monitor and report on the disposal of process wastes.

WORDS

Chapter 17.   HANDLING AND DISPOSAL OF PROCESS WASTES

CENTRIFUGE

CENTRIFUGE

A mechanical device that uses centrifugal or rotational forces to separate solids from liquids.

CONDITIONING

CONDITIONING

Pretreatment of sludge to facilitate removal of water in subsequent treatment processes.

DECANT

DECANT

To draw off the upper layer of liquid (water) after the heavier material (a solid or another liquid) has settled.

DEWATER

DEWATER

(1) To remove or separate a portion of the water present in a sludge or slurry. To dry sludge so it can be handled and disposed of.

(2) To remove or drain the water from a tank or trench.

SEPTIC (SEP-tick)

SEPTIC

A condition produced by bacteria when all oxygen supplies are depleted. If severe, the bottom deposits produce hydrogen sulfide, the deposits and water turn black, give off foul odors, and the water has a greatly increased chlorine demand.

SLUDGE (sluj)

SLUDGE

The settleable solids separated from water during processing.

SUPERNATANT (sue-per-NAY-tent)

SUPERNATANT

Liquid removed from settled sludge. Supernatant commonly refers to the liquid between the sludge on the bottom and the scum on the water surface of a basin or container.

THICKENING

THICKENING

Treatment to remove water from the sludge mass to reduce the volume that must be handled.

CHAPTER 17.   HANDLING AND DISPOSAL OF PROCESS WASTES

17.0   NEED FOR HANDLING AND DISPOSAL OF PROCESS WASTES

The need for handling and disposal of potable water treatment plant wastes is a problem that must be faced by all plant operators. Many articles and books have been published on potable water treatment processes. Their emphasis is usually on producing wholesome and pure water for human consumption in compliance with EPA, state and local health department regulations, but very few mention sludge handling and disposal in any great detail. In response to a growing population and increasing concern about pollution of natural water sources, pollution control agencies, health departments, and fish and game departments established programs to enforce rules to prevent any waste discharge that would tend to discolor, pollute, or generally be harmful to aquatic or plant life or the environment.

The law which restricts or prohibits the discharge of process wastes from water treatment plants is Public Law 92-500, the Water Pollution Control Act Amendments of 1972. This Act clearly includes treatment plant wastes such as sludge from a water treatment plant. These wastes are considered an industrial waste which requires compliance with the provisions of the Act. Under the National Pollutant Discharge Elimination System (NPDES) provisions, a permit must be obtained in order to discharge wastes from a water treatment plant. Water treatment plants are classified into three categories.

Category 1   Plants that use one of the following three processes: (1) coagulation, (2) oxidative iron and manganese removal, or (3) direct filtration.

Category 2   Plants that use only chemical softening processes.

Category 3   Plants that use combinations of coagulation and chemical softening, or oxidative iron-manganese removal and chemical softening.

Enforcement of PL 92-500 is the responsibility of each state. Many NPDES permits have been issued by the states to water treatment plants using state standards applicable to the local conditions at the time the permits were issued. Water quality indicators for which waste discharge limitations have been issued include pH, total suspended solids, settleable solids, total iron and manganese, flow rate, total dissolved solids (TDS), BOD, turbidity, total residual chlorine, temperature, floating solids, and visible forms of waste.

Water treatment plants can no longer simply discharge dirty backwash water or settled sludge into lakes, rivers, streams, or tributaries as was done in the past. Current regulations require daily monitoring of any discharge and analysis of such water quality indicators as pH, turbidity, TDS, settleable solids, or other harmful materials. The results of the analyses must be logged and reported frequently to the proper authorities and must conform to their rigid standards. For these reasons, it is absolutely necessary to make provisions for facilities to handle these wastes on a routine basis. The most important part of an operator's job is still the end product, good potable water, but an operator's duties are not complete until all by-products and wastes are disposed of in an acceptable and documented manner.

QUESTIONS

Write your answers in a notebook and then compare your answers with those on page 221.

17.0A   Why are strict laws needed regarding the disposal of process wastes?

17.0B   If a discharge results from the disposal of process wastes, what water quality indicators may require monitoring?

17.1   SOURCES OF TREATMENT PROCESS WASTES

Although there are many types of water treatment plants and methods for treating water, most of them probably operate in the following general manner. Alum or polymers are applied to the water in a rapid-mix chamber. The mixture is agitated by mechanical means or through a cylinder designed for hydraulic flash mixing for coagulation.

Following coagulation, the water passes through mechanical flocculators or a series of baffles for flocculation. The water then moves into the sedimentation tank where the floc is allowed to settle out before the water moves to the filters. The sedimentation tanks may be of various shapes and depths; however, they are most commonly rectangular or circular. Many large plants are equipped with either mechanical rakes or scrapers which periodically remove sludge from a hopper, or with a vacuum-type sludge removal device. The sludge is continuously scraped into the hopper. The hopper is emptied from one to three times per day for 20 to 30 minutes each time depending on the size of the hopper and the density of the sludge. Sludge is then usually moved to drying beds. The smaller and older plants may not have these sludge handling facilities available. Many new water treatment plants are equipped with sludge collection headers with squeegees. This system does not need any sludge hoppers. The collection headers are supported by a travelling bridge or floats. The sludge is pumped out of the bottom of the basin and into a sludge channel on the walkway level. This system is described in Chapter 5, "Sedimentation."

Another type of plant similar to the one above contains an upflow solids-contact unit with clarifiers. The clarifiers are usually circular and have sludge drawoff lines which must be monitored; the solids are then drawn off periodically as sludge.

For small plants and in areas where water must be pumped, pressure filters may be used and the coagulant is applied directly to the filter. Sedimentation tanks or clarifiers may occasionally accompany the use of pressure filters but this is not usually the case if the quality of the source water is good.

In another type of plant layout (not too commonly used), the sedimentation tank also functions as the backwash recovery area. In this case the backwash wastewater is pumped back to the head of the plant. Most of the solids will settle out when the water flows through the sedimentation basin. This method does eliminate the need for backwash recovery ponds or lagoons.

Diatomaceous earth filtration is different from all other types of filtration in its method of operation. There is usually no pretreatment of the water. Disposal of backwash wastes is still a problem. Table 17.1 summarizes the various sources of treatment process wastes and the methods of collecting, handling, and disposing of these wastes.

TABLE 17.1   COLLECTION, HANDLING, AND DISPOSAL OF PROCESS WASTES

SOURCES OF WASTES

1. Trash racks
2. Grit basins
3. Alum, ferric hydroxide, or polymer sludges from sedimentation basins
4. Filter backwash
5. Lime-soda softening
6. Ion exchange brine

COLLECTION OF SLUDGES

1. Mechanical scrapers or vacuum devices
2. Manual (hoses and squeegees)
3. Pumps (into tank trucks or dewatering facilities)
4. Floating headers

DEWATERING OF SLUDGES

1. Solar drying lagoons
2. Sand drying beds
3. Centrifuges[a]
4. Belt presses
5. Filter presses
6. Vacuum filters

DISPOSAL OF SLUDGES AND BRINES

1. Wastewater collection systems (sewers)
2. Landfills (usually dewatered sludges)
3. Spread on land

---

[a] Mechanical devices that use centrifugal or rotational forces to separate solids from liquids (sludge from water).

QUESTIONS

Write your answers in a notebook and then compare your answers with those on page 221.

17.1A   How is sludge removed from sedimentation tanks?

17.1B   How is sludge removed from an upflow solids-contact type of unit?

17.2   PROCESS SLUDGE VOLUMES

All of the different methods of sludge collection require some type of facilities for handling processed waste. The possibilities here include sedimentation tanks, backwash recovery ponds, drying beds, lagoons, ponds, holding tanks, adequate land, access to sewer systems, or vacuum trucks or similar equipment for removal and disposal of the waste material.

The amount of sludge accumulation depends on the type and amount of suspended matter in the source water being treated as well as on the level of dosage and the type of coagulant used. As an example, let's examine sludge production at two 5 MGD (19 MLD) plants. The annual water production at each was 800 to 900 million gallons (3,000 to 3,400 megaliters). Plant One had no source water stabilizing reservoir and the raw water turbidity ranged from 3 units during the summer months to over 100 units during the winter, with an annual average alum dosage of 11 mg/L. Yearly sludge accumulation was approximately 500,000 gallons (1.9 megaliters). Plant Two with a 15 million gallon (56.8 megaliters) source water stabilizing reservoir treated raw water which never exceeded 20 turbidity units at the intake with an average alum dosage of 8 mg/L. The annual sludge accumulation was approximately 300,000 gallons (1.14 megaliters). In both cases, non-ionic polymer was used for filter aid at approximately 15 ppb. The source water stabilizing reservoir reduced the turbidity level of the water to be treated and provided a more constant quality of water which required less alum and produced less sludge.

Organic polymers may be used instead of alum to reduce the quantity of sludge produced. Polymer sludges are relatively denser and easier to dewater for subsequent handling and disposal. Not all waters can be treated by using polymers instead of alum.

For plants without sludge collection devices, the volume of sludge produced and the frequency of cleaning the sedimentation tank are affected by several factors. Items to consider include:

1. Water demand,

2. Suspended solids loads and when peak demands occur,

3. Water temperature (as the temperature of the water increases, the settling rate of the solids will increase),

4. Detention time (as the detention time increases, the amount of solids that settle out will increase),

5. Volume of sludge deposited in basin (as the volume of sludge increases, the detention time decreases as well as the efficiency of the basin),

6. Volume of treated water storage for the system (the greater the volume of treated water storage, the more time is available for sludge removal),

7. Time required to clean and make any necessary repairs during the shutdown, and

8. Availability of adequate drying beds, lagoons, landfill, a vacuum tank truck, pumps or equipment, and adequate help with all necessary safety equipment and procedures.

Sedimentation tanks should be drained and cleaned at least twice a year and more often if the sludge buildup interferes with the treatment processes (filtration and disinfection). Alum or polymer sludge solids content is only 0.5 to 1 percent for continuous sludge removal and 2 to 4 percent when the sludge is allowed to accumulate and compact.

Therefore, the sludge can flow readily in pipes or be pumped, especially with wastewater-type pumps.

QUESTIONS

Write your answers in a notebook and then compare your answers with those on page 221.

17.2A How can a source water stabilizing reservoir reduce the volume of sludge handled?

17.2B How often should sedimentation tanks be drained and cleaned?

17.3 METHODS OF HANDLING AND DISPOSING OF PROCESS WASTES (Figure 17.1)

Various methods are used to handle and dispose of process wastes. The disposal facilities at your plant will depend on when the plant was built, the region where the plant is located (topography and climate), the sources of sludge, and the methods of ultimate disposal.

An effective method of handling sludge is to regularly during the day remove sludge from sedimentation tanks to a drying bed. When one drying bed is full of sludge, the sludge is allowed to dry while the other drying beds are being filled. A key to speedy drying is the regular removal of the water on top of the sludge.

Some plants require that portions of the facilities be shut down twice a year, the tanks drained, and the sludge removed. This is an excellent time to inspect the tanks and equipment and perform any necessary maintenance and repairs.

Backwash recovery ponds or lagoons are used to separate the water from the solids after the filters have been backwashed. The water is usually returned or recycled to the plant headworks for treatment with the source water. These ponds also may be used to concentrate or thicken sludges from sedimentation tanks. Sludges from the lime-soda softening process are usually stored in lagoons. The drainage water is removed and the sludge may be covered or hauled off to a disposal site. Lime softening sludges may be applied to agricultural lands to achieve the best soil pH for optimum crop yields.

Larger plants or plants that produce large volumes of sludge may use THICKENING,[1] CONDITIONING,[2] and DEWATERING[3] processes to reduce the volume of sludge that must be handled and ultimately disposed of. Sometimes polymers are added to sludges for conditioning prior to dewatering. Belt filter presses, centrifuges, solar lagoons, and sand drying beds are some of the processes used to dewater sludges.

Ultimately process wastes such as trash, grit, sludge, and brine must be disposed of in a manner that will not harm the environment. Trash and grit may be disposed of in landfills. Sometimes sludge and brine are discharged into wastewater collection systems (sewers); however, this procedure may cause operational problems for the wastewater treatment plant operator. To avoid upsetting wastewater treatment plants, discharges to sewers must be made very slowly to take advantage of the dilution provided by the wastewater. Sludges are commonly disposed of by spreading on land or dumping in landfills. The method used will depend on the volume of the sludge, sludge moisture content, land available, and distance from the plant to the ultimate disposal site.

The remainder of this chapter will discuss the detailed operational procedures that an operator must consider when handling and disposing of process wastes. Sections are also provided on equipment operation and maintenance as well as on monitoring and reporting.

QUESTIONS

Write your answers in a notebook and then compare your answers with those on pages 221 and 222.

17.3A When should sedimentation tanks be inspected and repaired?

17.3B List the methods that may be used to dewater sludge.

17.4 DRAINING AND CLEANING OF TANKS

Plants without mechanical or vacuum-type sludge collectors will require the use of manual labor to remove the sludge once or twice a year. When two or more sedimentation tanks are designed into a plant, the job of cleaning is made easier. While one sedimentation tank is down, the other(s) can remain in operation. The cleaning of sedimentation tanks should be done prior to and/or after peak demand months. Generally, early spring and the fall of the year are the better times to take some facilities out of service for cleaning.

---

[1] *Thickening. Treatment to remove water from the sludge mass to reduce the volume that must be handled.*
[2] *Conditioning. Pretreatment of sludge to facilitate removal of water in subsequent treatment processes.*
[3] *Dewatering. Treatment which removes or separates a portion of the water present in a sludge or slurry. To dry sludge so it can be handled and disposed of. Dewatering also means removing or draining the water from a tank or trench.*

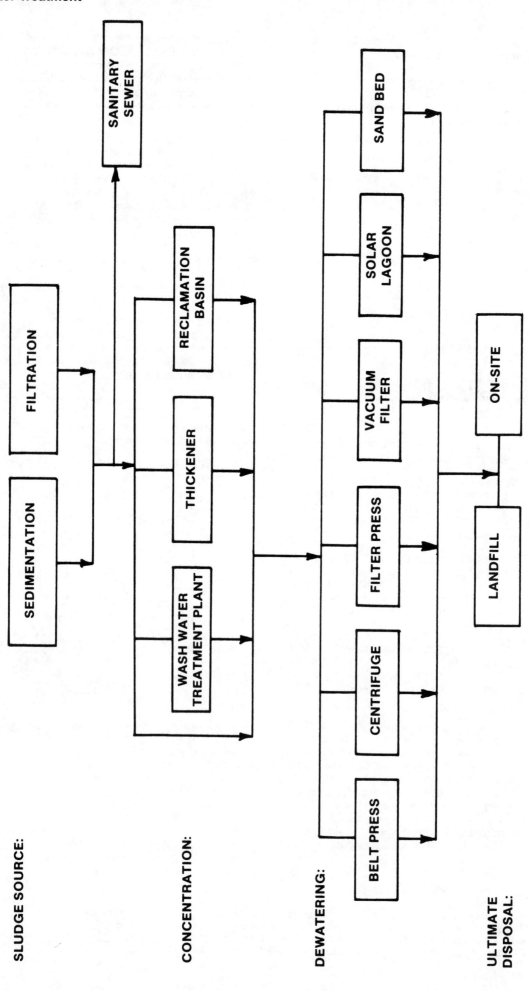

Fig. 17.1   Sludge processing alternatives

Before draining any in-ground tank, always determine the level of the water table. If the water table is high, an empty tank could float like a cork on the water surface and cause considerable damage to the tank and piping. A properly designed tank will have provisions to drain high water tables or will contain other protective features (bottom pressure-relief discs to let groundwater into the tank to prevent damage).

After any necessary intake valve(s) or gate(s) changes are made, drain the water down to the sludge blanket by partially opening the drain valve from the sedimentation tank into the lagoon or drying bed. After the first few minutes (if the valve is not wide open), the water will become clear. This portion of the water can be diverted from the lagoon or drying bed, if proper plumbing is available, and returned to the source to be reprocessed. Most drying beds will not handle this great a volume of water unless this draining process is extended over a period of a few days. Pump(s) can be used to transfer the settled water to another sedimentation tank that is still in operation.

As the water gets down to the sludge, fully open the drain valve into the drying bed(s). A large quantity of the sludge will drain by itself. As shown in Figure 17.2, the tank wall is 10 feet (3 m) high with the sludge level showing about five feet (1.5 m) from the top. When the level drops down to about two feet (0.6 m) of depth by the drain opening, the sludge will have to be assisted by an operator with a squeegee (Figure 17.3).

During the draining stages, the walls and all the equipment should be completely hosed down and inspected for damage. All necessary repairs should be made at this time. Once sludge dries on any coated surface, it is difficult to remove so it is important to hose everything down during the process of draining and while the sludge is still wet. All gears, sprockets, and moving parts should be lubricated immediately after hosing down to prevent "freeze up" resulting from exposure to the air during inspection and repair. By using drying beds and drying bed DECANT[4] pumps, ample amounts of water may be used for cleaning and assisting draining of the sludge. Under these conditions, two to three operators can clean out one sedimentation tank for a plant of 5 to 10 MGD (19 to 38 MLD) in one day. Additional time is required for initial drawdown, gathering up of tools and equipment, final cleanup, and any repairs that may be needed.

Sludge that settles out near the entrance to the sedimentation tank is more dense, especially when a polymer is used for flocculation aid. Therefore, the drain should be located in the headworks area. Once the sludge ceases to flow freely, even with the dilution water, then operators will have to push it toward the drain with squeegees (Figure 17.4).

The volume of sludge can vary with the size of the basin or clarifier, the quality of the source water being treated, the use of alum, polymer or combinations of both, and the frequency of cleaning. This volume may range from 100,000 to 200,000 gallons (0.38 to 0.76 ML), depending on the size of the basin and how long the sludge has accumulated in the basin.

Caution must be exercised whenever operators are in any closed tank (confined space):

1. Do not operate gasoline engines in the tank,

2. Test the atmosphere in the tank for flammable or explosive gases and oxygen deficiency, and provide adequate ventilation of clean air at all times,

3. Provide a source of water to clean off boots and tools where the operators come out of the tank, and

4. Use the buddy system. At least one person must be outside the tank and watching anyone inside the tank, and another person must be nearby and available to help in an emergency.

Before filling the tank, thoroughly inspect and repair all equipment and valves. Wash everything down with clean water or a solution of 200 mg/L chlorine to disinfect the basin. If a chlorine wash solution is not used, fill the tank 10 percent full with a 50 mg/L chlorine solution and then finish filling it with clean water from the plant. The final free chlorine residual should not be so high that water with a free chlorine residual greater than 0.5 mg/L reaches the consumers.

Although manually draining and cleaning tanks requires more operator hours and plant downtime than mechanical sludge removal, it does have its advantages. A more sanitary condition in the tank is obtained by cleaning up algae buildups or other deposits that are not picked up by mechanical collectors and regular inspection of equipment can eliminate many potential breakdown conditions. Even basins with continuous sludge collection systems should be drained once a year for inspection and maintenance.

QUESTIONS

Write your answers in a notebook and then compare your answers with those on page 222.

17.4A   How can sludge be removed from tanks without mechanical or vacuum-type sludge collectors?

17.4B   When draining a sedimentation tank, what should be done with the settled water above the sludge?

17.4C   What precautions must be exercised whenever an operator enters a closed tank (confined space)?

17.5 BACKWASH RECOVERY PONDS (SOLAR LAGOONS)

Because of water pollution control legislation enacted since the 1960s, many recently constructed water treatment plants now have backwash recovery ponds (Figure 17.5). In many instances these ponds can serve a dual purpose. In addition to their primary function as backwash recovery ponds, they can also be used to collect the sludge from sedimentation tanks and clarifiers with a few modifications. While these modified ponds are capable of performing both functions at the same time, it would be preferable to pay particular attention to timing these operations so that they do not overlap. Water for hosing down the sedimentation basin and assisting the flow of sludge should be used sparingly. Also, the backwash recovery pump suction pipe should be floated near the surface, by use of a flexible hose and tire tube or any similar float, so that any excess water can be recycled without also drawing out sludge. This will be very important if the filters must be backwashed at the same time sludge is being cleaned out of the backwash recovery ponds.

---

[4] Decant.   To draw off the upper layer of liquid (water) after the heavier material (a solid or another liquid) has settled.

Fig. 17.2   Sludge being drained from a clarifier

Fig. 17.3   Operator with a squeegee assisting sludge out of clarifier

Fig. 17.4   Operators pushing sludge toward drain with squeegees
and vacuum truck removing sludge

Fig. 17.5   Backwash recovery pond

A vacuum tank truck will be needed to move the wet sludge (a vacuum tank truck is shown in Figure 17.4). The capacity of the vacuum truck's tank in the picture is 5,000 gallons (19 cu m) and it has a 6-inch (150-mm) suction hose. About 15 minutes are required to fill the tank if sludge is fed to the suction end constantly without breaking the vacuum. A lift of 12 feet (3.6 m) can be obtained without too much difficulty.

Sludge is sometimes applied to land as a soil conditioner. Polymer sludges are suitable as a soil conditioner. Sludges produced by direct filtration, without coagulants, usually make excellent soil conditioners both with and without polymers. The sludge may be applied either wet or dry. Because commercial soil conditioner is becoming more expensive, sale of sludge as a soil conditioner can help to offset sludge handling and disposal costs.

Most plants that use the lime-soda ash softening process collect the sludge and dewater it in a lagoon. A variable length riser or discharge pipe is used to draw off the water that is separated from the sludge. When the lagoon is full and the sludge is dried, the surface may be covered with soil as in a landfill operation. In some plants where space is scarce, the dried sludge is hauled off to a landfill and the lagoon refilled. Lime softening sludges also can be disposed of by application to agricultural soils to adjust the pH for optimum crop yields.

Discharge of lime-soda sludges to the wastewater collection system (sewers) is a poor practice because (1) the sewers could become plugged regularly, and (2) the operator at the wastewater treatment plant will have to handle and dispose of the sludge. However, the lime-soda sludge may help the wastewater treatment plant operator by (1) adjusting the pH, or (2) serving as a coagulant aid in treating the incoming wastewater.

QUESTIONS

Write your answers in a notebook and then compare your answers with those on page 222.

17.5A   Why is timing critical if backwash recovery ponds are used to handle sludge from sedimentation basins?

17.5B   Why must the suction pipe for the backwash recovery pump be floated near the surface of the pond?

17.5C   How can lime-soda softening sludge be disposed of ultimately?

17.6   SLUDGE DEWATERING PROCESSES[5]

17.60   Solar Drying Lagoons

Solar drying lagoons are shallow, small-volume storage ponds in which treatment process sludge (sometimes concentrated) is stored for extended time periods. Sludge solids settle to the bottom of the lagoon by plain sedimentation (gravity settling) and the clear *SUPERNATANT*[6] water is skimmed off the top with the aid of an outlet structure that drains the clear surface waters. Evaporation removes additional water and the solar drying process proceeds until the sludge reaches a concentration of from 30 to 50 percent solids. At this point, the sludge can be disposed of on-site or at a sanitary landfill. Obviously, the solar drying process is dependent on environmental conditions (weather) and may take many months to complete. For this reason, several lagoons should be provided (a minimum of three) so that sludge loading and drying can be rotated from one lagoon to another.

17.61   Sand Drying Beds

Sand drying beds have been used extensively in municipal wastewater treatment where high solids volumes are handled. Sand drying beds are similar in construction to a sand filter, and consist of a layer of sand, a support gravel layer, an underdrain system, and some means for manual or mechanical removal of the sludge (see Figures 17.6, 17.7, and 17.8). They are built with underdrains covered with gradations of aggregate and sand. The drains discharge into a sump where recovery pumps can return the water drained from the sludge back to the plant to be reprocessed. Frequently, three beds are used so one can be dried out while one is being filled from the drawdown of wet sludge from the sedimentation tanks. The third bed contains dried sludge which is being hauled out.

The efficiency of the sand drying bed dewatering process can be greatly improved by preconditioning the process sludge with chemical coagulants. The drying time can vary from days to weeks, depending on weather conditions and the degree of preconditioning of the sludge. The frequency of removal of dried sludge will vary with different plants depending on the volume of sludge produced, size of drying beds, and drying conditions (weather).

---

[5] *Portions of this section were prepared by Jim Beard.*
[6] *Supernatant (sue-per-NAY-tent).   Liquid removed from settled sludge. Supernatant commonly refers to the liquid between the sludge on the bottom and the scum on the water surface of a basin or container.*

17.6   Sludge drying beds

Sludge has a unique characteristic about it that once it has even partially dried, it will not expand; therefore, layer after layer of wet sludge can be added over a period of time. This procedure will work as long as the solids content of the applied sludge is at least 2 to 3 percent. When drying this type of sludge, large cracks and checks will develop on the surface and extend down through the sludge to the sand. The proper time to remove this dried sludge is when no more than one foot (0.3 m) has accumulated and dried into a checkered pattern. A piece of dry sludge can then be picked up off the sand. The dried sludge can easily be removed with a front-end loader onto a dump truck and be hauled off to a landfill. However, the operator must exercise extreme caution so that only the dried sludge is picked up with the minimum possible disturbance to the sand and aggregate. The loader bucket should be operated carefully since there may be only about ten inches (36 cm) of sand cover over the underdrains. The loader bucket capacity should be limited to one or two cubic yards of sludge. Concrete tracks should be provided for larger equipment to collect the dried sludge.

QUESTIONS

Write your answers in a notebook and then compare your answers with those on page 222.

17.6A   What is the minimum recommended number of solar drying lagoons?

17.6B   Describe a typical sludge drying bed.

17.6C   When is the proper time to remove dried sludge from the drying bed?

17.6D   What precautions must be exercised when operating a front-end loader to remove sludge from a drying bed?

17.62   Belt Filter Presses

Continuous-belt filter presses are popular because of their relative ease of operation, low energy consumption, small land requirements, and their ability to produce a relatively dry filter cake (material removed from the filter press has about 35 to 40 percent solids). There are two primary mechanisms by which free water is separated from the sludge solids in a belt press:

1. Gravity drainage, and

2. Pressure dewatering.

Sludge is conveyed and dewatered between two endless belts (Figure 17.9). After the sludge is initially mixed with a polymer in a rotary drum conditioner, it is dewatered in three distinct zones:

1. A horizontal zone for gravity drainage,

2. A vertical sandwich draining zone, and

3. A final dewatering zone containing an arrangement of staggered rollers which produce a multiple-shear force action which squeezes out the remaining free water.

Each belt is washed with a high pressure/low volume water spray.

17.63   Centrifuges

Centrifuges have been used to dewater municipal sludges for some time. Problems with the earlier units included erosion of surfaces hit by high-speed particles, and poor performance capacity. Design improvements and the use of polymers have generally eliminated these problems. The principal advantage of this dewatering technique is that the density of the sludge cake can be varied from a thickened liquid slurry to a dry cake. The major limitation of using centrifuges is high energy consumption.

There are two basic types of centrifuges, the scroll type and the basket type. The scroll centrifuge operates continuously, while the basket centrifuge is a batch-type unit. Solids capture is generally greater with the basket centrifuge.

Fig. 17.7   Sludge drying beds

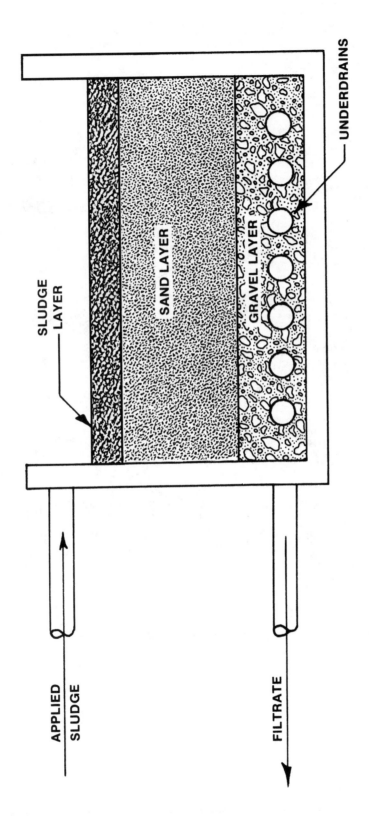

Fig. 17.8 Sectional view of sludge drying bed

Fig. 17.9   Flow diagram of Winklepress (a continuous-belt filter press)

(Permission of Ashbrook-Simon-Hartley)

In the scroll centrifuge (Figure 17.10), solids are introduced horizontally into the center of the unit. The spinning action forces the solids against the outer wall of the bowl, where they are transported to the discharge end by a rotating screw conveyor. Clear supernatant liquid is discharged over an adjustable weir on the opposite end of the unit.

In the basket centrifuge (Figure 17.11), sludge is introduced vertically into the bottom of the bowl and the supernatant is discharged over a weir at the top of the bowl. When the solids concentration in the supernatant becomes too high, the operation is stopped and the dense solids cake is removed by a knife unloader.

17.64 Filter Presses

Filter presses have been successfully used to process difficult-to-dewater sludges (alum sludges). These machines are best suited for sludges with a high specific resistance (the internal resistance of a sludge cake to the passage of water). Filter presses produce very dry cakes, a clear filtrate, and have a very high solids capture.

A filter press consists of a series of vertical plates covered with cloth which supports and retains the filter cake (Figure 17.12). These plates are rigidly held in a frame. Sludge is fed into the press at increasing pressures for about half an hour. The plates are then pressed together for one to four hours at pressures as high as 225 psi (15.8 kg/sq cm or 1,551 kiloPascals). Water passes through the cloth while the solids are retained, forming a cake which is removed when the press is depressurized.

17.65 Vacuum Filters

Vacuum filtration was once the main chemical sludge dewatering process. However, its use has declined due to development of devices such as the belt press which consumes less energy, is less sensitive to polymer dosage, and does not require use of a precoat (a substance applied to the filter before applying sludge for dewatering).

A vacuum filter consists of a cylindrical drum which rotates partially submerged in a tank of chemically conditioned sludge (Figure 17.13). As the drum slowly rotates, a vacuum is applied under the filter medium (belt) to form a cake on the surface. As the belt rotates suction is maintained to promote additional dewatering. As the belt passes the top of the drum, it separates from the drum and passes over a small-diameter roller for discharge of the cake. The belt is then washed before it re-enters the vat. A precoat of diatomaceous earth is required to dewater gelatinous (jelly-like) alum sludge.

QUESTIONS

Write your answers in a notebook and then compare your answers with those on page 222.

17.6E List the methods available for dewatering sludges.

17.6F List the major advantages and limitations of using centrifuges to dewater sludges.

17.6G When is a precoat of diatomaceous earth required on vacuum filters?

17.7 DISCHARGE INTO COLLECTION SYSTEMS (SEWERS)

The easiest method of sludge disposal would be to send the sludge down the wastewater collection (sewer) system. This does create some complications even if the wastewater treatment plant has the capacity to handle the load. Sludge discharged to sewers could cause sewer blockages. Also, the fees charged by the wastewater treatment plant to process and dispose of the sludge could be prohibitive. The charges are usually based upon annual flow, chemical or biochemical oxygen demand, suspended solids, and peak and average discharge. There are also increased monitoring requirements and costs associated with a sewer discharge. The water treatment plant must have a holding tank so that the sludge can be released at a uniform rate throughout the day or released only during the wastewater treatment plant's low-flow period.

Brine from ion exchange units may be discharged into wastewater collection systems. Usually the brine is discharged during the day to take advantage of high flows for dilution. When you plan such a discharge, notify the operator of the downstream wastewater treatment plant to be sure you won't create any unnecessary problems.

QUESTIONS

Write your answers in a notebook and then compare your answers with those on page 222.

17.7A What are the complications of discharging sludge to sewers?

17.7B When is brine from ion exchange units usually discharged into wastewater collection systems?

17.8 DISPOSAL OF SLUDGE [7]

Sludge is commonly disposed of in sanitary landfills. Other methods of ultimate disposal include lagoons, land application, and sanitary sewers. The method of disposal depends on the source and type of sludge, as well as economic and environmental considerations.

Water treatment plant lime sludge is an excellent liming agent for agricultural purposes. Lime sludge must be applied at a rate to achieve the best soil pH for optimum crop yield. Optimum levels of nitrogen and phosphorus are also important to achieve high crop yields.

---

[7] Portions of this section were obtained from ILLINOIS EPA SLUDGE REGULATION GUIDANCE DOCUMENT, Illinois Environmental Protection Agency, 1021 North Grand Avenue East, PO Box 19276, Springfield, IL 62702.

Fig. 17.10   Solid-bowl scroll centrifuge
(Permission of Sharples-Stokes Division, Pennwalt Corporation)

Fig. 17.11   Imperforate basket centrifuge
(Permission of Sharples-Stokes Division, Pennwalt Corporation)

Filter plates

Movable head

Stationary head

Gasket

Slurry inlet

Cloth

Cake

Filtrate outlet

FILTER CHAMBER ASSEMBLY

Fig. 17.12   Filter press

(Permission of Shriver Division, Eimco Process Equipment Co.)

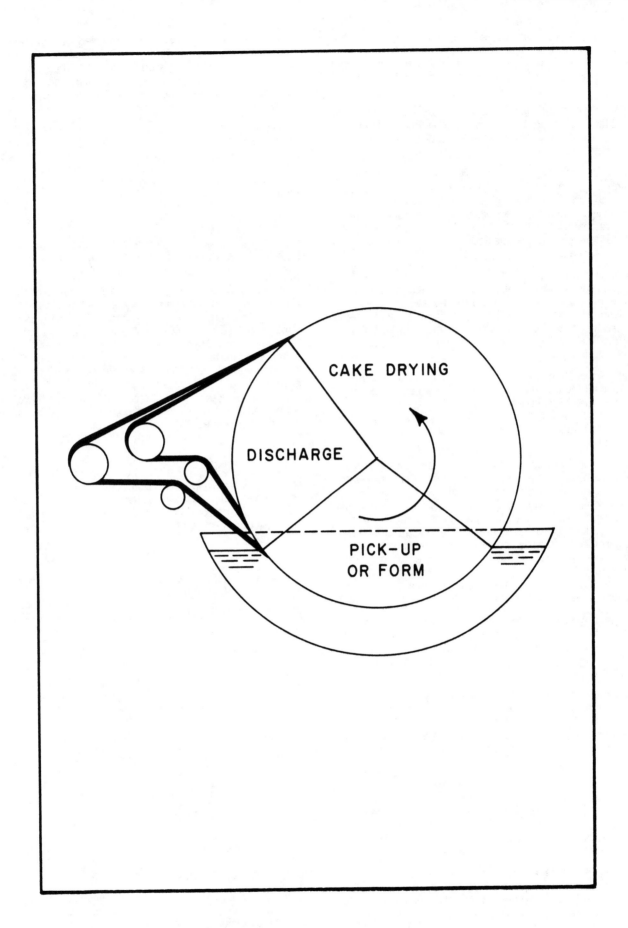

Fig. 17.13 Operating zones of a vacuum filter
(Permission of Metropolitan Water District of Southern California)

The application of nitrogen fertilizers causes a reduction in soil pH. If optimum soil pH conditions do not exist, crop yields will be reduced. Therefore, sufficient quantities of lime must be applied as a means of counteracting the fertilizer applications.

Lime softening sludges can also aid in the reclamation of spoiled lands by neutralizing acid soils. Disposal of lime softening sludge on strip mine land will help minimize the discharge of acidic compounds and low pH drainage waters.

Although most lime softening sludges are an excellent liming agent for agricultural and land reclamation purposes, some lime softening sludges must be disposed of in a sanitary landfill due to the lack of availability of agricultural land or excessive costs. Landfilling of lime softening sludge is a practical alternative where this method is cost-effective (minimum cost of disposal).

Alum sludge has a tendency to cause soils to harden and does not provide any beneficial value. For this reason water treatment plant alum sludge must not be applied to agricultural land. The sludge may be applied to a dedicated land disposal site. The sludge is applied to the land and plowed into the soil. Landfilling is another method of ultimate disposal of alum sludge.

Some water treatment plants use a slow sand filter or settling pond for the treatment of iron filter backwash wastewater. The slow sand filter must be cleaned occasionally by removing the top 2 to 3 inches (50 to 75 mm) of sand and iron sludge. The material removed must be disposed of in a sanitary landfill.

Water treatment plants which soften water by the ion exchange (zeolite) softening method produce a wastewater which has high concentrations of total dissolved solids and chloride compounds. Ion exchange softening wastes should not be discharged untreated into low flow streams. The wastewater treatment processes capable of reducing the total dissolved solids and chloride concentrations to acceptable levels are very energy consumptive and expensive. Ion exchange softener regeneration wastewater may be very carefully and slowly discharged into a sanitary sewer system. The operator at the wastewater treatment plant must be notified in advance.

If a sanitary sewer system is not available for the disposal of ion exchange softening wastes, holding tanks should be installed to store the liquid from the regeneration and rinse cycles. This liquid should be ultimately disposed of in a sanitary landfill.

Filter backwash wastewater may be recycled through the water treatment plant, placed in wastewater storage ponds for additional treatment and disposal or discharged into a sanitary sewer. The remainder of this section discusses some of the procedures used by operators to dispose of sludges.

Wet sludge can be disposed of in an open field by use of spray bars or dumped out for landfill (Figure 17.14). When releasing the wet sludge at one spot, the back of the truck should face downhill so it will drain faster and be emptied out completely (Figure 17.15). This practice will also reduce the chances of the truck getting stuck in the sludge. Usually it takes about 10 minutes to empty a truck.

Sometimes individuals will request the sludge for fill and some contractors have used the sludge to mix with decomposed granite (DG) (a type of rock found in some regions) for fill purposes.

Sludge drying beds for sedimentation tank wastes also can be used to dry sludge from nearby backwash recovery ponds,

but this requires the sludge to be handled for a second time. An open field spray bar application is one method for disposing of backwash recovery sludges because after a few weeks, the residual is hardly noticeable. PVC pipe may be used to dispose of backwash recovery sludges instead of using a spray bar.

Where sludge is repeatedly spread in a single landfill site, be prepared to mix the sludge in with the native soil because it is unsightly. Obviously a location as close to the plant as possible would be the most cost-effective solution. Process wastes also can be dried in lagoons and covered over permanently.

In plants with a size range from 5 to 10 MGD (19 to 38 MLD), it will take four operators approximately two days to complete the job of draining and cleaning a sedimentation tank or a backwash recovery pond and disposing of the sludge.

In plants where a backwash pond is not available, the sludge can be moved to a sump. A smaller suction hose must be used to empty small sumps; instead of the 6-inch (150-mm) hose, use either a 3- or 4-inch (75- or 100-mm) hose. With a smaller suction hose, it will take 25 minutes or more to fill the vacuum tank. Five or six operators will be needed to keep the sump filled. Of course, during the time that the truck is on the road to the dump site and back again, the operators are standing by and the sludge cannot be moved. If two trucks were used, this disadvantage could be overcome, but the cost may also increase. Obviously, the larger the sump and the truck's tank, the cheaper the operation from the standpoint of labor costs.

Plants of one MGD (3.8 MLD) capacity may be able to use some of the local septic tank pumpers or vacuum trucks to an advantage. Such companies usually have made arrangements for the use of dump sites that may be used to dispose of the sludge they pump.

QUESTIONS

Write your answers in a notebook and then compare your answers with those on page 222.

17.8A   List the methods of ultimate sludge disposal.

17.8B   Why should sludge be disposed of as close as possible to the water treatment plant?

17.9 EQUIPMENT

17.90 Vacuum Trucks

The use of a vacuum truck is highly recommended because these trucks develop the fewest problems with clogging. The larger the suction pipe the better. Any object smaller than the hose size can be readily sucked through unless there are too many objects in the sludge. Wedging of several rocks or sticks

Fig. 17.14   Use of sludge for a landfill

Fig. 17.15   Emptying sludge from a truck

can occur, slowing up the process of sludge removal. Obviously any object that is sighted should be removed by hand picking and tossed out. Any well-operated plant should be void of these solids, but they are sometimes accidentally dropped in or thrown in by vandals. Leaves and other small objects that may get by the plant inlet screens are not too much of a problem unless an excessive amount exists. Under these conditions, the heavily accumulated portions should be scooped out to prevent any clogging of drain pipes or suction hoses.

17.91 Sludge Pumps

Many small treatment plants exist, especially in rural areas, where disposal of sludge would appear less troublesome. A couple of thousand gallons of sludge can be moved by gravity or pumped out to an open field and mixed (disked) into the soil. Even a quarter of an acre can handle many years of dried sludge from a small plant. Unfortunately, most of these plants do not have the land available, so the sludge in its wet form must be hauled out to a disposal site or a small lagoon or pond must be excavated for sludge collection. If sludge must be moved wet, use a sludge pump[8] to pump it into a tank or hire a septic tank pumper. Septic tank pumps, especially the suction hose, must be thoroughly rinsed and disinfected before use in any water treatment plant facilities. This applies also to all tools and equipment used.

A sludge pump can be an advantage over a self-priming centrifugal pump because of its large suction and discharge hose (usually three inches (75 mm) in diameter). These pumps are rated at about 60 GPM (3.8 L/sec) and can handle more solids. However, there are also self-priming types of wastewater pumps available that are designed so that solids do not actually pass through the impellers. These pumps may be used to pump sludges from water treatment plants. In either case, an excessive amount of foreign solids other than sludge itself can cause some pumping problems.

Wet sludge from a sedimentation tank will flow through pipes by gravity even if there are some ups and downs in the line provided the sludge is under some head. If difficulty arises, add some water for dilution or raise the end of the suction hose closer to the surface of the sump where the sludge is more diluted.

Because of the differences in volume between wet and dried sludge, it is always preferable to contain the wet sludge at the plant for drying. If the plant water source is a canal or reservoir close to the site, construct a small pond parallel to it and return the supernatant to the source for recycling by removing baffle boards. Only fresh backwash wastewater should be recycled. Water separated or drained from old sludge can cause serious problems if recycled. This water is likely to be *SEPTIC*[9] and could cause taste and odor problems. Also this water will contain millions of bacteria and microorganisms which should not be recycled through a water treatment plant.

If necessary, semi-dry or dried sludge can be hauled out of the pond.

17.10 PLANT DRAINAGE WATERS

There are several sources of drainage waters in a water treatment plant which must be properly handled and disposed of. These sources include the laboratory, shops, and plant drainage water from leaks and spills. If continuous sampling pumps provide the lab with continuously flowing water from various plant processes, this water could be discharged to a sewer. Any reagents, toxics, or potentially pathogenic wastes from the lab must be properly treated and packaged before ultimate disposal in landfills. Drainage waters from leaks and other sources in the plant may be discharged to sewers. These drainage waters may be recycled through the plant; however, extreme caution must be exercised at all times to avoid contributing to taste and odor problems, health hazards, or operational problems.

17.11 MONITORING AND REPORTING

The location of the water treatment plant and the methods used to ultimately dispose of the process wastes will dictate the monitoring and reporting requirements. These reporting requirements may be established by local or state health or pollution control agencies. Monitoring and reporting will usually involve measuring and recording volumes of sludges or brines, percent solids, and other measurements which will prove that these processes are not creating any adverse environmental impacts.

17.12 ADDITIONAL READING

1. *WATER TREATMENT PLANT WASTE MANAGEMENT.* Customer Services, AWWA, 6666 W. Quincy Ave., Denver, CO 80235. Order No. 90527. Price to members, $38.50; nonmembers, $57.75; price includes cost of shipping and handling.

QUESTIONS

Write your answers in a notebook and then compare your answers with those on page 222.

17.9A   How do objects that plug sludge suction hoses get into water treatment plants?

17.9B   What type of pump can be used to pump sludge into a tank on a truck?

17.10A   List the sources of plant drainage waters.

17.11A   What factors will dictate the monitoring and reporting requirements for your sludge disposal program?

Please answer the discussion and review questions before continuing with the Objective Test.

---

[8] *Types of sludge pumps include types of diaphragm, nonclog, and progressive cavity pumps.*
[9] *Septic (SEP-tick).   A condition produced by bacteria when all oxygen supplies are depleted. If severe, the bottom deposits produce hydrogen sulfide, the deposits and water turn black, give off foul odors, and the water has a greatly increased chlorine demand.*

DISCUSSION AND REVIEW QUESTIONS

Chapter 17. HANDLING AND DISPOSAL OF PROCESS WASTES

Write the answers to these questions in your notebook before continuing with the Objective Test on page 223. The purpose of these questions is to indicate to you how well you understand the material in the chapter.

1. The amount of sludge produced by a conventional water filtration plant depends on what factors?

2. What items should be considered when determining the frequency of cleaning a sedimentation basin?

3. What happens to the water separated from sludges in backwash recovery ponds or lagoons?

4. What precautions must be taken before draining a tank?

5. What duties should be performed by operators as the sludge is being drained from a sedimentation tank?

6. How would you fill a sedimentation tank after the tank has been emptied, inspected, and the necessary repairs completed?

7. How is sludge from the lime-soda softening process dewatered?

8. Why are at least three sludge drying beds installed at water treatment plants?

9. Why should the back of the sludge truck face downhill when releasing wet sludge at one point?

10. What is the purpose of monitoring and reporting for a sludge disposal program?

SUGGESTED ANSWERS

Chapter 17. HANDLING AND DISPOSAL OF PROCESS WASTES

Answers to questions on page 201.

17.0A Strict laws are needed regarding the disposal of process wastes to prevent rivers and streams from becoming more polluted. These laws are designed to prevent any waste discharge that could discolor, pollute, or generally be harmful to aquatic or plant life or the environment.

17.0B If a discharge results from the disposal of process wastes, such water quality indicators as pH, turbidity, TDS, settleable solids, and any other harmful materials may require monitoring.

Answers to questions on page 202.

17.1A Sludge is removed from sedimentation tanks by mechanical rakes or scrapers which periodically draw out sludge from a hopper, or a vacuum-type sludge removal device may be used.

17.1B Sludge is removed from upflow solids-contact units through sludge drawoff lines which must be monitored.

Answers to questions on page 203.

17.2A A source water stabilizing reservoir can reduce the volume of sludge handled by reducing the turbidity in the water being treated. Lower turbidities reduce the amount of alum required and thus the volume of sludge that settles out.

17.2B Sedimentation tanks should be drained and cleaned at least twice a year and more often if the sludge buildup interferes with the treatment processes.

Answers to questions on page 203.

17.3A Sedimentation tanks should be inspected and repaired (if necessary) when the tanks are drained and cleaned.

17.3B   Sludge may be dewatered by the use of belt presses, centrifuges, filter presses, vacuum filters, solar lagoons, and sand drying beds.

Answers to questions on page 205.

17.4A   Sludge must be removed manually from tanks without mechanical or vacuum-type sludge collectors. The tanks must be drained and then operators must push the sludge to the drain lines with squeegees or the sludge must be pumped out into tank trucks.

17.4B   When draining a sedimentation tank, do not drain the settled water above the sludge to the lagoons or sludge drying beds. Divert or pump this water to sedimentation tanks that are in operation, to the headworks for reprocessing, or return the water to the source.

17.4C   Whenever an operator enters a closed tank (confined space), be sure that:

1. No gasoline engines are operated in the tank,
2. The tank atmosphere is tested for flammable or explosive gases and oxygen deficiency, and adequate ventilation of clean air is provided at all times,
3. Clean running water is available to wash down boots and equipment when leaving the tank, and
4. Use the buddy system. Someone must be outside the tank and watching anyone inside the tank, and another person must be available nearby.

Answers to questions on page 208.

17.5A   Timing is critical if backwash recovery ponds are used to handle sludge from sedimentation basins because you want to avoid having to backwash the filters while you are draining a sedimentation tank.

17.5B   The suction pipe for the backwash recovery pump must be floated near the surface of the pond so that any excess water can be recycled, but the sludge will not be pumped out of the pond.

17.5C   Lime-soda softening sludge can be disposed of ultimately by

1. Covering the lagoon with soil,
2. Hauling the dried sludge to a landfill, or
3. Spreading on agricultural soils to adjust the pH for optimum crop yields.

Answers to questions on page 209.

17.6A   The minimum recommended number of solar drying lagoons is three.

17.6B   Sludge drying beds are made with underdrains covered with gradations of aggregate and sand. The drains terminate into a sump where recovery pumps can return the water drained from the sludge back to the plant to be reprocessed.

17.6C   The proper time to remove sludge from the drying bed is when no more than one foot of sludge has accumulated and a checkered-shaped piece of dry sludge can be picked up off the sand.

17.6D   When operating a front-end loader to remove sludge from a drying bed, be careful so only the dried sludge is picked up with a minimum of disturbance to the sand and aggregate. The loader bucket capacity should be limited to one or two cubic yards of sludge because there may be only about 10 inches of sand cover over the underdrains.

Answers to questions on page 213.

17.6E   Sludges may be dewatered using: (1) solar lagoons, (2) sand drying beds, (3) belt filter presses, (4) centrifuges, (5) filter presses, and (6) vacuum filters.

17.6F   The principal advantage of using centrifuges to dewater sludges is that the density of the sludge cake can be varied from a thickened liquid slurry to a dry cake. The major limitation of using centrifuges is high energy consumption.

17.6G   A precoat of diatomaceous earth is required to dewater gelatinous alum sludge.

Answers to questions on page 213.

17.7A   The complications of discharging sludge to sewers include:

1. Fees charged by wastewater treatment plants could be very high,
2. Increased monitoring requirements and costs,
3. A holding tank may be necessary so the sludge is released at a uniform rate,
4. Possibility of causing a sewer blockage, and
5. Wastewater treatment plant will have to handle and dispose of sludge.

17.7B   Brine from ion exchange units is usually discharged into wastewater collection systems during the day to take advantage of high flows for dilution.

Answers to questions on page 218.

17.8A   Methods of ultimate sludge disposal include disposal in sanitary landfills, lagoons, land application, and discharge to sanitary sewers.

17.8B   Sludge should be disposed of as close as possible to the water treatment plant to reduce hauling costs.

Answers to questions on page 220.

17.9A   Objects that plug sludge suction hoses get into water treatment plants by being accidentally dropped in or thrown in by vandals.

17.9B   A diaphragm pump can be used to pump sludge into a tank on a truck. Nonclog and progressive cavity pumps are also sometimes used.

17.10A   Sources of plant drainage waters include the laboratory, shops, and plant drainage water from leaks and spills.

17.11A   Monitoring and reporting requirements for a sludge disposal program are dictated by the location of your water treatment plant and the methods used to ultimately dispose of your process wastes.

OBJECTIVE TEST

Chapter 17. HANDLING AND DISPOSAL OF PROCESS WASTES

Please write your name and mark the correct answers on the answer sheet, as directed at the end of Chapter 1. There may be more than one correct answer to each multiple-choice question.

True-False

1. Alum may sometimes be used instead of organic polymers to reduce the quantity of sludge produced.

    1. True
    2. False

2. Basins with continuous sludge collection systems never need to be drained for inspection and maintenance.

    1. True
    2. False

3. Polymer sludges are suitable as a soil conditioner.

    1. True
    2. False

4. Filter presses have been used to process difficult-to-dewater sludges (alum sludges).

    1. True
    2. False

5. Water treatment plant alum sludge may be applied to agricultural land.

    1. True
    2. False

Best Answer (Select only the closest or best answer.)

6. How often should sedimentation tanks be drained and cleaned?

    1. When adequate sludge density is achieved
    2. When sludge buildup interferes with the treatment processes
    3. When the designer/manufacturer recommends
    4. When the operator has the time

7. What is a key to speedy sludge drying?

    1. Dewater sludge using a filter press
    2. Rake up dried sludge
    3. Regularly remove water on top of sludge
    4. Remove sludge during day to a drying bed

8. How is sludge removed from tanks in plants without mechanical sludge collectors?

    1. Comminutors
    2. Continuously using vacuum pumps
    3. Manual labor
    4. Moving bridge systems

9. What should be done before draining any in-ground tank?

    1. Check movement of sludge scrapers
    2. Determine the level of water table
    3. Inspect tank for short-circuiting
    4. Measure depth of water in tank

10. Why must wet sludge be washed off all gears, sprockets, and moving parts after tanks are drained?

    1. Corrosion problems develop under wet sludge
    2. Dried sludge is difficult to remove from coated surfaces
    3. Wet sludge drains unevenly off equipment
    4. Wet sludge produces odors

11. Why must chlorine be applied to a tank before filling?

    1. Coating
    2. Disinfection
    3. Removal of algae
    4. Sealing

12. What is a benefit of applying sludge to land?

    1. Erosion control
    2. Fertilizer
    3. Soil conditioner
    4. Weed control

13. How can the efficiency of the sand drying bed dewatering process be improved?

    1. Apply greater depths of wet sludge
    2. Precondition process sludge with chemical coagulants
    3. Prevent formation of cracks in drying sludge
    4. Treat sludge using a centrifuge

14. What is the principal advantage of dewatering sludge using a centrifuge?

    1. Density of sludge cake can be varied
    2. High solids concentration in the supernatant
    3. Low energy consumption
    4. Requires low spinning action forces

15. Why are vacuum trucks recommended for removing sludge from tanks?

    1. Few problems with clogging
    2. Small suction pipes can be used effectively
    3. Trucks are mobile
    4. Unlimited sludge handling capacity

Multiple Choice (Select all correct answers.)

16. How do water treatment plants dispose of sludges?

    1. Lakes
    2. Landfills
    3. Rivers
    4. Spread on land
    5. Wastewater collection systems

17. What factors influence the amount of sludge accumulation to be handled and disposed of?

    1. Amount of suspended matter
    2. Level of dosage
    3. Size of sludge hopper
    4. Type of coagulant
    5. Type of suspended matter

18. What are the advantages of polymer sludge over alum sludge?

    1. Denser
    2. Easier to dewater
    3. Less costly
    4. Removes hardness
    5. Treats all waters

19. Facilities at a water treatment plant to handle and dispose of process wastes depend on what factors?

    1. Climate
    2. Methods of ultimate disposal
    3. Sources of sludge
    4. When plant was built
    5. Where plant is located

20. What additional work should be performed when tanks are drained and sludge removed?

    1. Adjust coagulant doses
    2. Backwash filters
    3. Inspect tanks
    4. Inventory spare parts
    5. Perform necessary repairs to tanks

21. What sludge treatment processes are used by plants that produce large volumes of sludge to reduce the volume of sludge that must be handled and ultimately disposed of?

    1. Coagulation
    2. Conditioning
    3. Dewatering
    4. Elutriation
    5. Thickening

22. What sludge treatment processes are used to dewater sludges?

    1. Belt filter presses
    2. Centrifuges
    3. Sand drying beds
    4. Screw pumps
    5. Solar lagoons

23. Why are continuous-belt filter presses popular?

    1. Ease of operation
    2. Low energy consumption
    3. Maintenance-free equipment
    4. Production of dry filter cake
    5. Small land requirements

24. How can sludge be disposed of in wastewater collection systems?

    1. At a uniform rate throughout the day
    2. Released during wastewater treatment plant's high flow period
    3. Released during wastewater treatment plant's low flow period
    4. Released when filters are backwashed
    5. Released when sludge is removed from sedimentation tanks

25. What are the sources of drainage waters in a water treatment plant?

    1. Kitchen
    2. Laboratory
    3. Leaks and spills
    4. Shops
    5. Toilets

End of Objective Test

CHAPTER 18

MAINTENANCE

by

Parker Robinson

TABLE OF CONTENTS

Chapter 18.   MAINTENANCE

Page

OBJECTIVES 231

WORDS 232

LESSON 1

18.0   TREATMENT PLANT MAINTENANCE — GENERAL PROGRAM 236

    18.00   Preventive Maintenance Records 236

    18.01   Library of Manufacturers' Operation and Parts Manuals 236

    18.02   Emergencies 238

    18.03   Lockout/Tagout Procedure 238

18.1   ELECTRICAL EQUIPMENT 240

    18.10   Beware of Electricity 240

        18.100   Attention 240

        18.101   Recognize Your Limitations 240

    18.11   Electrical Fundamentals 241

        18.110   Introduction 241

        18.111   Volts 241

        18.112   Direct Current (D.C.) 241

        18.113   Alternating Current (A.C.) 241

        18.114   Amps 242

        18.115   Watts 242

        18.116   Power Requirements 243

        18.117   Conductors and Insulators 243

    18.12   Tools, Meters, and Testers 243

        18.120   Voltage Testing 243

        18.121   Ammeter 245

        18.122   Megger 248

        18.123   Ohmmeters 249

    18.13   Switch Gear 250

        18.130   Equipment Protective Devices 250

        18.131   Fuses 250

        18.132   Circuit Breakers 250

        18.133   Overload Relays 250

       18.134 Motor Starters 251

  18.14 Electric Motors 251

       18.140 Classifications 251

       18.141 Troubleshooting 256

       18.142 Recordkeeping 256

  18.15 Auxiliary Electrical Power 256

       18.150 Safety First 256

       18.151 Standby Power Generation 256

       18.152 Emergency Lighting 264

       18.153 Batteries 265

  18.16 High Voltage 266

       18.160 Transmission 266

       18.161 Switch Gear 266

       18.162 Power Distribution Transformers 266

  18.17 Electrical Safety Checklist 267

  18.18 Additional Reading 267

DISCUSSION AND REVIEW QUESTIONS 268

LESSON 2

18.2 MECHANICAL EQUIPMENT 269

  18.20 Repair Shop 269

  18.21 Pumps 269

       18.210 Centrifugal Pumps 269

       18.211 Let's Build a Pump! 269

       18.212 Vertical Centrifugal Pumps 277

       18.213 Horizontal Centrifugal Pumps 277

       18.214 Reciprocating or Piston Pumps 277

       18.215 Progressive Cavity (Screw-Flow) Pumps 278

       18.216 Chemical Metering Pumps 278

  18.22 Lubrication 282

       18.220 Purpose of Lubrication 282

       18.221 Properties of Lubricants 282

       18.222 Lubrication Schedule 282

       18.223 Precautions 283

       18.224 Pump Lubrication 283

       18.225 Equipment Lubrication 283

DISCUSSION AND REVIEW QUESTIONS 284

LESSON 3

  18.23 Pump Maintenance 285

       18.230 Section Format 285

18.231 Preventive Maintenance 285

    1. Pumps, General 285

    2. Reciprocating Pumps, General 292

    3. Propeller Pumps, General 293

    4. Progressive Cavity Pumps, General 293

    5. Pump Controls 293

    6. Electric Motors 294

    7. Belt Drives 294

    8. Chain Drives 297

    9. Variable Speed Belt Drives 298

    10. Couplings 298

    11. Shear Pins 300

18.24 Pump Operation 302

  18.240 Starting a New Pump 302

  18.241 Pump Shutdown 302

  18.242 Pump-Driving Equipment 302

  18.243 Electrical Controls 302

  18.244 Operating Troubles 303

  18.245 Starting and Stopping Pumps 304

    18.2450 Centrifugal Pumps 304

    18.2451 Positive Displacement Pumps 306

DISCUSSION AND REVIEW QUESTIONS 307

LESSON 4

18.25 Compressors 307

18.26 Valves 309

  18.260 Uses of Valves 309

  18.261 Gate Valves 309

  18.262 Maintenance of Gate Valves 311

    12. Gate Valves 311

  18.263 Globe Valves 312

  18.264 Eccentric Valves 312

  18.265 Butterfly Valves 312

  18.266 Check Valves 316

  18.267 Maintenance of Check Valves 325

    13. Check Valves 325

  18.268 Automatic Valves 325

DISCUSSION AND REVIEW QUESTIONS 325

LESSON 5

18.3 INTERNAL COMBUSTION ENGINES 327

    18.30 Gasoline Engines 327

        18.300 Need to Maintain Gasoline Engines 327

        18.301 Maintenance 327

        18.302 Starting Problems 327

        18.303 Running Problems 327

        18.304 How to Start a Gasoline Engine 328

            18.3040 Small Engines 328

            18.3041 Large Engines 328

    18.31 Diesel Engines 329

        18.310 How Diesel Engines Work 329

        18.311 Operation 329

        18.312 Fuel System 329

        18.313 Water-Cooled Diesel Engines 332

        18.314 Air-Cooled Diesel Engines 332

        18.315 How to Start Diesel Engines 332

        18.316 Maintenance and Troubleshooting 332

    18.32 Cooling Systems 333

    18.33 Fuel Storage 335

        18.330 Code Requirements 335

        18.331 Diesel 335

        18.332 Gasoline 335

        18.333 Liquified Petroleum Gas (LPG) 335

        18.334 Natural Gas 335

    18.34 Standby Engines 336

18.4 CHEMICAL STORAGE AND FEEDERS 336

    18.40 Chemical Storage 336

    18.41 Drainage From Chemical Storage and Feeders 336

    18.42 Use of Feeder Manufacturer's Manual 337

    18.43 Solid Feeders 337

    18.44 Liquid Feeders 337

    18.45 Gas Feeders 337

    18.46 Calibration of Chemical Feeders 337

        18.460 Large-Volume Metering Pumps 337

        18.461 Small-Volume Metering Pumps 337

        18.462 Dry-Chemical Systems 337

    18.47 Chlorinators 340

18.5   TANKS AND RESERVOIRS 341

    18.50   Scheduling Inspections 341

    18.51   Steel Tanks 341

    18.52   Cathodic Protection 341

    18.53   Concrete Tanks 341

18.6   BUILDING MAINTENANCE 342

18.7   ARITHMETIC ASSIGNMENT 342

18.8   ADDITIONAL READING 342

18.9   ACKNOWLEDGMENTS 342

DISCUSSION AND REVIEW QUESTIONS 343

SUGGESTED ANSWERS 343

OBJECTIVE TEST 348

OBJECTIVES

Chapter 18.   MAINTENANCE

Following completion of Chapter 18, you should be able to:

1. Develop a maintenance program for your plant, including equipment, buildings, grounds, channels, and tanks;

2. Start a maintenance recordkeeping system that will provide you with information to protect equipment warranties, to prepare budgets, and to satisfy regulatory agencies;

3. Schedule maintenance of equipment at proper time intervals;

4. Perform maintenance as directed by manufacturers;

5. Recognize symptoms that indicate equipment is not performing properly, identify the source of the problem, and take corrective action;

6. Recognize the serious consequences that could occur when inexperienced, unqualified, or unauthorized persons attempt to troubleshoot or repair electrical panels, controls, circuits, wiring, or equipment;

7. Communicate with electricians by indicating possible causes of problems in electrical panels, controls, circuits, wiring, and motors;

8. Properly select and use the following pieces of equipment (if qualified and authorized):

    a. Voltage tester,

    b. Ammeter,

    c. Megger, and

    d. Ohmmeter;

9. Safely operate and maintain auxiliary electrical equipment, including during standby and emergency situations;

10. Describe how a pump is put together;

11. Discuss the application or use of different types of pumps;

12. Start and stop pumps;

13. Maintain the various types of pumps;

14. Operate and maintain a compressor;

15. Develop and conduct an equipment lubrication program; and

16. Start up, operate, maintain, and shut down gasoline engines, diesel engines, heating, ventilating, and air conditioning systems.

NOTE: Special maintenance information is given in the previous chapters on treatment processes where appropriate.

WORDS

Chapter 18.   MAINTENANCE

AIR GAP

An open vertical drop, or vertical empty space, that separates a drinking (potable) water supply to be protected from another water system in a water treatment plant or other location. This open gap prevents the contamination of drinking water by backsiphonage or backflow because there is no way raw water or any other water can reach the drinking water.

AIR GAP

ALTERNATING CURRENT (A.C.)

ALTERNATING CURRENT (A.C.)

An electric current that reverses its direction (positive/negative values) at regular intervals.

AMPERAGE (AM-purr-age)

AMPERAGE

The strength of an electric current measured in amperes. The amount of electric current flow, similar to the flow of water in gallons per minute.

AMPERE (AM-peer)

AMPERE

The unit used to measure current strength. The current produced by an electromotive force of one volt acting through a resistance of one ohm.

AMPLITUDE

AMPLITUDE

The maximum strength of an alternating current during its cycle, as distinguished from the mean or effective strength.

AXIAL TO IMPELLER

AXIAL TO IMPELLER

The direction in which material being pumped flows around the impeller or flows parallel to the impeller shaft.

AXIS OF IMPELLER

AXIS OF IMPELLER

An imaginary line running along the center of a shaft (such as an impeller shaft).

BRINELLING (bruh-NEL-ing)

BRINELLING

Tiny indentations (dents) high on the shoulder of the bearing race or bearing. A type of bearing failure.

CATHODIC (ca-THOD-ick) PROTECTION

CATHODIC PROTECTION

An electrical system for prevention of rust, corrosion, and pitting of metal surfaces which are in contact with water or soil. A low-voltage current is made to flow through a liquid (water) or a soil in contact with the metal in such a manner that the external electromotive force renders the metal structure cathodic. This concentrates corrosion on auxiliary anodic parts which are deliberately allowed to corrode instead of letting the structure corrode.

CAVITATION (CAV-uh-TAY-shun)

CAVITATION

The formation and collapse of a gas pocket or bubble on the blade of an impeller or the gate of a valve. The collapse of this gas pocket or bubble drives water into the impeller or gate with a terrific force that can cause pitting on the impeller or gate surface. Cavitation is accompanied by loud noises that sound like someone is pounding on the impeller or gate with a hammer.

CIRCUIT

CIRCUIT

The complete path of an electric current, including the generating apparatus or other source; or, a specific segment or section of the complete path.

CIRCUIT BREAKER CIRCUIT BREAKER

A safety device in an electric circuit that automatically shuts off the circuit when it becomes overloaded. The device can be manually reset.

CONDUCTOR CONDUCTOR

A substance, body, device or wire that readily conducts or carries electric current.

COULOMB (COO-lahm) COULOMB

A measurement of the amount of electrical charge carried by an electric current of one ampere in one second. One coulomb equals about 6.25×10^{18} electrons (6,250,000,000,000,000,000 electrons).

CROSS CONNECTION CROSS CONNECTION

A connection between a drinking (potable) water system and an unapproved water supply. For example, if you have a pump moving nonpotable water and hook into the drinking water system to supply water for the pump seal, a cross connection or mixing between the two water systems can occur. This mixing may lead to contamination of the drinking water.

CURRENT CURRENT

A movement or flow of electricity. Water flowing in a pipe is measured in gallons per second past a certain point, not by the number of water molecules going past a point. Electric current is measured by the number of coulombs per second flowing past a certain point in a conductor. A coulomb is equal to about 6.25×10^{18} electrons (6,250,000,000,000,000,000 electrons). A flow of one coulomb per second is called one ampere, the unit of the rate of flow of current.

CYCLE CYCLE

A complete alternation of voltage and/or current in an alternating current (A.C.) circuit.

DATEOMETER (day-TOM-uh-ter) DATEOMETER

A small calendar disc attached to motors and equipment to indicate the year in which the last maintenance service was performed.

DIRECT CURRENT (D.C.) DIRECT CURRENT (D.C.)

Electric current flowing in one direction only and essentially free from pulsation.

ELECTROLYTE (ee-LECK-tro-LITE) ELECTROLYTE

A substance which dissociates (separates) into two or more ions when it is dissolved in water.

ELECTROMOTIVE FORCE (E.M.F.) ELECTROMOTIVE FORCE (E.M.F.)

The electrical pressure available to cause a flow of current (amperage) when an electric circuit is closed. Also called VOLTAGE.

ELECTRON ELECTRON

(1) A very small, negatively charged particle which is practically weightless. According to the electron theory, all electrical and electronic effects are caused either by the movement of electrons from place to place or because there is an excess or lack of electrons at a particular place.

(2) The part of an atom that determines its chemical properties.

END BELLS END BELLS

Devices used to hold the rotor and stator of a motor in position.

FUSE FUSE

A protective device having a strip or wire of fusible metal which, when placed in a circuit, will melt and break the electric circuit if heated too much. High temperatures will develop in the fuse when a current flows through the fuse in excess of that which the circuit will carry safely.

GROUND GROUND

An expression representing an electrical connection to earth or a large conductor which is at the earth's potential or neutral voltage.

HERTZ HERTZ

The number of complete electromagnetic cycles or waves in one second of an electric or electronic circuit. Also called the frequency of the current. Abbreviated Hz.

HYGROSCOPIC (HI-grow-SKOP-ick)   HYGROSCOPIC

Absorbing or attracting moisture from the air.

JOGGING   JOGGING

The frequent starting and stopping of an electric motor.

LEAD (LEE-d)   LEAD

A wire or conductor that can carry electric current.

MANDREL (MAN-drill)   MANDREL

A special tool used to push bearings in or to pull sleeves out.

MEG   MEG

A procedure used for checking the insulation resistance on motors, feeders, bus bar systems, grounds, and branch circuit wiring. Also see MEGGER.

MEGGER (from megohm)   MEGGER

An instrument used for checking the insulation resistance on motors, feeders, bus bar systems, grounds, and branch circuit wiring. Also see MEG.

MEGOHM   MEGOHM

Meg means one million, so 5 megohms means 5 million ohms. A megger reads in millions of ohms.

MULTI-STAGE PUMP   MULTI-STAGE PUMP

A pump that has more than one impeller. A single-stage pump has one impeller.

NAMEPLATE   NAMEPLATE

A durable metal plate found on equipment which lists critical installation and operating conditions for the equipment.

OSHA (O-shuh)   OSHA

The Williams-Steiger Occupational Safety and Health Act of 1970 (OSHA) is a federal law designed to protect the health and safety of industrial workers and also the operators of water supply systems and treatment plants. The Act regulates the design, construction, operation and maintenance of water supply systems and water treatment plants. OSHA also refers to the federal and state agencies which administer the OSHA regulations.

OHM   OHM

The unit of electrical resistance. The resistance of a conductor in which one volt produces a current of one ampere.

POLE SHADER   POLE SHADER

A copper bar circling the laminated iron core inside the coil of a magnetic starter.

POWER FACTOR   POWER FACTOR

The ratio of the true power passing through an electric circuit to the product of the voltage and amperage in the circuit. This is a measure of the lag or lead of the current with respect to the voltage. In alternating current the voltage and amperes are not always in phase; therefore, the true power may be slightly less than that determined by the direct product.

PRUSSIAN BLUE   PRUSSIAN BLUE

A blue paste or liquid (often on a paper like carbon paper) used to show a contact area. Used to determine if gate valve seats fit properly.

RADIAL TO IMPELLER   RADIAL TO IMPELLER

Perpendicular to the impeller shaft. Material being pumped flows at a right angle to the impeller.

RESISTANCE   RESISTANCE

That property of a conductor or wire that opposes the passage of a current, thus causing electric energy to be transformed into heat.

ROTOR   ROTOR

The rotating part of a machine. The rotor is surrounded by the stationary (non-moving) parts (stator) of the machine.

SEIZE UP
SEIZE UP

Seize up occurs when an engine overheats and a part expands to the point where the engine will not run. Also called "freezing."

SHEAVE (SHE-v)
SHEAVE

V-belt drive pulley which is commonly made of cast iron or steel.

SHIM
SHIM

Thin metal sheets which are inserted between two surfaces to align or space the surfaces correctly. Shims can be used anywhere a spacer is needed. Usually shims are 0.001 to 0.020 inch thick.

SINGLE-STAGE PUMP
SINGLE-STAGE PUMP

A pump that has only one impeller. A multi-stage pump has more than one impeller.

STATOR
STATOR

That portion of a machine which contains the stationary (non-moving) parts that surround the moving parts (rotor).

STETHOSCOPE
STETHOSCOPE

An instrument used to magnify sounds and convey them to the ear.

VOLTAGE
VOLTAGE

The electrical pressure available to cause a flow of current (amperage) when an electric circuit is closed. Also called ELECTRO-MOTIVE FORCE (E.M.F.).

WATER HAMMER
WATER HAMMER

The sound like someone hammering on a pipe that occurs when a valve is opened or closed very rapidly. When a valve position is changed quickly, the water pressure in a pipe will increase and decrease back and forth very quickly. This rise and fall in pressures can cause serious damage to the system.

CHAPTER 18.   MAINTENANCE

(Lesson 1 of 5 Lessons)

18.0   TREATMENT PLANT MAINTENANCE — GENERAL PROGRAM

A water treatment plant operator has many duties. Most of them have to do with the efficient operation of the plant. An operator has the responsibility to produce a water that will meet all the requirements established for the plant. By doing this, the operator develops a good working relationship with the regulatory agencies, water users, and plant neighbors.

Another duty an operator has is that of *PLANT MAINTENANCE*. A good maintenance program is a must in order to maintain successful operation of the plant. A successful maintenance program will include everything from mechanical equipment to the care of the plant grounds, buildings, and structures.

Mechanical maintenance is of prime importance as the equipment must be kept in good operating condition in order for the plant to maintain peak performance. Manufacturers provide information on the mechanical maintenance of their equipment. You should thoroughly read their literature on your plant equipment and *UNDERSTAND* the procedures. Contact the manufacturer or the local representative if you have any questions. Follow the instructions very carefully when performing maintenance on equipment. You also must recognize tasks that may be beyond your capabilities or repair facilities, and you should request assistance when needed.

For a successful maintenance program, your supervisors must understand the need for and benefits from equipment that operates continuously as intended. Disabled or improperly working equipment is a threat to the quality of the plant output, and repair costs for poorly maintained equipment usually exceed the cost of maintenance.

18.00   Preventive Maintenance Records

Preventive maintenance programs help operating personnel keep equipment in satisfactory operating condition and aid in detecting and correcting malfunctions before they develop into major problems.

A frequent occurrence in a preventive maintenance program is the failure of the operator to record the work after it is completed. When this happens the operator must rely on memory to know when to perform each preventive maintenance function. As days pass into weeks and months, the preventive maintenance program is lost in the turmoil of everyday operation.

The only way an operator can keep track of a preventive maintenance program is by *GOOD RECORDKEEPING*. Whatever record system is used, it should be kept up to date on a daily basis and not left to memory for some other time. Equipment service record cards (Figure 18.1) are easy to set up and require little time to keep up to date.

An *EQUIPMENT SERVICE CARD* (master card) should be filled out for each piece of equipment in the plant. Each card should have the equipment name on it, such as Raw Water Intake Pump No. 1.

1. List each required maintenance service with an item number.

2. List maintenance services in order of frequency of performance. For instance, show daily service as items 1, 2, and 3 on the card; weekly items as 4 and 5; monthly items as 6, 7, 8, and 9; and so on.

3. Describe each type of service under work to be done.

Make sure all necessary inspections and services are shown. For reference data, list paragraph or section numbers as shown in the pump maintenance section of this lesson (Section 18.23, p. 285). Also list frequency of service as shown in the time schedule columns of the same section. Under time, enter day or month service is due. Service card information may be changed to fit the needs of your plant or particular equipment as recommended by the equipment manufacturer. Be sure the information on the cards is complete and correct.

The *SERVICE RECORD CARD* should have the date and work done, listed by item number and signed by the operator who performed the service. Some operators prefer to keep both cards clipped together, while others place the service record card near the equipment.

When the service record is filled, it should be filed for future reference and a new card attached to the master card. The *EQUIPMENT SERVICE CARD* tells what should be done and when, while the *SERVICE RECORD CARD* is a record of what you did and when you did it. Many operators keep this information on a computer.

18.01   Library of Manufacturers' Operation and Parts Manuals

A plant library can contain helpful information to assist in plant operation. Material in the library should be cataloged

EQUIPMENT SERVICE CARD

EQUIPMENT: #1 Raw Water Intake Pump

Item No.	Work To Be Done	Reference[a]	Frequency	Time
1	Check water seal and packing gland	Par. 1	Daily	
2	Listen for unusual noises	Par. 6	Daily	
3	Alternate operating pump	Par. 1	Weekly	Monday
4	Inspect pump assembly	Par. 1	Weekly	Wednesday
5	Inspect and lube bearings	Par. 1	Quarterly	1-4-7-10[b]
6	Check operating temperature of bearings	Par. 1	Quarterly	1-4-7-10[b]
7	Check alignment of pump and motor	Par. 1	Semiann.	4 & 10
8	Inspect and service pumps	Par. 1	Semiann.	4 & 10
9	Drain pump before shutdown	Par. 1		

SERVICE RECORD CARD

EQUIPMENT: #1 Raw Water Intake Pump

Date	Work Done (Item No.)	Signed	Date	Work Done (Item No.)	Signed
1-5-97	1-2-3	J.B.			
1-6-97	1-2	J.B.			
1-7-97	1-2-4-5-6	R.W.			

[a] Par. 1 refers to Paragraph 1 in Section 18.23 of this manual. Par. 6 is also in Section 18.23.
[b] 1-4-7-10 represent the months of the year when the equipment should be serviced — 1-January, 4-April, 7-July, and 10-October.

Fig. 18.1 Equipment service card and service record card

and filed for easy use. Items in the library should include:

1. Plant operation and maintenance instruction manuals,

2. Plant plans and specifications,

3. Manufacturers' instructions,

4. Reference books on water treatment,

5. Professional journals and publications,

6. First-aid book,

7. Reports from other plants, and

8. A dictionary.

18.02 Emergencies

If your plant has not developed procedures for handling potential emergencies, do it *NOW*. Emergency procedures must be established for operators to follow when emergencies are caused by the release of chlorine, hazardous or toxic chemicals into the raw water supply, power outages or broken transmission lines or distribution mains. These procedures should include a list of emergency phone numbers located near all telephones, especially one that is unlikely to be affected by the emergency.

1. Police

2. Fire

3. Hospital and/or Physician

4. Responsible Plant Officials

5. Local Emergency Disaster Office

6. CHEMTREC (800) 424-9300

7. Emergency Team (if your plant has one)

The CHEMTREC toll-free number may be called at any time. Personnel at this number will give information on how to handle emergencies created by hazardous materials and will notify appropriate emergency personnel.

An emergency team for your plant may be trained and assigned the task of responding to SPECIFIC EMERGENCIES such as chlorine leaks. This emergency team must meet the following strict specifications at all times.

1. Team personnel must be physically and mentally qualified.

2. Proper equipment must be available at all times, including:

    a. Protective equipment, including self-contained breathing apparatus,

    b. Repair kits,

    c. Repair tools, and

    d. First-aid supplies.

3. Proper training must take place on a regular basis and include instruction about:

    a. Properties and detection of hazardous chemicals,

    b. Safe procedures for handling and storage of chemicals,

    c. Types of containers, safe procedures for shipping containers, and container safety devices,

    d. Installation of repair devices, and

    e. First-aid procedures.

4. Team members must be exposed regularly to simulated field emergencies or practice drills. Team response must be carefully evaluated and any errors or weaknesses corrected.

5. Emergency team performance must be reviewed annually on a specified date. Review must include:

    a. Training program,

    b. Response to actual emergencies, and

    c. Team physical and mental examinations.

WARNING. One person should never be permitted to attempt an emergency repair alone. Always wait for trained assistance. Valuable time, needed to correct a serious emergency, could be lost rescuing a foolish individual.

For additional information on emergencies, see Chapter 7, "Disinfection," Section 7.52, "Chlorine Leaks," Chapter 10, "Plant Operation," Section 10.9, "Emergency Conditions and Procedures," and Chapter 23, "Administration," Section 23.10, "Emergency Response." Chapter 23 contains information on what to do if a toxic substance gets into your water supply.

18.03 Lockout/Tagout Procedure

OSHA standards require that all equipment that could unexpectedly start up or release stored energy must be locked out and tagged whenever it is being worked on. Common forms of stored energy are electrical energy, spring-loaded equipment, hydraulic pressure, and compressed gases which are stored under pressure.

The operator who will be performing the work on the equipment is the person who installs a lock (either key or combination) on the energy isolating device (switch, valve) to positively lock the switch or valve in a safe position, preventing the equipment from starting or moving. At the same time, a tag such as the one shown in Figure 18.2 is installed at the lock indicating why the equipment is locked out and who is working on it. NO OTHER PERSON IS AUTHORIZED TO REMOVE THE TAG OR LOCKOUT DEVICE unless the employer has provided specific procedures and training for removal by others.

Even after equipment is locked out and tagged, it still may not be safe to work on. Stored energy in gas, air, water, steam, and hydraulic systems (such as water pumping systems) must be drained or bled down to release the stored energy. Elevated machine members, flywheels, and springs should be physically blocked and/or secured in place to prevent movement.

Before bleeding down pressurized systems, think about the pressures involved and what will be discharged to the atmosphere and work area (toxic or explosive gases, corrosive chemicals). Will other safety precautions have to be taken? What volume of bleed down material will there be and where will it go? If dealing with chemicals, greases, or lubricants, how can they be cleaned up or contained? Many times an operator has removed a pump volute cleanout only to find that the discharge check valve wasn't seated or one of the isolation valves was not fully seated. Once the pump was open, however, the pump intake structure drained into the pump room through the opened pump.

All rotating mechanical equipment must have guards installed to protect operators from becoming entangled or caught up in belts, pulleys, drive lines, flywheels, and couplings. Keep the guards installed even when no one is working on the equipment.

Various pieces of machinery are equipped with travel limit switches, pressure sensors, pressure reliefs, shear pins, and stall or torque switches to ensure proper and safe operation of the equipment. Never disconnect a device, or install larger shear pins than those specified on the original design, or modify pressure or temperature settings.

The basic elements of a proper lockout/tagout procedure are as follows:

1. Notify all affected employees that a lockout or tagged system is going to be used and the reason why. The authorized employee shall know the type and level of energy that the equipment uses and shall understand the hazard presented by the equipment.

2. If the equipment is operating, shut it down using the procedures established for the equipment.

3. Operate the switch, valve, or other energy isolating device(s) so that the equipment is isolated from its energy source(s). Stored energy such as that in springs, elevated machine parts, rotating flywheels, hydraulic systems, and air, gas, steam, or water pressure must be released or restrained by methods such as repositioning, blocking, or bleeding down.

4. Lock out and/or tag out the energy isolating device with your assigned individual lock or tag.

5. After ensuring that no personnel are exposed, and as a check that the energy source is disconnected, operate the pushbutton or other normal operating controls to make certain the equipment will not operate. A common problem when motor control centers (MCCs) contain many breakers is to lock out the wrong equipment (locking pump #3 and thinking it is #2). Always confirm the dead circuit. CAUTION! RETURN OPERATING CONTROLS TO THE NEUTRAL OR OFF POSITION AFTER THE TEST.

6. The equipment is now locked out or tagged out and work on the equipment may begin.

7. After the work on the equipment is complete, all tools have been removed, guards have been reinstalled, and employees are in the clear, remove all lockout or tagout devices. Operate the energy isolating devices to restore energy to the equipment.

8. Notify affected employees that the lockout or tagout device(s) has been removed before starting the equipment.

DANGER

OPERATOR WORKING ON LINE

DO NOT CLOSE THIS SWITCH WHILE THIS TAG IS DISPLAYED

TIME OFF: _____

DATE: _____

SIGNATURE: _____

This is the ONLY person authorized to remove this tag.

INDUSTRIAL INDEMNITY/INDUSTRIAL UNDERWRITERS/
INSURANCE COMPANIES

4E210—R66

Fig. 18.2 Typical warning tag
(Source: Industrial Indemnity/Industrial Underwriters/Insurance Companies)

QUESTIONS

Write your answers in a notebook and then compare your answers with those on page 343.

18.0A   Why should you plan a good maintenance program for your treatment plant?

18.0B   What general items would you include in your maintenance program?

18.0C   Why should you have a good recordkeeping system for your maintenance program?

18.0D   What is the difference between an *EQUIPMENT SERVICE CARD* and a *SERVICE RECORD CARD?*

18.0E   Prepare a list of emergency phone numbers for your treatment plant.

18.0F   Why is it necessary to bleed down pressurized systems before making repairs?

18.1 ELECTRICAL EQUIPMENT

18.10 Beware of Electricity

18.100 Attention

A. *DO NOT ATTEMPT TO INSTALL, TROUBLESHOOT, MAINTAIN, REPAIR, OR REPLACE ELECTRICAL EQUIPMENT, PANELS, CONTROLS, WIRING, OR CIRCUITS UNLESS YOU*

1. *KNOW WHAT YOU ARE DOING,*

2. *ARE QUALIFIED, AND*

3. *ARE AUTHORIZED.*

Section 18.11, "Electrical Fundamentals," is presented to provide you with an understanding and awareness of electricity. *THE PURPOSE OF THE SECTION IS TO HELP YOU PROVIDE ELECTRICIANS WITH THE INFORMATION THEY WILL NEED WHEN YOU CONTACT THEM AND REQUEST THEIR ASSISTANCE. YOU MUST BE EXTREMELY FAMILIAR WITH ELECTRICITY BEFORE ATTEMPTING ANY MAJOR REPAIRS.*

B. Due to the wide variety of equipment and manufacturers in the water treatment field, detailed procedures for the maintenance of some types of equipment were very difficult to include in this chapter. Also manufacturers are continually improving their products and some details would soon be out of date. *FOR DETAILS CONCERNING THE OPERATION, MAINTENANCE, AND REPAIR OF A PARTICULAR PIECE OF EQUIPMENT, REFER TO THE O & M INSTRUCTION MANUAL OR CONTACT THE MANUFACTURER.*

C. Effective equipment maintenance is the key to successful system performance. The better your maintenance, the better your facilities will perform. Abuse your equipment and facilities and they will abuse you. Everyone must realize that if the equipment can't work, no one can work.

18.101 Recognize Your Limitations

In the water departments of all cities, there is a need for maintenance operators to know something about electricity. Duties could range from repairing a taillight on a trailer or vehicle to repairing complex pump controls and motors. *VERY FEW MAINTENANCE OPERATORS DO THE ACTUAL ELECTRICAL REPAIRS OR TROUBLESHOOTING BECAUSE THIS IS A HIGHLY SPECIALIZED FIELD AND UN-*

QUALIFIED PEOPLE CAN SERIOUSLY INJURE THEMSELVES AND DAMAGE COSTLY EQUIPMENT. For these reasons, you must be familiar with electricity, *KNOW THE HAZARDS,* and *RECOGNIZE YOUR OWN LIMITATIONS* when you must work with electrical equipment.

Most municipalities employ electricians or contract with a commercial electrical company that they call when major problems occur. However, the maintenance operator should be able to *EXPLAIN HOW THE EQUIPMENT IS SUPPOSED TO WORK AND WHAT IT IS DOING OR IS NOT DOING WHEN IT FAILS.* After studying this section, you should be able to tell an electrician what appears to be the problem with electrical panels, controls, circuits, and equipment.

The need for safety should be apparent. If proper safe procedures are not followed in operating and maintaining the various electrical equipment used in water treatment facilities, accidents can happen that cause injuries, permanent disability, or loss of life. Some of the serious accidents that have happened and could have been avoided occurred when machinery was not shut off, locked out, and tagged properly (Figure 18.2). Possible accidents include:

1. Maintenance operator could be cleaning pump and have it start, thus losing an arm, hand, or finger;

2. Electric motors or controls not properly grounded could lead to possible severe shock, paralysis, or death; and

3. Improper circuits such as a wrong connection, safety devices jumped, wrong fuses, or improper wiring can cause fires or injuries due to incorrect operation of machinery.

Another consideration for having a basic working knowledge of electricity is to prevent financial losses resulting from motors burning out and from damage to equipment, machinery and control circuits. Additional costs result when damages have to be repaired, including payments for outside labor.

WARNING

DO NOT TOUCH EQUIPMENT IN ELECTRICAL PANELS, CONTROLS, CIRCUITS, WIRING OR EQUIPMENT UNLESS YOU ARE QUALIFIED AND AUTHORIZED. BY THE TIME YOU FIND OUT WHAT YOU DON'T KNOW ABOUT ELECTRICITY, YOU COULD FIND YOURSELF TOO DEAD TO USE THE KNOWLEDGE.

QUESTIONS

Write your answers in a notebook and then compare your answers with those on page 343.

18.10A Why must unqualified or inexperienced people be extremely careful when attempting to troubleshoot or repair electrical equipment?

18.10B What could happen when machinery is not shut off, locked out, and tagged properly?

18.11 Electrical Fundamentals

18.110 Introduction

This section contains a basic introduction to electrical terms and information plus directions on how to troubleshoot problems with electrical equipment.

Most electrical equipment used in water treatment plants is labeled with nameplate information indicating the proper voltage and allowable current in amps.

18.111 Volts

Voltage (E) is also known as Electromotive Force (E.M.F.), and is the electrical pressure available to cause a flow of current (amperage) when an electric circuit is closed.[1] This pressure can be compared with the pressure or force that causes water to flow in a pipe. Some pressure in a water pipe is required to make the water move. The same is true of electricity. A force is necessary to push electricity or electric current through a wire. This force is called voltage. There are two types of current: Direct Current (D.C.) and Alternating Current (A.C.).

18.112 Direct Current (D.C.)

Direct Current (D.C.) flows in one direction only and is essentially free from pulsation. Direct current is seldom used in water treatment plants except in electronic equipment, some control components of pump drives, and standby lighting. Direct current is used exclusively in automotive equipment, certain types of welding equipment, and a variety of portable equipment. Direct current is found in various voltages such as 6 volts, 12 volts, 24 volts, 48 volts, and 110 volts. All batteries are direct current. D.C. voltage can be measured by holding the positive and negative leads of a D.C. voltmeter on the corresponding terminals of the D.C. device such as a battery. Direct current usually is not found in higher voltages (over 24 volts) around plants except in motor-generator sets. Care must be taken when installing battery cables and wiring that Positive (+) and Negative (−) poles are connected properly to wires marked (+) and (−). If not properly connected, you could get an arc of electricity across the unit that could cause an explosion.

18.113 Alternating Current (A.C.)

An alternating current circuit is one in which the voltage and current periodically change direction and *AMPLITUDE*.[2] In other words, the current goes from zero to maximum strength, back to zero and to the same strength in the opposite direction. Most A.C. circuits have a frequency of 60

CYCLES[3] per second. "Hertz" is the term we use to describe the frequency of cycles completed per second so our A.C. voltage would be 60 Hertz (Hz).

Alternating current is classified as:

1. Single phase,

2. Two phase, and

3. Three phase, or polyphase.

The most common of these are single phase and three phase. The various voltages you probably will find on your job are 110 volts, 120 volts, 208 volts, 220 volts, 240 volts, 277 volts, 440 volts, 480 volts, 2,400 volts and 4,160 volts.

Single-phase power is found in lighting systems, small pump motors, various portable tools, and throughout our homes. This power is usually 120 volts and sometimes 240 volts. Single phase means that only one phase of power is supplied to the main electrical panel at 240 volts and has three wires or leads. Two of these leads have 120 volts each, the other lead is neutral and usually is coded white. The neutral lead is grounded. Many appliances and power tools have an extra ground (commonly a green wire) on the case for additional protection.

Three-phase power is generally used with motors and transformers found in water treatment plants, and usually is 208, 220, 240 volts, or 440, 460, 480 and 550 volts. Higher voltages are used in some pump stations. Three phase is used when higher power requirements or larger motors are used because efficiency is usually higher and motors require less maintenance. Generally speaking, all motors above two horsepower are three phase unless there is a problem with the power company getting three phase to the installations. Three-phase power usually is brought in to the point of use with three leads. There is power on all three leads and the fuse switches will generally appear as shown in Figure 18.3.

When making voltage measurements on three-phase power circuits, take three readings: (1) between lead 1 and lead 2, (2) between 1 and 3, and (3) between 2 and 3. The imbalance between readings should not exceed five percent of the average of the three readings and the average should not be below the nominal voltage (208, 220, 240, 460) nor should it exceed the nominal voltage by more than five percent. Voltages that do not meet these limits will place undue stress on electrical equipment, especially motors.

---

[1] *Electricians often talk about closing an electric circuit. This means they are closing a switch that actually connects circuits together so electricity can flow through the circuit. Closing an electric circuit is like opening a valve on a water pipe.*

[2] *Amplitude. The maximum strength of an alternating current during its cycle, as distinguished from the mean or effective strength.*

[3] *Cycle. A complete alternation of voltage and/or current in an alternating current (A.C.) circuit.*

Fig. 18.3   Fuse switches
(Courtesy of Consolidated Electrical Distributors, Inc.)

When there is power in three leads and a fourth lead is brought in, it is a neutral lead. Incoming power goes through a meter and then some type of disconnecting switch. This switch could be a fuse switch or a circuit breaker. The purpose of the disconnect switch is to open whenever a short or fault occurs and thus protect both the electric circuits and electrical equipment.

Circuit breakers (Figure 18.4) are used to protect electric circuits from overloads. Most circuit breakers are metal conductors that de-energize the main circuit when excess current passes through a metal strip causing it to overheat and open the main circuit.

Fig. 18.4   Circuit breakers
(Courtesy of Consolidated Electrical Distributors, Inc.)

Two-phase systems will not be discussed because they are seldom found in water treatment facilities.

18.114   Amps

An Ampere (I) is the practical unit of electric current. This is the current produced by a pressure of one volt in a circuit having a resistance of one ohm. Amperage is the measurement of current or electron flow and is an indication of work being done or "how hard the electricity is working."

In order to understand amperage, one more term must be explained. The OHM is the practical unit of electrical resistance (R). "Ohm's Law" states that in a given electrical circuit the amount of current (I) in amperes is equal to the pressure in volts (E) divided by the resistance (R) in ohms. The following three formulas are given to provide you with an indication of the relationships among current, resistance, and E.M.F. (electromotive force).

$$\text{Current, amps} = \frac{\text{E.M.F., volts}}{\text{Resistance, ohms}} \qquad I = \frac{E}{R}$$

$$\text{E.M.F., volts} = (\text{Current, amps})(\text{Resistance, ohms}) \qquad E = IR$$

$$\text{Resistance, ohms} = \frac{\text{E.M.F., volts}}{\text{Current, amps}} \qquad R = \frac{E}{I}$$

These equations are used by electrical engineers for calculating circuit characteristics. If you memorize the following relationship, you can always figure out the correct formula.

To use the above triangle you cover up with your finger the term you don't know or are trying to find out. The relationship between the other two known terms will indicate how to calculate the unknown. For example, if you are trying to calculate the current, cover up I. The two knowns (E and R) are shown in the triangle as E/R. Therefore, I = E/R. The same procedure can be used to find E when I and R are known or to find R when E and I are known.

18.115   Watts

Watts (W) and kilowatts (kW) are the units of measurement of the rate at which power is being used or generated. In D.C. circuits, watts (W) equal the voltage (E) multiplied by the current (I).

Power, watts = (Current, amps)(Electromotive Force, volts)

or P, watts = (I, amps)(E, volts)

In A.C. polyphase circuits the formula becomes more complicated because of the inclusion of two additional factors. First, there is the square root of 3, for three-phase circuits, which is equal to 1.73. Secondly, there is the power factor which is the ratio of the true or actual power passing through an electric circuit to the product of the voltage times the amperage in the circuit. For standard three-phase induction motors the power factor will be somewhere near 0.9. The formula for power input to a three-phase motor is:

$$\text{Power, kilowatts} = \frac{(E, \text{volts})(I, \text{amps})(\text{Power Factor})(1.73)}{1,000 \text{ watts/kilowatt}}$$

Since 0.746 kilowatt equals 1.0 horsepower, then the power output of a motor is

$$\begin{array}{l}\text{Power Output,} \\ \text{horsepower}\end{array} = \frac{(\text{Power Input, kilowatts})(\text{Efficiency, \%})}{(0.746 \text{ kilowatt/horsepower})(100\%)}$$

18.116 Power Requirements

Power requirements (PR) are expressed in kilowatt hours. 500 watts for two hours or one watt for 1,000 hours equals one kilowatt hour. The power company charges so many cents per kilowatt hour.

Power Req, kW-hr = (Power, kilowatts)(Time, hours)

PR, kW-hr　　　= (P, kW)(T, hr)

18.117 Conductors and Insulators

A material, like copper, which permits the flow of electric current is called a conductor. Material which will not permit the flow of electricity, like rubber, is called an insulator. Such material when wrapped or cast around a wire is called insulation. Insulation is commonly used to prevent the loss of electrical flow by two conductors coming into contact with each other.

QUESTIONS

Write your answers in a notebook and then compare your answers with those on page 343.

18.11A How can you determine the proper voltage and allowable current in amps for a piece of equipment?

18.11B What are two types of current?

18.11C Amperage is a measurement of what?

18.12 Tools, Meters, and Testers

WARNING
NEVER ENTER AN ELECTRICAL PANEL OR ATTEMPT TO TROUBLESHOOT OR REPAIR ANY PIECE OF ELECTRICAL EQUIPMENT OR ANY ELECTRICAL CIRCUIT UNLESS YOU ARE QUALIFIED AND AUTHORIZED.

18.120 Voltage Testing

In order to maintain, repair, and troubleshoot electrical equipment and circuits, the proper tools are required. You will need a VOLTAGE TESTER to check for voltage. There are several types on the market and all of them work. They are designed to be used on energized circuits and care must be exercised when testing. By holding one lead on ground and the other on a power lead, you can determine if the circuit is energized.

Be sure the voltage tester that you are using has sufficient range to measure the voltage you would expect to find. In other words do not use a tester with a limit of 600 volts on a circuit that normally is energized at 2,400 volts. With the voltage tester you can tell if the current is A.C. or D.C. and the intensity or voltage which will probably be one of the following: 120, 208, 240, 480, 2,400, or 4,160.

Do not work on any electric circuits unless you are qualified and authorized. Use a voltage tester and other circuit testers to determine if a circuit is energized, or if all voltage is off. This should be done after the main switch is turned off to make sure it is safe to work inside the electrical panel. Always be aware of the possibility that even if the disconnect to the unit you are working on is off, the control circuit may still be energized if the circuit originates at a different distribution panel. Also a capacitor in the unit may have sufficient energy stored to cause considerable harm to an operator, such as a power factor correction capacitor on a motor. Test for voltage both before and during the time the switch is pulled off to have a double-check. This procedure ensures that the voltage tester is working and that you have good continuity to your tester. Use circuit testers to measure voltage or current characteristics to a given piece of equipment and to make sure that you have or do not have a "live" circuit.

Besides using the voltage tester for checking power, it can be used to test for open circuits, blown fuses, single phasing of motors, grounds, and many other uses. Some examples are illustrated in the following paragraphs.

In the circuit shown below (Figure 18.5), test for power by holding one lead of the tester on point "A" and the other at point "B." If no power is indicated, the switch is open or faulty. The sketch shows the switch in the "open" position.

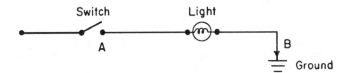

Fig. 18.5　Single-phase circuit (switch in open position)

To test for power at Point "A" and Point "B" in Figure 18.6, open the switch as shown. Using a voltmeter or voltage tester, connect a lead on Line 1 and a lead on Line 2, at points A and B, between the fuses and the load. Bring the voltage tester and leads out of the panel and close the panel door as far as possible without cutting or damaging the meter leads. Some switches cannot be closed if the panel door is open. The panel door is closed when testing because hot copper sparks could seriously injure you when the circuit is energized and the voltage is high. Close the switch.

1. Voltage tester should register at 220 volts. If there is no reading at points "A" and "B," the fuse or fuses could be blown.

Fig. 18.6   Single-phase, three-lead circuit

2. Move voltage tester to L1 and L2. If there is still no reading on the voltage tester, check for an open switch in another location, or call the power company to find out if power is out.

3. If a 220-volt reading is registered at L1 and L2, move the test leads to point "A" and the "neutral" lead. If a reading of 110 volts is observed, the fuse on line "A" is OK. If there isn't a voltage reading, the fuse on line "A" could be "blown." Move the lead from line "A" to line "B." Observe the reading. If 110-volt power is not observed, the fuse on line "B" could be "blown." Another possibility to consider is that the neutral line could be broken.

```
┌─────────────── WARNING ───────────────┐
│                                        │
│  TURN OFF POWER AND BE SURE THAT THERE IS │
│  NO VOLTAGE IN EITHER POWER LINE BEFORE   │
│  CHANGING FUSES. Use a FUSE PULLER. Test  │
│  circuit again in the same manner to make sure │
│  fuses or circuit breakers are OK. 220 volts power │
│  or voltage should be present between points "A" │
│  and "B." If fuse or circuit breaker trips again, shut │
│  off and determine the source of the problem.  │
│                                        │
└────────────────────────────────────────┘
```

Referring to Figure 18.7, test for voltage in three-phase circuits as follows — with the switch closed and the load disconnected, check for voltage (probably either 220 or 440)

between points A3-B3, A3-C3, and between B3-C3. A zero voltage reading on any or all of the three tests indicates a problem ahead of this location that could be at another switch or a power company problem. Assuming normal readings were found at A3, B3, and C3, repeat the three readings at points A2, B2, and C2 with the switch closed. Any zero voltage readings are an indication of a defective switch. Assuming normal readings were found at A2, B2, and C2, repeat the three readings at points A1, B1, and C1 with the switch closed. If any two voltage readings are zero, one fuse is blown and it will be the one in the line that was common to the two zero readings. If all three voltage readings are zero, either two or three fuses are blown. To determine which fuses are blown, refer to Table 18.1. Note that a zero voltage reading indicates a blown fuse.

Fig. 18.7 Three-phase circuit, 220 volts

TABLE 18.1 LOCATING A BLOWN FUSE

Blown Fuse in Line	Use Either Test
L1	A1-B2 or A1-C2
L2	B1-A2 or B1-C2
L3	C1-A2 or C1-B2

Another way of checking the fuses with the load connected on this three-phase circuit would be to take your voltage tester and place one lead on the bottom and one lead on the top of each fuse. You should *NOT* get a voltage reading on the voltmeter. This is because electricity takes the path of least resistance. If you get a reading across any of the fuses (top to bottom), that fuse is bad.

ALWAYS MAKE SURE THAT WHEN YOU USE A VOLTMETER IT IS SET FOR THE PROPER VOLTAGE. IF VOLTAGE IS UNKNOWN AND THE METER HAS DIFFERENT SCALES THAT ARE MANUALLY SET, ALWAYS START WITH THE HIGHEST VOLTAGE RANGE AND WORK DOWN. Otherwise the voltmeter could be damaged. Look at the equipment instruction manual or nameplate for the expected voltage. Actual voltage should not be much higher than given unless someone goofed when the equipment was wired and inspected.

18.121 Ammeter

Another meter used in electrical maintenance and testing is the AMMETER. The ammeter records the current or "amps" flowing in the circuit. There are several types of ammeters, but only two will be discussed in this section. The ammeter generally used for testing is called a "clamp-on" type. The term "clamp-on" means that it can be clamped around a wire supplying a motor, and no direct electrical connection needs to be made. Each "leg" or lead on a three-phase motor must be individually checked.

The first step should be to read the motor nameplate data and find what the amperage reading should be for the particular motor or device you are testing. After you have this information, set the ammeter to the proper scale. Set it on a higher scale than necessary if the expected reading is close to the top of the meter scale. Place the clamp around one lead at a time. Record each reading and compare with the nameplate rating. If the readings are not similar to the nameplate rating, find the cause, such as low voltage, bad bearings, poor connections or excessive load. If the ammeter readings are higher than expected, the high current could produce overheating and damage the equipment. Try to find the problem and correct it.

Current imbalance is undesirable because it causes uneven heating in a motor that can shorten the life expectancy of the insulation. However, a small amount of current imbalance is to be expected in the leads to a three-phase motor. This imbalance can be caused by either peculiarities in the motor or by a power company imbalance. To isolate the cause, make the following test. Note that this test should be done by a qualified electrician. Refer to Figure 18.8.

If the current readings on Lines L1, L2, and L3 are about the same both before and after the wiring change, this is an indication that the imbalance is being caused by the power company and they should be asked to make adjustments to correct the condition. However, if the current readings followed the motor terminal (T) numbers rather than the power line (L) numbers, the problem is within the motor and there

isn't much that can be done except contact the motor manufacturer for a possible exchange.

When using a clamp-on ammeter, be sure to set the meter on a high enough range or scale for the starting current if you are testing during start-up. Starting currents range from 500 to 700 percent higher than running currents and using too low a range can ruin an expensive and delicate instrument. Newer clamp-on ammeters automatically adjust to the proper range and can measure both starting or peak current and normal running current.

Another type of ammeter is one that is connected in line with the power lead or leads. Generally they are not portable

Fig. 18.8   Determination of current imbalance

1. With the motor wired to its starter, L1 to T1, L2 to T2, and L3 to T3, measure and record the amperage on L1, L2, and L3.

2. De-energize the circuit and reconnect the motor as follows: L1-T3, L2-T1, L3-T2. This wiring change will not change the direction of the rotation of the motor.

3. Start up the motor and again measure and record the amperage on L1, L2, and L3.

and are usually installed in a panel or piece of equipment. They require physical connections to put them in series with the motor or apparatus being tested. Current transformers (CT) are commonly used with this type of ammeter so that the meter does not have to conduct the full motor current. These ammeters are usually more accurate than the clamp-on type and are used in motor control centers and pump panels.

PROBLEM: Voltage imbalance. A common problem found in pump stations with a high rate of motor failure is voltage imbalance or unbalance. Unlike a single-phase condition, all three phases are present but the phase-to-phase voltage is not equal in each phase.

Voltage imbalance can occur in either the utility side or the pump station electrical system. For example, the utility company may have large single-phase loads (such as residential services) which reduce the voltage on a single phase. This same condition can occur in the pump station if a large number of 120/220 volt loads are present. Slight differences in voltage can cause disproportional current imbalance; this may be six to ten times as large as the voltage imbalance. For example, a two-percent voltage imbalance can result in a 20-percent current imbalance. A 4.5-percent voltage imbalance will reduce the insulation life to 50 percent of the normal life. This is the reason a dependable voltage supply at the motor terminals is critical. Even relatively slight variations can greatly increase the motor operating temperatures and burn out the insulation.

It is common practice for electrical utility companies to furnish power to three-phase customers in open delta or wye configurations. An open delta or wye system is a two-transformer bank that is a suitable configuration where LIGHTING LOADS ARE LARGE AND THREE-PHASE LOADS ARE LIGHT. This is the exact opposite of the configuration needed by most pumping facilities where THREE-PHASE LOADS ARE LARGE. (Examples of three-transformer banks include Y-delta, delta-Y, and Y-Y.) In most cases three-phase motors should be fed from three-transformer banks for proper balance. The capacity of a two-transformer bank is only 57 percent of the capacity of a three-transformer bank. The two-transformer configuration can cause one leg of the three-phase current to furnish higher amperage to one leg of the motor, which will greatly shorten its life.

Operators should acquaint themselves with the configuration of their electric power supply. When an open delta or wye configuration is used, operators should calculate the degree of current imbalance existing between legs of their polyphase motors. If you are unsure about how to determine the configuration of your system or how to calculate the percentage of current imbalance, ALWAYS consult a qualified electrician. CURRENT IMBALANCE BETWEEN LEGS SHOULD NEVER EXCEED 5 PERCENT UNDER NORMAL OPERATING CONDITIONS (NEMA Standards MGI-14.35).

Loose connections will also cause voltage imbalance as will high-resistance contacts, circuit breakers, or motor starters.

Another serious consideration for operators is voltage fluctuation caused by neighborhood demands. A pump motor in near perfect balance (for example, 3 percent unbalance) at 9:00 AM could be as much as 17 percent unbalanced by 4:00 PM on a hot day due to the use of air conditioners by customers on the same grid. Also, the hookup of a small market or a new home to the power grid can cause a significant change in the degree of current unbalance in other parts of the power grid. Because energy demands are constantly changing, water system operators should have a qualified electrician check the current balances between legs of their three-phase motors at least once a year.

SOLUTION: Motor connections at the circuit box should be checked frequently (semiannually or annually) to ensure that the connections are tight and that vibration has not rubbed through the insulation on the conductors. Measure the voltage at the motor terminals and calculate the percentage imbalance (if any) using the procedures below.

Do not rely entirely on the power company to detect unbalanced current. Complaints of suspected power problems are frequently met with the explanation that all voltages are within the percentages allowed by law and no mention is made of the percentage of current unbalance which can be a major source of problems with three-phase motors. A little research of your own can pay large benefits. For example, a small water company in Central California configured with an Open Delta system (and running three-phase unbalances as high as 17 percent as a result) was routinely spending $14,000 a year for energy and burning out a 10-HP motor on the average of every 1.5 years (six 10-HP motors in 9 years). After consultation, the local power utility agreed to add a third transformer to each power board to bring the system into better balance. Pump drop leads were then rotated, bringing overall current unbalances down to an average of 3 percent, heavy-duty three-phase capacitors were added to absorb the prevalent voltage surges in the area, and computerized controls were added to the pumps to shut them off when pumping volumes got too low. These modifications resulted in a saving in energy costs the first year alone of $5,500.00.

FORMULAS

Percentage of current unbalance can be calculated by using the following formulas and procedures:

$$\text{Average Current} = \frac{\text{Total of Current Value Measured on Each Leg}}{3}$$

$$\text{\% Current Unbalance} = \frac{\text{Greatest Amp Difference From the Average}}{\text{Average Current}} \times 100\%$$

PROCEDURES

A. Measure and record current readings in amps for each leg. (Hookup 1.) Disconnect power.

B. Shift or roll the motor leads from left to right so the drop cable lead that was on terminal 1 is now on 2, lead on 2 is now on 3, and lead on 3 is now on 1. (Hookup 2.) Rolling the motor leads in this manner will not reverse the motor rotation. Start the motor, measure and record current reading on each leg. Disconnect power.

C. Again shift drop cable leads from left to right so the lead on terminal 1 goes to 2, 2 goes to 3, and 3 to 1. (Hookup 3.) Start pump, measure and record current reading on each leg. Disconnect power.

D. Add the values for each hookup.

E. Divide the total by 3 to obtain the average.

F. Compare each single leg reading to the average current amount to obtain the greatest amp difference from the average.

G. Divide this difference by the average to obtain the percentage of unbalance.

H. Use the wiring hookup which provides the lowest percentage of unbalance.

CORRECTING THE THREE-PHASE POWER UNBALANCE

Example: Check for current unbalance for a 230-volt, 3-phase 60-Hz submersible pump motor, 18.6 full load amps.

Solution: Steps 1 to 3 measure and record amps on each motor drop lead for Hookups 1, 2, and 3 (Figure 18.9).

		Step 1 (Hookup 1)	Step 2 (Hookup 2)	Step 3 (Hookup 3)
(T_1)		DL_1 = 25.5 amps	DL_3 = 25 amps	DL_2 = 25.0 amps
(T_2)		DL_2 = 23.0 amps	DL_1 = 24 amps	DL_3 = 24.5 amps
(T_3)		DL_3 = 26.5 amps	DL_2 = 26 amps	DL_1 = 25.5 amps
Step 4	Total = 75 amps		Total = 75 amps	Total = 75 amps
Step 5	Average Current =		Total Current =	$\frac{75}{3}$ = 25 amps
			$\frac{}{3\ readings}$	
Step 6	Greatest amp difference	(Hookup 1) = 25 − 23	= 2	
	from the average:	(Hookup 2) = 26 − 25	= 1	
		(Hookup 3) = 25.5 − 25	= .5	
Step 7	% Unbalance	(Hookup 1) = 2/25 x 100	= 8	
		(Hookup 2) = 1/25 x 100	= 4	
		(Hookup 3) = 0.5/25 x 100	= 2	

As can be seen, Hookup 3 should be used since it shows the least amount of current unbalance. Therefore, the motor will operate at maximum efficiency and reliability on Hookup 3.

By comparing the current values recorded on each leg, you will note the highest value was always on the same leg, L_3. This indicates the unbalance is in the power source. If the high current values were on a different leg each time the leads were changed, the unbalance would be caused by the motor or a poor connection.

If the current unbalance is greater than 5 percent, contact your power company for help.

Acknowledgment

Material on unbalanced current was provided by James W. Cannell, President, Canyon Meadows Mutual Water Company, Inc., Bodfish, California. His contribution is greatly appreciated.

18.122 Megger

A MEGGER is a device used for checking the insulation resistance on motors, feeders, bus bar systems, grounds, and branch circuit wiring.

WARNING

USE A MEGGER ONLY ON DE-ENERGIZED CIRCUITS OR MOTORS.

There are three general types of meggers: crank operated, battery operated, and instrument. There are two leads to connect. One lead is clamped to a ground lead and the other to the lead you are testing. The readings on the megger will range from "0" (ground) to Infinity (perfect), depending on the condition of your circuit.

The megger is usually connected to a motor terminal at the starter, and the other lead to the ground lead. Results of this test indicate if the insulation is deteriorating or cut.

Insulation resistance of electrical equipment is affected by many variables such as the equipment design, the type of

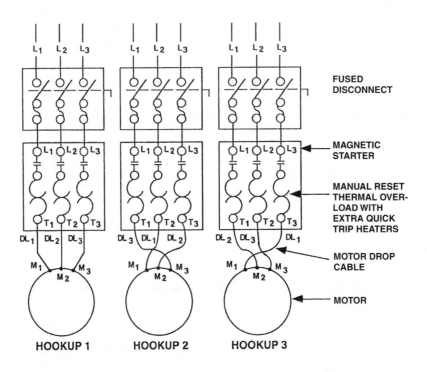

Fig. 18.9 Three hookups used to check for current unbalance

insulating material used, including binders and impregnating compounds, the thickness of the insulation and its area, cleanliness (or uncleanliness), moisture, and temperature. For insulation resistance measurements to be conclusive in analyzing the condition of equipment being tested, these variables must be taken into consideration.

Such factors as the design of the equipment, the kind of insulating material used, and its thickness and area cease to be variables after the equipment has been put into service, and minimum insulation resistance values can be established within reasonable tolerances. The variables that must be considered after the equipment has been put into service, and at the time that the insulation resistance measurements are being made, are uncleanliness, moisture, temperature, and damage such as fractures.

The most important requirements in the reliable operation of electrical equipment are cleanliness and the elimination of moisture penetration into the insulation. This is merely good housekeeping but it is essential in the maintenance of all types of electrical equipment. The very fact that insulation resistance is affected by moisture and dirt, with due allowances for temperature, makes the "megger" insulation test the valuable tool that it is in electrical maintenance. The test is an indication of cleanliness and good housekeeping as well as a detector of deterioration and impending trouble.

Suggested safe levels or "minimum values" of insulation resistance have been developed. These values should be provided by the equipment manufacturer and should serve as a guide for equipment in service. However, periodic tests on equipment in service will usually reveal readings considerably higher than the suggested minimum safe values. Records of periodic tests must be kept because persistent downward trends in insulation resistance usually give fair warning of impending trouble, even though the actual values may be HIGHER than the suggested minimum safe values.

Also, allowances must be made for equipment in service showing periodic test values LOWER than the suggested minimum safe values, so long as the values remain stable or consistent. In such cases, after due consideration has been given to temperature and humidity conditions at the time of the test, there may be no need for concern. THIS CONDITION MAY BE CAUSED BY UNIFORMLY DISTRIBUTED LEAKAGES OF A HARMLESS NATURE, AND MAY NOT BE THE RESULT OF A DANGEROUS LOCALIZED WEAKNESS. Here again, records of insulation resistance tests over a period of time reveal changes which may justify investigation. The "trend of the curve" may be more significant than the numerical values themselves.

For many years ONE MEGOHM[4] has been widely used as a fair allowable lower limit for insulation resistance of ordinary industrial electrical equipment rated up to 1,000 volts. This value is still recommended for those who may not be too familiar with insulation resistance testing practices, or who may not wish to approach the problem from a more technical point of view.

For equipment rated above 1,000 volts, the "one megohm" rule is usually stated: "A minimum of one megohm per thousand volts." Although this rule is somewhat arbitrary, and may

be criticized as lacking an engineering foundation, it has stood the test of a good many years of practical experience. This rule gives some assurance that equipment is not too wet or not too dry and has saved many an unnecessary breakdown.

More recent studies of the problem, however, have resulted in formulas for minimum values of insulation resistance that are based on the kind of insulating material used and the electrical and physical dimensions of the types of equipment under consideration.[5]

Motors and wirings should be megged at least once a year, and twice a year if possible. The readings taken should be recorded and plotted in some manner so that you can determine when insulation is breaking down. Meg motors and wirings after a pump station has been flooded. If insulation is wet, excessive current could be drawn and cause pump motors to "kick out."

18.123 Ohmmeters

OHMMETERS, sometimes called circuit testers, are valuable tools used for checking electrical circuits. An ohmmeter is used only when the electrical circuit is OFF, or de-energized. The ohmmeter supplies its own power by using batteries. An ohmmeter is used to measure the resistance (ohms) in a circuit. These are most often used in testing the control circuit components such as coils, fuses, relays, resistors, and switches. They are used also to check for continuity.

An ohmmeter has several scales which can be used. Typical scales are: R x 1, R x 10, R x 1,000, and R x 10,000. Each scale has a level of sensitivity for measuring different resistances. To use an ohmmeter, set the scale, start at the low point (R x 1), and put the two leads across the part of the circuit to be tested such as a coil or resistor and read the resistance in ohms. A reading of infinity would indicate an open circuit, and a "0" would read no resistance. These usually would be used only by skilled technicians because they are very delicate instruments.

All meters should be kept in good working order and calibrated periodically. They are very delicate, susceptible to damage, and should be well protected during transportation. When readings are taken, they should always be recorded on a machinery history card for future reference. Meters are a good way to determine pump and equipment performance. NEVER USE A METER UNLESS QUALIFIED AND AUTHORIZED.

[4] Megohm. Meg means one million, so 5 megohms means 5 million ohms. A megger reads in millions of ohms.
[5] Portions of the preceding paragraphs were taken from INSTRUCTION MANUAL FOR MEGGER INSULATION TESTERS, No. 21-J, pages 42 and 43, published by AVO International. For ordering information, write to AVO International Bookstore, 4651 South Westmoreland Road, Dallas, TX 75237. For additional information see Biddle's A STITCH IN TIME, also available from AVO International. Order number, AVTM21-P8B; price, $5.00.

QUESTIONS

Write your answers in a notebook and then compare your answers with those on pages 343 and 344.

18.12A   How can you determine if there is voltage in a circuit?

18.12B   What are some of the uses of a voltage tester?

18.12C   What precautions should be taken before attempting to change fuses?

18.12D   How do you test for voltage with a voltmeter when the voltage is unknown?

18.12E   What could be the cause of amp readings different from the nameplate rating?

18.12F   How often should motors and wirings be megged?

18.12G   An ohmmeter is used to check the ohms of resistance in what control circuit components?

18.13   Switch Gear

18.130   Equipment Protective Devices

Operators need safety devices to protect themselves and plant equipment from the destructive effects of electricity. Water systems have pressure valves, pop-offs, and different safety equipment to protect the pipes and equipment. So must electricity have safety devices to contain the voltage and amperage that comes in contact with the wiring and equipment. The first piece of equipment which must be protected is the main electrical panel or control unit where the power enters. This protection is provided by either fuses or a circuit breaker.

18.131   Fuses

Let's start with fuses. The power company has installed fuses on their power poles to protect their equipment from damage. We also must install something to protect the main control panel and wiring from damage due to excessive voltage or amperage.

A FUSE is a protective device having a strip or wire of fusible metal which, when placed in a circuit, will melt and break the electrical circuit when subjected to an excessive temperature. This temperature will develop in the fuse when a current flows through the fuse in excess of what the circuit will carry safely. This means that the fuse must be capable of de-energizing the circuit before any damage is done to the wiring it is safely protecting. Fuses are used to protect operators, main circuits, branch circuits, heaters, motors, and various other electrical equipment.

There are several types of fuses, each being used for a certain type of protection. Some of these are:

1. CURRENT-LIMITING FUSES: These fuses open so quickly while clearing a short-circuit current that the potential fault current is not allowed to reach its peak. They are used to protect power distribution circuits.

2. DUAL-ELEMENT FUSES: These fuses provide a time delay in the low overload range and a fast-acting element for short-circuit protection. These fuses are used for motor protection circuits.

There are many other types of fuses used for special application, but the above are the most common.

A fuse must *NEVER* be bypassed or jumped. This is the only protection the circuit has; without it, serious damage to equipment and possible injury to operators can occur. Make sure that all fuses are replaced with the proper size and type indicated for that circuit. If you have any doubt, check the electrical blueprints or contact your electrical engineer.

18.132   Circuit Breakers

The CIRCUIT BREAKER (Figure 18.4) is another safety device and is used in the same place as a fuse. Most circuit breakers consist of a switch that opens automatically when the current or the voltage exceeds or falls below a certain limit. Unlike a fuse that has to be replaced each time it "blows," a circuit breaker can be reset after a short delay to allow time for cooling. This is done by moving the handle to the OFF position or slightly past, and then moving it back to the ON position. Also, unlike a fuse, a circuit breaker can be visually inspected to find out if it has been tripped. The handle will be at the mid position between ON and OFF. Several different types of circuit breakers are being used today and each one is selected for a special protective purpose.

18.133   Overload Relays

Three-phase motors are usually protected by OVERLOAD RELAYS. This is accomplished by having heater strips, bimetal, or solder pots which open on current rise (overheating), and open the control circuit. This in turn opens the power control circuit, which de-energizes the starter and stops power to the motor. Such relays are also known as heaters or "thermal overloads." Sizing of these overloads is very critical and should coincide with the nameplate rating on the motor. Sizing depends on the service factor of the electric motor. Usually they range from 100 to 110 percent of the motor nameplate ratings and should never exceed 125 percent (usually 115 percent) of the motor rating. For example, if the motor is rated for 10 amps, the overloads should be sized from 10 to 11 amps.

Again, *NEVER INCREASE THE RATING OF THE OVERLOAD HEATERS BECAUSE OF TRIPPING. YOU SHOULD FIND THE PROBLEM AND REPAIR IT.* There are many other protective devices for electricity such as motor winding thermostats, phase protectors, low voltage protectors, and ground fault protectors. Each has its own special applications and should never be tampered with or jammed.

GROUND is an expression representing an electrical connection to earth or a large conductor which is at the earth's potential or neutral voltage. Motor frames and all electrical tools and equipment enclosures should be connected to ground. This is generally referred to simply as grounding, or equipment ground.

The third prong on cords from electric hand tools is the equipment ground and must never be removed. When an adapter is used with a two-prong receptacle, the green wire on the adapter should be connected under the center screw on the receptacle cover plate. Many times equipment grounding, especially at home, is achieved by connecting onto a water pipe or drain rather than a rod driven into the ground. This practice generally is not recommended when plastic pipes and other non-conducting pipe materials are used unless it is known that the piping is all metal and not interrupted. Also corrosion can be accelerated if pipes of different metals are used. A rod driven into dry ground isn't very effective as a ground.

18.134 Motor Starters

A motor starter is a device or group of devices which are used to connect the electrical power to a motor. These starters can be either manually or automatically controlled.

Manual and magnetic starters range in complexity from a single ON-OFF switch to a sophisticated automatic device using timers and coils. The simplest motor starter is used on single-phase motors where a circuit breaker is manually turned on and the motor starts. This type of starter also is used on three-phase motors of smaller horsepower, and on fan motors, machinery motors, and several other applications where it isn't necessary to have automatic control.

MAGNETIC STARTERS (Figures 18.10 and 18.11) are commonly used to start pumps, compressors, blowers, and anything where automatic or remote control is desired. They permit low power circuits to energize the starter of equipment at a remote location or to start larger starters (Figure 18.12). A magnetic starter is operated by electromagnetic action. This starter has contactors and they operate by energizing a coil which closes the contact, thus starting the motor. The circuit which energizes the starter is called the control circuit and it may operate on a lower voltage (115 volts) than the motor. Whenever a starter is used as a part of an integrated circuit (such as for flow, pressure, or temperature control), a magnetic starter or controller is necessary.

Magnetic starters are sized for their voltage and horsepower ratings. These are divided into classes. The most common starter is Class "A." A Class "A" starter is an "Alternating Current air-break and oil immersed manual, or magnetic controller for service on 600 volts or less. It is capable of interrupting operating overloads up to and including 10 times their normal motor rating, but not short circuits or faults beyond operating overloads."

Additional class information can be found in electrical catalogs, manuals, and manufacturers' brochures.

There are a number of different types of three-phase magnetic motor starters available. The simplest and most common is the "across-the-line" full voltage starter. This starter consists of three contacts, a magnetic actuating device, and overload detection. This starter subjects the power system to the full surge current on start-up and may cause the lights in the treatment plant to dim momentarily.

To reduce the in-rush current when starting polyphase motors, a number of other types of starters are available.

1. Auto-Transformer Type Reduced Voltage Starters. These begin the motor start sequence by applying a reduced voltage to the motor for a few seconds. The voltage is controlled by a time delay relay within the starter. The reduced voltage is obtained from transformers that are a part of the starter. These transformers are designed to operate for only a few seconds at a time and can easily be burned out if the motor is started too frequently.

2. Solid-State Reduced Voltage Starters. These starters do the same job as the auto-transformer type reduced voltage starters but they do not need transformers because the voltage and current are electrically controlled.

3. Part Winding Starters. These starters are used with special motors that have two separate sets of windings on the same motor frame. By energizing the windings about one second apart, the in-rush current is limited to about half that of a normal motor with a full voltage starter.

4. Wye-Delta Starters. These starters are used with motors that have all leads brought out to the terminal box. The motor is first started with wye connected coils and switched over to a delta connection for running. The result is the same as if you used a reduced voltage starter.

QUESTIONS

Write your answers in a notebook and then compare your answers with those on page 344.

18.13A What are two types of safety devices found in main electrical panels or control units?

18.13B What are fuses used to protect?

18.13C Why must a fuse never be bypassed or jumped?

18.13D How does a circuit breaker work?

18.13E How are motor starters controlled?

18.13F When are magnetic starters used?

18.14 Electric Motors

18.140 Classifications

Electric motors are the machines most commonly used to convert electrical energy into mechanical energy. A motor usually consists of a STATOR,[6] ROTOR,[7] END BELLS,[8] and windings. The rotor has an extended shaft which allows a machine to be coupled to it.

Motors are of many different types (Figure 18.13), such as squirrel cage induction motors, wound rotor motors, synchronous motors, and many others. The most common of these is the squirrel cage induction motor. Some pumping stations use wound rotor induction motors when speed control is needed.

Three-phase electric motors are used for operating pumps, compressors, fans, and other machinery. Motors are generally trouble free and, when lubricated properly, cause very few

---

[6] Stator. That portion of a machine which contains the stationary (non-moving) parts that surround the moving parts (rotor).
[7] Rotor. The rotating part of a machine. The rotor is surrounded by the stationary (non-moving) parts (stator) of the machine.
[8] End Bells. Devices used to hold the rotor and stator of a motor in position.

Housing

Contacts

DUAL VOLTAGE COIL
PART NO. D71221-32

CY   60 208-240V   50 190-220V   25 ....115V

CY   60 440-480V   50 380-440V   25 ....230V

Coil

FB
FURNAS

FURNAS ELECTRIC CO.
BATAVIA · ILLINOIS

V   W

Heater Overloads

Fig. 18.10   Three-phase magnetic starter
(Courtesy of Furnas Electric Company)

Fig. 18.11   Wiring diagram of three-phase magnetic starter

Fig. 18.12   Application of magnetic starter

DRIP PROOF

ITEM NO.	PART NAME
1	Wound Stator w/ Frame
2	Rotor Assembly
3	Rotor Core
4	Shaft
5	Bracket
6	Bearing Cap
7	Bearings
8	Seal, Labyrinth
9	Thru Bolts/Caps
10	Seal, Lead Wire
11	Terminal Box
12	Terminal Box Cover
13	Fan
14	Deflector
15	Lifting Lug

TOTALLY ENCLOSED **FAN COOLED**

ITEM NO.	PART NAME
1	Wound Stator w/ Frame
2	Rotor Assembly
3	Rotor Core
4	Shaft
5	Brackets
6	Bearings
7	Seal, Labyrinth
8	Thru Bolts/Caps
9	Seal, Lead Wire
10	Terminal Box
11	Terminal Box Cover
12	Fan, Inside
13	Fan, Outside
14	Fan Grill
15	Fan Cover
16	Fan Cover Bolts
17	Lifting Lug

Fig. 18.13   Typical motors
(Courtesy of Sterling Power Systems, Inc.)

problems. The amperage and voltage readings on motors should be taken periodically to ensure proper operation.

Motors are classified by NEMA (National Electrical Manufacturers Association) with code letters from A through V with "A" having the lowest starting torque and in-rush current and "V" having the highest starting torque and in-rush current. The most commonly available motors have code letters from "F" through "L" which have in-rush currents on start of from 500 to 1,000 percent of full load.

Another important consideration in selecting a motor is the class of insulation. This determines how hot a motor may operate and is listed as degree rise on the motor nameplate (Figure 18.14).

Motor insulation classes are as follows:

Class	Temperature Rating
A	105°C (221°F)
B	130°C (266°F)
F	155°C (311°F)
H	180°C (356°F)

At present most motors are Class B insulated. Try to keep the actual operating temperature below the temperature rating or limit in order to prolong the life of the insulation.

All of this information can be found on the motor nameplate and should be taken into consideration when evaluating a motor. Most of the trouble encountered with electric motors results from bad bearings, shorted windings due to insulation breakdown, or excessive moisture.

All of the information on the motor nameplate (Figure 18.14) should be recorded and placed in a file for future reference. Many times the nameplate is painted, corroded or missing from the unit when the information is needed to repair the motor or replace parts. Also record the date of installation and service start-up. See Section 18.142, "Recordkeeping," for a typical data sheet for recording the essential information. This information also should be on the manufacturer's data sheet and in the instruction manual. Compare the information for consistency and file in an appropriate location. Be sure you have the correct serial and/or model numbers.

QUESTIONS

Write your answers in a notebook and then compare your answers with those on page 344.

18.14A How is electrical energy converted into mechanical energy?

18.14B What are the important parts of an electric motor?

18.14C How can motors be kept trouble free?

18.14D What should be done with motor nameplate data?

NOTE: 1. The motor for this unit is rated at 1,750 RPM and the maximum speed for the variable drive unit is 1,200 RPM.

2. The 40°C rating is the allowable operating temperature above ambient temperature.

Fig. 18.14 Typical nameplate
(Courtesy of Sterling Power Systems, Inc.)

18.141 Troubleshooting

Practical step-by-step procedures combined with a common-sense approach is the key to effective troubleshooting.

"NEVER TAKE ANYTHING FOR GRANTED"

A. Gather preliminary information. The first step in troubleshooting any motor control which has developed trouble is to understand the circuit operation and other related functions. In other words, what is supposed to happen, operate, and so forth when it's working right? Also, what is it doing now? The qualified maintenance operator should be able to do the following:

1. *KNOW WHAT SHOULD HAPPEN WHEN A SWITCH IS PUSHED:* When switches are pushed or tripped, know what coils go in, contacts close, relays operate, and motors run.

2. *EXAMINE ALL OTHER FACTORS:* What other unusual things are happening in the plant now that this circuit doesn't work properly? Lights dimmed, other pumps stopped, lights went out when it broke, everything was flooded, operators were hosing down area, and many other possible factors.

3. *ANALYZE WHAT YOU KNOW:* What part of it is working correctly? Is switch arm tripped? Is it a mechanical failure or an electrical problem caused by a mechanical failure?

4. *SELECT SIMPLE PROCEDURES:* To localize the problem, select logical ways to investigate the problem that can be simply and quickly accomplished.

5. *MAKE A VISUAL INSPECTION:* Look for burned wires, loose wires, area full of water, coil burned, or contacts loose. Also note any unusual odors.

6. *CONVERGE ON SOURCE OF TROUBLE:* Mechanical or electrical. Motor or control, whatever it might be. Electrical problems result from some type of mechanical failure.

7. *PINPOINT THE PROBLEM:* Exactly where is the problem and what do you need for repair?

8. *FIND THE CAUSE:* What caused the problem? Moisture, wear, poor design, voltage, or overloading?

9. *REPAIR THE PROBLEM AND ELIMINATE THE CAUSE IF POSSIBLE.* If the problem is inside switch gear or motors, call an electrician. Give the electrician the information you have regarding the equipment. Do not attempt electrical repairs unless qualified and authorized, otherwise you could cause excessive damage to yourself and to the equipment.

B. Some of the things to look for when troubleshooting are given in the remainder of this section.

18.142 Recordkeeping

Records are a very important part of electrical maintenance. They must be accurate and complete. Whenever something is changed, repaired, or tested, it should be recorded on a material history card of some type. Pages 262 and 263 are examples of typical record sheets.

QUESTIONS

Write your answers in a notebook and then compare your answers with those on page 344.

18.14E What is the key to effective troubleshooting?

18.14F What are some of the steps that should be taken when troubleshooting electrical equipment?

18.14G What kind of information should be recorded regarding electrical equipment?

18.15 Auxiliary Electrical Power

18.150 Safety First

Always remember that a QUALIFIED ELECTRICIAN should perform most of the necessary maintenance and repair of electrical equipment. If you don't know the how, why, and when of the job, don't do it. You could endanger your life as well as your fellow operators. Never attempt work that you are not qualified to do or are not authorized to perform.

18.151 Standby Power Generation

There are three ways of providing standby power. One is by providing the treatment plant with an engine-driven generator set. The limit of how much power can be produced is determined only by the size of the generator. The second possibility for standby power is batteries. Batteries should only be considered for low power consumption uses such as emergency lighting, communication, and possibly some control and instrumentation functions. The other possibility for standby power is a connection to an alternate power source, such as a different substation or another power company.

Because the treatment of water is considered a critical service, it is important to be able to provide drinking water even with the loss of commercial power. A power outage of a short duration probably will not have adverse effects on plant operation. The question you must ask yourself is, "Can my plant meet the needs of the public if a 'brownout' or catastrophic event eliminates commercial power for an extended length of time?" If the answer is "no," then perhaps a form of standby power generation should be considered.

The following six conditions must be analyzed to determine the need for and size of standby power generation.

1. Frequency of power outages in last 10 to 15 years.

2. Duration of the power outage in each occurrence.

3. Availability of additional source of power supply from a different substation in the vicinity.

4. Method by which raw water reaches plant (is flow by gravity or by a raw water pumping station?).

5. Total storage capacity of reservoirs in the distribution system.

6. Possibility of obtaining a potable water supply from adjacent cities (is there a reasonably sized pipe connection between your system and the distribution system of an adjacent city?).

ELECTRIC MOTOR TROUBLESHOOTING

1. Contacts

Trouble	Possible Causes	Remedy
Contact chatter	1. Broken *POLE SHADER*.[9]	1. Replace.
	2. Poor contact in control circuit.	2. Improve contact or use holding circuit interlock.
	3. Low voltage.	3. Correct voltage condition. Check momentary voltage dip.
Welding or freezing	1. Abnormal surge of current.	1. Use larger contactor and check for grounds, shorts, or excessive motor load current.
	2. Frequent *JOGGING*.[10]	2. Install larger device rated for jogging service or caution operator.
	3. Insufficient contact pressure.	3. Replace contact spring; check contact carrier for damage.
	4. Contacts not positioning properly.	4. Check for voltage dip during start-up.
	5. Foreign matter preventing magnet from seating.	5. Clean contacts.
	6. Short circuit.	6. Remove short fault and check that fuse or breaker are right.
Short contact life or overheating of tips	1. Contacts poorly aligned, spaced, or damaged.	1. Do not file silver-faced contacts. Rough spots or discoloration will not harm contacts.
	2. Excessively high currents.	2. Install larger device. Check for grounds, shorts, or excessive motor currents.
	3. Excessive starting and stopping of motor.	3. Caution operators. Check operating controls.
	4. Weak contact pressure.	4. Adjust or replace contact springs.
	5. Dirty contacts.	5. Clean with approved solvent.
	6. Loose connections.	6. Check terminals and tighten.
Coil, overheated	1. Starting coil may not kick out.	1. Repair coil.
	2. Overload won't let motor reach minimum speed.	2. Remove overload.
	3. Overvoltage or high ambient temperature.	3. Check application and circuit.
	4. Incorrect coil.	4. Check rating and if incorrect, replace with proper coil.
	5. Shorted turns caused by mechanical damage or corrosion.	5. Replace coil.
	6. Undervoltage, failure of magnet to seal it.	6. Correct system voltage.
	7. Dirt or rust on pole faces increasing air gap.	7. Clean pole faces.

---

[9] *Pole Shader.   A copper bar circling the laminated iron core inside the coil of a magnetic starter.*
[10] *Jogging.   The frequent starting and stopping of an electric motor.*

ELECTRIC MOTOR TROUBLESHOOTING (continued)

1. Contacts (continued)

Trouble	Possible Causes	Remedy
Overload relays tripping	1. Sustained overload.	1. Check for grounds, shorts, or excessive motor currents. Mechanical overload.
	2. Loose connection on all or any lead wires.	2. Check, clean, and tighten.
	3. Incorrect heater.	3. Replace with correct size heater unit.
	4. Fatigued heater blocks.	4. Inspect and replace.
Failure to trip overload relay	1. Mechanical binding, dirt, or corrosion.	1. Clean or replace.
	2. Wrong heater, or heaters omitted and jumper wires used.	2. Check ratings. Apply heaters of proper rating.
	3. Motor and relay in different temperatures.	3. Adjust relay rating accordingly, or install temperature compensating relays.

2. Magnetic and Mechanical Parts

Trouble	Possible Causes	Remedy
Noisy magnet (humming)	1. Broken shading coil.	1. Replace shading coil.
	2. Magnet faces not mating.	2. Replace magnet assembly or realign.
	3. Dirt or rust on magnet faces.	3. Clean and realign.
	4. Low voltage.	4. Inspect system voltage and voltage dips during starting.
Failure to pick up and seal	1. Low voltage.	1. Inspect system voltage and correct.
	2. Coil open or shorted.	2. Replace.
	3. Wrong coil.	3. Check coil number and voltage rating.
	4. Mechanical obstruction.	4. With power off, check for free movement of contact and armature assembly. Repair.
Failure to drop out	1. Gummy substance on pole.	1. Clean with solvent.
	2. Voltage not removed from coil.	2. Check coil circuit.
	3. Worn or rusted parts causing binding.	3. Replace or clean parts as necessary.
	4. Residual magnetism due to lack of air gap in magnet path.	4. Replace worn magnet parts or align if possible.
	5. Welded contacts.	5. Replace contacts.

TROUBLESHOOTING GUIDE FOR ELECTRIC MOTORS

Symptoms	Cause	Result*	Remedy
1. Motor does not start. (Switch is on and not defective.)	a. Incorrectly connected.	a. Burnout.	a. Connect correctly per diagram.
	b. Incorrect power supply.	b. Burnout.	b. Use only with correctly rated power supply.
	c. Fuse out, loose or open connection.	c. Burnout.	c. Correct open circuit condition.
	d. Rotating parts of motor may be jammed mechanically.	d. Burnout.	d. Check and correct: 1. Bent shaft. 2. Broken housing. 3. Damaged bearing. 4. Foreign material in motor.
	e. Driven machine may be jammed.	e. Burnout.	e. Correct jammed condition.
	f. No power supply.	f. None.	f. Check for voltage at motor and work back to power supply.
	g. Internal circuitry open.	g. Burnout.	g. Correct open circuit condition.
2. Motor starts but does not come up to speed.	a. Same as 1-a, b, c above.	a. Burnout.	a. Same as 1-a, b, c above.
	b. Overload.	b. Burnout.	b. Reduce load to bring current to rated limit. Use proper fuses and overload protection.
	c. One or more phases out on a 3-phase motor.	c. Burnout.	c. Look for open circuits.
3. Motor noisy electrically.	a. Same as 1-a, b, c above.	a. Burnout.	a. Same as 1-a, b, c above.
4. Motor runs hot (exceeds rating).	a. Same as 1-a, b, c above.	a. Burnout.	a. Same as 1-a, b, c above.
	b. Overload.	b. Burnout.	b. Reduce load.
	c. Impaired ventilation.	c. Burnout.	c. Remove obstruction.
	d. Frequent start or stop.	d. Burnout.	d. 1. Reduce number of starts or reversals. 2. Secure proper motor for this duty.
	e. Misalignment between rotor and stator laminations.	e. Burnout.	e. Realign.
5. Noisy (mechanically)	a. Misalignment of coupling or sprocket.	a. Bearing failure, broken shaft, stator burnout due to motor drag.	a. Correct misalignment.
	b. Mechanical unbalance of rotating parts.	b. Same as 5-a.	b. Find unbalanced part, then balance.
	c. Lack of or improper lubricant.	c. Bearing failure.	c. Use correct lubricant, replace parts as necessary.
	d. Foreign material in lubricant.	d. Same as 5-c.	d. Clean out and replace bearings.
	e. Overload.	e. Same as 5-c.	e. Remove overload condition. Replace damaged parts.
	f. Shock loading.	f. Same as 5-c.	f. Correct causes and replace damaged parts.
	g. Mounting acts as amplifier of normal noise.	g. Annoying.	g. Isolate motor from base.
	h. Rotor dragging due to worn bearings, shaft, or bracket.	h. Burnout.	h. Replace bearings, shaft, or bracket as needed.
6. Bearing failure	a. Same as 5-a, b, c, d, e.	a. Burnout, damaged shaft, damaged housing.	a. Replace bearings and follow 5-a, b, c, d, e.
	b. Entry of water or foreign material into bearing housing.	b. Same as 6-a.	b. Replace bearings and seals and shield against entry of foreign material (water, dust). Use proper motor.

* Many of these conditions should trip protective devices rather than burn out motors.

TROUBLESHOOTING GUIDE FOR ELECTRIC MOTORS (continued)

Symptom	Caused By	Appearance
1. Shorted motor winding	a. Moisture, chemicals, foreign material in motor, damaged winding.	a. Black or burned with remainder of winding good.
2. All windings completely burned	a. Overload. b. Stalled. c. Impaired ventilation. d. Frequent reversal or starting. e. Incorrect power.	a. Burned equally all around winding. b. Burned equally all around winding. c. Burned equally all around winding. d. Burned equally all around winding. e. Burned equally all around winding.
3. Single-phase condition	a. Open circuit in one line. The most common causes are loose connection, one fuse out, loose contact in switch.	a. If 1,800 RPM motor — four equally burned groups at 90° intervals. b. If 1,200 RPM motor — six equally burned groups at 60° intervals. c. If 3,600 RPM motor — two equally burned groups at 180° intervals. NOTE: If Y-connected each burned group will consist of two adjacent phase groups. If delta-connected each burned group will consist of one phase group.
4. Other	a. Improper connection. b. Ground.	a. Irregularly burned groups or spot burns.

Many burnouts occur within a short period of time after motor is started up. This does not necessarily indicate that the motor was defective, but usually is due to one or more of the above-mentioned causes. The most common of these are improper connections, open circuits in one line, incorrect power supply, or overload.

TROUBLE/REMEDY CHART FOR INDUCTION MOTORS

A. Motor will not start.

Overload control tripped. Wait for overload to cool, then try to start again. If motor still does not start, check for the causes outlined below.

1. Open fuses: test fuses.

2. Low voltage: check nameplate values against power supply characteristics. Also check voltage at motor terminals when starting motor under load to check for allowable voltage drop.

3. Wrong control connections: check connections with control wiring diagram.

4. Loose terminal-lead connection: turn power off and tighten connections.

5. Drive machine locked: disconnect motor from load. If motor starts satisfactorily, check driven machine.

6. Open circuit in stator or rotor winding: check for open circuits.

7. Short circuit in stator winding: check for short.

8. Winding grounded: test for grounded wiring.

9. Bearing stiff: free bearing or replace.

10. Overload: reduce load.

B. Motor noisy.

1. Three-phase motor running on single phase: stop motor, then try to start. It will not start on single phase. Check for open circuit in one of the lines.

2. Electrical load unbalanced: check current balance.

3. Shaft bumping (sleeve-bearing motor): check alignment and conditions of belt. On pedestal-mounted bearing check cord play and axial centering of rotor.

4. Vibration: driven machine may be unbalanced. Remove motor from load. If motor is still noisy, rebalance.

5. Air gap not uniform: center the rotor and if necessary replace bearings.

6. Noisy ball bearing: check lubrication. Replace bearings if noise is excessive and persistent.

7. Rotor rubbing on stator: center the rotor and replace bearings if necessary.

8. Motor loose on foundation: tighten hold-down bolts. Motor may possibly have to be realigned.

9. Coupling loose: insert feelers at four places in coupling joint before pulling up bolts to check alignment. Tighten coupling bolts securely.

C. Motor at higher than normal temperature or smoking. (Measure temperature with thermometer or thermister and compare with nameplate value.)

1. Overload: measure motor loading with ammeter. Reduce load.

2. Electrical load unbalance: check for voltage unbalance or single-phasing.

3. Restricted ventilation: clean air passage and windings.

4. Incorrect voltage and frequency: check nameplate values with power supply. Also check voltage at motor terminals with motor under full load.

5. Motor stalled by driven tight bearings: remove power from motor. Check machine for cause of stalling.

6. Stator winding shorted or grounded: test windings by standard method.

7. Rotor winding with loose connection: tighten, if possible, or replace with another rotor.

8. Belt too tight: remove excessive pressure on bearings.

9. Motor used for rapid reversing service: replace with motor designed for this service.

D. Bearings hot.

1. End shields loose or not replaced properly: make sure end shields fit squarely and are properly tightened.

2. Excessive belt tension or excessive gear side thrust: reduce belt tension or gear pressure and realign shafts. See that thrust is not being transferred to motor bearing.

3. Bent shaft: straighten shaft or send to motor repair shop.

E. Sleeve bearings.

1. Insufficient oil: add oil — if supply is very low, drain, flush, and refill.

2. Foreign material in oil or poor grade of oil: drain oil, flush, and relubricate using industrial lubricant recommended by a reliable oil manufacturer.

3. Oil rings rotating slowly or not rotating at all: oil too heavy; drain and replace. If oil ring has worn spot, replace with new ring.

4. Motor tilted too far: level motor or reduce tilt and realign if necessary.

5. Rings bent or otherwise damaged in reassembling: replace rings.

6. Rings out of slot (oil-ring retaining clip out of place): adjust or replace retaining clip.

7. Defective bearings or rough shaft: replace bearings. Resurface shaft.

F. Ball bearings.

1. Too much grease: remove relief plug and let motor run. If excess grease does not come out, flush and relubricate.

2. Wrong grade of grease: flush bearing and relubricate with correct amount of proper grease.

3. Insufficient grease: remove relief plug and grease bearing.

4. Foreign material in grease: flush bearing, relubricate; make sure grease supply is clean (keep can covered when not in use).

PUMP RECORD CARD

NAME_____MAKE_____MODEL_____

TYPE_____SIZE_____SERIAL #_____

ORDER NUMBER_____SUPPLIER_____DATE PURCHASED_____

DATE INSTALLED_____APPLICATION_____PLANT #_____

Name Plate Data and Pump Info   Stuffing Box Data   Motor Data

GPM _____   Diameter_____Depth_____Name_____Serial #_____

TDH _____   Pack. Size____Type_____H.P._____Speed_____

RPM _____   Length_____No. Rings_____Ambient°_____

Gage Press Disc____ _____Lantern Ring_____Flushed_____RPM_____Frame_____

Gage Press Suc ____ _____Mech. Seal Name_____Size____Volts_____Amps_____

Shut off Press   ____ _____   Type_____Phase_____Cycle_____

Suction Head   ____ _____   Shaft Size_____Key_____

Rotation   ____ _____Casing_____Bearing Front_____

Impeller Type_____Shaft_____   Rear_____

Impeller Dia._____Wearing Rings Casing _____Code_____Type_____

Impeller Clear_____Wearing Rings Impeller_____Amps @ Max. Speed_____

Coupl Type & Size_____Shaft Sleeve_____Amps @ Shut Off_____

Front Brg #_____Slinger_____Control Data Info

Rear Brg #_____Shims_____Starter_____

Lub Interval_____Gaskets_____MENA Size_____

Lubricant_____"O" Rings_____Cat. #_____

Wearing Rings_____Brg. Seals Front_____Heater Size_____

Shaft Sleeve Size_____   Rear_____Rated @_____

Pump Shaft Size_____Casing Wear Ring Size ID_____Control Voltage_____

Pump Keyway_____   OD_____Variable Speed
                                                            Type_____

_____   Width_____Speed Max_____

Other Related Information: Impeller Wear Ring ID_____Speed Min_____

                                        OD_____

                                   Width_____

Pump Materials

MOTOR STARTERS   Number _____

Title:_____

Mfg.:_____Address_____

Style:_____Class_____Size_____

Type:_____   _____   _____

==

O.L. HEATERS   O.L. TRIP UNITS

Style_____Code_____   Mfg:_____Style:_____

Amps_____   _____   Type:_____   _____

_____   _____   Amps Range:_____   _____

==

CIRCUIT BREAKER

Mfg:_____Address_____

Style:_____Frame:_____Volts_____Amps Setting_____

Cat. No._____   _____   _____   _____

MOTOR   Number _____

TITLE_____

Mfg:_____Address_____

HP:_____Volts:_____Ser. No._____Duty:_____

Phase:_____Amps:_____Frame:_____Temp:_____

Cycles:_____RPM:_____Type_____Class:_____

Code:_____S.F.:_____Model_____Spec.:_____

SO#_____S#_____Style:_____CSA App:_____

Form_____Spec._____Shft. Brg._____Rear Brg._____

50 Cycle Data_____

Suitable for 208V Network:_____   Connection Diagram

Additional data_____   (6) (5) (4)   (6) (5) (4)

_____   (7) (8) (9)   (7) (8) (9)

_____   (1) (2) (3)   (1) (2) (3)

_____

If the frequency of power outages is once or twice a year with a 10- to 30-minute duration, the capacity of a standby power generator can be relatively small. The minimum size of a standby power generator may require sufficient capacity to operate essential equipment such as:

1. Coagulant and chlorine feeders,

2. One-third of flocculators,

3. Major electric valve operators and plant control system,

4. One-third of pumping capacity (if necessary), and

5. Minimum lighting.

Where do you begin? You have to consider whether you would like to have all of your facility operating or whether just the vital or key equipment would be sufficient. Since the characteristics and operating conditions of every plant are different, it is difficult to make specific suggestions.

For the sake of illustration, let us pose a hypothetical situation. Consider a 10-MGD (38-MLD) capacity plant with an average flow rate of 6 MGD (23 MLD). Prepare a list of needs that must be met to ensure minimal operation:

1. Raw water pumping,

2. Clarification,

3. Clear water pumping,

4. Chlorination, and

5. Minimal lighting.

Calculate the maximum horsepower or total kilowatts necessary to maintain the limited operation:

1. Raw Water Pump — 75 horsepower		56.00 kW
2. Clarification — 2½ horsepower		2.24 kW
3. Clear Water Pump — 40 horsepower		30.00 kW
4. Chlorination — 15 horsepower		11.20 kW
5. Lighting		5.00 kW
		104.44 kW

The minimum power required is 104.44 kW. When sizing a generator for emergency power, you have to make sure that the operator will be able to start the needed motors. Since the locked rotor current of the 75-horsepower induction motor on the raw water pump is approximately four times running current, the generator must be able to handle 224 kW at that instant. Size the generator not only by total load, but also for the highest horsepower motor being started. Consider the sequence in which motors will be started. The starting of all the motors simultaneously (without sequence starting) would be nearly impossible. Consult experts in power generation for

answers to your specific questions regarding your plant because each plant has different needs. If you are considering standby power, shop around and get ideas from the equipment manufacturers. You may be able to reduce the size of the generator by using reduced voltage starters on the larger motors.

After you have determined the size of generator needed, you must be able to connect it to your power distribution system. This may require some sophisticated switch gear. Besides the mechanical functions necessary in connecting the emergency power with your normal system, it is important that the two systems cannot be electrically coupled. (Two electrical systems must be "in phase" with each other before parallel coupling.) For this reason, mechanical interlocks are used to ensure that one circuit is always open. A "kirk-key" system, where one key is used for two locks, locking one switch open before the other can be closed, is sometimes used. The manufacturers of most packaged motor-generator systems can provide automatic transfer switches that will automatically start the generator when a power failure occurs and connect the generated power into the plant power distribution wiring.

Looking back at the plant described, a generator of 125 kW with intermittent overload capabilities should handle the load. (Note: This is an assumption. Actual calculation may indicate a different size.) An engine-generation system of this size could handle your minimal power needs. If your water distribution system has ample capacity, it may be possible to cut the plant production rate to reduce power requirements to what can be handled with a smaller capacity generator.

If you do not have standby power generation at your facility, talk to others in the water treatment field who do and obtain ideas and information. After due consideration, take the necessary steps to ensure yourself against interrupted power.

Standby power generators should be operated on a regular basis (once a week) to be sure they will operate properly when needed. Be sure to operate your generator at full load for at least an hour. Commercial power into your plant must be shut off to operate standby power at full load.

18.152 Emergency Lighting

The most practical form of emergency lighting in most instances is that provided by battery-powered lighting units. Because they are used primarily for exit lighting, they are more economical than engine-driven power sources. If you have a momentary power outage, the system responds without an engine-generator start-up. All emergency lighting unit equipment is basically the same and consists of a rechargeable battery, a battery charger, low voltage flood lights, and test monitoring and control accessories. Proper selection of a unit for a particular location requires careful consideration of the following items:

1. Initial cost,

2. Types of batteries,

3. Maintenance requirements, and

4. Lighting requirements.

The three types of batteries most commonly used are: lead acid, lead calcium, and nickel cadmium. Because poor battery maintenance is quite common in emergency lighting systems, "maintenance-free" batteries are becoming increasingly popular. These batteries can have a gelatin or acid (wet)

ELECTROLYTE.[11] The gelatin type is completely spillproof and can be handled safely without the dangers of acid spills. These batteries have a shorter life span than the wet type. Since all batteries undergo evaporation, the gelatin electrolyte will be exhausted before that of a battery containing liquid. Wet-type, maintenance-free batteries require no refilling and, when handled properly, acid spillage is minimal.

In terms of cost, the maintenance-free battery is more expensive; but when you consider the human factor, they may be more reliable and cheaper in the long run. Most systems use a battery charger that monitors the battery voltage. When required, the charger then charges the batteries. In older units, a trickle charger was used. This constant charging resulted in inoperative batteries in a short time because of overcharging.

The lamps used are normally 6- to 12-volt, sealed-beam, 25-watt lamps. The light pattern provided is most effective when illuminating a work area. A rule of thumb is that one lamp will be sufficient for about 1,000 square feet, providing that the full light pattern can be used. Consult emergency light level codes (Table 18.2) for your particular application.

When selecting an emergency lighting system, check it very thoroughly to ensure that it will give you the protection needed. If it fails to work when the chips are down and the main power is out, you've wasted your money.

18.153 Batteries

This section will discuss wet storage batteries since they are the most prevalent. Automotive and equipment batteries are usually of the lead-acid type in which the dissimilar plates are made of two types of lead and the electrolyte is sulfuric acid. Wet-type batteries can also be nickel cadmium or nickel iron.

Most batteries are a series of cells enclosed in a common case. Each of these cells develops a potential (voltage) of 2.3 volts per cell when fully charged. Hence, a six-volt battery contains three cells and a 12-volt battery has six cells. The voltage output of a 12-volt battery is 13.8 volts when fully charged. Once a lead-acid battery has been placed in service, the addition of sulfuric acid is not necessary. The water portion of the electrolyte solution evaporates as the battery is charged and discharged. Lost water must be replaced. Deionized or distilled water should be used. Tap water contains impurities that shorten the life span of a battery if used to replace lost water. These minute particles become attached to the lead plates and do not allow the battery to rejuvenate itself fully when charged.

When batteries are placed on charge, remove the cell covers to allow the gas (hydrogen) caused by charging to escape and not to build excessive pressure in the battery. A battery on charge is as lethal as a small bomb if you ignite the gas. Do not smoke or cause electrical arcing near the battery. Do not breathe the gas and make sure that the area where a battery is being charged is well ventilated.

The keys to prolonged life of a battery are to keep the electrolyte level above the cell plates, to keep the battery fully charged, and above all, to keep the terminals and top clean. When dirt and residue accumulate on the top of a battery, it

TABLE 18.2   IES[a] RECOMMENDED EMERGENCY LIGHT LEVELS[b]

Hazard requiring visual detection	Slight		High	
NORMAL ACTIVITY LEVEL[c]	LOW	HIGH	LOW	HIGH
Areas	Conference rooms Reception rooms Exterior floodlighting Closets	Lobbies Corridors Concourse Restrooms, washrooms Telephone switchboard rooms Exterior entrance Exterior floodlighting	Elevators (freight) File rooms Mail rooms Offices Stairways Stockrooms Exterior entrance with stairs	Elevators Escalators Computer rooms Drafting rooms Offices Stairways Transformer vaults Engine rooms Electrical, mechanical, plumbing rooms
Footcandles	0.5	1.0	2.0	5.0
Dekalux	0.54	1.1	2.2	2.2

a Illuminating Engineering Society
b Reprinted from December, 1978 issue Electrical Construction and Maintenance. Copyright 1978 McGraw-Hill, Inc. All rights reserved. (IES does not have a more current recommendation at the time of this publication.)
c Special conditions may require different levels of illumination. In some cases higher levels may be required as for example where security is a factor. In some other cases greatly reduced levels of illumination, including total darkness, may be necessary, specifically in situations involving manufacturing, handling, use, or processing of light-sensitive materials (notably in connection with photographic products). In these situations alternate methods of ensuring safe operation must be relied upon. EMERGENCY LIGHT LEVEL codes and standards vary widely throughout the country. Recommended minimum lighting levels of the Illuminating Engineering Society are being considered as a possible standard by ANSI and the Life Safety Code. These are minimum lighting levels recommended for safety of personnel.

---

[11] *Electrolyte (ee-LECK-tro-LITE). A substance which dissociates (separates) into two or more ions when it is dissolved in water.*

forms a path for current to flow between the negative and positive posts. Take a multimeter, connect one lead to the proper post (it will cause up-scale deflection) and slowly slide the other lead across the top of the battery toward the other post. If the top is dirty, the meter will deflect more as you proceed across the top.

To clean the battery, use a stiff-bristled brush (not a wire brush) and remove the heavy material. Then wash with a solution of baking soda and water (four teaspoons of baking soda to one quart of water). This will remove the acid film from the top and neutralize corrosion on the battery terminals. Rinse with fresh water and dry the top with a dry, lintless cloth. Remove cell caps and wipe between them, then replace. At this time check to be sure that the battery terminals are clean and tight. If a battery is charged, but the terminals are loose, proper voltage and current cannot be delivered.

QUESTIONS

Write your answers in a notebook and then compare your answers with those on page 344.

18.15A   Why should a qualified electrician perform most of the necessary maintenance and repair of electrical equipment?

18.15B   What is the purpose of a "kirk-key" system?

18.15C   Why are battery-powered backup lighting units considered better than engine-driven power sources?

18.15D   Why should the water lost from a lead-acid battery be replaced with deionized or distilled water?

18.16   High Voltage

18.160   Transmission

In general terms, high voltage is the voltage transmitted to the plant site by the utility company. The voltage level can vary, but 12,000 volts is quite common. After the power reaches the plant, it is transformed down to a usable voltage (460 to 480 volts) either through utility-owned or customer-owned transformers. The NEC (National Electrical Code) denotes high voltages as those over 600 volts.

Why have high voltage? Since current (amperes) varies inversely with voltage, a load of 500 amps on the low voltage side of the transformer would create a 20-amp load on the high voltage side of a 12,000-volts/480-volt transformer. Transmission lines would have to be enormous in order to carry the load if a lower voltage were used. Where high voltage cables terminate at a transformer or switch gear, certain conditions must be adhered to. If outdoor transformers are used that have high voltage wires exposed, an eight-foot (2.4-m) high fence is required to prevent accessibility by unqualified or unauthorized persons. Signs attached to the fence must indicate "High Voltage." Specifications for clearances, grounding, access, and enclosures vary with installations. Any modifica-

tion or repair work must be completed by qualified people only.

18.161   Switch Gear

When we see the term "switch gear," it is usually associated with the equipment used in the interruption, transfer, or disconnecting of voltages over 600 volts. The enclosure is designed and manufactured to safely control high-voltage switching. Most distribution systems have a load-interrupting switch that is capable of disconnecting high voltage lines that are under load. Because of the arc that is caused in breaking the circuit, special "arc shoes" (arc-suppressant devices) are used to ensure that the contact points are not pitted. A keyed lock system is used to prevent opening of the enclosure in the energized state.

Probably the best preventive maintenance that a treatment plant operator can provide for switch gear is to keep the exterior and its surroundings clean. If you encounter difficulties in the course of operating the switches, please obtain qualified help to do the inspection or repairs needed. Check with your particular manufacturer to determine what is needed and when this has to be done to keep your system functioning as designed. If your equipment is in a corrosive atmosphere, it may be necessary to remove it from service and epoxy paint the internal buses. All pivoting points should be lubricated with a lubricant specified by the manufacturer.

18.162   Power Distribution Transformers

If the high voltage transformers are owned by the utility, the inspection and maintenance is carried out by the utility. Any peculiar changes, smells, or noises should be reported to the utility. When transformers are customer owned, a regular inspection program should be established.

Most transformers use an oil to insulate as well as to cool the windings. As heat is generated in the windings, it is transferred to the oil. The oil is then cooled by air passing the "cooling fins" of the transformer. The primary requirements of the oil are:

1. High dielectric strength;

2. Freedom from inorganic acid, alkali, and sulfur to prevent injury to insulation and conductors;

3. Low viscosity to provide good heat transfer; and

4. Freedom from sludging under normal operation conditions.

The principal causes of deterioration of insulating oil are water and oxidation. The oil may be exposed to moisture through condensation of moist air due to "breathing" of the transformer, especially when the transformer is not continuously in service. The moist air condenses on the surface of the oil and on the inside of the tank. Oxidation causes sludging. The amount of sludge formed in a given oil depends upon the temperature and the time of exposure of the oil to the air. Excessive operating temperatures may cause sludging of any transformer oil. Check with the manufacturer to determine how often the oil should be tested. Oil can be revitalized by a cleaning procedure that is accomplished at the transformer site.

Any symptoms such as unusual noises, high or low oil levels, oil leaks, or high operating temperatures should be investigated at once. If your transformer has a thermometer, it is of the alcohol type and should be replaced with that type only. A mercury-type thermometer could cause insulation failures by reason of proximity of a metallic substance, regardless of whether it is intact or broken.

The tank of every power transformer should be grounded to eliminate the possibility of obtaining static shocks from it or from being injured by accidental grounding of the winding to the case.

If repairs are indicated, use the expertise of a qualified person to ensure that the repairs are made safely as well as correctly. Your life and the lives of others may depend on the use of qualified people.

QUESTIONS

Write your answers in a notebook and then compare your answers with those on page 344.

18.16A Why is electricity transmitted at high voltage?

18.16B What precautions must be taken if outdoor transformers have exposed high voltage wires?

18.16C What kind of maintenance should a treatment plant operator perform on switch gear?

18.16D What symptoms indicate that a power distribution transformer may be in need of maintenance or repair?

18.17 Electrical Safety Checklist

Throughout this manual and throughout this chapter the need for electrical safety is always being stressed. This section contains an electrical safety checklist which is provided to help you ensure that you have minimized electrical hazards in your plant. This list is provided to make you aware of potential electrical hazards. You should add to the list additional electrical hazards that could injure someone at your water treatment plant.

1. Are there any conduits rusted to the point where they might have lost their explosion-proof integrity?

2. Are there any electrical conduit hangers that are rusted so bad that they are allowing the conduit to sag?

3. Are there any fasteners on the conduit hangers that are rusted and allowing the conduit to hang by the wires?

4. Do all of the extension cords and power tools meet code requirements for use in wet areas?

5. Does the agency or utility have a policy covering the proper placement of portable ventilation equipment when operators work inside enclosed tanks, vaults, and other confined spaces?

6. Does the agency use proper grounding units (ground fault interrupters) when working in wet areas?

7. Is the grounding of electrical equipment and systems inspected regularly?

8. Are electrical breakers and controls clearly marked?

9. Is there a formal program for locking out, tagging, and blocking out of electrical devices?

If you can answer these questions properly, you are working in the right direction to minimize electrical hazards in your water treatment plant.

QUESTIONS

Write your answers in a notebook and then compare your answers with those on page 344.

18.17A What is the purpose of an electrical safety checklist?

18.17B Why are rusted conduits of concern to a water treatment plant operator?

18.18 Additional Reading

1. *BASIC ELECTRICITY* by Van Valkenburgh, Nooger & Neville, Inc. This book is available from Howard W. Sams & Company, 2647 Waterfront Parkway East Drive, Indianapolis, IN 46214, or call 800-428-7267. ISBN No. 0-7906-1041-8; price, $24.95.

2. "Maintenance" by Stan Walton, Volume II, Chapter 15, in *OPERATION OF WASTEWATER TREATMENT PLANTS*, Kenneth D. Kerri, California State University, Sacramento, 6000 J Street, Sacramento, CA 95819. Price for Volume II, $25.00.

3. "Instrumentation" by Leonard Ainsworth, Chapter 9, in *ADVANCED WASTE TREATMENT*, Kenneth D. Kerri, California State University, Sacramento, 6000 J Street, Sacramento, CA 95819. Price, $20.00.

4. *INDUSTRIAL ELECTRICITY: PRINCIPLES AND PRACTICES* by Adams, Glencoe Division of McGraw-Hill, PO Box 543, Blacklick, OH 43004-0543. Order No. 007000327-0. Price: $47.48.

5. "Control and Automation," Chapter XII in *WATER DISTRIBUTION OPERATOR TRAINING HANDBOOK,* by I.E. Nichols and B.W. Jex. Obtain from Customer Services, American Water Works Association, 6666 W. Quincy Ave., Denver, CO 80235. Order No. 20103. Price, members of AWWA, $21.00; nonmembers, $31.00. Price includes cost of shipping and handling.

6. *MAINTENANCE ENGINEERING HANDBOOK* by Higgins, Glencoe Division of McGraw-Hill Publishing Company. PO Box 543, Blacklick, OH 43004-0543. Order No. 0070288119. Price: $110.00.

End of Lesson 1 of 5 Lessons on
MAINTENANCE

Please answer the discussion and review questions next.

DISCUSSION AND REVIEW QUESTIONS

Chapter 18.   MAINTENANCE

(Lesson 1 of 5 Lessons)

At the end of each lesson in this chapter you will find some discussion and review questions. The purpose of these questions is to indicate to you how well you understand the material in the lesson. Write the answers to these questions in your notebook before continuing.

1. Why should operators thoroughly read and understand manufacturers' literature before attempting to maintain plant equipment?

2. Why must administrators or supervisors be made aware of the need for an adequate maintenance program?

3. What is the purpose of a maintenance recordkeeping program?

4. What items should be included in a plant library?

5. Why should your plant have an emergency team to repair chlorine leaks?

6. Why should one person never be permitted to repair a chlorine leak alone?

7. Why should inexperienced, unqualified, or unauthorized persons and even qualified and authorized persons be extremely careful around electrical panels, circuits, wiring, and equipment?

8. What protective or safety devices are used to protect operators and equipment from being harmed by electricity?

9. Why must motor nameplate data be recorded and filed?

10. What might be the cause of a pump motor failing to start?

11. Why should a water treatment plant have standby power?

12. How would you determine the capacity of standby generation equipment?

CHAPTER 18. MAINTENANCE

(Lesson 2 of 5 Lessons)

18.2 MECHANICAL EQUIPMENT

Mechanical equipment commonly used in water treatment plants is described and discussed in this section. Equipment used with specific treatment processes such as flocculation and filtration is not discussed. You must be familiar with equipment and understand what it is intended to do before developing a preventive maintenance program and maintaining equipment.

18.20 Repair Shop

Many large plants have fully equipped machine shops staffed with competent mechanics. But for smaller plants, adequate machine shop facilities often can be found in the community. In addition, most pump manufacturers maintain pump repair departments where pumps can be fully reconditioned.

The pump repair shop in a large plant commonly includes such items as welding equipment, lathes, drill press and drills, power hacksaw, flame-cutting equipment, micrometers, calipers, gages, portable electric tools, grinders, a forcing press, metal-spray equipment, and sandblasting equipment. You must determine what repair work you can and should do and when you need to request assistance from an expert.

Some agencies have their own repair shops or local machine shops rebuild parts rather than buying direct from manufacturers. Many agencies try to select equipment on the basis of the reputations of distributors for supplying repair parts when needed. A parts inventory is essential for key pieces of equipment.

18.21 Pumps

Pumps serve many purposes in water treatment plants. They may be classified by the character of the material handled, such as raw or filtered water. Or, they may relate to the conditions of pumping: high lift, low lift, or high capacity. They may be further classified by principle of operation, such as centrifugal, propeller, reciprocating, and turbine (Figure 18.15).

The type of material to be handled and the function or required performance of the pump vary so widely that the designing engineer must use great care in preparing specifications for the pump and its controls. Similarly, the operator must conduct a maintenance and management program adapted to the peculiar characteristics of the equipment.

18.210 Centrifugal Pumps

A centrifugal pump is basically a very simple device: an impeller rotating in a casing called the volute. The impeller is supported on a shaft which is, in turn, supported by bearings. Liquid coming in at the center (eye of the impeller (Figure 18.16)) is picked up by the vanes and by the rotation of the impeller and then is thrown out by centrifugal force into the discharge.

To help you understand how pumps work and the purpose of the various parts, a section titled "Let's Build a Pump!" has been included on the following pages. This material has been reprinted with the permission of Allis-Chalmers Corporation. Originally, the material was printed in Allis-Chalmers Bulletin No. OBX62568.

18.211 Let's Build a Pump!

A student of medicine spends long years learning exactly how the human body is built before attempting to prescribe for its care. Knowledge of *PUMP* anatomy is equally basic in caring for centrifugal pumps!

But whereas the medical student must take a body apart to learn its secrets, it will be far more instructive to us if we put a pump *TOGETHER* (on paper, of course). Then we can start at the beginning — adding each new part as we need it in logical sequence.

As we see *WHAT* each part does, *HOW* it does it . . . we'll see how it must be *CARED FOR!*

Another analogy between medicine and maintenance: there are various types of human bodies, but if you know basic anatomy, you understand them all. The same is true of centrifugal pumps. In building one basic type, we'll learn about *ALL* types.

Part of this will be elementary to some maintenance people . . . but they will find it a valuable "refresher" course, and, after all, maintenance just can't be too good.

So, with a glance at the centrifugal principle on page 272, let's get on with building our pump . . .

FIRST WE REQUIRE A DEVICE TO SPIN LIQUID AT HIGH SPEED . . .

That paddle-wheel device is called the "impeller". . . and it's the heart of our pump.

Note that the blades curve out from its hub. As the impeller spins, liquid between the blades is impelled outward by centrifugal force.

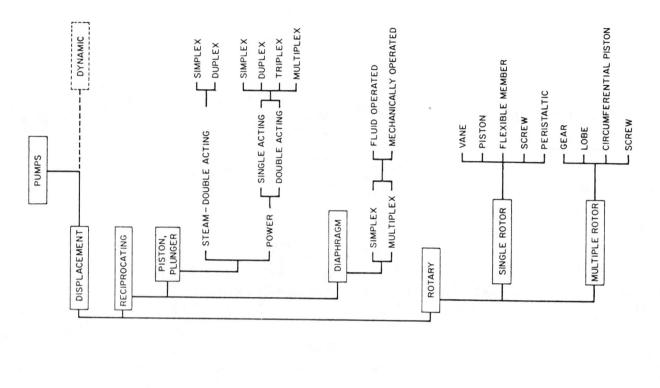

Displacement types of pumps

Dynamic types of pumps

Fig. 18.15   Classification of pumps

Discharge

Suction

Volute

Vanes

Impeller
eye

Refer to Figure 18.19, pages 278 and 279, for location of impeller in pump

Fig. 18.16   Diagram showing details of centrifugal pump impeller
(Source: *CENTRIFUGAL PUMPS* by Karassik and Carter of Worthington Corporation)

Note, too, that our impeller is open at the center — the "eye." As liquid in the impeller moves outward, it will suck more liquid in behind it through this eye . . . *PROVIDED IT'S NOT CLOGGED!*

That brings up Maintenance Rule No. 1: if there's any danger that foreign matter (sticks, refuse) may be sucked or drawn into the pump — clogging or wearing the impeller unduly — *PROVIDE THE INTAKE END OF THE SUCTION PIPING WITH A SUITABLE SCREEN.*

1ST. LINE OF PUMP DEFENSE IN WATER CARRYING STICKS, ETC!

NOW WE NEED A SHAFT TO SUPPORT AND TURN THE IMPELLER . . .

Our shaft looks heavy — and it *IS*. It must maintain the impeller in precisely the right place.

But that ruggedness does *NOT* protect the shaft from the corrosive or abrasive effects of the liquid pumped . . . so we must protect it with sleeves slid on from either end.

THESE SLEEVES WILL PROTECT THE SHAFT

CENTRIFUGAL FORCE IN ACTION—

ALL MOVING BODIES TEND TO TRAVEL IN A STRAIGHT LINE. WHEN FORCED TO TRAVEL IN A CURVE, THEY CONSTANTLY _TRY_ TO TRAVEL ON A TANGENT...

... IN AN "AIRPLANE RIDE"

Centrifugal force pushes dummy planes swung in a circle _away_ from center of rotation.

... IN A WHIRLPOOL

Centrifugal force tends to push swirling water outward ... forming vortex in center.

What these sleeves — and the impeller, too — are made of depends on the nature of the liquid we're to pump. Generally they're bronze, but various other alloys, ceramics, glass, or even rubber-coating are sometimes required.

Maintenance Rule No. 2: *NEVER PUMP A LIQUID FOR WHICH THE PUMP WAS NOT DESIGNED.*

Whenever a change in pump application is contemplated and there's any doubt as to the pump's ability to resist the different liquid, *CHECK WITH YOUR PUMP MANUFAC-TURER!*

WE MOUNT THE SHAFT ON SLEEVE, BALL OR ROLLER BEARINGS . . .

As we'll see later, clearances between moving parts of our pump are *QUITE SMALL.*

If bearings supporting the turning shaft and impeller are allowed to wear excessively and lower the turning units within a pump's closely-fitted mechanism, the life and efficiency of that pump will be seriously threatened.

Maintenance Rule No. 3: *KEEP THE RIGHT AMOUNT OF THE RIGHT LUBRICANT IN BEARINGS AT ALL TIMES. FOLLOW YOUR PUMP MANUFACTURER'S LUBRICATION INSTRUCTIONS TO THE LETTER.*

Main points to keep in mind are . . .

1. Although too much oil won't harm sleeve bearings, too much grease in antifriction type bearings (ball or roller) *PROMOTE* friction and heat. The main job of grease in antifriction bearings is to protect steel elements against corrosion, not friction.

2. Operating conditions vary so widely that no one rule as to frequency of changing lubricant will fit all pumps. So play it safe: if anything, change lubricant *BEFORE* it's too worn or too dirty.

TO CONNECT WITH THE MOTOR, WE ADD A COUPLING FLANGE . . .

Some pumps are built with pump and motor on one shaft and, of course, offer no alignment problem.

But our pump is to be driven by a separate motor . . . and we attach a flange to one end of the shaft through which bolts will connect with the motor flange.

USE FEELER GAUGES BETWEEN FLANGES, A STRAIGHT-EDGE ACROSS TOPS AND SIDES.

Maintenance Rule No. 4: *SEE THAT PUMP AND MOTOR FLANGES ARE PARALLEL VERTICALLY AND AXIALLY . . . AND THAT THEY'RE KEPT THAT WAY!*

If shafts are eccentric or meet at an angle, every revolution throws tremendous extra load on bearings of both pump and motor. Flexible couplings will *NOT* correct this condition if excessive.

Checking alignment should be regular procedure in pump maintenance. Foundations can settle unevenly, piping can change pump position, bolts can loosen. Misalignment is a *MAJOR* cause of pump and coupling wear.

NOW WE NEED A "STRAW" THROUGH WHICH LIQUID CAN BE SUCKED . . .

Notice two things about the suction piping: (1) the horizontal piping slopes *UPWARD* toward the pump; (2) any reducer which connects between the pipe and pump intake nozzle should be horizontal at the top — (*ECCENTRIC,* not concentric).

AIR POCKET   AIR POCKET

ALLOWED BY DOWN-SLOPING PIPE   ALLOWED BY TAPERED REDUCER

This up-sloping prevents air pocketing in the top of the pipe . . . through which air might be drawn into the pump and cause loss of suction.

Maintenance Rule No. 5: *ANY DOWNSLOPING TOWARD THE PUMP IN SUCTION PIPING (AS EXAGGERATED IN THE DIAGRAMS ABOVE) SHOULD BE CORRECTED.*

This rule is *VERY* important. Loss of suction greatly endangers a pump . . . as we'll see shortly.

WE CONTAIN AND DIRECT THE SPINNING LIQUID WITH A CASING . . .

We got a little ahead of our story in the previous paragraphs . . . because we didn't yet have the casing to which the suction piping bolts. And the manner in which it is attached is of great importance.

Maintenance Rule No. 6: *SEE THAT PIPING PUTS ABSOLUTELY NO STRAIN ON THE PUMP CASING.*

THE WEIGHT OF PIPING CAN EASILY **RUIN** A PUMP!

When the original installation is made, all piping should be in place and self-supporting before connection. Openings should meet with no force. Otherwise the casing is apt to be cracked . . . or sprung enough to allow closely-fitted pump parts to rub.

It's good practice to check the piping supports regularly to see that loosening, or settling of the building, hasn't put strains on the casing.

NOW OUR PUMP IS ALMOST COMPLETE, BUT IT WOULD LEAK LIKE A SIEVE . . .

We're far enough along now to trace the flow of water through our pump. It's not easy to show suction piping in the cross-section view above, so imagine it stretching from your eye to the lower center of the pump.

Our pump happens to be a "double suction" pump, which means that water flow is divided inside the pump casing . . . reaching the eye of the impeller from either side.

LIQUID GOES IN HERE (UNDER SUCTION)

AND IT COMES OUT HERE (UNDER PRESSURE)

BUT SOME OF IT LEAKS BACK FROM PRESSURE TO SUCTION!

As water is sucked into the spinning impeller, centrifugal force causes it to flow outward . . . building up high pressure at the outside of the pump (which will force water *OUT*) and creating low pressure at the center of the pump (which will suck water *IN*). This situation is diagrammed in the upper half of the pump, above.

So far so good . . . except that water tends to be sucked back from pressure to suction through the space between impeller and casing — as diagrammed in the lower half of the pump, above — and our next step must be to plug this leak, if our pump is to be very efficient!

SO WE ADD WEARING RINGS TO PLUG INTERNAL LIQUID LEAKAGE . . .

You might ask why we didn't build our parts closer fitting in the first place — instead of narrowing the gap between them by inserting wearing rings.

The answer is that those rings are removable and *REPLACEABLE* . . . when wear enlarges the tiny gap between them and the impeller. (Sometimes rings are attached to impeller rather than casing — or rings are attached to *BOTH* so they face each other.)

PRIME

DESTRUCTIVE FRICTION AND HEAT

YOUR PUMP

A LOT DEPENDS ON MAINTAINING PRIME!

Maintenance Rule No. 7: *NEVER ALLOW A PUMP TO RUN DRY* (either through lack of proper priming when starting or through loss of suction when operating). Water is a LUBRICANT between rings and impeller.

Maintenance Rule No. 8: *EXAMINE WEARING RINGS AT REGULAR INTERVALS.* When seriously worn, their replacement will greatly improve pump efficiency.

TO KEEP AIR FROM BEING SUCKED IN, WE USE STUFFING BOXES . . .

We have two good reasons for wanting to keep air out of our pump: (1) we want to pump water, not air; and (2) air leakage is apt to cause our pump to lose suction.

Each stuffing box we use consists of a casing, rings of packing, and a gland at the outside end. A mechanical seal may be used instead.

Maintenance Rule No. 9: *PACKING SHOULD BE REPLACED PERIODICALLY — DEPENDING ON CONDITIONS — USING THE PACKING RECOMMENDED BY YOUR PUMP MANUFACTURER.* Forcing in a ring or two of new packing instead of replacing worn packing is *BAD PRACTICE.* It's apt to displace the seal cage (see next column).

Put each ring of packing in separately, seating it firmly before adding the next. Stagger adjacent rings so the points where their ends meet do not coincide.

Maintenance Rule No. 10: *NEVER TIGHTEN A GLAND MORE THAN NECESSARY* . . . as excessive pressure will wear shaft sleeves unduly.

Maintenance Rule No. 11: *IF SHAFT SLEEVES ARE BADLY SCORED, REPLACE OR REPAIR THEM IMMEDIATELY* . . . or packing life will be entirely too short.

TO MAKE PACKING MORE AIRTIGHT, WE ADD WATER SEAL PIPING . . .

In the center of each stuffing box is a "seal cage." By connecting it with piping to a point near the impeller rim, we bring liquid *UNDER PRESSURE* to the stuffing box.

This liquid acts both to block out air intake and to lubricate the packing. It makes both packing and shaft sleeves wear longer . . . *PROVIDING IT'S CLEAN LIQUID!*

WATER IS A LUBRICANT!

Maintenance Rule No. 12: *IF THE LIQUID BEING PUMPED CONTAINS GRIT, A SEPARATE SOURCE OF SEALING LIQUID SHOULD BE OBTAINED* (in some cases, it may be possible to direct a portion of the pumped liquid into a container and allow the grit to settle out).

To control liquid flow, draw up the gland just tight enough so that there will be a leakage of approximately one drop per second from the stuffing box during pump operation.

DISCHARGE PIPING COMPLETES THE PUMP INSTALLATION — AND NOW WE CAN ANALYZE THE VARIOUS FORCES WE'RE DEALING WITH . . .

SUCTION. At least 75% of centrifugal pump troubles trace to the suction side. To minimize them . . .

1. Total suction lift (distance between centerline of pump and liquid level when pumping, plus friction losses) generally should not exceed 15 feet.

2. Piping should be at least a size larger than pump suction nozzle.

3. Friction in piping should be minimized . . . use as few and as easy bends as possible . . . avoid scaled or corroded pipe.

DISCHARGE lift, plus suction lift, plus friction in the piping from the point where liquid enters the suction piping to the end of the discharge piping equals total head.

PUMPS SHOULD BE OPERATED NEAR THEIR RATED HEADS.

Otherwise, the pump is apt to operate under unsatisfactory and unstable conditions which reduce efficiency and operating life of the unit.

Note the description of "cavitation" below. Cavitation can seriously damage your pump.

PUMP CAPACITY generally is measured in gallons per minute. A new pump is guaranteed to deliver its rating in capacity and head.

But whether a pump *RETAINS* its actual capacity depends to a great extent on its maintenance.

Wearing rings must be replaced when necessary — to keep internal leakage losses down.

Friction must be minimized in bearings and stuffing boxes by proper lubrication . . . and misalignment must not be allowed to force scraping between closely-fitted pump parts.

POWER of the driving motor, like capacity of the pump, will not remain at a constant level without proper maintenance.

HAVE A HEALTHY RESPECT FOR CAVITATION!

IF PUMP CAPACITY, SPEED, HEAD, AND SUCTION LIFT AREN'T FIGURED PROPERLY, CAVITATION CAN EAT AN IMPELLER AWAY *FAST!* A LABORATORY WATER HAMMER INDICATES ITS EROSIVE FORCE . . .

1 VESSEL FILLED WITH WATER DROPPED TO BOTTOM OF TANK

2 MOMENTUM OF WATER & WEIGHT PRODUCE CAVITY BENEATH INSERTED BRASS PLATE

3 PRESSURE CLOSES CAVITY - WATER PUNCHES HOLE IN BRASS PLATE!

1 FAST MOVEMENT OF IMPELLER BLADE THROUGH WATER . . .

2 PRODUCES CAVITY BEHIND BLADE . . .

3 LOCAL PRESSURE INCREASE DRIVES WATER INTO METAL WITH TERRIFIC FORCE.

MORAL: BE SURE YOUR HEAD IS RIGHT FOR YOUR PUMP!

Starting load on motors can be reduced by throttling or closing the pump discharge valve (*NEVER* the suction valve!) . . . but the pump must not be operated for long with the discharge valve closed. Power then is converted into friction — overheating the water with serious consequences.

Cavitation is a condition that can cause a drop in pump efficiency, vibration, noise and rapid damage to the impeller of a pump. Cavitation occurs due to unusually low pressures within a pump. These low pressures can develop when pump inlet pressures drop below the design inlet pressures or when the pump is operated at flow rates considerably higher than design flows. When the pressure within the flowing water drops very low, the water starts to boil and vapor bubbles form. These bubbles then collapse with great force which knocks metal particles off the pump impeller. This same action can and does occur on pressure reducing valves and partially closed gate and butterfly valves.

18.212 Vertical Centrifugal Pumps
(Figures 18.17 and 18.18)

Another common configuration for centrifugal pumps is the vertical-suction cased centrifugal pump. This is an adaptation of the deep-well turbine pump for booster pump service. They are very flexible in design as the engineers can specify either single- or multistage in a wide variety of sizes and characteristics.

Besides the usual lubrication of the electric motor, the only routine maintenance required is to adjust and repair, as needed, the single packing gland.

18.213 Horizontal Centrifugal Pumps (Figure 18.19)

Horizontal centrifugal pumps, like the one we just constructed on paper in Section 18.211, are available in a number of configurations. The one we built is best described as a single-stage, horizontal, double-suction, split-case centrifugal pump. The pump is a single-stage pump because it has only one impeller. Some horizontal pumps have two impellers that are working in series to create higher heads than can readily be obtained with only one impeller. Our paper pump was double suction in that water entered the impeller from both sides. The advantage of this design is that the longitudinal thrust from the water entering the impeller is balanced. This greatly reduces the thrust load that the pump's bearings must carry. The split-case designation indicates that the pump case is made in two halves. Some centrifugal pumps have a single suction in line with the shaft. These are described as single-stage, end-suction centrifugal pumps.

18.214 Reciprocating or Piston Pumps

The word "reciprocating" means moving back and forth, so a reciprocating pump is one that moves a liquid by a piston that moves back and forth. A simple reciprocating pump is shown in Figure 18.20. If the piston is pulled to the left, Check Valve A will be open and the liquid will enter the pump and fill the casing. When the piston reaches the end of its travel to the left and is pushed back to the right, Check Valve A will close, Check Valve B will open, and the liquid will be forced out the exit line.

A piston pump is a positive-displacement pump. Never operate it against a closed discharge valve or the pump, valve, and/or pipe could be damaged by excessive pressures. Also, the suction valve should be open when the pump is started. Otherwise an excessive suction or vacuum could develop and cause problems.

Fig. 18.17 *Vertical centrifugal pump (multistage)*
(Permission of Aurora Pump Company)

Adjusting Nut
Drive Key
Vertical Hollow Shaft Motor
Top Shaft
Deflector Ring
Packing Gland
Packing
Lantern Ring
Packing Box
Discharge Head
Packing Box Bushing
Drain Line
Top Column Flange
Shaft Coupling
Column Pipe
Bowl Shaft
Discharge Case Cap
Discharge Case Coupling
Discharge Case
Discharge Case Bearing
Impeller
Intermediate Bowl
Impeller Lock Collet
Intermediate Bowl Bearing
Bowl Wear Ring
Suction Case Bearing
Suction Flange

Fig. 18.18 *Vertical centrifugal pump (single stage)*
(Permission of Aurora Pump Company)

18.215 Progressive Cavity (Screw-Flow) Pumps
(Figure 18.21)

The progressive cavity pump consists of a screw-shaped rotor snugly enclosed in a non-moving stator or housing. The threads of the screw-like rotor (commonly manufactured of chromed steel) make contact along the walls of the stator (usually made of synthetic rubber). The gaps between the rotor threads are called "cavities." When water is pumped through an inlet valve, it enters the cavity. As the rotor turns, the material is moved along until it leaves the conveyor (rotor) at the discharge end of the pump. The size of the cavities along the rotor determines the capacity of the pump.

All progressive cavity pumps operate on the basic principle described above. To further increase capacity, some models have a shaped inside surface of the stator (housing) with a similarly shaped rotor. In addition, some models use a rotor that moves up and down inside the stator as well as turning on its axis (Figure 18.22). This allows a further increase in the capacity of the pump.

Progressive cavity pumps are recommended for materials containing higher concentrations of suspended solids. They are commonly used to pump sludges. Progressive cavity pumps should *NEVER* be operated dry (without liquid in the cavities), and should *NEVER* be run against a closed discharge valve.

18.216 Chemical Metering Pumps

Many chemical metering pumps are a type of positive displacement pump. For information on chemical metering pumps, see Chapter 13, "Fluoridation," Section 13.30, "Chemical Feeders," and Section 18.4, "Chemical Storage and Feeders," in this chapter.

QUESTIONS

Write your answers in a notebook and then compare your answers with those on pages 344 and 345.

18.20A List the pieces of equipment and special tools commonly found in a pump repair shop.

18.21A What is the purpose of a pump impeller?

18.21B Why should the intake end of suction piping have a suitable screen?

18.21C Why must suction piping always be up-sloping?

18.21D What is cavitation?

18.21E What is an advantage of a *DOUBLE-SUCTION* pump over a *SINGLE-SUCTION* pump?

1. Motor frame	6. Casing	11. Impeller	16. Wearing ring
2. Impeller	7. Shaft sleeve	12. Bearings	17. Oil reservoir
3. Oil seal	8. Back pull-out	13. Shaft sleeve	18. Rear support foot
4. Mechanical seal	9. Lubrication fittings	14. Close coupled motor support	
5. Frame	10. Shaft	15. Impeller	

Fig. 18.19 Centrifugal pump parts

(Permission of Aurora Pump Company)

1. Motor frame
2. Impeller
3. Oil seal
4. Mechanical seal
5. Frame
6. Casing
7. Shaft sleeve
8. Back pull-out
9. Lubrication fittings
10. Shaft
11. Impeller
12. Bearings
13. Shaft sleeve
14. Close coupled motor support
15. Impeller
16. Wearing ring
17. Oil reservoir
18. Rear support foot

Fig. 18.19   Centrifugal pump parts (continued)

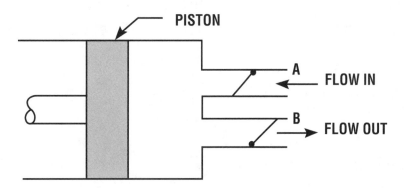

Fig. 18.20   Simple reciprocating pump

Fig. 18.21 Progressive cavity (screw-flow) pump
(Permission of Moyno Pump Division, Robbins & Meyer, Inc.)

Pumping principle

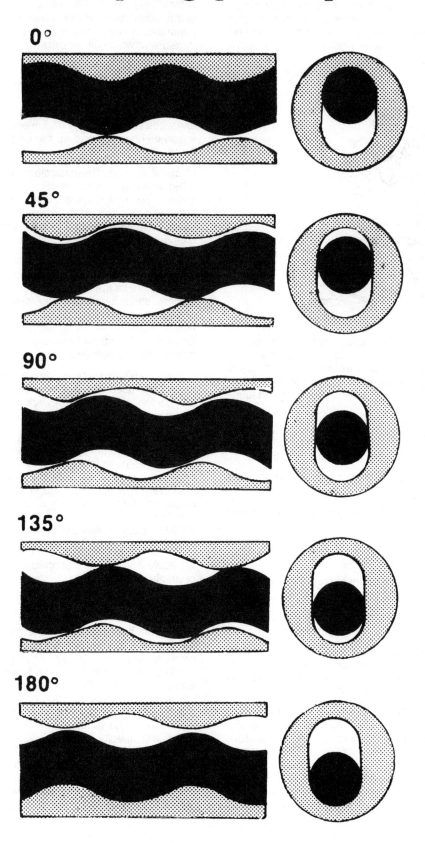

0°

45°

90°

135°

180°

Fig. 18.22 Pumping principle of a progressive cavity pump
(Permission of Allweiler Pumps, Inc.)

18.22   Lubrication

18.220   Purpose of Lubrication

Lubrication of equipment is probably one of the most important phases of a maintenance operator's job. Without proper lubrication, the tools and equipment used for operating and maintaining water treatment plants would fail. Proper lubrication of tools and equipment is probably one of the maintenance operator's easiest jobs, but often it is the most neglected.

The purpose of lubrication is to reduce friction between two surfaces. Lubrication also removes heat that is caused by friction. Solid friction of two dry surfaces in contact is changed to a fluid friction of a separating layer of liquid or liquid lubricant. Actually, water is a lubricant, although not a good lubricant.

18.221   Properties of Lubricants

A good lubricant must have the following properties:

1. Form a slippery coating on contacting surfaces so they can slide freely past each other, and

2. Exert sufficient pressure to keep the surfaces apart when running.

To be a good lubricant for a particular job, the lubricant used must have the following qualities:

1. Thickness of the lubricant layer must be sufficient to keep the roughness of the metal parts from touching.

2. Lubricity (slipperiness) must be sufficient to allow molecules to slide freely past each other, and

3. Viscosity (resistance to flow) must be sufficient to build up a pressure necessary to keep the surfaces apart. If viscosity alone cannot provide enough pressure, an external pressure must be supplied by a pump.

Viscosity in the United States is the number of seconds it takes 60 cubic centimeters (cc) of an oil to flow through the standard orifice of a Saybolt Universal Viscometer at 100, 130, or 210 degrees Fahrenheit. A 300 - *SSU*[12] @ 130 oil means that it took 300 seconds for 60 cc to flow through a Saybolt Universal Viscometer at 130 degrees Fahrenheit. Viscosity decreases with temperature rise because oil becomes thinner. The specific gravity of an oil is measured by comparing the weight of oil with an equal volume of water, both at 60 degrees Fahrenheit.

Some other important information to know about lubricants is their "Pour Point," "Flash Point," and "Fire Point." "Pour Point" is the temperature at which a lubricant refuses to run. This is important in low temperature work. "Flash Point" is the temperature at which oil vaporizes enough to ignite momentarily when near a flame. A low flash point means that oil evaporates more readily in service. "Fire Point" is the temperature at which oil vaporizes enough to keep on burning. Oils in service tend to become acid and may cause corrosion, deposits, sludging, and other problems. This condition may not be visible when you look at the oil. Therefore, do not extend the time for an oil change because the oil looks clean.

To detect acid conditions in oils, the neutralization number of an oil is used. The neutralization number is the weight in milligrams of potassium hydroxide required to neutralize one gram of oil. This is used by laboratories that test the oil on large engines, turbines, compressors, and other equipment which have large volume oil reservoirs to determine when oil changes or additives are needed.

Most lubricants in general use are fluid at room temperature. Mostly, these are petroleum based, but others are used. Greases are mixtures of petroleum products with soaps such as lime, soda, aluminum, and metallic. Metallic soaps, forms of calcium, sodium, potassium, and lithium, have good retention in bearings and can withstand high temperatures and pressures. A sodium base grease has sodium as the soap mixed with the petroleum.

Solid materials such as graphite and finely ground mica are sometimes used as lubricants. Some recently developed silicon compounds (silicones) work very well under heavy loads and widely varying temperatures.

There are many oil additives on the market today and they are worth investigating. Oil additives are chemical compounds added to an oil to improve certain chemical or physical properties such as stability, lubricity, and foaming. They are used to prevent rust or deposits and many other items that could cause problems.

18.222   Lubrication Schedule

To have proper lubrication you must first set up a lubrication schedule. This can be a simple check-off sheet or card system or an elaborate computer system. The first thing to do is make a list of everything that needs lubrication down to the smallest item, including chains, rollers, and sprockets. After you have listed every item on paper, go through the manufacturer's instruction books to determine the frequency and type of lubrication required. Is the frequency daily, weekly, monthly, semiannually, or annually? The manufacturer's literature usually lists several different name brands of lubricants which are equal. If you need help determining the type of lubricant or cross-referencing it to your particular brand, contact your supplier. Most oil distributors have a service representative who will come to your facility and go over the individual equipment and specify which lubricants you should use. Next, determine the amount of each lubricant required. This is achieved by counting the number of grease fittings. Determine the locations of fill plugs, drain plugs, oil levels, sight glasses, dipsticks, and other important items. To find these locations, physically inspect each piece of equipment thoroughly and

---

[12] *SSU.   Standard Saybolt Units.*

look for all lubrication points. Also, the manufacturer's maintenance manual should show the lubrication points for each piece of equipment.

When you have gathered all this information, transfer it to the equipment history cards for future reference. From this information you can make up a lubrication chart or form.

As stated earlier, use whatever type of lubrication form you prepare, but follow it. Always record each lubrication job when completed and have the operator who did the job initial the record card. Always keep your lubrication schedules up to date. If there are failures due to the wrong or insufficient lubricant, change or increase the lubrication frequency on the schedule. Also, new equipment must be added and discarded equipment removed from the schedule. Someone must be assigned to take care of the lubrication and records. Assign more than one operator or rotate this job so if an individual is off work or leaves the crew, there is a continuity in the lubrication schedule.

18.223 Precautions

When handling or storing oils and greases, some special precautions must be followed. Make sure the storage area does not create a fire hazard. Most lubricants are highly flammable and shouldn't be stored where there is an open flame. "NO SMOKING" signs must be posted outside the building. Be sure to keep any spills wiped up and make sure that all the lids are tight on their containers.

Keep materials and containers clean. Sand, grit, and other substances can contaminate lube supplies and create an equipment failure that lubrication maintenance is intended to prevent. Another good idea is to direct the first shot of grease from a gun into a waste can.

18.224 Pump Lubrication

Pumps, motors, and drives should be oiled and greased in strict accordance with the recommendations of the manufacturer. Cheap lubricants may often be the most expensive in the end. Oil should not be put in the housing while the pump shaft is rotating because the rotary action of the ball bearings will pick up and retain a considerable amount of oil. When the unit comes to rest, an overflow of oil around the shaft or out of the oil cup will result.

Greased bearings should be lubricated as follows:

1. Shut off, lock out, tag, and block the unit if moving parts that might be a safety hazard are close to the grease fitting or drain plugs.

2. Remove the drain plug from the bearing housing.

3. Remove the grease fitting protective cap and wipe off the grease fitting. Be sure that you do not force dirt into the bearing housing along with the clean grease.

4. Pump in clean grease until the grease coming out of the drain hole is clean. Don't pump grease into a bearing with the drain plug in place. This could easily build up enough pressure to blow out the seals.

5. Put the protective cap back on the grease fitting.

6. With the drain plug still removed, put the unit back in service. As the bearing warms up, excess grease will be expelled from the drain hole. After the unit has been running for a few hours, the drain plug may be put back in place. Special drain plugs with spring-loaded check valves are recommended because they will protect against further buildup.

7. Unless you intend to be very careful, we recommend that bearing grease be purchased in cartridge form to minimize the chance of getting dirt into the lubricant.

QUESTIONS

Write your answers in a notebook and then compare your answers with those on page 345.

18.22A What is the purpose of lubrication?

18.22B What happens to oils in service?

18.22C What should be done to ensure proper lubrication of equipment?

18.225 Equipment Lubrication

Different authorities may make conflicting lube recommendations for essentially the same item; however, general reference material is available to help select the correct lubricant for a specific application.

Grease is graded on a number scale, or viscosity index, by the National Lubricating Grease Institute. For example, No. 0 is very soft; No. 6 is quite stiff. A typical grease for most treatment plant applications might be a No. 2 lithium or sodium compound grease, which is used for operating temperatures up to 250°F (120°C).

Generally, the time between flushing and repacking for greased bearings should be divided by 2 for every 25°F (14°C) above 150°F (65°C) operating temperature. Also, generally, the time between lubrications should not be allowed to exceed 48 months, since lube component separation and oxidation can become significant after this period of time, regardless of amount of use.

Another point worth noting is that grease is normally not suitable for moving elements with speeds exceeding 12,000 in/min (5 m/sec). Usually, oil lubricating systems are used for higher speeds. Lighter viscosity oils are recommended for high speeds, and, within the same speed and temperature range, a roller bearing will normally require one grade heavier viscosity than a ball bearing.

A good rule of thumb is to change and flush oil completely at the end of 600 hours of operation, or every 3 months, whichever occurs first. More specific procedures for flushing and changing lubricants are outlined by most equipment manufacturers.

Every operator should be aware of the dangers of overfilling with either grease or oil. Overfilling can result in high pressures and temperatures, and ruined seals or other components. It has been observed that more antifriction bearings are ruined by overgreasing than by neglect.

A thermometer can tell a great deal about the condition of a bearing. Ball bearings are generally in trouble above 180°F (82°C). Grease-packed bearings typically run 10 to 50 degrees above ambient temperature.

For clarifier drive units, which are almost always located outdoors, condensation presents a dangerous problem for the lubrication system. Most units of current design have a condensate bailing system to remove water from the gear housing by displacement. These units should be checked often for proper operation, particularly during seasons of wide air temperature fluctuation.

Pumps incorporate many types of seals and gaskets constructed of combinations of elastomers and metals. As for lubricants, conflicting advice can be obtained. A file containing data on general properties of materials used can help in the choice of lubricant.

QUESTIONS

Write your answers in a notebook and then compare your answers with those on page 345.

18.22D Does a soft grease have a high or low viscosity index as compared with a hard grease?

18.22E Is oil or grease used with higher speeds?

18.22F What problems can result from overfilling with oil or grease?

End of Lesson 2 of 5 Lessons on MAINTENANCE

Please answer the discussion and review questions next.

DISCUSSION AND REVIEW QUESTIONS

Chapter 18. MAINTENANCE

(Lesson 2 of 5 Lessons)

Write the answers to these questions in your notebook before continuing. The question numbering continues from Lesson 1.

13. What is the purpose of a pump shaft?

14. What is the purpose of pump sleeves?

15. Why should a pump never be allowed to run dry?

16. How would you develop a lubrication schedule for a pump?

17. Why is cleanliness important in the storage and use of lubricants?

CHAPTER 18.   MAINTENANCE

(Lesson 3 of 5 Lessons)

18.23   Pump Maintenance

18.230   Section Format

The format of this section differs from the other chapters. This format was designed specifically to assist you in planning an effective preventive maintenance program. The paragraphs are numbered for easy reference when you use the Equipment Service Cards and Service Record Cards mentioned in Section 18.00, page 236, and shown in Figure 18.1.

An entire book could be written on the topics covered in this section. Step-by-step details for maintaining equipment are not provided because manufacturers are continually improving their products and these details could soon be out of date. You are assumed to have some familiarity with the equipment being discussed. *FOR DETAILS CONCERNING A PARTICULAR PIECE OF EQUIPMENT, YOU SHOULD CONTACT THE MANUFACTURER.* This section indicates to you the kinds of maintenance you should include in your program and how you could schedule your work. Carefully read the manufacturer's instructions and be sure you clearly understand the material before attempting to maintain and repair equipment. If you have any questions or need any help, do not hesitate to contact the manufacturer or your local representative.

A glossary is not provided in this section because of the large number of technical words that require familiarization with the equipment being discussed. The best way to learn the meaning of these new words is from manufacturers' literature or from their representatives. Some new words are described in the lessons where necessary.

18.231   Preventive Maintenance

The following paragraphs list some general preventive maintenance services and indicate frequency of performance. There are many makes and types of equipment and the wide variation of functions cannot be included; therefore, you will have to use some judgment as to whether the services and frequencies will apply to your equipment. If something goes wrong or breaks in your plant, you may have to disregard your maintenance schedule and fix the problem now.

NOTE: If you need to shut a unit down, make sure it is also locked out and tagged properly. (Figure 18.23)

CODE
D MEANS DAILY; W, WEEKLY; M, MONTHLY; Q, QUARTERLY; S, SEMIANNUALLY; A, ANNUALLY

Paragraph 1: Pumps, General

This paragraph lists some general preventive maintenance services and indicates frequency of performance. Typical centrifugal pump sections are shown in Figure 18.19.

**Frequency
of
Service**

D   1. CHECK WATER-SEAL PACKING GLANDS FOR LEAKAGE. See that the packing box is protected with a clear water supply from an outside source, make sure that water seal pressure is at least 5 psi (35 kPa or 0.35 kg/sq cm) greater than maximum pump suction pressure. See that there are no *CROSS CONNECTIONS.*[13] Check packing glands for leakage during operation. Allow a slight seal leakage when pumps are running to keep packing cool and in good condition. The proper amount of leakage depends on equipment and operating conditions. Sixty drops of water per minute is a good rule of thumb. If excessive leakage is found, HAND TIGHTEN glands' nuts evenly, but not too tight. After adjusting packing glands, be sure shaft turns freely by hand. If serious leakage continues, renew packing, shaft, or shaft sleeve.

D   2. CHECK GREASE-SEALED PACKING GLANDS. When grease is used as a packing gland seal, maintain constant grease pressure on packing during operation. When a spring-loaded grease cup is used, keep it loaded with grease. Force grease through packing at a rate of about one ounce (30 gm) per day. When water is used, adjust seal pressure to 5 psi (35 kPa or 0.35 kg/sq cm) above maximum pump suction pressure. Never allow the seal to run dry.

---

[13] *Cross Connection.   A connection between a drinking (potable) water system and an unapproved water supply. For example, if you have a pump moving nonpotable water and hook into the drinking water system to supply water for the pump seal, a cross connection or mixing between the two water systems can occur. This mixing may lead to contamination of the drinking water.*

DANGER

OPERATOR WORKING ON LINE

DO NOT CLOSE THIS SWITCH WHILE THIS TAG IS DISPLAYED

TIME OFF: _____

DATE: _____

SIGNATURE: _____

This is the ONLY person authorized to remove this tag.

INDUSTRIAL INDEMNITY/INDUSTRIAL UNDERWRITERS/
INSURANCE COMPANIES

4E210—R66

Fig. 18.23   Typical warning tag
(Source: Industrial Indemnity/Industrial Underwriters/Insurance Companies)

**Frequency
of
Service**

W   3. OPERATE PUMPS ALTERNATELY. If two or more pumps of the same size are installed, alternate their use to equalize wear, keep motor windings dry, and distribute lubricant in bearings.

W   4. INSPECT PUMP CONTROL. Inspect the pump controls to see that the pump responds properly to changes in the controlling variable. This variable may be either a pressure or a water level. This check could be done physically or by analyzing recording gage records.

D   5. CHECK MOTOR CONDITION. See Paragraph 6: Electric Motors.

W   6. CHECK PACKING GLAND ASSEMBLY. Check packing gland, the unit's most abused and troublesome part. If stuffing box leaks

excessively when gland is pulled up with mild pressure, remove packing and examine shaft sleeve carefully. Replace or repair grooved or scored shaft sleeve because packing cannot be held in stuffing box with roughened shaft or shaft sleeve. Replace the packing a strip at a time, tamping each strip thoroughly and staggering joints. (See Figure 18.24.) Position lantern ring (water-seal ring) properly. If grease sealing is used, completely fill lantern ring with grease before putting remaining rings of packing in place. The type of packing used (Figure 18.25) is less important than the manner in which packing is placed. Never use a continuous strip of packing. This type of packing wraps around and scores the shaft sleeve or is thrown out against the outer wall of the stuffing box, allowing water to leak through and score the shaft. The proper size of packing should be available in your plant's equipment files. See Figure 18.26 for illustrated steps on how to pack a pump.

Fig. 18.24 Method of packing shaft
(Source: War Department Technical Manual TM5-666)

Teflon Packing

Graphite Packing

Fig. 18.25 Packing
(Courtesy A.W. Chesteron Co.)

**Frequency
of
Service**

If a bronze shaft sleeve is not too badly scored, the shaft sleeve can be restored to service. The repair procedure consists of turning the sleeve down to a uniform diameter with a rough cut. Then spray the sleeve with stainless steel to a slightly oversized outside diameter followed by machining and polishing to bring the sleeve back to its original diameter. You will probably find that these reworked sleeves will outlast the originals.

W   7. CHECK MECHANICAL SEALS. Mechanical seals usually consist of two sub-assemblies: (1) a rotating ring assembly, and (2) a stationary assembly.

Inspect seal for leakage and excessive heat. If any part of the seal needs replacing, replace the entire seal (both sub-assemblies) with a new seal that has been provided by the manufacturer. Before installing a new seal, be sure that there are no chips or cracks on the carbide sealing surface. Keep a new mechanical seal clean at all times.

Always be sure that a mechanical seal is surrounded with water before starting and running the pump.

Q   8. INSPECT AND LUBRICATE BEARINGS. Unless otherwise specifically directed for a particular pump model, lubricate according to the procedures covered in Section 18.224, page 283. Check sleeve bearings to see that oil rings turn freely with the shaft. Repair or replace if defective.

Measure sleeve bearings and replace those worn excessively. Generally, allow clearance of 0.002 inch plus 0.001 inch for each inch or fraction of inch of shaft-journal diameter.

Q   9. CHECK OPERATING TEMPERATURE OF BEARINGS. Check bearing temperature with thermometer, not by hand. If antifriction bearings are running hot, check for overlubrication and relieve if necessary. If sleeve bearings run too hot, check for lack of lubricant. If proper lubrication does not correct condition, disassemble and inspect bearings. Check alignment of pump and motor if high temperatures continue.

S   10. CHECK ALIGNMENT OF PUMP AND MOTOR. For method of aligning pump and motor, see Paragraph 10: Couplings. If misalignment recurs frequently, inspect entire piping system. Unbolt piping at suction and discharge nozzles to see if it springs away, indicating strain on casing. Check all piping supports for soundness and effective support of load.

Vertical pumps usually have flexible shafting which permits slight angular misalignment;

however, if solid shafting is used, align exactly. If beams carrying intermediate bearings are too light or are subject to contraction or expansion, replace beams and realign intermediate bearings carefully.

S   11. INSPECT AND SERVICE PUMPS.

a. Remove rotating element of pump and inspect thoroughly for wear. Order replacement parts where necessary. Check impeller clearance between volute.

b. Remove any deposit or scaling. Clean out water-seal piping.

c. Determine pump capacity by pumping into empty tank of known size or by timing the draining of pit or sump.

$$\text{Pump Capacity, GPM} = \frac{\text{Volume, gallons}}{\text{Time, minutes}}$$

or

$$\text{Pump Capacity, } \frac{\text{liters}}{\text{sec}} = \frac{\text{Volume, liters}}{\text{Time, seconds}}$$

See Example 1 (page 292) for procedures on how to calculate pump capacity.

d. Test pump efficiency. Refer to pump manufacturer's instructions on how to collect data and perform calculations. Also see Chapter 3, Section 3.17, "Pump Testing and Evaluation," in *SMALL WATER SYSTEM OPERATION AND MAINTENANCE* in this series of manuals.

e. Measure total dynamic suction head or lift and discharge head to test pump and pipe condition. Record figures for comparison with later tests.

f. Inspect foot and check valves, paying particular attention to check valves, which can cause water hammer when pump stops. (See Paragraph 13: Check Valves also.) Foot valves are a type of check valve which are used when pumping raw water.

g. Examine wearing rings. Replace seriously worn wearing rings to improve efficiency. Check wearing ring clearances which generally should be no more than 0.003 inch per inch of wearing ring diameter.

CAUTION: To protect rings and casings, never allow pump to run dry through lack of proper priming when starting or loss of suction when operating.

A   12. DRAIN PUMP FOR LONG-TERM SHUTDOWN. When shutting down pump for a long period, open motor disconnect switch, and if so equipped, turn on the electric motor winding heaters. Shut all valves on suction, discharge, water-seal, and priming lines; drain pump completely by removing vent and drain plugs. This procedure protects pump against corrosion, sedimentation, and freezing. Inspect pump and bearings thoroughly and perform all necessary servicing. Drain

1 Remove *all* old packing. Aim packing hook at bore of the box to keep from scratching the shaft. Clean box thoroughly so the new packing won't hang up

2 Check for bent rod, grooves or shoulders. If the neck bushing clearance in bottom of box is great, use stiffer bottom ring or replace the neck bushing

3 Revolve rotary shaft. If the indicator runs out over 0.003-in., straighten shaft, or check bearings, or balance rotor. Gyrating shaft beats out packing

6 Cutting off rings while packing is wrapped around shaft will give you rings with parallel ends. This is very important if packing is to do job

7 If you cut packing while stretched out straight, the ends will be at an angle. With gap at angle, packing on either side squeezes into top of gap and ring, cannot close. This brings up the question about gap for expansion. Most packings need none. Channel-type packing with lead core may need slight gap for expansion

HOW
TO PACK
A PUMP

(*Editor's Note:* This step-by-step illustration of a basic maintenance duty was brought to our attention by Anthony J. Zigment, Director, Municipal Training Division, Department of Community Affairs.)

11 Open ring joint sidewise, especially lead-filled and metallic types. This prevents distorting molded circumference—breaking the ring opposite gap

12 Use split wooden bushing. Install first turn of packing, then force into bottom of box by tightening gland against bushing. Seat each turn this way

Cross expansion   Sectional   Diagonal

15 Always install cross-expansion packing so plies slope toward the fluid pressure from housing. Place sectional rings so slope between inside and outside ring is toward the pressure. Diagonal rings must also have slope toward the fluid pressure. Watch these details for best results when installing new packing in a box

Fig. 18.26   How to pack a pump

(Source: Water Pollution Control Association of Pennsylvania Magazine, January-February, 1976)

4 To find the right size of packing to install, measure stuffing-box bore and subtract rod diameter, divide by 2. Packing is too critical for guesswork.

5 Wind packing, needed for filling stuffing box, snugly around rod (for same size shaft held in vise) and cut through each turn while coiled, as shown. If the packing is slightly too large, never flatten with a hammer. Place each turn on a clean newspaper and then roll out with pipe as you would with a rolling pin

8 Install foil-wrapped packing so edges on inside will face direction of shaft rotation. This is a must; otherwise, thin edges flake off, reduce packing life

9 Neck bushing slides into stuffing box. Quick way to make it is to pour soft bearing metal into tin can, turn and bore for sliding fit into place

10 Swabbing new metallic packings with lubricant supplied by packing maker is OK. These include foil types, lead-core, etc. If the rod is oily, don't swab it

13 Stagger joints 180 degrees if only two rings are in stuffing box. Space at 120 degrees for three rings, or 90 degrees if four rings or more are in set

14 Install packing so lantern ring lines up with cooling-liquid opening. Also, remember that this ring moves back into box as packing is compressed. Leave space for gland to enter as shown. Tighten gland with wrench—back off finger-tight. Allow the packing to leak until it seats itself, then allow a slight operating leakage.

Hydraulic-packing pointers

First, clean stuffing box, examine ram or rod. Next, measure stuffing-box depth and packing set—find difference. Place 1/8-in. washers over gland studs as shown. Lubricate ram and packing set (if for water). If you can use them, endless rings give about 17% more wear than cut rings. Place male adapter in bottom, then carefully slide each packing turn home—don't harm lips. Stagger joints for cut rings. Measure from top of packing to top of washers, then compare with gland. Never tighten down new packing set until all air has chance to work out. As packing wears, remove one set of washers, after more wear, remove other washer.

Fig. 18.26   How to pack a pump (continued)

bearing housings and replenish with fresh oil, purge old grease and replace. When a pump is out of service, run it monthly to warm it up and to distribute lubrication so the packing will not "freeze" to the shaft. Resume periodic checks after pump is put back in service.

FORMULAS

To find the volume of a rectangle in cubic feet, multiply the length times width times depth.

Volume, cu ft = (Length, ft)(Width, ft)(Depth, ft)

To find the volume of a cylinder in cubic feet, multiply 0.785 times the diameter squared times the depth.

Volume, cu ft = (0.785)(Diameter, ft)^2(Depth, ft)

To convert a volume from cubic feet to gallons, multiply the volume in cubic feet times 7.48 gallons per cubic foot.

Volume, gal = (Volume, cu ft)(7.48 gal/cu ft)

To calculate the output or capacity of a pump in gallons per minute, divide the volume pumped in gallons by the pumping time in minutes.

$$\text{Pump Capacity, GPM} = \frac{\text{Volume Pumped, gallons}}{\text{Pumping Time, minutes}}$$

EXAMPLE 1

A pump's capacity is measured by recording the time in minutes for water to rise 3 feet in an 8-foot diameter tank. What is the pumping rate or capacity in gallons per minute when the pumping time is 9 minutes?

Known	Unknown
Diameter, ft = 8 ft	Pump Capacity, GPM
Depth, ft = 3 ft	
Time, min = 9 min	

Calculate the tank volume in cubic feet.

Volume, cu ft = (0.785)(Diameter, ft)^2(Depth, ft)

= (0.785)(8 ft)^2(3 ft)

= 151 cu ft

Convert the tank volume from cubic feet to gallons.

Volume, gal = (Volume, cu ft)(7.48 gal/cu ft)

= (151 cu ft)(7.48 gal/cu ft)

= 1,129 gallons

Calculate the pump capacity in gallons per minute.

$$\text{Pump Capacity, GPM} = \frac{\text{Volume Pumped, gal}}{\text{Pumping Time, min}}$$

$$= \frac{1,129 \text{ gal}}{9 \text{ min}}$$

$$= 125 \text{ GPM}$$

QUESTIONS

Write your answers in a notebook and then compare your answers with those on page 345.

18.23A   What is a cross connection?

18.23B   Is a slight water-seal leakage desirable when a pump is running? If so, why?

18.23C   How would you measure the capacity of a pump?

18.23D   Estimate the capacity of a pump (in GPM) if it lowers the water in a 10-foot wide by 15-foot long wet well 1.7 feet in five minutes.

18.23E   What should be done to a pump before it is shut down for a long time, and why?

Paragraph 2: Reciprocating Pumps, General

The general procedures in this paragraph apply to all reciprocating pumps described in this section.

W   1.   CHECK SHEAR PIN ADJUSTMENT. Set eccentric by placing shear pin through proper hole in eccentric flanges to give required stroke. Tighten the two $^5/_8$- or $^7/_8$-inch hexagonal nuts on connecting rods just enough to take spring out of lock washers. (See Paragraph 11: Shear Pins.) When a shear pin fails, eccentric moves toward neutral position, preventing damage to the pump. Remove cause of obstruction and insert new shear pin. Shear pins fail because of one of three common causes:

(1) Solid object lodged under piston,

(2) Clogged discharge line, and

(3) Stuck or wedged valve.

D   2.   CHECK PACKING ADJUSTMENT. Give special attention to packing adjustment. If packing is too tight, it reduces efficiency and scores piston walls. Keep packing just tight enough to keep sludge from leaking through gland. Before pump is installed or after it has been idle for a time, loosen all nuts on packing gland. Run pump with sludge suction line closed and valve covers open for a few minutes to break in the packing. Turn down gland nuts no more than necessary to prevent sludge from getting past packing. Tighten all packing nuts uniformly.

When packing gland bolts cannot be taken up farther, remove packing. Remove old packing and thoroughly clean cylinder and piston walls. Place new packing into cylinder, staggering packing-ring joints, and tamp each ring into place. Break in and adjust packing as explained above. When chevron type packing is used, tighten gland nuts only finger tight because excessive pressure ruins packing and scores plunger.

Frequency of Service

Q 3. CHECK BALL VALVES. When valve balls are so worn that diameter is $5/8$-inch (1.5-cm) smaller than original size, they may jam into guides in valve chamber. Check size of valve balls and replace if badly worn.

Q 4. CHECK VALVE-CHAMBER GASKETS. Valve-chamber gaskets on most pumps serve as a safety device and blow out under excessive pressure. Check gaskets and replace if necessary. Keep additional gaskets on hand for replacement.

A 5. CHECK ECCENTRIC ADJUSTMENT. To take up babbitt bearing, remove brass shims provided on connecting rod. After removing shims, operate pump for at least one hour and check to see that eccentric does not run hot.

D 6. NOTE UNUSUAL NOISES. Check for noticeable water hammer when pump is operating. This noise is most pronounced when pumping water or very thin sludge; it decreases or disappears when pumping heavy sludge. Eliminate noise by opening the $1/4$-inch (0.6-cm) petcock on pump body slightly; this draws in a small amount of air, keeping discharge air chamber full at all times.

D 7. CHECK CONTROL VALVE POSITIONS. Because any plunger pump may be damaged if operated against closed valves in the pipeline, especially the discharge line, make all valve setting changes with pump shut down; otherwise pumps which are installed to pump from two sources or to deliver to separate tanks at different times may be broken if all discharge line valves are closed simultaneously for a few seconds or discharge valve directly above pump is closed.

W 8. GEAR REDUCER. Check oil level by removing plug on the side of the gear case. Unit should not be in operation.

Q 9. CHANGE OIL AND CLEAN MAGNETIC DRAIN PLUG.

W 10. CONNECTING RODS. Set oilers to disperse two drops per minute.

W 11. PLUNGER CROSSHEAD. Fill plunger as required to half cover the wrist pin with oil.

D 12. PLUNGER TROUGH. Keep small quantity of oil in trough to lubricate the plunger.

M 13. MAIN SHAFT BEARING. Grease bearings monthly. Pump should be in operation when lubricating to avoid excessive pressure on seals.

14. CHECK ELECTRIC MOTOR. See Paragraph 6: Electric Motors.

Paragraph 3: Propeller Pumps, General

D 1. CHECK MOTOR CONDITION. See Paragraphs 6.1 and 6.2.

D 2. CHECK PACKING GLAND ASSEMBLY. See Paragraph 1.6.

W 3. INSPECT PUMP ASSEMBLY. See Paragraph 1.4.

W 4. LUBE LINE SHAFT AND DISCHARGE BOWL BEARING. Maintain oil in oiler at all times. Adjust feed rate to approximately four drops per minute.

W 5. LUBE SUCTION BOWL BEARING. Lube through pressure fitting. Usually three or four strokes of gun are enough.

W 6. OPERATE PUMPS ALTERNATELY. See Paragraph 1.3.

A 7. LUBE MOTOR BEARINGS. See Paragraph 6.3.

Paragraph 4: Progressive Cavity Pumps, General
(Figure 18.21, page 280).

D 1. CHECK MOTOR CONDITION. See Paragraphs 6.1 and 6.2.

D 2. CHECK PACKING GLAND ASSEMBLY. See Paragraph 1.6.

D 3. CHECK DISCHARGE PRESSURE. A higher than normal discharge pressure may indicate a line blockage or a closed valve downstream. An abnormally low discharge pressure can mean reduced rate of discharge.

S 4. INSPECT AND LUBRICATE BEARINGS — GREASE. If possible, remove bearing cover and visually inspect grease. When greasing, remove relief plug and cautiously add 5 or 6 strokes of the grease gun. Afterward, check bearing temperature with thermometer. If over 220°F (104°C), remove some grease.

S 5. LUBEFLUSH MOTOR BEARINGS. See Paragraph 6.3.

S 6. CHECK PUMP OUTPUT. Check how long it takes to fill a vessel of known volume or quantity; or check performance against a meter, if available. See Paragraph 1.11 c.

A 7. SCOPE MOTOR BEARINGS. See Paragraph 6.4.

A 8. SCOPE PUMP BEARINGS. See Paragraph 6.4.

Paragraph 5: Pump Controls

To ensure the best operation of the pump, a systematic inspection of the controls should be made at least once a week.

W 1. CHECK CONTROLS. Controls respond to the control variable.

W   2. START-UP. The unit starts when the control system makes contact, and the pump stops at the prescribed control setting.

W   3. MOTOR SPEED. The motor comes up to speed quickly and is maintained.

W   4. SPARKING. A brush-type motor does not spark profusely in starting or running.

W   5. INTERFERENCE WITH CONTROLS. Grease and dirt are not interfering with controls.

W   6. ADJUSTMENTS. Any necessary adjustments are properly completed.

QUESTIONS

Write your answers in a notebook and then compare your answers with those on page 345.

18.23F What are some of the common causes of shear pin failure in reciprocating pumps?

18.23G What may happen when water or a thin sludge is being pumped by a reciprocating pump?

18.23H What could be the causes of a higher than normal discharge pressure in a progressive cavity pump?

Paragraph 6: Electric Motors (Figure 18.27)

In order to ensure the proper and continuous function of electric motors, the items listed in this paragraph must be performed at the designated intervals. If operational checks indicate a motor is not functioning properly, these items will have to be checked to locate the problem.

D   1. CHECK MOTOR CONDITIONS.

    a. Keep motors free from dirt, dust, and moisture.

    b. Keep operating space free from articles which may obstruct air circulation.

    c. Check for excessive grease leakage from bearings.

D   2. NOTE ALL UNUSUAL CONDITIONS.

    a. Unusual noises in operation.

    b. Motor failing to start or come to speed normally, sluggish operation.

    c. Motor or bearings that feel or smell hot.

    d. Continuous or excessive sparking at commutator or brushes. Blackened commutator.

    e. Intermittent sparking at brushes.

    f. Fine dust under coupling having rubber buffers or pins.

    g. Smoke, charred insulation, or solder whiskers extending from armature.

    h. Excessive humming.

    I. Regular clicking.

    j. Rapid knocking.

    k. Brush chatter.

    l. Vibration.

    m. Hot commutator.

A   3. LUBRICATE BEARINGS (Figure 18.28). Check grease in ball bearing and relubricate when necessary.

Follow instructions in Section 18.224, "Pump Lubrication," when lubricating greased bearings.

A   4. USING A *STETHOSCOPE*,[14] CHECK BOTH BEARINGS.

    Listen for whines, gratings, or uneven noises. Listen all around the bearing and as near as possible to the bearing. Listen while the motor is being started and shut off. If unusual noises are heard, pinpoint the location.

    5. IF YOU THINK THE MOTOR is running unusually hot, check with a thermometer. Place the thermometer on the casing near the bearing, holding it there with putty or clay. Check the current on each leg to determine if the currents are balanced and within the motor nameplate limits.

A   6. *DATEOMETER*.[15] If there is a dateometer on the motor, after changing the oil in the motor, loosen the dateometer screw and set to the corresponding year.

QUESTIONS

Write your answers in a notebook and then compare your answers with those on page 345.

18.23I What are the major items you would include when checking an electric motor?

18.23J What is the purpose of a stethoscope?

Paragraph 7: Belt Drives

    1. GENERAL. Maintaining a proper tension and alignment of belt drives ensures long life of belts and sheaves. Incorrect alignment causes poor operation and excessive belt wear. Inadequate tension reduces the belt grip, causes high belt loads, snapping, and unusual wear.

---

[14] *Stethoscope. An instrument used to magnify sounds and convey them to the ear.*

[15] *Dateometer (day-TOM-ut-ter). A small calendar disc attached to motors and equipment to indicate the year in which the last maintenance service was performed.*

DRIP PROOF

ITEM NO.	PART NAME
1	Wound Stator w/ Frame
2	Rotor Assembly
3	Rotor Core
4	Shaft
5	Bracket
6	Bearing Cap
7	Bearings
8	Seal, Labyrinth
9	Thru Bolts/Caps
10	Seal, Lead Wire
11	Terminal Box
12	Terminal Box Cover
13	Fan
14	Deflector
15	Lifting Lug

TOTALLY ENCLOSED FAN COOLED

ITEM NO.	PART NAME
1	Wound Stator w/ Frame
2	Rotor Assembly
3	Rotor Core
4	Shaft
5	Brackets
6	Bearings
7	Seal, Labyrinth
8	Thru Bolts/Caps
9	Seal, Lead Wire
10	Terminal Box
11	Terminal Box Cover
12	Fan, Inside
13	Fan, Outside
14	Fan Grill
15	Fan Cover
16	Fan Cover Bolts
17	Lifting Lug

Fig. 18.27 Typical motors
(Courtesy of Sterling Power Systems, Inc.)

ELECTRIC MOTOR

MOTOR LUBRICATION

1　FRONT BEARING BRACKET
2　FRONT AIR DEFLECTOR
3　FAN
4　ROTOR
5　FRONT BEARING
6　END COVER
7　STATOR

8　SCREENS
9　CONDUIT BOX
10　BACK AIR DEFLECTOR
11　BACK BEARING
12　BACK BEARING BRACKET
13　OIL LUBRICATION CAP

Fig. 18.28　Electric motor lubrication

a. Cleaning belts. Keep belts and sheaves clean and free of oil, which causes belts to deteriorate. To remove oil, take belts off sheaves and wipe belts and sheaves with a rag moistened in a non-oil base solvent. Carbon tetrachloride is *NOT* recommended because exposure to its fumes has many toxic effects on humans. Carbon tetrachloride also is absorbed into the skin on contact and its effects become stronger with each contact.

b. Installing belts. Before installing belts, replace worn or damaged sheaves, then slack off on adjustments. Do not try to force belts into position. Never use a screwdriver or similar lever to get belts onto sheaves. After belts are installed, adjust tension; recheck tension after eight hours of operation. (See Table 18.3.)

c. Replacing belts. Replace belts as soon as they become frayed, worn, or cracked. *NEVER REPLACE ONLY ONE V-BELT ON A MULTIPLE DRIVE.* Replace the complete set with a set of matched belts, which can be obtained from any supplier. All belts in a matched set are machine-checked to ensure equal size and tension.

d. Storing spare belts. Store spare belts in a cool, dark place. Tag all belts in storage to identify them with the equipment on which they can be used.

2. V-BELTS. A properly adjusted V-belt has a slight bow in the slack side when running; when idle it has an alive springiness when thumped with the hand. An improperly tightened belt feels dead when thumped.

If the slack side of the drive is less than 45° from the horizontal, vertical sag at the center of the span may be adjusted in accordance with Table 18.3 below:

TABLE 18.3 HORIZONTAL BELT TENSION

Span (inches)		10	20	50	100	150	200
Vertical Sag (inches)	From	.01	.03	.20	.80	1.80	3.30
	To	.03	.09	.58	2.30	4.90	8.60
Span (millimeters)		250	500	1,250	2,500	3,750	5,000
Vertical Sag (millimeters)	From	0.25	0.75	5.00	20.0	45.0	82.5
	To	0.75	2.25	14.50	57.5	122.5	215.0

M   a. Check tension. If tightening belt to proper tension does not correct slipping, check for overload, oil on belts, or other possible causes. Never use belt dressing to stop belt slippage. Rubber wearings near the drive are a sign of improper tension, incorrect alignment, or damaged sheaves.

M   b. Check sheave (pulley) alignment. Lay a long straightedge or string across outside faces of pulley, and allow for differences in dimensions from centerlines of grooves to outside faces of the pulleys being aligned. Be very careful in aligning drives with more than one V-belt on a sheave, as misalignment can cause unequal tension.

Paragraph 8: Chain Drives

1. GENERAL. Chain drives may be designated for slow, medium, or high speeds.

a. Slow-speed drives. Because slow-speed drives are usually enclosed, adequate lubrication is difficult. Heavy oil applied to the outside of the chain seldom reaches the working parts; in addition, the oil catches dirt and grit and becomes abrasive. For lubricating and cleaning methods, see 5 and 6 below.

b. Medium- and high-speed drives. Medium-speed drives should be continuously lubricated with a device similar to a sight-feed oiler. High-speed drives should be completely enclosed in an oil-tight case and the oil maintained at proper level.

D   2. CHECK OPERATION. Check general operating condition during regular tours of duty.

Q   3. CHECK CHAIN SLACK. The correct amount of slack is essential to proper operation of chain drives. Unlike other belts, chain belts should not be tight around the sprocket; when chains are tight, working parts carry a much heavier load than necessary. Too much slack is also harmful; on long centers particularly, too much slack causes vibrations and chain whip, reducing life of both chain and sprocket. A properly installed chain has a slight sag or looseness on the return run.

S   4. CHECK ALIGNMENT. If sprockets are not in line or if shafts are not parallel, excessive sprocket and chain wear and early chain failure result. Wear on inside of chain, side walls, and sides of sprocket teeth are signs of misalignment. To check alignment, remove chain and place a straightedge against sides of sprocket teeth.

S   5. CLEAN. On enclosed types, flush chain and enclosure with a petroleum solvent (kerosene). On exposed types, remove chain and soak and wash it in solvent. Clean sprockets, install chain, and adjust tension.

S   6. CHECK LUBRICATION. Soak exposed-type chains in oil to restore lubricating film. Remove excess lubricant by hanging chains up to drain.

Do not lubricate underwater chains which operate in contact with considerable grit. If water is clean, lubricate by applying waterproof grease with brush while chain is running.

**Frequency
of
Service**

Do not lubricate chains on elevators or on conveyors of feeders which handle dirty or gritty materials. Dust and grit combine with lubricants to form a cutting compound which reduces chain life.

S   7. CHANGE OIL. On enclosed types only, drain oil and refill case to proper level.

S   8. INSPECT. Note and correct abnormal conditions before serious damage results. Do not put a new chain on worn sprockets. Always replace worn sprockets when replacing a chain because out-of-pitch sprockets cause as much chain wear in a few hours as years of normal operation.

9. TROUBLESHOOTING. Some common symptoms of improper chain drive operation and their remedies follow:

a. Excessive noise. Correct alignment, if misaligned. Adjust centers for proper chain slack. Lubricate in accordance with aforementioned methods. Be sure all bolts are tight. If chain or sprockets are worn, reverse or renew if necessary.

b. Wear on chain, side walls, and sides of teeth. Remove chain and correct alignment.

c. Chain climbs sprockets. Check for poorly fitting sprockets and replace if necessary. Make sure tightener is installed on drive chain.

d. Broken pins and rollers. Check for chain speed which may be too high for the pitch, and substitute chain and sprockets with shorter pitch if necessary. Breakage also may be caused by shock loads.

e. Chain clings to sprockets. Check for incorrect or worn sprockets or heavy, tacky lubricants. Replace sprockets or lubricants if necessary.

f. Chain whip. Check for too-long centers or high, pulsating loads and correct cause.

g. Chains get stiff. Check for misalignment, improper lubrication, or excessive overloads. Make necessary corrections or adjustments.

Paragraph 9: Variable Speed Belt Drives (Figure 18.29)

D   1. CLEAN DISCS. Remove grease, acid, and water from disc faces.

D   2. CHECK SPEED-CHANGE MECHANISM. Shift drive through entire speed range to make sure shafts and bearings are lubricated and discs move freely in lateral direction on shafts.

W   3. CHECK V-BELT. Make sure it runs level and true. If one side rides high, a disc is sticking on shaft because of insufficient lubrication or

wrong lubricant. In this case, stop the drive at once, remove V-belt, and clean disc hub and shaft thoroughly with petroleum solvent until disc moves freely. Relubricate with soft ball-bearing grease and replace V-belt in opposite direction from that in which it formerly ran.

M   If drive is not operated for 30 days or more, shift unit to minimum speed position, placing spring on variable-speed shaft at minimum tension and relieving belt of excessive pressure.

4. LUBRICATE DRIVE. Make sure to apply lubricant at all the six force-feed lubrication fittings (Figure 18.29: A, B, D, E, G, and H) and the one cup-type fitting (C).

NOTE: If the drive is used with a reducer, fitting E is not provided.

W   a. Once every ten days to two weeks, use two or three strokes of a grease gun through fittings A and B at ends of shifting screw and variable-speed shaft, respectively, to lubricate bearings of movable discs. Then, with unit running, shift drive from one extreme speed position to the other to ensure thorough distribution of lubricant over disc-hub bearings.

Q   b. Add two or three shots of grease through fittings D and E to lubricate frame bearing on variable-speed shaft.

Q   c. Every 90 days, add two or three cupfuls of grease to Cup C which lubricates thrust bearing on constant-speed shaft.

Q   d. Every 90 days, use two or three strokes of grease gun through fittings G and H to lubricate motor frame bearings.

CAUTION: Be sure to follow manufacturer's recommendation on type of grease. After lubricating, wipe excessive grease from sheaves and belt.

QUESTIONS

Write your answers in a notebook and then compare your answers with those on pages 345 and 346.

18.23K   How can you tell if a belt on belt-drive equipment has proper tension and alignment?

18.23L   Why should worn sprockets be replaced when replacing a chain in a chain drive unit?

Paragraph 10: Couplings

1. GENERAL. Unless couplings between the driving and driven elements of a pump or any other piece of equipment are kept in proper alignment, breaking and excessive wear results in either or both the driven machinery and the driver. Burned-out bearings, sprung or broken shaft, and excessively worn or ruined gears are some of the damages caused by misalignment. To prevent outages and the expense of installing replacement parts, check the alignment of all equipment before damage occurs.

MOTOR
REDUCER

MOTOR

V-BELT

DISCS

SPEED-
CHANGE
MECHANISM

NOTE: A, B, D, E, G, and H are force-feed lubrication fittings.
C is a cup-type lubrication fitting.

Fig. 18.29   Reeves varidrive
(Source: War Department Technical Manual TM5-666)

**Frequency
of
Service**

a. Improper original installation of the equipment may not necessarily be the cause of the trouble. Settling of foundations, heavy floor loadings, warping of bases, excessive bearing wear, and many other factors cause misalignment. A rigid base is not always security against misalignment. The base may have been mounted off level, which could cause it to warp.

b. Flexible couplings permit easy assembly of equipment, but they must be aligned as exactly as flanged couplings if maintenance and repair are to be kept to a minimum. Rubber-bushed types cannot function properly if the bolts cannot move in their bushings.

S   2. CHECK COUPLING ALIGNMENT (straightedge method). Excessive bearing and motor temperatures caused by overload, noticeable vibration, or unusual noises may all be warnings of misalignment. Realign when

necessary (Figure 18.30) using a straightedge and thickness gage or wedge. To ensure satisfactory operation, level up to within 0.005 inch (0.13 mm) as follows:

a. Remove coupling pins.

b. Rigidly tighten driven equipment; slightly tighten bolts holding drive.

c. To correct horizontal and vertical misalignment, shift or shim drive to bring coupling halves into position so no light can be seen under a straightedge laid across them. Place straightedge in four positions, holding a light in back of straightedge to help ensure accuracy.

d. Check for angular misalignment with a thickness or feeler gage inserted at four places to make certain space between coupling halves is equal.

e. If proper alignment has been secured, coupling pins can be put in place easily using only finger pressure. Never hammer pins into place.

f. If equipment is still out of alignment, repeat the procedure.

Fig. 18.30   Testing alignment, straightedge
(Source: Unknown)

S   3. CHECK COUPLING ALIGNMENT (dial indicator method). Dial indicators also are used to measure coupling alignment. This method produces better results than the straightedge method. The dial indicates very small movements or distances which are measured in mils (one mil equals 1/1,000 of an inch). The indicator consists of a dial with a graduated face (with "plus" and "minus" readings), a pedestal, and a rigid indicator bar (or "fixture") as shown in Figure 18.31.

The dial indicator is attached to one coupling via the fixture and adjusted to the zero position or reading. When the shaft of the machine is rotated, misalignment will cause the pedestal to compress (a "plus" reading), or extend (a "minus" reading). Literature provided by the manufacturer of machinery usually will indicate maximum allowable tolerances or movement.

Carefully study the manufacturer's literature provided with your dial indicator before attempting to use the device.

A   4. CHANGE OIL IN FAST COUPLINGS. Drain out old oil and add oil to proper level. Correct quantity is given on instruction card supplied with each coupling.

Paragraph 11: Shear Pins

Some water treatment units use shear pins as protective devices to prevent damage in case of sudden overloads. To serve this purpose, these devices must be in operational condition at all times. Under some operating conditions, shearing surfaces of a shear pin device may freeze together so solidly that an overload fails to break them.

Manufacturers' drawings for particular installations usually specify shear pin material and size. If this information is not available, obtain the information from the manufacturer, giving the model, serial number, and load conditions of unit. When necessary to determine shear pin size, select the lowest strength that does not break under the unit's usual loads. When proper size is determined, never use a pin of greater strength, such as a bolt or a nail.

If necked pins are used, be sure the necked-down portion is properly positioned with respect to shearing surfaces. When a shear pin breaks, determine and remedy the cause of failure before inserting new pin and starting drive in operation.

M   1. GREASE SHEARING SURFACES.

Q   2. REMOVE SHEAR PIN. Operate motor for a short time to smooth out any corroded spots.

A   3. CHECK SPARE INVENTORY. Make sure an adequate supply is on hand, properly identified and with record of proper pin size, necked diameter, and longitudinal dimensions.

QUESTIONS

Write your answers in a notebook and then compare your answers with those on page 346.

18.23M What factors could cause couplings to become out of alignment?

18.23N What is the purpose of shear pins?

DIAL INDICATORS

DIAL

PEDESTAL

25 MILS

25 MILS

REVERSE DIALING PARALLEL MISALIGNMENT

INDICATOR BAR (FIXTURE)

20 MILS

20 MILS

ILLUSTRATION INDICATES
A TOTAL OFFSET OF
40 MILS (20 MILS + 20 MILS)

Fig. 18.31   Use of a dial indicator
(Permission of DYMAC, a Division of Spectral Dynamics Corporation)

18.24   Pump Operation

18.240   Starting a New Pump

The initial start-up work described in this paragraph should be done by a competent and trained person, such as a manufacturer's representative, consulting engineer, or an experienced operator. The operator can learn a lot about pumps and motors by accompanying and helping a competent person put new equipment into operation.

Before starting a pump, lubricate it according to the lubrication instructions. Turn the shaft by hand to see that it rotates freely. Then check to see that the shafts of the pump and motor are aligned and the flexible coupling adjusted. (Refer to Paragraph 10: Couplings, page 298; also see Section 18.23, "Pump Maintenance," page 285.) If the unit is belt driven, sheave (pulley) alignment and belt adjustment should be checked. (Refer to Paragraph 7: Belt Drives.) Check the electric voltage with the motor characteristics and inspect the

wiring. See that thermal overload units in the starter are set properly. Turn on the motor just long enough to see that it turns the pump in the direction indicated by the rotational arrows marked on the pump. If separate water seal units or vacuum primer systems are used, these should be started. Finally, make sure lines are open. Sometimes there is an exception (see following paragraph) in the case of the discharge valve.

A pump should not be run without first having been primed. To prime a pump, the pump must be completely filled with water. In some cases, automatic primers are provided. If they are not, it is necessary to vent the casing. Most pumps are provided with a valve to accomplish this. Allow the trapped air to escape until water flows from the vent; then replace the vent cap. In the case of suction lift applications, the pump must be filled with water unless a self-primer is provided. In nearly every case, you may start a pump with the discharge valve open. Exceptions to this, however, are where water hammer or pressure surges might result, or where the motor does not have sufficient margin of safety or power. Sometimes there are no check valves in the discharge line. In this case (with the exception of positive displacement pumps) it is necessary to start the pump and then open the discharge lines. Where there are common discharge headers, it is essential to start the pump and then open the discharge valve. A positive displacement pump (reciprocating or piston types) should never be operated against a closed discharge line.

After starting the pump, again check to see that the direction of rotation is correct. Packing gland boxes (stuffing boxes) should be observed for slight leakage (approximately 60 drops per minute) as described in Paragraph 1: Pumps, General. Check to see that the bearings do not overheat from over- or underlubrication. The flexible coupling should not be noisy; if it is, the noise may be caused by misalignment or improper

clearance or adjustment. Check to be sure pump anchorage is tight. Compare delivered pump flows and pressures with pump performance curves. If pump delivery falls below performance curves, look for obstructions in the pipelines and inspect piping for leaks.

18.241   Pump Shutdown

When shutting down a pump for a long period, the motor disconnect switch should be opened, locked out, and tagged with reason for tag noted. If the electric motor is equipped with winding heaters, check to be sure they are turned on. This helps to prevent condensation from forming which can weaken the insulation on the windings. All valves on the suction, discharge, and water-seal lines should be shut tightly. Completely drain the pump by removing the vent and drain plugs.

Inspect the pump and bearings thoroughly so that all necessary servicing may be done during the inactive period. Drain the bearing housing and then add fresh lubricant. Follow any additional manufacturer's recommendations.

18.242   Pump-Driving Equipment

Driving equipment used to operate pumps includes electric motors and internal combustion engines. In rare instances, pumps are driven with steam turbines, steam engines, air and hydraulic motors.

In all except the large installations, electric motors are used almost exclusively, with synchronous and induction types being the most commonly used. Synchronous motors operate at constant speeds and are used chiefly in large sizes. Three-phase, squirrel-cage induction motors are most often used in water treatment plants. These motors require little attention and, under average operating conditions, the factory lubrication of the bearing will last approximately one year. (Check with the manufacturer for average number of operating hours for bearings.) When lubricating motors, remember that too much grease may cause bearing trouble or damage the winding.

Clean and dry all electrical contacts. Inspect for loose electrical contacts. Make sure that hold-down bolts on motors are secure. Check voltage while the motor is starting and running. Examine bearings and couplings.

18.243   Electrical Controls

A variety of electrical equipment is used to control the operation of pumps or to protect electric motors. If starters, disconnect switches, and cutouts are used, they should be installed in accordance with the local regulations (city and/or county codes) regarding this equipment. In the case of larger motors, the power company often requires starters that do not overload the power lines.

The electrode-type, bubbler-type, and diaphragm-type water level control systems are all similar in effect to the float-switch system. Scum is a problem with most water-level controls that operate pumps, and it must be removed on a regular basis.

QUESTIONS

Write your answers in a notebook and then compare your answers with those on page 346.

18.24A   Where would you find out how to lubricate a pump?

18.24B   What problems can develop if too much grease is used in lubricating a motor?

18.244 *Operating Troubles*

The following list of operating troubles includes most of the causes of pump failure or reduced operating efficiency. The remedy or cure is either obvious or may be identified from the description of the cause.

SYMPTOM A — PUMP WILL NOT START

CAUSES:

1. Blown fuses or tripped circuit breakers due to:

    A. Rating of fuses or circuit breakers not correct,

    B. Switch (breakers) contacts corroded or shorted,

    C. Terminal connections loose or broken somewhere in the circuit,

    D. Automatic control mechanism not functioning properly,

    E. Motor shorted or burned out,

    F. Wiring hookup or service not correct,

    G. Switches not set for operation,

    H. Contacts of the control relays dirty and arcing,

    I. Fuses or thermal units too warm,

    J. Wiring short-circuited, and

    K. Shaft binding or sticking due to rubbing impeller, tight packing glands, or clogging of pump.

2. Loose connections, fuse, or thermal unit

SYMPTOM B — REDUCED RATE OF DISCHARGE

CAUSES:

1. Pump not primed
2. Air in the water
3. Speed of motor too low
4. Improper wiring
5. Defective motor
6. Discharge head too high
7. Suction lift greater than anticipated
8. Impeller clogged
9. Discharge line clogged
10. Pump rotating in wrong direction
11. Air leaks in suction line or packing box
12. Inlet to suction line too high, permitting air to enter
13. Valves partially or entirely closed
14. Check valves stuck or clogged
15. Incorrect impeller adjustment
16. Impeller damaged or worn
17. Packing worn or defective
18. Impeller turning on shaft because of broken key
19. Flexible coupling broken
20. Loss of suction during pumping may be caused by leaky suction line, ineffective water or grease seal
21. Belts slipping
22. Worn wearing ring

SYMPTOM C — HIGH POWER REQUIREMENTS

CAUSES:

1. Speed of rotation too high
2. Operating heads lower than rating for which pump was designed, resulting in excess pumping rates
3. Sheaves on belt drive misaligned or maladjusted
4. Pump shaft bent
5. Rotating elements binding
6. Packing too tight
7. Wearing rings worn or binding
8. Impeller rubbing

SYMPTOM D — NOISY PUMP

CAUSES:

1. Pump not completely primed
2. Inlet clogged
3. Inlet not submerged
4. Pump not lubricated properly
5. Worn impellers
6. Strain on pumps caused by unsupported piping fastened to the pump
7. Foundation insecure
8. Mechanical defects in pump
9. Misalignment of motor and pump where connected by flexible shaft
10. Rocks in the impeller
11. Cavitation

QUESTIONS

Write your answers in a notebook and then compare your answers with those on page 346.

18.24C What items would you check if a pump will not start?

18.24D How would you attempt to increase the discharge from a pump if the flow rate is lower than expected?

18.245 Starting and Stopping Pumps

The operator must determine what treatment processes will be affected by either starting or stopping a pump. The pump discharge point must be known and valves either opened or closed to direct flows as desired by the operator when a pump is started or stopped.

18.2450 CENTRIFUGAL PUMPS

Basic rules for the operation of centrifugal pumps include the following items.

1. Do not operate the pump when safety guards are not installed over or around moving parts.

2. Do not start a pump that has been locked or tagged out for maintenance or repairs. An operator working on the pump could be injured or the equipment could be damaged.

3. Never run a centrifugal pump when the impeller is dry. Always be sure the pump is primed.

4. Never attempt to start a centrifugal pump whose impeller or shaft is spinning backward.

5. Do not operate a centrifugal pump that is vibrating excessively after start-up. Shut unit down and isolate pump from system by closing the pump suction and discharge valves. Look for a blockage in the suction line and the pump impeller.

There are several situations in which it may be necessary to start a *CENTRIFUGAL* pump against a *CLOSED* discharge valve. Once the pump is primed, running, and indicating a discharge pressure, slowly open the pump discharge valve until the pump is fully on line. This procedure is used with treatment processes or piping systems with vacuums or pressures that cannot be dropped or allowed to fluctuate greatly while an alternate pump is put on the line.

Most centrifugal pumps used in water treatment plants are designed so that they can be easily started even if they haven't been primed. This is accomplished with a positive static suction head or a low suction lift. On most of these arrangements, the pump will not require priming as long as the pump and the piping system do not leak. Leaks would allow the water to drain out of the pump volute. When pumps in water systems lose their prime, the cause is often a faulty check valve on the pump discharge line. When the pump stops, the discharge check valve will not seal (close) properly. Water previously pumped then flows back through the check valve and through the pump. The pump is drained and has lost its prime.

About ninety-five percent of the time, the centrifugal pumps in water treatment plants are ready to operate with suction and discharge valves open and seal water turned on. When the automatic start or stop command is received by the pump from the controller, the pump is ready to respond properly.

When the pumping equipment must be serviced, take it off the line by locking and tagging out the pump controls until all service work is completed.

QUESTIONS

Write your answers in a notebook and then compare your answers with those on page 346.

18.24E Why should a pump that has been locked or tagged out for maintenance or repairs not be started?

18.24F Under what conditions might a centrifugal pump be started against a closed discharge valve?

STOPPING PROCEDURES

This section contains a typical sequence of procedures to follow to stop a centrifugal pump. Exact stopping procedures for any pumping system depend upon the condition of the discharge system. The sudden stoppage of a pump could cause severe *WATER HAMMER*[16] problems in the piping system.

1. Inspect process system affected by pump, start alternate pump if required, and notify supervisor or log action.

2. Before stopping an operating pump, check its operation. This will give an indication of any developing problems, required adjustments, or problem conditions of the unit. This procedure only requires a few minutes. Items to be inspected include:

   a. Pump packing gland.

      (1) Seal water pressure

      (2) Seal leakage (too much, sufficient, or too little leakage)

      (3) Seal leakage drain flowing clear

      (4) Mechanical seal leakage (if equipped)

   b. Pump operating pressures.

      (1) Pump suction (pressure, vacuum)

         A higher vacuum than normal may indicate a partially plugged or restricted suction line. A lower vacuum may indicate a higher suction water level or a worn pump impeller or wearing rings.

---

[16] *Water Hammer.   The sound like someone hammering on a pipe that occurs when a valve is opened or closed very rapidly. When a valve position is changed quickly, the water pressure in a pipe will increase and decrease back and forth very quickly. This rise and fall in pressures can cause serious damage to the system.*

(2) Pump discharge pressure

System pressure is indicated by the pump discharge pressure. Lower than normal discharge pressures can be caused by:

(a) Worn impeller or wearing rings in the pump;

(b) A different point of discharge can change discharge pressure conditions; and

(c) A broken discharge pipe can change the discharge head.

NOTE: To determine the maximum head a centrifugal pump can develop, slowly close the discharge valve at the pump. Read the pressure gage between the pump and the discharge valve when the valve is fully closed. This is the maximum pressure the pump is capable of developing. Do not operate the pump longer than a few minutes with the discharge valve closed completely because the energy from the pump is converted to heat and water in the pump can become hot enough to damage the pump.

c. Motor temperature and pump bearing temperature.

If motor or bearings are too hot to touch, further checking is necessary to determine if a problem has developed or if the temperature is normal. High temperatures may be measured with a thermometer.

d. Unusual noises, vibrations, or conditions about the equipment.

If any of the above items indicate a change from the pump's previous operating condition, additional service or maintenance may be required during shutdown.

3. Actuate stop switch for pump motor and lock out switch. If possible use switch next to equipment so that you may observe the equipment stop. Observe the following items:

a. Check valve closes and seats.

Valve should not slam shut, or discharge piping will jump or move in their supports. There should not be any leakage around the check valve shaft. If check valve is operated automatically, it should close smoothly and firmly to the fully closed position.

NOTE: If the pump is not equipped with a check valve, close discharge valve before stopping pump.

b. Motor and pump should wind down slowly and not make sudden stops or noises during shutdown.

c. After equipment has completely stopped, pump shaft and motor should not start back-spinning. If back-spinning is observed in a pump with a check valve or foot valve, close the pump discharge valve SLOWLY! Be extra careful if there is a plug valve on a line with a high head because when the discharge valve is partway

closed, the plug valve could slam closed and damage the pump or piping.

4. Go to power control panel containing the pump motor starters just shut down and OPEN motor breaker switch, lock out, and tag.

5. Return to pump and close:

a. Discharge valve,

b. Suction valve,

c. Seal water supply valve, and

d. Pump volute bleed line (if so equipped).

6. If required, close and open appropriate valves along piping system through which pump was discharging.

STARTING PROCEDURES

This section contains a typical sequence of procedures to follow to start a centrifugal pump.

1. Check motor control panel for lock and tags. Examine tags to be sure that NO item is preventing start-up of equipment.

2. Inspect equipment.

a. Be sure stop switch is locked out at equipment location.

b. Guards over moving parts must be in place.

c. Cleanout on pump volute and drain plugs should be installed and secure.

d. Valves should be in closed position.

e. Pump shaft must rotate freely.

f. Pump motor should be clean and air vents clear.

g. Pump, motor, and auxiliary equipment lubricant levels must be at proper elevations.

h. Determine if any special considerations or precautions are to be taken during start-up.

3. Follow pump discharge piping route. Be sure all valves are in the proper position and that the pump flow will discharge where intended.

4. Return to motor control panel.

a. Remove tag.

b. Remove padlock.

c. Close motor main breaker.

d. Place selector switch to manual (if you have automatic equipment).

5. Return to pump equipment.

a. Open seal water supply line to packing gland. Be sure seal water supply pressure is adequate.

b. Open pump suction valve slowly.

c. Bleed air out of top of pump volute in order to prime pump. Some pumps are equipped with air relief valves or bleed lines back to the wet well for this purpose.

d. When pump is primed, slowly open pump discharge valve and recheck prime of pump. Be sure no air is escaping from volute.

e. Unlock stop switch and actuate start switch. Pump should start.

6. Inspect equipment.

   a. Motor should come up to speed promptly. If ammeter is available, test for excessive draw of power (amps) during start-up and normal operation. Most three-phase induction motors used in water treatment plants will draw 5 to 7 times their normal running current during the brief period when they are coming up to speed.

   b. No unusual noise or vibrations should be observed during start-up.

   c. Check valve should be open and no chatter or pulsation should be observed.

   d. Pump suction and discharge pressure readings should be within normal operating range for this pump.

   e. Packing gland leakage should be normal.

   f. If a flowmeter is on the pump discharge, record pump output.

7. If the unit is operating properly, return to the motor control panel and place the motor mode of operation selector in the proper operating position (MANUAL-AUTO-OFF).

8. The pump and auxiliary equipment should be inspected routinely after the pump has been placed back into service.

QUESTIONS

Write your answers in a notebook and then compare your answers with those on page 346.

18.24G What should be done before stopping an operating pump?

18.24H What could cause a pump shaft or motor to spin backward?

18.24I Why should the position (open or closed) of all valves be checked before starting a pump?

18.2451 *POSITIVE DISPLACEMENT PUMPS*

Steps for starting and stopping positive displacement pumps are outlined in this section. There are two basic differences in the operation of positive displacement pumps as compared with centrifugal pumps. Centrifugal pumps (due to their design) will permit an operator error, but a positive displacement pump will not and someone will have to pay for correcting the damages.

Important rules for operating positive displacement pumps include:

1. NEVER, NEVER OPERATE A POSITIVE DISPLACEMENT PUMP AGAINST A CLOSED VALVE, ESPECIALLY A DISCHARGE VALVE.

Excessive pressure could rupture the equipment and possibly seriously injure or kill someone nearby.

2. Positive displacement pumps are used to pump solids (sludge) and meter chemicals. Certain precautions must be taken to prevent injury or damage. If the valves on both ends of a sludge line are closed tightly, the line becomes a closed vessel. Gas from decomposition of the sludge can build up and rupture pipes or valves.

3. Positive displacement pumps also are used to meter and pump chemicals. Care must be exercised to avoid venting chemicals to the atmosphere.

4. Never operate a positive displacement pump when it is dry or empty, especially the progressive-cavity types that use rubber stators. A small amount of liquid is needed for lubrication in the pump cavity between the rotor and the stator.

In addition to *NEVER* closing a discharge valve on an operating positive displacement pump, the only other difference (when compared with a centrifugal pump) may be that the positive displacement pump system may or may not have a check valve in the discharge piping after the pump. Installation of a check valve depends upon the designer and the material being pumped.

Other than the specific differences mentioned in this section, the starting and stopping procedures for positive displacement pumps are similar to the procedures for centrifugal pumps.

QUESTIONS

Write your answers in a notebook and then compare your answers with those on page 346.

18.24J What is the most important rule regarding the operation of positive displacement pumps?

18.24K What could happen if a positive displacement pump is started against a closed discharge valve?

18.24L Why should both ends of a sludge line never be closed tight at the same time?

End of Lesson 3 of 5 Lessons on MAINTENANCE

Please answer the discussion and review questions next.

DISCUSSION AND REVIEW QUESTIONS

Chapter 18. MAINTENANCE

(Lesson 3 of 5 Lessons)

Write the answers to these questions in your notebook before continuing. The question numbering continues from Lesson 2.

18. When two or more pumps of the same size are installed, why should they be operated alternately?

19. What should be checked if pump bearings are running hot?

20. What happens when the packing is too tight on a reciprocating pump?

21. Why should adjustments in control valves for reciprocating pumps be made when the pump is shut down?

22. Why would you use a stethoscope to check an electric motor?

23. How would you determine if a motor is running unusually hot?

24. How would you clean belts on a belt drive?

25. Why should you never replace only one belt on a multiple-drive unit?

26. What do rubber wearings near a belt drive indicate?

27. How can you determine if a chain in a chain-drive unit has the proper slack?

28. What happens when couplings are not in proper alignment?

29. How can you determine if a new pump will turn in the direction intended?

30. How can you determine if a new pump is delivering design flows and pressures?

31. When shutting down a pump for a long period, what precautions should be taken with the motor disconnect switch?

CHAPTER 18. MAINTENANCE

(Lesson 4 of 5 Lessons)

18.25 Compressors

Compressors (Figure 18.32) are commonly used in the operation and maintenance of water treatment plants. They are used to activate and control pump control systems (bubblers), valve operators, and water pressure systems. They are also used to operate portable pneumatic tools, such as jackhammers, compactors, air drills, sandblasters, tapping machines, and air pumps.

A compressor is a device used to increase the pressure of air or gas. It can be of a very simple diaphragm or bellows type such as are found in aquarium pumps, or an extremely complex rotary, piston, or sliding vane type compressor. A compressor usually has a suction pipe with a filter and a discharge pipe which connects to an air receiver or storage tank. The compressed air or gas is then used from the air receiver.

Due to the complexity of compressors, the water treatment plant operator usually will not be repairing them. You will, however, be required to maintain these compressors. With proper maintenance a compressor should give years of trouble-free service.

The first step for compressor maintenance, and this pertains to any mechanical equipment, is to get the manufacturer's instruction book and read it completely. Each compressor is different and the particular manufacturer will provide its recommended maintenance schedules and procedures. Some of the maintenance procedures are discussed in the following paragraphs.

1. Inspect the suction filter of the compressor regularly. The frequency of cleaning depends upon the use of the compressor and the atmosphere around it. Under normal operations the filter should be inspected at least monthly

Fig. 18.32   Two-stage piston compressor
(Courtesy Worthington Corporation)

and cleaned or replaced every three to six months. Inspect and replace the filter more frequently in areas with excavation and dust. When breaking up concrete, inspect the filters daily.

There are several types of filters, such as paper, cloth, wire screen, oil bath, and others. The impregnated paper filters must be replaced when dirty. The cloth-type filters can be washed with soap and water, dried and reinstalled. If a cloth-type filter is used, it is recommended that a spare be kept so one can be cleaned while the other is being used. The wire mesh and oil-bath type filters can be cleaned with a standard solvent, reoiled or oil bath filled and used again. Never operate a compressor without the suction filter because dirt and foreign materials will collect on the rotors, pistons, or blades and cause excessive wear.

2. Lubrication. Improper or lack of lubrication is probably the biggest cause of compressor failures. Most compressors require oiling of the bearings. They can have crankcase reservoirs, oil cups, grease fittings, a pressure system or separate pump. Whatever type, it must be inspected daily. Examine the reservoir dipstick or sight glass. Make sure that drip-feed oilers are dripping at the proper rate, force-feed oilers have the proper pressure, and grease fittings

are greased at the proper interval. Compressors use a certain amount of oil in their operation and special attention is needed to keep the reservoirs full. Care also must be used to not overfill the crankcase. On some compressors it is possible for the oil to get into the compression side and lock up the compressor, or damage it. Remember!

A LIQUID CANNOT BE COMPRESSED.

When air or gas is compressed, it gives off heat and the compressor becomes very hot. This tends to break down oil faster, so most compressor manufacturers have special oils recommended for their particular compressor. Also, due to the heat and contamination, it is necessary to change oil quite frequently. Compressor oil should be changed at least every three months, unless the manufacturer states differently. If there are filters in the oil system, these also should be changed.

3. Cylinder or casing fins should be cleaned weekly with compressed air or vacuumed off. The fins must be clean to ensure proper cooling of the compressor.

4. Unloader. Many compressors have unloaders that allow the compressor to start under a no-load condition. These can be inspected by observing the compressor. When the compressor starts, it should come up to speed and the unloader will change, starting the compression cycle. This can usually be heard by a change in sound. When it stops, you can hear a small pop and hear the air bleed off the cylinders. If the unloader is not working properly, the compressor will stall when starting, not start, or if belt-driven, burn off the belts.

5. Test the safety valves weekly. The pop-off or safety valves are located on the air receiver or storage tank. They prevent the pressure from building up above a specified pressure by opening and venting to the atmosphere. In gas compressors, they vent to the suction side of the compressor. Some compressors have high pressure cut-off switches, low oil pressure switches, and high temperature cutoff switches. These switches have preset cutoff settings and must not be changed without proper authorization. If for any reason any of the safety switches are not functioning properly, the problem must be corrected before starting the compressor again. The safety switch settings should be recorded and kept in the equipment file.

6. Drain the condensate (condensed water) from the air receiver daily. Due to temperature changes, the air receiver will fill with condensate. Each day the condensate should be drained from the bottom of the tank. There is usually a small valve at the bottom of the air receiver for this purpose. Some air receivers are equipped with automatic drain valves. These must be inspected periodically to ensure they are operating satisfactorily.

7. Inspect belt tension on compressors. Usually you should be able to press the belt down with hand pressure approximately three-fourths of an inch. This is done at the center between the two pulleys. *MAKE SURE THE COMPRESSOR IS LOCKED OFF BEFORE MAKING THIS TEST.* Do not overtighten belts because it will cause overheating and excessive wear on bearings and motor overloading.

8. Examine operating controls. Make sure the compressor is starting and stopping at the proper settings. If it is a dual installation, make sure they are alternating if so designed; inspect gage for accuracy. Compare readings with recorded start-up values or other known, accurate readings.

9. Many portable compressors are equipped with tool oilers on the receivers. These are used for mixing a small quantity of oil with the compressed air for lubrication of the tools being used. Tool oilers are located on the discharge side of the air receiver. They have a reservoir which must be filled with rock drill oil.

10. All compressors should be thoroughly cleaned at least monthly. Dirt, oil, grease, and other material must be thoroughly cleaned off the compressor and surrounding area. Compressors have a tendency to lose oil around piping, fittings, and shafts; therefore, constant cleaning is required by the maintenance operator to ensure proper and safe operation.

QUESTIONS

Write your answers in a notebook and then compare your answers with those on page 346.

18.25A List some of the uses of a compressor in connection with operation and maintenance of a water treatment plant.

18.25B How often should the suction filter of a compressor be cleaned?

18.25C How often should compressor oil be changed?

18.25D How often should the condensate from the air receiver be drained?

18.25E What must be done before testing belt tension on compressors with your hands?

18.26 Valves[17]

18.260 Uses of Valves

Valves are the controlling devices placed in piping systems to stop, regulate, check, divert, or otherwise modify the flow of liquids or gases. There are specific valves that are more suitable for certain jobs than others. The five most common valves that you will find in a water treatment facility are discussed in this section.

18.261 Gate Valves (Figures 18.33 and 18.34)

The basic parts of a gate valve are: the operator (handle), the shaft packing assembly, the bonnet, the valve body with seats, the stem, and the disc. Gate valves come in a large number of sizes, but the principle of operation is quite similar for all sizes. One could associate the action of a gate valve to that of a guillotine having a screw shaft instead of the rope. The valve disc is raised or lowered by a threaded shaft and is guided on each side to ensure that it will not hang up in the operation. The disc is screwed down until it wedges itself between two machined valve seats. This makes a leakproof seat on both sides of the disc. The discs are replaceable. Some gate valves have discs with wedges inside. As more force is applied to the screwed stem, the wedges force the discs into tighter contact with the valve seats.

Gate valves are either of the rising (Figure 18.33) or non-rising stem (Figure 18.34) type. The rising stem has companion threads in the valve bonnet. As the valve is opened, the stem is threaded out, lifting the wedged disc. In the non-rising type, the stem is held in place in the bonnet by a collar. The stem is threaded with companion threads in the wedged disc. As the valve opens, the disc rises on the stem. Consequently, the handwheel stays on the same plane.

Gate valves are not commonly used to control flows. With the valve partially open, the water velocity is increased through the valve and minute particles transported in the water can cause undue seat wear. However, the vee-ported gate valve can be used in controlling flows. As the valve is opened, the vee is widened to allow more flow. Because of the valve design, little damage is done to the valve seats in the vee-ported type of gate valve.

Suggested gate valve operation and maintenance procedures are listed below:

1. Open valve fully. When at stop, reverse and close valve one-half turn.

2. Operate all large valves at least yearly to ensure proper operation.

3. Inspect valve stem packing for leaks. Tighten as needed.

4. If the valve has a rising stem, keep stem threads clean and lubricated.

---

[17] For additional information on valves, see WATER DISTRIBUTION SYSTEM OPERATION AND MAINTENANCE, Chapter 3, "Distribution System Facilities," Section 3.670, "Valves," in this series of manuals.

Fig. 18.33   Rising stem gate valve
(Permission of Stockham Valves & Fittings, Copyright, 1976)

Fig. 18.34   Non-rising stem gate valve
(Permission of Stockham Valves & Fittings, Copyright, 1976)

5. Close valves slowly in pressure lines to prevent water hammer.

6. If a valve will not close by using the handwheel, check for the cause. Using a "cheater" (bar-pipe wrench) will only aggravate your problem.

18.262 Maintenance of Gate Valves

Paragraph 12: Gate Valves

The most common maintenance required by gate valves is oiling, tightening, or replacing the stem stuffing box packing.

**Frequency
of
Service**

A 1. REPLACE PACKING. Modern gate valves can be repacked without removing them from service. Before repacking, open valve wide. This prevents excessive leakage when the packing or the entire stuffing box is removed. It draws the stem collar tightly against the bonnet on a non-rising stem valve, and tightly against the bonnet bushing on a rising stem valve.

    a. Stuffing box. Remove all old packing from stuffing box with a packing hook or a rat-tail file with bent end. Clean valve stem of all adhering particles and polish it with fine emery cloth. After polishing remove the fine grit with a clean cloth to which a few drops of oil have been added.

    b. Insert packing. Insert new split-ring packing in stuffing box and tamp it into place with packing hook. Stagger ring splits. After stuffing box is filled, place a few drops of oil on stem, assemble gland, and tighten it down on packing.

S 2. OPERATE VALVE. Operate inactive gate valves to prevent sticking.

A 3. LUBRICATE GEARING. Lubricate gate valves as recommended by manufacturer. Lubricate thoroughly any gearing in large gate valves. Wash open gears with solvent and lubricate with grease.

S 4. LUBRICATE RISING STEM THREADS. Clean threads on rising stem gate valves and lubricate with grease.

5. LUBRICATE BURIED VALVES. If a buried valve works hard, lubricate it by pouring oil down through a pipe which is bent at the end to permit oiling the packing follower below the valve nut.

A 6. REFACE LEAKY GATE VALVE SEATS. If gate valve seats leak, reface them immediately, using the method discussed below. A solid wedge disc valve is used for illustration, but the general method also applies to other types of repairable gate valves. Proceed as follows:

a. Remove bonnet and clean and examine disc and body thoroughly. Carefully determine extent of damage to body rings and disc. If corrosion has caused excessive pitting or eating away of metal, as in guide ribs in body, repairs may be impractical.

b. Check and service all parts of valve completely. Remove stem from bonnet and examine it for scoring and pitting where packing makes contact. Polish lightly with fine emery cloth to put stem in good condition. Use soft jaws if stem is put in vise.

c. Remove all old packing and clean out stuffing box. Clean all dirt, scale, and corrosion from inside of valve bonnet and other parts.

d. Do not salvage an old gasket. Remove it completely and replace with one of proper quality and size.

e. After cleaning and examining all parts, determine whether valve can be repaired by removing cuts from disc and body seat faces or by replacement of body seats. If repair can be made, set disc in vise with face leveled, wrap fine emery cloth around a flat tool, and rub or lap off entire bearing surface on both sides to a smooth, even finish. Remove as little metal as possible.

f. Repair cuts and scratches on body rings, lapping with an emery block small enough to permit convenient rubbing all around rings. Work carefully to avoid removing so much metal that disc will seat too low. When seating surfaces of disc and seat rings are properly lapped in, coat faces of disc with *PRUSSIAN BLUE*[18] and drop disc in body to check contact. When good, continuous contact is obtained, the valve is tight and ready for assembly. Insert stem in bonnet, install new packing, assemble other parts, attach disc to stem, and place assembly in body. Raise stem to prevent contact with seats so bonnet can be properly seated on body before tightening the joint.

g. Test repaired valve before putting it back in line to ensure that repairs have been properly made.

h. If leaky gate valve seats cannot be refaced, remove and replace seat rings with a power lathe. Chuck up body with rings vertical to lathe and use a strong steel bar across ring lugs to unscrew them. They can be removed by hand with a diamond point chisel if care is taken to avoid damaging threads. Drive new rings home tightly. Use a wrench on a steel bar across lugs when putting in rings by hand. Always coat threads with a good lubricant before

---

[18] *Prussian Blue.*   *A blue paste or liquid (often on a paper like carbon paper) used to show a contact area. Used to determine if gate valve seats fit properly.*

putting threads into the valve body. This helps to make the threads easier to remove the next time the seats have to be replaced. Lap in rings to fit disc perfectly.

18.263 Globe Valves (Figure 18.35)

The globe valve seating configuration is quite different from the gate valve. Globe valves use a circular disc to make a flat surface contact with a ground-fitted valve seat. This is similar to placing your thumb over the end of a tube. The parts of the valve are similar in name and function to the gate valve. They can be of the rising or non-rising stem type.

What is unique about the globe valve is its internal design (Figure 18.35). This design enables the valve to be used in a controlling mode. The valve seats are not subject to excessive wear when partially opened like the gate valve. After extended use, the valve may not have a positive shutoff but it will still be effective in throttling flows. Procedures for operating and maintaining globe valves are similar to the procedures outlined for gate valves in Section 18.262.

18.264 Eccentric Valves (Figures. 18.36 and 18.37)

The eccentric valve has many desirable features. These features include allowance for high flow capacity, quarter-turn operation, no lubrication, excellent resistance to wear, and good throttling characteristics. The eccentric valve uses a cam-shaped plug to match an eccentric valve seat. As the valve is closed, the plug throttles the flow yet maintains a smooth flow rate. The plug does not come into contact with the valve seat until it is in the closed position.

Because the plug has a resilient coating, it ensures a leak-tight seal at the valve seats. The Buna-N, neoprene, or viton plug coating is a very wear-resistant compound and can function well under a wide temperature range. This valve is excellent for controlling the flows of slurries and sludges found in water treatment facilities.

18.265 Butterfly Valves (Figure 18.38)

The butterfly valve is used primarily as a control valve. The flow characteristics allow the water to move in straight lines with little turbulence in the area of the valve disc (butterfly). Complete flow shutoff can be accomplished but the psi rating is relatively low in comparison to eccentric or gate valves.

The butterfly valve uses a machined disc that can be opened to 90 degrees to allow full flow through the valve. Quarter-turn operation moves the valve from the "closed" to "open" position. The disc is mounted on a shaft eccentric that allows the disc to come into its seat with minimum seating torque and scuffing of the rubber seat. There is no contact between the disc and the seat until the last few degrees of valve closure.

A resilient rubber is used as the seat and is of a continuous form that is not interrupted by a shaft connection. Wear resistance characteristics are good when used in slurry and sludge applications.

When the valve is closed, the disc is forced against the rubber seat. Wedges with jacking screws compress the rubber seat via a jack ring. The rubber seat then conforms to the entire disc circumference. The rubber can be readily replaced when necessary without complete valve dismantling. Large valves do not need to be removed from the line for seat replacement.

Fig. 18.35 Globe valve
(Permission of Stockham Valves & Fittings)

ECCENTRIC ACTION

The DeZurik design matches a single-faced eccentric or cam-shaped plug with an eccentric raised body seat. With rotary motion only, the plug advances against the seat as it closes. Here's how it works:

OPEN—The plug is out of the flow path. There is no bonnet or other cavity to fill with slurry material. Flow is straight-through with minimum pressure drop.

CLOSING—At any position between open and closed, the eccentric plug still has not touched the seat. There is no friction to cause wear or binding. Flow is still smooth and straight. Throttling action is excellent on all types of services from slurries to gas.

CLOSED—The eccentric plug makes contact with the eccentric seat only in the fully closed position. Action is easy, without binding or scraping. There is no continual seat wear. The plug is moved firmly into the seat to provide a positive, drip-tight, long-lasting seal.

Fig. 18.36   How eccentric valves work
(Permission of DeZurik Corporation, Sartell, MN)

Fig. 18.37 Eccentric valve
(Permission of DeZurik Corporation, Sartell, MN)

Fig. 18.38   Butterfly valve
(Permission of American-Darling Valve, Birmingham, AL)

18.266 Check Valves (Figure 18.39)

The term "check valve" describes its function. A check valve allows water to flow in one direction only. If the water attempts to flow in the opposite direction, an internal mechanism closes the valve and "checks" (prevents) the flow. Three types of check mechanisms may be used — the swing check, the water check, or the lift check. In the swing check, a movable disc rests at a right angle to the flow and seats against a ground seat. The movable disc is called the clapper. The clapper can be one of three types: gravity operated, lever and weight operated, or lever and spring operated. In many installations the water being pumped must be delivered at a desired flow rate and pressure. A clapper with an external means of adjusting the opening in the check valve may be necessary to produce desired flows and pressures. By positioning the weight on the lever or adjusting the spring tension, a check valve can be made to operate either partially or fully open at various pressures and flows. The spring or counterweight also ensures that the check valve closes at "no flow." This is very helpful if the valve is not in a position that will enable gravity alone to operate the clapper. The gravity-operated clapper does not have an external adjustment and relies on the weight of the clapper to close the valve at "no flow" conditions.

Most swing check valves provide for full opening, that is, the clapper can move up into the bonnet and thus be completely out of the flow. Head loss in swing check valves may be relatively high and this factor must be considered in selecting the device for a particular application. This type of check valve is quite common in pump installations and often has a dampening feature to cushion the closing of the clapper.

The wafer check has a circular disc that hinges in the center (diameter) of the disc. Water passing through collapses the disc and the stoppage of flow allows the disc to return to its circular form. Because the valve has a tendency to be fouled up by stringy material, it is not commonly used in handling raw water. Wafer check valves are very effective when used with clean water.

The lift check uses a vertical lift disc or ball. When there is flow, the disc or ball is lifted from its ground seat and fluid passes through the valve. As flow stops, the check realigns itself with its seat and checks or prevents water backflow. The movable portion can be a spring or gravity return.

The foot valves used in pump suctions are nearly always of the vertical lift disc design. A check valve of this type is usually applied to handle clean water.

Backflow prevention by check valves is essential in many applications to:

1. Prevent pumps from reversing when power is removed,
2. Protect water systems from being cross-connected,
3. Aid in pump operation as a dampener, and
4. Ensure "full pipe" operation (pipe is full of water).

Table 18.4 provides a comparison of various types of check valves with features of these valves. Figures 18.40 through 18.46 provide drawings and photographs of the different types of check valves listed in Table 18.4.

Tight closing assured since clapper arm shaft is set slightly back of vertical seat face.

Bronze clapper arm shaft can be extended through body when lever with weight or spring is required.

Fully revolving disc seats in different position on seat ring face and distributes wear uniformly over the entire seating face.

Bronze seat ring is screwed in body and made with lugs and can be replaced with body in line. It can be furnished with a resilient insert for bottle-tight service on gas or air.

Bronze bushed ductile iron clapper arm for added strength and impact resistance.

Bronze or alloy disc ring is securely peened into machined dove-tailed groove.

Body design permits removal of clapper arm assembly through bonnet opening.

Vertical seating surfaces provide sensitive seating action.

Fig. 18.39 Check valve
(Permission of American-Darling Valve, Birmingham, AL)

TABLE 18.4 COMPARISON OF FEATURES OF DIFFERENT TYPES OF CHECK VALVES[a]

Globe Silent Check Valve	Wafer Silent Check Valve	Double Door Check Valve	Rubber Flapper Check Valve	Cushion Swing Check Valve	Slanting Disc Check Valve	Automatic Control Check Valve		Feature
		X					1.	Lowest initital cost
		X					2.	Shortest laying length
	X						3.	Highest head loss (see head loss curves)
X	X	X		X			4.	Resilient seat (optional)
			X	X			5.	For waste and raw sewage
X	X	X			X	X	6.	Clean water only
		X	X	X	X		7.	Cushion closing
X	X					X	8.	Silent closing (positively silent)
			X		X		9.	Free open – Free close
				X	X	X	10.	Control open or close or both (optional)
X	X					X	11.	Vertical installation flow up or down
			X	X		X	12.	Can be rubber lined
				X	X	X	13.	Disc position indicator
			X				14.	Buried service
				X			15.	Outside lever
					X	X	16.	Surge pressure control
			X	X		X	17.	Reverse flow
X	X				X	X	18.	Up to 600# class
	X						19.	Up to 1500# class
					X		20.	Lowest head loss (see head loss curves)
		X					21.	Up to 2500# class
						X	22.	Control open and close standard
						X	23.	Shut off valve
						X	24.	Throttling valve
		X	X	X	X		25.	Vertical installation flow up only
						X	26.	Electric motor operated
						X	27.	Remote control
						X	28.	Control closure upon power failure
		X	X	X		X	29.	Resilient seat standard
		X			X	X	30.	Velocities in excess of 15 FPS
				X			31.	Velocities up to 5 FPS
X	X		X				32.	Velocities up to 10 FPS

[a] Permission of APCO/Valve and Primer Corporation.

Fig. 18.40   Swing check valves (single disc)

(Permission of APCO / Valve and Primer Corporation)

Fig. 18.41 Double disc swing check valves (split swing discs)
(Permission of APCO / Valve and Primer Corporation)

Fig. 18.42   Rubber flapper check valves (angle seating)

(Permission of APCO/Valve and Primer Corporation)

Fig. 18.43   *Slanting disc check valves (pivot off center)*

(Permission of APCO/Valve and Primer Corporation)

Fig. 18.44   Silent check valves (wafer)

(Permission of APCO/Valve and Primer Corporation)

Fig. 18.45 Silent check valves (globe)
(Permission of APCO/Valve and Primer Corporation)

Fig. 18.46   Automatic control check valves
(Permission of APCO/Valve and Primer Corporation)

18.267 Maintenance of Check Valves

Paragraph 13: Check Valves

Frequency of Service		
A	1.	INSPECT DISC FACING. Open valves to observe condition of facing on swing check valves equipped with leather or rubber seats on disc. If metal seat ring is scarred, dress it with a fine file and lap with fine emery paper wrapped around a flat tool.
A	2.	CHECK PIN WEAR. Check pin wear on balanced disc check valve, since disc must be accurately positioned in seat to prevent leakage.

18.268 Automatic Valves

Water treatment plants usually have a number of automatically operated valves. The simplest type is either open or closed and is not required to operate in an intermediate position. Frequently these valves are similar to gate valves that have had their threaded stems and handwheels replaced by a smooth shaft and hydraulic piston. Maintenance on these valves is essentially the same as for gate valves.

Other automatically operated valves are used to control flow in water treatment plants and are usually located at some point between tight shut and wide open. These are commonly called modulating valves. A butterfly valve with a hydraulic cylinder operator can be used for this type of service.

The diaphragm-operated globe valve (Figure 18.47) is also used for modulating service. These valves can be equipped with pilot control devices to control pressure, flow, or level either singly or in combination. Maintenance on these valves consists of the following:

1. Periodically clean any strainers in the pilot control system. Scheduling should be adjusted to accommodate the rate at which the strainer collects foreign material.

2. Check the operation of the valve to see that the controls are, in fact, correctly positioning the valve to accomplish the job.

3. If the valve is used in an application where it seldom or never is wide open, it should periodically be exercised manually to cycle from tight shut to wide open. This is to ensure that there is no buildup on the stem that could jam the valve. These valves can be opened wide by drawing all the pressure from the cover chamber. If water does not stop flowing out of the cover chamber when the valve is wide open, this is an indication that the diaphragm is leaking and should be replaced.

QUESTIONS

Write your answers in a notebook and then compare your answers with those on page 346.

18.26A What is the purpose of valves?

18.26B List five common types of valves found in water treatment facilities.

18.26C What maintenance is required by gate valves?

18.26D What is the purpose of a check valve?

18.26E Why is backflow prevention by check valves essential in many applications?

End of Lesson 4 of 5 Lessons on
MAINTENANCE

Please answer the discussion and review questions next.

DISCUSSION AND REVIEW QUESTIONS
Chapter 18. MAINTENANCE
(Lesson 4 of 5 Lessons)

Write the answers to these questions in your notebook before continuing. The question numbering continues from Lesson 3.

32. What are the uses of a compressor?

33. What items should be maintained on a compressor?

34. What factors can cause wear on gate valve seats?

35. Why should inactive gate valves be operated periodically?

CLAYTON 100 HYTROL VALVE

COVER
COVER BEARING
STUD
SPRING
COVER RETAINING NUT
STEM NUT
DIAPHRAGM
DIAPHRAGM WASHER
SPACER WASHER
DISC RETAINER
DISC GUIDE
DISC
SEAT
BODY
STEM

CLAYTON 100P POWERTROL VALVE

COVER BEARING
UPPER STEM NUT
STEM
DIAPHRAGM WASHER
DIAPHRAGM
POWER UNIT BODY STUD
BEARING RETAINER
COVER RETAINING NUT
COVER
POWER UNIT BODY
DISC RETAINER
DISC
LOWER STEM NUT
BODY
SEAT

Fig. 18.47   Diaphragm-operated globe valve
(Permission of CLA-VAL Co.)

CHAPTER 18.   MAINTENANCE

(Lesson 5 of 5 Lessons)

18.3   INTERNAL COMBUSTION ENGINES

18.30   Gasoline Engines

18.300   *Need to Maintain Gasoline Engines*

In the water treatment departments of all cities there is occasion to use gasoline-powered engines that drive pumps, generators, tractors, and vehicles. Although we all drive automobiles that are powered by internal combustion engines, are you aware of the fundamentals?

Very few operators actually do the repair of gasoline-powered engines. Although you may not be able to perform the duties of an engine mechanic, there are a number of steps you can take to ensure that your particular engine is well maintained.

At the end of this section you will have an adequate knowledge of how a gasoline engine operates in order to maintain it so as to provide many hours at optimum performance.

18.301   *Maintenance*

In order to have an engine that will provide you with many hours of trouble-free operation, it must be well cared for. *PLEASE REFER TO THE OWNER/OPERATOR MANUAL FOR YOUR PARTICULAR ENGINE.* Typical maintenance procedures are as follows:

1. Change engine oil regularly every 25 hours;

2. Clean carburetor air filter every 25 hours;

3. Blow dust and chaff from louvered engine vanes regularly;

4. Clean carburetor fuel filter/screen every 100 hours;

5. Lubricate generator and/or starter motor as recommended, every 100 hours;

6. Lubricate throttle linkage every 100 hours;

7. Clean, gap, or replace spark plug every 100 hours; and

8. Remove carbon deposits from top of piston and valves every 100 to 300 hours.

18.302   *Starting Problems*

Listed below are some items to check if you have problems starting a gasoline engine.

1. No fuel in tank, valve closed

2. Carburetor not choked

3. Water or dirt in fuel lines or carburetor

4. Carburetor flooded

5. Low compression

6. Loose spark plug, and

7. No spark at plug

   a. Dirty and/or improperly gapped plug

   b. Broken or wet ignition cables

   c. Breaker points not opening or closing, and

   d. Magneto grounded

18.303   *Running Problems*

Check the following items if a gasoline engine does not run properly.

1. Engine misses

   a. Faulty spark plug/gapping

   b. Weak ignition spark

   c. Loose ignition cable

   d. Worn breaker points

   e. Water in fuel

   f. Poor compression

2. Engine surges

   a. Carburetor flooding

   b. Governor spring connected improperly

3. Engine stops

   a. Fuel tank empty

   b. Vapor lock

   c. Tank air vent plugged

4. Engine overheats

   a. Low crankcase oil

   b. Ignition timing wrong

   c. Engine overloaded

   d. Restricted air circulation/high ambient temperature

   e. Poor grade of gasoline

5. Engine knocks

   a. Poor grade of gasoline

   b. Engine under heavy load at low speed

   c. Carbon deposits in cylinder head

   d. Spark advanced too far

   e. Loose connecting rod bearing

   f. Worn or loose piston pin

6. Engine backfires through carburetor

   a. Water or dirt in fuel

   b. Cold engine

   c. Poor grade of gasoline

   d. Sticking inlet valves

   e. Spark plug heat range too hot

QUESTIONS

Write your answers in a notebook and then compare your answers with those on pages 346 and 347.

18.30A List some possible uses of gasoline engines in water treatment plants.

18.30B What items would you check if you had problems starting a gasoline engine?

18.30C What items could cause a gasoline engine to not run properly?

18.304 How to Start a Gasoline Engine

Because of the wide variety of uses for gasoline-powered engines, no one starting sequence will apply to all engines. In general, gasoline engines can be divided into two groups. In the first group are small engines with magneto ignition and recoil start. Larger engines with battery-powered ignition and electric start are in the second group.

18.3040 SMALL ENGINES

The procedure for starting small engines is as follows:

1. Check fuel tank for adequate fuel;

2. Ensure fuel shutoff valve from the tank to the carburetor is open;

3. Disengage ignition ground ("kill" switch or mechanism that grounds the spark plug);

4. Check crankcase lubricating oil;

5. Set throttle to start position or 3/4-full throttle;

6. Set choke lever or pull out choke on carburetor;

7. Pull recoil starter twice;

8. If engine has started, push choke to OFF; and

9. If engine does not start after two pulls, disengage the choke and try three or four more times.

If repeated efforts at starting have been unsuccessful, remove the high tension voltage wire from the spark. Hold the end of the wire (grasp the insulated portion, *NOT* the connector) 1/8 inch (3 mm) from the spark plug. Pull the recoil starter. You should see a small blue spark. This will indicate that the points are opening and closing and providing ignition voltage.

The next step is to remove the spark plug from the cylinder head (use a 13/16-inch (20.6-mm) deep socket). Check for a carbon buildup on the electrode. A piece of carbon may have lodged between the center electrode and the side electrode. Also check to see if the plug is wet with fuel or oil. This could indicate that you have flooded the cylinder with fuel by having the choke on too long. If there is oil residue, it could indicate worn piston rings.

Replace the spark plug with a new one if in doubt. If you must use the one you have, clean it by buffing with a wire brush. Check the "gap" between the center electrode and side electrode; it should be approximately 0.030 inch (30 thousandths of an inch or 0.76 mm).

Try starting the engine as previously described. If the engine does not sputter or pop, close the fuel shutoff valve, remove fuel sedimentation bowl and clean. Open fuel valve. Catch a small amount of fuel in the palm of your hand and examine the fuel for grit or water. If everything looks OK, replace sediment bowl and open fuel valve.

Try to start the engine. If you still cannot achieve ignition, you may have other problems that will require further checking by a small-engine mechanic. Do not feel disgruntled; you have checked for the most common problems.

18.3041 LARGE ENGINES

The procedure for starting large engines is as follows:

1. Check fuel tank for fuel;

2. Check crankcase for oil;

3. Check radiator for coolant (if water-cooled);

4. Set throttle to 1/2-full position;

5. Pull out choke;

6. Turn on ignition switch and press start button;

7. After four or five engine revolutions, push in the choke; and

8. Engine should start.

After repeated tries, further investigation by a mechanic may be needed.

NOTE: Do not crank engine with the starter motor for more than one minute initially. Wait two minutes and try again for 45 seconds. After three tries, let starter motor cool for 5 minutes before trying again. This will avoid starter motor damage.

Preliminary checks for a large engine that won't start are similar to procedures for small engines. Remove spark plug wires. Test each one by holding it 1/8 inch (3 mm) from the spark plug or ground, and turn engine over with the starter. You should see a small blue spark. If you have no spark, the points are not opening or high tension voltage is not present from the ignition coil. Check further as needed. If spark is present, inspect spark plugs. Clean or replace if needed.

After checking the ignition system, make sure fuel is present at the carburetor. Remove the fuel line at the carburetor and direct it away from you and the engine. Engage starter motor for two revolutions. Fuel should spurt from the line if the fuel pump is working satisfactorily. Replace fuel line and wipe away any fuel that may be present on the engine.

With fuel and ignition voltage present, the engine should start. Repeat start procedure. If you still cannot start the engine, call on your mechanic to look for the problem.

NOTE: Some engines have a low oil pressure switch that must be manually held in until sufficient oil pressure is present.

Do not use a starting fluid on gasoline engines unless it is a LAST RESORT effort to get a critical piece of equipment running. Hard-starting engines should be inspected and repaired by a reliable mechanic.

After an engine has been started, give it an opportunity to warm up before applying the load. Follow manufacturer's recommendations for the starting procedure since there is some variation between different makes of engines.

QUESTIONS

Write your answers in a notebook and then compare your answers with those on page 347.

18.30D If a gasoline engine will not start and the spark plug is wet with fuel or oil, what has happened?

18.30E If a gasoline engine will not start and there is an oil residue on the spark plug, what has happened?

18.30F After an engine has started, what should be done before applying the load?

18.31 Diesel Engines

18.310 How Diesel Engines Work (Figure 18.48)

Diesel engines are similar to gasoline engines and are either two or four cycle. They can be air or water cooled. In general the diesel engine is of heavier construction to withstand the higher pressures resulting from higher compression ratios.

The diesel does not use spark plugs, but instead relies on heat generated by air compressed in the cylinder (1,000 degrees F (540°C)) to ignite the fuel mixture. The fuel is a petroleum product that is heavier than gasoline and has a higher flash point. Gasoline cannot be used in a diesel because it would start to burn from the heat generated by compression before the piston reached the top of the stroke.

A diesel has no carburetor. The fuel is sprayed (injected) into the cylinder while the cylinder is compressing air. The heat of compression ignites the fuel-air mixture and burns, producing power similar to a gasoline engine. The introduction of fuel into the cylinder must be "timed" in the same manner as spark to the plug in a gasoline engine. Fuel is pumped by a pumping device that is geared to the crankshaft.

Diesel fuel, unlike gasoline, does not vaporize readily. The fuel must be broken up into fine particles and sprayed into the cylinder. The atomization of fuel is accomplished by forcing the fuel through a nozzle at the top of the combustion chamber. As the fuel combines with the air in the cylinder, it becomes a combustible mixture. Since the diesel engine depends upon the heat of compressed air to ignite the fuel-air mixture, compression pressure must be maintained. Leaking valves or piston rings (causing "blow by") cannot be tolerated.

The fuel is also important. The automotive-type diesel is designed to run on a specific type or grade of fuel. Trouble can be expected if an attempt is made to use other than the proper type.

18.311 Operation

In the two-cycle engine, intake and exhaust take place during part of the compression and power strokes; whereas, the four-cycle engine requires four strokes to complete the operating cycle. During one-half of the cycle, the four-stroke acts as an air pump. The two-stroke must have a blower (air pump) to provide the necessary air to expel the exhaust gases and recharge the cylinder with fresh air.

In the two-cycle, a series of ports surround the cylinder at a point higher than the lowest position of the piston. These are the intake ports that allow air into the cylinder. The four-cycle engine uses intake valves. The incoming air forces the expended gases out the exhaust valve, leaving the cylinder full of clean air.

As the piston starts its upward stroke, the exhaust valve closes, the intake ports are sealed off by the piston, and the air in the cylinder is compressed. Shortly before the piston reaches the top of the stroke, the required amount of fuel is sprayed into the combustion chamber by the fuel injector. The intense heat of compression ignites the fuel-air mixture with the resulting combustion driving the piston down on its power stroke.

As the piston nears the bottom of the stroke, the exhaust valve opens and the spent gases are released, assisted by the incoming fresh air. The cycle is complete.

18.312 Fuel System (Figure 18.49)

The basic parts of the fuel system are:

1. Primary fuel filter,

2. Secondary fuel filter,

3. Fuel injection pump, and

4. Fuel injector.

Scavenging and Compression

Power and Exhaust

Fig. 18.48   How diesel engines work

(Source: GMC Truck Overhaul Manual Series 53, permission of General Motors Corp.)

1 Nozzle Valve and Body
2 Nozzle Valve Spring
3 Leak-off Lines
4 Hydraulic Head Assembly
5 Fuel Metering Sleeve
6 Pump Plunger

7 Face Gear
8 Tappet and Roller
9 Cam
10 Governor Gears
11 Governor Weights

12 Governor Stop Plate
13 Fulcrum Lever
14 Stop Lever
15 Shut-off (when used)
16 Fuel Return Line

T-2347

Fig. 18.49 Diesel engine fuel system
(Source: Maintenance Manual, permission of General Motors Corp.)

The primary filter removes all coarse particles from the fuel and the secondary filter removes any minute particles that remain. This ensures a clean fuel that will not clog the injector pump or fuel injectors. The heart of the fuel system is the injection pump (Figure 18.50). This pump is a gear-type positive-displacement pump that can deliver fuel to the injector at a very high pressure. Incorporated into the pump is a timing advance mechanism to advance or retard the instant when fuel is injected into the cylinder. At high engine speed, injection would take place sooner in the cycle. The reverse happens for lower speeds.

A governor, which uses centrifugal weights and is driven by the pump shaft, activates a fuel control unit. When engine speed increases, the weights are thrown toward their outer limit. Geared to the assembly, the fuel control valve is opened wider allowing more fuel to flow to the injector.

We now have higher engine speed, advanced "timing" of injection, and the necessary fuel to sustain the faster operation. When the engine is slowed, the reverse takes place.

Fuel under pressure is fed from the injection pump to the appropriate fuel nozzles. When the pressure reaches approximately 3,000 psi (20,700 kPa or 207 kg/sq cm), the valve in the injector opens allowing fuel to be injected into the combustion chambers. As line pressure drops, the return spring closes the nozzle valve. Fuel left in the line is fed back to the pump through "leak off" lines.

18.313 Water-Cooled Diesel Engines

Usually the larger diesel engines are of the water-cooled type, similar to gasoline engines. In order to deliver a sustained amount of high horsepower, an effective cooling system is necessary to dissipate the extreme heat of combustion. Because of this fact, a water-cooled engine of comparative horsepower to the air-cooled will cost more to manufacture, and subsequently to maintain.

18.314 Air-Cooled Diesel Engines

When a lighter weight, lower horsepower, and more compact engine is desired, the air-cooled engine will serve your needs. You get the benefits of a diesel engine in a smaller package.

There are some definite advantages to the diesel engine over the gasoline engine. The initial cost is greater for the diesel; however, the diesel:

1. Requires less maintenance because there are:

   a. No plugs,

   b. No contact points to pit,

   c. No ignition coils or high tension wires, and

   d. Fewer tune-ups.

2. Is cheaper to operate because:

   a. Diesel fuel may be cheaper, and

   b. Fuel efficiency is better.

Perhaps the biggest drawbacks against diesel engines are:

1. Initial investment costs, and

2. Repair costs.

The pros and cons must be weighed to provide you with an engine that will meet your particular needs. Whichever engine you select, remember that a well-cared-for engine will be there to serve you when it is needed and will provide trouble-free operation that is essential to most users.

18.315 How to Start Diesel Engines

Diesel engines vary in size and use and have varied starting procedures. Follow the manufacturer's suggested procedures for your particular engine. As with the gasoline engine, check fuel, oil, and coolant.

To start a diesel engine, the procedures are as follows:

1. Push in "stop" control,

2. Set throttle to 1/3-full,

3. Turn on switch and engage starter, and

4. Engine should start.

Some engines have glow plugs that are energized when the switch is placed in the start position. They preheat the air-fuel mixture in the cylinder to aid in starting. After the engine is started, maintain the lower RPMs on the engine tachometer and allow the engine to warm up. The warm-up period is vital to the diesel engine for efficient engine performance. When operating the engine, maintain adequate engine RPMs as recommended by the manufacturer.

When a diesel engine will not start after repeated tries, a small amount of starting fluid sprayed into the air intake may be needed to start the engine. If you use starting fluid, do not get carried away with its use; a little goes a long way. Use it only as a last resort or as specified by the manufacturer. If your efforts have failed to start the engine, have a mechanic who is familiar with diesel engines determine the cause of the problem.

18.316 Maintenance and Troubleshooting

For detailed maintenance procedures for your diesel engine, see your diesel manufacturer's service manual.

TROUBLESHOOTING

Certain abnormal conditions which sometimes interfere with satisfactory engine operation are listed in this section.

Satisfactory engine operation depends primarily on:

1. An adequate supply of air compressed to a sufficiently high compression pressure.

2. The injection of the proper amount of fuel at the right time.

Lack of power, uneven running, excessive vibration, stalling at idle speed, and hard starting may be caused by either low compression, faulty injection in one or more cylinders, or lack

Fig. 18.50 *Cutaway view of fuel injection pump for 6-cylinder engine*
(Source: Maintenance Manual, permission of General Motors Corp.)

of sufficient air. Several problems which can reduce engine performance are listed below:

1. Misfiring cylinders,

2. Improper compression pressure,

3. Engine out of fuel,

4. Inadequate fuel flow,

5. Excessive crankcase pressure,

6. Excessive back pressure,

7. Improper air box pressure,

8. Restricted air inlet,

9. Low oil pressure, and

10. Improper engine coolant operating temperature.

Solutions to these problems can be found in the operation and maintenance instructions for the engines.

18.32 Cooling Systems (Figure 18.51)

In an air-cooled engine, the heat generated by combustion is dissipated by the air circulating past the louvered cylinder block. With a water-cooled system, the same effect is achieved by using water. Each cylinder is surrounded with a water jacket through which the coolant water circulates. This is accomplished by a water pump that is belt driven from the crankshaft. The heat transfers from the cylinder wall to the water which, in turn, is pumped back to the radiator where the heat is dissipated. A fan mounted on the same shaft as the water pump ensures that a large volume of air is blown across the radiator coils to facilitate rapid dispersal of heat. The cooled water is then pumped back into the engine.

Internal combustion engines operate more efficiently when their temperature is maintained within narrow limits. This objective is achieved with the insertion of a thermostat in the cooling system which is called a "temperature actuated valve." When the engine is cold, the thermostat remains closed, not allowing the water to circulate back to the radiator. As the engine temperature increases to normal operating temperature, the thermostat opens.

The radiator cap provides a function other than preventing coolant from splashing out the filter opening. The cap is designed to seal the cooling system so that it operates under pressure. This improves cooling efficiency and prevents evaporation of coolant. The boiling point of water is 212 degrees F (100°C). However, for every pound of pressure applied to the system, the boiling point rises 3.25 degrees F (1.8°C). If your cooling system had a 15 psi (100 kPa or 1 kg/sq cm) radiator cap and used water for coolant, it would have a boiling point near 260 degrees F (127°C).

Engine temperatures are regulated by transferring excess heat to surrounding air.

Shaft ball bearings are sealed at each end to keep lubricant in and water out of bearings. A spring-loaded seal (in color) is used to avoid water leakage around pump shaft. Note clearance between impeller and cover plate.

With water jackets entirely around each cylinder and valve, there is a great amount of area exposed to the circulating coolant.

Fig. 18.51 Water cooling system
(Source: Automotive Encyclopedia, permission of the Goodheart-Wilcox Co., Inc.)

The use of coolant/antifreeze provides protection against the radiator coolant freezing and rupturing the system and also provides better heat transfer and heat dissipation characteristics than water. Most of the name-brand coolants contain rust inhibitors. Rust buildup in the cooling system interferes with good heat transfer and the sloughing of rust scale can block narrow passages.

Stationary internal combustion engines, such as those that are used to drive pumps and generators at water treatment plants, are often installed in a building where free circulation of air for radiator cooling may not be possible. For these installations, a liquid-to-liquid heat exchanger often replaces the radiator (which is a liquid-to-air heat exchanger). In this case, instead of the heat in the cooling jacket water being transferred to the surrounding air, it is transferred to another liquid, usually tap water. This water may be wasted if the engine is a standby unit and not operated very much, or the cooling water may be recovered in a cooling tower if the engine is in regular use.

In liquid-to-liquid heat exchanger systems a thermostatically controlled valve is usually installed to regulate the flow of cooling water through the exchanger. This valve should be checked periodically to see that it: (1) provides sufficient water flow when the engine is running, and (2) closes off tight when the engine is shut down to prevent waste.

Cooling water from a heat exchanger should not be put back into a potable water system. Any leakage in the heat exchanger could result in engine jacket coolant contaminating the potable water supply.

QUESTIONS

Write your answers in a notebook and then compare your answers with those on page 347.

18.31A Why is gasoline not used as a fuel in diesel engines?

18.31B List the four basic parts of a diesel fuel system.

18.31C What is the purpose of the fuel injection pump?

18.32A How is heat removed from the cylinders in a water-cooled engine?

18.33 Fuel Storage

18.330 Code Requirements

Storage and use of fuels for internal combustion engines must always be in accordance with local building and fire codes. In addition, the water treatment plant operator should be familiar with the particular problems associated with each of the commonly used fuels.

18.331 Diesel

This fuel comes in two grades known as #1 and #2. Be sure to use the grade recommended by the engine manufacturer. Be aware that the fuel grade recommendation may vary with the season. Diesel fuel is often stored in above-ground tanks. The fuel may be kept in storage for years without deteriorating. To protect stored diesel from water contamination, keep the storage tanks full and use special additives.

18.332 Gasoline

Except for very small quantities, gasoline is stored in underground tanks. This can result in problems for the operator. If the storage tank develops a leak, either fuel can leak out or water can leak in. Either condition is undesirable. Fuel loss cannot only be an unwanted operating expense, but can be a danger to underground plant piping. Gasoline deteriorates rubber and if the piping is put together with rubber gaskets or rings, the deterioration can result in major leaks and broken couplings. The owner of a leaking underground tank can be liable for any resulting environmental damage and also responsible for the cleanup. Fuel loss can best be monitored by careful accounting.

Water leakage into underground fuel tanks can result in engine stoppages and possible damage to the engine. Special devices are available for detecting water in gasoline tanks and such a test should be run routinely. These devices can be obtained by contacting your local wholesale fuel distributor.

Gasoline, unlike diesel, deteriorates in storage. For engines that are in normal everyday use, this is not a problem. However, fuel storage for standby, engine-driven equipment requires further consideration. Engine operation and fuel tank replenishment should be scheduled so that at least half of the gasoline in storage is used each year. Failure to do this can result in engines that are hard to start and in the formation of varnish and gummy deposits that can cause malfunctions in the parts of the fuel system.

18.333 Liquified Petroleum Gas (LPG)

LPG is usually a mixture of propane and butane. The proportion of each is varied according to the weather temperature. The cooler the weather, the greater the proportion of propane.

This fuel is always stored under pressure in above-ground tanks that are located out in the open. LPG does not deteriorate in storage and therefore can be kept for many years.

LPG is heavier than air and will collect in low areas if there is any leakage. This poses an extremely dangerous explosive threat that treatment plant operators must constantly guard against.

18.334 Natural Gas

This fuel is usually obtained from the local gas company through a metered connection from their distribution system. There is no on-site storage.

Natural gas, being lighter than air, tends to rise and dissipate from leaks and therefore is less dangerous to handle than LPG. Explosions can occur, however, if the leakage is confined inside a building.

18.34 Standby Engines

Internal combustion engines must be run periodically to ensure that, when needed, they will function properly. An engine that is not in regular service should be started up and test run at least once a week. The test run should be long enough for the engine to come up to its normal operating temperature before the engine is shut down. If at all possible, run the engine under its normal load. Just idling an engine for 20 minutes doesn't give you much of an indication whether it can handle a load. Check and make note of the engine instruments. Look for changes that may indicate a need for repairs. Lube oil pressure and intake manifold pressure (on spark ignition engines without supercharging or fuel injection) are two key indicators of engine condition.

QUESTIONS

Write your answers in a notebook and then compare your answers with those on page 347.

18.33A The storage and use of fuels for internal combustion engines must be in accordance with what codes?

18.33B List four types of fuels commonly used by internal combustion engines.

18.34A How often should standby internal combustion engines be test run when not in regular service?

18.34B Under what conditions should standby engines be test run?

18.4 CHEMICAL STORAGE AND FEEDERS[19]

18.40 Chemical Storage

Certain dry chemicals such as alum, ferric chloride, and soda ash are *HYGROSCOPIC.*[20] These chemicals require special considerations to protect them from moisture during storage. Dry quicklime should be kept dry because of the tremendous heat which is generated when it comes in contact with water. This heat is sufficient to cause a fire.

Some liquid chemicals such as sodium hydroxide (caustic soda) should not be exposed to air because of the formation of calcium carbonate (a solid) due to the carbon dioxide in the air. Also some liquid chemicals may "freeze." A 50-percent sodium hydroxide solution becomes crystalized (forms a solid) at temperatures below 55°F (13°C). Therefore a heater may be required to keep the storage area warm or the solution may have to be diluted down to a 25-percent solution.

Potassium permanganate ($KMnO_4$)can be kept indefinitely if stored in a cool dry area in closed containers. The drums should be protected from damage that could cause leakage. Potassium permanganate should be stored in fire-resistant buildings, having concrete floors as opposed to wooden floors. It should not be exposed to intense heat, or stored next to heated pipes. Any organic solvent, such as greases and oils in general, should be kept away from stored $KMnO_4$.

Potassium permanganate spills should be swept up and removed immediately. Flushing with water is an effective way to eliminate spillage on floors. Potassium permanganate fires should be extinguished with water.

Carbon should be stored in a clean, dry place, in single or double rows, and with access aisles around every stack for frequent fire inspections. The removal of burning carbon will thus be facilitated. Carbon should never be stored in large stacks.

The storage area should be of fireproof construction, with self-closing fire doors separating the carbon room from other sections. Storage bins for dry bulk carbon should be of fireproof construction equipped for fire control by the installation of carbon dioxide equipment, or should be so arranged that they can be flooded with a fine spray of water.

Carbon storage areas should be protected from contact with flammable materials. (Carbon dust mixed with oily rags or chlorine compounds can ignite in spontaneous combustion.) *SMOKING SHOULD BE PROHIBITED AT ALL TIMES DURING THE HANDLING AND UNLOADING OF CARBON AND IN THE STORAGE AREA.* Carbon should not be stored where a spark from overhead electric equipment could start a fire. If a fire occurs, the carbon monoxide hazard should be taken into account.

Electric equipment should be protected from carbon dust and cleaned frequently or, better, explosion-proof electric wiring and equipment should be used. (The heat from a motor may ignite the accumulated carbon dust; this material, especially when damp, is a good conductor of electricity and could short-circuit the mechanism.)

Polymer solutions will be degraded (lose their strength) by biological contamination. A good cleaning of polymer storage tanks is recommended before a new shipment is delivered to the plant.

Liquid chemical storage tanks should have a berm or earth bank around the tanks to contain any chemicals released if the tank fails due to an earthquake, corrosion or any other reason.

Some chemicals such as chlorine and fluoride compounds are harmful to the human body when they are released as the result of a leak. Continual surveillance and maintenance of the storage and feeding systems are required.

18.41 Drainage From Chemical Storage and Feeders

Safety regulations prohibit a single drainage pit which can accept and contain both acid and alkali chemicals because of the possibility of an explosion whenever these two types of chemicals come in contact. Also, any organic chemical waste such as a polymer solution should not be allowed to be discharged into a pit or sump which could also receive a waste from oxidizing chemicals such as potassium perman-

---

[19] *For additional information on chemical feeders, see Chapter 13, "Fluoridation," Section 13.30, "Chemical Feeders."*
[20] *Hygroscopic (HI-grow-SKOP-ick).   Absorbing or attracting moisture from the air.*

ganate ($KMnO_4$) because of the possibility of a fire. Therefore, separate drainage systems or a high dilution of certain chemicals is necessary for a safe drainage system.

18.42 Use of Feeder Manufacturer's Manual

Water treatment plants will have a number of chemical feeders to accurately control the rate at which chemicals are fed into the water as a part of the treatment processes. There are many types of feeders and they work on many different principles. Study the feeder manufacturer's manual that you should find in the treatment plant library for details on maintaining the equipment. Additional information on chemical feeders is contained in specific chapters on treatment processes that require the use of chemical feeders.

18.43 Solid Feeders

Solid feeders usually handle powdered material and usually have many moving mechanical parts that need adjustment, lubrication, and replacement when worn. The chemical supply is usually stored in a hopper. Keep the hopper and feeder clean and dry in order to prevent "bridging" (a hardened layer which can form an arch and prevent flow) of the chemical in the hopper and clogging in the feeder.

18.44 Liquid Feeders

Liquid feeders handle many types of chemicals, some of which may be corrosive and/or have a tendency to plug up the mechanism. The key to reliable operations is constant vigilance and cleaning as needed.

18.45 Gas Feeders

The principal chemical found in gaseous form at water treatment plants is chlorine. Chlorine is quite poisonous to humans and must be handled with great caution.

18.46 Calibration of Chemical Feeders[21]

To ensure the accuracy of chemical feed rates, liquid-chemical metering pumps and dry-chemical feed systems should be tested and calibrated when first installed and at regular intervals thereafter. This section presents general procedures for calibrating several types of liquid- and dry-chemical feeders.

18.460 Large-Volume Metering Pumps

Pumps metering chemicals such as liquid alum deliver a relatively large volume of chemical in a short time period. These pumps can be accurately calibrated with a clear plastic sight tube and a stopwatch (Figure 18.52).

To calibrate the pump, fill the sight tube from the chemical solution tank, then set the valve so the tube is the only source of liquid chemical entering the pump. Run the pump for exactly one minute (use the stopwatch) at each of five or six representative settings of the pump-control scale. Record the amount pumped at each setting as observed in the sight tube. Use this information to develop curves of pump setting vs. chemical dose in mg/L or chemical feed in gallons per day for your plant (Figure 18.53).

The graph developed by this process is called a calibration curve. It can be used to determine the pump setting needed to deliver a required chemical feed rate, or the commonly

used range of feed rates can be marked in gallons per day directly on the pump control panel.

18.461 Small-Volume Metering Pumps

Pumps metering a chemical such as sodium hexametaphosphate, a lime feed solubility enhancer, feed a very small volume per day. The procedure for calibration of these pumps is similar to the procedure for large-volume units. For very low feed rates, pumping times of longer than one minute may be required to give accurately measurable results.

Once the test data have been recorded, convert the test results to appropriate units and draw a calibration curve to be used as for the larger pumps.

18.462 Dry-Chemical Systems

Dry-chemical feed systems are used for chemicals such as activated carbon, fluoride, and lime. Two types of systems are common, the rocker-dump type and the helix-feed type. The rocker-dump chemical feed uses a scraper moving back and forth on a platform located at the bottom of a hopper filled with dry chemical. The platform may be adjusted up and down to regulate the thickness of the ribbon of chemical, and the length of stroke for the scraper can be adjusted, usually by means of an indicator on an exterior arm.

The helix-type feeder feeds the dry chemical with a rotating screw (helix). The feed rate is adjusted by varying the drive-motor speed. The speed can usually be varied from 0 to 100 percent.

To calibrate either type of feed system, choose five or six representative settings of the arm (rocker-dump) or of the motor speed control (helix type), and at each of the settings catch the amount of chemical fed during a precisely measured time interval. Next, weigh each volume of chemical as accurately as possible and convert the information into pounds per day. Use the data to construct a calibration curve with one axis representing feeder settings and the other representing pounds per day. The curve is used in the same manner as the curves for liquid-feed pumps.

THE FEED RATE OF A CHEMICAL SOLUTION FEED PUMP CAN BE DETERMINED BY MEASURING THE AMOUNT OF SOLUTION WITHDRAWN FROM A GRADUATED CYLINDER IN A GIVEN TIME PERIOD. ALLOW THE CYLINDER TO FILL WITH SOLUTION. THEN CLOSE THE VALVE ON THE LINE FROM THE TANK SO THE FEED PUMP TAKES SUCTION FROM THE CYLINDER ONLY. OBSERVE THE MILLILITERS OF SOLUTION USED IN ONE MINUTE. COMPARE THIS RESULT WITH THE DESIRED FEED RATE AND ADJUST THE FEED PUMP ACCORDINGLY.

Fig. 18.52   Calibration of a chemical feed pump

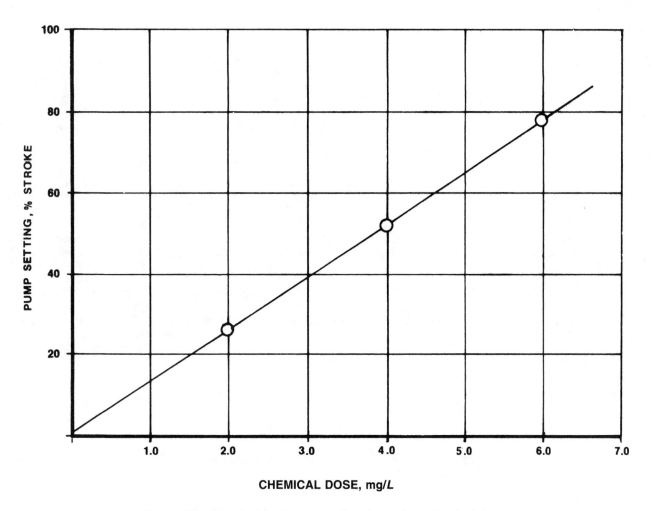

Fig. 18.53   Chemical feed pump settings for various chemical doses

FORMULAS

To determine the chemical feed rate or flow from a chemical feeder, we need to know the amount or volume fed during a known time period. The flow from a chemical feeder can be calculated by knowing the volume pumped from a chemical storage tank and the time period.

$$\text{Flow, GPM} = \frac{\text{Volume Pumped, gal}}{\text{Pumping Time, minutes}}$$

$$\text{or Flow, GPD} = \frac{(\text{Volume Pumped, gal})(24 \text{ hr/day})}{\text{Pumping Time, hour}}$$

Liquid polymer feed rates are often measured in pounds per day. To calculate this feed rate we need to know the strength of the polymer solution as a percent or as milligrams per liter, the specific gravity of the solution, the volume pumped and the time period.

$$\text{Polymer Feed, lbs/day} = \frac{(\text{Poly Conc, mg/}L)(\text{Vol Pumped, m}L)(60 \text{ min/hr})(24 \text{ hr/day})}{(\text{Time Pumped, min})(1{,}000 \text{ m}L/L)(1{,}000 \text{ mg/gm})(454 \text{ gm/lb})}$$

To determine the actual feed from a dry chemical feeder, we need to know the pounds of chemical fed and the time period.

$$\text{Chemical Feed, lbs/day} = \frac{(\text{Chemical Fed, lbs})(60 \text{ min/hr})(24 \text{ hr/day})}{\text{Time, minutes}}$$

EXAMPLE 2

A chemical feed pump lowered the chemical solution in a four-foot diameter chemical storage tank two feet during a seven-hour period. Estimate the flow delivered by the pump in gallons per minute and gallons per day.

Known		Unknown
Tank Diameter, ft	= 4 ft	Flow, GPM
Chemical Drop, ft	= 2 ft	Flow, GPD
Time, hr	= 7 hr	

1. Determine the volume of water pumped in gallons.

   Volume, gal = (0.785)(Diameter, ft)^2(Drop, ft)(7.48 gal/cu ft)

   = (0.785)(4 ft)^2(2 ft)(7.48 gal/cu ft)

   = 188 gal

2. Calculate the flow from the chemical feed pump in gallons per minute.

   $$\text{Flow, GPM} = \frac{\text{Volume Pumped, gal}}{(\text{Pumping Time, hr})(60 \text{ min/hr})}$$

   $$= \frac{188 \text{ gal}}{(7 \text{ hr})(60 \text{ min/hr})}$$

   = 0.45 GPM

3. Calculate the flow from the chemical feed pump in gallons per day.

$$\text{Flow, GPD} = \frac{(\text{Volume Pumped, gal})(24 \text{ hr/day})}{\text{Pumping Time, hr}}$$

$$= \frac{(188 \text{ gal})(24 \text{ hr/day})}{7 \text{ hr}}$$

$$= 645 \text{ GPD}$$

EXAMPLE 3

Determine the chemical feed in pounds of polymer per day from a chemical feed pump. The polymer solution is 2.0 percent or 20,000 mg polymer per liter. Assume a specific gravity of the polymer solution of 1.0. During a test run the chemical feed pump delivered 750 mL of polymer solution during six minutes.

Known	Unknown
Polymer Solution, % = 2.0%	Polymer Feed, lbs/day
Polymer Conc, mg/L = 20,000 mg/L	
Polymer Sp Gr = 1.0	
Volume Pumped, mL = 750 mL	
Time Pumped, min = 6 min	

Calculate the polymer feed by the chemical feed pump in pounds of polymer per day.

$$\frac{\text{Polymer Feed,}}{\text{lbs/day}} = \frac{(\text{Poly Conc, mg/}L)(\text{Vol Pumped, m}L)(60 \text{ min/hr})(24 \text{ hr/day})}{(\text{Time Pumped, min})(1{,}000 \text{ m}L/L)(1{,}000 \text{ mg/gm})(454 \text{ gm/lb})}$$

$$= \frac{(20{,}000 \text{ mg/}L)(750 \text{ m}L)(60 \text{ min/hr})(24 \text{ hr/day})}{(6 \text{ min})(1{,}000 \text{ m}L/L)(1{,}000 \text{ mg/gm})(454 \text{ gm/lb})}$$

$$= 7.9 \text{ lbs polymer/day}$$

EXAMPLE 4

Determine the actual chemical fed in pounds per day from a dry chemical feeder. A pie tin placed under a chemical feeder collected 1,000 grams of chemical in five minutes.

Known	Unknown
Dry Chemical, gm = 1,000 gm	Chemical Feed, lbs/day
Time, min = 5 min	

Determine the chemical feed in pounds of chemical applied per day.

$$\frac{\text{Chemical Feed,}}{\text{lbs/day}} = \frac{(\text{Chemical Applied, gm})(60 \text{ min/hr})(24 \text{ hr/day})}{(454 \text{ gm/lb})(\text{Time, min})}$$

$$= \frac{(1{,}000 \text{ gm})(60 \text{ min/hr})(24 \text{ hr/day})}{(454 \text{ gm/lb})(5 \text{ min})}$$

$$= 635 \text{ lbs/day}$$

18.47 Chlorinators

Chlorine gas leaks around chlorinators or containers of chlorine will cause corrosion of equipment. Check every day for leaks. Large leaks will be detected by odor; small leaks may go unnoticed until damage results. A green or reddish deposit on metal indicates a chlorine leak. Any chlorine gas leakage in the presence of moisture will cause corrosion. Always plug the ends of any open connection to prevent moisture from entering the lines. Never pour water on a chlorine leak because this will only create a bigger problem by enlarging the leak. Chlorine gas reacts with water to form hydrochloric acid.

> **WARNING**
>
> ANOTHER IMPORTANT REASON FOR PREVENTING CHLORINE LEAKS IS THAT THE GAS IS TOXIC TO HUMANS.

Ammonia water will detect any chlorine leak. A small piece of cloth, soaked with ammonia water[22] and wrapped around the end of a short stick, makes a good leak detector. Wave this stick in the general area of the suspected leak (do not touch the equipment with it). If chlorine gas leakage is occurring, a white cloud of ammonium chloride will form. You should make this test at all gas pipe joints, both inside and outside the chlorinators, at regular intervals. Bottles of ammonia water should be kept tightly capped to avoid loss of strength. All pipe fittings must be kept tight to avoid leaks. *NEW GASKETS SHOULD BE USED FOR EACH NEW CONNECTION.*

Do not use a spray bottle in a room where large amounts of chlorine gas have already leaked into the air. After one squeeze, the entire area may be full of white smoke and you will have trouble locating the leak. Under these conditions, use a cloth soaked in ammonia water to look for leaks.

> **CAUTION**
>
> TO LOCATE A CHLORINE LEAK, DO NOT SPRAY OR SWAB EQUIPMENT WITH AMMONIA WATER! WAVE AN AMMONIA-SOAKED RAG OR PAINT BRUSH IN THE GENERAL AREA AND YOU CAN DETECT THE PRESENCE OF MANY LEAKS. SOME OPERATORS PREFER TO WAVE A STICK WITH A CLOTH ON THE END IN FRONT OF THEM WHEN THEY ARE LOOKING FOR CHLORINE LEAKS.

The exterior casing of chlorinators should be painted as required; however, most chlorinators manufactured recently have plastic cases that do not require protective coatings. A clean machine is a better operating machine. Parts of a chlorinator handling chlorine gas must be kept dry to prevent the chlorine and moisture from forming hydrochloric acid. Some parts may be cleaned, when required, first with water to remove water-soluble material, then with wood alcohol, followed by drying. The above chemicals leave no moisture residue. Another method would be to wash them with water and dry them over a pan or heater to remove all traces of moisture.

Water strainers on chlorinators frequently clog and require attention. They may be cleaned by flushing with water or, if badly fouled, they may be cleaned with diluted hydrochloric acid, followed with a water rinse.

The atmosphere vent lines from chlorinators must be open and free. These vent lines evacuate the chlorine to the outside

---

[22] *Use a concentrated ammonia solution containing 28 to 30 percent ammonia as NH_3 (this is the same as 58 percent ammonium hydroxide, NH_4OH, or commercial 26° Baume).*

atmosphere when the chlorinator is being shut down. Place a screen over the end of the pipe to keep insects from building a nest in the pipe and clogging it.

When chlorinators are removed from service, as much chlorine gas as possible should be removed from the supply lines and machines. The chlorine valves at the containers are shut off and the chlorinator injector is operated for a period to remove the chlorine gas. In "V" notch chlorinators, the rotameter goes to the bottom of the manometer tube when the chlorine gas has been expelled.

All chlorinators will give continuous trouble-free operation if properly maintained and operated. Each chlorinator manufacturer provides with each machine a maintenance and operations instruction booklet with line diagrams showing the operation of the component parts of the machine. Manufacturer's instructions should be followed for maintenance and lubrication of your particular chlorinator. If you do not have an instruction booklet, you may obtain one by contacting the manufacturer's representative in your area.

QUESTIONS

Write your answers in a notebook and then compare your answers with those on page 347.

18.4A   How can an operator locate information on how to operate, control, and maintain chemical feeders?

18.4B   List three common types of chemical feeders.

18.4C   Why should chlorine leaks be detected and repaired?

18.4D   How would you search for chlorine leaks?

18.5   TANKS AND RESERVOIRS [23]

18.50   Scheduling Inspections

Plant tanks should be drained and inspected at regular intervals. If the interior is well protected, five-year intervals between inspections may be sufficient. If the tank is below the surface of the ground, be sure the groundwater level is down far enough (below the bottom of the tank) so the tanks will not float on the groundwater when empty or develop cracks from groundwater pressure.

Schedule inspections of tanks and channels during periods of low plant demand so that plant operation won't be disrupted.

18.51   Steel Tanks

All steel tanks must be protected from rusting. Once metal is lost because of rusting, it can't be recovered. The exteriors of the tanks are easily inspected — don't forget the roof — and should be repainted, as needed, not only to protect the steel surface but to provide a pleasing appearance. The interiors of steel tanks are exposed to a much harsher environment due either to being constantly submerged or to constant high humidity.

Protective coatings for steel tank interiors must be carefully selected to provide superior protection and at the same time impart neither taste nor odors to the water. Proper surface

preparation and application is as important as the coating materials in getting interior protection that will last a reasonable period of time.

When interior tank recoating is required, schedule the work when plant demand is low but not during rainy weather when it may be impossible to maintain a dry steel surface warm enough to ensure proper curing of the coating. This type of work is usually done by outside contractors. Constant inspection is a must if the work is going to be completed according to the specifications.

18.52   Cathodic Protection [24]

An alternative to repainting the submerged interior surfaces of a steel water tank is installation of a cathodic protection system. The rusting of steel is accompanied by the flow of small electrical currents. Cathodic protection systems prevent rusting of bare steel surfaces by causing an electrical current to flow from anodes hung in the water to the tank surface. The polarity of this current is opposite to what it would be if rust were forming. The current can be obtained from sacrificial anodes that make the tank into a giant low voltage battery, or from electronic rectifiers that are powered from the commercial power lines.

Cathodic protection systems provide protection only so long as they are operating and properly adjusted. Systems with rectifiers should be checked weekly. The inspection consists of reading and recording the D.C. voltmeter and ammeter readings. Compare the readings with previous readings and with the readings recommended by the corrosion engineer or technician. Deviations from normal should be investigated without delay.

Once a year, a corrosion specialist should be called in to take potential profile readings on the inside of the tank and to set the rectifier and recommend new normal current settings. Over the years, as more and more of the interior tank coating fails, the bare surface area to be protected by the cathodic protection system will increase. For this reason, it is to be expected that the current required to provide protection will increase in small amounts or increments each year.

18.53   Concrete Tanks

Concrete tanks are not usually coated on the inside and are painted on the exterior for appearance purposes only. This would seem to indicate that maintenance on concrete tanks is minimal, but this may not be true. Concrete tanks are all reinforced with steel. Steel can rust. If too much steel is lost to rust, the structural strength of the tank can be threatened. Periodically inspect the tank for signs of rusting. This is particularly important for pre-stressed concrete tanks that have a tensioned wire wrap on the exterior. The wires are small in

---

[23] Also see WATER DISTRIBUTION SYSTEM OPERATION AND MAINTENANCE, Chapter 2, "Storage Facilities," Section 2.4, "Maintenance," in this series of manuals.

[24] Also see Chapter 8, "Corrosion Control," Section 8.45, "Cathodic Protection," in WATER TREATMENT PLANT OPERATION, Volume I.

diameter and even a small amount of rust could reduce the size of the wire to the point where it might fail.

QUESTIONS

Write your answers in a notebook and then compare your answers with those on page 347.

18.5A   How often should tanks and reservoirs be drained and inspected?

18.5B   Why must the groundwater level be below the bottom of a tank before it is drained?

18.5C   What is an alternative to applying a protective coating to prevent corrosion of a steel tank?

18.6 BUILDING MAINTENANCE

Building maintenance is another program that should receive attention on a regular schedule. Buildings in a treatment plant are usually built of sturdy materials to last for many years, if they are kept in good repair. In selecting paint for a treatment plant, it is always a good idea to have a painting expert help the operator select the types of paint needed to protect the buildings from deterioration. The expert also will have some good ideas as to color schemes to help blend the plant in with the surrounding area. Consideration should also be given to the quality of paint. A good quality, more expensive material will usually give better service over a longer period of time than the economy-type products.

Building maintenance programs depend on the age, type, and use of a building. New buildings require a thorough check to be certain essential items are available and working properly. Older buildings require careful watching and prompt attention to keep ahead of leaks, breakdowns, replacements when needed, and changing uses of the building. Attention must be given to the maintenance requirements of many items in all plant buildings, such as electrical systems, plumbing, heating, cooling, ventilating, floors, windows, roofs, and drainage around the buildings. Regularly scheduled examinations and necessary maintenance of these items can prevent many costly and time-consuming problems in the future.

In each plant building, periodically check all stairways, ladders, catwalks, and platforms for adequate lighting, head clearance, and sturdy and convenient guardrails. Protective devices should surround all moving equipment. Whenever any repairs, alterations, or additions are built, avoid building accident traps such as pipes laid on top of floors or hung from the ceiling at head height, which could create serious safety hazards.

Organized storage areas should be provided and maintained in an accessible and neat manner.

KEEP ALL BUILDINGS CLEAN AND ORDERLY. Janitorial work should be done on a regular schedule. All tools and plant equipment should be kept clean and in their proper place. Floors, walls, and windows should be cleaned at regular intervals in order to maintain a neat appearance. A treatment plant kept in a clean, orderly condition makes a safe place to work and aids in building good public and employee relations.

QUESTIONS

Write your answers in a notebook and then compare your answers with those on page 347.

18.6A   What items should be included in a building maintenance program?

18.6B   What factors influence the type of building maintenance program that might be needed for your water treatment plant?

18.7 ARITHMETIC ASSIGNMENT

Turn to the appendix at the back of this manual and read Section A.35, "Maintenance." Also work the example problems and check the arithmetic using your calculator. You should be able to get the same answers.

18.8 ADDITIONAL READING

1. *NEW YORK MANUAL*, Chapter 19*, "Treatment Plant Maintenance and Accident Prevention."

2. *TEXAS MANUAL*, Chapter 13*, "Pumps and Measurement of Pumps."

3. *PUMP HANDBOOK*, Second Edition, by Igor J. Karassik, William C. Krutzsch, Warren H. Fraser, and Joseph P. Messina. Obtain from McGraw-Hill, Inc., PO Box 182604, Columbus, OH 43272-3031. Price $115.50.

* Depends on edition.

18.9 ACKNOWLEDGMENTS

Major portions of this chapter were taken from the following California State University, Sacramento, Operator Manuals:

1. *OPERATION OF WASTEWATER TREATMENT PLANTS*, Volume II, Chapter 15, "Maintenance," by Norman Farnum, Stan Walton, John Brady, Roger Peterson, and Malcolm Carpenter.

2. *OPERATION AND MAINTENANCE OF WASTEWATER COLLECTION SYSTEMS*, Volume II, Chapter 9, "Equipment Maintenance," by Lee Doty.

3. *INDUSTRIAL WASTE TREATMENT*, Volume II, Chapter 8, "Maintenance," by Norman Farnum, Stan Walton, John Brady, Roger Peterson, and Malcolm Carpenter.

End of Lesson 5 of 5 Lessons
on
MAINTENANCE

Please answer the discussion and review questions before continuing with the Objective Test.

DISCUSSION AND REVIEW QUESTIONS

Chapter 18. MAINTENANCE

(Lesson 5 of 5 Lessons)

Write the answers to these questions in your notebook before continuing with the Objective Test on page 348. The question numbering continues from Lesson 4.

36. What factors could cause gasoline engine starting problems?

37. What is the purpose of the filters in the diesel fuel system?

38. What are the advantages of air-cooled diesel engines as compared with water-cooled types?

39. Why is rust a problem in water-cooled systems?

40. How should large quantities of gasoline be stored?

41. Why is "idling" not a satisfactory method of testing standby engines?

42. Why should dry chemical feeders and hoppers be kept clean and dry?

43. What problems can be caused by chlorine gas leaks around chlorinators or containers of chlorine?

44. Why should a treatment plant be kept in a clean and orderly condition?

SUGGESTED ANSWERS

Chapter 18. MAINTENANCE

ANSWERS TO QUESTIONS IN LESSON 1

Answers to questions on page 240.

18.0A A good maintenance program is essential for a water treatment plant to operate at peak efficiency.

18.0B The most important item is maintenance of the mechanical equipment — pumps, valves, scrapers, and other moving equipment. Other items include plant buildings and grounds.

18.0C A good record system tells when maintenance is due and also provides a record of equipment performance.

18.0D Both cards are vital in a good recordkeeping system. The equipment service card is a permanent or master card that indicates what maintenance is required and how often each service item should be performed. The service record card is a record of who did what work on what date and is helpful in determining when the future maintenance work is due.

18.0E Emergency phone numbers for a treatment plant should include the phone numbers for police, fire, hospital and/or physician, responsible plant officials, local emergency disaster office, emergency team, and CHEMTREC, (800) 424-9300.

18.0F Stored energy must be bled down to prevent its sudden release, which could injure an operator working on the system or equipment.

Answers to questions on page 241.

18.10A Unqualified or inexperienced people must be extremely careful when attempting to troubleshoot or repair electrical equipment because they can be seriously injured and damage costly equipment if a mistake is made.

18.10B When machinery is not shut off, locked out, and tagged properly, the following accidents could occur:

1. Maintenance operator could be cleaning pump and have it start, thus losing an arm, hand, or finger;

2. Electric motors or controls not properly grounded could lead to possible severe shock, paralysis, or death; and

3. Improper circuits such as a wrong connection, safety devices jumped, wrong fuses, or improper wiring can cause fires or injuries due to incorrect operation of machinery.

Answers to questions on page 243.

18.11A The proper voltage and allowable current in amps for a piece of equipment can be determined by reading the nameplate information or the instruction manual for the equipment.

18.11B The two types of current are Direct Current (D.C.) and Alternating Current (A.C.).

18.11C Amperage is a measurement of work being done or "how hard the electricity is working."

Answers to questions on page 250.

18.12A You test for voltage by using a voltage tester.

18.12B A voltage tester can be used to test for voltage, open circuits, blown fuses, single phasing of motors and grounds.

18.12C Before attempting to change fuses, turn off power and check both power lines for voltage. Use a fuse puller.

18.12D If the voltage is unknown and the voltmeter has different scales that are manually set, always start with the highest voltage range and work down. Otherwise the voltmeter could be damaged.

18.12E Amp readings different from the nameplate rating could be caused by low voltage, bad bearings, poor connections, or excessive load.

18.12F Motors and wirings should be megged at least once a year, and twice a year if possible.

18.12G An ohmmeter is used to test the control circuit components such as coils, fuses, relays, resistors, and switches.

Answers to questions on page 251.

18.13A The two types of safety devices in main electrical panels or control units are fuses or circuit breakers.

18.13B Fuses are used to protect operators, wiring, circuits, heaters, motors, and various other electrical equipment.

18.13C A fuse must never be bypassed or jumped because the fuse may be the only protection the circuit has; without it, serious damage to equipment and possible injury to operators can occur.

18.13D A circuit breaker is a switch that is opened automatically when the current or the voltage exceeds or falls below a certain limit. Unlike a fuse that has to be replaced each time it "blows," a circuit breaker can be reset after a short delay to allow time for cooling.

18.13E Motor starters can be either manually or automatically controlled.

18.13F Magnetic starters are generally used to start pumps, compressors, blowers, and anything where automatic or remote control is desired.

Answers to questions on page 255.

18.14A Electrical energy is commonly converted into mechanical energy by electric motors.

18.14B An electric motor usually consists of a stator, rotor, end bells, and windings.

18.14C Motors can be kept trouble free with proper lubrication and maintenance.

18.14D Motor nameplate data should be recorded, compared with manufacturer's data sheets and instructions, and placed in a file for future reference. Many times the nameplate is painted, corroded, or is missing from the unit when the information is needed to repair the motor or replace parts.

Answers to questions on page 256.

18.14E The key to effective troubleshooting is combining practical, step-by-step procedures with a common-sense approach.

18.14F When troubleshooting:

A. Gather preliminary information.
B. Inspect:
1. Contacts,
2. Mechanical parts, and
3. Magnetic parts.

18.14G Types of information that should be recorded regarding electrical equipment include nameplate data and every change, repair, and test.

Answers to questions on page 266.

18.15A A qualified electrician should perform most of the necessary maintenance and repair of electrical equipment to avoid endangering lives and to avoid damage to equipment.

18.15B The purpose of a "kirk-key" system (one key is used for two locks) is to ensure proper connection of standby power into your power distribution system. The commercial power system must be locked out by the use of switch gear before the standby power is connected to your power distribution system.

18.15C Battery-powered backup lighting units are considered better than engine-driven power sources because they are more economical. If you have a momentary power outage, the system responds without an engine-generator start-up.

18.15D If water lost from a lead-acid battery is replaced with tap water, the impurities in the water will become attached to the lead plates and shorten the life of the battery.

Answers to questions on page 267.

18.16A Electricity is transmitted at high voltage to reduce the size of transmission lines.

18.16B If outdoor transformers have exposed high voltage wires, the following precautions must be taken:

1. An eight-foot (2.4-m) high fence is required to prevent accessibility by unqualified or unauthorized persons; and
2. Signs attached to the fence must indicate "High Voltage."

18.16C The treatment plant operator must keep the exterior and surroundings of the switch gear clean.

18.16D Symptoms that a power distribution transformer may be in need of maintenance or repair include unusual noises, high or low oil levels, oil leaks, or high operating temperatures.

Answers to questions on page 267.

18.17A Electrical safety checklists are used to make operators aware of potential electrical hazards in their water treatment plant.

18.17B Rusted conduits are of concern because they could become the source of a spark which could cause an explosion.

ANSWERS TO QUESTIONS IN LESSON 2

Answers to questions on page 278.

18.20A Pieces of equipment and special tools commonly found in a pump repair shop include welding equipment, lathes, drill press and drills, power hacksaw, flame-cutting equipment, micrometers, calipers, gages, portable electric tools, grinders, a forcing press, metal-spray equipment, and sandblasting equipment.

18.21A The purpose of a pump impeller is to suck water in the suction piping and to throw water out between the impeller blades.

18.21B A suitable screen should be installed on the intake end of suction piping to prevent foreign matter (sticks, refuse) from being sucked into the pump and clogging or wearing the impeller.

18.21C Suction piping must be up-sloping to prevent air pockets from forming in the top of a pipe where air could be drawn into the pump and cause the loss of suction.

18.21D Cavitation is the formation and collapse of a gas pocket or bubble on the blade of an impeller. The collapse of this gas pocket or bubble drives water into the impeller with a terrific force that can cause pitting on the impeller surface.

18.21E An advantage of a double-suction pump is that the longitudinal thrust from the water entering the impeller is balanced.

Answers to questions on page 283.

18.22A The purpose of lubrication is to reduce friction between two surfaces and to remove heat caused by friction.

18.22B Oils in service tend to become acid (contaminated) and may cause corrosion, deposits, sludging, and other problems.

18.22C To ensure proper lubrication of equipment, determine the proper lubrication schedule, lubricant, and amount of lubricant, and prepare a lubrication chart.

Answers to questions on page 284.

18.22D A soft grease has a low viscosity index as compared with a hard grease.

18.22E Oil is used with higher speeds.

18.22F Overfilling with oil or grease can result in high pressures and temperatures, and ruined seals or other components.

ANSWERS TO QUESTIONS IN LESSON 3

Answers to questions on page 292.

18.23A A cross connection is a connection between two piping systems where an undesirable water (water from water seal) could enter a domestic water supply.

18.23B Yes. A slight leakage is desirable when a pump is running to keep the packing cool and in good condition.

18.23C To measure the capacity of a pump, measure the volume pumped during a specific time period.

$$\text{Capacity, GPM} = \frac{\text{Volume, gallons}}{\text{Time, minutes}}$$

or

$$\text{Capacity, } \frac{\text{liters}}{\text{sec}} = \frac{\text{Volume, liters}}{\text{Time, sec}}$$

18.23D

$$\text{Capacity, GPM} = \frac{\text{Volume, gallons}}{\text{Time, minutes}}$$

$$= \frac{(10 \text{ ft})(15 \text{ ft})(1.7 \text{ ft})(7.5 \text{ gal/cu ft})}{5 \text{ minutes}}$$

$$= 382.5 \text{ GPM}$$

or

$$\text{Capacity, } \frac{\text{liters}}{\text{sec}} = \frac{\text{Volume, liters}}{\text{Time, sec}}$$

$$= \frac{(3 \text{ m})(5 \text{ m})(0.5 \text{ m})(1,000 \text{ } L/\text{cu m})}{(5 \text{ minutes})(60 \text{ sec/min})}$$

$$= 25 \text{ liters/sec}$$

18.23E Before a prolonged shutdown, the pump should be drained to prevent damage from corrosion, sedimentation, and freezing. Also, the motor disconnect switch should be opened to disconnect the motor.

Answers to questions on page 294.

18.23F Shear pins commonly fail in reciprocating pumps because of (1) a solid object lodged under piston, (2) a clogged discharge line, or (3) a stuck or wedged valve.

18.23G A noise may develop when pumping thin sludge due to water hammer, but it will disappear when heavy sludge is pumped.

18.23H Higher than normal discharge pressures in a progressive cavity pump may indicate a line blockage or a closed valve downstream.

Answers to questions on page 294.

18.23I When checking an electric motor, the following items should be checked periodically, as well as when trouble develops:

1. Motor condition,
2. Note all unusual conditions,
3. Lubricate bearings,
4. Listen to motor, and
5. Check temperature.

18.23J The purpose of a stethoscope is to magnify sounds and carry them to the ear. This instrument is used to detect unusual sounds in electric motors such as whines, gratings, or uneven noises.

Answers to questions on page 298.

18.23K A properly adjusted horizontal belt has a slight bow in the slack side when running. When idle, it has an alive springiness when thumped with the hand. Vertical belts should have a springiness when thumped. To check for proper alignment, place a straightedge against the pulley face or faces. If a ruler won't work, use a transit for long runs, or the belt may be examined for wear.

18.23L Always replace worn sprockets when replacing a chain because old, out-of-pitch sprockets cause as much chain wear in a few hours as years of normal operation.

Answers to questions on page 300.

18.23M Improper original installation of equipment, settling of foundations, heavy floor loadings, warping of bases, and excessive bearing wear could cause couplings to become out of alignment.

18.23N Shear pins are designed to fail if a sudden overload occurs that could damage expensive equipment.

Answers to questions on page 302.

18.24A Pumps must be lubricated in accordance with manufacturer's recommendations. Quality lubricants should be used.

18.24B In lubricating motors, too much grease may cause bearing trouble or damage the winding.

Answers to questions on page 303.

18.24C If a pump will not start, check for blown fuses or tripped circuit breakers and the cause. Also check for a loose connection, fuse, or thermal unit.

18.24D To increase the rate of discharge from a pump, you should look for something causing the reduced rate of discharge, such as pumping air, motor malfunction, plugged lines or valves, impeller problems, or other factors.

Answers to questions on page 304.

18.24E If a pump that has been locked or tagged out for maintenance or repairs is started, an operator working on the pump could be seriously injured and also equipment could be damaged.

18.24F Normally a centrifugal pump should be started after the discharge valve is opened. Exceptions are treatment processes or piping systems with vacuums or pressures that cannot be dropped or allowed to fluctuate greatly while an alternate pump is put on the line. (If the pump is not equipped with a check valve and the discharge pressure is higher than the suction pressure under static conditions, the pump could run backward and cause damage to the equipment.)

Answers to questions on page 306.

18.24G Before stopping an operating pump:

1. Start another pump (if appropriate); and
2. Inspect the operating pump by looking for developing problems, required adjustments, and problem conditions of the unit.

18.24H A pump shaft or motor will spin backward if water being pumped flows back through the pump when the pump is shut off. This will occur if there is a faulty check valve or foot valve in the system.

18.24I The position of all valves should be checked before starting a pump to ensure that the water being pumped will go where intended.

Answers to questions on page 306.

18.24J The most important rule regarding the operation of positive displacement pumps is to NEVER start the pump against a closed discharge valve.

18.24K If a positive displacement pump is started against a closed discharge valve, the pipe, valve, or pump could rupture from excessive pressure. The rupture will damage equipment and possibly seriously injure or kill someone standing nearby.

18.24L Both ends of a sludge line should never be closed tight at the same time because gas from decomposition can build up and rupture pipes or valves.

ANSWERS TO QUESTIONS IN LESSON 4

Answers to questions on page 309.

18.25A Compressors are used with water ejectors, pump control systems (bubblers), valve operators, and water pressure systems. Also they are used to operate portable pneumatic tools such as jackhammers, compactors, air drills, sandblasters, tapping machines, and air pumps.

18.25B The frequency of cleaning a suction filter on a compressor depends on the use of a compressor and the atmosphere around it. The filter should be inspected at least monthly and cleaned or replaced every three to six months. More frequent inspection, cleaning, and replacement are required under dusty conditions such as near jackhammer operation on a street.

18.25C Compressor oil should be changed at least every three months, unless the manufacturer states differently. If there are filters in the oil system, these also should be changed.

18.25D Drain the condensate from the air receiver daily.

18.25E Before testing belt tension on a compressor with your hands, MAKE SURE THE COMPRESSOR IS LOCKED OFF.

Answers to questions on page 325.

18.26A Valves are the controlling devices placed in piping systems to stop, regulate, check, divert, or otherwise modify the flow of liquids or gases.

18.26B Five common types of valves found in water treatment facilities include gate valves, globe valves, eccentric valves, butterfly valves, and check valves.

18.26C The most common maintenance required by gate valves is oiling, tightening, or replacing the stem stuffing box packing.

18.26D The purpose of the check valve is to allow water to flow in one direction only.

18.26E Backflow prevention by check valves is essential in many applications to:

1. Prevent pumps from reversing when power is removed,
2. Protect water systems from being cross-connected,
3. Aid in pump operation as a dampener, and
4. Ensure "full pipe" operation.

ANSWERS TO QUESTIONS IN LESSON 5

Answers to questions on page 328.

18.30A Gasoline engines may be used in water treatment plants to drive pumps, generators, tractors, and vehicles.

18.30B If a gasoline engine will not start, check the following items:

1. No fuel in tank, valve closed,
2. Carburetor not choked,
3. Water or dirt in fuel lines or carburetor,
4. Carburetor flooded,
5. Low compression,
6. Loose spark plug, and
7. No spark at plug.

18.30C A gasoline engine may not run properly due to:

1. Engine misses,
2. Engine surging,
3. Engine stopping,
4. Engine overheating,
5. Engine knocking, and
6. Engine backfiring through carburetor.

Answers to questions on page 329.

18.30D If a gasoline engine will not start and the spark plug is wet with oil or fuel, this could indicate that the cylinder is flooded with fuel from having the choke on too long.

18.30E If a gasoline engine will not start and there is an oil residue on the spark plug, this could indicate worn piston rings.

18.30F After an engine has started, give it an opportunity to warm up before applying the load.

Answers to questions on page 335.

18.31A Gasoline is not used as a fuel in diesel engines because it would start to burn from the heat generated by compression before the piston reached the top of the stroke.

18.31B The four basic parts of a diesel fuel system are:

1. Primary fuel filter,
2. Secondary fuel filter,
3. Fuel injection pump, and
4. Fuel injector.

18.31C The purpose of the fuel injection pump is to deliver fuel to the injector at a very high pressure.

18.32A Heat is removed from the cylinders by a water cooling system. Each cylinder is surrounded with a water jacket through which the coolant (water) circulates and pulls heat from the cylinder. This is accomplished by a water pump that is belt driven from the crankshaft.

Answers to questions on page 336.

18.33A The storage and use of fuels for internal combustion engines must be in accordance with building and fire codes.

18.33B Four types of fuels commonly used by internal combustion engines include (1) diesel, (2) gasoline, (3) liquified petroleum gas (LPG), and (4) natural gas.

18.34A Standby internal combustion engines not in regular service should be started up and test run at least once a week.

18.34B Standby engines should be test run long enough for the engine to come up to its normal operating temperature. If at all possible, the engine should be run under its normal load.

Answers to questions on page 341.

18.4A Information on how to operate, control, and maintain chemical feeders may be found in the feeder manufacturer's literature.

18.4B The three common types of chemical feeders are (1) solid feeders, (2) liquid feeders, and (3) gas feeders.

18.4C Chlorine is toxic to humans and will cause corrosion damage to equipment.

18.4D Large chlorine leaks can be detected by smell. Small leaks are detected by soaking a cloth with ammonia water and holding the cloth near areas where leaks might develop. A white cloud will indicate the presence of a leak.

Answers to questions on page 342.

18.5A Tanks and reservoirs should be drained and inspected at least once every five years if the interior is well protected, more often if it is not well protected.

18.5B The groundwater level should be below the bottom of a tank before it is drained so the tank will not float on the groundwater when empty or develop cracks from groundwater pressure.

18.5C Cathodic protection is an alternative to applying a protective coating to prevent corrosion of a steel tank.

Answers to questions on page 342.

18.6A A building maintenance program will keep the building in good shape and includes painting when necessary. Attention also must be given to electrical systems, plumbing, heating, cooling, ventilating, floors, windows, and roofs. The building should be kept clean, tools should be stored in their proper place, and essential storage should be available.

18.6B Factors that influence the type of building maintenance program needed by a water treatment plant include the age, type, and use of each building.

OBJECTIVE TEST

Chapter 18.   MAINTENANCE

Please write your name and mark the correct answers on the answer sheet, as directed at the end of Chapter 1. There may be more than one correct answer to each multiple-choice question.

True-False

1. Repair costs for poorly maintained equipment usually exceed the cost of maintenance.
   1. True
   2. False

2. One person should never attempt an emergency repair alone.
   1. True
   2. False

3. Electricity will flow through a circuit when a switch is open.
   1. True
   2. False

4. A fuse must never be bypassed or jumped.
   1. True
   2. False

5. A rod driven into dry ground is very effective as an electrical ground.
   1. True
   2. False

6. All of the information on a motor nameplate should be recorded and placed in a file for future reference.
   1. True
   2. False

7. Electrical problems result from some type of mechanical failure.
   1. True
   2. False

8. Never attempt electrical work that you are not qualified to do or are not authorized to perform.
   1. True
   2. False

9. Transformer oil can be revitalized by a cleaning procedure that is accomplished at the transformer site.
   1. True
   2. False

10. Keep the right amount of the right lubricant in bearings at all times.
    1. True
    2. False

11. Too much oil will harm sleeve bearings.
    1. True
    2. False

12. Too much grease in antifriction type bearings (ball or roller) promotes friction and heat.
    1. True
    2. False

13. The main job of grease in antifriction bearings is to protect steel elements against friction.
    1. True
    2. False

14. Never operate a piston pump against a closed discharge valve.
    1. True
    2. False

15. Water is a good lubricant.
    1. True
    2. False

16. Lighter viscosity oils are recommended for low speeds.
    1. True
    2. False

17. Replace only damaged V-belts on a multiple-drive unit.
    1. True
    2. False

18. Lubricate underwater chains which operate in contact with considerable grit.
    1. True
    2. False

19. A pump should be run before being primed.
    1. True
    2. False

20. Safety guards must be installed over and around all centrifugal pump moving parts.
    1. True
    2. False

Best Answer (Select only the closest or best answer.)

21. What should you do when maintenance tasks are beyond your capabilities or repair facilities?
    1. Read manufacturer's literature
    2. Request assistance
    3. Substitute alternative procedures
    4. Try to perform maintenance task

22. What is the best way an operator can keep track of a preventive maintenance program?

    1. Good recordkeeping
    2. Keeping supervisor informed of completed work
    3. Remembering when tasks were performed
    4. Telling another operator what work was done

23. What should a maintenance operator know about electricity?

    1. Enough to explain to an electrician what is happening when equipment fails
    2. How to wire electrical control panels
    3. Repair electrical problems when equipment fails
    4. Troubleshoot and solve electrical problems when equipment fails

24. What could happen if battery cables are not properly connected?

    1. An arc of electricity across the battery could cause an explosion
    2. The battery will be "dead" again
    3. The engine will consume too much gas
    4. The vehicle will run too fast

25. What does electrical voltage measure?

    1. Electrical pressure available to cause a flow of current
    2. Indication of work being done
    3. Rate at which power is being used
    4. Resistance to the flow of current

26. Why should the electrical panel door be closed when using a voltage tester if the circuit is energized and the voltage is high?

    1. Circuit breakers could open and cause serious injury
    2. Electricity flowing through an open door could cause serious injury
    3. Hot copper sparks could cause serious injury
    4. Voltage readings may be inaccurate

27. Why is current imbalance undesirable?

    1. Decreases power consumption
    2. Loosens connections
    3. Overheats motors
    4. Shortens life expectancy of insulation

28. What is the use of a megger?

    1. Checks circuit breakers
    2. Checks electrical circuits
    3. Checks insulation resistance on motors
    4. Checks power drawn by a motor

29. How are three-phase motors usually protected?

    1. Amp meters
    2. Circuit breakers
    3. Fuses
    4. Overload relays

30. Why should amperage and voltage readings on motors be taken periodically?

    1. To check on need for maintenance
    2. To determine remaining life of motor
    3. To ensure proper operation
    4. To evaluate effectiveness of maintenance program

31. What should be the status of commercial power into a plant when operating standby power at full load?

    1. Allowed to handle peak demands
    2. Left on
    3. Shut off
    4. Used to power noncritical equipment

32. How can the starting load on pump motors be reduced?

    1. By increasing cavitation
    2. By increasing suction lift
    3. By throttling or closing the pump discharge valve
    4. By throttling or closing the pump suction valve

33. What is the cause of pump cavitation?

    1. Impeller RPM too low
    2. Pressures above design inlet pressures
    3. Pump operating at below-design flows
    4. Unusually low pressures within a pump

34. Why should bearing grease be purchased in cartridge form?

    1. Because the cartridge form is cheaper
    2. For ease of applying the lubricant
    3. To facilitate ultimate disposal of used cartridges
    4. To minimize the chance of getting dirt into the lubricant

35. What should be checked if pump sleeve bearings run too hot?

    1. Ambient temperature
    2. Antifriction bearings
    3. Lack of lubrication
    4. Overlubrication

36. Why is maintaining proper tension and alignment of belt drives important?

    1. Creates proper working conditions
    2. Ensures long life of belts and sheaves
    3. Keeps belts clean
    4. Requires intensive maintenance

37. What should be done if a centrifugal pump is vibrating excessively after start-up?

    1. Lower pump speed
    2. Reduce discharge pressure head
    3. Reduce flows
    4. Shut unit down and isolate pump

38. What problem could develop if a pump is stopped suddenly?

    1. Cavitation damage could result
    2. Pump vibrations could continue
    3. Water demands might not be met
    4. Water hammer damage could result

39. What could be the cause of a higher than normal pump suction vacuum?

    1. Higher suction water level
    2. Partially plugged suction line
    3. Worn pump impeller
    4. Worn wearing rings

40. What is the primary use of a butterfly valve?

1. Control flow
2. Measure flow
3. Regulate flow pressure
4. Stop flow

Multiple Choice (Select all correct answers.)

41. What items are included in a successful maintenance program?

1. Buildings
2. Mechanical equipment
3. Operation
4. Plant grounds
5. Structures

42. What information should be included on an equipment service card?

1. Date each maintenance task was completed
2. Description of each required maintenance service
3. Frequency of required services
4. References that provide instructions for each task
5. Signature of the person who performed the task

43. Emergency procedures must be established for operators to follow for what types of emergencies?

1. Broken distribution main
2. Discharge of toxic chemicals into raw water supply
3. Power outage
4. Release of chlorine
5. Taste or odor complaint from outraged consumer

44. A voltage tester can be used to check or test for which items?

1. Blown fuses
2. Electrical grounds
3. Open circuits
4. Power
5. Single phasing of motors

45. What factors could cause ammeter readings that are different from the nameplate rating?

1. Bad bearings
2. Excessive load
3. Low voltage
4. Overheating
5. Poor connections

46. What are fuses installed to protect?

1. Circuits
2. Electrical equipment
3. Heaters
4. Motors
5. Operators

47. What are the causes of most of the trouble encountered with electric motors?

1. Bad bearings
2. Excessive moisture
3. Overloaded circuits
4. Shorted windings
5. Tripped circuit breakers

48. What are the possible causes of coils overheating in electric motors?

1. High ambient temperature
2. Overload
3. Overvoltage
4. Rust on pole faces increasing air gap
5. Shorted turns caused by corrosion

49. What are possible causes of a motor not starting when the switch is on and not defective?

1. Driven machine may be jammed
2. Incorrect power supply
3. Incorrectly connected
4. Internal circuitry open
5. Rotating parts of motor may be jammed mechanically

50. What are possible causes of bearing failures?

1. Entry of water into bearing housing
2. Frequent starts and stops
3. Lack of or improper lubricant
4. Mechanical unbalance of rotating parts
5. Misalignment of coupling

51. What are possible causes of pump and motor misalignment?

1. Bolts loosening
2. Electrical overload
3. Piping can change pump position
4. Pumping overload
5. Uneven settling of foundations

52. Cavitation can cause what types of problems?

1. Drop in pump efficiency
2. Excessive pressures on impeller
3. Noise
4. Rapid damage to impeller
5. Vibration

53. What special precautions must be followed when handling or storing oils and greases?

1. Avoid creating a fire hazard
2. Keep any spills wiped up
3. Keep materials and containers clean
4. Make sure lids are tight on containers
5. Post "NO SMOKING" signs in area

54. What dangers can result from overfilling with either grease or oil?

1. High pressures
2. High temperatures
3. More frequent lubrication
4. Ruined antifriction bearings
5. Ruined seals

55. Why should a pump be drained for long-term shutdown? To protect pump against

1. Corrosion.
2. Freezing.
3. Improper start-up.
4. Overheating.
5. Sedimentation.

56. What are some unusual conditions for electric motors?

1. Bearings smelling hot
2. Excessive humming
3. Excessive sparking at brushes
4. Rapid knocking
5. Vibration

57. Which pump valves should be shut tightly when a pump is shut down?

1. Air relief
2. Check valves
3. Discharge
4. Suction
5. Water-seal lines

58. What could be the causes of a reduced rate of discharge from a pump?

    1. Air in water
    2. Check valves stuck or clogged
    3. Discharge head too high
    4. Pump not primed
    5. Suction lift greater than anticipated

59. Estimate the pumping capacity of a pump in gallons per minute if it takes 14 minutes for the water level in a tank to drop 3 feet. The tank is 8 feet in diameter.

    1. 14 GPM
    2. 31 GPM
    3. 72 GPM
    4. 80 GPM
    5. 90 GPM

60. Calculate the feed rate of a dry chemical feeder in pounds per day if 4.0 pounds of chemical are caught in a weighing tin during 14 minutes.

    1. 180 lbs/day
    2. 206 lbs/day
    3. 310 lbs/day
    4. 410 lbs/day
    5. 1,440 lbs/day

End of Objective Test

CHAPTER 19

INSTRUMENTATION

by

Leonard Ainsworth

TABLE OF CONTENTS

Chapter 19. INSTRUMENTATION

Page

OBJECTIVES 356

WORDS 357

SYMBOLS 361

LESSON 1

19.0   IMPORTANCE AND NATURE OF MEASUREMENT AND CONTROL SYSTEMS 365

    19.00   Need for Understanding Measurement and Control Systems 365

    19.01   Importance to Waterworks Operator 365

    19.02   Purpose and Nature of the Measurement Process 365

    19.03   Explanation of Control Systems 366

19.1   SAFETY HAZARDS OF INSTRUMENTATION WORK 368

    19.10   Be Careful 368

    19.11   Electrical Hazards 368

    19.12   Mechanical Hazards 370

    19.13   Vaults and Other Confined Spaces 371

    19.14   Falls 371

19.2   MEASURED VARIABLES AND TYPES OF SENSORS/TRANSMITTERS 371

    19.20   How Variables Are Measured 371

    19.21   Pressure 372

    19.22   Level 372

    19.23   Flow (Rate of Flow and Total Flow) 379

    19.24   Chemical Feed Rate 383

    19.25   Process Instrumentation 383

    19.26   Signal Transmitters/Transducers 383

DISCUSSION AND REVIEW QUESTIONS 386

LESSON 2

19.3   CATEGORIES OF INSTRUMENTATION 386

    19.30   Measuring Elements 386

    19.31   Panel Instruments 386

        19.310   Indicators 386

        19.311   Indicators/Recorders 386

        19.312   Recorders 387

	19.313	Totalizers	390
	19.314	Alarms	390
	19.32	Automatic Controller	391
	19.33	Pump Controllers	391
	19.34	Telemetering Links (Phone Lines)	393
	19.35	Air Supply Systems	395
	19.36	Laboratory Instruments	397
	19.37	Test and Calibration Equipment	397
19.4		OPERATION AND PREVENTIVE MAINTENANCE	398
	19.40	Proper Care of Instruments	398
	19.41	Indications of Proper Function	398
	19.42	Start-up/Shutdown Considerations	401
	19.43	Maintenance Procedures and Records	401
	19.44	Operational Checks	402
	19.45	Preventive Maintenance	402
19.5		ADDITIONAL READING	403
DISCUSSION AND REVIEW QUESTIONS			403
SUGGESTED ANSWERS			404
OBJECTIVE TEST			406

OBJECTIVES

Chapter 19.   INSTRUMENTATION

Following completion of Chapter 19, you should be able to:

1. Explain the purpose and nature of measurement and control systems,

2. Identify, avoid, and correct safety hazards associated with instrumentation work,

3. Recognize various types of sensors and transducers,

4. Operate and maintain measurement and control instruments,

5. Read instruments and make proper adjustments in operation of waterworks facilities, and

6. Determine location and cause of measurement and control system failures and take corrective action.

WORDS

Chapter 19. INSTRUMENTATION

ACCURACY ACCURACY

How closely an instrument measures the true or actual value of the process variable being measured or sensed.

ALARM CONTACT ALARM CONTACT

A switch that operates when some preset low, high or abnormal condition exists.

ANALOG ANALOG

The readout of an instrument by a pointer (or other indicating means) against a dial or scale.

ANALYZER ANALYZER

A device which conducts periodic or continuous measurement of some factor such as chlorine, fluoride or turbidity. Analyzers operate by any of several methods including photocells, conductivity or complex instrumentation.

CALIBRATION CALIBRATION

A procedure which checks or adjusts an instrument's accuracy by comparison with a standard or reference.

CONTACTOR CONTACTOR

An electric switch, usually magnetically operated.

CONTROL LOOP CONTROL LOOP

The path through the control system between the sensor, which measures a process variable, and the controller, which controls or adjusts the process variable.

CONTROL SYSTEM CONTROL SYSTEM

An instrumentation system which senses and controls its own operation on a close, continuous basis in what is called proportional (or modulating) control.

CONTROLLER CONTROLLER

A device which controls the starting, stopping, or operation of a device or piece of equipment.

DESICCANT (DESS-uh-kant) DESICCANT

A drying agent which is capable of removing or absorbing moisture from the atmosphere in a small enclosure.

DESICCATION (DESS-uh-KAY-shun) DESICCATION

A process used to thoroughly dry air; to remove virtually all moisture from air.

DETECTION LAG DETECTION LAG

The time period between the moment a process change is made and the moment when such a change is finally sensed by the associated measuring instrument.

DIGITAL READOUT DIGITAL READOUT

Use of numbers to indicate the value or measurement of a variable. The readout of an instrument by a direct, numerical reading of the measured value. The signal sent to such readouts is usually an analog signal.

DRIFT DRIFT

The difference between the actual value and the desired value (or set point); characteristic of proportional controllers that do not incorporate reset action. Also called OFFSET.

EFFECTIVE RANGE   EFFECTIVE RANGE

That portion of the design range (usually from 10 to 90+ percent) in which an instrument has acceptable accuracy. Also see RANGE and SPAN.

FEEDBACK   FEEDBACK

The circulating action between a sensor measuring a process variable and the controller which controls or adjusts the process variable.

HERTZ   HERTZ

The number of complete electromagnetic cycles or waves in one second of an electric or electronic circuit. Also called the frequency of the current. Abbreviated Hz.

INTEGRATOR   INTEGRATOR

A device or meter that continuously measures and calculates (adds) a process rate variable in cumulative fashion; for example, total flows displayed in gallons, million gallons, cubic feet, or some other unit of volume measurement. Also called a TOTALIZER.

INTERLOCK   INTERLOCK

An electric switch, usually magnetically operated. Used to interrupt all (local) power to a panel or device when the door is opened or the circuit is exposed to service.

LEVEL CONTROL   LEVEL CONTROL

A float device (or pressure switch) which senses changes in a measured variable and opens or closes a switch in response to that change. In its simplest form, this control might be a floating ball connected mechanically to a switch or valve such as is used to stop water flow into a toilet when the tank is full.

LINEARITY (LYNN-ee-AIR-it-ee)   LINEARITY

How closely an instrument measures actual values of a variable through its effective range; a measure used to determine the accuracy of an instrument.

MEASURED VARIABLE   MEASURED VARIABLE

A characteristic or component part that is sensed and quantified (reduced to a reading of some kind) by a primary element or sensor.

OFFSET   OFFSET

The difference between the actual value and the desired value (or set point); characteristic of proportional controllers that do not incorporate reset action. Also called DRIFT.

ORIFICE (OR-uh-fiss)   ORIFICE

An opening (hole) in a plate, wall, or partition. An orifice flange or plate placed in a pipe consists of a slot or a calibrated circular hole smaller than the pipe diameter. The difference in pressure in the pipe above and at the orifice may be used to determine the flow in the pipe.

PRECISION   PRECISION

The ability of an instrument to measure a process variable and repeatedly obtain the same result. The ability of an instrument to reproduce the same results.

PRESSURE CONTROL   PRESSURE CONTROL

A switch which operates on changes in pressure. Usually this is a diaphragm pressing against a spring. When the force on the diaphragm overcomes the spring pressure, the switch is actuated (activated).

PRIMARY ELEMENT   PRIMARY ELEMENT

The hydraulic structure used to measure flows. In open channels, weirs and flumes are primary elements or devices. Venturi meters and orifice plates are the primary elements in pipes or pressure conduits.

PROCESS VARIABLE   PROCESS VARIABLE

A physical or chemical quantity which is usually measured and controlled in the operation of a water treatment plant or an industrial plant.

RANGE   RANGE

The spread from minimum to maximum values that an instrument is designed to measure. Also see EFFECTIVE RANGE and SPAN.

RECEIVER RECEIVER

A device which indicates the result of a measurement. Most receivers in the water utility field use either a fixed scale and movable indicator (pointer) such as a pressure gage or a movable scale and movable indicator like those used on a circular flow-recording chart. Also called an INDICATOR.

RECORDER RECORDER

A device that creates a permanent record, on a paper chart or magnetic tape, of the changes in a measured variable.

REFERENCE REFERENCE

A physical or chemical quantity whose value is known exactly, and thus is used to calibrate instruments or standardize measurements. Also called a STANDARD.

ROTAMETER (RODE-uh-ME-ter) ROTAMETER

A device used to measure the flow rate of gases and liquids. The gas or liquid being measured flows vertically up a tapered, calibrated tube. Inside the tube is a small ball or bullet-shaped float (it may rotate) that rises or falls depending on the flow rate. The flow rate may be read on a scale behind or on the tube by looking at the middle of the ball or at the widest part or top of the float.

SENSOR SENSOR

A device that measures (senses) a physical condition or variable of interest. Floats and thermocouples are examples of sensors. Also called a PRIMARY ELEMENT.

SET POINT SET POINT

The position at which the control or controller is set. This is the same as the desired value of the process variable.

SOFTWARE PROGRAMS SOFTWARE PROGRAMS

Computer programs; the list of instructions that tell a computer how to perform a given task or tasks. Some software programs are designed and written to monitor and control water distribution systems and treatment processes.

SOLENOID (SO-luh-noid) SOLENOID

A magnetically (electric coil) operated mechanical device. Solenoids can operate small valves or electric switches.

SPAN SPAN

The scale or range of values an instrument is designed to measure. Also see RANGE.

STANDARD STANDARD

A physical or chemical quantity whose value is known exactly, and thus is used to calibrate instruments or standardize measurements. Also called a REFERENCE.

STANDARDIZE STANDARDIZE

To compare with a standard.

(1) In wet chemistry, to find out the exact strength of a solution by comparing it with a standard of known strength. This information is used to adjust the strength by adding more water or more of the substance dissolved.

(2) To set up an instrument or device to read a standard. This allows you to adjust the instrument so that it reads accurately, or enables you to apply a correction factor to the readings.

STARTERS (MOTOR) STARTERS (MOTOR)

Devices used to start up large motors gradually to avoid severe mechanical shock to a driven machine and to prevent disturbance to the electrical lines (causing dimming and flickering of lights).

TELEMETRY (tel-LEM-uh-tree) TELEMETRY

The electrical link between the transmitter and the receiver. Telephone lines are commonly used to serve as the electrical line.

THERMOCOUPLE THERMOCOUPLE

A heat-sensing device made of two conductors of different metals joined at their ends. An electric current is produced when there is a difference in temperature between the ends.

TIME LAG TIME LAG

The time required for processes and control systems to respond to a signal or to reach a desired level.

TIMER

TIMER

A device for automatically starting or stopping a machine or other device at a given time.

TOTALIZER

TOTALIZER

A device or meter that continuously measures and calculates (adds) a process rate variable in cumulative fashion; for example, total flows displayed in gallons, million gallons, cubic feet, or some other unit of volume measurement. Also called an INTEGRATOR.

TRANSDUCER (trans-DUE-sir)

TRANSDUCER

A device that senses some varying condition measured by a primary sensor and converts it to an electrical or other signal for transmission to some other device (a receiver) for processing or decision making.

TURN-DOWN RATIO

TURN-DOWN RATIO

The ratio of the design range to the range of acceptable accuracy or precision of an instrument. Also see EFFECTIVE RANGE.

VARIABLE, MEASURED

VARIABLE, MEASURED

A factor (flow, temperature) that is sensed and quantified (reduced to a reading of some kind) by a primary element or sensor.

VARIABLE, PROCESS

VARIABLE, PROCESS

A physical or chemical quantity which is usually measured and controlled in the operation of a water treatment plant or an industrial plant.

WATER HAMMER

WATER HAMMER

The sound like someone hammering on a pipe that occurs when a valve is opened or closed very rapidly. When a valve position is changed quickly, the water pressure in a pipe will increase and decrease back and forth very quickly. This rise and fall in pressures can cause serious damage to the system.

SYMBOLS

Chapter 19. INSTRUMENTATION

Special symbols are used for simplicity and clarity on circuit drawings for instruments. Usually instrument manufacturers and design engineers provide lists of symbols they use with an explanation of the meaning of each symbol. This section contains a list of typical instrumentation abbreviations and symbols used in this chapter and also used by the water-works profession.

ABBREVIATIONS

A — **A**nalyzer, such as a device used to measure a water quality indicator (pH, temperature).

C — **C**ontroller, such as a device used to start, operate, or stop a pump.

D — **D**ifferential, such as a "differential pressure" (**D. P.**) cell used with a flowmeter.

E — **E**lectrical or Voltage.
Element, such as a primary element.

F — **F**low rate (*NOT* total flow).

H — **H**and (manual operation).
High as in hi-level.

I — **I**ndicator, such as the indicator on a flow recording chart.
I = E/R where I is the electrical current in amps.

L — **L**evel, such as the level of water in a tank.
Low, as in a lo-level switch.
Light, as in indicator light.

M — **M**otor.
Middle, as in a mid-level switch.

P — **P**ressure (or vacuum).
Pump.
Program, as in a software program.

Q — **Q**uantity, such as a totalized volume (Σ for summation is also used).

R — **R**ecorder (or printer), such as a chart recorder.
Receiver.
Relay.

S — **S**witch.
Speed, such as the RPM (revolutions per minute) of a motor.
Starter, such as a motor starter.
Solenoid.

T — **T**ransmitter.
Temperature.
Tone.

V — **V**alve.
Voltage.

W — **W**eight.
Watt.

X — Special or unclassified variable.

Y — **C**omputing function, such as a square root ($\sqrt{}$) extraction.

Z — Position, such as a percent valve opening.

TYPICAL PROCESS AND ELECTRICAL SYMBOLS

1.   Pressure transmitter #1

2. Level indicator/recorder #2

3. 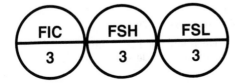   Flow indicator/controller #3 with hi-low control switches in the same instrument

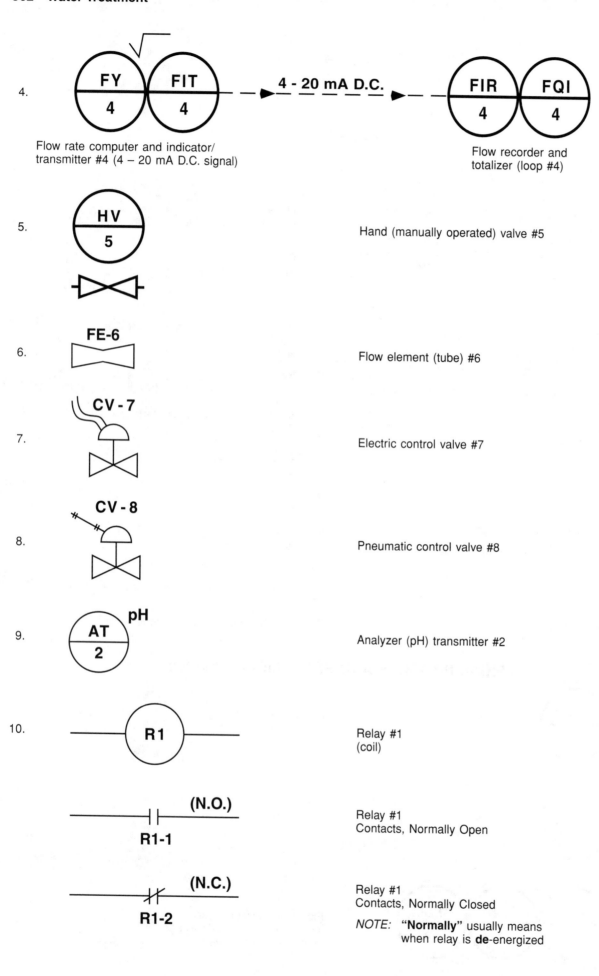

4.   Flow rate computer and indicator/
     transmitter #4 (4 – 20 mA D.C. signal)

     Flow recorder and
     totalizer (loop #4)

5.   Hand (manually operated) valve #5

6.   Flow element (tube) #6

7.   Electric control valve #7

8.   Pneumatic control valve #8

9.   Analyzer (pH) transmitter #2

10. Relay #1
     (coil)

     Relay #1
     Contacts, Normally Open

     Relay #1
     Contacts, Normally Closed

     NOTE: "Normally" usually means
            when relay is de-energized

11.

Hi

Red

Hi-level
indicator light (red)

12.

100 Ω

Resistor, 100 ohms

13.

480 V A.C.

110 V A.C.

Power transformer
(step-down)

14.

S-1

OFF

ON

Hand switch #1 (SPST)*

15.

S-2

Hand switch #2 (DPST)*

16.

S-3

Hand switch #3 (SPDT)*

17.

S-4

Hand switch #4 (DPDT)*

18.

PB-1

PB-2

L.O.S.

Manual push button switches:
PB #1 push to make
PB #2 push to break
"Lockout stop" safety feature

* SPST means single-pole, single-throw; DPST means double-pole, single-throw; SPDT means single-pole, double-throw; DPDT
  means double-pole, double-throw

FUSES/CIRCUIT BREAKERS

19.   **10A**   10-amp cartridge fuse

1A   1-amp in-line fuse

O.L.s   Thermal overload contacts
(motor)

20A
or
20A   20-amp circuit breaker

20.   **L1   L2 (OR N)**

110 V A.C.   Line 1 and Line 2 (neutral) to
standard duplex wall plug outlet

H - O - A Function Switch

21.   From
power   H
O   To control
circuits   (**H**and - **O**ff - **A**utomatic)
A

22.   **M
25 HP**   Electric motor, 3-phase power,
25 horsepower

CHAPTER 19.   INSTRUMENTATION

(Lesson 1 of 2 Lessons)

19.0   IMPORTANCE AND NATURE OF MEASUREMENT AND CONTROL SYSTEMS

19.00   Need for Understanding Measurement and Control Systems

In this chapter, you will learn some basic concepts about waterworks measurement instruments and their associated control systems. Since the water treatment plant operator frequently must monitor, and sometimes control, the distribution system supplied from the plant, both in-plant and field-type instrumentation will be discussed. You will become generally acquainted with the *WHAT, HOW,* and *WHY* instrument systems measure, and how some measured quantities are controlled automatically. However, this chapter is not intended to teach you how to fix a malfunctioning instrument, though some general preventive maintenance steps are included in the discussion.

Your understanding of the measurement and control basics presented here enhances the efficient and effective operation of your plant and/or system. Specifically, if you can recognize a meter as faulty (by the way the pointer acts, for example), your treatment/distribution decisions will then be based on that knowledge rather than a blind-faith-in-the-black-box attitude you might otherwise have to assume.

Also, the operator who recognizes the general operating principles of typical instrumentation systems is prepared to perform not only routine preventive maintenance, but also to take the minor corrective action sometimes really necessary to keep the system operating. The operator who knows enough to free a stuck pen, safely replace a fuse, or drain an air line can avoid a lot of personal worry and the expense of an electrician's service call while still protecting the operational integrity of the plant or system.

19.01   Importance to Waterworks Operator

In a real sense, measurement instruments can be considered extensions of your human senses, comparable in many ways to your own wide-ranging and exact eyes and ears. The associated automatic control systems, in turn, are like having extra sets of far-reaching and strong hands to constantly and precisely manipulate valves, motors, and switches.

In effect then, instrumentation provides you with a staff of hard-working assistants, always on the job to help you operate your plant and system easily. If you have failed to adequately appreciate the advantages of automation, consider the alternative methods of operating your plant. For example, in the recent past, or for some older operations in existence today, the situation described in the following paragraph could have occurred.

You have a complete and unrestorable power failure in the circuit which supplies all of the instruments and control systems in your conventional water filtration plant. As the operator you must try to keep the plant on line manually by controlling influent and effluent flows, basin levels, pump operation, chemical feeders, and filter valves. You must do all of this by watching and listening, and running to manipulate valves, start and stop pumps, and reset chemical feeders. Even if you could do it (and some nights on shift it seems like that *IS* what you have to do) for a small plant, you certainly couldn't exercise close control and do it for a long time. If you are trying to operate a larger plant, continued operation would be impossible without the instrumentation systems functioning. Accordingly, you would do well to familiarize yourself now with these "eyes, ears, and hands" that are so essential to your effective performance as a professional waterworks operator.

19.02   Purpose and Nature of the Measurement Process

Instrument capabilities can greatly extend our range of personal observations. They also have an additional and quite important advantage over our senses in that instruments provide quantitative or measurable information, whereas only qualitative information is available from our senses. That is to say, instruments provide us with numbers; the direct senses

can only tell us that an observation is "more than" or "less than" what the observation was the last time it was recently observed. Some very simple water supply operations can and do get by with such imprecise visual observations of a chemical process, rate of flow, or basin level.

However, modern water facilities must operate "by the numbers" so to speak, and only instrumentation can provide these numbers (Figure 19.1).

A measurement is, by definition, the comparison of the quantity or *PROCESS VARIABLE*[1] in question to an accepted standard unit of measure. Certain basic units of length, volume, weight, and time have been agreed upon by international convention to serve as primary standards. All measurements of length (level), area, volume, capacity, weight, pressure, and rate of flow encountered in waterworks practice ultimately refer to these standards. Thus, the weight of a 100-pound sack of chemicals, for instance, amounts to 100 times that of the standard pound; or, the capacity of a tank could be 1,000 times larger than the standard gallon. Some important terms often encountered in measurement practice will be discussed in the following paragraphs.

ACCURACY refers to how closely an instrument determines the true or actual value of the process variable being measured. Accuracy depends upon the *PRECISION*, or general quality and condition of the instrument and its ability to repeatedly obtain the same result. Precision also depends on an instrument's *CALIBRATION*. An instrument is calibrated in order to standardize its measurements. That is, the instrument itself is made to measure the value of a standard unit or reference and its indicator is adjusted accordingly. *STANDARDIZATION* is a simple calibration procedure done regularly (by the operator). Most instruments are accurate to about one or two parts in one hundred; this is expressed as ±1 to 2 percent error (or at times 98 to 99 percent accuracy). The *RANGE* of an instrument is the spread between the minimum and the maximum value of the variable it is designed to measure accurately. The *EFFECTIVE RANGE* is that portion of its complete range within which acceptable accuracy can

be expected; usually from 10 to 90+ percent of its nominal (design) range. *LINEARITY* refers to how closely the instrument measures actual values of the variable through its effective range, and thus bears upon its stated accuracy. An *ANALOG* readout of an instrument has a pointer (or other indicating means) reading against a dial or scale; a *DIGITAL* display provides a direct, numerical reading.

QUESTIONS

Write your answers in a notebook and then compare your answers with those on page 404.

19.0A   How can measurement instruments be considered an extension of your human senses?

19.0B   What water treatment processes and equipment could be monitored or controlled by measurement and control systems?

19.0C   What is an advantage of instruments over our human senses?

19.0D   What is an analog readout?

19.03   Explanation of Control Systems

The terms "controller" and "control systems" are used in the waterworks field in two different senses. The electrical panel which controls only the starting/stopping of an electric motor is referred to as a "controller." This controller may control a pump's operation or a chemical feeder motor. The control exercised may be manual, through push buttons or switches, or automatic with a switch responding to a value of level, pressure, or other variable such as is usually the case with a "Hand/Off/Automatic" (H.O.A.) function switch.

Fig. 19.1   *Main control panel of a modern water treatment plant*

---

[1] *Process Variable.   A physical or chemical quantity which is usually measured and controlled in the operation of a water treatment plant or an industrial plant.*

This type of so-called controller is more correctly termed a motor control station or panel, and will be discussed later. The other, technically proper, usage of the terms controller and control system identifies a system which senses and controls its own operation on a close, continuous basis, in what is called proportional (or modulating) control. This type of true controller will be discussed first (Figure 19.2).

In order for a process variable, whether pressure, level, weight, or flow, to be closely controlled, it must be measured precisely and continuously. The measuring device sends a signal (electrical or pneumatic, as discussed in a following section), proportional to the value of the variable, to the actual controller. Within the controller, the signal is compared to the desired or set point value (Figure 19.3). A difference between the actual and desired values results in the controller sending out a command signal to the controlled element, usually a valve, pump, or feeder. Such an error signal produces an adjustment in the system that causes a corresponding change in the original measured variable making it more closely match the set point. This continuous "cut-and-try" process can result in very fine, ongoing control of variables requiring constant values, such as some flow rates, pressures, levels, or chemical feeds. The term applied to this circulating action of the variable in such a controller is *FEEDBACK*. The path through the control system is the *CONTROL LOOP*. The internal settings of the true controller can be quite critical since close control depends upon sensitive adjustments. Thus, you should not try to adjust any such control system unless you know exactly what you are doing. Many plant and system operations have been drastically upset due to such efforts, however well intentioned, of unqualified personnel.

Examples of proportional control of waterworks operations which may be encountered are: (1) chlorine residual analyzer/controller; (2) chemical feed, flow-paced (open loop); (3) pressure- or flow-regulating valves; (4) continuous level control of filter basins; and (5) variable-speed pumping systems for flow/level control.

The *MOTOR CONTROL STATION* (Figures 19.4 and 19.5), as mentioned, essentially provides only for ON/OFF operation of an electric motor, which in turn powers a pump, valve, or chemical feeder. Primarily it is a standard electric motor panel, with manual operation push buttons, overload relays,

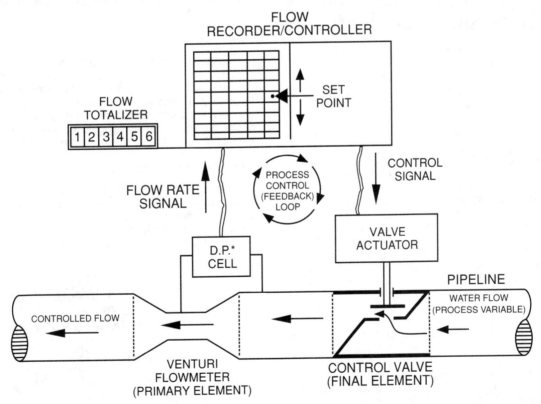

NOTE: Measurement and control system instruments may be electric or pneumatic.
* D.P. means differential pressure

Fig. 19.2 Automatic flow control system diagram
(closed-loop, proportional)

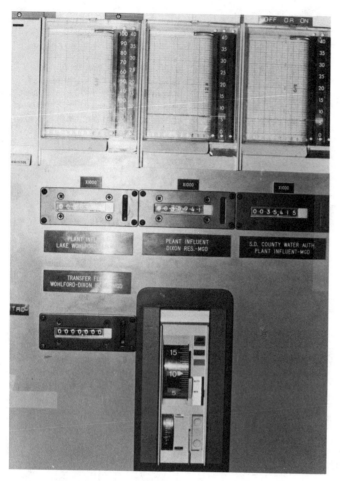

NOTE: Controller in photo is the lower instrument with set point at 10 MGD.

Fig. 19.3   Photo of flow recorder/controller shown in Figure 19.2

and function switch (H.O.A. or Hand/Off/Automatic). Additionally it may include, in good electrical design practice, provisions for power failure or loss of phase (fail-safe circuitry), and such protective devices as high or low pressure/temperature/level cutoff switches. For this type of panel even to be considered a controller (within our secondary meaning of the term), its operation must be controlled by the value or values of some variable, not merely by a device such as a timer. In other words, it must be turned on and off as a result of a measurement of a level, pressure, flow, chemical concentration, or other variable which reaches a predetermined setting. In the automatic mode (A on the H.O.A. switch) then, its operation is in fact automatic in the sense that the variable is controlled, even though the limits of its value are quite wide compared to those attainable with a true controller as previously described. Whereas a filter basin level controller may allow only an inch or so of water level change, an ON/OFF system might operate within a few feet of level difference. In many applications, however, such wide control is of no particular disadvantage, and sometimes is even desirable (such as with a distribution system reservoir level). However, one problem with level controllers in some water treatment plants is that small changes in the water level over the filters will cause the effluent controller to modulate suddenly. In cases of rising levels the effluent valve will open suddenly and

turbid water from within the filter may be discharged as treated water.

Terms used in control practice can now be defined operationally in this paragraph. *FEEDBACK* and *CONTROL LOOP* have been mentioned previously; however, the term *CONTROL LOOP* needs qualification. An *OPEN-LOOP* control system controls one variable on the basis of another. A good example of this is a chlorinator paced by flow signals (rather than by the chlorine residual analyzer). *CLOSED-LOOP* control remains as discussed previously, the true controller. *PROPORTIONAL-BAND*, *RESET*, and *DERIVATIVE* actions are adjustments of the controller that bear on effectiveness and speed of control action. *OFFSET* is the difference between the desired value of the variable (the *SET POINT*) and the controlled (actual) value. *DETECTION LAG*, common to chlorinator control systems, refers to the prolonged period between the moment when a change in control occurs and the moment when such change is finally sensed by the associated measuring instrument.

QUESTIONS

Write your answers in a notebook and then compare your answers with those on page 404.

19.0E   What does an ON/OFF type "controller" control?

19.0F   List three examples of "proportional control" in waterworks operations.

19.0G   What is the purpose of a motor control station?

19.1   SAFETY HAZARDS OF INSTRUMENTATION WORK

19.10   Be Careful

The general principles for safe performance on the job, summed up as always avoiding unsafe acts and correcting unsafe conditions, apply as much to instrumentation work as to other plant operations. However, there are some special dangers associated with instrument systems, mainly electric shock hazards, that merit special mention in this section. Repetition is well justified for the sake of safe practice!

19.11   Electrical Hazards

A hidden aspect of energized electrical equipment is that it looks normal, that is, there are no obvious signs that tend to discourage one from touching. In fact, there seems to be a peculiar fascination to see if it's really live by touching circuit components with a tool, often a screwdriver (usually having

an insulated handle, fortunately) but even with the finger. Only training, coupled with bad experience at times, is effective in squelching this morbid curiosity. Even so, most practicing electricians' tools have an "arc-mark trademark" or two, evidence of the need for continuing self-discipline in this area.

Fig. 19.4 Motor control panel
(simplified double-line schematic)

Fig. 19.5   Photo of motor control panel

Though such mention may conjure up humorous images of the maintenance person's surprise and "shock" upon such an incident, one only need consider that electric shock can and does regularly cause disfigurement and even death (by asphyxiation due to paralysis of the muscles used in breathing and/or burning) to bring the problem into sober perspective. Also, the expense and effort caused by a needless shorting-out of an electrical device could be significant. The point is, *RESIST THE URGE* to "test" any electrical device with a tool or part of your body!

If there is *ANY* doubt in your mind that *ALL* sources of voltage (not merely the local switch) have been switched off, then *DON'T TOUCH*, except possibly with the probes of a test meter. Remember, you can't "see" even the highest voltage, and an unverified presumption of a dead circuit is worthless and may be deadly.

Do not simulate a known electrical action, for example pressing down a relay armature, within an electrical panel without a *POSITIVE* understanding of the circuitry. Your innocent action may cause an electrical "explosion" to shower you with molten metal, startle you into a bumped head or elbow, or cause a bad fall. Again the adage, *WHEN IN DOUBT — DON'T.*

Usually the operator does not have the test equipment or the technical knowledge to correct an electrical malfunction, other than possibly resetting a circuit breaker, regardless of how critical the device's function is to plant operations. Though the foregoing applies mainly to motor control centers, there also may be a shock hazard within measurement instrument cases — and the sure destruction of expensive components — when the foolhardy "tool touch test" is used.

Most panels have an *INTERLOCK* on the door that interrupts all (local) power to a panel or device when the door is opened or the circuit is exposed for service. Do not disconnect or disable interlocks that interrupt all (local) power. Warning labels, insulating covers (over "hot" terminals), safety switches, lockouts, and other safety provisions on electrical equipment must be used at all times. Your attention to this crucial aspect of your workplace may save a life and, as the slogan goes, it could be your own!

QUESTIONS

Write your answers in a notebook and then compare your answers with those on page 404.

19.1A   What are the general principles for safe performance on the job?

19.1B   How can electric shock cause death?

19.1C   What could happen to you as a result of an electrical "explosion"?

19.12   Mechanical Hazards

There exists a special danger when working around powered mechanical equipment, such as electric motors, valve operators, and chemical feeders, which are operated remotely or by an automatic control system. Directly stated, the machinery may START or MOVE when you are not expecting it! Most devices are powered by motors with enough torque or

RPM to severely injure anyone in contact with a moving part. Even when the exposed rotating or meshing elements are fitted with guards in compliance with safety regulations, a danger may exist. A motor started remotely may catch a shirttail, finger, or tool hanging near a loose or poorly fitted shaft guard.

The sudden, automatic operation of equipment, even if half-expected, may startle one nearby into a fall or slip. Signs indicating that "This equipment may start at any time" tend to be ignored after a while. Accordingly, you must stay alert to the fact that any automatic device may begin to operate at any time. Always stay well clear of automatic equipment, especially when it is not operating.

Lockout devices on electric switches must be respected at all times. The electrician who inserts one to physically prevent the operation of an electric circuit is, in effect, trusting his or her life and health to the device. Once the lockout device is attached to the switch (whether the switch is tagged off or actually locked with lock and key), the electrician will consider the circuit de-energized and safe and will feel free to work on it. Consider the potential consequences then of an unauthorized operator who removes a lockout to place needed equipment back into service, presuming the electrician is finished (as might occur after several hours' work). The point cannot be overstressed:

RESPECT ALL LOCKOUT DEVICES AND ALL TAGGED OFF EQUIPMENT AS IF A LIFE IS ENTRUSTED TO YOU,

IT MAY WELL BE.

Operators often use power tools on instrumentation and associated equipment. All power tools present not only a shock hazard, waterworks being damp places at times, but a mechanical hazard as well. The use of power tools in the performance of instrumentation work, with its special nature, should wait until the operator can have an observer on hand in case of an accident.

19.13 Vaults and Other Confined Spaces

Included as part and parcel of measurement and control systems are those remotely installed sensors and control valves. Quite often these are found in meter or valve vaults, or other closed concrete structures. There are some special precautions beyond those stated in Chapter 20, "Safety." Be sure the ventilation equipment is working properly before entering. The use of power tools, including a soldering iron, can be even more dangerous in wet environments. *NEVER* stand in water with a power tool, even when OFF. Brace yourself, if necessary, in such a way that electric current cannot flow from arm to arm in case of an ungrounded tool. Shocks through the upper body involve your heart and/or your head, whose importance to you is self-evident!

19.14 Falls

All the general safety measures to guard the operator against falls, a leading cause of lost-time accidents, are covered in Chapter 20, "Safety," and need not be repeated in this instrumentation chapter. However, if one considers that an electric shock of even minor intensity can result in a serious fall, a special mention herein is justified. When working above ground on a ladder, even though you position it safely, use the proper nonconductive type (such as fiberglass), are duly cau-

tious on the way up, and comply with all other considerations of safety, a slight shock can still ruin all your precautions! When required to do preventive maintenance from a ladder, turn off the power to the equipment if at all possible. If not feasible, take special care to stay out of contact with any component inside the enclosure of a measuring or operating mechanism, and well away from terminal strips, unconduited wiring, and "black boxes." Though not commonly considered essential, the wearing of thin rubber or plastic gloves can reduce your chances of electric shock markedly (whether on a ladder or off).

Make provisions for carrying tools or other required objects on an electrician's belt rather than in your hands when climbing up or down ladders. Finally, never leave tools or any object on a step or platform of the ladder when you climb down, even temporarily. *YOU* might be the one upon whom they fall if the ladder is moved or even steadied from below. In this regard, it is always a good idea (even if not required) for preventive maintenance personnel to wear a hard hat whenever working on or near equipment, especially when a ladder must be used.

QUESTIONS

Write your answers in a notebook and then compare your answers with those on page 404.

19.1D   Why should operators be especially careful when working around powered, automatic, mechanical equipment?

19.1E   What is the purpose of an electrical lockout device?

19.1F   Why should you brace yourself when operating power equipment so that electric current cannot flow from arm to arm in case of an ungrounded tool?

19.1G   What kind of specific protective clothing items could be worn to protect you from electric shock?

19.2 MEASURED VARIABLES AND TYPES OF SENSORS/TRANSMITTERS

19.20 How Variables Are Measured

A measured variable is any quantity which is sensed and quantified (reduced to a reading of some kind) by a primary element or sensor. In waterworks practice, pressure, level, and flow are the most commonly measured variables; sometimes chemical feed rates and some physical or chemical water quality characteristics are also sensed.

The sensor is often a transducer of some type, in that it converts energy of one kind into some other form to produce a readout or signal. For example, one type of flowmeter converts the hydraulic action of the water into the mechanical motions necessary to drive a meter indicator, and also into an electrical signal for a remote readout device. If such a signal is produced, be it electric or pneumatic, the sensor is then considered a transmitter.

The signal produced is frequently not a continuous one proportional to the variable (such as an analog signal), but merely a switch which is set to detect when the variable goes above or below preset limits. In this type of ON/OFF control, the predetermined settings are called control points. This distinction between continuous and set point operation bears upon the two types of controllers discussed previously. The remainder of this section discusses each of the common variables sensed in waterworks practice.

19.21 Pressure

Since pressure is defined as a force per unit of area (pound per square inch or kiloPascal), you might expect that sensing pressure would entail the movement of some flexible element subjected to a force. In fact, that is how pressure is always measured. Such pressure elements (a class of primary elements) consist of strain gages and mechanically deformable devices such as the Bourdon tube (Figures 19.6 and 19.7), bellows, and diaphragm arrangements. The slight motion each exhibits, proportional to the applied force, is then amplified mechanically by levers or gears to position a pointer on a scale or to provide an input for an associated transmitter. (*NOTE:* A "blind" transmitter, of any variable, has no local indicator.) Again, the sensing of pressure can take place only at important points, such as with pump control systems.

There being many classes and brands of pressure sensors, it serves no purpose to elaborate further on specific types. Some sensors are fitted with surging and overrange protection (dampeners) to limit the effect pressure spikes or water hammer have on the sensor. Most protection devices function by restricting flow into the sensing element. Surge protection equipment prevents sudden pressure surges from overranging instrumentation which can easily damage many pressure sensors. One type of overrange protection uses a mechanical device to prevent the pressure element from exceeding its upper limit. The actual degree of protection necessary depends on the type and range of the sensor.

A second surge protection device is a snubber (Figure 19.8) which consists of a restrictor through which the pressure-producing fluid must flow. A simple restrictor is made of a short section of capillary (very small) tubing fitted into a plug in the pressure pipe to form an orifice. A more elaborate mechanical snubber responds to surges by moving a piston or plunger that effectively controls the size of the orifice. Some snubbers are subject to clogging or being adjusted so tight as to prevent any response at all to pressure changes. If a pressure sensor is not performing properly, look first for clogging or adjustment that is too tight.

A third device is an air cushion chamber (Figure 19.9) which is simply constructed yet very effective. The top half of the chamber contains air. Water flows into the bottom half. A sudden change in water pressure compresses the air within the chamber. The rate of response can easily be regulated by placing a small orifice in the pipe on the water side of the air cushion chamber.

QUESTIONS

Write your answers in a notebook and then compare your answers with those on page 404.

19.2A   What is a sensor?

19.2B   How is pressure measured?

19.2C   Why are some pressure sensors fitted with surging and overrange protection?

19.22 Level

Systems for sensing the level of water or any other liquid level, either continuous or single point, are probably the most common sensors found in waterworks. Pumps are controlled, filters operated, clear wells monitored, basins and tanks filled, chemicals fed and ordered, sumps emptied, and distribution system reservoirs controlled on the basis of liquid level. Fortunately, level sensors usually are simple devices. A float, for example, is a reliable liquid level sensor. Other types of level sensing devices include direct pressure, pneumatic bubblers, sonar, and capacitance probes. Single-point detection of level is very common to levels controlled by pumps and valve operation.

A float on the end of a cable (see Figure 19.10) is frequently used to continuously measure and/or to key pump/valve operation at control points. For distribution reservoir or local tank measurement only, the cable rides over a pulley on the lip of the tank, the other end terminating at a target which moves and reads against a vertical scale on the tank's side. These simple systems read out backward (for example, high levels result in lower scale readings as shown in Figure 19.10), but are entirely satisfactory for many purposes. Though the action of the float can key switches to signal high or low levels, no continuous transmission of level to a remote instrument is commonly used with the simple float/cable system. Targets are often read through binoculars when this system is used on a remote distribution system reservoir.

Variations on this scheme to measure liquid levels use either a perforated steel tape riding on a toothed pulley or fine cable riding over a grooved drum. The cable transmits the level sensed as a signal (electrical) proportional to pulley or drum rotation (Figures 19.11a and 19.11b). Most of these devices use a counterweight on the end of the tape/cable opposite the float to ensure tautness. Also, all types of float-operated sensors work best with the float traveling within a long tube called a stilling well, which dampens out unwanted liquid turbulence or waves.

An industrial pressure gage with a Bourdon pressure sensing element

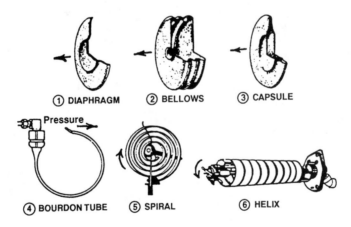

① DIAPHRAGM ② BELLOWS ③ CAPSULE

④ BOURDON TUBE ⑤ SPIRAL ⑥ HELIX

Elastic deformation elements. Pressure tends to expand or unroll elements to indicate pressure as shown by arrows.

Fig. 19.6 *Bourdon tube and other pressure sensing elements*
(Permission of Heise Guage, Dresser Industries)

NOTE: Capsule (round disk) below gage protects sensing
element from corrosion by chlorine gas.

Fig. 19.7   Photo of a chlorine pressure gage

Fig. 19.8   Internal parts of a plunger-type
snubber for surge protection

Fig. 19.9   Air cushion chamber and snubber for surge
protection of pressure gage

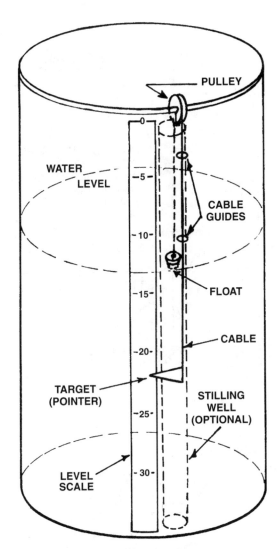

NOTE: As liquid level drops, float falls and pointer (target) rises and vice versa. Therefore, pointer indicates depth of water in tank "backward."

Fig. 19.10 Reservoir level gage, float/target type

Another common system of level sensing is the displacer type (Figure 19.11c). By its nature only single-point determinations of level can be obtained, but this type of sensing for ON/OFF control is adequate for many purposes. The displacer is a weight, usually of a noncorroding heavy material such as porcelain, which hangs down on a cable into the liquid within a stilling well. The cable is supported by a spring which is sized so as to keep an electric switch (a mercury vial, usually) in one position with the displacer immersed, but allowing it to switch to another position when the displacer is out of the liquid. The basic principle is that the weight is buoyed up by the liquid when immersed, thus weighing less. Accordingly, the motion of the displacer is very slight, typically less than one inch (25 mm) so this design is more reliable than a float device which may be subject to sticking in its stilling well.

An alternative to a float or displacer, both of which are mechanical systems, is the use of electrical probes to sense liquid level (Figure 19.11d). Again, only single-point determinations can be made this way, though several probes can be set up to detect several different levels. Level probes are used where a mechanical system is impractical, such as

within sealed or pressurized tanks, or with chemically active liquids.

The probes are small-diameter, stainless-steel rods that are inserted into a tank through a special fitting, usually through the top but at times in the side of the vessel. Each rod is cut to length corresponding to a specific liquid level in the case of the top-entering probes; in the side-entering setup, a short rod merely enters the vessel at the appropriate height or depth. One problem encountered with probes is the accumulation of scum or caking (by $CaCO_3$) on the surface of the rods.

A small voltage is applied to the probe(s) by the system's power supply, with current flowing only when the probe "sees liquid," that is, becomes immersed. When current flow is sensed, a switch activates a pump/valve control or alarm(s) at as many control points as necessary. Though at times only a single probe is used, with the metal tank completing the circuit as a ground, usually at least two probes are found — the ground probe extending all the way to the bottom of the tank so as to be in constant contact with the electricity-conducting liquid (a liquid ground as it were).

Levels can be sensed continuously by measurement of liquid pressure near the bottom of a vessel or basin. The pressure elements used for level sensing must be quite sensitive to the low pressures created by liquid level (23 feet of water column equals only 10 psi, or 7 meters of water column equals 7 kPa (0.7 kg/sq cm)). Therefore, simple pressure gages such as are found on pumps are not used to measure water levels. Water level sensors are used to measure levels of water in systems on filter basins, or in chemical storage tanks where control or monitoring must be close, continuous, and positive. Rather than being calibrated in units of pressure (psi), these gages read directly in units of liquid level (feet). Single-point control/alarm contacts can be made a part of this or any continuous type of level sensor.

A very precise method of measuring liquid level is the bubbler tube, with its associated pneumatic instrumentation (Figure 19.12). The pressure created by the liquid level is sensed, but not directly as with a mechanical pressure element. Air pressure is created in a bubbler tube to just match the pressure applied by the liquid above the open end immersed to some predetermined depth in the tank or basin. This *AIR* pressure is then measured (sensed) as proportional to liquid level *ABOVE THE END OF THE TUBE*. This indirect determination of level using air permits the placement of the instrumentation anywhere above or below the liquid's surface, whereas direct pressure-to-level gages must be installed at the very point where liquid pressure must be sensed.

These pneumatic devices are adjusted so air *JUST BEGINS* to bubble out of the submerged end of the sensing

Fig. 19.11a *Float and cable (continuous)*

Fig. 19.11b *Float and tape (continuous)*

Fig. 19.11c *Displacer (single-point)*

Fig. 19.11d *Electrical probes (multi-point)*

Fig. 19.11 *Liquid level sensing systems
(level measurement and single- and multi-point sensing)*

FUNCTIONAL DIAGRAM

Constant-flow regulator and rotameter on left, back-
pressure sensor (DP cell) to right.

Fig. 19.12   Bubbler tube system for measuring liquid level tube. They automatically compensate for changes in liquid level by providing a small, constant flow of air. There is no advantage to turning up the amount of air to create more intense bubbling (the pressure will still depend on the water level). In fact, such action may create a sizeable measuring error in the system and any air flow changes should be left to qualified instrument service personnel.

Bubbler tube systems are common in filter level controllers which must maintain water levels within a range of a few inches (or centimeters). Usually the level transmitter for this use is "blind" since it only controls liquid level and does not provide an indication or readout of the level.

QUESTIONS

Write your answers in a notebook and then compare your answers with those on page 404.

19.2D   List the major types of liquid level sensors.

19.2E   How can a level signal be generated by a float element?

19.2F   Under what circumstances are probes used to measure liquid level instead of mechanical systems (floats)?

19.2G   How does a bubbler measure the level of a liquid?

Rotameters (*RATE* of flow)

Fig. 19.13   Flow sensing devices

19.23   Flow (Rate of Flow and Total Flow)

The term "flow" can be used to refer to either *RATE OF FLOW,* such as MGD, CFS, and GPM (volume per unit of time), or to *TOTAL FLOW* in simple units of volume such as gallons or cubic feet. Such volumes are usually obtained as a running total, with a comparatively long time period for the flow delivery (such as a month). This distinction is important in the understanding of flow instrumentation, most of which provides *BOTH* values (for rate of flow and total flow). Some flowmeters, however, provide only total flow readings.

While it is possible in principle to measure flow directly, such as is done with pressure and most level sensing devices, it is quite impractical. Direct measurement would involve the constant filling and emptying of, say, a gallon container with water flowing from a pipe on a timed basis. This method is simply not practical. Therefore, sensing of flows in waterworks practice is done *INFERENTIALLY,* that is by inferring what the flow is from the observation of some associated hydraulic action of the water. The inferential techniques that are used in waterworks flow measurement are: (1) velocity sensing, (2) differential-pressure sensing, (3) magnetic, and (4) ultrasonic. First, let's look at a few other methods used in flow sensing for specialized applications before studying velocity sensing devices.

ROTAMETERS (Figure 19.13, previous page) are transparent tubes with a tapered bore containing a ball (or float). The ball rises up within the tube to a point corresponding to a particular rate of flow. The rotameter tube is set against, or has etched upon the tube, marks calibrated in whatever flow rate unit is appropriate. Rotameters are used to indicate ap-proximate liquid flow or gas flow, such as those installed at the readout device of a gas chlorinator. Sometimes a simple rotameter is installed merely to indicate a flow or no-flow condition in a pipe, such as on chlorinator injector supply lines.

Service meters are the type of flowmeters used to record total water usage through individual service connections in a distribution system (Figure 19.14). The smaller service meters are usually one of the positive-displacement types. The larger service meters use the velocity-sensing principle.

VELOCITY SENSING DEVICES measure water speed within a pipeline. This can be done by sensing the rate of rotation of a special impeller (Figure 19.15) placed within the flowing stream; the rate of flow is directly proportional to impeller RPM (within certain limits). Since normal water velocities in pipes and channels are well under 10 feet per second (about 7 MPH or 3 m/sec), the impeller turns rather slowly. This rotary motion drives a train of gears which finally indicates *RATE* of flow as a speedometer-type readout. *TOTAL* flow appears as the cumulative number, similar to the odometer (total mileage) on your car.

Rotation of the velocity sensing element is not always transferred by gears, but may be picked up as a magnetic or electric signal (pulses) by the instrument system. Nor is velocity always sensed mechanically; it may also be detected or measured purely electrically (the thermister type) or hydraulically (the pitot tube), but the principle of equating water velocity with rate of flow within a constant flow area is the same. Of course, all such flowmeters are calibrated to read out in an appropriate unit of flow rate, rather than velocity units.

Service meter (*TOTAL* flow)

Fig. 19.14   Flow sensing device

METER HEAD
(Rate of and Total Flow)

IMPELLER
(or Propeller)

FLOW TUBE (Exact
cross-section Area)

SIGNAL

**RATE-OF-FLOW
INDICATOR
AND/OR
RECORDER**

1 2 3 4 5 6 7 **FLOW TOTALIZER**

**FLOW
TRANSDUCER/
TRANSMITTER**

*

FLOW

PIPE   FLOWMETER

*
NOTE: MOTION OF PROPELLER
CAN BE SENSED/TRANSMITTED
MECHANICALLY, MAGNETICALLY
OR ELECTRICALLY, OR ANY OF
THESE IN COMBINATION.

Fig. 19.15   Propeller (velocity) meter

Typically, this type of flow element transmits its reading to a remote site as electrical pulses, although other devices can be used in order to convert to any standard electrical or pneumatic signal.

Preventive maintenance of impeller-type flowmeters centers around regular lubrication of rotating parts. Propeller meters, as they are called, have a long history of reliability and acceptable accuracy in waterworks practice. When propeller meters become old, they become susceptible to under-registration (read low) due to bearing wear and gear train friction. Accordingly, annual teardown for inspection is indicated. An over-registration is a physical impossibility as far as the operating principle goes, but a partially full pipeline, wrong gears installed, or a malfunctioning transmitter can cause high readings.

DIFFERENTIAL PRESSURE SENSING DEVICES (Figures 19.16 and 19.17), also called Venturi or just differential meters, depend for their operation on a basic principle of hydraulics. When a liquid is forced to go faster in a pipe or tube, its internal pressure drops. If a carefully sized restriction is placed within the pipe or flow channel, the flowing water must speed up to get through it. In doing so, its pressure drops a little, and it always drops the same amount for the same flow. This small pressure drop, the differential, is the difference between the water pressure before the restriction and within the restriction. This difference is proportional to the rate of flow. The difference in pressure is measured very precisely by the instrumentation associated with the particular flow tube or Venturi installed. Typically, only a difference of a few psi is required. This small value of pressure difference is often described in inches of water (head).

Measuring flow by this method removes a little hydraulic energy from the water. However, the classical Venturi tube, with its carefully tapered form, allows recovery of well over 95 percent of the original pressure throughout its range of flows. Other ways of constricting the flow do not allow such high recoveries of pressure, nor the accuracy possible with modern Venturi flow tubes. The Dall tube is a shortened form of the Venturi, with acceptable accuracies for many in-plant purposes (filter wash water flows).

The orifice plate (Figures 19.16 and 19.17) is inserted between flanges in a pipe and is a stainless-steel plate with a calculated size hole (orifice) in it. The pressure drop is sensed right at the orifice, or immediately downstream to yield a comparatively rough flow indication. This drop in pressure is permanent; that is, a permanent pressure loss occurs with orifice plate installations.

Differential devices require little if any preventive maintenance by the operator since there are no real moving parts. Occasionally, flushing of the hydraulic sensing lines is good practice. This flushing should only be done by a qualified person. When dealing with an instrument sensitive to small fractions of psi, opening the wrong valve can damage the internal parts. Also, if an instrument containing mercury is used, this toxic (and expensive) metal can easily be blown out of the device and *INTO THE WATER PIPELINE!* Thus, all valve manipulations must be understood and done deliberately after careful planning.

In nearly all cases, the instrumentation associated with the larger flow tubes is transmitted to a remote readout station. Local readout is also provided (sometimes inside the case only), for purposes of calibration. Differential meter flow transmitters may be electrical or pneumatic types (with signal transmitted proportional to the square root of the differential pressure).

Venturi system (flow rate)

Orifice plate installation (flow rate)

Fig. 19.16   Schematic diagrams of differential pressure flow metering

Venturi meters have been in use for many decades and can produce very close accuracies year after year. Older flow tubes are quite long physically (to yield maximum accuracy and pressure recovery). Newer units are much shorter but have even better accuracy. With no moving parts, the Venturi-type meter is not subject to mechanical failure as is the propeller meter. Flow tubes, however, must be kept clean and without obstructions upstream and downstream to provide designed accuracy.

These flowmeter types all provide rate of flow indication. The rate of flow is continuously totalized, usually at the readout instrument, as the total flow up to that point in time (recorded in gallons or cubic feet).

54-inch Venturi tube

24-inch orifice plate

Fig. 19.17   Differential pressure flowmeters

Flowmeters in pipes will produce accurate flowmeter readings when the meter is located at least five pipe diameters distance downstream from any pipe bends, elbows, or valves and also at least two pipe diameters distance upstream from any pipe bends, elbows, or valves. Flowmeters also should be calibrated in place to ensure accurate flow measurements.

QUESTIONS

Write your answers in a notebook and then compare your answers with those on page 404.

19.2H   What are two types of flow readings?

19.2I   List the two main types of (larger) flow measurement devices.

19.2J   Smaller service meters are what type of flowmeter?

19.2K   How do velocity-sensing devices measure flows?

19.2L   How are flows measured with Venturi meters?

19.24 Chemical Feed Rate

Chemical feed rate indicators are usually a necessary part of the particular chemical feed system and thus are usually not considered instrumentation as such. For example, a dry feeder for lime or dry polymer may be provided with an indicator for feed rate in units of weight per time, such as lbs/hr or grams/minute. In a fluid (liquid or gas) feeder, the indication of quantity/time, such as gallons/hour or pounds/day, may be provided by use of a rotameter (Figure 19.13).

19.25 Process Instrumentation

Process instrumentation provides for continuous checking of physical or chemical indicators of water quality in a treatment plant. These instruments do not include laboratory instruments (unless set up to measure sample water continuously), although the operating principles are usually quite similar. The process variables of turbidity and pH are always monitored closely in a modern water treatment plant (Figure 19.18). Very frequently chlorine residuals are also continuously measured and controlled. Usually these three variables are measured at several locations. For example, turbidity of raw, settled, and filtered water is frequently measured. Additionally, other indicators of water quality may be sensed on a continuous basis such as fluoride, electrical conductivity (for TDS), water hardness and alkalinity, and temperature. In every case, the instrumentation is specific as to operating principle, standardization procedures, preventive maintenance, and operational checks. The manufacturer's technical manual sets forth routine procedures to check and operate the equipment.

Operators must realize that most process instrumentation is quite sensitive and thus requires careful handling and special training to service. No adjustments should be made without a true understanding of the device. Generally speaking, this category of instrumentation must be maintained by the water agency's instrument specialist or the factory representative rather than by an operator (unless specially instructed).

19.26 Signal Transmitters/Transducers

Common practice measures a variable at one location and provides a readout of the value at a remote location, such as a main panel board. Except in the case of a blind transmitter, a local indication is provided at the field site as well as being available at the remote site. Associated with the remote (panel) readout system quite often are alarm set points, an integrator, or a controller (though any of these may exist at the measuring site also). Usually a recorder is found only on a panel board along with all other recorders remote from the sensor in the field. These system components will be discussed further in Section 19.3, "Categories of Instrumentation."

In order to transmit a measured value to a remote location for readout, it is necessary to generate a signal proportional to the value measured. This signal is then transmitted to a receiver which provides a reading based on the signal. Also, a controller may use the signal to control the measured variable.

Presently, two general systems for transmission of signals, electrical and pneumatic, are used in waterworks and most other industrial situations. Electricity, of course, requires wiring (though radio transmission or microwave are possible). Pneumatic systems require small-diameter tubing (usually ¼ inch or 6 mm) between transmitter and receiver. When the transmitter is quite far removed from the receiving station, a special terminology is used for the electrical link between the two; this is called telemetry. The wiring used is telephone lines leased from the local telephone company or owned by the water agency. Telemetry will be discussed separately in Section 19.34, "Telemetering Links (Phone Lines)," since the signals are usually a special type.

Electric signals used within a water treatment plant are either voltage (1 to 5 volts D.C.), current (4 to 20 milliamps D.C.), or pulse types. Milliamp signals (4 to 20 ma) are the most common electrical signals for most instrumentation and control systems in recent years. In any of these, a low voltage is applied so no severe shock hazard exists (though shorting signal wires may still destroy electrical components). Signal transmission is limited to several hundred feet, with signal strength usually set up for the specific connecting lines.

A power supply to generate the required electrical energy may be at the transmitter, the receiver, or at another location. The transmitter may be an integral part of the measurement sensor/transducer, or separately housed. In any case, the transmitter adjusts the signal to a corresponding value of the measured variable, and the receiver in turn converts this signal to a visible indication which is the readout.

Turbidimeter

pH meter

Fig. 19.18 Water treatment plant instrumentation
(continued on the next page)

Chlorine residual analyzer

Fig. 19.18 Water treatment plant instrumentation
(continued from previous page)

Pneumatic signal systems are restricted to comparatively short distances. Components include a compressor to provide air under pressure, as well as the necessary air filters and an air dryer. The precision of signal transmission by pneumatics is comparable to electrical signals so both systems are found about equally in waterworks.

Compressed air presents no shock hazard and most plants must have compressors available for other purposes.

Also, pneumatic systems seem to be more understandable to operating personnel and thus easier to keep functioning as desired. As with electrical signal circuits, the transmitter and receivers perform as their names imply. Pneumatic controllers, and all other types of pneumatic equipment, are as available as their electrical counterparts. Pneumatic signals are generated by causing pressures from 3 to 15 psi (20 to 100 kPa (0.2 to 1.1 kg/sq cm)), proportional to the variable, in almost every installation, with 9 psi (62 kPa (0.65 kg/sq cm)) then representing a 50-percent signal.

Preventive maintenance of pneumatic components centers around ensuring a clean, dry air supply at all times which requires alert operators.

QUESTIONS

Write your answers in a notebook and then compare your answers with those on page 405.

19.2M How are chemical feed rates measured?

19.2N What process variables are commonly monitored and/or controlled by instruments?

19.2O By what means can values measured at one site be read out at a remote location?

19.2P What are the two general systems used to transmit measurement signals?

Please answer the discussion and review questions next.

End of Lesson 1 of 2 Lessons
on
INSTRUMENTATION

DISCUSSION AND REVIEW QUESTIONS

Chapter 19.   INSTRUMENTATION

(Lesson 1 of 2 Lessons)

At the end of each lesson in this chapter you will find some discussion and review questions. The purpose of these questions is to indicate to you how well you understand the material in the lesson. Write the answers to these questions in your notebook before continuing.

1. Why should operators understand measurement and control systems?

2. How can measurement and control systems make an operator's job easier?

3. What is the difference between precision and accuracy?

4. Why should a screwdriver not be used to test an electric circuit?

5. What precautions should an operator take before entering a vault?

6. How can water levels be measured?

7. What problems can develop with propeller meters when they become old?

CHAPTER 19.   INSTRUMENTATION

(Lesson 2 of 2 Lessons)

19.3   CATEGORIES OF INSTRUMENTATION

19.30   Measuring Elements

Measuring (or primary) elements are those devices which make the actual measurement of the variable. Transducers are usually associated with sensors to convert the sensor's signal to another magnified action producing a more usable indication. If remote transmission of the value is required, a transmitter may become part of the transducer. An illustrative example of these three components is the typical Venturi meter: (1) the flow tube is the primary element, (2) the differential pressure device (D.P. cell) is the transducer, and (3) the signal-producing components are the transmitter. An understanding of the separate functions of each section of the flowmeter is important to the proper understanding of equipment problems.

19.31   Panel Instruments (See Figure 19.1, page 366)

19.310   Indicators

The components of measurement and control systems found on the water plant's main panel board are generally thought of as the plant instrumentation. These components are important to the operator, and hence to plant operation itself, because they display the variable directly. These panel devices can produce alarm signals to indicate if a variable is outside its range of expected values. In addition, the controllers are often installed on (or behind) the main panel along with the operating buttons and switches for the plant's equipment.

An operator can easily be lulled into an overdependence on automation to operate the plant processes more or less blindly. However there is no substitute for critical evaluation

and informed judgment regarding important plant functions. You must not rely solely upon the readings of any single instrument to ensure proper plant operation, but must consult other instruments and closely watch the other indicators of plant operation. Even the most sophisticated and expensive instrument systems do malfunction at times and require constant maintenance work by specialists.

19.311   Indicators/Recorders

The major components found on the plant's main panel are indicators and recorders. Indicators give a visual presentation of a variable's value, either as an analog or as a digital display (Figures 19.19 and 19.20). The analog display uses some manner of pointer (or other indicator) against a scale. A digital display is a direct numerical readout. Recorders, which can also serve as indicators, give a permanent record of how the variable changes with time by way of a moving chart. Whereas there are usually several indicators out in the plant or field, recorders are usually housed at a central location in the plant. We will discuss both indicators and recorders in the following paragraphs.

Since there are two types of signal transmission available, panel indicators may be of the electric or the pneumatic type. The digital readout is a relatively recent development, with both advantages and disadvantages. Digitals may be read more quickly and precisely from a longer distance, and can respond virtually instantly to variable changes. But analog indicators are cheaper, more rugged, and may not even require electrical power (the pneumatic type), an advantage during a power failure.

Another advantage of the electric or pneumatic analogs or gages is that a wrong indication (value) is more recognizable than with a digital system.

An analog device can sometimes be repaired easily by the operator. For example, the pointer on a flowmeter gage may merely be stuck, as evidenced by a perfectly constant reading. With a digital reading there is no practical way for the operator to see whether a problem actually does exist, nor is there any way for the operator to attempt a repair, such as freeing a pointer. Erratic or unreliable operation, while always a problem, seems to be worse when digitals are involved since there is no way out for the operator. You often can't tell if the problem is real, and you can't do anything to get by 'til 8 A.M., as is often required on a night shift.

With all-electronic instrumentation, as advantageous as it may seem from a technical and economic standpoint, the operator has little recourse in case of malfunction of critical instrumentation. Temporary power failures, tripped panel circuit breakers, voltage surges (lightning) resulting in blown fuses, and problems of excessive heat can all result in electronic instrument problems. However, electromechanical or pneumatic instruments may keep operating, or recover operation readily, after such power or heat problems. Electronic systems may require the services of an instrument technician, or even the factory technician, to become fully operable again. Accordingly, the operator should insist upon some input into the design phase of instrument systems to ensure that the plant is still operable during power outages, hot weather, and other contingencies. Standby power generators and/or batteries are used to keep plants operating during power outages.

QUESTIONS

Write your answers in a notebook and then compare your answers with those on page 405.

19.3A   What is the purpose of indicators?

19.3B   Describe an analog display.

19.3C   Where are recorders usually found at a water treatment plant?

19.3D   What factors can cause electronic instrument problems?

19.312 Recorders

Recorders are indicators designed to show how the value of the variable has changed with time (Figure 19.20). Usually this is done by attaching a pen (or stylus) to the indicating arm, which then marks or scribes the value of the variable onto a continuously moving chart. The chart is marked on a horizontal or circular scale in time units. Some models of recorders reverse the scales by indicating time on the vertical and variable on the horizontal scales.

The chart is driven along at a precise speed under the pen, to correspond with the time markings on the chart. Chart speeds range from several inches to a fraction of an inch per minute, with the pen and drying time of the ink specific to a given range of speeds.

There are two main types of recorder charts and recorders: the horizontal strip-chart type and the circular type

Fig. 19.19 Analog chlorine residual indicator

Fig. 19.20   *Digital indicator/recorder combination (24-hour circular chart)*
(Permission of Leopold Company, Division of Sybron Corporation)

(Figure 19.21). The horizontal strip chart carries its chart on a roll or as folded stock, typically with several months' supply of chart available. Several hours of charted data are usually visible or easily available for the operator to read. On a circular recorder, the chart makes one revolution every day, week, or month, and the record of the entire elapsed time period is visible at any time.

Changing of charts is usually the operator's duty, and is easier with circular recorders, though not that difficult with most strip-chart units.

Recorders may be electric or pneumatic. Pneumatic models frequently have electric chart drives. Purely mechanical units, useful at a remote, unpowered pressure gaging sta-

Strip-chart recorders

Seven-day circular-chart recorder

Fig. 19.21   Recorders, strip-chart and circular-chart

tion, have hand-wound chart drives and are of the circular-chart type. Other models are battery powered. Recorders are most commonly described by the nominal size of the strip-chart width or circular-chart diameter (for example, a 4-inch (100-mm) strip-chart, or a 10-inch (250-mm) circular-chart recorder).

19.313 Totalizers

The rate of flow as a variable is a time rate; that is, it involves time directly, such as in gallons per minute, or million gallons per day, or cubic feet per second. Flow rate units become units of volume with the passage of time. For example, flow in gallons per minute accumulates as total gallons during an hour or day. The process of calculating and presenting an on-going, running total of flow volumes passing through a meter is termed "integration" or totalizing.

An integrator, also called a totalizer, continually adds up gallons or cubic feet as a cumulative total up to that point in time. Virtually all flow indicators and recorders are equipped with totalizers, though sometimes as separate units (Figure 19.20). Many flowmeters ONLY measure the total quantity of fluid passing through them; the domestic service meter (common water meter) is an example of this type of flowmeter.

Large quantities of water (or liquid chemical) are commonly measured in units of hundreds or thousands of gallons or cubic feet. This is simply a shorthand means of expressing the measurement. On the face of a totalizer you will find a multiplier such as x 100 or x 1,000. This indicates that the reading is to be multiplied by this (or another) factor to yield the full amount of gallons or cubic feet. If the readout uses a large unit, such as "mil gal," a decimal will appear between appropriate numbers on the display, or a fractional multiplier (x 0.001, for example) will appear on the face of the totalizer.

Every operator should personally be able to *CALCULATE* total flow for a time period in order to verify that the integrator is actually producing the correct value. Accuracy to one or two parts in a hundred (1 or 2 percent) is usually acceptable in a totalizer. There are methods to integrate (add up) the area under the flow rate curve on a recorder chart to check for long-term accuracy of total flow calculations.

19.314 Alarms

Alarms are visual and/or audible signals that a variable is out of bounds or that a condition exists in the plant requiring the operator's attention. For noncritical conditions, the glow of a small lamp or light on (or outside of) an indicating instrument is sufficient notice. For more important variables

or conditions, an attention-getting annunciator panel (Figure 19.22) with flashing lights and an unmistakable and penetrating alarm horn is commonly used.

Annunciator panels all have "acknowledge" and "reset" features to allow the operator to squelch the alarm sound (leaving the visible indication alone) and to reset the system after the alarm condition is corrected. The alarm contacts (switches) activating the system commonly use the same

Fig. 19.22 Annuniciator (alarm) panel
(each rectangle represents a monitored location)

instrument as the variables presented on the main panel, or are wired in from remote alarm sensors in the plant or field. The operator is usually responsible for setting these alarm contacts and the operator must use judgment as to the actual limits of the particular variables that will ensure meeting proper operational goals. Each system is different so no attempt will be made here to instruct operating personnel in alarm resetting procedures.

Sometimes operators fail to reset alarm limits as conditions and judgments change in the plant. It is not uncommon to see the annunciator panel "lit up," with the operator ignoring all the alarm conditions as the normal status quo! *SUCH PRACTICE IS NOT ADVISED BECAUSE A TRUE ALARM CONDITION REQUIRING IMMEDIATE OPERATOR ATTENTION MAY BE LOST IN THE RESULTING GENERAL INDIFFERENCE TO THE ALARM SYSTEM.* For some operators, acknowledging an alarm sound to get rid of the noise is second nature, without due attention to each and every activating condition. Alarm contact limits should always be reset (or deactivated) as necessary to ensure that the operator is as attentive to the alarm system as possible to prevent real emergencies.

QUESTIONS

Write your answers in a notebook and then compare your answers with those on page 405.

19.3E   What is the purpose of recorders?

19.3F   What are the two types of charts used on recorders?

19.3G   How are charts driven in remote locations where electricity is not available?

19.3H   List two types of warnings that are produced by alarms.

19.32 Automatic Controller

Section 19.0 explains the nature of control systems, especially as they are used in waterworks operations. Indications of proper and improper control need to be recognized even though actual adjustment of the controller should be left to a qualified instrument technician. By shifting to the manual mode, you can bypass the operation of any controller, whether electric, pneumatic, or even hydraulic. Learn how to shift all controllers to manual operation. This will allow you to take over control of a critical system when necessary in an emergency, as well as at any other time it suits your purposes. For example, you could quickly correct a "cycling" or "sluggish" recorder indication rather than waiting for the controller to correct the condition in time, if it does at all.

A controller, while admittedly "superhuman" in some of its abilities, is still limited. It can only do what it has been programmed to do. You, the operator, can and should exercise *JUDGMENT* based on your experience and observations, so do not hesitate to intervene if a controller is not exercising control within sensible limits. Of course, you must be *SURE* of your conclusions, and competent to take over control if you decide to operate manually.

To repeat a few of the more important operational control considerations, remember that ON/OFF control is quite different in operation than proportional control. Both methods may exercise close control of a variable; however, proportional control may be better suited to the purpose. Attempting to set up an ON/OFF control system to maintain a variable within too close a tolerance may result in rapid ON/OFF operation of equipment. Such operation can damage both the equipment and the switching devices. Therefore, do not attempt to set a level controller, for instance, to cycle the pump or valve more often than actually necessary for plant operation.

In the case of a proportional controller, it too may begin to cycle its final control element (pump or valve) through a wide range if any of the internal settings, namely proportional band or reset, are adjusted so as to gain closer control of the variable than is reasonable. Accordingly, it may be better to accommodate to a small offset (difference between set point and control point) than risk an upset in control by attempting too much control.

19.33 Pump Controllers

Control of pumping systems can be achieved by an automatic controller which determines the output of a variable-speed pump, or by an ON/OFF type of controller starting/stopping the pump(s) according to a level, pressure, or flow measurement. The control of a variable-speed system was discussed earlier in the description of the automatic (proportional) control method, so this section will restrict comments to ON/OFF pump control.

Usually an ON/OFF pump control system responds to level changes in a tank or a reservoir of some type. Water level can be sensed directly or by pressure change at the pump site. The pump is turned off or on as the tank level rises above or falls below predetermined level or pressure limits. Control is rather simple in this case. However, such systems may include several extra features to ensure fail-safe operation. To prevent the pump from running after a loss of signal, electrical circuitry should be designed so the pump will turn OFF on an *OPEN* signal circuit, and ON only with a *CLOSED* circuit. Ideally, the sensor can distinguish between an open or closed remote level/pressure contact and an open or shorted telemetry line. Larger pump systems will usually have a low-pressure cutoff switch on the suction side to prevent the pump from running when no water is available, such as with a dry wet well or a closed suction valve.

Pumps may also be protected against overheating, caused by continuing to pump into a closed discharge situation, by a high-pressure cutoff switch on the discharge piping. Both the high- and low-pressure switches may shut off the pump through a time-delay circuit, so that short-term pressure surges can be tolerated within the pump piping. Usually the low- or high-pressure switches also key an alarm to notify the operator of the condition. For remote stations, the plant's main panel may include indicator lights to show the pump's operating condition. Figure 19.23 shows a typical pump control circuitry.

REFER TO FIG. 19.4, page 369, FOR LEGEND OF TERMS AND SYMBOLS

*Fig. 19.23   Pump control station ladder diagram (ON/OFF control)
(simplified double-line schematic)*

Fig. 19.24   Pump control station

Pump control panels (Figure 19.24) may also include automatic or manual sequencers. This provision allows the total pump operating time required for the particular system to be distributed equally among all the pumps at a pump station. A manual switch for a two-pump station, for example, will read "1-2" in one position and "2-1" in the other position. In the first position, pump #1 is the lead pump (which runs most of the time) and #2 the lag pump (which runs less). When the operator changes the switch to "2-1," the lead/lag order of pump operation is reversed, as it should be periodically, to keep the running time (as read on the elapsed time (E.T.) meters, or as estimated) of both pumps to about the same number of total hours. In a station with multiple pumping units, an automatic sequencer regularly changes the order of the pumps' start-up to maintain similar operating times for all pumps.

QUESTIONS

Write your answers in a notebook and then compare your answers with those on page 405.

19.3I   Under what conditions might an operator decide to bypass a proportional-type controller? How could this be done?

19.3J   What basic principle should guide you in programming the frequency of operation of an ON/OFF control?

19.3K   How can pumps be prevented from running upon loss of signal?

19.3L   How can you ensure that all pumps in a pump station operate for roughly equal lengths of time?

19.34   Telemetering Links (Phone Lines)

Remote monitoring or controlling of water distribution system operational variables, such as level, pressure, and flow, may require the use of long signal transmission lines. These lines may be wires (two being required for each circuit) owned by the water agency, or telephone lines leased from the local telephone company (Figure 19.25). (Radio or microwave transmission also is sometimes used). This lease line arrangement is being used by many utility agencies. In most cases, a transmitter generates an audio frequency or tone on the line. For example, a frequency of 1,000 Hz[2] produces a medium high-pitched hum on the tone channel (line). Each variable to be transmitted and received has its own tone. This helps limit the number of phone lines needed to and from the remote sites. A very limited number of different tones can be sent over the same phone lines and then be unscrambled by their individual receivers. A remote sensing and control station can send tone signals to the water plant and simultaneously receive tone signals to effect control at the same site. An example would be a flow/pressure/level sensing station across town, with a control valve or pump there under remote manual control. The term "telemetry" is used to denote such use of remote signaling to monitor and/or control remote station operation. The term "supervisory control" applies to the remote control feature exercised through telemetry systems.

With or without use of tone equipment (which mainly serves to allow multiple signals on single phone lines), the actual signal is of the pulse-duration or the pulse-frequency type in virtually every application in waterworks.[3] Pulse duration, also called pulse width or time duration depending on the brand of

---

[2] *Hz or Hertz.   The number of complete electromagnetic cycles or waves in one second of an electric or electronic circuit. Also called the frequency of the current. Abbreviated Hz.*
[3] *Some short-distance signals operate only by sensing opening or closing of an electric contact, exactly like a local (in-plant) level or pressure switch.*

FIELD (REMOTE) STATION

FLOW →

SYSTEM RESERVOIR

PRES.

FLOW

VALVE CONTROL

LEVEL

1 RCVR. 3 TRANS.

110 V AC

TONE UNITS

LEASED PHONE LINE (ONE PAIR ONLY)

LOCAL TELEPHONE COMPANY OFFICE (OR RELAY STATION)

LEASE-LINE (P.L. # - - -)

(FOUR CHANNELS)

1 TRANS. 3 RCVRS.

OTHER SYSTEMS

TONE CABINET

PRES. IND.

FLOW REC.

SET FLOW

LEVEL REC.

CONTROL STATION

CENTRAL CONTROL (WATER PLANT OR STATION)

NOTES:

1. SINGLE PAIR OF PHONE LINES TRANSMIT SEVERAL TONE SIGNALS TO/FROM SITES SIMULTANEOUSLY.

2. TONE UNITS ARE TRANSMITTERS (TRANS) OR RECEIVERS (RCVRS). POWER SUPPLY ALSO NECESSARY.

3. AS SHOWN, FIELD STATION PRESSURE, FLOW AND TANK LEVEL MONITORED, DIRECT CONTROL EXERCISED OVER FLOW (WITH PRESSURE AND LEVEL CHANGING ACCORDINGLY).

Fig. 19.25   Diagram of telemetry system
(monitoring and supervisory control)

equipment, functions by creating a 15-second (sometimes less) regular signal cycle within the transmitter. The value of the variable transmitted occupies more or less of this basic time cycle; a 50-percent signal would produce a 7½-second tone (during the remaining 7½ seconds the circuit would be silent). Each manufacturer has selected some standard, usable portion of the 15-second cycle. For example, one company uses only 9 seconds (from 3 seconds to 12 seconds) of the time to proportion 0 to 100 percent of the variable's value. If the panel indicator shows that the depth of water in a remote tank can range from 0 to 9 feet, a tone lasting 6 seconds (67-percent signal) out of the possible 9 seconds, would cause the indicator to show a depth of water of 6 feet. In any case the corresponding receiver is set up to accept and relay the proper signal to the indicating/controlling instrumentation. This form of signal telemetry is very popular, being easy to understand, requiring no sophisticated instrumentation to check or calibrate, and being virtually insensitive to improper signals originating in the telephone lines or at the phone company.

A limitation of this form of signal (time duration) is when it is used for the pacing of chemical feeders, especially coagulants. During a low-flow period, alum feeders will be feeding alum intermittently which will produce very poor coagulation/flocculation results. A loss of signal or interference causes the indicator to go to zero or to maximum scale. If you have the opportunity, ask the instrumentation service person to allow you to listen to a tone channel, or better, to a phone line carrying several channels.

From an operational standpoint, there isn't much you can do if you lose a channel, no matter how important it is to plant operations. Fuse replacement can be tried, then a call to the telephone company to check on its status (phone lines may be down in an accident or incident), after which the instrument service person must be called in. At times, tone channels may be lost for several minutes (pens go to top or bottom), only to return to normal service later; therefore, you may wish to try to wait out the interruption. An indicator pointer/pen cannot move from its last position during a power outage if the readout instrument (electronic) has no internal power. If you push a pointer/pen up or down and it remains in the new position, you have an internal power problem. Thus a different action would then be required of the operator, not related to a telemetry problem.

19.35 Air Supply Systems

Pneumatic instrumentation depends upon a constant source of clean, dry, pressurized air for reliable operation. Given a quality air supply, pneumatics can operate seemingly forever without significant problems. Without a quality air supply, operational problems can be frequent. The operator of a plant is usually assigned the task of ensuring that the "instrument air" is available and dry, though rarely are operators told how to accomplish this (it being assumed evidently that clean air will "be there" automatically).

The plant's instrument air supply system consists of a compressor with its controls, master air pressure regulator, air filter and air dryer, as well as the individual pressure regulator/filters in the line at each pneumatic instrument (Figure 19.26). Only the instrument air is filtered and dried; the plant air usually does not require such measures since it is being used only for pneumatic tools.

As air passes through a compressor, it not only picks up oil but the air's moisture content is concentrated by the compression process. Special measures must be taken to remove both of these liquids. You can remove oil by filtering the air through special oil-absorbent elements. A process called *DESICCATION*[4] can be used to remove the water. This is simply a matter of either passing the moisture-laden air through desiccant columns, which regenerate their absorption capacity periodically through heating, or of refrigerating the instrument air. The refrigeration method is based upon the principle that cold air can hold comparatively little moisture within it. You must recognize that the capacity of any of these systems of oil or water removal is limited to amounts of liquid encountered under normal conditions.

If the compressor is so worn as to pass more oil than usual, the oil separation process may permit large amounts of oil to pass into the air supply. If the air storage tank contains excessive liquid water (due to irregular or improper drainage), the air drying system may not handle the excess moisture. Learn enough about the instrument air system to be able to open the drain valves, cycle the desiccator, or bypass the tank, in order to prevent instrumentation problems due to an oily, moisture-saturated air supply.

Operators should regularly crack the regulator/filter drain valves at the site of the plant instruments. An unusual quantity of liquid drainage may indicate an overloading or failure in the instrument air filter/drying parts. Also, pneumatic indicators/recorders should be watched for erratic pointer/pen movements which may well be indicative of air quality or supply problems.

The seriousness of temporary plant or compressor station power failures can be lessened if you temporarily turn off all nonessential usages of compressed air in the plant. The air storage tank is usually sized so that there is enough clean, dry air on hand to last for several hours, if conserved. Knowing this, you may be able to wait out a power failure without undue drastic action by observing remaining available pressure at the air supply.

---

[4] Desiccation (DESS-uh-KAY-shun).   A process used to thoroughly dry air; to remove virtually all moisture from air.

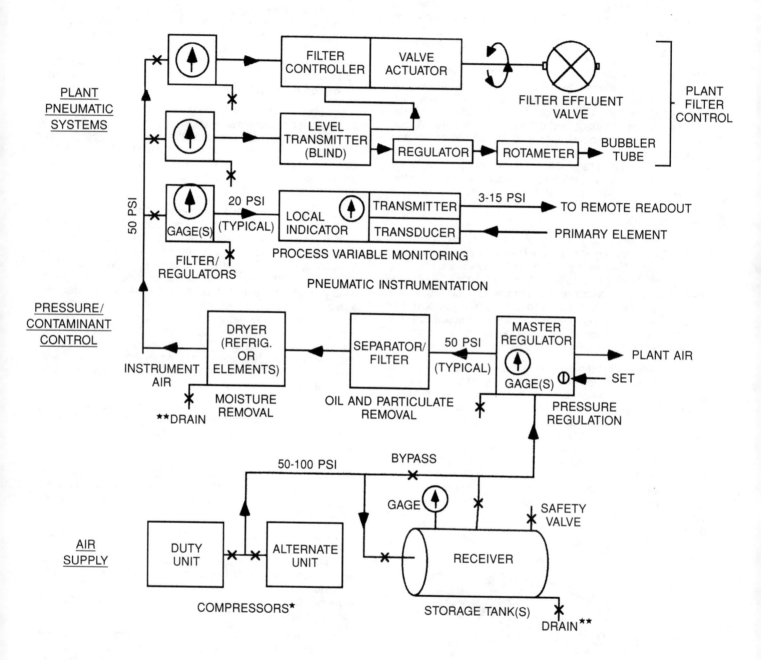

PLANT
PNEUMATIC
SYSTEMS

FILTER
CONTROLLER

VALVE
ACTUATOR

FILTER EFFLUENT
VALVE

PLANT
FILTER
CONTROL

LEVEL
TRANSMITTER
(BLIND)

REGULATOR

ROTAMETER

BUBBLER
TUBE

50 PSI

20 PSI
(TYPICAL)

GAGE(S)

LOCAL
INDICATOR

TRANSMITTER

3-15 PSI

TO REMOTE READOUT

TRANSDUCER

PRIMARY ELEMENT

FILTER/
REGULATORS

PROCESS VARIABLE MONITORING

PNEUMATIC INSTRUMENTATION

PRESSURE/
CONTAMINANT
CONTROL

DRYER
(REFRIG.
OR
ELEMENTS)

SEPARATOR/
FILTER

50 PSI
(TYPICAL)

MASTER
REGULATOR

GAGE(S)

PLANT AIR

SET

INSTRUMENT
AIR

**DRAIN

MOISTURE
REMOVAL

OIL AND PARTICULATE
REMOVAL

PRESSURE
REGULATION

50-100 PSI

BYPASS

GAGE

SAFETY
VALVE

AIR
SUPPLY

DUTY
UNIT

ALTERNATE
UNIT

RECEIVER

COMPRESSORS*

STORAGE TANK(S)

DRAIN**

Notes:

   * Compressor and "Receiver" (tank) are often an integral unit in small installations.
   ** Drains may be automatic type (on timer).

Fig. 19.26   Instrument air system functional diagram
(simplified, not all valves and piping shown)

QUESTIONS

Write your answers in a notebook and then compare your answers with those on page 405.

19.3M   How are signals transmitted over long distances, such as from a water storage reservoir to pumps at a water treatment plant?

19.3N   What happens to a remote indicator when a signal is lost?

19.3O   What are the essential qualities of the air supply needed for reliable operation of pneumatic instrumentation pressure systems?

19.3P   How are moisture and oil removed from instrument air?

19.36   Laboratory Instruments

This category of instrumentation includes the analytical units usually found in larger water treatment plant laboratories. Turbidimeters, colorimeters and comparators, pH, conductivity (TDS), dissolved oxygen (DO), and temperature indicators fit in this classification of instruments (Figure 19.27). We have already seen that process models of each of the units monitor these same variables out in the plant. Operators rarely are required to do anything more than make periodic readings from lab instruments, though standardizing the particular instrument is often required before the determination of a sample's turbidity or color is made. Preventive, and certainly corrective, maintenance (if any) is handled by the chemist, factory rep, or instrument technician since each unit is quite specialized and complex. Some of these countertop instruments or devices are very delicate and replacement parts, such as turbidimeter tubes or pH electrodes, are relatively expensive. Moreover, the use of many of these instruments requires the regular handling of laboratory glassware and other breakable items. The operator who, through carelessness, lack of knowledge, or simple hurrying, consistently breaks glassware or "finds the *!* meter broken" does not become popular with the chemist, supervisor, nor the other operators. The byword in the lab is *WORK WITH CAUTION*. Protect valuable and essential equipment and instrumentation.

19.37   Test and Calibration Equipment

In most larger water plant operations, the plant operating staff have little occasion to use testing and calibration meters and devices on the plant instrumentation systems. A trained technician will usually be responsible for maintaining such systems. There are, however, some general considerations the operator should understand concerning the testing and calibration of plant measuring and control systems. With this basic knowledge, you may be able to discuss needed repairs or adjustments with an instrument technician and perhaps actually assist with that work. A greater understanding of your plant's instrument systems may enable you to analyze instrument problems as they bear upon continued plant operation and handle emergency situations created by instrument failure. Your skills in instrument testing and calibration equipment may also result in a job promotion and/or pay raise.

Fig. 19.27   Water laboratory instruments

The most useful piece of test equipment is the V-O-M, that is the **V**olt-**O**hm-**M**illiammeter, commonly called the "multimeter" (Figure 19.28). To use this instrument you will need a workable understanding of electricity, but once you learn to use it, the V-O-M has potential for universal usage in instrument and general electrical work. Local colleges and other educational institutions may offer courses in basic electricity which undoubtedly include practice with a V-O-M. You, as a professional plant/system operator, are unlikely to find technical training of greater practical value than this type of course or program. Your future use of test and calibration equipment in general certainly should be preceded by instruction in the fundamentals of electricity.

QUESTIONS

Write your answers in a notebook and then compare your answers with those on page 405.

19.3Q   Why should an operator be especially careful when working in a laboratory?

19.3R   Why should an operator become familiar with the testing and calibration of plant measuring and control systems?

19.3S   What is a V-O-M?

19.4   OPERATION AND PREVENTIVE MAINTENANCE

19.40   Proper Care of Instruments

Usually instrumentation systems are remarkably reliable year after year, assuming proper application, setup, operation and maintenance. Measurement systems may be found still in service at some utilities up to 50 years after installation. To a certain extent, good design and application account for such long service life, but most important is the careful operation and regular maintenance of the instrument's parts or components. The key to such proper O & M is the operator's practical understanding of the system. Operators must know how to (1) recognize properly functioning instruments, so as to prevent prolonged and damaging malfunction, (2) shut down and prepare devices for seasonal or prolonged non-operation, and (3) perform preventive (and minor corrective) maintenance tasks to ensure proper operation in the long term. By contrast, a sensitive instrumentation system can be quite easily ruined in short order with neglect of *ANY ONE* of the three principles listed.

Operators should be familiar with the Technical Manual (also called the "Instruction Book" or "Operating Manual") of each piece of equipment and instrument encountered in a plant. Each manual will have a section devoted to the operation of some component of a measuring or control system (though frequently not for the entire system). Detailed descriptions of maintenance tasks and operating checks will usually be found in the same section of the manual. Depending upon the general type of instrument (electromechanical, pneumatic,

or electronic), the suggested frequency of the operation and maintenance/checking tasks can range from none to monthly. Accordingly, this section of the course only addresses those general tasks an operator might be expected to perform to operate and maintain instrumentation systems. These general tasks can be summed up from the *OPERATIONS STANDPOINT AS LEARNING AND CONSTANT ATTENTION TO WHAT CONSTITUTES NORMAL FUNCTION, AND FROM A MAINTENANCE STANDPOINT, ENSURING PROPER AND CONTINUING PROTECTION AND CARE OF EACH COMPONENT.*

QUESTIONS

Write your answers in a notebook and then compare your answers with those on page 405.

19.4A   List the three principles which are the keys to proper instrument O & M.

19.4B   What generally is expected of an operator of instrumentation systems from (1) an operations standpoint, and (2) a maintenance standpoint?

19.41   Indications of Proper Function

The usual pattern of day-to-day operation of every measuring and control system in a plant should become so familiar that operators almost unconsciously sense any significant change. This will be especially evident and true for systems with recorders where the pen trace is visible. An operator should watch indicators and controllers for their characteristic actions. With analog instruments, each pen or pointer may display its own unique characteristics (though some may be virtually the same). Thus, the pen for "Flow Recorder A" may normally scribe out a one-eighth-inch (3-mm) wide track due to inherent sensitivity or flow variations, whereas "Level Recorder B" may normally produce a trace as steady as a rock (Figure 19.29). However, if the flow pen is noticed as steady one day, or the level indication widens due to a quiver, then the operator should suspect a problem. In this regard, signs of possible improper function (though not *NECESSARILY* so) include:

1. Very flat or steady pen trace (is the system working at all, or is the variable really that constant?);

2. Excessive pen/pointer quiver (causes undue wear on parts, can usually be adjusted out); and

3. Constant or periodic hunting, or spikes, in a pen/pointer (improper adjustment, control, or other problem).

Additionally, it is not uncommon for a pointer or pen to become stuck at some position on its scale, usually at the extreme limits of movement. Pens are particularly prone to sticking, getting hung up on the chart edge or in a tear or hole. Therefore, operators should become observant not only of unusual pointer/pen movement, but unusual *LACK* of movement by indicators and recorders. In the case of recorders, you may *LIGHTLY TAP* an instrument to check on the pointer/pen motion. If a gentle tap does not cause slight movement, a problem may well exist. Anyone hitting or shaking a delicate instrument hard, however, in an attempt to check it out, only reveals a lack of training in this area.

At times, firmly pushing an instrument into its case, or closing the door completely, may close the interlock switch and switch the system on, as designed. However, jamming the device into its case, or slamming a door is *NEVER* considered proper action. If a device still doesn't begin to work, check the power connection and instrument fuse(s), if any.

Front Panel Controls, Jacks, and Indicators

Controls, Jacks, and Indicator

1. Range Switch: Has 12 positions. May be turned in either direction. There are 5 voltage positions, 4 direct-current positions, and three resistance positions used to select desired ranges.

2. Function Switch: Has 3 positions: –D.C., +D.C., and A.C. To measure D.C. voltage, current, or resistance, the function switch is set to –D.C. or +D.C. according to the polarity of the applied current or voltage. Turning this switch reverses the test lead connections without removing the leads from the circuit under test.

3. Zero Ohms: This control is used to compensate for variation in the voltage of the internal batteries.

4. Circuit Jacks: There are 8 jacks, two in each corner of the sub-panel. They provide an electrical connection to the test leads.

5. Meter: 4-1/2" indicating instrument. Has a scale for each function and range.

Fig. 19.28 Volt-Ohm-Milliammeter (V-O-M)

MEASURING/MONITORING SYSTEMS

← CHARTS MOVE FROM RIGHT TO LEFT ←

1. Normal function: Ink trace dark and steady, variable within expected range.
2. Pen skips: Pen dirty, dry, or not on chart; clean pen/tubing, re-ink, check contact.
3. Wide trace: "Noisy" system, too sensitive; causes inking problems, can be adjusted out.
4. Flat trace (upscale): OK if usual for system, otherwise check sensor or process.
5. Trace to max. scale: Instrumentation problem (sudden or constant 100% unlikely).
6. Trace to min. scale: Process or sensor off, also may be signal loss.

CONTROL SYSTEMS

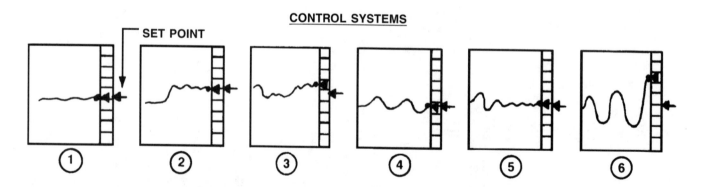

1. Normal control: Pen trace steady, process or set point changes controlled well.
2. Normal control: Small oscillations normal with process or set point change.
3. Abnormal control: Excessive departure from set point, "sloppy" controller.
4. Cycling or hunting: Unstable control, controller settings need adjustment.
5. Damped oscillations: Process upset, control OK if acceptable for process.
6. Worsening oscillations: System out of control due to process or set point change, service required. Do not use "auto," switch to "manual" control.

Fig. 19.29   Indications of proper and abnormal function
(systems with strip-chart recorders; circular chart indications are similar)

For pneumatic systems, an unnoticed failure of the instrument air supply is the most common reason for an inoperable instrument. Such a failure of the air supply extends the inoperable situation to all pneumatic systems in the plant. Complete functional loss of a single pneumatic instrument is rather rare, but erratic operation is not uncommon, due to previously mentioned water or oil in the air supply.

One of the surest indications of a serious electrical problem in instrument or power circuits is, of course, smoke and/or a burning odor. Such signs of a problem should never be ignored. Smoke or a burning odor means heat, and no device can operate long at unduly high temperatures. Any electrical equipment which begins to show signs of excessive heating must be shut down immediately, regardless of how critical it is to plant operation. Overheated equipment will very likely fail soon anyway, with the damage being aggravated by continued usage. Fuses and circuit breakers are not always designed to de-energize circuits before damage occurs, and cannot be relied upon to do so.

Finally, operators frequently forget to reset an individual alarm, either after an actual occurrence or after a system test. This is especially prevalent when an annunciator panel is allowed to operate day after day with lit up alarm indicators (contrary to good practice) and one more light is not easily noticeable. Also, when a plant operator must be away from the main duty station, the system may be set so the audible part of the alarm system is temporarily squelched. When the operator returns, the audible alarm system may inadvertently not be reset. In both instances (individual or collective loss of audible alarm) the consequences of such inattention can be serious. Therefore, get in the habit of checking and resetting your annunciator system often.

QUESTIONS

Write your answers in a notebook and then compare your answers with those on pages 405 and 406.

19.4C   List three possible signs of an improperly functioning flow recorder.

19.4D   Where or how are recording pens most likely to become stuck or hung up?

19.4E   What is a common reason for nonoperation of pneumatic systems?

19.4F   What is an indication of a serious problem in an electrical instrument or power circuit?

19.42   Start-up/Shutdown Considerations

The start-up and periodic (seasonal) or prolonged shutdown of instrumentation equipment requires very little extra work by the operator. Start-up is limited mainly to undoing or reversing the shutdown measures taken.

When shutting down any pressure, flow, or level measuring system, valve off the access of water to the measuring element. Exercise particular care, as explained previously, regarding the ORDER in which the valves are manipulated for any flow-tube installation. Also, the power source of some instruments may be shut off, unless the judgment is made that keeping an instrument case warm (and thus dry) is in order. In such cases, constantly moving parts, such as chart drives, should be turned off. With an electrical panel room containing instrumentation, it is good practice to leave some power components on (such as a power transformer) to provide space heat for moisture control. In a known moist environment, sealed instrument cases may be protected for a while with a container of *DESICCANT*[5] (indicating silica gel which is blue if OK and pink when the moisture-absorbent capacity is exhausted).

Though preventing the access of insects and rodents into any area appears difficult, general cleanliness seems to help considerably. Rodenticides are available to control mice; this is good preventive maintenance practice in any electrical space. Mice will chew off wire and transformer insulation, and may urinate on other insulator material, leading to serious damage.

Nest-building activities of some birds can also be a problem. Screening buildings and equipment against entry by birds has become a design practice of necessity. Insects and spiders are not known to cause specific functional problems, but start-up and operation of systems invaded by ants, bees, or spiders should await cleanup of each such component of the system. All of these pests can bite or sting, so take care!

With pneumatic instrumentation, it is desirable to purge each device with dry air before shutdown. This measure helps rid the individual parts of residual oil and moisture to minimize internal corrosion while standing idle. As before, periodic blowoff of air receivers and filters keeps these liquids out of the instruments to a large degree. Before shutdown, however, extra attention should be paid to instrument air quality for purging. Before start-up, each filter/receiver should again be purged.

Finally, pay attention to the pens and chart drives of recorders upon shutdown. Ink containers (capsules) may be removed if deemed necessary, and chart drives turned off. A dry pen bearing against one track (such as zero) of a chart for weeks on end is an invitation to start-up problems. Re-inking and chart replacement at start-up is an easy matter if the proper shutdown procedures were followed.

QUESTIONS

Write your answers in a notebook and then compare your answers with those on page 406.

19.4G   How can moisture be controlled in an instrument?

19.4H   Why should pneumatic instrumentation be purged before shutdown?

19.43   Maintenance Procedures and Records

Preventive maintenance means that attention is given periodically to equipment in order to *PREVENT* future malfunctions. Corrective maintenance involves actual, significant repairs which are beyond the responsibility of the operator (in most cases). Routine operational checks are part of all P.M.

---

[5] Desiccant (DESS-uh-kant).   A drying agent which is capable of removing or absorbing moisture from the atmosphere in a small enclosure.

(preventive maintenance) programs in that a potential problem may be discovered and thereby corrected before it becomes serious.

P.M. duties for instrumentation should be included in the plant's general P.M. program. If your plant has no formal, routine P.M. program, it should have. Such a program must be set up on paper. That is, the regular duties required are printed on forms or cards which the operator (or technician) uses as a reminder, guide, and record of P.M. tasks performed. Without such explicit measures, experience shows that preventive maintenance will almost surely be put off indefinitely. Eventually, the press of critical corrective maintenance (often due to lack of preventive maintenance) and even equipment replacement projects may well eliminate forever any hope of a regular P.M. program. The fact that instrumentation is usually very reliable (being of quality design) may keep it running long after unmaintained pumps and other equipment have failed. Nevertheless, instrumentation does require proper attention periodically to maximize its effective life. P.M. tasks and checks on modern instrument systems are quite minimal (even virtually nonexistent on some), so there are no valid reasons for failing to ever perform these tasks.

19.44 Operational Checks

Operational checks are most efficiently performed by always observing each system for its continuing signs of normal operation. However, some measuring systems may be cycled within their range of action as a check on the responsiveness of components. For instance, if a pressure-sensing system indicates only one pressure for months on end, and some doubt arises as to whether it's working or not, the operator may bleed off a little pressure at the primary element to produce a small fluctuation. Or, if a flow has appeared constant for an overly long period, the bypass valve in the D.P. (**D**ifferential **P**ressure) cell piping[6] may be cracked open briefly to cause a drop in reading. Be sure you crack the bypass valve. If you open the wrong valve the pressure may be excessive and be beyond the range of the D.P. cell which could cause some problems. If a float is suspected of being stuck (very constant level indication), try jiggling its cable to free the float or take other measures to cause a slight fluctuation in the reading.

Whenever an operator or a technician disturbs normal operation during checking or for any reason, operating personnel must be informed — ideally *PRIOR TO* the disturbance. If a recorder trace is altered from its usual pattern in the process, the person causing the upset should initial the chart appropriately, with time noted. Some plants require operators to mark or date each chart at midnight (or noon) of each day for easy filing and retrieval.

In the case where a pen/pointer is thought to be stuck mechanically, that is, it does not respond at all to simulated or actual change in the measured variable, it is normally permissible to open an instrument's case and try to move the pointer/pen, *BUT ONLY TO THE MINIMUM* extent possible to establish its freedom. Further deflection may well bend or break the device's linkage. A "dead" pen often is due only to loss of power or air to the readout mechanism. Any hard or repeated striking of an instrument to make it work identifies the striker as ignorant of good operational practice and can ruin the equipment. Insertion of tools into an instru-

ment case in a random fix-it attempt could damage the instrument. Generally speaking, any extensive operating check of instrumentation should be performed by the instrument technician during routine P.M. program activities.

QUESTIONS

Write your answers in a notebook and then compare your answers with those on page 406.

19.4I   Why should regular preventive maintenance duties be printed on forms or cards?

19.4J   How are operational checks performed on instrument equipment?

19.4K   What should be done if a recorder trace is altered from its usual pattern during the process of checking an instrument?

19.45 Preventive Maintenance

The technical manual for each item of instrumentation in your plant should be available so you can refer to it for O & M purposes. When a manual cannot be located, contact the manufacturer of the unit. Be sure to give all relevant serial/model numbers in your request for the manual. Request two manuals, one to use and one to put in reserve. All equipment manuals should be kept in one protected location, and signed out as needed. Become familiar with the sections of these manuals related to O & M, and follow their procedures and recommendations closely.

A good practice is to have on hand any supplies and spare parts which are or may be necessary for instrument operation (such as charts) or service (such as pens, pen cleaners, and ink). Some technical manuals contain a list of recommended spare parts which you could use as a guide. Try to obtain these supplies/parts for your equipment. A new pen on hand for a critical recorder can be a lifesaver at times.

Since P.M. measures can be so diverse for different types, brands, and ages of instrumentation, only the few general considerations applicable to all will be covered in this section.

1. Protect all instrumentation from moisture (except as needed by design), vibration, mechanical shock, vandalism (a very real problem in the field), and unauthorized access.

2. Keep instrument components clean on the outside, and closed/sealed against inside contamination. This specifically includes spiderwebs and rodent wastes.

---

[6] *There is no similar easy way to check a propeller meter's response.*

3. *DON'T* presume to lubricate, adjust, fix, calibrate, free up, or modify any component of a system arbitrarily. If you are not qualified to take any of these measures, then don't do it.

4. *DO* keep record pens and charts functioning as designed by frequent checking and service, bleed pneumatic systems regularly as instructed, ensure continuity of power for electrical devices, and don't neglect routine analytical instrument cleanings (such as turbidimeters) and standardizing duties as required by your own plant's established procedures.

As a final note, it is a good idea to get to know and cooperate fully with your plant's instrument service person. Good communication between this person and the operating staff can only result in a better all-around operation. If your agency is too small to staff such a specialist (most are), it may be a good idea to enter into an instrumentation service contract with an established company or possibly even with the manufacturers of the majority of the components. With rare exceptions, general maintenance persons (even journeyman electricians) are not qualified to perform extensive maintenance on modern instrumentation. Be sure that someone takes good care of your instruments and your instruments will take good care of you.

QUESTIONS

Write your answers in a notebook and then compare your answers with those on page 406.

19.4L How can the technical manual for an instrument be obtained if the only copy in a plant is lost?

19.4M What instrument supplies and spare parts should always be available at your plant?

19.5 ADDITIONAL READING

1. *TEXAS MANUAL*, Chapter 14*, "Instrumentation."

2. *AUTOMATION AND INSTRUMENTATION* (M2). Obtain from Customer Services, American Water Works Association, 6666 West Quincy Avenue, Denver, CO 80235. Order No. 30002. Price to members, $34.00; nonmembers, $49.00; includes cost of shipping and handling.

* Depends on edition.

Please answer the discussion and review questions before continuing with the Objective Test.

End of Lesson 2 of 2 Lessons on INSTRUMENTATION

DISCUSSION AND REVIEW QUESTIONS

Chapter 19. INSTRUMENTATION

(Lesson 2 of 2 Lessons)

Write the answers to these questions in your notebook before continuing with the Objective Test on page 406. The question numbering continues from Lesson 1.

8. What are the advantages and limitations of analog versus digital indicators?

9. Why is it poor practice to ignore many of the lamps that are "lit up" (alarm conditions) on an annunciator panel?

10. How should the constantly "lit up" lamps (alarm conditions) on an annunciator panel be handled?

11. What controls are available to protect pumps from damage?

12. What problems are created by oil and moisture in instrument air, and how can these contaminants be removed?

13. Why should a plant operator have a basic understanding of how measuring and control systems are tested and calibrated?

14. What could cause erratic operation of pneumatic instruments?

15. Why should insects and rodents be kept out of instruments?

16. How could you tell if a float might be stuck and how would you determine if it was actually stuck?

SUGGESTED ANSWERS

Chapter 19.   INSTRUMENTATION

ANSWERS TO QUESTIONS IN LESSON 1

Answers to questions on page 366.

19.0A   Measurement instruments can be considered an extension of your human senses because they can perform the same duties as your eyes and ears can directly.

19.0B   Water treatment processes and equipment that could be monitored or controlled by measurement and control systems include influent and effluent flows, basin levels, pump operation, chemical feeders, and filter valves.

19.0C   An advantage of instruments over our senses is that instruments provide quantities or measurable information, whereas only qualitative information is available from our senses.

19.0D   The analog readout of an instrument has a pointer (or other indicating means) that reads against a dial or scale.

Answers to questions on page 368.

19.0E   An ON/OFF type "controller" controls the automatic starting/stopping of a pump or a chemical feeder motor.

19.0F   Examples of "proportional control" in waterworks operations include: (1) chlorine residual analyzer/controller; (2) chemical feed, flow-paced (open loop); (3) pressure- or flow-regulating valves; (4) continuous level control of filter basins; and (5) variable-speed pumping systems for flow control.

19.0G   The motor control station provides for ON/OFF operation of electric motors.

Answers to questions on page 370.

19.1A   The general principles for safe performance on the job are to ALWAYS avoid unsafe acts and correct unsafe conditions.

19.1B   Electrical shock can cause death by asphyxiation and/or burning.

19.1C   An electrical "explosion" could shower you with molten metal, startle you into a bumped head or elbow, or cause a bad fall.

Answers to questions on page 371.

19.1D   Operators should be especially careful when working around powered, automatic, mechanical equipment because the equipment could start unexpectedly and cause serious injury.

19.1E   The purpose of an electrical lockout device is to positively prevent the operation of an electrical circuit, or to de-energize the circuit temporarily.

19.1F   If electrical current flows through your upper body, electrical shock could harm your heart and/or your head.

19.1G   Thin rubber or plastic gloves can be worn to reduce markedly your chances of electric shock.

Answers to questions on page 372.

19.2A   A sensor is the primary element that measures a variable. The sensor is often a transducer of some type that converts energy of one kind into some other form to produce a readout or signal.

19.2B   Pressure is measured by the movement of a flexible element or a mechanically deformable device subjected to the force of the pressure being measured.

19.2C   Some sensors are fitted with surging and overrange protection to limit the effect of pressure spikes or water hammer on the sensor.

Answers to questions on page 378.

19.2D   Liquid level sensors include floats, displacers, probes, pressure sensors, and bubbler tubes.

19.2E   A level signal can be generated by a float element by attaching the float to a steel tape or cable that is wrapped around a drum or pulley. The level sensed is transmitted as a signal (electrical) proportional to the rotation (position) of the pulley or drum.

19.2F   Probes are used instead of mechanical systems to measure liquid levels in sealed or pressurized tanks, or with chemically active liquids.

19.2G   A bubbler measures the level of a liquid by sensing (measuring) air pressure necessary to cause bubbles to just flow out the end of the tube.

Answers to questions on page 383.

19.2H   The two types of flow readings are (1) rate of flow, and (2) total flow (volume).

19.2I   The two main types of larger flow measurement devices are (1) velocity sensing, and (2) differential-pressure sensing. Magnetic and ultrasonic devices are also used.

19.2J   Smaller service meters are usually one of the positive-displacement types of total flowmeters.

19.2K   Velocity-sensing devices measure flows by sensing the rate of rotation of a special impeller placed within the flowing stream.

19.2L   Flows are measured with Venturi meters by sensing the pressure differential between the water pressure before the restriction in the meter or tube, and the pressure within the restriction.

Answers to questions on page 385.

19.2M Chemical feed rates are measured on a weight or volumetric basis if the chemical is in a dry solid form. If the chemical is in liquid form, a volumetric flow measuring device such as a rotameter may be used.

19.2N Process variables commonly measured and/or controlled by instruments include turbidity, pH, chlorine residual, fluoride, electrical conductivity, hardness, alkalinity, and temperature.

19.2O Values measured at one site are transmitted by a signal to a receiver at a remote location.

19.2P The two general systems used to transmit measurement signals are electrical and pneumatic systems.

ANSWERS TO QUESTIONS IN LESSON 2

Answers to questions on page 387.

19.3A The purpose of indicators is to give a visual presentation of a variable's value, either as an analog or as a digital display.

19.3B An analog display uses some type of pointer (or other indicator) against a scale.

19.3C Recorders are usually found in a central location at a water treatment plant.

19.3D Factors that can cause electronic instrument problems include temporary power failures, tripped panel circuit breakers, voltage surges (or lightning) resulting in blown fuses, and excessive heat.

Answers to questions on page 391.

19.3E Recorders are indicators designed to show how the value of the variable has changed with time.

19.3F Recorder charts may be circular or strip types.

19.3G In remote locations where no electricity is available, charts are driven by hand-wound drives or batteries.

19.3H Alarms may produce visual and/or audible signals.

Answers to questions on page 393.

19.3I An operator might bypass a proportional-type controller in an emergency or when, in the judgment of the operator, the controller is not exercising control within sensible limits. To bypass a controller, switch to the manual mode of operation.

19.3J ON/OFF controls should be programmed to operate or cycle associated equipment on and off no more often than actually necessary for plant or system operation.

19.3K Pumps can be prevented from running upon loss of signal by electrical circuitry designed so the pump will turn OFF on an *OPEN* signal circuit, and ON only with a *CLOSED* circuit.

19.3L Pumps in a pump station can be operated for similar lengths of time by the use of manual or automatic sequencers which switch different pumps to the lead pump position and the other(s) to the lag position periodically.

Answers to questions on page 397.

19.3M Signals are transmitted over long distances by the use of signal transmission lines. These lines may be wires owned by the water agency, or telephone lines leased from the local telephone agency. Radio or microwave transmission is sometimes used.

19.3N A loss of signal causes the indicator to go to zero or to maximum scale, depending on type of signal.

19.3O Pneumatic instrumentation pressure systems must have a constant source of clean, dry, pressurized air for reliable operation.

19.3P Oil is removed by filtration through special oil-absorbent elements, and a dryer/desiccator or refrigeration is used to remove moisture from instrument air.

Answers to questions on page 398.

19.3Q Care must be exercised when working in the laboratory so as not to break the sensitive instruments, delicate equipment, or fragile glassware.

19.3R Operators should become familiar with the testing and calibration of plant measuring and control systems in order to assist instrument technicians, and to better understand the plant's instrumentation system. Also, development of skills in instrument testing and calibration equipment may result in a job promotion and/or pay raise.

19.3S V-O-M stands for **V**olt-**O**hm-**M**illiammeter, commonly referred to as a multimeter.

Answers to questions on page 398.

19.4A The three principles which are the keys to proper instrument O & M are:

1. Recognizing properly functioning instruments, so as to prevent prolonged and damaging malfunctions,
2. Shutting down and preparing devices for seasonal or prolonged nonoperation, and
3. Performing preventive (and minor corrective) maintenance tasks to ensure proper operation in the long term.

19.4B General tasks expected of operators of instrumentation systems can be summed up (1) from an operations standpoint as learning and constant attention to what constitutes normal function, and (2) from a maintenance standpoint, as ensuring proper and continuing protection and care of each component.

Answers to questions on page 401.

19.4C Three signs that a flow recorder may not be functioning properly are:

1. Very flat or steady pen trace (is the system working at all, or is the variable really that constant?);
2. Excessive pen/pointer quiver (causes undue wear on parts, can usually be adjusted out); and
3. Constant or periodic hunting, or spikes, in a pen/pointer (improper adjustment, control, or other problem).

19.4D   Recording pens are most likely to become stuck or hung up on the chart edge or in a tear or hole.

19.4E   A common reason for nonoperation of a pneumatic system is the failure of the instrument air supply caused by water and oil.

19.4F   An indication of a serious problem in an electrical instrument or power circuit is the presence of smoke and/or a burning odor.

Answers to questions on page 401.

19.4G   Moisture can be controlled in instruments by a space-heat source (such as a power transformer) or by inserting a container of desiccant into its case.

19.4H   Pneumatic instrumentation should be purged with dry air before shutdown to rid the individual parts of residual oil and moisture and to minimize internal corrosion.

Answers to questions on page 402.

19.4I   Regular preventive maintenance duties should be printed on forms or cards for use by operators as a reminder, guide, and record of preventive maintenance.

19.4J   Operational checks are performed by always observing each system for its continuing signs of normal operation, and cycling some indicators by certain testing methods.

19.4K   If a recorder trace is altered from its usual pattern during the process of checking an instrument, the operator causing the upset should initial the chart appropriately, with the time noted.

Answers to questions on page 403.

19.4L   To obtain a technical manual for an instrument, write to the manufacturer. Be sure to provide all relevant serial/model numbers in your request to the manufacturer for a manual.

19.4M   Instrument supplies and spare parts that should always be available include charts, pens, pen cleaners and ink, and any other parts necessary for instrument operation or service.

OBJECTIVE TEST

Chapter 19. INSTRUMENTATION

Please write your name and mark the correct answers on the answer sheet, as directed at the end of Chapter 1. There may be more than one correct answer to each multiple-choice question.

True-False

1. The operator's senses provide quantitative or measurable information regarding plant performance.
   1. True
   2. False

2. Most electrical panels have an interlock on the door that interrupts all (local) power to a panel or device when the door is opened or the circuit is exposed for service.
   1. True
   2. False

3. Lockout devices on electric switches must be respected at all times.
   1. True
   2. False

4. Flowmeters are calibrated to read out flows in velocity units.
   1. True
   2. False

5. When propeller meters become old, they become susceptible to over-registration (read high).
   1. True
   2. False

6. When water is forced to go faster in a pipe, the pressure in the pipe increases.
   1. True
   2. False

7. Flowmeters should be calibrated in place to ensure accurate flow measurements.
   1. True
   2. False

8. An analog display is a direct numerical readout.
   1. True
   2. False

9. During the design phase of a plant, operators must ensure that a plant is operable during power outages.

   1. True
   2. False

10. A remote sensing and control station can send tone signals and simultaneously receive tone signals at the same site.

    1. True
    2. False

11. The most common reason for an inoperable instrument is an unnoticed failure of the instrument air supply.

    1. True
    2. False

12. If a gentle tap on an instrument causes a slight pen movement, the instrument is functioning properly.

    1. True
    2. False

Best Answer (Select only the closest or best answer.)

13. What does accuracy refer to?

    1. How closely an instrument determines the actual value
    2. The direct numerical reading from an instrument
    3. The general quality and condition of the instrument
    4. The standardization of measurements

14. The motor control station provides only for ON/OFF operation of which piece of equipment?

    1. Chemical feeder
    2. Electric motor
    3. Pump
    4. Valve

15. What is a leading cause of operator lost-time accidents?

    1. Asphyxiation
    2. Drowning
    3. Electric shock
    4. Falls

16. How can you reduce your chances of electric shock?

    1. Be very careful on ladders
    2. Carry tools on an electrician's belt
    3. Wear hard hat
    4. Wear thin rubber or plastic gloves

17. What is a snubber?

    1. Air cushion chamber
    2. Mechanical pressure element
    3. Primary element
    4. Surge protection device

18. What is a problem encountered when using probes to measure water levels?

    1. Accumulation of scum on probe
    2. Measuring entire range of depth readings
    3. Rods move up and down
    4. Signals can't be transmitted electronically

19. What is the most precise method of measuring liquid level?

    1. Bubbler
    2. Float
    3. Probe
    4. Target pointer

20. Preventive maintenance of pneumatic components in pneumatic systems centers around which factor?

    1. Adjusting flow rate of air supply
    2. Ensuring a clean, dry air supply
    3. Keeping conduits clear at all times
    4. Providing an acceptable vent system

21. Annunciator panels all have "acknowledge" and "reset" features which allow the operator to perform which task?

    1. Change the alarm set points to stop the alarm
    2. Correct the alarm condition from the panel
    3. Squelch the alarm sound
    4. Turn off the visible alarm

22. Why do larger pump systems usually have a low-pressure cutoff switch on the suction side of the pump?

    1. To control impacts from water hammer
    2. To prevent pump from running when no water is available
    3. To reduce corrosion problems
    4. To stop cavitation damage

Multiple Choice (Select all correct answers.)

23. Which of the following are process variables?

    1. Flow
    2. Level
    3. Pressure
    4. Records
    5. Weight

24. Which of the following are level sensing devices?

    1. Capacitance probe
    2. Direct pressure
    3. Float
    4. Pneumatic bubbler
    5. Sonar

25. Which inferential techniques are used to measure flows?

    1. Differential pressure sensing
    2. Direct measurement
    3. Magnetic
    4. Ultrasonic
    5. Velocity sensing

26. Which factors could cause a propeller meter to over-register (read high)?

    1. Bearing wear
    2. Gear train friction
    3. Malfunctioning transmitter
    4. Partially full pipeline
    5. Wrong gears installed

27. Which process variables are usually monitored closely and continuously in a water treatment plant?

    1. Chlorine residual
    2. Coliforms
    3. Nitrate
    4. pH
    5. Turbidity

28. What must a plant's instrument air be free of?

    1. Carbon dioxide
    2. Moisture
    3. Nitrogen
    4. Oil
    5. Particulates

29. What is required for instrumentation systems to be reliable year after year? Proper

1. Application
2. Maintenance
3. Operation
4. Setup
5. Warranty

30. What are the causes of erratic instrument operation?

1. Fluctuating process variable
2. Low temperature
3. Oil in air supply
4. Water in air supply
5. Windy conditions

31. An operator should be alert for which of the pen movements that could indicate a potential problem?

1. Constant hunting
2. Periodic spikes
3. Quivering pen movement
4. Similar cycles
5. Very flat pen trace

32. What are the limitations of a time-duration (or pulse-width) type of signal transmission in a telemetry system?

1. Equipment such as chemical feeders cannot be operated continuously
2. It must be calibrated frequently with sophisticated instruments
3. Loss of power can damage strip or chart recorders
4. Stray line noise may produce incorrect tone
5. The concept is difficult for operators to understand

End of Objective Test

CHAPTER 20

SAFETY

by

Joe Monscvitz

TABLE OF CONTENTS
Chapter 20. SAFETY

Page

OBJECTIVES 413

WORDS 414

LESSON 1

20.0 IMPORTANCE OF SAFETY 416

   20.00 What Is Safety? 416

   20.01 Causes of Accidents 416

   20.02 Steps to Avoid Accidents 416

20.1 CHEMICAL HANDLING 417

   20.10 Safe Handling of Chemicals 417

   20.11 Acids 417

      20.110 Acetic Acid (Glacial) 417

      20.111 Hydrofluosilicic Acid 418

      20.112 Hydrogen Fluoride 420

      20.113 Hydrochloric Acid 420

      20.114 Nitric Acid 420

      20.115 Sulfuric Acid 420

   20.12 Bases 421

      20.120 Ammonia 421

      20.121 Calcium Hydroxide 422

      20.122 Sodium Hydroxide (Caustic Soda) 422

      20.123 Sodium Silicate 423

      20.124 Hypochlorite 423

      20.125 Sodium Carbonate 423

   20.13 Gases 424

      20.130 Chlorine (Cl_2) 424

      20.131 Carbon Dioxide (CO_2) 426

      20.132 Sulfur Dioxide (SO_2) 426

   20.14 Salts 428

      20.140 Aluminum Sulfate (Alum) 428

      20.141 Ferric Chloride 429

      20.142 Ferric Sulfate 429

20.143   Ferrous Sulfate 429

20.144   Sodium Aluminate 429

20.145   Fluoride Compounds 429

20.15   Powders 430

20.150   Potassium Permanganate ($KMnO_4$) 430

20.151   Powdered Activated Carbon 430

20.152   Other Powders 431

20.16   Labeling of Chemical Containers 432

20.17   Chemical Storage Drains 432

DISCUSSION AND REVIEW QUESTIONS 432

LESSON 2

20.2   FIRE PROTECTION 433

20.20   Fire Prevention 433

20.21   Classification 433

20.22   Extinguishers 433

20.23   Fire Hoses 434

20.24   Storage of Flammables 435

20.25   Exits 435

20.3   PLANT MAINTENANCE 436

20.30   Maintenance Hazards 436

20.31   Cleaning 436

20.32   Painting 436

20.33   Cranes 436

20.34   Confined Spaces 437

20.35   Manholes 438

20.36   Power Tools 440

20.37   Welding 441

20.38   Safety Valves 441

20.4   VEHICLE MAINTENANCE AND OPERATION 441

20.40   Types of Vehicles 441

20.41   Maintenance 441

20.42   Seat Belts 443

20.43   Accident Prevention 443

20.44   Forklifts 444

DISCUSSION AND REVIEW QUESTIONS 444

LESSON 3

20.5   ELECTRICAL EQUIPMENT 446

20.50   Electrical Safety 446

20.51   Current — Voltage 446

20.52   Transformers 446

20.53   Electric Starters 446

20.54   Electric Motors 447

20.55   Instrumentation 447

20.56   Control Panels 447

20.57   Lockout/Tagout Procedure 447

20.6   LABORATORY SAFETY 449

20.60   Laboratory Hazards 449

20.61   Glassware 449

20.62   Chemicals 449

20.63   Biological Considerations 450

20.64   Radioactivity 450

20.65   Laboratory Equipment 450

20.650   Hot Plates 450

20.651   Water Stills 450

20.652   Sterilizers 450

20.653   Pipet Washers 450

20.7   OPERATOR PROTECTION 451

20.70   Operator Safety 451

20.71   Respiratory Protection 451

20.72   Safety Equipment 451

20.73   Eye Protection 452

20.74   Foot Protection 452

20.75   Hand Protection 452

20.76   Head Protection 453

20.77   Water Safety 453

20.8   PREPARATION FOR EMERGENCIES 454

20.9   ARITHMETIC ASSIGNMENT 456

20.10   ADDITIONAL READING 456

DISCUSSION AND REVIEW QUESTIONS 456

SUGGESTED ANSWERS 457

OBJECTIVE TEST 460

OBJECTIVES

Chapter 20.   SAFETY

Following completion of Chapter 20, you should be able to:

1. List the responsibilities of operators and management for waterworks safety,

2. Identify and safely handle hazardous chemicals,

3. Recognize fire hazards and properly extinguish various types of fires,

4. Safely maintain waterworks equipment and facilities,

5. Properly operate and maintain vehicles,

6. Recognize electrical hazards,

7. Safely perform duties in a laboratory, and

8. Protect other operators and yourself while working in and around waterworks facilities.

WORDS

Chapter 20.   SAFETY

ARCH   ARCH

(1) The curved top of a sewer pipe or conduit.

(2) A bridge or arch of hardened or caked chemical which will prevent the flow of the chemical.

ACUTE HEALTH EFFECT   ACUTE HEALTH EFFECT

An adverse effect on a human or animal body, with symptoms developing rapidly.

CONFINED SPACE   CONFINED SPACE

Confined space means a space that:

A.   Is large enough and so configured that an employee can bodily enter and perform assigned work; and

B.   Has limited or restricted means for entry or exit (for example, tanks, vessels, silos, storage bins, hoppers, vaults, and pits are spaces that may have limited means of entry); and

C.   Is not designed for continuous employee occupancy.

(Definition from the Code of Federal Regulations (CFR) Title 29 Part 1910.146.)

CONFINED SPACE, CLASS "A"   CONFINED SPACE, CLASS "A"

A confined space that presents a situation that is immediately dangerous to life or health (IDLH). These include but are not limited to oxygen deficiency, explosive or flammable atmospheres, and/or concentrations of toxic substances.

(Definition from NIOSH, "Criteria for a Recommended Standard: Working in Confined Spaces.")

CONFINED SPACE, CLASS "B"   CONFINED SPACE, CLASS "B"

A confined space that has the potential for causing injury and illness, if preventive measures are not used, but not immediately dangerous to life and health.

(Definition from NIOSH, "Criteria for a Recommended Standard: Working in Confined Spaces.")

CONFINED SPACE, CLASS "C"   CONFINED SPACE, CLASS "C"

A confined space in which the potential hazard would not require any special modification of the work procedure.

(Definition from NIOSH, "Criteria for a Recommended Standard: Working in Confined Spaces.")

CONFINED SPACE, PERMIT-REQUIRED   CONFINED SPACE, PERMIT-REQUIRED
(PERMIT SPACE)   (PERMIT SPACE)

A confined space that has one or more of the following characteristics:

• Contains or has a potential to contain a hazardous atmosphere,

• Contains a material that has the potential for engulfing an entrant,

• Has an internal configuration such that an entrant could be trapped or asphyxiated by inwardly converging walls or by a floor which slopes downward and tapers to a smaller cross section, or

• Contains any other recognized serious safety or health hazard.

(Definition from the Code of Federal Regulations (CFR) Title 29 Part 1910.146.)

DECIBEL (DES-uh-bull)   DECIBEL

A unit for expressing the relative intensity of sounds on a scale from zero for the average least perceptible sound to about 130 for the average level at which sound causes pain to humans. Abbreviated dB.

MATERIAL SAFETY DATA SHEET (MSDS)

MATERIAL SAFETY DATA SHEET (MSDS)

A document which provides pertinent information and a profile of a particular hazardous substance or mixture. An MSDS is normally developed by the manufacturer or formulator of the hazardous substance or mixture. The MSDS is required to be made available to employees and operators whenever there is the likelihood of the hazardous substance or mixture being introduced into the workplace. Some manufacturers are preparing MSDSs for products that are not considered to be hazardous to show that the product or substance is *NOT* hazardous.

OSHA (O-shuh)

OSHA

The Williams-Steiger **O**ccupational **S**afety and **H**ealth **A**ct of 1970 (OSHA) is a federal law designed to protect the health and safety of industrial workers and also the operators of water supply systems and treatment plants. The Act regulates the design, construction, operation and maintenance of water supply systems and water treatment plants. OSHA also refers to the federal and state agencies which administer the OSHA regulations.

OLFACTORY (ol-FAK-tore-ee) FATIGUE

OLFACTORY FATIGUE

A condition in which a person's nose, after exposure to certain odors, is no longer able to detect the odor.

PERMIT-REQUIRED CONFINED SPACE
  (PERMIT SPACE)

PERMIT-REQUIRED CONFINED SPACE
(PERMIT SPACE)

See CONFINED SPACE, PERMIT-REQUIRED (PERMIT SPACE).

TAILGATE SAFETY MEETING

TAILGATE SAFETY MEETING

Brief (10 to 20 minutes) safety meetings held every 7 to 10 working days. The term *TAILGATE* comes from the safety meetings regularly held by the construction industry around the tailgate of a truck.

CHAPTER 20.   SAFETY

(Lesson 1 of 3 Lessons)

20.0   IMPORTANCE OF SAFETY

20.00   What Is Safety?

Webster states that safety is the following:

"The condition of being safe; freedom from exposure to danger; exemption from hurt, injury or loss; to protect against failure, breakage or other accidents; knowledge of or skill in methods of avoiding accident or disease."

Safety is more than words. Safety is the action of Webster's definition. Safety is using one's knowledge or skill to avoid accidents or to protect oneself and others from accidents. Safety is a form of preventive maintenance which includes equipment and machinery and its proper handling. Who is responsible for safety? Everyone should be responsible, from top management to all employees.

Management has its responsibilities for safety; its main function is to set the tone and provide the training and monies for an effective safety program. (See Chapter 23, "Administration," for a description of the elements of an effective safety program and a detailed discussion of management's responsibilities for safety.) Management should be responsible for the following:

1. Establish a safety policy,

2. Assign responsibility for accident prevention, which includes description of the duties and responsibilities of a safety officer, department heads, line supervisors, safety committees, and operators,

3. Appoint a safety officer or coordinator,

4. Establish realistic goals and periodically revise them to ensure continuous and maximum effort, and

5. Evaluate the results of the program.

While management has its responsibilities, the operators also have their particular responsibilities. Operators should:

1. Perform their jobs in accordance with established safe procedures,

2. Recognize the responsibility for their own safety and that of fellow operators,

3. Report all injuries,

4. Report all observed hazards, and

5. Actively participate in the safety program.

QUESTIONS

Write your answers in a notebook and then compare your answers with those on page 457.

20.0A   What are management's responsibilities for safety?

20.0B   What are the operators' responsibilities for safety?

20.01   Causes of Accidents

A SAFETY PROGRAM HAS ONE OBJECTIVE: TO PREVENT ACCIDENTS. Accidents do not happen, they are caused. They may be caused by unsafe acts of operators or result from hazardous conditions or may be a combination of both. An analysis of accident statistics reveals that operator negligence and carelessness are the causes of most accidents. We know how to do our job safely, but we just don't do it safely.

Accidents reduce efficiency and effectiveness. An accident is that occurrence in a sequence of events that usually produces unintended injury, death, or property damage. Accidents affect the lives and morale of operators. They raise the costs not only to management but also to operators.

Safety authorities tell us that nine out of ten injuries are the result of unsafe acts of either the person injured or someone else. Here are some of the principal reasons for unsafe acts.

IGNORANCE. This may be due to lack of experience or training, or to a temporary condition that prevents the recognition of a hazard.

INDIFFERENCE. Some people know better but don't care. They take unnecessary risks and disregard the rules or instructions.

POOR WORK HABITS. Some people either don't learn the right way of doing things, or they develop a wrong way. Supervisors or fellow operators who see things done unsafely must speak up.

LAZINESS. Laziness affects speed and quality of work. Laziness also affects safety because safety requires an effort. In most jobs you cannot reduce your "safety effort" and still maintain the same level of safety, even if you slow down or lower your quality standards.

HASTE. When we rush, we work too fast to think about what we are doing, we take dangerous shortcuts, and we are more likely to be injured.

POOR PHYSICAL CONDITION. Some of us just won't take reasonable care of ourselves. We ignore our bodily needs in regard to exercise, rest, and diet, lessening our endurance and alertness.

TEMPER. Impatience and anger cause many accidents. Again, our thinking is interfered with and the way prepared for an accident.

Every one of these unsafe acts could be considered due to operator negligence or carelessness.

20.02   Steps to Avoid Accidents

Some specific steps you can take to avoid accidents are the following:

1. Ask about the safety program established by management and then actively participate in safety training sessions and *TAILGATE SAFETY MEETINGS*,[1]

2. Routinely use the safety equipment described in Section 20.7 (for example, lockout/tagout devices and self-contained breathing apparatus) and personal protective gear (hard hat, safety goggles, gloves) provided by your employer, and

3. Follow safe procedures at all times. This means taking the time needed to do every job *SAFELY*.

QUESTIONS

Write your answers in a notebook and then compare your answers with those on page 457.

20.0C   What is an accident?

20.0D   List the principal reasons for unsafe acts.

20.0E   What problems are caused by laziness?

20.1   CHEMICAL HANDLING

20.10   Safe Handling of Chemicals

The water treatment plant operator may be required to handle a wide variety of chemicals, depending on the type of plant. In a simple well system, chlorine may be the only chemical used. In more complicated plants, there may be chlorine, other gases, sulfuric acid, lime, alum, powdered activated carbon, and anhydrous ammonia. All of these chemicals fall into groups: acids, hydroxides, gases, salts, organics, and solvents. Each group requires you, the operator, to have a good understanding of all types of chemicals. You must know how to handle the many problems associated with each of these elements or compounds. For example, you must know how to store chemicals, understand the fire problem, be aware of the tendency of chemicals to *ARCH*[2] in a storage bin, know how to feed dry, how to feed liquid, and how to make up solutions. All of these situations may cause an unsafe condition. Overheating gas containers, dust problems with powdered carbon, burns caused by acid, reactivity of each chemical under a variety of conditions that may cause fire and explosions are other safety hazards. You will need to know the usable limits of each chemical because of toxicity, the protective equipment required for each chemical, each chemical's antidote, and how to control fires caused by each chemical.

Although you may not regularly handle all of the chemicals listed here, you may come into contact with them from time to time. Try at least to learn all of the characteristics of the chemicals you will use regularly. For example, learn the boiling point, explosive limits, reactivity, flammability, first aid used for each chemical, and other characteristics that may prove helpful in preventing a safety hazard. Study the chemistry of each chemical used in the plant in order to have a safe plant in which to work. The following discussions concentrate on the characteristics of each compound and point out its hazards, reactivity, and the information needed to avoid conditions that may cause a safety problem.

20.11   Acids

Acids are used extensively in water treatment. For example, hydrofluoric acid is used in fluoride addition and hydrochloric acid is often used in cleaning. Table 20.1 lists many of the acids used in water treatment and gives their characteristics. This section can serve as a quick reference and a guide for learning some of each acid's limitations and its reactivity with other compounds.

The antidote to all acids is neutralization. However, one must be careful in how this is performed. Most often large amounts of water will serve the purpose, but if the acid is ingested (swallowed), then milk of magnesia may be needed. If vapors are inhaled, first aid usually consists of providing fresh air, artificially restoring breathing (CPR), or supplying oxygen. In general, acids are neutralized by a base or alkaline substance. Baking soda is often used to neutralize acids on skin because it is not harmful on contact with your skin. To understand these reactions, you will need to know some acid/base chemistry. The knowledge of acid/base chemistry and fast reactions on your part may reduce the safety hazards involved in handling acids in water treatment.

20.110   Acetic Acid (Glacial)

This chemical is stable when stored and handled properly. However, it may react violently with certain compounds such as ammonium nitrate, potassium hydroxide, and other alkaline materials. Strong oxidizing glacial acetic acid is a combustible material. Fires involving the acid may be extinguished with water, dry chemical, or carbon dioxide. Under such conditions as adding water, the diluted acid may produce hydrogen gas when it comes in contact with metals. When the chemical is involved in a fire situation, a self-contained breath-

---

[1] *Tailgate Safety Meeting.   Brief (10 to 20 minutes) safety meetings held every 7 to 10 working days. The term TAILGATE comes from the safety meetings regularly held by the construction industry around the tailgate of a truck.*

[2] *Arch.   A bridge or arch of hardened or caked chemical which will prevent the flow of the chemical.*

TABLE 20.1   ACIDS USED IN WATER TREATMENT

Name, Formula	Common Name	Available Forms	Specific Gravity	Flammability	Color	Odor	Containers
Acetic Acid, CH_3COOH	Ethanoic Acid	Solution	1.05	Yes	Clear	Sharp, pungent	Carboys, drums
Hydrofluosilicic Acid, H_2SiF_6	Fluosilicic Acid	Solution	1.4634	N/A[a]	Clear	Pungent fumes	Drums, trucks, R.R. tank cars
Hydrogen Fluoride Acid, HF	Hydrofluoric Acid	Liquid	0.987	N/A	Clear	Fumes, toxic	Drums, tank cars
Hydrochloric Acid, HCl	Muriatic Acid	Solution	1.16	N/A	Clear to yellow	Pungent, suffocating	Drums, carboys
Nitric Acid, HNO_3	—	Liquid	1.5027	N/A	Colorless, yellowish	Toxic fumes in presence of light	Drums, carboys, bottles
Sulfuric Acid, H_2SO_4	Oil of Vitriol; Vitriol	Solution	(60-66° Bé[b]) 1.841	N/A	Clear	Odorless	Bottles, carboys, drums, trucks, tank cars

[a] N/A = Not Applicable
[b] Bé = Baumé scale, a scale for measuring specific gravity of liquids

ing apparatus must be used to protect the operator against suffocation and problems caused by corrosive vapors.

Most people find inhalation of acetic acid vapors in concentrations over 50 ppm (parts per million) intolerable, resulting in nose and throat irritations. Repeated exposure to high concentrations may produce congestion of the larynx. Skin contact with concentrated acetic acid can produce deep burns with skin destruction. High vapor concentration may blacken the skin and produce allergic reactions and eye irritation. Possible permanent damage or immediate burns are caused when the acid comes into contact with the eye. If the acid is ingested, severe intestinal irritation will result as well as burns to the mouth and upper respiratory tract.

Operators should be protected by adequate exhaust facilities to ensure ventilation when working with acetic acid. At a minimum, exhaust hoods should have air velocity of 100 FPM (30 m/min). Wear rubber gloves and an apron to prevent skin contact. Wear splash-proof goggles or a face shield to prevent any eye contact. Gas-tight goggles may also be needed to prevent vapors from irritating your eyes. An eye wash station must be readily available where this chemical is being handled. Also, respiratory equipment should be available for emergency use. Acetic acid can be handled safely by using adequate ventilation and safety equipment to prevent skin and eye contact. Remember also that acetic acid vapors can cause OLFACTORY (ol-FAK-tore-ee) FATIGUE. This is a condition in which a person's nose, after exposure to certain odors, is no longer able to detect the odor. Acetic acid is detectable by your nose at 1 ppm, but documentation has shown operators tolerating up to 200 ppm.

If a leak or spill should occur, notify safety personnel and provide adequate ventilation. When cleaning up large spills, wear a self-contained breathing apparatus and equipment to prevent contact with eyes and skin. To clean up spill areas and remove chemical residue, cover the area with sodium bicarbonate and flush away with large quantities of water.

First aid for acetic acid exposure calls for removal of the victim to fresh air, rinsing the mouth and nasal passages with water, and checking for inhalation problems. If the acid made contact with the eyes, immediately irrigate with water for at

least 15 minutes. Obtain medical attention. For skin contact problems, wash with water immediately; if the acid was swallowed, give three glasses of milk or water and obtain medical attention quickly. Acetic acid exposure, like all other acids, must be treated immediately to prevent damage to the victim.

20.111 Hydrofluosilicic Acid

This chemical is hazardous to handle under any conditions. Be extremely careful using this acid. The acid is colorless, transparent, fuming, corrosive, and is a liquid. A pungent odor is created by the acid and contact causes skin irritation. When the acid vaporizes, it decomposes into hydrofluoric acid and silicon tetrafluoride. Hydrofluoric acid can attack glass.

When handling hydrofluosilicic acid, always use complete protective equipment, rubber gloves, goggles or face shield, rubber apron, rubber boots, and have lime slurry barrels, epsom salt solution, and safety showers (Figure 20.1) available. Always provide adequate ventilation because its vapor can cause irritation to the respiratory system. Careful maintenance of protective equipment is essential because the fumes of the acid corrode metal or etch glass on the protective equipment.

First aid for eye contact is to thoroughly flush with water for 15 minutes and get medical aid as soon as possible. For skin

Fig. 20.1   Safety shower with face/eye wash
(Permission of Nevada Safety & Supply)

contact, wash the affected areas with water. For gross (large) contact, remove contaminated clothing under a safety shower and thoroughly wash entire body for 15 minutes or longer. In case of inhalation, remove operator to fresh air, restore breathing, if required, and get medical aid.

20.112 Hydrogen Fluoride

This acid is extremely poisonous, and it produces terrible sores when allowed to come into contact with the skin. The acid is a clear, corrosive liquid that has a pungent odor. All of the precautions discussed for hydrofluosilicic acid apply to this acid also.

20.113 Hydrochloric Acid

This acid is used most often for cleaning in and around the treatment plant and is known as muriatic acid. The acid is also used very frequently in the laboratory. Hydrochloric acid is stable when properly contained and handled. This acid is one of the strong mineral acids and, therefore, is highly reactive with metals and these oxides: hydrocarbon, amine, and carbonate compounds. The acid liberates significant levels of hydrogen chloride gas (HCl) because of its vapor pressure at room temperature, and gives off large amounts of gas when heated. In reactions with most metals, hydrochloric acid will produce hydrogen gas.

Inhalation of HCl vapors or mists for long periods can cause damage to teeth and irritation to the nasal passages. Concentrations of 750 ppm or more will cause coughing, choking, and produce severe damage to the mucous membranes of the respiratory tract. In concentrations of 1,300 ppm, HCl is dangerous to life. Ingestion can cause burns of the mouth and digestive tract.

When handling HCl, provide adequate exhaust facilities to ensure ventilation and wear protective clothing and equipment to prevent body contact with the acid. Use rubber gloves, rubber apron, rubber boots, and wear a long-sleeved shirt when handling hydrochloric acid. To protect your eyes against splashing of the acid, you must wear safety goggles and/or a face shield. There should always be an eye wash station and safety shower located near areas where this acid is to be used.

First aid consists of thoroughly flushing the eyes with running water for 15 minutes and securing medical aid. If hydrochloric acid comes in contact with skin, wash the affected areas with water. For gross contact, remove clothing under the safety shower and continue showering for 15 minutes or longer. Should the acid be ingested, give water and milk of magnesia. Do not induce vomiting; get medical aid. In case of inhalation, remove the victim to fresh air, restore breathing if required, and get medical aid.

Store acid containers closed in a clean, cool, open, and well-ventilated area. Keep out of the sun. Keep the acid away from oxidizing agents or alkaline materials. Provide emergency neutralization materials in use areas.

20.114 Nitric Acid

Like hydrochloric acid, nitric acid is one of the most commonly used acids in the water treatment laboratory and plant. The acid is a powerful oxidizing agent and attacks most metals. Nitric acid is stable when properly handled and placed into a proper container. The acid is one of the strong mineral acids, and is highly reactive with materials such as metals. When handling nitric acid, use protective clothing and equipment to prevent body contact with the liquid. Such equipment includes rubber gloves, rubber apron, and safety goggles or a face shield for eye protection against splashing of the acid. Nitric acid is a strong, poisonous, and highly corrosive liquid and must be handled carefully. The acid forms toxic fumes in the presence of light; therefore, it should be kept out of the sun.

Like other acids, nitric acid should be stored in clean, cool, well-ventilated areas. The areas should have an acid-resistant floor and adequate drainage. Keep it away from oxidizing agents and alkaline materials. Protect containers from damage or breakage. Avoid contact with skin and provide emergency neutralization materials and safety equipment in use areas.

First aid for skin contact is to flush thoroughly with water for 15 minutes. Get medical aid if needed. This acid will cause burns, but these can be greatly reduced if the contact area is immediately flushed. For gross (large) contact, remove contaminated clothing under a safety shower. For eye contact, flush with water for 15 minutes and get medical aid. If acid is ingested, give water with milk of magnesia; get medical aid. For inhalation, remove to fresh air, restore breathing if required, and get medical aid.

20.115 Sulfuric Acid

This mineral acid is highly corrosive and will attack most metals. Sulfuric acid is also very reactive to the skin and must be handled with extreme care or you will suffer severe burns. Even when the acid is diluted, it is highly corrosive and must be contained in rubber-, glass-, or plastic-lined equipment. The acid will decompose clothing and shoes. Sulfuric acid should not come in contact with potassium permanganate or similar compounds. Sulfuric acid reacts violently with water. *ALWAYS POUR ACID INTO WATER* while stirring to prevent the generation of steam and hot water which could boil over the container and cause serious acid burns.

As with other mineral acids, this material is stable when properly contained and handled. When you are handling sulfuric acid, you must use protective clothing and equipment to prevent body contact with the acid. Wear rubber gloves, safety goggles, and/or a face shield for eye protection against splashing. Also wear a rubber apron, rubber boots, and long-sleeved shirt. The eye wash station and safety shower must be located nearby where the acid is being handled. The area should be well ventilated, the acid should be stored in closed containers in a clean, cool, open area. The area should have an acid-resistant floor which is well drained. Keep away from oxidizing agents and alkaline materials and protect the containers from damage or breakage.

Because the acid is highly corrosive and causes severe burns, first aid for sulfuric acid exposure must be immediate to avoid substantial damage to human tissue. For eye contact, flush thoroughly with running water for 15 minutes, get medical aid — the first seconds are important. For skin contact, wash affected areas thoroughly with water. For gross (large) contact, remove contaminated clothing under the safety shower with prolonged washing for at least 15 minutes. In cases of ingestion, give water and milk of magnesia; get medical aid. When working with sulfuric acid, avoid skin contact and always provide emergency neutralization materials and a safety shower near the work areas.

QUESTIONS

Write your answers in a notebook and then compare your answers with those on page 457.

20.10A What does an operator need to know about chemicals used in a water treatment plant?

20.11A What should be done if an operator inhales acid vapors?

20.11B Acetic acid will react violently with which compounds?

20.11C Under what conditions can acetic acid be handled safely?

20.11D What protective equipment is necessary for handling hydrofluosilicic acid?

20.11E How can the inhalation of hydrochloric acid (HCl) vapors or mists cause damage to operators?

20.11F How should nitric acid be stored?

20.12 Bases

The bases that are used in water treatment are known as hydroxides. From a functional standpoint they are used to raise pH. Most common bases are compounds of sodium, calcium, and ammonium which are strong bases. However, there are other weak bases, such as silicate, carbonate, and hypochlorite. From the standpoint of safety, both weak and strong bases must be given the same consideration when being handled. Some are very toxic and will attack human tissue very rapidly and cause burns. Explosive reactions will occur when bases come in contact with an acid and hazardous decomposition products are created under certain conditions.

Bases must be neutralized with dilute acids. However, the operator must work carefully because under some conditions there may be other reactions, such as with hypochlorite compounds. Therefore, you should understand acid/base chemistry before handling any of the basic compounds used in water treatment. Table 20.2 gives some of the common basic compounds used in water treatment. The following sections will discuss some of their characteristics and the precautions the operator must use to safely handle such compounds.

12.120 Ammonia

The operator may use one of two forms of ammonia: anhydrous or hydroxide. The first (anhydrous) is in a gas form and requires one type of consideration. The hydroxide is a liquid and requires another type of consideration. Anhydrous ammonia in the gaseous state is colorless; it is about 0.6 times as heavy as air. In a liquid state, ammonia is also colorless, 0.68 times as heavy as water, and it vaporizes rapidly. The ammonia gas is capable of forming explosive mixtures with air. For your own safety, be aware of the possibility of suffocation since the gas can displace air which contains oxygen. Although the vapors are not poisonous, they can and will irritate the mucous membranes of the eyes, nose, throat, and lungs. Irritation will be detected in concentrations of 5.0 ppm and when human tissue comes in contact with the liquid, it will cause severe burns.

When handling ammonia or working in an ammonia environment, respiratory protection is a requirement. For entry into emergency areas, use only a self-contained breathing apparatus. Install a good ventilation system to control vapors in the application room. Use protective clothing, rubber gloves, apron, boots, and face and eye protection if you are going to work with ammonia for long periods.

Care must be used when storing or transporting containers. Always keep cylinder caps in place when cylinders are not in

TABLE 20.2 BASES USED IN WATER TREATMENT

Name, Formula	Common Name	Available Forms	Spec. Grav. or lbs/cu ft	Flammability	Color	Odor	Containers
Ammonia, NH_3	Ammonia	Liquid, gas	0.04813 lbs/ cu ft @ 0°C	Explosive with air; will burn in air	Colorless	Irritating	Cylinders, tanks, trucks
Calcium Hydroxide and Oxide, $Ca(OH)_2$ and CaO	Hydrated Lime and Quicklime	Dry powder, lump	50-70 lbs per cu ft	N/A[a]	White	Dust	Bags, bulk, trucks
Sodium Hydroxide, $NaOH$	Caustic Soda, Lye	Lump, liquid, flake	1.524	May cause flammable condition	Opaque white	Toxic, pungent	Drums, bulk, trucks
Sodium Silicate, Na_2SiO_2	Water Glass	Liquid	1.35-1.42	N/A	Opaque	N/A	Drums, bulk, trucks
Hypochlorite Compounds, $NaOCl$, $Ca(OCl)_2$	HTH	Powder, liquid	—	Explosive with antifreeze	White	Toxic Cl_2, pungent	Cans, drums
Sodium Carbonate, Na_2CO_3	Soda Ash	Powder	23, 35, and 65 lbs/cu ft	N/A	White	Dust	Bags, bulk, trucks

[a] N/A = Not Applicable

use. Store cylinders in a cool, dry location away from heat, and protect from direct sunlight. Storage near radiators, steam pipes, or other sources of heat may raise the pressure to a dangerous point, whereas dampness may cause excessive corrosion. Do not store in the same room with chlorine. Always use lifting clamps or cradles. Avoid hoisting the cylinders using ropes, cables, or slings, and never drop the containers. Control ammonia leaks. They can be detected by odor or by using a cloth swab soaked with hydrochloric acid. This will form a white cloud of ammonium chloride.

Ammonia gas will burn if it is blended with air in a mixture containing 15 to 28 percent ammonia by volume. Check cylinder valve stems for leaks; tighten the packing gland nut only with a special wrench provided for such purposes. If a serious leak in a cylinder cannot be controlled, place the container in a vat of water. Fifty-three pounds of ammonia will dissolve in 100 pounds of water at 68°F (20°C). *NEVER* neutralize liquid ammonia with an acid. The reaction generates a lot of heat which may speed up the release of ammonia gas.

First aid for skin contact with ammonia is to flush with large amounts of water for 5 to 10 minutes, and get medical aid. Remove contaminated clothing under a safety shower. For eye contact, flush thoroughly with water for 15 minutes immediately, and get medical aid. In the case of inhalation, remove to fresh air and restore breathing. If required, get medical aid. Throat burns should be rinsed with two percent boric acid solution. Urge the patient to drink large amounts of milk. For irritation of nose and throat because of exposure, see a physician.

Ammonium hydroxide is an aqueous (watery) solution of anhydrous ammonia and is quite volatile (will evaporate) at atmospheric temperatures and pressures. This solution can cause local skin irritations. A strong solution will cause human tissue destruction on contact with eyes, skin, and mucous membranes of the respiratory system, so avoid contact with the compound. The solution will cause severe burns depending upon solution concentration and length of contact time. The solution's vapor causes the same effects as the gas. First aid should be the same as for anhydrous ammonia.

20.121 Calcium Hydroxide

Hydrated lime (calcium hydroxide) and quicklime (calcium oxide) are two forms of lime commonly used in water treatment plants. Hydrated lime is the least troublesome of the two forms. Hydrated lime is less caustic and is therefore less irritating to the skin, but can cause injury to eyes. However, as a dust it is just as hazardous as quicklime. Quicklime is a strong caustic and irritating to personnel exposed to the compound. When quicklime is mixed with water, a great deal of heat is generated which can cause explosions.

Both quicklime and hydrated lime should be stored in cool, dry areas. Care must be taken to avoid mixtures of alum and quicklime, since quicklime tends to absorb the water away from the alum that forms as alum crystallizes (water of crystallization). In a closed container this could lead to a violent explosion. Equal care should be taken to avoid mixtures of ferric sulfate and lime.

When handling both forms of lime, the operator should use chemical goggles and a suitable dust mask to protect the eyes and mucous membranes. Also wear proper clothing to protect the skin because, with long contact, the lime can cause dermatitis (skin irritation) or burns, particularly at perspiration points. Always shower after handling quicklime. All operators should wear a face shield when inspecting lime slakers. Hot lime suspension that splatters on the operator may cause severe burns of the eyes or skin. The hot mist coming from the slakers is also dangerous. The loss of water supply to a lime slaker can create explosive temperatures.

First aid for lime burns, which are like burns from other caustics, consists of alternately washing with water and a mild acetic acid solution. One may also use large amounts of soap and water. For eye contact, wash immediately with large amounts of warm water and rinse with a boric acid solution. Get medical aid. For irritation of nose and throat because of exposure, see a physician.

20.122 Sodium Hydroxide (Caustic Soda)

Sodium hydroxide is available in pellet, liquid, and flake forms. Caustic soda usually comes as a 50-percent solution of sodium hydroxide. This base is a strong caustic alkali and very hazardous to the operator. This compound is extremely reactive. Sodium hydroxide absorbs carbon dioxide from the air, reacting violently or explosively with acid and a number of organic compounds. Caustic soda (1) dissolves human skin, (2) generates heat when mixed with water, and (3) reacts with amphoteric metals (such as aluminum) generating hydrogen gas which is flammable and may explode if ignited. Sodium hydroxide can be dissolved in water; the resulting solution is often used for the adjustment of pH because it is a liquid and easy to feed. This base is extensively used in water treatment. Because of its everyday use, you may forget just how hazardous this compound is, and through neglect may injure yourself or another operator. Only trained and protected operators should undertake spill cleanup. The operator must act cautiously, dilute the spill with water, and neutralize with a dilute acid, preferably acetic.

When handling caustic soda, control the mists with good ventilation. Protect your nose and throat with an approved respiratory system. For eye protection, you must wear chemical worker's goggles and/or a full face shield to protect your eyes. There must be an eye wash and safety shower at or near the work station for this chemical. Protect your body by being fully clothed, and by using impervious gloves, boots, apron, and face shield.

Special precautions to be taken when handling or storing caustic soda include (1) prevent eye and skin contact, (2) do not breathe dusts or mists, and (3) avoid storing this chemical next to strong acids. Dissolving sodium hydroxide in water or other substances generates excessive heat, causes splattering and mists. Solutions of sodium hydroxide are viscous (thick) and slippery. Caustic can quickly and permanently cloud vision if not immediately flushed out of eyes. Determine location of safety showers and eye wash stations *BEFORE* starting to work with caustic soda.

First aid for the eyes consists of irrigating the eyes immediately and continuously with flowing water for at least 30 minutes. Prompt medical attention is essential. For skin burns, immediate and continuous, thorough washing in flowing water for 30 minutes is important to prevent damage to the

skin. Consult a physician if required. In case of inhalation, remove victim to fresh air, call physician, or transport injured person to a medical facility. For ingestion, give large amounts of water or milk and immediately transport injured person to a medical facility; *DO NOT INDUCE VOMITING.*

You may also have occasion to use sodium hydroxide as flakes or pellets. All of the precautions stated for liquid caustic also apply for the flake form.

20.123 Sodium Silicate

This chemical is a liquid as used in water treatment. However, it is nontoxic, nonflammable, and nonexplosive, but presents the same hazards to the eyes and skin as any other base compounds. Sodium silicate is a strong alkali and should be handled with care by using goggles or face shield, wearing gloves and protective clothing. The chemical will cause damage to the eyes and skin, but it is less dangerous than other alkaline compounds used in water treatment.

First aid for the eyes is to flush immediately and thoroughly with flowing water for at least 15 minutes. Get medical attention. If sodium silicate makes contact with skin, wash thoroughly with water, particularly if the solution is hot. Then wash the skin with a 10-percent solution of ammonium chloride or 10 percent acetic acid. For ingestion, give plenty of water and dilute vinegar, lemon, or orange juice. Follow this with milk, white of eggs beaten with water, or olive oil. Call a physician.

20.124 Hypochlorite

A number of hypochlorite compounds are commercially available for use in water treatment. If you understand the precautions for one such compound, you will know what steps must be taken with other hypochlorite compounds, such as calcium, sodium, or lithium. These chemicals may be used in either a liquid or dry form. There are several grades of hypochlorite compounds, but all are good oxidizers and are used for disinfection. When these compounds come into contact with organic materials, their decomposition releases heat very rapidly and produces oxygen and chlorine. Although hypochlorite compounds are nonflammable, they may cause fires when they come in contact with heat, acids, organic matter, or other oxidizable substances.

All solutions of hypochlorite compounds attack the skin, eyes or other body tissues with which they come into contact. When handling hypochlorite, liquid or dry, use suitable protective clothing such as rubber gloves, aprons, goggles, and/

or a face shield. Be aware that many times these compounds are stored in containers and give off chlorine gas when opened. Store these compounds in a cool, dry, dark area.

First aid for eyes is to flush with plenty of water for at least 15 minutes and see a physician. If hypochlorite compounds come in contact with the skin, flush thoroughly with water for at least 15 minutes, and get medical attention as needed. In case of ingestion, wash out mouth thoroughly with water, give plenty of water to drink, and get medical attention. For inhalation, move the victim into fresh air and get medical attention.

Overexposure to any of the hypochlorite compounds may produce severe burns, so avoid contact with these compounds. They are hazardous and can attack skin, eyes, mucous membranes, and clothing.

20.125 Sodium Carbonate

Soda ash (sodium carbonate) is a mild alkaline compound, but requires safety precautions to minimize hazards when handling the chemical. An adequate ventilation system is needed to control the dust generated by the compound. Wear protective gear, such as chemical safety goggles and/or a face shield, a well-fitting dust respirator, and protective clothing to avoid skin contact. You should protect yourself by using a suitable cream or petroleum jelly on exposed skin surfaces, such as neck and hands. This compound's dust irritates the mucous membranes and prolonged exposure can cause sores in your nasal passage.

First aid for exposure to eyes (dust or solution) requires irrigation with water immediately for at least 15 minutes. Consult a physician if the exposure has been severe. For skin exposure, wash with large amounts of water; for contaminated clothing, wash before reusing. For inhalation or irritation of the respiratory tract, gargle or spray with warm water, and consult a physician as needed.

QUESTIONS

Write your answers in a notebook and then compare your answers with those on page 457.

20.12A   What are the two forms of ammonia used by operators?

20.12B   How should ammonia be stored?

20.12C   What are the two forms of lime used in water treatment plants?

20.12D   What would you do if someone swallowed sodium hydroxide?

20.12E   What would you do if sodium silicate came in contact with your skin?

20.13   Gases

There are a number of gases used in water treatment (Table 20.3). Most are supplied in steel drum containers; others must be generated on site. Some gases can be seen; others call the operator's attention by odor; and still others cannot be seen or detected by odor, yet are deadly. In this section we will only discuss those which are supplied in containers that the operator must connect, disconnect, handle or store. (See Section 12.120 for a discussion of ammonia.)

Exposure to the liquid forms of these gases usually will cause damage to human tissue, such as skin burns, but the most important factor to remember is the displacement of oxygen. Most gases are heavier than air and remove air from a room by displacement. Therefore, it is very important to have the right type of ventilation and respiratory protection. Use only the self-contained breathing apparatus when working in emergency areas.

20.130   Chlorine (Cl₂)

Safety is of the utmost importance when handling chlorine. Do not treat chlorine cylinders roughly; never drop them or permit collision of two or more cylinders. Never hoist chlorine cylinders by the neck. Always use lifting clamps or cradles — do not use ropes, cables, or chains. Store the cylinders in such a way that they cannot fall. Do not store chlorine cylinders below ground level and always keep the protective cap

on the cylinder when it is not in use. Mark the empty containers and store them apart from full cylinders. Always store containers in an upright position in a clean, dry location free of flammable materials. The storage area must be equipped with forced-exhaust ventilation with starting switches located on the outside of the storage room. Ventilation must provide at least one complete air change per minute. The temperature of the storage room should never be permitted to approach 140°F (60°C). Protect the chlorine cylinder from heat sources and never use an open flame on cylinders or pipes carrying chlorine. If chlorine is heated, the increase in temperature will cause an expansion of the gas which results in an increase in pressure inside of the cylinders or piping, resulting in rupture of the containers.

When working with chlorine, be equipped to control chlorine leaks which are most often found in the control valve. Repair kits are available for the 100- and 150-pound (45- and 68-kg) cylinders, as is emergency equipment for the one-ton (909-kg) tanks for controlling leaks. Each operator must be trained in the use of these emergency kits and must practice with the equipment at least once a year. Always check out even the slightest odor of chlorine; it may indicate a leak. Chlorine leaks only get worse. Small leaks can grow very rapidly causing serious problems that could have been easily solved as a small leak. There should always be two operators attending a chlorine leak, one to do the repairs and the other to act as safety observer. Some repairs require two operators to do the job (depends on leak and repair kit). Once again, use only the self-contained breathing apparatus when repairing a chlorine leak.

When connecting chlorine cylinders, be very careful with the threaded connections; never use two washers, use only one. If it does not work well, remove the washer and use another one. Do not reuse an old or used washer; always use a new washer. By taking this precaution, by cleaning the threads and washer, and by being careful with the thread setting, many chlorine leaks will be prevented. You *MUST* be aware whether you are using gas or liquid when connecting the container. On the one-ton (909-kg) tank, the top valve is for gas, the bottom valve is for liquid. If liquid chlorine is allowed into a gas feed system it will cause "freezing"[3] and shut down (plug) the system. Similarly, if liquid gets into the gas outlet, it will cause problems by "freezing." You must not panic in this situation. *DO NOT* do anything as foolish as

TABLE 20.3   GASES USED IN WATER TREATMENT

Name, Formula	Common Name	Available Forms	Spec. Grav. or lbs/cu ft	Flam- mability	Color	Odor	Containers
Ammonia, NH_3	Ammonia	Liquid, gas	0.04813 lbs/ cu ft @ 0°C	Explosive with air; will burn in air	Colorless	Irritating	Cylinders, tanks, trucks
Chlorine, Cl_2	Liquid Chlorine	Liquid, gas	1.468 @ 0°C	None	Greenish yellow	Irritating	Cylinders, one-ton units, tank cars
Carbon Dioxide, CO_2	Dry Ice	Liquid, gas	0.914	None	Colorless	Odorless	Bulk liquid under pressure
Sulfur Dioxide, SO_2	Sulfuric Acid Anhydride	Liquid, gas	1.436 @ 0°C	None	Colorless	Suffocating, pungent	Cylinders, one-ton units, tank cars

---

[3] *Liquid chlorine becomes a solid around −103 to −105°C. The liquid can plug a chlorine gas line which operators refer to as a "frozen" line.*

adding heat by open flame or electrical heaters to clear a "frozen" (plugged) gas line. Get help from someone experienced with chlorine cylinders.

Never make repairs to the valve or chlorine container. Just stop the leak, perhaps by tightening the packing on the valve stem or placing the safety device onto the cylinder. Let the chlorine supplier repair the container. Never use a wrench longer than six inches (15 cm) to open the cylinder valve; make only one complete turn of the valve stem in a counterclockwise direction. The one turn will open the valve sufficiently for the maximum discharge. As a safety consideration, cylinders are equipped with fusible metal plugs which are designed to melt at 158 to 168°F (70 to 76°C). This will allow the cylinder contents to discharge and prevent rupturing of the tank. On 100- to 150-pound (45- to 68-kg) cylinders, the plug is located just below the valve seat. The one-ton (909-kg) tanks have six such plugs, three on each end. Should one of these plugs melt, permitting liquid chlorine to discharge, place the tank in a position with the leak at the top of the tank so that it permits the chlorine gas (rather than the liquid) to discharge. This action will reduce the amount of chlorine being discharged because the liquid will change to a gas to escape. In doing so, it will lower the temperature of the container, reducing the discharge rate.

All employees, maintenance personnel and operators who handle chlorine, must have access to an approved chlorine gas mask (Figure 20.2). They must be instructed in the use and maintenance of this equipment. A monthly program should be conducted to familiarize and train each user of the safety equipment. Those employees who are to use the chlorine emergency equipment should practice with this equipment every six months while wearing a self-contained breathing apparatus. The emergency kit consists of clamps, gaskets, drift pins, hammers, wrenches, and other tools needed for repairing leaks. The operator may not be able to practice with all of the tools, but inspection and practice gives the operator an opportunity to do maintenance on the emergency equipment.

All operators working with chlorine should be familiar with methods of detecting chlorine leaks. When testing for leaks, use ammonia water on a small cloth or swab on a stick or use an aspirator containing ammonia water. This will form a white cloud of ammonium chloride. Leaks should be repaired immediately. Do not apply the ammonia swab directly to the equipment surface. Also do not spray ammonia into a room full of chlorine because a white cloud will form and you won't be able to see anything.

Many plants are equipped with chlorine gas detectors. This equipment must be maintained weekly. If not properly maintained, it may not be operable when you need it. Change the electrolyte regularly, test the alarm, and keep the detectors clean and in good repair.

Someone must be assigned the responsibility for maintenance of the self-contained breathing apparatus. That opera-

SCOTT PRESUR-PAK IIa

SPECIFICATIONS	BACK-PAK STYLE
AIR SUPPLY	
Rated Duration at moderate exertion (MESA/NIOSH test procedure)*	30 min.
Cylinder Capacity at 2216 psi	45 cu. ft.
USE FACTORS	
Weight, as worn, fully charged (approx.)	32 lbs.
Donning Speed (trained personnel)	under 30 secs.
Facepiece (Scottoramic w/nose cup)	Wide vision, anti-fogging
Cylinder and Valve Connection	Straight thread, gasket seal
Cylinder Change	Hand disconnect, no tools req'd
Harness Webbing (replaceable without tools or rivets)	Polypropylene
Transport and Storage	Custom Molded High Density Polyethylene Case
SHIPPING WEIGHT	48 lbs.
NOTES: * POSITIVE PRESSURE	

Fig. 20.2   Chlorine gas mask
(Permission of Nevada Safety & Supply)

tor must keep records of the maintenance problems and of monthly drills using the gear. The assigned operator should check the masks for leaks, loose eyepieces, faulty tubing, or other worn or defective spots. If inspection indicates any defective parts, they should be discarded or repaired by a properly trained employee. Remember, in high concentrations of chlorine within a confined space where oxygen can be displaced, *DO NOT USE THE CANISTER TYPE OF MASK. NO CANISTER CAN PROVIDE OXYGEN.* Therefore, use only a self-contained breathing apparatus or a hose-type mask supplied with air (Figure 20.3).

If you are caught in an area containing chlorine, do not panic, but leave immediately. Do not breathe or cough, and keep your head high until you are out of the affected area.

The first safety measure you can take when entering a chlorination room is to make sure the ventilating system is working. The ventilating system for the chlorination room should be working all the time. Doors of chlorination rooms should have panic bars as door openers so that in an emergency you will not have to search for the door opener. All safety equipment should be located outside of the chlorination room, but close enough so you can find the equipment when needed.

First aid for eyes exposed to liquid chlorine is immediate irrigation with flowing water for at least 30 minutes. Medical attention is essential. If the eyes are exposed to chlorine gas, immediately irrigate with flowing water for a period of 15 minutes. Get medical aid. If skin is exposed to liquid chlorine, it will most likely cause burns. The skin should be washed with flowing water for 30 minutes. If the skin is burned, get medical attention. Chlorine gas can become trapped in the clothing and react with body moisture to form hydrochloric acid which could burn the skin. Remove the clothing of the victim and wash the body down with water. In case of inhalation, remove the victim to fresh air, administer oxygen if available, call a physician, or transport the injured person to a medical facility. Ingestion is not a problem because chlorine is a gas at room temperature.

Each operator should have a copy of the Chlorine Institute's *CHLORINE MANUAL.*[4] You should read this manual and review it at least once every year. The manual gives data concerning chlorine as an element and gives you suggestions for safely handling this hazardous liquid or gas.

20.131 Carbon Dioxide (CO_2)

Water treatment plant operators are not often exposed to carbon dioxide because of its limited use, but it is hazardous and can cause suffocation due to the lack of oxygen. Therefore, when using CO_2 keep in mind the carbon dioxide safety considerations. The problem with carbon dioxide is that it is odorless, colorless, and will accumulate at the lowest possible level because it is heavier than air.

Carbon dioxide is obtained in bulk lots, as a liquid (under pressure) which must be vaporized before using. CO_2 is also prepared by generation on site. In either case, good ventila-

tion will reduce the hazards of using CO_2. This will control the accumulating effects of the gas. If you must go into a room filled with CO_2, use a self-contained breathing apparatus, not a canister gas mask. Carbon dioxide displaces oxygen and you may suffocate with the canister type of mask. Exposure to carbon dioxide does not require any protection of the eyes, skin, or other parts of the body, but take precautions when entering rooms, low spots, or manholes that may be filled with carbon dioxide.

First aid involves moving the victim to fresh air, giving resuscitation if the victim has stopped breathing, and getting medical attention.

20.132 Sulfur Dioxide (SO_2)

This gas is about 2.3 times as heavy as air and therefore will accumulate in low areas. Sulfur dioxide is colorless in the gaseous form. As a liquid it is also colorless and, when unconfined, will vaporize rapidly into a gas. The gas is extremely irritating and, like chlorine, will react readily with the respiratory system if inhaled. Sulfur dioxide causes varying degrees of irritation to the mucous membranes — eyes, nose, throat, and lungs. The damage is caused by the formation of sulfurous acid in reaction with moisture in these locations. Sulfur dioxide can be readily detected in concentrations of 3 to 5 ppm. In higher concentrations, it is unlikely that you will remain in the area unless you are unconscious or trapped. If the liquid comes into contact with the skin, it may cause local freezing as the liquid evaporates.

Always use a self-contained breathing apparatus around sulfur dioxide and never use the canister type. As with other gases, good ventilation is essential in a room where sulfur dioxide is being used. The fans should be used to dissipate any gas vapors that may occur. There should always be an eye wash fountain close to the work area where sulfur dioxide is used.

---

[4] *CHLORINE MANUAL (6th Edition), The Chlorine Institute, Inc., 2001 L Street, NW, Suite 506, Washington, DC 20036. Price to members, $15.00; nonmembers, $30.00. Cost of shipping is about 5 percent of the purchase price.*

Dual air supply cylinder being used with 900007 series hoseline Air-Pak with Egress.

Typical fixed air supply installation using high pressure air cylinders.

Fig. 20.3   Hose-type mask supplied with air
(Permission of Nevada Safety & Supply)

First aid for eyes exposed to or splashed with sulfur dioxide is washing immediately with water for at least 15 minutes, then getting medical attention. In case of inhalation, remove victim to fresh air, give resuscitation if needed, consult a physician, or transport the injured person to a medical facility. Sulfur dioxide leaks and injuries should be treated similar to chlorine problems.

QUESTIONS

Write your answers in a notebook and then compare your answers with those on page 458.

20.13A   Where are chlorine leaks most often found?

20.13B   What is the purpose of the fusible metal plugs on chlorine cylinders?

20.13C   How can chlorine leaks be detected?

20.13D   Why is carbon dioxide a safety hazard and what safety precautions must be taken when using it?

20.14   Salts

There are many salts (chemicals) used in water treatment. Table 20.4 lists the salts that will be discussed in this section. If you would like additional information about compounds not listed, request a data sheet about specific compounds from the suppliers of the chemicals. Review the chemistry of the compounds in Table 20.4 and become familiar with each chemical's characteristics. You should become well trained in how to handle each chemical and know and observe the appropriate safety precautions. For most of these salts, ven-

tilation, respiratory protection, and eye protection will prove adequate. Other problems may involve chemical solutions and dust. The solution may attack skin and clothing. The dust may attack the respiratory system or cause an explosion. Even though these chemicals do not normally react violently, use the following procedures when handling such salts to reduce the hazards and to provide a safe working location.

When handling, storing or preparing solutions of chemicals, treat them all as being hazardous. All chemicals require careful consideration. They may be sources of an explosion, violent reaction, loss of eyesight, burns, and illness.

Do not store acidic or basic compounds with salts. Keep these chemicals in a clean, dry area. When handling dry, bulk materials, store in a fire-safe area. Keep all lids on containers and follow the instructions on the container. Make sure that the operator who is mixing or dispensing these chemicals is well trained and wears proper clothing to meet all safety requirements, such as chemical goggles, face shield, rubber gloves, rubber boots, rubber apron, and chemical respirator. When working with chemical salts, be aware that fumes, gases, vapors, dusts, or mists may be given off and this represents a hazard to the safety of the operator. *PROTECT YOURSELF!*

20.140   Aluminum Sulfate (Alum)

There are two forms of alum: dry and liquid. Both have to be handled with care. Dry alum is available in lump, ground, or powdered forms and should be stored in a dry location because moisture can cause caking. Liquid alum is acidic and

TABLE 20.4   SALTS USED IN WATER TREATMENT

Name, Formula	Common Name	Available Forms	Density, lbs/cu ft	Flammability	Color	Odor	Containers
Aluminum Sulfate, $Al_2(SO_4)_3 \cdot 14H_2O$	Alum, Filter Alum	Liquids, powder, lump	1.69 (S.G.) 38-67	None	Ivory	N/A[a]	Bags, tank truck, bulk
Ferric Chloride, $FeCl_3$	Ferrichlor, Chloride of Iron	Syrup, liquid, lump	60-90	None	Dark brown, yellow-brown	N/A	Carboys, tank cars
Ferric Sulfate, $Fe_2(SO_4)_3$	Ferrifloc, Ferrisul	Powder, granule	70-72	None	Red-brown	N/A	Bags, drums
Ferrous Sulfate, $FeSO_4 \cdot 7H_2O$	Coppras, Green Vitriol	Crystal, liquid, granule, lump	63-66	None	Green	N/A	Bags, drums, bulk
Sodium Aluminate, $Na_2O \cdot Al_2O_3$	Soda Alum	Dry crystal, liquid	(27° Bé[b])	None	White, green-yellow	N/A	Bags, bulk
Fluoride Compounds, NaF and H_3SiF_6	—	Liquid and powder	50-75	None	Blue, white	Dust	Bags, carboys, tank trucks
Sodium Hexametaphosphate, $(NaPO_3)_6$	Calgon, Glassy Phosphate	Crystal, flake	47	None	White	N/A	Bags, drums
Copper Sulfate, $CuSO_4$	Blue Vitriol, Blue Stone	Crystal, lump, powder	60-90	None	Blue	None	Bags, drums
Sodium Chlorite, NaOCl	Technical Sodium Chlorite	Powder, flake, liquid	70 dry	Oxidizer	Light orange	None	Tank truck, 100-lb drums
Potassium Permanganate, $KMnO_4$	Permanganate	Crystal, powder	90-100	Oxidizer	Purple	None	Drums, bulk

[a]   N/A = Not Applicable
[b]   Bé = Baumé scale, a scale for measuring specific gravity of liquids

very corrosive. Store liquid alum in corrosion-resistant storage tanks such as:

1. Steel, wood (Douglas Fir), or concrete-lined, all lined with a material corrosion-resistant to alum,

2. Steel, lined with 3/16-inch (5-mm) soft rubber,

3. Stainless steel,

4. Steel, lined with plastic if temperature remains below 150°F (65°C), and

5. Glass-reinforced epoxy or polyester plastic.

When working with dry alum, use respiratory protection and ensure adequate ventilation of the work area. There should be a good mechanical dust collection system to minimize any dust accumulation. Exposure to alum dust concentrations greater than 15 milligrams per cubic meter of air for more than an 8-hour period is dangerous. Avoid skin exposure to this chemical by using long-sleeved, loose-fitting, dust-proof clothing.

Never use the same conveyor for quicklime and alum. This mixture may explode under proper conditions.

Liquid alum is an acidic solution and should be handled as you would handle a weak acid. Reduce exposures to the skin and eyes. Avoid ingestion. Although the chemical will not cause any lasting internal damage, it will cause discomfort. Use good ventilation for removing any mists. Rubber gloves and protective clothing are recommended.

As a general precaution, avoid prolonged exposure to dry or liquid forms of alum. If used dry, a dust mask and goggles are desirable for the comfort of the operator. Alum dust can be extremely irritating to the eyes. When handling the liquid, normal precautions should be used to prevent splashing of the compound onto the operator, particularly if the liquid is hot. Wear a face shield to protect your eyes and a rubber apron to protect clothing.

First aid for liquid or dry alum is immediate flushing of the eyes for 15 minutes with large amounts of water. Alum should also be washed off the skin with water because prolonged contact will cause irritation.

20.141 Ferric Chloride

This is a very corrosive compound and should be treated as you would treat any acid. The salt is highly soluble in water, but in the presence of moist air or light, it decomposes to give off hydrochloric acid, which may cause other safety hazards.

Avoid prolonged exposure to this liquid (there is a dry form but it is not often used). When handling liquid ferric chloride, normal precautions should be taken to prevent splashing, particularly if the liquid is hot. Use a face shield to protect your eyes and rubber aprons to protect clothing. This compound will not only attack the clothing, but also stain it. First aid for eyes exposed to the liquid is that the eyes must be flushed out immediately for 15 minutes with large amounts of water. Ferric chloride should also be washed off the skin with water because prolonged contact will cause irritation and staining of the skin.

20.142 Ferric Sulfate

This compound produces an acidic solution when mixed with water. Because of its acidic nature, operators using this compound should be provided with protection suitable for dry or liquid alum. The hazards associated with the use of dry ferric sulfate are those usually connected with an acid. Use protective clothing, neck cloths, gloves, goggles or face shield, and a respirator. Avoid prolonged exposure to the dry form because of its acidic reaction with moisture on the skin, eyes, and throat. The normal precautions should be used including a dust mask and protective clothing. First aid for exposure to the eyes requires the eyes to be flushed immediately with lots of water. The skin should also be flushed with large amounts of water. Prolonged contact may cause irritation.

20.143 Ferrous Sulfate

This chemical may be obtained in liquid or dry form. The safety hazards are some of those for dry or liquid forms of alum. The operator should be provided with adequate ventilation and respiratory protection. The material should be stored in a clean, dry location. Mechanical dust collecting equipment must be used to minimize the dust. Wear chemical goggles or a face shield, loose-fitting, long-sleeved clothing, and make an effort to minimize all skin exposure.

First aid for ferrous sulfate in the eyes is to flush out immediately with large amounts of water for 15 minutes. The chemical should be washed off the skin to reduce irritations.

20.144 Sodium Aluminate

Sodium aluminate dissolved in water produces a noncorrosive solution. In the dry form, its powder consistency raises the usual dust problems. There are few hazards with this compound, but as with other chemicals, you should use precautions when handling it. Use respiratory protection when handling the dry compound to prevent the inhalation of dust. First aid for eyes that are exposed is to flush with water; keep the skin clean with water.

20.145 Fluoride Compounds

All fluoride compounds should be treated with care when you are handling them because of their long-term accumulative effects. Provide good ventilation; always wear respiratory protection; and be careful not to expose any open cuts, lesions (wounds), or sores to fluoride compounds. Clean up any spills promptly and wash immediately after handling such compounds.

When handling acid compounds of fluoride, always wear a face shield and/or chemical goggles, rubber gloves, rubber apron, and rubber boots. Your wearing apparel should always be washed after working around fluoride, and the respirator should be kept clean and sanitary. Keep the acid feeder for fluoride in good repair. Use plastic guards to prevent acid spray from glands or other parts of the chemical feeder. This prevents attack upon the equipment and protects operators. All fluoride compounds must be regarded as hazardous chemicals that are toxic to operators. Every means possible must be taken to prevent exposure to these compounds by use of a respirator and protective clothing.

Once it is established that fluoride is the cause of the poisoning, first aid should be started while waiting for medical help. The following are recommended first-aid procedures:

1. Move the person away from any contact with fluoride and keep warm,

2. Give the person three teaspoons (one tablespoon) of table salt in a glass of warm water,

3. If the person is conscious, induce vomiting by rubbing the back of the throat with a spoon or your finger; if available use syrup of ipecac,

4. Give the person a glass of milk,

5. Repeat the salt and vomiting several times, and

6. Take the person to the hospital as soon as possible.

First aid for a person with a nosebleed from inhaling a high concentration of fluoride is:

1. Take the person away from the source of the fluoride,

2. Tip the person's head back while placing cotton, cloth, or paper towels inside the nostrils (change these often), and

3. Take the person to a doctor if you cannot stop the bleeding.

QUESTIONS

Write your answers in a notebook and then compare your answers with those on page 458.

20.14A   What kind of protection does an operator need when handling salts?

20.14B   What is the recommended first aid when either liquid or dry alum comes in contact with your skin or your eyes?

20.14C   What happens when ferric chloride is exposed to moist air or light?

20.15 Powders

20.150 Potassium Permanganate (KMnO₄)

Under normal conditions in a water treatment plant, potassium permanganate is considered to be a safe chemical (see Table 20.4). However, potassium permanganate is a strong oxidizing agent and will react with certain easily oxidizable substances. Keep potassium permanganate away from the possibility of reacting with sulfuric acid, hydrogen peroxide, metallic powders, elemental sulfur, phosphorus, carbon, hydrochloric acid, hydrazine, hydroxylamine, and metal hydrides. When in contact with potassium permanganate, the following compounds may ignite: ethylene glycol (antifreeze), glycerine, sawdust compounds, propylene glycol, and sulfuric oxide.

Potassium permanganate is available as pellets, as a powder, or in crystal form. This chemical can be kept indefinitely if stored in a cool, dry area in closed containers. The drums should be protected from damage that could cause leaks or spills. Potassium permanganate should be stored in fire-resistant buildings having concrete floors instead of wooden floors. The chemical must not be exposed to intense heat, or stored next to heated pipes. Organic solvents, such as greases and oils, should be kept away from stored potassium permanganate.

Potassium permanganate spills should be swept up and removed immediately. Flushing with water is an effective way to eliminate any residue remaining on floors. Potassium permanganate fires should be extinguished with water.

To avoid inhalation of potassium permanganate dust, use an approved mask which is an air-purifying, half-mask respirator with an outblower. Safety glasses or a full face shield should be worn to protect your eyes. Protective clothing that should be worn includes rubber or plastic gloves and apron, and a long-sleeved shirt for handling both dry and dissolved potassium permanganate.

Mild exposure will cause sneezing and mild irritation of the mucous membranes. Prolonged inhalation of potassium permanganate should be avoided. If potassium permanganate gets on your skin, flood the contacted skin with water. If it gets in your eyes, flush with plenty of water and call a physician immediately.

20.151 Powdered Activated Carbon

Powdered activated carbon is the most dangerous powder that you will be exposed to as a treatment plant operator. If you understand how to handle activated carbon properly, other dust problems or powdered chemicals will not be very difficult for you to handle.

There are two problems when handling activated carbon. One is dust and the second is fire. The two may or may not be related. The dust causes uncomfortable working conditions; fire causes damage to equipment and a hazard to personnel. If the two problems are treated together, it will reduce the hazards to operators. Left unattended they may cause loss of life and property. If you will use the following safety precautions, you can minimize the hazards of handling activated carbon and aid the other operators in handling other powders.

Store activated carbon in a clean, dry, fireproof location. Keep clear of dust, protect from flammable materials, and do not permit smoking in the area at any time when handling or unloading activated carbon. Install carbon dioxide fire extinguishers. Store bagged carbon in single rows. Keep access aisles clear to prevent damage to the bags and thus reduce the dust and fire potential.

Electrical equipment in and around activated carbon storage should be explosion-proof and protected from the carbon dust. Keep the equipment clean and dry. Wet or damp carbon is a good conductor of electrical current and can cause short-circuit fires. Heat can also build up from the motors if covered with carbon dust, causing fires. The key to controlling fires with activated carbon is keeping the storage area clean and dust free.

Next to electrical fires, activated carbon gives the operator the most difficult fire to control. The carbon gives off an intense heat; it burns without smoke or visible flame. The fires are difficult to locate and are very hard to control. They cannot readily be detected in a large storage bin or in large stacks of bags.

Bags of activated carbon should be stored in single rows.

You will detect the indications of the fire, such as the smell of charred paper, burned paint, or other odor, before seeing any evidence of flames.

Do not douse a carbon fire with a stream of water. The water may cause burning carbon particles to fly, resulting in a greater fire problem. The carbon fire should be controlled with carbon dioxide (CO_2) extinguishers or hoses equipped with fog nozzles. However, when using CO_2, be aware that there is a potential of carbon monoxide formation and take the precaution of using a self-contained breathing apparatus.

Activated carbon supports fire without atmospheric oxygen because it may have adsorbed sufficient oxygen for combustion. The best means of controlling a carbon fire is to reduce its temperature below the ignition point. This can be done by applying cold water with fog or spray nozzles and soaking the burning carbon, but do not hit the carbon with a stream of water. For a small fire involving just a few bags, move the bags to a safe location and use CO_2 or spray nozzles to extinguish the fire. Blocks of dry ice may help control fires in storage bins or other confined areas, but do not expect this method to be very effective.

A final word about fire and explosions involving activated carbon. Tests performed by carbon manufacturers have not shown that dust mixtures of carbon have explosive tendencies. Activated carbon is a charcoal and performs in a like manner; the carbon burns without smoke or visible flame, burns very hot, and will spread if doused with a large stream of water.

There are no specific first-aid methods for carbon exposure because the carbon will not attack the human body. Carbon does sometimes cause problems with the nasal passages, however, and may be difficult to wash off your hands and body. Therefore, methods here are those of prevention. Provide good dust collection at the point where carbon is being unloaded, in storage bins for liquid preparation, and in dry storage bins. Wear an approved dust mask, loose-fitting and dust-proof clothing. If there is an excess of dust, you should use chemical goggles, close your shirt collar, and tape your trousers to cover your ankles. You will need adequate shower facilities and should use mild liquid soap. Most, if not all, hard soap bars are ineffective in removing activated carbon dust from pores of the human body.

20.152 Other Powders

You may come in contact with other powdered compounds in the water treatment plant, but they do not present the problem in handling that activated carbon does. Bentonite creates no significant hazard other than dust, and this can be controlled by using dust collection systems.

Similarly, calcium carbonate presents a slight dust hazard that can be controlled by a dust collection system. Also, when handling calcium carbonate in bags, use the same methods of control that you would use with bags of carbon.

Of the many organic coagulant aids used in water treatment, only a few are applied in powder form. Most of these compounds are used in the liquid form which reduces the danger to operators. The dry compounds present a slight

hazard in dust irritation to the nasal passages; this can be prevented by use of approved dust masks. The liquid compounds can and will attack the skin, but can be treated by washing with ample amounts of water and/or soap and water. Organic coagulant aids (polymers) are extremely slippery when wet. Floors and walkways should be clean and dry to prevent slips and falls. Spilled polymers may be cleaned up using inert, absorbent materials, such as sand or earth.

As new compounds are introduced to the waterworks field, ask for training in their use. Such a training program should provide information about detailed safety precautions, the toxicity of the compound, and the appropriate first-aid methods. Supervisors have the responsibility to provide this type of training, either in conjunction with the supplier or sponsored entirely by the utility. The training must be reinforced periodically for those compounds that are not often used by the operator. A review and updating of information will go a long way in preventing accidents.

QUESTIONS

Write your answers in a notebook and then compare your answers with those on page 458.

20.15A How can potassium permanganate spills be cleaned up?

20.15B What is the most dangerous powder the water treatment plant operator will be exposed to?

20.15C How should activated carbon be stored?

20.15D How can fires caused by activated carbon be prevented?

20.15E How should an activated carbon fire be extinguished?

20.16 Labeling of Chemical Containers

For information on proper labeling of chemical containers, see Section 4.11, "Hazard Communication (Worker Right-To-Know Laws)," in *OPERATION AND MAINTENANCE OF WASTEWATER COLLECTION SYSTEMS*, Volume I, in this series of operator training manuals.

20.17 Chemical Storage Drains

Safety regulations prohibit the use of a common drain and sump for acid and alkali chemicals, oxidizing chemicals, and organic chemicals because of the possibility of the release of toxic gases, explosions, and fires. If both an acid and an alkali chemical come in contact, an explosion could occur. If an organic chemical such as a polymer solution comes in contact with an oxidizing chemical, such as potassium permanganate, a fire could develop. Be sure that if a leak develops from any chemical container or storage facility, the chemical will not be able to reach, mix, or react with another chemical.

QUESTIONS

Write your answers in a notebook and then compare your answers with those on page 458.

20.17A Why should drains from chemical storage areas not use common drains and sumps?

20.17B What could happen if a leak from a polymer storage container comes in contact with potassium permanganate?

End of Lesson 1 of 3 Lessons on SAFETY

Please answer the discussion and review questions next.

DISCUSSION AND REVIEW QUESTIONS

Chapter 20.   SAFETY

(Lesson 1 of 3 Lessons)

At the end of each lesson in this chapter you will find some discussion and review questions. The purpose of these questions is to indicate to you how well you understand the material in the lesson. Write the answers to these questions in your notebook before continuing.

1. What is safety?

2. Who is responsible for safety?

3. What are the causes of accidents?

4. What does an operator need to know about chemicals used in a water treatment plant?

5. How can hydrochloric acid be handled safely?

6. How should hydrochloric acid be stored?

7. How can ammonia leaks be detected?

8. What is the first-aid treatment for lime burns?

9. What special precautions should be taken when handling and storing caustic soda?

10. How should hypochlorite be handled and stored?

11. What first aid is required for a person overcome by carbon dioxide?

12. What safety hazards may be caused by salt dust?

13. What types of safety hazards might an operator encounter when handling alum?

14. What are the two major problems encountered when handling activated carbon?

15. How can an operator detect an activated carbon fire?

CHAPTER 20. SAFETY

(Lesson 2 of 3 Lessons)

20.2 FIRE PROTECTION

20.20 Fire Prevention

Fire prevention is the best fire protection the plant operator can afford. Fire protection is just good housekeeping. The word "housekeeping" best describes the action any water plant operator can take to protect from or prevent fires. This means a well-kept, neat, and orderly plant represents a good fire safety policy.

Fire hazards can be easily removed. The prompt disposal of cartons, crates, and other packing materials, a system of waste paper collection, and the removal of other debris can greatly reduce fire hazards. Provide suitable containers for used wiping cloths and have fire extinguishers conspicuously located in hallways, near work areas, and near potential fire problem areas. All of these housekeeping activities are low-cost measures that also improve the appearance of the plant and create a better work environment.

You can call upon the local fire department for advice on fire prevention in and around the treatment plant. You may also ask the utility insurance underwriter for cooperation in your fire prevention program. All operators should be trained in the proper use and maintenance of fire control equipment. These simple steps can reduce fire losses to a minimum and prevent most fires from happening at very low cost to the utility.

You should make a fire analysis of your plant once a year to determine what new measures should be taken to prevent fires. As activity changes occur, there may be a need to change the location of hoses and extinguishers or it may be necessary to add fire control equipment. Fire and police departments' telephone numbers must be posted in a conspicuous location along with escape routes. Post emergency numbers near all telephones throughout the plant. In hazardous locations the means of exit should be lighted and all doors should be equipped with "panic bars." As indicated above, your best fire protection or prevention is good housekeeping.

20.21 Classification

Fire classifications are important for determining the type of fire extinguisher needed to control the fire. Classifications also aid in recordkeeping and for comparison with other agencies. Fires are classified as "A" — Ordinary combustibles, "B" — Flammable liquids, "C" — Electrical equipment, and "D" — Combustible metals.

A. Class A fires involve miscellaneous combustible materials. These include fabrics, paper, wood, dried grass, hay, and stubble.

B. Class B fires involve flammable liquids and vapors. This may include oils, lacquers, fats, waxes, paints, petroleum products, and gas. This class is subdivided into two sub-classes:

B-2 - are those fires in which the source of flammable vapors is substantially in a single place such as tanks, vats, spills, and trenches.

B-3 - are those fires that are complicated by a falling stream. LPG and other vapor fires are in this class.

C. The Class C fire involves electrical equipment such as starters, breakers, and motors. The circuits should always be killed (de-energized) before extinguishing this type of fire.

D. Class D fires involve metals such as sodium, zinc, magnesium, and other similar metals. Operators rarely encounter this type of fire.

20.22 Extinguishers

There are many types of hand-held fire extinguishers. All are classified for class of fires. There is no one extinguisher that is effective for all fires, so it is important that you understand the class of fire you are trying to control. You must be trained in the use of the different types of extinguishers, and the proper type should be located near the area where that class of fire may occur.

A. There are four types of water extinguishers: stored pressure, cartridge operated, water pump tank, and soda-acid. All of these perform well in Class A fires, but they do require maintenance. A preventive maintenance schedule on all water extinguishers should include a monthly check by the operator responsible for the maintenance and completion of appropriate maintenance records. Some agencies make the safety officer responsible for ensuring that an operator checks the fire extinguishers and records each inspection.

1. The method of operation for a stored pressure extinguisher is simply to squeeze the handle or turn a valve. The maintenance is also simple: check air pressure and recharge the extinguisher as needed.

2. For the cartridge type, the maintenance consists of weighing the gas cartridge and adding water as required. To operate, turn upside down and pump.

3. To use the water pump tank type of extinguisher, simply operate the pump handle. For maintenance, one has only to discharge the contents and refill with water annually or as needed.

4. The soda-acid type must be turned upside down to operate; it also requires annual recharging.

B. The foam type of extinguishers will control Class A and Class B fires well. They, like soda-acid types, operate by turning upside down, and require annual recharging.

The foam and water type extinguishers should not be used for fires involving electrical equipment. However, they can be used in controlling flammable liquids such as gasoline, oil, paints, grease, and other Class B fires.

C. The carbon dioxide (CO_2) extinguishers are common (Figures 20.4 and 20.5). They are easy to operate, just pull the pin and squeeze the lever. For maintenance, they must be weighed at least semiannually. Many of these extinguishers will discharge with age. They can be used on a Class C (electrical) fire. All electric circuits should be killed, if possible, before trying to control this type of fire. A carbon dioxide extinguisher is also satisfactory for Class B fires, such as gasoline, oil, and paint, and may be used on surface fires of the Class A type.

D. There are two types of dry chemical extinguishers. These extinguishers are either (1) cartridge operated, or (2) stored pressure. These are recommended for Class B and C fires and may work on small surface Class A fires.

1. The cartridge-operated extinguishers only require you to rupture the cartridge, usually by squeezing the lever. The maintenance is a bit more difficult, requiring weighing of the gas cartridge and checking the condition of the dry chemical.

2. For the stored-pressure extinguishers, the operation is the same as the CO_2 extinguisher. Just pull the pin and squeeze the lever. The maintenance requires a check of the pressure gages and condition of the dry chemical.

As suggested above, a preventive maintenance program for fire extinguishers requires a considerable amount of time from the operator and requires a system of recordkeeping. You might consider hiring a local fire prevention agency to perform this part of your maintenance program. These service agencies will check and maintain the plant's firefighting equipment on a regular basis. This does not relieve the operator of ultimate responsibility for the equipment, but ensures that the equipment is in proper working order when needed.

20.23 Fire Hoses

Fire hoses are usually stationed throughout the treatment and pumping plants. These are the type of firefighting equipment that an operator may see every day, but never give due consideration to their maintenance. Without proper maintenance, the hoses may develop dry rot and be untrustworthy at the time they are needed. Under some conditions, you may be tempted to use these hoses for cleaning settling basins or filters. The fire hoses should only be used for fighting fires, and after their use, they must be cleaned and stored properly. The hose should be tested periodically and replaced as required, or at regular time intervals. Check with the local fire department for recommendations.

SPECIFICATIONS	CARBON DIOXIDE			
Size/Type	5 Horn	10 Hose	15 Hose	20 Hose
Model Number	322	330	331	332
U/L Rating	5B:C	10B:C	10B:C	10B:C
Capacity (lbs.)	5	10	15	20
Shipping Wt. (lbs.)	15	29½	39½	51½
Height	17¾"	24"	30"	30"
Width	8¼"	12"	12"	13"
Depth (Diam.)	5¼"	7"	7"	8"
Range (Ft.)	3-8	3-8	3-8	3-8
Discharge Time— Seconds	10	10	12.5	19
Coast Guard App.	Yes	Yes	Yes	Yes
◇FM◇ Approved	Yes	Yes	Yes	Yes
Bracket	Wall	Wall	Wall	Wall

Fig. 20.4 Carbon dioxide extinguishers

(Permission of Nevada Safety & Supply)

SPECIFICATIONS	ABC						
Size/Type	2½ Nozzle	5 Nozzle	6 Nozzle	5 Hose	10 Short Hose	10 Tall Hose	20 Hose
Model Number	417T	425	442	424	419	441	423
U/L Rating	1A:10 B:C	2A:10 B:C	3A:40 B:C	2A:10 B:C	4A:60 B:C	4A:60 B:C	20A:120 B:C
Capacity (lbs.)	2½	5	6	5	10	10	20
Ship. Wt. (lbs.)	5½	8½	11	10½	19½	18	40
Height	14⅛″	14⅝″	15½″	14⅝″	17″	20½″	24″
Width	3⅞″	5″	5″	8″	9½″	9″	10″
Depth (Diam.)	3″	4¼″	5″	4¼″	6″	5″	7″
Range (Ft.)	9-15	12-18	12-18	12-18	15-21	15-21	15-21
Discharge Time- Seconds	10	10	14	10	17	17	30
Coast Guard Ap.	Yes	Yes	Yes	Yes	Yes	Yes	Yes
⬥ Approved	Yes	Yes	Pending	Yes	Yes	Yes	Yes
Bracket	Veh/Mar	Wall	Wall	Wall	Wall	Wall	Wall

Fig. 20.5   Typical carbon dioxide extinguishers
(Permission of Nevada Safety & Supply)

20.24   Storage of Flammables

The storage of flammable material should be isolated, if possible, from other plant structures. Ideally, these storage areas should have explosion-proof lighting. The floor should be grounded and the operator should only use spark-proof tools when working near or handling flammable materials. The room should have an alarm system, be equipped with automatic extinguishers and have supplementary equipment located outside of the room. In and around the storage area, smoking or welding must be prohibited. The flammable storage areas must be clearly marked with distinctive signs and all entrances should be lighted.

More often than not, however, you will be compelled to use rooms within the plant for storage of flammable material. Here you must make the room fireproof, equip the room with a fire door, automatic extinguishers, and alarms. Keep passageways free from obstructions. Station firefighting equipment at a suitable location, readily accessible and with plainly labeled operating instructions. The room must be equipped with explosion-proof lights, grounded floor, no smoking permitted, and distinctive signs indicating that this room is a flammable storage area.

20.25   Exits

Access and exit are very important in plant safety. Therefore, all exit signs should be distinctly marked and well lighted. All doors should open outward and, in hazardous areas, there should be "panic bars" on the doors. To provide positive protection around the filter and sedimentation basins, install handrails or other enclosures for the protection of operating personnel as well as visitors.

In high-fire-hazard occupied areas, there should be at least two means of emergency exit located, if possible, at opposite ends of the room or building. These would include areas containing woodworking and paint spraying residues that burn rapidly or give off poisonous fumes.

QUESTIONS

Write your answers in a notebook and then compare your answers with those on page 458.

20.2A   Class A fires involve what types of materials?

20.2B   What kinds of fires can be controlled by a foam type of extinguisher?

20.2C   How can an electrical fire be extinguished?

20.3   PLANT MAINTENANCE

20.30   Maintenance Hazards

Plant maintenance, housekeeping, cleaning up, or whatever you wish to call it, is a very important function of the treatment plant and essential for plant equipment. This function requires the use of cleaning materials and hand tools. Maintenance may require you to go into a manhole, repair electric motors, lift boxes, and use power tools. All of these functions may in some way be hazardous and may cause injury, fire, disease, or even death unless proper safety precautions are taken.

20.31   Cleaning

Any effort spent keeping the entire plant clean and sanitary will provide a much nicer place for you to work and will also make visitors feel as if the water being produced is safe. Even if you can just keep all working areas free of tripping hazards, this will add greatly to the safety in the plant.

Cleaning duties should be performed at such times of day or night as to cause a minimum of exposure to other operators. For example, floors become slippery when wet so give some consideration to the time of day and the type of wax to be used. When cleaning floors, there are problems of exposure to others of cleaning equipment, mops, mop and broom handles, other tools, cleaning compounds and, most of all, wet floors. When cleaning, try to keep others out of the area. Warn others about newly waxed floors. Use wax compounds containing nonslip ingredients. Try to do such cleaning and waxing on weekends or at night when foot traffic through the plant is minimal.

As part of your maintenance program, provide trash containers for collecting waste paper and for separating used, oily rags. Dispose of garbage and flammable refuse on a routine, frequent basis. Hazardous waste, acids, and caustics should be cleaned up immediately. These steps will add to the safety in the plant and to the safety of operators in the plant.

Keeping aisles, doorways, stairs, and work areas free of refuse reduces hazards of tripping and other injuries, as well as reducing the possibility of fires.

Cleaning windows is a hazardous occupation, but the operator who gives due consideration to the task can perform it safely. If windows are high, time of day is important. Clean-

ing tools may be dropped and fall on pedestrians or vehicles. There may be a need for safety harnesses; check the harness each time it is used. Make sure all parts of the harness are in good working condition. Cleaning compounds that are acidic or alkaline may attack the harness or the safety rope. Also, such compounds may attack human skin; therefore, use rubber gloves when appropriate.

20.32   Painting

There are a number of considerations when painting in a treatment plant. First, is the paint exposed to the drinking water being treated and are there toxic compounds in the paint? Next, is the paint being applied by brush or spray? In either case, is there sufficient ventilation if the operator is painting indoors or in a closed area?

When working with toxic paints, for example, those containing lead, zinc, or organics, be sure to clean your hands before eating or handling food. Also, avoid exposing your skin to solvents and thinners and try not to use compounds such as carbon tetrachloride. When spray painting, always use a respirator to avoid inhaling fumes. Do not allow smoking or open flames of any kind around areas being painted. Also, when painting or cleaning the spraying equipment, avoid closed containers where heat is involved. At a certain temperature, called the flash point, spray or vapors could ignite and burn the operator or start fires. Always clean the spray equipment in an area having sufficient ventilation. If the painting operation is taking place in a paint booth, use only explosion-proof lighting and permit no open flame and no electric switch that may cause a spark.

Some of the other hazards when painting include scaffolding, rags, and threats to your personal health. Be very careful when using scaffolding and ladders. The scaffolding must be in good repair and conform to current safety regulations. Ladders must also be in good repair. If they are broken or badly worn, they should be replaced with new ones.

Rags are always a problem if they contain oils, paint, or other cleaning compounds; there is always the possibility of fire. The rags should be placed into a closed metal container to reduce the fire hazard.

To protect your skin, consider using creams to help reduce direct exposure to paint and solvents. Always use an approved respirator to reduce inhalation of fumes and paint mists.

20.33   Cranes

Overhead traveling cranes require safety considerations. First, only authorized personnel should be allowed to operate them. Inspections should be made to check out the circuit breaker, limit switches, the condition of the hook, the wire rope, and other safety devices. The load limits should be posted on the crane and you should never overload the unit. Always check out each lift for proper balance. Use only a standard set of hand signals, and make sure that each operator involved with the crane knows all of the signals. Personnel in and around an overhead crane should be required to wear hard hats. When making repairs to the crane, lock out the main power switch, physically block any movable parts, and allow only authorized personnel to make repairs.

Never move loads over areas where operators or other people are working. Do not let the load remain over the heads of operators or other workers or allow anyone to work under loaded cranes. If loads must be moved over populated areas, give a warning signal and make sure everyone is in a safe location. Set up monthly safety inspection forms to be filled out and placed into the maintenance file. The plant supervisor should review the forms and authorize any maintenance necessary on the crane in addition to following a good preventive maintenance program.

20.34 Confined Spaces[5]

Special safety rules and regulations have been developed to protect the life and health of persons who must enter confined spaces. A confined space may be defined as an area which has limited means for entry and exit and which is not intended for continuous occupancy. One easy way to identify a confined space is by whether or not you can enter it by simply walking while standing fully upright. In general, if you must duck, crawl, climb, or squeeze into the space, it is considered a confined space. Typical examples of confined spaces found in water treatment plants and within water systems are pits, tanks, basins, and manholes.

Dangerous air contamination presents a threat of causing death, injury, *ACUTE* [6] illness, or disablement due to the presence of flammable and/or explosive, toxic, or otherwise injurious or incapacitating substances. Accumulations of gases or vapors, for example, may produce an explosive or flammable atmosphere. Similarly, if particles of chemical dust become airborne when filling hoppers or during operation of chemical feed equipment, the dust concentration in a poorly ventilated space may reach a level where a spark could cause the dust to ignite or explode.

An oxygen-deficient atmosphere is one in which the air with its oxygen content has been reduced by another gas or the oxygen has been removed. Normal air contains approximately 20.9 percent oxygen at sea level with the remaining constituents being primarily nitrogen (about 78.1 percent), argon (about 1 percent), and a few traces of other inert gases. When the oxygen content of air drops below 19.5 percent by volume, a potentially dangerous condition exists. A person breathing air with only 17 percent oxygen will experience shortness of breath. Loss of consciousness occurs rapidly when the oxygen content drops to 6 to 10 percent, and death occurs rapidly (within minutes) at less than 6 percent.

Oxygen deficiency in an enclosed atmosphere can occur for several reasons. Some of the more common causes include bacterial action which uses up the oxygen, displacement by other gases (can be both toxic and/or inert gases like nitrogen or carbon dioxide), oxidation of metals or other materials that deplete the oxygen level, adsorption of the oxygen onto surfaces, and combustion. Since the oxygen content of an enclosed atmosphere can change quickly, it must be continually monitored to ensure that the oxygen content does not drop below an acceptable level. High levels of oxygen (above 22.5 percent) are also dangerous because they increase the possibility of an explosion.

To check the safety of the atmosphere in a confined space, use a gas-detection instrument (Figure 20.6). These devices can detect explosive gases, oxygen deficiency, and/or toxic conditions. Remember, just because there are no toxic or explosive gases present does not mean that you may not lose your life because of a deficiency of oxygen.

Fig. 20.6   Gas-detection instruments (toxic gas, combustible gas, and oxygen deficiency)
(Permission of ENMET Corporation)

---

[5] *Confined Space. Confined space means a space that:*
  A. Is large enough and so configured that an employee can bodily enter and perform assigned work; and
  B. Has limited or restricted means for entry or exit (for example, tanks, vessels, silos, storage bins, hoppers, vaults, and pits are spaces that may have limited means of entry); and
  C. Is not designed for continuous employee occupancy.
  (Definition from the Code of Federal Regulations (CFR) Title 29 Part 1910.146.)
[6] *Acute Health Effect. An adverse effect on a human or animal body, with symptoms developing rapidly.*

According to OSHA law, each entry into a confined space requires a confined space entry permit (Figure 20.7). The purpose of the permit is to ensure that a supervisor or other qualified person has taken the necessary steps to identify any hazards associated with entry into the confined space and has taken appropriate safety measures to protect operators from injury. The permit should be renewed each time the space is left and re-entered, even for a break or lunch, or to go get a tool.

A comprehensive set of written, understandable operating procedures should be developed and provided to all persons whose duties may involve work in *PERMIT-REQUIRED*[7] or non-permit confined spaces. Training in the use of procedures should be provided, along with training in the use of safety equipment, rescue techniques, and cardiopulmonary resuscitation (CPR). Exact procedures for work in confined spaces may vary with different agencies and geographical locations and must be confirmed with the appropriate regulatory safety agency.

The following steps are recommended *PRIOR* to entry into a confined space.

1. Identify and close off or reroute any lines which may convey harmful substance(s) to, or through, the work area.

2. Empty, flush, or purge the space of any harmful substance(s) to the extent possible.

3. Monitor the atmosphere at the work site and within the space to determine if dangerous air contamination and/or oxygen deficiency exists.

4. Record the atmospheric test results and keep them at the site throughout the work period.

5. If the space is interconnected with another space, each space should be tested and the most hazardous conditions found should govern subsequent steps for entry into the space.

6. If an atmospheric hazard is noted, use portable blowers to further ventilate the area; retest the atmosphere after a suitable period of time.

7. If dangerous air contamination and/or oxygen deficiency does not exist prior to or following ventilation, entry into the area may proceed.

8. Provide appropriate, approved respiratory protective equipment for the standby person and place it where it will be readily available for immediate use in case of emergency.

WHENEVER AN ATMOSPHERE FREE OF DANGEROUS AIR CONTAMINATION AND/OR OXYGEN DEFICIENCY CANNOT BE ENSURED THROUGH SOURCE ISOLATION, VENTILATION, FLUSHING, OR PURGING, OBSERVE THE FOLLOWING PROCEDURES.

1. If the confined space has both side and top openings, enter through the side opening whenever possible.

2. Wear appropriate, approved respiratory protective equipment.

3. Wear an approved safety belt with an attached line. The free end of the line should be secured outside the entry point.

4. Station at least one person to stand by on the outside of the confined space and at least one additional person within sight or call of the standby person.

5. Maintain frequent, regular communication between the standby person and the entry person.

6. The standby person, equipped with appropriate respiratory protection, should only enter the confined space in case of emergency.

7. If the entry is made through a top opening, use a hoisting device with a harness that suspends a person in an upright position.

8. If the space contains, or is likely to develop, flammable or explosive atmospheric conditions, do not use any tools or equipment (including electrical) which may provide a source of ignition.

9. Wear appropriate protective clothing when entering a confined space that contains corrosive substances, or other substances harmful to the skin.

10. At least one person trained in first aid and cardiopulmonary resuscitation (CPR) should be immediately available during any confined space job.

Confined space work can present serious hazards if you are uninformed and/or untrained. The procedures presented are only guidelines and exact requirements for confined space work for your locale may vary. *CONTACT YOUR LOCAL REGULATORY SAFETY AGENCY FOR SPECIFIC REQUIREMENTS.*

20.35 Manholes

There are many hazards involved with manholes and all of them can cause injury to the operator. Just removing the manhole cover can cause the loss of hands or fingers. You should never remove the manhole cover with your hands. Use a manhole hook or special tool such as a pick with a bent point to remove the lid. Be very careful when lifting the lid. Use your legs, not your back, for lifting. This will help prevent back

---

[7] *Permit-Required Confined Space (Permit Space).   A confined space that has one or more of the following characteristics:*
 • *Contains or has a potential to contain a hazardous atmosphere,*
 • *Contains a material that has the potential for engulfing an entrant,*
 • *Has an internal configuration such that an entrant could be trapped or asphyxiated by inwardly converging walls or by a floor which slopes downward and tapers to a smaller cross section, or*
 • *Contains any other recognized serious safety or health hazard.*
 (Definition from the Code of Federal Regulations (CFR) Title 29 Part 1910.146.)

Confined Space Pre-Entry Checklist/Confined Space Entry Permit

Date and Time Issued: _____ Date and Time Expires: _____ Job Site/Space I.D.: _____

Job Supervisor: _____ Equipment to be worked on: _____ Work to be performed: _____

Attendant personnel: _____   _____   _____

1. Atmospheric Checks: Time _____ Oxygen _____ %   Toxic _____ ppm

   Explosive _____ % LFL   Carbon Monoxide _____ ppm

2. Tester's signature: _____

3. Source isolation: (No Entry)   N/A   Yes   No

   Pumps or lines blinded,
   disconnected, or blocked   ( )   ( )   ( )

4. Ventilation Modification: N/A   Yes   No

   Mechanical   ( )   ( )   ( )

   Natural ventilation only   ( )   ( )   ( )

5. Atmospheric check after isolation and ventilation:

   Oxygen _____ %   [19.5 – 23.5%]

   Explosive _____ % LFL [<10%]

   Toxic _____ ppm   [<10 ppm H_2S]

   Carbon Monoxide _____ ppm   [<35 ppm CO]

   Tester's signature: _____

   Time: _____

6. Communication procedures: _____

7. Rescue procedures: _____

   _____

8. Entry, attendant, and backup persons   Yes   No   Yes   No

   Successfully completed required training?   ( )   ( )   Is training current?   ( )   ( )

9. Equipment: N/A   Yes   No

   Direct reading gas monitor tested   ( )   ( )   ( )

   Safety harnesses and lifelines for entry and attendant persons   ( )   ( )   ( )

   Hoisting equipment   ( )   ( )   ( )

   Powered communications   ( )   ( )   ( )

   SCBAs for entry and attendant persons   ( )   ( )   ( )

   Protective clothing   ( )   ( )   ( )

   All electric equipment listed for Class I, Division I, Group D
   and nonsparking tools   ( )   ( )   ( )

10. Periodic atmospheric tests:

    Oxygen: ____% Time ____;   ____% Time ____;   ____% Time ____;   ____% Time ____;

    Explosive: ____% Time ____;   ____% Time ____;   ____% Time ____;   ____% Time ____;

    Toxic: ____% Time ____;   ____% Time ____;   ____% Time ____;   ____% Time ____;

    Carbon Monoxide: ____% Time ____;   ____% Time ____;   ____% Time ____;   ____% Time ____;

We have reviewed the work authorized by this permit and the information contained herein. Written instructions and safety procedures have been received and are understood. Entry cannot be approved if any brackets ( ) are marked in the "No" column. This permit is not valid unless all appropriate items are completed.

	Name	Signature
Permit Prepared By: (Supervisor)	_____	_____
Approved By: (Unit Supervisor)	_____	_____
Reviewed By: (Authorized Entrant(s))	_____	_____
(Attendant(s))	_____	_____
(Entry Supervisor)	_____	_____

This permit to be kept at job site. Return job site copy to Safety Office following job completion.

Fig. 20.7   Confined space pre-entry checklist/permit

strains. Locate the cover outside the working area to provide adequate working area around the manhole opening.

Next is the problem of traffic around an open manhole. The public, other operators, and vehicles must be protected. Therefore, barricades, warning devices, and lights must conform to local and state regulations. There also should be a barricade around the manhole to protect the operators. All personnel around manholes should wear hard hats for their safety.

Always inspect and test the ladder rungs in the manhole before using them. They may become loose or corroded and could collapse under your full weight. One should never enter a manhole alone; there should be at least one other person standing by at the top and at least one or more people within hearing distance in case of injury.

Perhaps the greatest threats to operators working in manholes are air contamination or depletion of oxygen. Many operators have lost their lives because of leaking gas mains, gases produced by decaying vegetation, or other gases. Never enter a manhole without checking the atmosphere for (1) sufficient oxygen, (2) presence of toxic gases (hydrogen sulfide), or (3) explosive conditions (methane or natural gas). In any event, always provide adequate ventilation. This will remove any hazardous gases.

Smoking should never be permitted in or around manholes. Always use a mechanical lifting aid (rope and bucket) for raising or lowering tools and equipment in and out of a manhole. The use of a bucket or basket will keep your hands free when climbing down into or out of the manhole.

To review the hazards of underground structures, remember to use the proper tools for opening and closing the manhole. Keep in mind the need for barricades and lights to warn traffic and to prevent endangering other operators. Be sure that operators are trained in cardiopulmonary resuscitation (CPR) methods, and in the way to test the manhole for oxygen deficiency, explosive gases, and toxic gases.

QUESTIONS

Write your answers in a notebook and then compare your answers with those on page 458.

20.3A   What safety precautions should be taken when waxing floors?

20.3B   How should rags containing oils, paint, or other cleaning compounds be stored?

20.3C   What safety precautions should be exercised when operating an overhead crane?

20.3D   How can traffic be warned that operators are working in a manhole?

20.3E   How should tools and equipment be lowered into and removed from manholes?

20.36   Power Tools

The two general classes of portable power tools are (1) pneumatic, and (2) electrical. Safety precautions for handling these types of tools are much the same for both types. Wear eye and ear protection when operating grinding, chipping, buffing, or pavement-breaking equipment. When using grinding or buffing tools you will sometimes encounter toxic materials and will need respiratory protection. At other times there is a need for full face protection because of flying particles; you should use a face shield or at least goggles. In the use of electrical tools, always replace worn extension cords, and never expose cords to oils or chemicals. Extension cords also present a tripping hazard if left in the way. Avoid leaving extension cords in aisles or in work areas. Do not hang extension cords over sharp edges which could cut the cord, and always store the cords in a clean, dry location.

When working in a wet or damp location, consider using rubber mats or insulated platforms. As indicated above, use only grounded tools. When using pneumatic tools, never use the compressed air to clean off your clothing or parts of your body. Air can enter your tissues or other openings and cause problems. Always check hose clamps. If they are loose or worn, tighten or replace as needed. Air hoses, like extension cords, are a tripping hazard. Therefore, consider their location when working with pneumatic tools. For the large (¾-inch or 18-mm) hoses, always use an approved safety-type hose connection with a short safety chain or other safety device attached. Air hoses that come apart can cause injuries as they are whipping about. Like electrical cords, keep air hoses away from oils, chemicals, or sharp objects.

Sandblasting with a pneumatic tool requires some special precautions. The operator should protect all skin surfaces with protective clothing, wear eye and face protection, use a respirator, and be very careful of toxic fumes which are discharged from a blasting operation.

The grinding wheel, pneumatic or electric, requires the same safety considerations. Eye and face protection is required. Do not use this tool without safety guards. Be careful of gloves being caught on the grinding wheel. Never operate a wheel with loose nuts on its spindle. When the grinding wheel is badly worn, replace it and use the proper wheel and speed of rotation.

All persons using power tools must be trained in their use and maintenance. Use the manufacturer's operations and maintenance guide for details of proper training. Most injuries by power tools are caused by incorrect setup and operation due to poor training.

Finally, power tools often produce a high level of noise. For example, air drills produce 95 *DECIBELS*[8] and circular saws, 105 dB. Ear protection must be provided when operators are exposed to long periods of high levels of noise. In areas of noise exposure, all operators should be provided with approved ear protective devices.

---

[8] *Decibel (DES-uh-bull).   A unit for expressing the relative intensity of sounds on a scale from zero for the average least perceptible sound to about 130 for the average level at which sound causes pain to humans. Abbreviated dB.*

20.37 Welding

The first safety rule in operation of gas or electric welding equipment is that the operator be thoroughly trained in the correct operating procedures. The second rule concerns fire protection. The third rule is personnel protection. None of these rules is first or last — they should *ALL* be followed.

If you are not thoroughly trained in the use of the welding equipment, do not use it. If you absolutely must use the equipment, do so only under the supervision of a trained welder. Whenever such work must be performed in or around a water treatment plant, take time to consider the fire problem. For example, welding can be very dangerous in an oxidizing chemical location, near powdered activated carbon storage, and in storage areas for other bagged chemicals. Avoid welding around oil and grease when possible; and when that's not possible, at least provide for ventilation of fumes. When welding or cutting is done in the vicinity of any combustible material, you must take special precautions to prevent sparks or slag from reaching the combustible material and causing a fire. Some insurance companies require a fire watch to be present during welding operations. The fire watch is responsible for making the welder immediately aware of fire and to assist in putting out any fires that develop.

Regarding the safety of other personnel in the welding area, eye protection comes first. The person using the welding equipment must wear protective clothing, gloves, helmet, and goggles. Others in and around the welding operation should be kept at a safe distance. Always be careful of overhead welding because of falling sparks and slag. If other operators are (or must be) working in the vicinity of the welding operation, they too must be protected from the rays of arc welding; never look at the welding operation without eye protection.

Store welding gas cylinders in the same manner as other gas cylinders. They are stored upright, kept out of radiation of heat and sunlight, and stored with protective covers in place when not in use. Store cylinders away from elevators and stairs, and secure them with a chain or other suitable device.

20.38 Safety Valves

There are quite a number of safety valves in a water treatment plant; operators are not always aware of their locations or functions. For example, most operators know of the safety plugs on chlorine cylinders, but there are also large safety valves in any plant that stores large amounts of chlorine on site. These containers take on truck load lots of 17 tons (15,540 kilograms). The safety valves on such containers should be certified at least every two years or as often as the state requires. Such relief valves must be maintained on a regular basis. Inspect the inside of these tanks at regular time intervals and keep a record of the findings, for example, evidence of deposits and corrosion.

Water heater safety valves should be checked on an annual basis and maintained or replaced as needed. If the plant has a boiler room, the steam safety valve should be maintained and checked for proper operating pressures. These valves should not discharge in such a manner as to be a hazard to operating personnel.

There also may be surge relief valves on discharge piping (high lift) of the treatment plant. These valves also act as a safety valve to the pumping equipment and must be maintained on some regular time interval. They should be checked for proper pressure setting, with all pilot valves being reconditioned or replaced as needed.

There may be other safety valves located in the pumping plant's hydraulic system for opening and closing discharge valves that require maintenance. In the maintenance of water treatment plants, you or your supervisor must set up a maintenance system for all equipment. Hand tools, power tools, and other maintenance equipment must also be kept in safe working condition. Operators must be furnished protection for the eyes, the ears, the hands, the head, feet and, at other times, the body. Work areas should be well ventilated and noise should be reduced whenever possible. Each operator should always be on the lookout for additional ways of making the treatment plant a safer place to work.

QUESTIONS

Write your answers in a notebook and then compare your answers with those on pages 458 and 459.

20.3F   What type of protection do operators need when operating portable power tools?

20.3G   How can operators be protected from high noise levels when operating air drills and circular saws?

20.3H   What personal protection should be used when operating welding equipment?

20.4 VEHICLE MAINTENANCE AND OPERATION

20.40 Types of Vehicles

Many types of vehicles are used in the waterworks industry. However, the plant operator may only come into contact with a few. Cars, pickup trucks, forklifts, dump trucks, and some electrically driven cars are the types of vehicles the operator is most likely to be involved with and to need to maintain. In addition to motor vehicle safety, this section will also consider the storage of fuel for these and other engines in the plant.

20.41 Maintenance

To have a safe motor vehicle, there must be a preventive maintenance program. Figure 20.8 gives a checklist for finding potential safety problems and a means of recording the preventive maintenance.

Tire inflation is a good example of proper safety checks. Not only is it unsafe to operate on underinflated tires, but it also causes undue wear on the tire. Therefore, tires should be checked regularly for wear, which may be caused by misalignment or low inflation. If tires are badly worn, they should be replaced. Always maintain the recommended pressure in the

	Month _____	Vehicle Number _____		Assignment _____		
		WEEKS				
	CHECK	1st	2nd	3rd	4th	5th
1	Oil					
2	Water					
3	Tires					
4	Horn					
5	Headlights, High - Low					
6	Tail Lights					
7	Turn Signals					
8	Stop Lights					
9	Battery Water					
10	Fire Extinguisher					
11	First Aid Kits					
12	Windshield Wipers					
13	Visual Inspection - Wire Rope					
14	" " - Hook					
15	" " - Sheaves					
16	" " - Boom					
17	" " - Hydraulic Level					
18	Operational Test Controls					

SERVICE MILEAGE READINGS				FUEL CONSUMPTION	
Week	Present	Last Service	Difference	Start Mileage	
1st				End Mileage	
2nd				Total Miles	
3rd				Fuel Used	
4th				MPG Average	
5th					

Fig. 20.8   Mobile equipment checklist

tires; when checking, set the hand brake and turn off the motor.

Next, when changing tires, be sure the jack you are using has sure footing. Position the jack at right angles to the direction of the lift. Jacks are a problem in general, and you should make sure that proper jacks are in each vehicle. In other words, select the proper jack for each job and choose only one that is safe and strong enough. If blocking is required, only use safe supports, avoid leaning on the jack, and protect hands. Always stay a safe distance from the jack handle as many injuries are caused by flying jack handles. Also, injuries are caused by overloading jacks. In addition, where needed, use braces or other supports to prevent tipping the vehicle over, another cause of serious injuries.

Fueling motor vehicles also involves some hazards. Always stop the vehicle's engine. Remember to remove the fuel hose immediately after using it. You could start a fire if you carelessly drive off with the hose still attached. Also, make sure the cap is replaced tightly on the tank. Do not permit smoking in the vicinity of gas delivery pumps at any time. Avoid any sparks, and skin contact. Use only high flash-point solvent for cleaning up any gasoline. Some other safety tips when refueling are: do not let the tank overflow, always set the brake, hang nozzle up properly onto the pump, and eliminate any leaks on the hose connections.

Most small water treatment plants do not have hoists or pits for vehicle lubrication. However, most of the following suggestions are applicable. First, keep all walkways, steps, tools, and containers free from grease, oil, and dirt. This will reduce the possibility of accidents caused by these items. As when maintaining any equipment, use the right tools, keep shoes free of all oil or grease, and wear only shoes with nonslip soles.

If the plant is equipped with a hoist, do not permit anyone to remain inside the vehicle when it is on the hoist. When lifting the vehicle, do not permit tools on the hoist or vehicle that may fall onto you or other personnel in the work area. Keep the driveway free of hoses, tools, and cars, and always keep your hand on the operating lever when raising or lowering the vehicle.

Most water treatment plants have assigned specific areas for washing or steam cleaning vehicles. If your plant does not have such an area, you should have one assigned. This area does not have to be elaborate, but should have water hoses and steam-cleaning equipment and be adequately drained. The same safety rules apply to makeshift installations as apply to completely equipped cleaning areas. The most important consideration is the steam cleaner. Keep the nozzle clean, check water level on coils before turning on the flame, and always wear protection for your eyes and face. Make sure that the cleaner is adequately grounded and be careful of cleaning compounds (see Section 20.1, "Chemical Handling,"

for precautions to prevent burns). Maintain steam hoses, check connections and never permit horseplay with steam-cleaning equipment. As in other work areas, keep the wash rack free from grease and oil and oily rags. Hoses should be stored on the rack when not in use. Always use scaffolding or platforms when cleaning the tops of vehicles.

20.42 Seat Belts

Many water treatment plant operators have some excuse for not wearing seat belts. The excuses may sound good, but they won't protect you in the event of an accident. Many lives would have been saved if seat belts were used. The water utility should equip all vehicles with seat belts and require every operator to use them.

20.43 Accident Prevention

The best overall means of preventing vehicle accidents is defensive driving. This method requires training and a certain mental outlook on the part of the vehicle operator. Most, if not all, drivers think they are good at what they do and this may be true to some extent. However, if each driver would operate all vehicles as if all other drivers were the world's worst drivers, accidents would be greatly reduced.

Good drivers check out their vehicles each time they use them and have any maintenance performed when needed. They use proper signals for directional change, always observe traffic regulations, and show courtesy to others. Remember that drivers in an agency vehicle represent the agency. Therefore, good driving skills are good for public relations.

Another way to avoid accidents is,

"Do Not Tailgate"

Tailgating is a very unwise practice which is dangerous to the vehicle and hazardous to its operator. A good rule to use when following another vehicle is the old one-car-length for every 10 MPH, and if there is limited visibility, increase that distance. Another rule is the "Three Second Rule" which says you must be at least three seconds behind the car in front of you. Take precautions when backing up. Always set the brake and/or shift to "Park" when parking the vehicle. Be cautious at intersections. As a defensive driver always be ready to give the right of way. No right of way is worth injuring oneself.

In some cases, even the most defensive and careful driver has an accident. Because of this, each vehicle should carry flashlights, flares, flags, and a fire extinguisher, along with a first-aid kit. In the event of an accident, the driver should know how to fill out all the forms, a supply of which should be provided in the vehicle.

Remember, when operating a vehicle, an accident can be prevented by defensive driving. The plant supervisor should have each member of the staff take a defensive driver training course. Each driver should develop a defensive driver frame of mind. Developing a good attitude and driving skills are the key to accident prevention when operating a vehicle. All new employees should be given road tests in operating the types of vehicles they will be using.

Here are a few reminders when operating a vehicle. During a storm, roadways or pavement are likely to be slippery. Slow down, pump the brakes when stopping, and remember the minimum distance rules. No driver should be required to operate an unsafe vehicle. Keep copies of a suitable form for reporting mechanical problems in each vehicle and encourage operators to use them.

20.44   Forklifts

Most water treatment plants and pumping stations have a forklift. Most, if not all, plant operators use this vehicle to move chemicals, repair parts, and even use it when making repairs to lift heavy objects. Therefore, every plant operator should be trained in the use of the forklift.

Following are a few points regarding safe operation of the forklift with suggestions for operator safety as well as protection of others who may be in the operating area of the forklift.

Keep all aisles free of boxes and other debris. Do not permit anyone to ride on the forklift except the operator. Never overload the forklift. Always be sure the warning signals are operational and never leave the power on when leaving the forklift. Like other vehicles, check out the brakes before operating. Be careful at intersections of aisles and always face the direction of travel. If a loaded forklift is to be placed on an elevator, be sure that the load on the forklift and the weight of the vehicle do not exceed the weight limit of the elevator. Also, make sure the forklift load is stacked properly before lifting or moving. When handling drums, special lifting and retaining devices are needed.

Figure 20.9 is a typical forklift inspection form.

QUESTIONS

Write your answers in a notebook and then compare your answers with those on page 459.

20.4A   What causes tire wear on motor vehicles?

20.4B   Motor vehicles should contain what safety devices?

End of Lesson 2 of 3 Lessons on SAFETY

Please answer the discussion and review questions next.

DISCUSSION AND REVIEW QUESTIONS

Chapter 20.   SAFETY

(Lesson 2 of 3 Lessons)

Write the answers to these questions in your notebook before continuing. The question numbering continues from Lesson 1.

16. How can an operator prevent fires in a water treatment plant?

17. How would you maintain water-type fire extinguishers?

18. How would you maintain fire hoses in your water treatment plant?

19. What precautions should be taken in areas where flammable material is stored?

20. How can an operator make visitors feel as if the water being produced is safe to drink?

21. How would you remove a manhole cover?

22. What precautions should be taken when operating power tools in a wet or damp location?

23. What fire hazards should be considered before doing any welding?

24. How would you safely refuel a motor vehicle?

25. What safety precautions should be taken when driving during a storm?

HOW WHAT HOW WHAT HOW WHAT HOW WHAT

Operator	Brake	Boom		Tilt		Back-up Horn	Horn	Wheel	Remarks
		Up	Dn.	F	R				

SOUTHERN NEVADA WATER SYSTEM
For Truck Operator Inspection

FORM #268 — S.N.W.S.

Fig. 20.9   Forklift inspection form

CHAPTER 20.   SAFETY

(Lesson 3 of 3 Lessons)

20.5   ELECTRICAL EQUIPMENT

20.50   Electrical Safety

As a water plant operator, you are not expected to be an expert in electrical equipment, but you must have a working understanding of electricity. This includes an understanding of the safety precautions needed to operate the electrical equipment. After all, electrical energy is required to power most of the treatment plant operations. The objective of this section is to show you how to operate safely and to become involved to a limited degree in the maintenance of electrical equipment. Electricity is unforgiving to the careless treatment plant operator. If you have any doubts about your understanding of this section, you may wish to reread Chapter 18, "Maintenance," Section 18.1, "Electrical Equipment."

20.51   Current — Voltage

Many types of electrical current are used in water treatment plants and the associated pumping plant. Each day the plant operator is exposed to this equipment, giving little thought to the potential hazards of the equipment. Current may come into the plant at a high voltage, for example, 69 KVA, reduced to 4,160 volts or 2,300 volts. This current may power pump motors, blowers and other equipment at lower voltages of 440, 220, or 120 volts and within starters may be reduced to 24 or 12 volts or changed over into D.C. voltages. Given all of these various voltages, the operator must be careful not to become careless working with equipment. Therefore, become familiar with the types of current and voltage in the plant. By knowing this, you will avoid the mistake of becoming involved with unsafe electrical currents or practices for which you are not trained. This will also enable you to know when to ask for a qualified person to perform any necessary repairs.

20.52   Transformers

Electrical power entering a plant is routed through transformers to reduce the voltage in most cases. There are many types of transformers although the operator may only think of the larger ones that bring the power into the plant. Sometimes these are owned by the waterworks agency and therefore the maintenance is the responsibility of the operator. There are few, if any, plant operators who are qualified to perform such maintenance. Never attempt to work on a high voltage transformer without the assistance of qualified personnel. Such personnel can be located at the power company or contact an electrical contractor who specializes in the repair and maintenance of electrical transformers. You will, however, need to keep records of the transformer's operation. This information is helpful to repair personnel and is useful to operators who need to know the status of the transformer.

There are many small transformers within the plant's operating gear and it is these you may have to maintain. Most often these low-voltage transformers become overworked; they overheat and burn out. Any fire in the electrical gear can be hazardous. Be very careful when opening a starter, breaker box or indicating instrumentation if a fire or overheated transformer is suspected. Operators have been badly burned by not thinking before opening such devices when they smell smoke in pumping stations or treatment plants. When solving problems with hot, overheated, or burning transformers, remember what you learned in Section 20.2 about electrical fires. For the safety of operating personnel and the safety of the plant, regularly inspect or have someone inspect both large and small transformers. If you detect any overheating, have a qualified electrician inspect and replace any transformer that is not functioning properly.

There should be a fence around the transformer station, with a locked gate and only a limited number of keys issued to plant personnel. The operator may perform routine preventive maintenance such as removing weeds, brush and general cleanup. Replacing fuses and major maintenance or repairs should be made by the power company or qualified electricians. Maintenance must be performed by qualified and well-trained personnel.

20.53   Electric Starters

As a treatment plant operator, your most frequent contact with electrical power will probably be with electric starters on the motor control panels. These devices are used throughout the plant and provide an interface between the operator and the flow of energy. The starter may be located on a switch panel or there may be a switch that is remotely located from the starter. One of the first safety procedures you should take is to use a special insulated mat on the floor at all switchboards. The starter should be provided with adequate lighting and clearly marked Start/Stop buttons. Replace indicating lights as needed without delay. There should always be clear and adequate working space around the starter or switch panels. To reduce the hazards of fire in electric starters, they should be cleaned and maintained on a regular basis. Such maintenance must be performed by trained, qualified personnel. In electrical starting equipment, fires can easily occur because of accumulation of dust and dirt on the contactors. When they become so badly burned that they do not make proper contact they could overheat and start fires. The key to preventing fires in starting equipment is a good preventive maintenance program.

20.54 Electric Motors

The treatment plant operator is exposed to many types and sizes of electric motors. In some plants, the motors are old and require more attention because of exposed parts. The newer electric motors are enclosed and have all parts protected. For the old motors, you should install guards or guardrails to prevent accidental contact with live parts of the motors.

Some of the electric motors may have exposed couplings, pulleys, gears, or sprockets that also require consideration. For these and other moving devices, a wire cloth gear guard may be installed. The gear guard can also be made of sheet metal. However, no matter which type of guard is used, it must be securely fastened onto the floor or some other solid support. The safeguards must be constructed and fitted to prevent material being handled by operators from coming into contact with the moving parts driven by the motors.

Another consideration is projections on couplings, pulley shafts, and other revolving parts on the motor or on the device being driven. These projections can be bolts, keys, set screws, or other projections. The projections should be removed, reduced, or protected by one of the above guards.

Check grounding on all electric motors as part of a routine maintenance program. The motor frames themselves must be grounded if the wires to the motor are not enclosed in an armored conduit or other metallic raceway. Check that all joints are mechanically secure to ensure good grounding. In the case of portable electric motors, the simplest way of grounding is an extra conductor in the cord serving the motor. The best way is to install a ground fault interrupter (G.F.I.) receptacle. This device will automatically disconnect the tool from the power supply if the ground is not connected and will supply the greatest protection to the operator and to the equipment.

When using portable electric motors always check the service cord. If the cord or receptacles are in poor condition or showing signs of wear, they should be replaced. A badly worn cord must never be used in a wet location.

20.55 Instrumentation

In this area of water treatment the operator is not exposed to a great deal of hazard, but must give some consideration to instrumentation devices since they are operated by electric current. This is also true of all other automatic equipment. Although most instruments protect the operator, there is still a degree of hazard when changing charts, calibrating, or performing other maintenance. First, when calibrating an instrument, you are exposed to at least 12 volts D.C. to 120 volts A.C. If you become grounded with the 120 volts A.C., you may be killed or severely injured. Also, when maintaining automatic control equipment, adjustment of one instrument may start another device, exposing another operator to a hazard because of an unexpected start. As mentioned above, electronic devices operate on low current, but don't forget that there is still high voltage located somewhere in the instrument.

20.56 Control Panels

Always provide adequate working space in and around control panels. As with electric motors, the panels must be well grounded. At some locations there may be a need for special insulating mats, such as in wet locations. Adequate lighting must be available inside the control panel as well as outside for those who do the maintenance. Moisture or corrosive gases must be kept away from the control panels. To reduce fire hazard, never store any hazardous material next to switchboards or control panels. Panels carrying greater than 600 volts must be permanently marked warning of the hazards. Areas of high voltage should be screened off and locked with a limited number of keys given to authorized personnel only.

> **CAUTION**
>
> UNLESS YOU ARE A QUALIFIED ELECTRICIAN, STAY OUT OF THE INSIDE OF ALL ELECTRICAL PANELS. IF YOU DO NOT KNOW OR ARE NOT FAMILIAR WITH THE EQUIPMENT, LEAVE IT ALONE!

20.57 Lockout/Tagout Procedure

Any equipment that could suddenly start up or release stored energy is a potential hazard to operators. Stored energy may be in the form of electrical power, hydraulic pressure, pneumatic pressure, or even the tension in a spring. Two hazards due to the lack of a good lockout procedure are: (1) accidentally starting a piece of equipment exposing a fellow operator to a hazard, and (2) turning electrical power on when someone is still working on the equipment, exposing that person to danger. Every water treatment plant should develop a standard operating procedure (SOP) (Figure 20.10) for lockout of equipment to protect personnel from accidental injury.

A lockout device is a positive means of holding a switch, valve, or other energy isolating device in a safe position to prevent the equipment from becoming energized, either directly or by release of stored energy. Positive control of the energy source is ensured by the use of a keyed lock or a combination lock. Besides physically locking out or isolating the source of energy, it is also important to warn other operators, by means of a tagout device, that the switch or piece of equipment has been shut down. A tagout device is a prominent warning tag which can be securely fastened to the energy isolating device to indicate that both it and the equipment being controlled may not be operated until the tagout device is removed.

Even after equipment is locked out and tagged, it still may not be safe to work on. Stored energy in gas, air, water, steam, and hydraulic systems (such as water pumping sys-

SOUTHERN NEVADA WATER SYSTEM
Standard Operating Procedure

SUBJECT: REMOVING EQUIPMENT FROM SERVICE	Number: 35
DIVISION: SAFETY	Prepared By: JAR 4/22/85

PURPOSE

This procedure prescribes the method for safely removing a piece of equipment from service prior to performing the required maintenance or repairs.

GENERAL

Equipment may be removed from service for the following reasons:

1. To prevent an unsafe or damaging operating condition.
2. To perform maintenance or repairs that would be unsafe or impractical to perform while equipment is in service.

Equipment should only be removed from service when one of the above conditions exists.

METHOD

RESPONSIBILITY: Operations or Maint. Employee

ACTION:

1. Upon receipt of a work order requiring removal of equipment from service or upon discovering a condition that requires removal of equipment from service, checks the following as applicable:
   – motor(s) is off
   – discharge valves are closed
   – selector switches are off
   – alarm system is bypassed
   – etc.
2. Attaches a "lock-out" device to the piece of equipment, if possible.

NOTE: Once a "lock-out" device is installed, it is not to be removed until repairs are complete, unless removal is authorized by the Director or a Division Head.

3. Prepares a "Do Not Operate" tag, entering the following:
   – date
   – reason for equipment being removed from service
   – signature of employee preparing tag
4. Affixes tag to the piece of equipment.
5. Notifies operations by radio or telephone of the removal from service.
6. If the removal from service was not initiated by a work order, checks to make sure that no work order is already scheduled for the repair.
7. If no active work order is on file for the repair, prepares and processes a work order in accordance with SOP #39, subject: "Work Orders."
8. Removes the "lock-out" device, if possible, or requests that the device be removed by the employee who installed it.

NOTE: If the employee who installed the device is unavailable, requests removal or authorization for removal from the Superintendent.

9. Performs scheduled maintenance or repairs and installs own "lock-out" device as needed until work is completed.
10. Maintenance Technician, upon completion of scheduled maintenance or repairs, removes the tag and the "lock-out" device, if applicable, and returns the piece of equipment to service status.
11. Notifies Operations that the equipment has been returned to service.

Fig. 20.10   Standard operating procedure for locking out electrical equipment

tems) must be drained or bled down to release the stored energy. Before bleeding down pressurized systems, think about the pressures involved and what will be discharged to the atmosphere and work area (toxic or explosive gases, corrosive chemicals). Will other safety precautions have to be taken? What volume of bleed down material will there be and where will it go? If dealing with chemicals, greases, or lubricants, how can they be cleaned up or contained? Many times an operator has removed a pump volute cleanout only to find that the discharge check valve wasn't seated or one of the isolation valves was not fully seated. Once the pump was open, however, the pump intake structure drained into the pump room through the opened pump.

Many types of equipment also require the use of a blockout procedure. Blockout means the insertion of some device that prevents moving parts in equipment from moving. Physically block and/or secure in place any elevated machine members, flywheels, and springs to prevent movement which could injure an operator working on the equipment.

All rotating mechanical equipment must have guards installed to protect operators from becoming entangled or caught up in belts, pulleys, drive lines, flywheels, and couplings. Keep the guards installed even when no one is working on the equipment.

Various pieces of machinery are equipped with travel limit switches, pressure sensors, pressure reliefs, shear pins, and stall or torque switches to ensure proper and safe operation of the equipment. Never disconnect a device, or install larger shear pins than those specified on the original design, or modify pressure or temperature settings.

In a safe lockout procedure, the switches are locked open and are properly tagged; only the operator who is doing the maintenance should have a key. In fact, all people who perform electrical maintenance should have their own individual lock and key so as to maintain control over the equipment being worked on by each individual. Only the operator who installed the lockout device and warning tag may remove them unless the employer has provided specific procedures and training for removal by others.

The basic elements of a proper lockout/tagout procedure[9] are as follows:

1. Notify all affected employees that a lockout or tagout system is going to be used and the reason why. The authorized employee is responsible for knowing the type and magnitude of energy that the equipment uses and must understand the potential hazards.

---

[9] *Adapted from* WASTEWATER SYSTEM OPERATIONS, *State of Oklahoma Certification Study Guide.*

2. If the equipment is operating, shut it down by the normal stopping procedure.

3. Operate the switch, valve, or other energy isolating device(s) so that the equipment is isolated from its energy source(s). Stored energy such as that in springs, elevated machine members, rotating flywheels, hydraulic systems, and air, gas, steam, or water pressure must be dissipated or restrained by methods such as repositioning, blocking, or bleeding down.

4. Lock out and tag the energy isolating device with assigned individual lock or tag.

5. After ensuring that no personnel are exposed and, as a check that the energy source is disconnected, operate the push button or other normal operating controls to make certain the equipment will not operate. A common problem when motor control centers (MCCs) contain many breakers is to lock out the wrong equipment (locking pump #3 and thinking it is #2). Always confirm the dead circuit. *CAUTION:* Return operating controls to the neutral or OFF position after the test.

6. The equipment is now locked out or tagged out and work on the equipment may begin.

7. After the work on the equipment is complete, all tools have been removed, guards have been reinstalled, and employees are in the clear, remove all lockout/tagout devices. Operate the energy isolating devices to restore energy to the equipment.

8. Notify affected employees that the lockout or tagout device(s) has been removed before starting the equipment.

QUESTIONS

Write your answers in a notebook and then compare your answers with those on page 459.

20.5A   Why should each plant operator become familiar with the type of current and voltage in the water treatment plant?

20.5B   List the moving parts on electric motors that require safety guards.

20.5C   What are two hazards created by the lack of a good lockout procedure for control panels and switchboards?

20.5D   List four examples of stored energy that could be hazardous to operators.

20.6   LABORATORY SAFETY [10]

20.60   Laboratory Hazards

In general, water plant operators do not experience a great deal of exposure to hazardous laboratory conditions. However, you will be in contact with glassware, toxic chemicals, flammable chemicals, corrosive acids, and alkalies. There may be times when you will be exposed to hazardous bacteriological agents. The seriousness of the hazards depends mainly upon the size of the plant and the operating procedures in the treatment plant. For your own safety, learn the proper procedures for handling laboratory equipment and chemicals.

20.61   Glassware

An important item in laboratory safety is handling of glassware. Almost all tests performed by an operator will require the use of some glassware. The operator's hands, of course, are exposed to the greatest hazard. To reduce accidents when handling glassware, never used chipped, cracked, or broken glassware in any testing procedures. All such glassware should be disposed of in a container marked "For Broken Glass Only." Never put broken glass in wastebaskets. Although it may not be a hazard to the operator, it is a danger to those who clean out the wastebaskets. Clean up any broken glass and/or spilled chemicals to reduce hazards to others. Never let broken pieces of glass remain in the sink or in sink drains. This may cause cuts to others who unknowingly try to clean the sink.

Washing glassware is always potentially hazardous. The glassware can be broken while being washed, causing cuts, or cuts can be caused by chipped or cracked glassware. Also, the cleaning compounds themselves can be a problem. Sometimes strong acid cleaners are used to remove stains from the glassware. Without protective gloves, your hands could be seriously burned by these acids.

20.62   Chemicals

When handling liquid chemicals, such as acids and bases, always use safety glasses or face shields. If working with ether or chloroform, avoid inhalation of fumes and always do this type of work under the ventilation hood. Be sure to turn the ventilation fan on. Of course, be careful of open flames when using flammables such as ether. As a general rule, do not permit smoking in the laboratory. All chemicals should be stored in proper locations; do not set chemicals on the laboratory benches where they may cause an accident if spilled or if the container is broken.

When handling laboratory gases, give consideration to their location and potential accident hazards. Gas cylinders must be prevented from falling by using safety retaining devices such as chains. The valve and cylinder regulator should be

---

[10] *See SAFETY PRODUCTS REFERENCE MANUAL, Bulletin Number 2363, Fisher Scientific Company, 2000 Park Lane, Pittsburgh, PA 15275. No charge.*

protected from being struck by stools, ladders, and other objects.

When mixing acid with water, always pour the acid into the water while stirring.

Never add water to acid because the water may remain on top of the acid, thus causing splattering and excess heat generation.

Always use safety goggles, gloves, and protective garments. When cleaning up acid or alkali spills, dilute with lots of water even if you flush them down the sink drain. Baking soda can be used to neutralize acids, and vinegar is used to neutralize bases. Never allow mercury, gasoline, oil, or organic compounds into the laboratory drains. Use only a toxic waste disposal drain system for these items. Pouring such compounds down sink drains can cause an explosion, allow toxic gases and vapors to enter the lab, or destroy the piping.

You must never use your mouth with the pipet for transferring toxic chemicals, acids, or alkalis. Use a suction bulb, aspirator, pump, or vacuum line. If you use your mouth, there is always the danger of getting the toxic solutions into your mouth.

20.63   Biological Considerations

Do not take chances with bacteria. A good policy is to have each operator immunized with anti-typhoid vaccine and to keep their booster shots current. Always use good sanitary practices, particularly when working with unknown bacteria or known pathogens. Never pipet bacteriological samples by mouth. *ALWAYS USE A PIPET BULB.*

When exposed to any bacteria, you should make it a habit to always wash your hands before eating or smoking. If you have any cuts or broken skin areas, these wounds should not come in contact with bacterial agents. You should wear protective gloves or cover the wound with a bandage when working with any kind of bacteria.

All work areas should be swabbed down with a good bactericidal disinfectant before and after preparing samples. As a general policy, the preparation or serving of food should never be permitted in the laboratory. Also, give some consideration to proper ventilation, because some bacteria may be transmitted through the air system.

20.64   Radioactivity

There are many laboratory and treatment plant instruments that use radioactive isotopes in laboratory tests and research. A plant operator may be exposed to radioactive compounds when calibrating sludge density meters or using research isotopes. From a safety standpoint, only qualified personnel should be involved in the use of radioactive compounds. If radioactive compounds are present in the laboratory, warning signs should be posted. The disposal of all radioactive compounds must be performed strictly by qualified laboratory personnel in accordance with government regulations.

20.65   Laboratory Equipment

20.650   Hot Plates

You will probably use a hot plate in your threshold odor number (TON) tests. You should turn the hot plate off when not in use; never place bare hands on the hot plate to check if it is hot. When using the hot plate, always use the hood and turn on the hood ventilation fan to remove gas or fumes. Never place glassware onto a hot plate if the outside of the glassware has water or moisture on the surface between the glass and the hot plate. Steam will form at this interface and cause the glass to break. When taking hot glassware off the hot plate, always use gloves.

20.651   Water Stills

Most water stills in the laboratory today are the electrical type. To observe good safety practices, check the items described in the electrical safety section of this chapter, such as good grounding. Set up a SOP (Standard Operating Procedure) for proper operation of the still and follow the manufacturer's instructions for proper starting and stopping. The still will require cleaning from time to time. Be very careful when disassembling the still. Parts may be frozen together because of hardness in the water and may require an acid wash to separate. Be sure that the boiler unit is full of water before turning the still on. Never allow cold water into a hot boiler unit because it may cause the unit to break.

20.652   Sterilizers

There are two types of sterilizers: (1) dry electrical sterilizers, and (2) wet sterilizers (autoclaves). In the dry electrical sterilizers, check the cords frequently because the high heat may damage the wiring. Always let the unit cool off before removing its contents. Wet sterilizers (autoclaves) are under pressure by steam and should be opened very slowly. Use gloves and protective clothing when unloading the autoclave. Cover the steam exhaust with an insulated covering to prevent burns. Any leakage around the door should be repaired by replacing door gaskets, or even the door if it is worn or bent. Always load the autoclave in accordance with the manufacturer's recommendations. Never allow an operator to work with this equipment without proper instruction in its operation.

20.653   Pipet Washers

Cleaning pipets can be hazardous. Many laboratories have a pipet cleaner which contains an acid compound or other cleaning agents. Always use protective clothing and a face shield when working with the washer unit. Try to avoid dripping or spilling the cleaning compound when transferring the pipets. If the acid comes into contact with your skin, use the remedies recommended in Section 20.11, "Acids."

QUESTIONS

Write your answers in a notebook and then compare your answers with those on page 459.

20.6A   Why is washing glassware always a potential hazard?

20.6B   What precautions should be taken when handling liquid chemicals such as acids and bases?

20.6C   Why should mercury, gasoline, oil, or organic compounds never be allowed into laboratory drains?

20.6D   How can an operator be exposed to radioactive compounds?

20.6E   Why should cold water never be allowed into the hot boiler unit of a water still?

20.7   OPERATOR PROTECTION

20.70   Operator Safety

So far in this chapter we have discussed many means by which you can protect yourself and your equipment. In this section we wish to discuss your own personal protection. Take a look at the means of protecting the eye, the foot, the head, and, most of all, look at water safety. After all, a plant operator is always in contact with water. The water may be found in raw water reservoirs, settling basins, clear wells, or filters. Operators have lost their lives by falling into the backwash gullet. Operators have lost their lives in the finished water reservoirs. As unlikely as it seems, fatal accidents have happened in the past and will happen again in the future. Therefore, it is the responsibility of each operator to watch for any safety problems in the plant's reservoirs, pumping stations, or filters. You, the operator, are responsible for yourself. You should never expose yourself to unsafe conditions.

A major problem confronting many operators is locating reliable safety vendors and equipment. State, regional and national professional meetings, such as those sponsored by the American Water Works Association, often have displays or exhibits featuring manufacturers of safety equipment. This is an excellent opportunity to meet the representatives of these companies and discuss with them what equipment they would recommend for your situation. Also, other operators who have had experience with safety equipment of interest to you often attend these meetings and are eager to share their experiences with you.

If you are unable to attend these meetings, the program announcements will often have a short description of the types of safety equipment that will be featured by each vendor exhibiting at the conference. You can obtain the vendor's address by looking in professional journals, buyers' guides, or by writing to the sponsor of the conference.

20.71   Respiratory Protection

There are many respiratory hazards in and around the treatment plant that an operator is exposed to daily including chemical dusts, chemical fumes, and chemical gases, such as chlorine, ammonia, sulfur dioxide, and acid fumes, to name only a few. Whenever working around or handling these and other compounds, you must take adequate precautions.

Two types of conditions for which you should be prepared are: (1) oxygen-deficient atmosphere, and (2) sufficient oxygen, but a contaminated atmosphere containing toxic gases or explosive conditions. In either circumstance you will need an independent oxygen supply. However, an independent oxygen supply will not protect you from an explosion.

Never enter a confined space with an explosive atmosphere.

Call your local gas company and ask their experts to enter the explosive area, if entry is essential. Your independent oxygen supply should be of the positive-pressure type to protect you if there are any leaks in your mask. Good ventilation can reduce explosive conditions.

20.72   Safety Equipment

All waterworks safety equipment, such as life lines, life buoys, fire extinguishers, fencing, guards, and respiratory apparatus, must be kept in good repair. This and other safety equipment is necessary to protect operators or visitors from injury or death. Safety equipment may fall into disrepair because it is only used occasionally and may deteriorate due to heat, time, and other environmental factors. First-aid equipment should also be provided and kept resupplied as it is used. The operating staff should be given regular instructions in the use and maintenance of the safety equipment.

Provide protective clothing for all operators handling chemicals or dangerous materials. Keep the clothing clean and store it in a protected area when not in use.

The water utility is responsible for providing outward opening doors, remote-controlled ventilation, inspection windows, and similar safety devices where appropriate. This equipment should be exercised, kept clean and well maintained so that it will operate when needed. Respiratory (self-contained breathing) apparatus must be stored in unlocked cabinets outside of chlorination, sulfur dioxide, carbon dioxide, ozone, and ammonia rooms. The storage cabinets must have a controlled environment to prevent deterioration of the equipment.

The operator has the responsibility to inspect each apparatus for deterioration and need for repair. Safety equipment is of no use to the operator if it fails when put to use, and may cost you your life if it is in poor condition. Some self-contained breathing apparatus (air packs) depend on compressed air to supply the oxygen. Under conditions of deficient oxygen supply, the canister type of respirator is useless. You could lose your life by entering a room containing chlorine gas (which is heavier than air) while depending on a poorly maintained respirator. Although you might have protection from the chlorine, you would not have adequate oxygen. Never take a chance with a toxic gas. In water treatment plants, use only the positive-pressure type of self-breathing apparatus.

Many newer plants are being constructed with independent air supplies consisting of a helmet, hose, and compressed air. The helmet is connected by a hose to an uncontaminated air source. The key word here is "uncontaminated." Not only should the operator follow a maintenance program for the hose and mouthpieces of the apparatus, but the operator must maintain the air supply. The air is supplied by mechanical equipment which requires maintenance. The air pressure is controlled by a reducer or regulator which must be kept clean and maintained to be available when needed. Set up a preventive maintenance program for this equipment. It should be checked out on a weekly basis, and records should be kept of each inspection. The record should show conditions of the hoses, regulators, air filters, compressors, helmet, and any other apparatus furnished with the system.

The old standby, of course, has been the air packs or self-breathing apparatus. These units are carried by the user, giving the operator an independent source of air (oxygen). The unit can be used in any concentration of contamination of gases, dust, or anywhere the atmosphere is oxygen deficient. There are two types of units. One type of unit depends on compressed air or oxygen, and the second system generates oxygen by use of chemicals in a canister. The oxygen is generated by the moisture exhaled by the user. Because this equipment is not used daily in the water treatment plant, there must be a preventive maintenance program, with records, inspection, and operator checkout. As with any system, self-breathing equipment requires maintenance. This is vital because the operator's life will depend on how well this apparatus performs.

Training is another important consideration. Even though you may have used the breathing apparatus many times in the past, you should be checked out each month on the equipment. There should be a maximum allowable time for putting on the apparatus. The apparatus should be checked out under field conditions, such as using ammonia or some other non-toxic gas. Remember, it is too late to learn how fast an operator can put on a self-breathing apparatus when a room is filled with chlorine.

Be aware that there have been cases where operators have been saved because they knew how to use the breathing apparatus properly. Only repeated practice will enable you to master this survival skill.

20.73   Eye Protection

The water treatment plant operator has only two eyes. You may think that everyone is aware of this fact. However, some operators behave as though they have many eyes and are very careless about protecting the eyes they *DO* have from hazards.

Because some operators fail to see the value of eye protection, it will take a maximum effort on the part of the supervisory staff to enforce an adequate eye protection program. There must be an intense program of education, persuasion, and appeal to guarantee compliance with an eye protection program.

Most conditions in which a plant operator needs eye protection are not too difficult to understand. Eye protection is needed when handling many of the liquid chemicals, acids, and caustics. Some of the tests performed in the laboratory require eye protection. Only a few moments are required to put on a face shield or safety glasses, and remember — the loss of an eye will last a lifetime.

QUESTIONS

Write your answers in a notebook and then compare your answers with those on page 459.

20.7A   When entering an oxygen-deficient atmosphere, what type of oxygen supply is recommended?

20.7B   Where should respiratory apparatus be stored?

20.7C   How frequently should independent air supply equipment be checked out and what should be inspected?

20.7D   How can compliance with an eye protection program be encouraged?

20.7E   Under what conditions does an operator need eye protection?

20.74   Foot Protection

There are few situations under which a water treatment plant operator needs foot protection. In the normal routine of daily operation of the plant, there are not many hazards to the operator's feet. But in some plants the operator also performs plant maintenance. Here the steel-toed safety shoes are useful. The shoe should be able to resist at least a 300-pound (136-kg) impact. An important consideration in any plant under operating conditions is the use of rubber boots. The rubber boots are needed when handling acid or caustic, or when the operator is working in wet conditions such as reservoirs, filters, or chemical tanks. Under these circumstances, the agency should have an adequate supply of boots with non-skid soles in various sizes. If these conditions are something that the operator is exposed to daily or weekly, the agency should give the operator a pair of boots for personal use.

20.75   Hand Protection

The treatment plant operator's hands are always exposed to hazards. These include not only minor scratches or cuts, but also exposure to chemicals that may not attack immediately. Some compounds, such as alum, attack the skin slowly. Because there is no immediate pain, you may think there is no damage. This is not true; the attack on the skin is slow and may cause an infection at a later date. Therefore, when handling chemicals, always use rubber gloves. As part of a safety package, each operator should be issued a pair of rubber gloves and also a pair of leather gloves. These gloves should be replaced when they no longer provide the necessary protection.

There are other compounds such as solvents that will absorb through the skin and can cause long-term effects. For such special problems, there is a need for neoprene gloves. Another problem is that of handling hot materials, such as laboratory flasks and beakers. Here you may need insulated fabric gloves. When working around machinery that is revolving, wearing gloves or other hand protection can be dangerous. If a glove gets caught in the machinery, you could become injured. Don't let your protective equipment itself become a hazard.

Be sure that the gloves you are wearing are the right type for the job you are doing. The gloves should allow for quick removal and be in good condition. Always check for cracks and holes, flexibility, and grip. Keep them clean and in good condition. There are many types of gloves and the proper type should be worn for each job.

1. *CLOTH GLOVES* protect from general wear, dirt, chafing, abrasions, wood slivers, and low heat.

2. *LEATHER GLOVES* protect from sparks, chips, rough material, and moderate heat.

3. *RUBBER GLOVES* protect against acids and some chemical burns.

4. *NEOPRENE AND CORK-DIPPED GLOVES* give better grip on slippery or oily jobs.

5. *ALUMINIZED GLOVES* are heat-resistant to protect against sparks, flames, and heat.

6. *METAL MESH GLOVES* protect from cuts, rough materials, and blows from edge tools.

7. *PLASTIC GLOVES* protect from chemicals and corrosive substances.

8. *INVISIBLE GLOVES* (barrier cream, such as petroleum jelly) protect from excessive water contact and from substances which dissolve in skin oil.

20.76 Head Protection

In most areas of a water treatment plant, there is really no need for a hard hat. However, there are certain hazardous conditions under which the operators should be required to wear a metal, plastic-impregnated fabric, or fiberglass hat. The hard hat should have a suspended crown with an adjustable head band; provide good ventilation; and be water resistant. Operators should be required to wear the hard hats when work is being performed overhead, or in any location where there is danger of tools or other materials falling, for example, working in filters, settling basins, manholes, or trenches. There has been a long history showing the value of hard hats in reducing injuries and death.

20.77 Water Safety

Every operator in a treatment plant is exposed to situations in which the operator's life can be lost due, either directly or indirectly, to water. Although during your daily activity you may never think in terms of drowning, this hazard is always present in the treatment plant. If you are working at a reservoir or a lake in a boat, you may think of water safety, but still never pay real attention to the danger.

Starting at the treatment plant, you can take simple measures that will reduce hazards. To reduce the hazard of slipping on catwalks or when working around clarifiers or settling basins, use nonskid surfaces on ladders and walkways going into and out of clarifiers or sedimentation basins. Be very cautious during cold or wet weather. Water freezes into ice which is slippery.

Keep all handrails or other guards in good repair; replace any that become unsafe. Many older plants do not have protective handrails; install rails or chain off the unsafe area to all employees and mark off with warning signs. The unsafe areas can be guarded with ⅜-inch (9-mm) manila rope, chains, or cables that you may have around the plant.

Filters are an important area of safety consideration because there is always activity in or around each filter, such as washing or maintenance. Make repairs to handrails immediately when needed. Station emergency gear around the filter areas; equipment such as life jackets are good, but buoys, ⅜-inch (9-mm) manila line, or a long wooden pole are much more useful. These types of devices can be used to rescue someone who has fallen into the filter. An operator should never work in the filter when it is being backwashed. There is always the danger of falling into the wash-water gullet and being unable to get out before drowning.

Sedimentation basins, flocculation basins, or clarifiers present many of the same problems as filters. Maintain handrails, place warning signs, or put up guard ropes or chains. Also keep life rings and manila or nylon lines in good repair. A lift ring, life pole, and lines should be stationed at each basin. A good idea is to shelter the safety gear from the weather, but do not cause the gear to become inaccessible.

In reservoir operation and maintenance you will encounter two types of water: (1) raw water, and (2) treated water. In a raw water reservoir or lake, you have to worry only about personnel safety. In a treated water reservoir, you must also be concerned about the safety of the water going to the customer. If you are working out of a boat, make sure that everyone in the boat is wearing a life jacket. Also take on board both a safety line and buoys. Cold weather conditions are an added problem. Even though you may be a good or excellent swimmer, the thermal shock of cold water may quickly paralyze you, making you unable to save yourself. Under such conditions, if a second operator goes into the water to save you, there may be two lives lost.

Of course, when taking a boat out on the water it should first be checked out for safety. Check the bilge pump, ventilation in the compartments, the safety cushions, fire extinguishers, battery, and the engine. Also check for safety equipment, oars, life jackets, lights, mooring lines, and fuel. If you are applying copper sulfate powder or solution, other safety equipment will be needed, such as respiratory and eye protection equipment. Prepare a detailed equipment checklist to use each time the boat goes out onto the lake or reservoir. The boat should never be taken out on choppy waters or when the wind is high.

On some occasions, there is a need for underwater examination of valves, intake, or other underwater equipment or apparatus. Such work should only be performed by employees who are trained in underwater diving. If there are no qualified divers on your staff, you should hire such personnel to do the diving and underwater inspections. There are organizations with people who do this type of work and they are well qualified in underwater examinations. If an operator on staff is to do the diving, the operator should be certified by a local diving school or other certifying agency. The operator's certificate should always be kept current and the operator should be required to perform the number of dives necessary to keep this certification current.

In closing, all plant operators should know how to swim. If they do not, they should take a Red Cross class and learn the minimum fundamentals to save their own lives. Any operator working over open water should be required to wear a buoyant vest. All basins should have approved safety vests, buoys, and life lines stationed at outside edges.

QUESTIONS

Write your answers in a notebook and then compare your answers with those on page 459.

20.7F   Under what operating conditions should an operator wear rubber boots?

20.7G   Under what specific conditions should an operator be very careful wearing gloves?

20.7H   Why should operators never work in a filter when it is being backwashed?

20.7I   What items should be checked before an operator takes a boat out on the water?

20.8   PREPARATION FOR EMERGENCIES [11]

Emergencies are very difficult to plan and prepare for because you never know what will happen and when it will occur. Catastrophic events could include floods, tornados, hurricanes, fires, and earthquakes. Serious injury to anyone on the plant grounds is an emergency.

Conduct periodic tours of your facilities with the local fire, police and emergency response organizations to familiarize them with the site, potentially hazardous locations, and location of fire hydrants. Their familiarity with the plant layout will be very helpful if an emergency ever occurs. Emphasize to these people that if a disaster occurs, it is important for your plant to be a top priority for assistance because the entire community relies on you for its drinking water.

You should know the names and phone numbers of your local and state civil preparedness coordinators.

If a chemical emergency occurs, such as a chemical spill, leak, fire, exposure, or accident, phone *CHEMTREC*, 800-424-9300. *CHEMTREC* (Chemical Transportation Emergency Center) provides immediate advice for those at the scene of a chemical emergency, and then quickly and promptly alerts experts from the manufacturers whose products are involved for more detailed assistance and appropriate followup.

Prepare a procedure for quick and efficient handling of all accidents or injuries occurring in your treatment facilities or involving your outside crews. All personnel must be familiar with these procedures and must be prepared to carry them out with a minimum amount of delay or confusion.

A copy of these procedures must be posted in all working areas accessible to a phone and in all vehicles containing work crews. Names, addresses, and phone numbers of operators in each working area should be listed in that area and also those immediately available (day or night) by telephone.

Everyone must study these procedures carefully and be able to respond properly and quickly. Your health and life may depend on these procedures.

Figure 20.11 is an example of a typical safety procedure and Figure 20.12 is a checklist of what must be done if someone is seriously injured.

QUESTIONS

Write your answers in a notebook and then compare your answers with those on page 459.

20.8A   What types of emergencies should operators be prepared to handle?

20.8B   Who should be contacted if a serious chemical emergency occurs, such as a chemical spill, leak, fire, exposure, or accident?

20.8C   What is *CHEMTREC?*

---

[11] *Some of the information in this section was provided by Mr. Richard R. Metcalf, Training Officer, County of Onondaga, NY.*

EMERGENCY SAFETY PROCEDURE

1. *DO NOT MOVE THE INJURED PERSON* except when conditions would cause additional injury, such as a gas leak or a fire.

2. *ADMINISTER ONLY SUCH AID AS NECESSARY TO PRESERVE LIFE — TREAT FOR SHOCK*
   (a) clear throat and restore breathing
   (b) stop bleeding
   (c) closed heart massage

3. *DO NOT ATTEMPT MEDICAL TREATMENT* such as
   (a) do not apply splints or attempt to set broken bones
   (b) do not remove foreign objects from the body
   (c) do not administer liquids or oxygen

4. *NOTIFY YOUR SUPERVISOR*
   IF AN AMBULANCE IS REQUIRED:
   1. CALL AMBULANCE — phone _____
   2. Give this information carefully and accurately:
      (a) Location of the injured — be specific
         1. Street location and number, Town or City
            **Remember some streets have north or south or east or west designation — use the full street name. Also, many streets in different towns have the same name — specify the Town.
         2. Location within the Plant area
      (b) Phone number from which you are calling
      (c) Number of persons injured and nature of the injury
      (d) Post an operator to direct the ambulance to the victim
   3. Upon arrival of the ambulance:
      (a) give name, address, and phone number of the injured person to the ambulance crew
      (b) notify relatives of injury and hospital to which person is being taken
         (Medical treatment cannot be given without the permission of the injured or a relative, if a minor)
   4. Call your supervisor

   IF AN AMBULANCE IS NOT REQUIRED:
   1. Take injured: (see map) (phone _____ ,
      ask for Emergency Room)
      Emergency Room
      St. Joseph's Hospital
      301 Prospect Avenue
   2. If possible, call ahead. Give the names of injured and nature of injury
   3. Notify relatives of injury and address of hospital
   4. Call your supervisor

Fig. 20.11 Emergency safety procedure

INJURED PERSON CHECKLIST

1. *CALL AMBULANCE SERVICE,* phone _____

   LOCATION OF INJURED _____ STREET

   _____ TOWN

   _____ BUILDING LOCATION

   _____ PHONE NUMBER

   NUMBER OF PERSONS INJURED _____

   NATURE OF INJURY _____

2. *POST OPERATOR TO DIRECT THE AMBULANCE*
   NAME, ADDRESS, PHONE OF INJURED PERSON

   NAME _____

   ADDRESS _____

   _____

   PHONE _____

3. *GIVE ABOVE INFORMATION TO AMBULANCE CREW*
   NAME AND LOCATION OF HOSPITAL

   HOSPITAL NAME _____

   ADDRESS _____

   _____

   PHONE _____

4. *NOTIFY RELATIVES*

5. *NOTIFY SUPERVISORS*

6. *MAKE OUT ACCIDENT REPORT AS SOON AS POSSIBLE*

Fig. 20.12 Injured person checklist

20.9 ARITHMETIC ASSIGNMENT

Turn to the Appendix at the back of this manual and read Section A.36, "Safety." Work the example problems on your electronic pocket calculator. You should be able to get the same answers.

20.10 ADDITIONAL READING

This chapter cannot provide you with all of the information you need to respond to the many safety problems that occur daily. You should have other sources of ready references. Because this chapter does not give all of the detail you may need, the following bibliography is given. You should have copies of these documents for your reference or have your employer obtain them.

1. *CHLORINE MANUAL* (6th Edition), The Chlorine Institute, Inc., 2001 L Street, NW, Suite 506, Washington, DC 20036. Price to members, $15.00; nonmembers, $30.00. Cost of shipping is about 5 percent of the purchase price.

2. *SAFETY PRODUCTS REFERENCE MANUAL*, Bulletin Number 2363, Fisher Scientific Company, 2000 Park Lane, Pittsburgh, PA 15275. No charge.

3. *STANDARD FIRST AID AND SAFETY*, American Red Cross, 430 17th Street, NW, Washington, DC 20006. May be obtained from local Red Cross offices. Price $11.00.

4. *SAFETY PRACTICES FOR WATER UTILITIES*, M3. Obtain from Customer Services, AWWA, 6666 W. Quincy Avenue, Denver, CO 80235. Order No. 30003. Price to members, $39.00; nonmembers, $60.75; price includes cost of shipping and handling.

5. *SAFETY TALKS*. A series of 52 lectures on common water utility safety practices. Price for one to five subscriptions, $22.00 each; six or more, $18.00 each (AWWA members); nonmembers, $34.00 each, and $26.00 each, respectively. Price includes cost of shipping and handling. Obtain from Customer Services, AWWA, 6666 W. Quincy Avenue, Denver, CO 80235. Order No. 70117.

6. Safety videos available from American Water Works Association:

   • Personal Protective Equipment (No. 65034), AWWA members only, $147.00.

   • Lockout/Tagout Protection (No. 65030), members, $122.00; nonmembers, $183.00.

   • Lockout/Tagout Participant's Guide (No. 65031), members, $7.00 each; nonmembers, $9.00 each.

   • Preventing Bloodborne Disease (No. 65037), AWWA members only, $147.00.

To order videos, write to AWWA, 6666 W. Quincy Avenue, Denver, CO 80235 or call 1-800-926-7337. Prices include cost of shipping and handling.

End of Lesson 3 of 3 Lessons on SAFETY

Please answer the discussion and review questions before continuing with the Objective Test.

DISCUSSION AND REVIEW QUESTIONS

Chapter 20. SAFETY

(Lesson 3 of 3 Lessons)

Write the answers to these questions in your notebook before continuing with the Objective Test on page 460. The question numbering continues from Lesson 2.

26. How can the hazards of fire be reduced in electric starters?

27. How should gas cylinders be stored in laboratories?

28. What safety precautions should be taken with regard to bacteria while working in the laboratory?

29. What is the most common reason safety equipment falls into disrepair?

30. How can an operator reduce the hazard of slipping when working around clarifiers or settling basins?

SUGGESTED ANSWERS

Chapter 20.   SAFETY

ANSWERS TO QUESTIONS IN LESSON 1

Answers to questions on page 416.

20.0A   Management's responsibilities for safety include:

1. Establishing a safety policy,
2. Assigning responsibility for accident prevention,
3. Appointing a safety officer or coordinator,
4. Establishing realistic goals and periodically revising them, and
5. Evaluating the results of the program.

20.0B   Operators' responsibilities for safety include:

1. Performing their jobs in accordance with established safe procedures,
2. Recognizing the responsibility for their own safety and that of fellow operators,
3. Reporting all injuries,
4. Reporting all observed hazards, and
5. Actively participating in the safety program.

Answers to questions on page 417.

20.0C   An accident is that occurrence in a sequence of events that usually produces unintended injury, death, or property damage.

20.0D   The principal reasons for unsafe acts include ignorance, indifference, poor work habits, laziness, haste, poor physical condition, and temper.

20.0E   Laziness affects the speed and quality of work. Laziness also affects safety because safety requires an effort. In most jobs you cannot reduce your "safety effort" and still maintain the same level of safety, even if you slow down or lower your quality standards.

Answers to questions on page 421.

20.10A   An operator needs to know how to handle the problems associated with the chemicals used in a water treatment plant. The operator needs to know how to store chemicals, understand the fire problem, be aware of the tendency of chemicals to "arch" in a storage bin, know how to feed dry, how to feed liquid, and how to make up solutions. Overheating gas containers, dust problems with powdered carbon, burns caused by acid, reactivity of each chemical under a variety of conditions that may cause fire and explosions are other safety hazards that an operator needs to know about and know how to control. Also, the operator needs to know the usable limits of each chemical because of toxicity, the protective equipment required for each chemical, each chemical's antidote, and how to control fires caused by each chemical.

20.11A   To give first aid when acid vapors are inhaled, remove the victim to fresh air, restore breathing, or give oxygen when necessary.

20.11B   Acetic acid will react violently with ammonium nitrate, potassium hydroxide, and other alkaline material.

20.11C   Acetic acid can be handled safely if the operator uses adequate ventilation and prevents skin and eye contact.

20.11D   When handling hydrofluosilicic acid, always use complete protective equipment including rubber gloves, goggles or face shield, rubber apron, rubber boots, and have lime slurry barrels, epsom salt solution, and safety showers available. Always provide adequate ventilation.

20.11E   Inhalation of hydrochloric acid (HCl) vapors or mists can cause damage to teeth and irritation to the nasal passages. Concentrations of 750 ppm or more will cause coughing, choking, and produce severe damage to the mucous membranes of the respiratory tract. In concentrations of 1,300 ppm, HCl is dangerous to life.

20.11F   Nitric acid should be stored in clean, cool, well-ventilated areas. The area should have an acid-resistant floor and adequate drainage. Keep away from oxidizing agents and alkaline materials. Protect containers from damage or breakage. Avoid contact with skin and provide emergency neutralization materials and safety equipment in use areas.

Answers to questions on page 423.

20.12A   Operators use two forms of ammonia: the gaseous form (anhydrous) and the liquid form (hydroxide).

20.12B   Care must be used when storing or transporting ammonia containers. Always keep cylinder caps in place when cylinders are not in use. Store cylinders in a cool, dry location away from heat, and protect from direct sunlight. Do not store in the same room with chlorine.

20.12C   The two forms of lime used in water treatment plants are (1) hydrated lime (calcium hydroxide), and (2) quicklime (calcium oxide).

20.12D   If someone swallowed sodium hydroxide, give large amounts of water or milk and immediately transport to a medical facility; *DO NOT INDUCE VOMITING*.

20.12E   If sodium silicate comes in contact with your skin, wash thoroughly with water, followed by washing with a 10-percent solution of ammonium chloride or 10 percent acetic acid.

Answers to questions on page 428.

20.13A   Chlorine leaks are most often found in the control valve.

20.13B   The purpose of the fusible metal plugs is to melt at 158 to 168°F. If a cylinder becomes overheated, the plugs will melt and let the gas escape rather than the cylinder bursting.

20.13C   Chlorine leaks can be detected by the odor, by the use of ammonia water on a small cloth or swab on a stick, or by the use of an aspirator containing ammonia water. (Remember not to spray ammonia into a room full of chlorine because a white cloud will form and you won't be able to see anything.) Also, a chlorine gas detector may be used.

20.13D   Carbon dioxide is a safety hazard because it is odorless, colorless, and will accumulate at the lowest possible level. Carbon dioxide will displace oxygen so you must use a self-contained breathing apparatus, not a canister gas mask.

Answers to questions on page 430.

20.14A   For handling most salts, ventilation, respiratory protection, and eye protection will prove adequate.

20.14B   First aid when liquid or dry alum gets into the eyes consists of flushing them immediately for 15 minutes with large amounts of water. Alum should be washed off the skin with water because prolonged contact will cause skin irritation.

20.14C   When exposed to moist air or light, ferric chloride decomposes and gives off hydrochloric acid.

Answers to questions on page 432.

20.15A   Potassium permanganate spills can be swept up. Flushing with water is an effective way to eliminate any residue remaining on floors.

20.15B   Powdered activated carbon is the most dangerous powder the water treatment plant operator will be exposed to.

20.15C   Activated carbon should be stored in a clean, dry, fireproof location. Keep free of dust, protect from flammable materials, and do not permit smoking in the area at any time when handling or unloading activated carbon.

20.15D   The key to preventing activated carbon fires is keeping the storage area clean and free of dust.

20.15E   Carbon fires should be controlled by carbon dioxide (CO_2) extinguishers or hoses equipped with fog nozzles. An activated carbon fire should not be doused with a stream of water. The water may cause burning carbon particles to fly, resulting in a greater fire problem.

Answers to questions on page 432.

20.17A   Safety regulations prohibit the use of common drains and sumps from chemical storage areas to avoid the possibility of chemicals reacting and producing toxic gases, explosions, and fires.

20.17B   If a polymer solution comes in contact with potassium permanganate, a fire could develop.

ANSWERS TO QUESTIONS IN LESSON 2

Answers to questions on page 436.

20.2A   Class A fires involve miscellaneous combustible materials. These include fabrics, paper, wood, dried grass, hay, and stubble.

20.2B   Foam extinguishers can control Class A and Class B fires. They can control ordinary combustibles ("A") such as fabrics, paper, wood, and grass, as well as flammable liquids and vapors ("B") such as oils, lacquers, fats, waxes, paints, petroleum products, and gas.

20.2C   An electrical fire can be extinguished by the use of carbon dioxide (CO_2) extinguishers or with a dry chemical extinguisher.

Answers to questions on page 440.

20.3A   When waxing floors use compounds containing non-slip ingredients. Warn others about newly waxed floors. Try to do cleaning and waxing during weekends or at night when foot traffic is light.

20.3B   Rags are always a problem and if they contain oils, paint or other cleaning compounds there is always the possibility of fire. The rags should be placed into a closed metal container to reduce the fire hazard.

20.3C   When operating an overhead crane, the following safety precautions must be exercised:

1. Allow only trained and authorized personnel to operate the overhead crane,
2. Inspect the circuit breaker, limit switches, condition of hook, wire rope, and other safety devices,
3. Post load limits on crane and never overload crane,
4. Check each lift for proper balance,
5. Use a standard set of hand signals,
6. Be sure everyone in vicinity wears a hard hat,
7. Allow only authorized personnel to make repairs,
8. Lock out the main power switch before repairs begin,
9. Try to avoid moving loads over populated areas, and
10. Set up monthly safety inspection forms to be filled out and placed into the maintenance file.

20.3D   Traffic can be warned that operators are working in a manhole by the use of barricades, signs, flags, lights, and other warning devices. Warning devices and procedures must conform to local and state regulations.

20.3E   Operators should always use a mechanical lifting aid (rope and bucket) for raising or lowering tools and equipment into and out of a manhole. The use of a bucket or basket will keep your hands free when climbing down into or out of a manhole.

Answers to questions on page 441.

20.3F   Operators should wear eye and ear protection when operating grinding, chipping, buffing, or pavement-breaking equipment. Sometimes when using grinding or buffing tools, operators encounter toxic dusts or fumes and therefore need respiratory protection. At other times there is a need for full face protection because of flying particles.

20.3G Operators can be protected from high noise levels by wearing approved ear protection devices.

20.3H When operating welding equipment, the operator should wear protective clothing, gloves, helmet, and goggles.

Answers to questions on page 444.

20.4A Tire wear is caused by misalignment and low inflation.

20.4B Motor vehicles should have flashlights, flares, flags, fire extinguisher, and first-aid kit.

ANSWERS TO QUESTIONS IN LESSON 3

Answers to questions on page 449.

20.5A Each operator should become familiar with the type of current and voltage in the plant in order to avoid any mistake of becoming involved with unsafe electric circuits or practices for which they are not trained. This will also permit operators to ask for a qualified person to perform any necessary repairs.

20.5B Moving parts on electric motors that require safety guards include exposed couplings, pulleys, gears, and sprockets, as well as projections such as bolts, keys, or set screws.

20.5C Two hazards due to the lack of a good lockout procedure for control panels and switchboards are (1) accidentally starting a piece of equipment exposing a fellow operator to a hazard, and (2) turning electrical power on when someone is still working on the equipment, exposing that person to danger.

20.5D Examples of stored energy that could be hazardous to operators include electrical power; air, gas, or steam pressure; water (hydraulic) pressure; spring tension; rotational forces in flywheels; and the energy in elevated machine parts if they suddenly swing free.

Answers to questions on page 451.

20.6A Washing glassware is always a potential hazard because the glassware can be broken while being washed, causing cuts, or cuts can be caused by chipped or cracked glassware. If your hands come in contact with strong acid cleaners, the acids may cause serious burns.

20.6B When handling liquid chemicals, such as acids and bases, always use safety glasses or face shields.

20.6C Never allow mercury, gasoline, oil, or organic compounds into the laboratory drains. Use only a toxic waste disposal drain system for these items. Flushing such compounds down sink drains can cause an explosion, allow toxic gases and vapors to enter the lab, or destroy the piping.

20.6D The plant operator may be exposed to radioactive compounds when calibrating sludge density meters or using research isotopes.

20.6E Never allow cold water into the hot boiler unit of a water still because it may cause the unit to break.

Answers to questions on page 452.

20.7A When entering an oxygen-deficient atmosphere, you should have an independent oxygen supply of the positive-pressure type to protect you if there are any leaks in your mask.

20.7B Respiratory apparatus must be stored outside of chlorinating, sulfur dioxide, carbon dioxide, ozone, and ammonia rooms in an unlocked cabinet. The storage cabinets must have a controlled environment to prevent deterioration of the equipment.

20.7C Independent air supply equipment should be checked out on a weekly basis, and records kept of each inspection. The record should show conditions of the hoses, regulators, air filters, compressors, helmet, and any other apparatus furnished with the system.

20.7D To obtain compliance with an eye protection program, supervisors should undertake an intense program of education, persuasion, and appeal.

20.7E An operator needs eye protection when handling many of the liquid chemicals, acids, and caustics. Many of the tests performed in the laboratory also require eye protection.

Answers to questions on page 454.

20.7F Rubber boots are needed when handling acid or caustic, or when the operator is working in wet conditions such as reservoirs, filters, or chemical tanks.

20.7G An operator should be very careful wearing gloves when working around machinery that is revolving.

20.7H Operators should never work in a filter when it is being backwashed because there is always the danger of falling into the wash-water gullet and being unable to get out before drowning.

20.7I Before taking a boat out on the water, it should be checked out for safety. The operator should check the bilge pump, ventilation in the compartments, the safety cushions, fire extinguishers, battery, and the engine. For safety equipment, check oars, life jackets, lights, mooring lines, and fuel.

Answers to questions on page 454.

20.8A Operators should be prepared for catastrophic events such as floods, tornados, hurricanes, fires, and earthquakes. Serious injury to anyone on the plant grounds is an emergency.

20.8B If a serious chemical emergency occurs, such as a chemical spill, leak, fire, exposure, or accident, phone *CHEMTREC*, 800-424-9300. Also local and state civil preparedness coordinators should be notified.

20.8C *CHEMTREC* is an emergency response service that provides immediate advice (by telephone) about what to do in a chemical emergency such as a spill, leak, fire, exposure, or accident.

OBJECTIVE TEST

Chapter 20. SAFETY

Please write your name and mark the correct answers on the answer sheet, as directed at the end of Chapter 1. There may be more than one correct answer to each multiple-choice question.

True-False

1. Safety is a form of preventive maintenance which includes equipment and machinery and its proper handling.
   1. True
   2. False

2. Hydrofluosilicic acid is a relatively weak acid which causes minor skin irritation after prolonged contact.
   1. True
   2. False

3. Nitric acid is stable when properly handled and placed into a proper container.
   1. True
   2. False

4. Always pour acid into water, never the reverse.
   1. True
   2. False

5. Bases are used to lower the pH.
   1. True
   2. False

6. From the standpoint of safety, both weak and strong bases must be given the same consideration when being handled.
   1. True
   2. False

7. Always shower after handling quicklime.
   1. True
   2. False

8. If someone ingests sodium hydroxide, induce vomiting immediately.
   1. True
   2. False

9. Hypochlorite compounds are flammable.
   1. True
   2. False

10. Always try to reuse old or used chlorine connection washers.
    1. True
    2. False

11. Chlorine lines that have become "frozen" should be quickly but carefully thawed with a welder's torch.
    1. True
    2. False

12. Acidic and basic compounds can be stored with salts.
    1. True
    2. False

13. Liquid alum is acidic and very corrosive.
    1. True
    2. False

14. Fire prevention is the best fire protection the plant operator can afford.
    1. True
    2. False

15. Always stop the vehicle's engine when fueling motor vehicles.
    1. True
    2. False

16. Once a lockout device is installed, it is not removed until repairs are complete unless removal is authorized by an appropriate official.
    1. True
    2. False

17. Never enter a confined space with an explosive atmosphere.
    1. True
    2. False

Best Answer (Select only the closest or best answer.)

18. How are bases neutralized?
    1. Dilute acids
    2. Dilute bases
    3. Salts
    4. Strong acids

19. What is the first safety measure an operator should take when entering a chlorination room?
    1. Determine location of self-contained breathing apparatus
    2. Look for chlorine leaks
    3. Make sure ventilating system is working
    4. Measure chlorine concentration in atmosphere

20. What is the most dangerous powder you will be exposed to as a treatment plant operator?
    1. Activated carbon
    2. Bentonite
    3. Polymers
    4. Potassium permanganate

21. When should water treatment plant fire hoses be used?

    1. Clean up chemical spills
    2. Cleaning settling basins
    3. Hose filters clean
    4. Only to fight fires

22. What is the operator's *BEST* approach to fire protection or prevention?

    1. Annually making a fire analysis of plant
    2. Good housekeeping
    3. Properly locating fire extinguishers
    4. Providing suitable containers for used wiping cloths

23. According to OSHA law, what type of paperwork must be completed before entering a confined space?

    1. Entry permit
    2. NPDES permit
    3. Safety and health permit
    4. Sewer-use permit

24. What is the most toxic gas encountered in manholes?

    1. Carbon monoxide
    2. Hydrogen sulfide
    3. Methane
    4. Natural gas

25. How can the hazards of fire in electric starters be reduced?

    1. Keep the starters clean
    2. Provide adequate working space around the starters
    3. Regularly overload the starters
    4. Replace indicating lights as needed

26. Which electrical ground protection device provides the greatest protection to the operator and to the equipment?

    1. Ground fault interrupter (G.F.I.)
    2. Plastic-handled screwdrivers
    3. Rubber mats to stand on
    4. Wire to rod in ground

27. How can mercury, gasoline, oil, or organic compounds be properly disposed of in a laboratory?

    1. Incineration
    2. Pour down sanitary drain
    3. Recycling
    4. Toxic waste disposal system

28. Why must storage cabinets for safety equipment have a controlled environment?

    1. Allow equipment to be available for training
    2. Keep equipment at comfortable temperature when worn
    3. Prevent deterioration of equipment
    4. Store equipment at a convenient location

29. Under what conditions must an operator use eye protection?

    1. Backwashing filters
    2. Driving vehicles
    3. Handling liquid chemicals
    4. Hosing sludge from tanks

30. What type of gloves would provide suitable protection against sparks, chips, rough material, and moderate heat?

    1. Aluminized
    2. Leather
    3. Neoprene or cork-dipped
    4. Rubber

Multiple Choice (Select all correct answers.)

31. What are an operator's general responsibilities for safety?

    1. Develop a safety program
    2. Investigate accidents
    3. Report all injuries
    4. Report observed hazards
    5. Use safe work procedures

32. What should an operator know about the safe handling of chemicals?

    1. How to feed the chemical
    2. How to make up solutions
    3. Storage of chemicals
    4. Understand the fire potential
    5. Where to purchase chemicals

33. Why is acetic acid extremely hazardous to operators?

    1. Contact with skin causes deep burns
    2. It is combustible
    3. It is very unstable at all times
    4. It reacts violently with alkaline materials
    5. Olfactory fatigue may delay detection of its presence

34. Hydrochloric acid is highly reactive with which chemicals?

    1. Amine
    2. Carbonate
    3. Glass
    4. Metals
    5. Porcelain

35. How can an operator prevent body contact with acids and bases?

    1. Face shield
    2. Rubber apron
    3. Rubber boots
    4. Rubber gloves
    5. Safety shower

36. Hypochlorite compounds may cause fires when they come in contact with which of the following items?

    1. Acids
    2. Bases
    3. Heat
    4. Organic matter
    5. Oxidizable substances

37. What tasks must an operator safely perform when dealing with gases?

    1. Connect
    2. Disconnect
    3. Handle
    4. Inhale
    5. Store

38. What steps should be taken immediately if one of the fusible plugs melts on a one-ton chlorine tank?

    1. If working alone, call for assistance
    2. Insert a new plug
    3. Position the tank with the leak on top
    4. Turn on the ventilation system
    5. Use an ammonia-soaked swab to check for leaking chlorine

39. Salts may be sources of what types of safety hazards?

    1. Burns
    2. Explosions
    3. Illness
    4. Loss of eyesight
    5. Violent chemical reactions

40. Potassium permanganate must be kept away from which chemicals and compounds?

    1. Glycol (antifreeze)
    2. Hydrochloric acid
    3. Hydrogen peroxide
    4. Sawdust
    5. Sulfuric acid

41. What are the major problems associated with the handling of powdered activated carbon?

    1. Dust
    2. Fire
    3. Regeneration
    4. Slippery
    5. Toxicity

42. Which of the following are procedures for safely handling and storing activated carbon?

    1. Increase the humidity in storage areas to control dust
    2. Install fire hoses with water jet nozzles to extinguish fires
    3. Store bags of activated carbon in single rows
    4. Use explosion-proof equipment and wiring in storage areas
    5. Warn operators to use caution when smoking near activated carbon

43. What safety questions must be considered when painting in a water treatment plant?

    1. Are there toxic compounds in the paint?
    2. How can fire hazards be avoided or minimized?
    3. Is the paint being applied by brush or spray?
    4. Is the paint exposed to drinking water?
    5. Is there sufficient ventilation?

44. What atmospheric conditions must be tested for in a confined space?

    1. Explosive gases
    2. Inert gases
    3. Nitrogen gases
    4. Oxygen deficiency
    5. Toxic gases

45. Which of the following are important safety considerations when operating gas or electric welding equipment?

    1. Atmospheric protection
    2. Fire protection
    3. Operator must be thoroughly trained
    4. Personnel protection
    5. Welding protection permit

46. Which of the following are practices performed by good defensive drivers?

    1. Always wear a seat belt
    2. Check out the vehicle before each use
    3. Do not permit others to tailgate
    4. Observe all traffic regulations
    5. Take weather conditions into account

47. Stored energy in equipment may be present in which forms?

    1. Electrical power
    2. Hydraulic pressure
    3. Pneumatic pressure
    4. Tension in a spring
    5. Unused mechanical power

End of Objective Test

CHAPTER 21

ADVANCED LABORATORY PROCEDURES

by

Jim Sequeira

TABLE OF CONTENTS

Chapter 21. ADVANCED LABORATORY PROCEDURES

Page

OBJECTIVES 465

LESSON 1

21.0 USE OF A SPECTROPHOTOMETER 466

21.1 TEST PROCEDURES* 467

    1. Algae Counts 467

    2. Calcium 468

    3. Chloride 469

    4. Color 471

    5. Dissolved Oxygen 472

    6. Fluoride 475

DISCUSSION AND REVIEW QUESTIONS 478

LESSON 2

    7. Iron (Total) 479

    8. Manganese 481

    9. Marble Test (Calcium Carbonate Saturation Test) 484

    10. Metals 485

    11. Nitrate 486

    12. pH
       by Jack Rossum 489

    13. Specific Conductance (Conductivity) 489

    14. Sulfate 490

    15. Taste and Odor 492

    16. Trihalomethanes 496

    17. Total Dissolved Solids 497

DISCUSSION AND REVIEW QUESTIONS 499

SUGGESTED ANSWERS 500

OBJECTIVE TEST 501

---

* Test Procedures in Chapter 11 (Volume I) include alkalinity, chlorine residual, chlorine demand, coliform bacteria, hardness, jar test, pH, temperature, and turbidity.

OBJECTIVES

Chapter 21.   ADVANCED LABORATORY PROCEDURES

Following completion of Chapter 21, you should be able to:

1. Explain how a spectrophotometer analyzes samples of water, and

2. Perform the following field or laboratory tests — algae counts, calcium, chloride, color, dissolved oxygen, fluoride, iron, manganese, marble test, metals, nitrate, pH, specific conductance, sulfate, taste and odor, trihalomethanes, and total dissolved solids.

CHAPTER 21.   ADVANCED LABORATORY PROCEDURES

(Lesson 1 of 2 Lessons)

21.0   USE OF A SPECTROPHOTOMETER

In the field of water analysis, many determinations such as iron, manganese, and phosphorus are based on the color intensity formed when a specific color developing reagent is added to the sample being tested. Measuring the intensity of the color enables the concentration of the substance to be determined. The simplest means of accomplishing this is through either Nessler tubes or a pocket comparator. The color developed in a sample is compared by the operator to a series of known standards, to each of which has been added the same color developing reagents. For the analysis of phosphorus present in a water sample, for example, ammonium molybdate reagent is added as the color developing reagent. If phosphorus is present, a blue color develops. The more phosphorus there is, the deeper and darker the blue color.

The human eye can detect some differences in color intensity; however, for very precise measurements an instrument called a spectrophotometer (SPEK-tro-fo-TOM-uh-ter) is used.

THE SPECTROPHOTOMETER. A spectrophotometer is an instrument generally used to measure the color intensity of a chemical solution. A spectrophotometer in its simplest form consists of a light source which is focused on a prism or other suitable light dispersion device to separate the light into its separate bands of energy. Each different wavelength or color may be selectively focused through a narrow slit. This beam of light then passes through the sample to be measured. The sample is usually contained in a glass tube called a cuvette (que-VET). Most cuvettes are standardized to have a 1.0 cm light path length; however, many other sizes are available.

After the selected beam of light has passed through the sample, it emerges and strikes a photoelectric cell. If the solution in the sample cell has absorbed any of the light, the total energy content will be reduced. If the solution in the sample cell does not absorb the light, then there will be no change in energy. When the transmitted light beam strikes the photoelectric tube, it generates an electric current that is proportional to the intensity of light energy striking it. By connecting the photoelectric tube to a galvanometer (a device for measuring electric current) with a graduated scale, a means of measuring the intensity of the transmitted beam is achieved.

The diagram at the top of the next column illustrates the working parts of a spectrophotometer.

The operator should always follow the working instructions provided with the instrument.

UNITS OF SPECTROSCOPIC MEASUREMENT. The scale on spectrophotometers is generally graduated in two ways:

(1)   In units of percent transmittance (%T), an arithmetic scale with units graded from 0 to 100%; and

(2)   In units of absorbance (A), a logarithmic scale of nonequal divisions graduated from 0.0 to 2.0.

Both the units, percent transmittance and absorbance, are associated with color intensity. That is, a sample which has a low color intensity will have a high percent transmittance but a low absorbance.

PERCENT TRANSMITTANCE

Absorbance

As illustrated above, the absorbance scale is ordinarily calibrated on the same scale as percent transmittance on spectrophotometers. The chief usefulness of absorbance lies in the fact that it is a logarithmic function rather than linear (arithmetic) and a law known as Beer's Law states that the concentration of a light-absorbing colored solution is directly proportional to absorbance over a given range of concentrations. If one were to plot a graph showing percent transmittance (%T) versus concentration on straight graph or line paper and another showing absorbance versus concentration on the same paper, the following curves (graphs) would result:

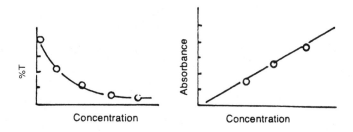

CALIBRATION CURVES: The calibration curve is used to determine the concentration of the water quality indicator (iron or manganese) contained in a sample. Three steps must be completed in order to prepare a calibration graph.

First, a series of standards must be prepared. A standard is a solution that contains a known amount of the same chemical constituent which is being determined in the sample.

Second, these standard solutions and a sample containing none of the constituent being tested for (usually distilled water and generally referred to as a blank) must be treated with the developing reagent in the same manner as the sample would be treated.

Third, using a spectrophotometer the absorbance or transmittance at the specified wavelength of the standards and blank must be determined. From the values obtained, a calibration curve of absorbance (or %T) versus concentration can be plotted. Once you have plotted these several points, you can then extend the plotted points by connecting the known points with a straight line. For example, with the data given below you could construct the following calibration curve.

Absorbance	Concentration, mg/L
0.0	0.0
0.30	0.25
0.55	0.50
0.80	0.75

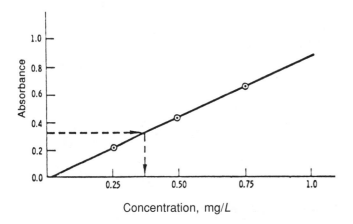

Once you have established a calibration curve for the water quality indicator in question, you can easily determine the amount of that substance contained in a solution of unknown concentration. You merely take an absorbance reading on the color developed by the unknown and locate it on the vertical axis. Draw a straight line to the right on the graph until it intersects with the experimental standard curve. Then drop a line to the horizontal axis; this value identifies the concentration of your unknown water quality indicator.

In this example, an absorbance reading of 0.32 was read on the unknown solution or sample, which indicates a concentration of about 0.37 mg/L.

QUESTIONS

Write your answers in a notebook and then compare your answers with those on page 500.

21.0A When measuring phosphorus concentrations, the intensity of what color is measured?

21.0B What are the units of measurements for spectrophotometers?

21.0C Using the previous absorbance vs. concentration calibration graph, if an absorbance of 0.60 was read on an unknown solution or sample, what would be the concentration of the unknown?

21.1 TEST PROCEDURES

1. Algae Counts

A. Discussion

The quality of water in any lake, reservoir, or stream has a very direct effect on the abundance and types of aquatic organisms found. By knowing the nature and numbers of these aquatic organisms one can obtain a good idea of the water quality. A biological method used for measuring water quality is the collection, counting, and identification of algae

contained in a particular body of water. Information from algae counts can serve one or more of the following purposes:

1. Help explain the cause of color and turbidity and the presence of tastes and odors in the water,

2. Help explain the clogging of screens or filters, and

3. Help document variability in the water quality.

Algae counting and identification may be done very simply or it may be developed into a highly technical operation. The beginner should use great caution applying the results of algae identifications until considerable experience has been gained.

Some operators perform algae counts on both the raw water and treated water. Taking algae counts on treated water is a means of studying the effectiveness of coagulation and the performance of filters. If the filters are performing properly, there should not be any countable algae in the treated water.

(Calcium)

B. Materials and Procedures

See page 10-2, *STANDARD METHODS*, 18th Edition.[1]

2. Calcium

A. Discussion

In most natural waters, calcium is the principal cation. The element is widely distributed in the common minerals of rocks and of soil. Calcium in the form of lime or calcium hydroxide may be used to soften water or to control corrosion through pH adjustment.

B. What is Tested?

Sample	Common Range, mg/L
Raw and Treated Surface Water	5 to 50
Well Water	10 to 100

C. Apparatus Required

Buret, 25 mL
Buret support
Graduated cylinder, 100 mL
Beaker, 100 mL
Magnetic stirrer
Magnetic stir-bar

D. Reagents

NOTE: Standardized solutions are commercially available for most reagents. Refer to *STANDARD METH-ODS* if you wish to prepare your own reagents.[2]

1. Sodium hydroxide (NaOH), 1 *N*.

2. Eriochrome Blue Black R indicator.

3. Standard EDTA titrant, 0.01 *M*. Standardize against Standard Calcium Solution and store in plastic polyethylene bottle.

4. Standard Calcium Solution. Store in polyethylene plastic bottle. 1 mL of this solution = 1 mg calcium hardness as $CaCO_3$ or 400.8 micrograms (μg) Ca.

5. 1 + 1 HCl: Carefully add 50 mL concentrated HCl to 50 mL distilled water.

6. Ammonium hydroxide, 3 *N*.

7. Methyl Orange indicator solution.

E. Procedure

1. Take a clean beaker and add 50 mL of sample.

2. Add 2.0 mL NaOH solution.

3. Add 0.1 to 0.2 gm indicator mixture.

4. Titrate immediately with EDTA titrant until last reddish-purple tinge disappears. Mix with magnetic stirrer during titration.

5. Calculate calcium concentration.

F. Example

Results from calcium testing of a treated water sample were as follows:

Sample size   = 50 mL

mL EDTA titrant used, A = 7.3 mL

OUTLINE OF PROCEDURE FOR CALCIUM

1. Add 50 mL to a clean beaker.

2. Add 2 mL NaOH and 0.2 gm indicator mixture.

mL OF EDTA

3. Titrate with EDTA. Mix with magnetic stirrer.

---

[1] *STANDARD METHODS FOR THE EXAMINATION OF WATER AND WASTEWATER*, 18th Edition, 1992, Product No. 10062. Available from Customer Services, American Water Works Association, 6666 W. Quincy Avenue, Denver, CO 80235. Price to members, $119.00; nonmembers, $168.00; price includes cost of shipping and handling. 19th Edition, 1995, Product No. 10071. Price to members, $147.00; nonmembers, $188.00; price includes cost of shipping and handling.
[2] See "Prepared vs. Do-It-Yourself Reagents," by Josephine W. Boyd, OPFLOW, Vol. 9, No. 10, October 1983.

(Chloride)

G. Calculation

$$mg\ Ca/L = \frac{A \times 400.8^*}{mL\ of\ sample}$$

$$= \frac{7.3\ mL \times 400.8}{50\ mL}$$

$$= 59\ mg/L$$

---

* 400.8 is a constant for this calculation. It contains the conversion units to produce mg/L.

H. Precautions

1. Titrate immediately after adding NaOH solution.

2. Use 50 mL or a smaller portion of sample diluted to 50 mL with distilled water so that the calcium content is about 5 to 10 mg.

3. For hard waters with alkalinity greater than 300 mg $CaCO_3/L$, use a smaller portion or neutralize alkalinity with acid, boiling for one minute, and cooling before beginning the titration.

I. Reference

See page 3-56, *STANDARD METHODS*, 18th Edition.

3. Chloride

A. Discussion

Chloride occurs in all natural waters, usually as a metallic salt. In most cases, the chloride content increases as mineral content increases. Mountain water supplies usually are quite low in chloride while groundwaters and valley rivers often contain a considerable amount. The maximum allowable chloride concentration of 250 mg/L in drinking water has been established for reasons of taste rather than as a safeguard against a physical or a health hazard. At concentrations above 250 mg/L, chloride may give a salty taste to the water which is objectionable to many people.

B. What is Tested?

Sample	Common Range, mg/L
Surface or Groundwater	2 to 100

C. Apparatus Required

Graduated cylinder, 100 mL
Buret, 50 mL
Erlenmeyer flask, 250 mL
Pipet, 10 mL
Magnetic stirring apparatus

D. Reagents

NOTE: Standard solutions may be purchased from chemical suppliers.

1. Chloride-free water — distilled or deionized water.

2. Potassium chromate (K_2CrO_4) indicator solution.

3. Standard Silver Nitrate Titrant, 0.0141 N.

4. Standard Sodium Chloride, 0.0141 N.

E. Procedure

1. Place 100 mL or a suitable portion of sample diluted to 100 mL in a 250-mL Erlenmeyer flask.

2. Add 1.0 mL K_2CrO_4 indicator solution.

3. Titrate with standard silver nitrate to a pinkish yellow end point. Be consistent in end point recognition. Compare with known standards of various chloride concentrations.

F. Calculation

$$Chloride\ (as\ Cl),\ mg/L = \frac{(A - B) \times N \times 35,450^*}{mL\ of\ sample}$$

A = mL $AgNO_3$ used for titration of sample

B = mL $AgNO_3$ used for blank

N = normality of $AgNO_3$

---

* 35,450 is a constant for this calculation. It contains the conversion units to produce mg/L.

G. Example

Sample size = 100 mL

A = mL $AgNO_3$ used for sample = 10.0 mL

B = mL $AgNO_3$ used for blank   = 0.4 mL

N = normality of $AgNO_3$ = 0.0141 N

$$Chloride,\ mg/L = \frac{(10.0\ mL - 0.4\ mL) \times (0.0141\ N) \times 35,450}{100\ mL}$$

$$= 48\ mg/L$$

H. Special Notes

1. Sulfide, thiosulfate, and sulfite ions interfere, but can be removed by treatment with 1 mL of 30 percent hydrogen peroxide (H_2O_2).

2. Highly colored samples must be treated with an aluminum hydroxide suspension and then filtered.

3. Orthophosphate in excess of 25 mg/L and iron in excess of 10 mg/L also interfere.

4. If the pH of the sample is not between 7 and 10, adjust with 1 N sulfuric acid or 1 N sodium hydroxide.

(Chloride)

1. Place 100 mL or other measured sample in flask.

2. Add 1 mL chromate indicator.

3. Place flask on magnetic stirrer and titrate with standard silver nitrate.

5. Procedure for standardization of $AgNO_3$:

   a. Add 10 mL (1 mg Cl) standard sodium chloride solution to a clean 250-mL Erlenmeyer flask.

   b. Add 90 mL distilled water.

   c. Titrate as in Section E above.

   d. Calculation

   $$\text{Normality, } N, \text{ } AgNO_3 = \frac{\text{mL CaCl standard x 0.0141}}{\text{mL } AgNO_3 \text{ used in titration}}$$

   e. Example

   10.0 mL NaCl standard used

   10.0 mL $AgNO_3$ used in titration

   0.0141 N = normality of NaCl standard

   $$\text{Normality, } N, \text{ } AgNO_3 = \frac{10.0 \text{ mL x 0.0141}}{10 \text{ mL}}$$

   $$= 0.0141$$

(Color)

I. Reference

See page 4-48, *STANDARD METHODS*, 18th Edition.

QUESTIONS

Write your answers in a notebook and then compare your answers with those on page 500.

21.1A   Does the quality of water in any lake, reservoir, or stream affect the abundance and types of aquatic organisms found in the water? Yes or No?

21.1B   How are calcium compounds used to treat water?

21.1C   How soon should a sample be titrated for calcium after the sodium hydroxide (NaOH) solution has been added?

21.1D   Why are concentrations of chloride above 250 mg/*L* objectionable to many people?

4. Color

A. Discussion

Color in water supplies may result from the presence of metallic ions (iron, manganese, and copper), organic matter of vegetable or soil origin, and industrial wastes. The most common colors which occur in raw water are yellow and brown. There are two general types of color found in water. True color results from the presence of dissolved organic substances or from certain minerals such as copper sulfate dissolved in the water. Suspended materials (including colloidal substances) can add what is called apparent color.

True color is normally removed or at least reduced by coagulation and chlorination or ozonation. The method given below is suitable only for the measurement of color in clear treated water supplies having a turbidity of less than one unit of turbidity. When greater amounts of turbidity are present in the sample, some form of pretreatment for turbidity removal must be used before measuring the color.

B. What is Tested?

Sample	Common Range, units
Treated Surface Water	1 to 10
Groundwater	0 to 5

C. Apparatus Required

Nessler tubes, matched, 50 m*L* tall form
Pipet, 1.0 m*L*

D. Reagents

1. Color Standard. Use a stock standard with a color of 500 units.

2. Prepare color standards by adding the following increments of stock color standard to a Nessler tube and diluting to 50 m*L*.

Color Unit Standard	m*L* of Stock Color Standard
1	0.1
2	0.2
3	0.3
4	0.4
5	0.5

Protect these standards against evaporation and contamination when not in use.

E. Procedure

1. Fill a clean matched Nessler tube to the 50 m*L* mark with sample.

2. Compare the sample with the various color standards by looking downward vertically through the tubes toward a white surface.

3. Match as closely as possible sample color with a color standard.

F. Other Procedures

Color may also be measured by the use of

1. Color comparator kits, and

2. Spectrophotometers.

G. Notes

1. If the color exceeds 70 units, dilute sample with distilled water in known proportions until the color is within range of the standards. Calculate color units by the following equation:

$$\text{Color units} = \frac{A \times 50}{B}$$

where:

A = estimated color of diluted sample

B = m*L* of sample taken from dilution

2. If turbidity is greater than one unit, consult *STANDARD METHODS* for pretreatment for turbidity removal.

H. Reference

See page 2-1, *STANDARD METHODS*, 18th Edition.

QUESTIONS

Write your answers in a notebook and then compare your answers with those on page 500.

21.1E   What are the most common colors which occur in raw water?

21.1F   How can true color be removed from water?

21.1G   When not in use, stock color standards should be protected against what?

(Dissolved Oxygen)

5. Dissolved Oxygen

A. Discussion

Dissolved oxygen (DO) is important to the water treatment plant operator for a number of reasons. In surface waters, dissolved oxygen must be present in order for fish and smaller aquatic organisms to survive. The taste of water is improved by dissolved oxygen. However, the presence of dissolved oxygen in water can contribute to corrosion of piping systems. Low or zero dissolved oxygen levels at the bottom of lakes or reservoirs often cause taste and odor problems in drinking water.

B. What is Tested?

Sample	Common Range, mg/L
Surface Water	5 to 11*
Groundwaters	0 to 2

* Some reservoirs and lakes may have zero DO near the bottom.

C. Apparatus Required

Method A (Sodium Azide Modification of Winkler Method)

Buret, graduated to 0.1 mL
Buret support
BOD bottle, 300 mL
Magnetic stirrer

Magnetic stir-bar
Pipets, 10 mL

Method B (Membrane Electrode Method)

Follow manufacturer's instructions. To ensure that the DO probe reading is accurate, the probe must be calibrated frequently. Take a sample that does not contain substances that interfere with either the probe reading or the Modified Winkler procedure. Split the sample. Measure the DO in one portion of the sample using the Modified Winkler procedure and compare this result with the DO probe reading on the other portion of the sample. Adjust the probe reading to agree with the results from the Modified Winkler procedure. To obtain good results when using a probe, you should be aware of the following *PRECAUTIONS:*

a. Periodically check the calibration of the probe,

b. Keep the membrane in the tip of the probe from drying out,

c. Dissolved inorganic salts, such as found in seawater, can influence the readings from a probe,

d. Reactive compounds, such as reactive gases and sulfur compounds, can interfere with the output of a probe, and

e. Don't place the probe directly over a diffuser because you want to measure the dissolved oxygen in the water being treated, not the oxygen in the air supply to the aerator.

OUTLINE OF PROCEDURE FOR COLOR

1. Fill Nessler tube to 50 mL.

2. Compare the sample to color standards.

(Dissolved Oxygen)

D. Reagents

(Standardized solutions may be purchased from chemical suppliers.)

1. Manganous Sulfate solution.

2. Alkaline Iodide-Sodium Azide solution.

3. Sulfuric Acid: Use concentrated reagent-grade acid (H_2SO_4). Handle carefully, since this material will burn hands and clothes. Rinse affected parts with tap water to prevent injury.

   CAUTION: When working with alkaline azide and sulfuric acid, keep a nearby water faucet running for frequent hand rinsing.

4. 0.025 N Phenylarsine Oxide (PAO) solution.

5. 0.025 N Sodium Thiosulfate solution.

   For preservation, add 0.4 gm or 1 pellet of sodium hydroxide (NaOH). Solutions of "thio" should be used within two weeks to avoid loss of accuracy due to decomposition of solution.

6. Starch solution.

E. Procedure

SODIUM AZIDE MODIFICATION OF THE WINKLER METHOD

NOTE: The sodium azide destroys nitrate which would otherwise interfere with this test.

The reagents are to be added in the quantities, order, and methods as follows:

1. Collect a sample to be tested in 300-mL BOD bottle taking special care to avoid aeration of the liquid being collected. Fill bottle completely and stopper.

2. Remove stopper and add 1 mL of manganous sulfate solution below surface of the liquid.

3. Add 1 mL of alkaline iodide-sodium azide solution below the surface of the liquid.

4. Replace the stopper, avoid trapping air bubbles, and mix well by inverting the bottle several times. Repeat this mixing after the floc has settled halfway. Allow the floc to settle halfway a second time.

5. Acidify with 1 mL of concentrated sulfuric acid by allowing the acid to run down the neck of the bottle above the surface of the liquid.

6. Restopper and mix well until the precipitate has dissolved. The solution will then be ready to titrate. Handle the bottle carefully to avoid acid burns.

7. Pour 201 mL from bottle into an Erlenmeyer flask.

8. If the solution is brown in color, titrate with 0.025 N PAO until the solution is a pale yellow color. Add a small quantity of starch indicator and proceed with Step 10. (Note: Either PAO or 0.025 N sodium thiosulfate can be used.)

9. If the solution has no brown color, or is only slightly colored, add a small quantity of starch indicator. If no blue color develops, there is zero dissolved oxygen. If a blue color does develop, proceed to Step 10.

10. Titrate to the first disappearance of the blue color. Record the number of mL of PAO used.

11. The amount of oxygen dissolved in the original solution will be equal to the number of mL of PAO used in the titration provided significant interfering substances are not present.

mg DO/L = mL PAO

F. Example

A sample is collected from just upstream of a river intake to a water treatment facility. The water temperature is 18°C. The sample is tested for DO and the operator uses 9.1 mL of 0.025 N PAO titrant.

G. Calculation

The DO titration of the 201 mL sample required 9.1 mL of 0.025 N PAO. Therefore, the dissolved oxygen (DO) concentration in the sample is 9.1 mg/L.

The percent saturation of DO in the river can be calculated using the dissolved oxygen saturation values given in Table 21.1. Note that as the temperature of water increases, the DO saturation value (Saturation column) decreases. Table 21.1 gives 100 percent DO saturation values for temperatures in °C and °F.

$$\text{DO Saturation, \%} = \frac{\text{DO of Sample, mg/L} \times 100\%}{\text{DO at 100\% Saturation, mg/L}}$$

For example, given

$$\text{DO Saturation, \%} = \frac{9.1 \text{ mg/L}}{9.5 \text{ mg/L}} \times 100\%$$

$$= 0.96 \times 100\%$$

$$= 96\%$$

where

9.1 mg/L = DO of Sample

9.5 mg/L = DO at 100% Saturation at 18°C (river temperature)

(Dissolved Oxygen)

OUTLINE OF PROCEDURE FOR DO

1. Take 300 mL sample.
2. Add 1 mL MnSO₄ below surface.
3. Add 1 mL KI + NaOH below surface.
4. Mix by inverting.

Brown floc; DO present.

White floc; no DO.

5. Add 1 mL H₂SO₄.

Reddish-brown iodine solution.

Titration of Iodine Solution:

1. Pour 201 mL into flask.
2. Titrate with PAO or Sodium Thiosulfate.

Reddish-Brown

Pale Yellow

3. Add Starch Indicator.

Blue

Clear

End Point

(Fluoride)

TABLE 21.1
EFFECT OF TEMPERATURE ON
DISSOLVED OXYGEN SATURATION FOR A
CHLORIDE CONCENTRATION OF ZERO mg/L

°C	°F	DO at 100% Saturation, mg/L
0	32.0	14.6
1	33.8	14.2
2	35.6	13.8
3	37.4	13.5
4	39.2	13.1
5	41.0	12.8
6	42.8	12.5
7	44.6	12.2
8	46.4	11.9
9	48.2	11.6
10	50.0	11.3
11	51.8	11.1
12	53.6	10.8
13	55.4	10.6
14	57.2	10.4
15	60.0	10.2
16	61.8	10.0
17	63.6	9.7
18	65.4	9.5
19	67.2	9.4
20	68.0	9.2
21	69.8	9.0
22	71.6	8.8
23	73.4	8.7
24	75.2	8.5
25	77.0	8.4

H. Precautions

1. Samples for dissolved oxygen measurements should be collected very carefully. Do not let sample remain in contact with air or be agitated. Collect samples in a 300-mL BOD bottle. Avoid entraining (trapping) or dissolving atmospheric oxygen.

2. When sampling from a water line under pressure, attach a tube to the tap and extend tube to bottom of bottle. Let bottle overflow two or three times its volume and replace glass stopper so no air bubbles are entrapped.

3. Use suitable sampler for streams, reservoirs, or tanks of moderate depth such as that shown in Figure 21.1. Use a Kemmerer-type sampler for samples collected from depths greater than 6½ feet (2 m).

4. Always record temperature of water at time of sampling.

5. Use the proper bottle with matched stopper.

6. When working with a lake or reservoir, examine the temperature and DO profile (measure temperature and DO at surface and at various depths all the way down to the bottom).

7. Measure the DO in the sample as soon as possible.

I. Reference

See page 4-100, *STANDARD METHODS*, 18th Edition.

6. Fluoride

A. Discussion

Fluoride may occur naturally or it may be added in controlled amounts. The concentration of fluoride in most natural waters is less than 1.0 mg/L. There are, however, several areas in the United States which have natural fluoride concentrations as high as 30 mg/L. The importance of fluoride in forming human teeth and the role of fluoride intake from drinking water in controlling the characteristics of tooth structure has been realized only within the past 40 to 50 years. Studies have shown that a fluoride concentration of approximately 1.0 mg/L reduces dental caries of young people without harmful effects on health.

B. What is Tested?

Sample	Common Range, mg/L
Fluoridated Water	0.8 to 1.2

C. Apparatus Required

Spectrophotometer for use at 570 nanometers wavelength
Pipets, 5 mL
Flasks, Erlenmeyer, 125 mL

D. Reagents

1. Stock fluoride solution. 1.0 mL = 0.100 mg F.

2. Standard fluoride solution: Dilute 100 mL stock fluoride solution to 1,000 mL with distilled water; 1.0 mL = 0.010 mg F.

3. SPADNS solution. This solution is stable indefinitely if protected from direct sunlight.

4. Zirconyl-acid reagent.

5. Acid zirconyl-SPADNS reagent: Mix equal volumes of SPADNS solution and zirconyl-acid reagent. The combined reagent is stable for at least 2 years.

6. Reference solution: Add 10 mL SPADNS solution to 100 mL distilled water. Dilute 7 mL concentrated HCl to 10 mL and add to the diluted SPADNS solution. The resulting solution, used for setting the instrument reference point (zero), is stable and may be reused indefinitely. Alternatively, use a prepared standard as a reference.

7. Sodium arsenite solution. (*CAUTION*: Toxic — avoid ingestion.)

(Fluoride)

Fig. 21.1   DO sampler

(Reprinted from *STANDARD METHODS*, 15th Edition, by
permission. Copyright 1980, the American Public Health Association)

E. Procedure

1. Measure 50 m*L* of sample and add to a clean 125-m*L* Erlenmeyer flask. (If sample contains residual chlorine, add one drop NaAsO$_2$ solution per 0.1 mg chlorine residual and mix.)

2. Add 5.0 m*L* each of SPADNS solution and zirconyl-acid reagent, or 10.0 m*L* acid zirconyl-SPADNS reagent. Mix.

3. Set spectrophotometer to 0.730 absorbance with reference solution containing zero mg/*L* of fluoride (see G. Example).

4. Read absorbance at 570 nm with spectrophotometer and determine the amount of fluoride from standard curve.

NOTE: A colorimeter may also be used to measure fluoride.

F. Construction of Standard Calibration Curve

1. Using the standard fluoride solution, prepare the following standards in 100 m*L* volumetric flasks.

m*L* of Standard Fluoride Solution Placed in 100 m*L* Volumetric Flask	Fluoride Concentration, mg/*L*
5.0	0.50
7.5	0.75
10.0	1.00
12.5	1.25

2. Dilute flasks to 100 m*L*.

3. Transfer 50 m*L* to 125-m*L* Erlenmeyer flask.

4. Determine amount of fluoride as outlined previously.

(Fluoride)

5. Prepare a standard curve by plotting the absorbance values of standards versus the corresponding fluoride concentrations.

G. Example

Results from a series of tests for fluoride were as follows:

Flask No.	Sample	Volume, mg/L	Absorbance
1	Distilled Water	50	0.730
2	C Street Well	50	0.470
3	Plant Effluent	50	0.520
4	0.5 mg/L F Standard	50	0.625
5	0.75 mg/L F Standard	50	0.560
6	1.0 mg/L F Standard	50	0.500
7	1.25 mg/L F Standard	50	0.444

H. Calculation

1. Prepare a standard curve by using data from prepared standards. From above example:

Fluoride Concentration, mg/L	Absorbance
0.0	0.730
0.5	0.625
0.75	0.560
1.0	0.500
1.25	0.444

The graph below is a result of plotting concentration of fluoride standards versus their corresponding absorbance.

OUTLINE OF PROCEDURE FOR FLUORIDE

1. Measure 50 mL of sample into flask. Dechlorinate, if necessary.

2. Add 5 mL each of SPADNS solution and zirconyl-acid reagent.

3. Measure absorbance at 570 nm with spectrophotometer.

(Fluoride)

2. Obtain concentration of unknown samples from curve.

FLUORIDE, mg/*L*

PLANT EFFLUENT = 0.90 mg/*L*
C STREET WELL = 1.12 mg/*L*

I. Precautions

1. Whenever any of the following substances are present in the listed quantities, the sample must be distilled prior to analysis.

Substance	Concentration, mg/*L*
Alkalinity	5,000
Aluminum	0.1
Chloride	7,000
Iron	10
Hexametaphosphate	1.0
Phosphate	16
Sulfate	200

2. Samples and standards should be at the same temperature throughout color development.

J. Reference

See page 4-62, *STANDARD METHODS*, 18th Edition.

QUESTIONS

Write your answers in a notebook and then compare your answers with those on page 500.

21.1H Why is the presence of dissolved oxygen (DO) in water in piping systems of concern to operators?

21.1I What is the common range of fluoride in fluoridated drinking water?

Please answer the discussion and review questions next.

DISCUSSION AND REVIEW QUESTIONS

Chapter 21. ADVANCED LABORATORY PROCEDURES

(Lesson 1 of 2 Lessons)

At the end of each lesson in this chapter you will find some discussion and review questions. The purpose of these questions is to indicate to you how well you understand the material in the lesson. Write the answers to these questions in your notebook before continuing.

1. What is the purpose of spectrophotometer calibration curves?

2. How would you prepare a spectrophotometer calibration graph?

3. Why are algae counts in raw water important to operators?

4. The maximum allowable chloride concentration in drinking water has been established on what basis?

5. What are the two general types of color found in water and what is the cause of each type?

6. Why is dissolved oxygen (DO) in water important to the treatment plant operator?

7. What precautions would you take when collecting a lake sample for a dissolved oxygen measurement?

8. How does fluoride get into drinking waters?

CHAPTER 21.   ADVANCED LABORATORY PROCEDURES

(Lesson 2 of 2 Lessons)

7. Iron (Total)

A. Discussion

Iron is an abundant and widespread constituent of rocks and soils. The most common form of iron in solution in groundwater and in water under anaerobic conditions (bottom of a lake or reservoir) is the ferrous ion, Fe^{2+}. Ferric iron can occur in soils, in aerated water, and in acid solutions as Fe^{3+}, ferric hydroxide and polymeric forms depending upon pH. Above pH of 4.8, however, the solubility of the ferric species is less than 0.1 mg/L. Colloidal ferric hydroxide is commonly present in surface water and small quantities may persist even in water that appears clear.

Iron in a domestic water supply can stain laundry, concrete, and porcelain. A bitter astringent taste can be detected by some people at levels above 0.3 mg/L. When iron reacts with oxygen, a red precipitate (rust) is formed.

B. What is Tested?

Source	Common Range, mg/L
Untreated Surface Water	0.10 to 1.0
Treated Surface Water	<0.01 to 0.20
Groundwater	<0.01 to 10

C. Apparatus Required

Spectrophotometer for use at 510 nm
Acid-washed glassware. Wash all glassware with concentrated HCl and rinse with distilled water to remove deposits of iron oxide.
Flasks, Erlenmeyer, 125 mL
Pipets, 5 and 10 mL
Flasks, Volumetric, 100 mL
Hot plate

D. Reagents

Use reagents low in iron. Use iron-free distilled water. Store reagents in glass-stoppered bottles. The hydrochloric acid and ammonium acetate solutions are stable indefinitely if tightly stoppered. The hydroxylamine, phenanthroline, and stock iron solutions are stable for several months. The standard iron solutions are not stable; prepare daily as needed by diluting the stock solution. Visual standards in Nessler tubes are stable for several months if sealed and protected from light.

1. Hydrochloric acid, HCl.

2. Hydroxylamine solution.

3. Ammonium acetate buffer solution. Because even a good grade of $NH_4C_2H_3O_2$ contains a significant amount of iron, prepare new reference standards with each buffer preparation.

4. Sodium acetate solution.

5. Phenanthroline solution. (*NOTE:* One milliliter of this reagent is sufficient for no more than 100 μg Fe.)

6. Stock iron solution: 1.00 mL = 0.200 mg Fe.

7. Standard iron solutions. Prepare daily for use. Pipet 50.00 mL stock solution into a one-liter volumetric flask and dilute to mark with iron-free distilled water; 1.00 mL = 0.010 mg Fe.

E. Procedure

For Total Iron

1. Measure 50 mL of thoroughly mixed sample into a 125-mL Erlenmeyer flask.

2. Add 2 mL concentrated HCl and 1 mL hydroxylamine solution.

3. Heat to boiling. Boil sample until volume is reduced to 20 mL. Cool to room temperature.

4. Transfer to 100-mL volumetric flask.

5. Add 10 mL acetate buffer solution and 2 mL phenanthroline solution. Dilute to 100-mL mark with iron-free distilled water. Mix thoroughly.

6. After 15 minutes, measure the absorbance at 510 nm and determine the amount of iron from the standard curve.

F. Construction of Standard Calibration Curve

1. Using the standard solution, prepare the following standards in 100 mL volumetric flasks.

mL of Standard Iron Solution Placed in 100 mL Volumetric Flask	Iron Concentration, mg/L
0	0
1.0	0.10
2.5	0.25
5.0	0.50
7.5	0.75
10.0	1.00

2. Dilute flasks to 100 mL.

(Iron)

OUTLINE OF PROCEDURE FOR IRON

1. Measure 50 mL into flask.

2. Add 2 mL conc. HCl and 1 mL hydroxylamine solution.

3. Heat to boiling. Reduce volume to 20 mL. Cool.

4. Transfer to 100-mL volumetric flask.

5. Add 10 mL acetate buffer and 2 mL phenanthroline solution. Dilute to 100 mL.

6. Measure absorbance at 510 nm with spectrophotometer.

3. Transfer 50 mL to 100-mL volumetric flask.

4. Add 1.0 mL hydroxylamine solution and 1 mL acetate solution to each flask.

5. Dilute to about 75 mL, add 10 mL phenanthroline solution, dilute to 100 mL mark. Mix thoroughly.

6. Measure absorbance at 510 nm against the reference blank.

7. Prepare a standard curve by plotting the absorbance values of standards versus the corresponding iron concentrations.

G. Example

A series of tests for total iron produced these results:

Flask #	Sample	Absorbance
1	Distilled Water	0.000
2	Plant Clear Well	0.100
3	River Sample	0.420
4	0.10 mg/L Fe Standard	0.066
5	0.25 mg/L Fe Standard	0.161
6	0.50 mg/L Fe Standard	0.328
7	0.75 mg/L Fe Standard	0.495
8	1.00 mg/L Fe Standard	0.658

H. Calculation

1. Prepare a standard curve by using data from prepared standards. From the above example:

Concentration Iron, mg/L	Absorbance
0.0	0.000
0.10	0.066
0.25	0.161
0.50	0.328
0.75	0.495
1.00	0.658

The graph below is a result of plotting concentration of standards versus their corresponding absorbance.

2. Obtain concentration of unknown clear well and river samples from curve.

PLANT CLEAR WELL = 0.16 mg/L Fe
RIVER SAMPLE = 0.66 mg/L Fe

I. Notes

1. Iron in well water or tap samples may vary in concentration and form with the duration and degree of flushing before and during sampling.

2. For precise determination of total iron, use a separate container for sample collection. Treat with acid at time of collection to place iron in solution and prevent deposition on walls of sample container.

3. Exercise caution when handling sulfuric acid.

J. Reference

See page 3-65, *STANDARD METHODS*, 18th Edition.

8. Manganese

A. Discussion

Although manganese is much less abundant than iron in the earth's crust, it is one of the most common elements and

(Manganese)

widely distributed in rocks and soils. Some groundwaters that contain objectionable amounts of iron also contain considerable amounts of manganese, but groundwaters that contain more manganese than iron are rather unusual. Manganese in surface waters occurs both in suspension and as a soluble complex. Although rarely present in excess of 1 mg/L, manganese imparts objectionable stains to laundry and plumbing fixtures. Manganese will also cause stains on the walls of tanks and driveways in treatment plants.

B. What is Tested?

Source	Common Range, mg/L
Treated and Untreated Surface Water	<0.01 to 0.10
Groundwater	<0.01 to 1.0

C. Apparatus Required

Spectrophotometer for use at 525 nm
Hot plate
Flask, Erlenmeyer, 250 mL
Pipets, 5 and 10 mL
Flask, Volumetric, 100 and 500 mL

D. Reagents

1. Special reagent.

2. Ammonium persulfate, $(NH_4)_2S_2O_8$, solid.

3. Standard manganese solution. 1 mL = 0.01 mg Mn. Prepare dilute solution daily.

4. 1% HCl: Add 10 mL concentrated HCl carefully to 990 mL distilled water.

5. Hydrogen peroxide, H_2O_2, 30 percent.

E. Procedure

1. Measure 100 mL of thoroughly mixed sample into a 250-mL Erlenmeyer flask which has been marked with a line at the 90-mL level.

2. Add 5 mL special reagent and 1 drop H_2O_2.

3. Concentrate to 90 mL by boiling. Add 1 gram ammonium persulfate. Cool immediately under water tap.

4. Dilute to 100 mL.

5. Measure the absorbance at 525 nm with a spectrophotometer and determine the amount of manganese from the standard curve.

F. Construction of Calibration Curve

1. Using the standard manganese solution, prepare the following standards in 100-mL volumetric flasks.

mL of Standard Manganese Solution Placed in 100-mL Volumetric Flask	Manganese Concentration, mg/L
0	0
1.0	0.10
2.0	0.20
3.0	0.30
4.0	0.40

2. Dilute flasks to 100 mL.

3. Transfer to 250-mL Erlenmeyer flask.

4. Determine amount of manganese as outlined previously.

5. Prepare a standard curve by plotting the absorbance values of standards versus the corresponding manganese concentrations.

G. Example

Results from a series of tests for manganese were as follows:

Flask	Sample	Absorbance
1	Distilled Water	0.000
2	Plant Effluent	0.000
3	Jones St. Well	0.030
4	0.05 mg/L Mn Standard	0.009
5	0.10 mg/L Mn Standard	0.018
6	0.20 mg/L Mn Standard	0.036
7	0.30 mg/L Mn Standard	0.053
8	0.40 mg/L Mn Standard	0.071

H. Calculation

1. Prepare a standard curve by using data from prepared standards. From the above example:

Concentration Manganese, mg/L	Absorbance
0.0 (distilled water)	0.000
0.05	0.009
0.10	0.018
0.20	0.036
0.30	0.053
0.40	0.071

The graph below is the result of plotting concentration of standards versus their corresponding absorbance.

MANGANESE, mg/L

(Manganese)

OUTLINE OF PROCEDURE FOR MANGANESE

1. Measure 100 mL into flask.

2. Add 5 mL special reagent and 1 drop H_2O_2.

3. Concentrate to 90 mL, then add 1 gm ammonium persulfate. Dilute to 100 mL after cooling.

4. Measure absorbance at 525 nm with spectrophotometer.

2. Obtain concentration of unknown plant effluent and well sample from curve.

PLANT EFFLUENT = <0.01 mg/L Mn
JONES ST. WELL   = 0.17 mg/L Mn

I. Notes

1. If turbidity or interfering color is present, use the following "bleaching" method: as soon as the spectrophotometer reading has been made, add 0.05 mL hydrogen peroxide solution directly to the optical cell. Mix and read again as soon as the color has faded. Deduct absorbance of bleached solution from initial absorbance to obtain absorbance due to manganese.

2. Determine manganese as soon as possible after sample collection. If this is not possible, acidify sample with nitric acid to pH less than 2.

J. Reference

See page 3-74, *STANDARD METHODS*, 18th Edition.

QUESTIONS

Write your answers in a notebook and then compare your answers with those on page 500.

21.1J   Iron in a domestic water supply may cause what problems?

21.1K   Why must all glassware be acid washed when analyzing samples for iron?

(Marble Test)

21.1L   In what forms does manganese occur in surface waters?

21.1M   If the manganese concentration in a sample cannot be measured immediately, what would you do?

9. Marble Test (Calcium Carbonate Saturation Test)

A. Discussion

The Marble Test is used to determine the degree to which a sample of water is saturated with calcium carbonate. Marble Test results are used in the lime-soda softening process and to control corrosion. Water in intimate contact with powdered calcium carbonate (calcite) will approach saturation. The water being tested should not be exposed to atmospheric carbon dioxide. The Marble Test must be conducted at the specific temperature because the solubility of calcium carbonate varies with temperature. However, equipment that will maintain a constant temperature (either lower or higher than room temperature) while mixing the solution is not commonly available in water treatment plants. The only other way to keep a reasonably uniform temperature is to run the test as rapidly as possible.

B. What is Tested?

Source	Common Range*
Untreated Surface Water	− 1 to +1
Treated Surface Water	− 0.2 to +0.2
Well Water	− 0.1 to +1

* Initial pH − Final pH

C. Apparatus Required

Bottle, BOD, 300 mL
Magnetic stirrer
Stir-bar
Thermometer
Funnel, glass, 125 mm
Filter paper, Whatman #50 (18.5 inch)
Equipment for determining pH and hardness

D. Reagents

1. Calcium carbonate, reagent grade.

2. Reagents for determining pH and hardness.

E. Procedure

1. Measure the temperature of the water to be tested.

2. Measure the pH, hardness and, if desired, the alkalinity of the sample being tested.

3. Insert the stirring bar in the BOD bottle and fill with the water being tested. Adjust the water temperature to within 1°C of the initial temperature. Add approximately one (1) gram of calcium carbonate and stir for five minutes at a rate high enough to keep the calcium carbonate in suspension and the sample vigorously agitated.

4. Recheck the temperature. If the temperature has changed more than one degree Celsius, repeat the stirring with a fresh sample whose temperature has been adjusted so that the final temperature will be within one degree Celsius of the initial temperature.

5. Immediately measure the final pH.

6. Filter the remaining sample. Determine the hardness and, if desired, the final alkalinity on the filtrate (water that passed through the filter).

F. Example

Results from a series of tests for the calcium carbonate precipitation potential were as follows:

Filtered Water Sample

Initial Temperature	14°C
Final Temperature	14°C
Initial pH	8.7
Final pH	9.1
Initial Hardness	34 mg/L
Final Hardness	38 mg/L
Initial Alkalinity	24 mg/L
Final Alkalinity	27 mg/L

G. Calculation

Calcium Carbonate
Precipitation   = Initial Hardness, mg/L − Final Hardness, mg/L
Potential, mg/L

The Langelier Index[3] is approximately equal to the initial pH − final pH. If the value of this index is less than 0.2, this value will indicate that the water is very near the saturation level. In any event, the sign of this value will be the same as the sign of the Langelier Index. That is to say, both the Langelier Index and the calcium carbonate precipitation potential will be negative if the water is undersaturated, and positive if the water is supersaturated.

---

[3] *Langelier Index (L.I.).   An index reflecting the equilibrium pH of a water with respect to calcium and alkalinity. This index is used in stabilizing water to control both corrosion and the deposition of scale.*

   Langelier Index = pH − pH$_s$
      where pH = actual pH of the water, and
         pH$_s$ = pH at which water having the same alkalinity and calcium content is just saturated with calcium carbonate.

(Marble Test)

OUTLINE OF PROCEDURE FOR MARBLE TEST

1. Measure temperature, pH, hardness, and alkalinity of sample being tested.

2. Transfer to BOD bottle and add 1 gm calcium carbonate. Mix.

3. Measure final pH and temperature.

4. Filter.

5. Determine hardness and alkalinity of filtrate.

From the example above:

Calcium Carbonate Precipitation Potential, mg/L = Initial Hardness, mg/L – Final Hardness, mg/L

= 34 mg/L – 38 mg/L

= – 4 mg/L

Langelier Index ≅ Initial pH – Final pH

≅ 8.7 – 9.1

≅ – 0.4

This water is undersaturated (and therefore corrosive) with respect to calcium carbonate.

Also see page 2-28, *STANDARD METHODS*, 18th Edition.

10. Metals

A. Discussion

The presence of certain metals in drinking water can be a matter of serious concern because of the toxic properties of these materials. The analyses of these metals are generally done by using atomic absorption spectroscopy or colorimetric methods. The term "metals" includes the following elements:

Aluminum	Cobalt	Potassium
Antimony	Copper	Selenium
Arsenic	Iron	Silver
Barium	Lead	Sodium
Beryllium	Magnesium	Thallium
Cadmium	Manganese	Tin
Calcium	Mercury	Titanium
Chromium	Molybdenum	Vanadium
	Nickel	Zinc

(Nitrate)

B. Reference

For materials and procedures see page 3-1, *STANDARD METHODS*, 18th Edition.

QUESTIONS

Write your answers in a notebook and then compare your answers with those on page 500.

21.1N Why is temperature important when running the Marble Test?

21.1O The results from the Marble Test produce an initial pH of 8.9 and a final pH of 8.6. Would this water be considered corrosive?

21.1P How are the concentrations of most metals in water measured?

11. Nitrate

A. Discussion

Nitrate represents the most completely oxidized form of nitrogen found in water. High levels of nitrate in raw water samples indicate biological wastes in the final stage of stabilization or runoff from fertilized areas. High nitrate levels degrade water quality by stimulating excessive algal growth. Drinking water that contains excessive amounts of nitrate can cause infant methemoglobinemia (blue babies). For this reason, a level of 10 mg/L (as nitrogen) has been established as a maximum level. The procedure given below measures the amount of both nitrate and nitrite nitrogen present in a sample by reducing all nitrate to nitrite through the use of a copper-cadmium column. The total nitrate (any nitrite present originally plus the reduced nitrate) is then measured colorimetrically.

B. What is Tested?

Sample	Common Range, mg/L
Treated Surface Water	<0.1 to 5
Groundwater	0.5 to 10

C. Apparatus

Reduction column. The column in Figure 21.2 was constructed from a 100-mL volumetric pipet by removing the top portion. This column may also be constructed from two pieces of tubing joined end to end. A 10-cm length of 3-cm I.D. tubing is joined to a 25-cm length of 3.5-mm I.D. tubing. A column may be purchased from HACH Company, PO Box 608, Loveland, CO 80539-0608. Catalog No. 14563-00. $157.50 plus $8.00 shipping and handling.

Spectrophotometer for use at 540 nm, providing a light path of 1 cm or longer
Beakers, 125 mL
Glass wool
Glass-fiber filter or 0.45-micron membrane filter
Filter holder assembly
Filter flask
pH meter
Separatory funnel, 250 mL
Pipets, volumetric, 1, 2, 5, and 10 mL

D. Reagents

1. Granulated cadmium: 40 to 60 mesh.

2. Copper-Cadmium: The cadmium granules (new or used) are cleaned with 6 N HCl and copperized with a 2-percent solution of copper sulfate in the following manner:

    a. Wash the cadmium with 6 N HCl and rinse with distilled water. The color of the cadmium should be silver.

    b. Swirl 25 gm cadmium in 100-mg/L portions of a 2-percent solution of copper sulfate for 5 minutes or until the blue color partially fades, decant, and repeat with fresh copper until a brown precipitate forms.

    c. Wash the copper-cadmium with distilled water at least 10 times to remove all the precipitated copper. The color of the cadmium should now be black.

3. Preparation of reaction column: Insert a glass wool plug into the bottom of the reduction column and fill with distilled water. Add sufficient copper-cadmium granules to produce a column 18.5 cm in length. Maintain a level of distilled water above the copper-cadmium granules to eliminate entrapment of air. Wash the column with 200 mL of dilute ammonium chloride-EDTA solution (reagent 5). The column is then activated by passing through the column 100 mL of solution composed of 25 mL of a 1.0-mg/L NO$_2$-N standard and 75 mL of concentrated ammonium chloride-EDTA solution. Use a flow rate of 7 to 10 mL per minute. Collect the reduced standard until the level of solution is 0.5 cm above the top of the granules. Close the screw clamp to stop flow. Discard the reduced standard.

4. Measure about 40 mL of concentrated ammonium chloride-EDTA and pass through column at 7 to 10 mL per minute to wash nitrate standard off column. Always leave at least 0.5 cm of liquid above top of granules. The column is now ready for use.

5. Dilute ammonium chloride-EDTA solution. Dilute 300 mL of concentrated ammonium chloride-EDTA solution (reagent 4) to 500 mL with distilled water.

6. Color reagent.

7. Zinc sulfate solution.

8. Sodium hydroxide, 6 N.

9. Ammonium hydroxide, concentrated.

10. Hydrochloric acid, 6 N. Dilute 50 mL concentrated HCl to 100 mL with distilled water.

11. Copper sulfate solution, 2 percent.

12. Nitrate stock solution. 1.0 mL = 1.00 mg NO$_3$-N. Preserve with 2 mL of chloroform per liter. This solution is stable for at least six months.

(Nitrate)

Fig. 21.2 *Reduction column*

(Nitrate)

13. Nitrate standard solution. 1.0 mL = 0.01 mg NO$_3$-N. Dilute 10.0 mL of nitrate stock solution (reagent 12) to 1,000 mL with distilled water.

14. Chloroform.

E. Procedure

Removal of Interferences (if necessary).

1. Turbidity removal. Use one of the following methods to remove suspended matter that can clog the reduction column.

    a. Filter sample through a glass-fiber filter or a 0.45-micron pore size filter as long as the pH is less than 8, or

    b. Add 1 mL zinc solution (reagent 7) to 100 mL sample and mix thoroughly. Add enough (usually 8 to 10 drops) sodium hydroxide solution (reagent 8) to obtain a pH of 10.5. Let treated sample stand a few minutes to allow the heavy flocculant precipitate to settle. Clarify by filtering through a glass-fiber filter.

Reduction of Nitrate to Nitrite.

1. Using a pH meter adjust the pH of sample (or standard) to between 5 and 9 either with concentrated HCl or concentrated NH$_4$OH.

2. To 25 mL of sample (or standard) or aliquot diluted to 25 mL, add 75 mL of concentrated ammonium chloride-EDTA solution and mix.

3. Pour sample into column and collect reduced sample at a rate of 7 to 10 mL per minute.

4. Discard the first 25 mL. Collect the rest of the sample (approximately 70 mL) in the original sample flask. Reduced samples should not be allowed to stand longer than 15 minutes before addition of color reagent.

5. Add 2.0 mL of color reagent to 50 mL of sample. Allow 10 minutes for color development. Within two hours measure the absorbance at 540 nm against a reagent blank (50 mL distilled water to which 2.0 mL color reagent has been added).

F. Construction of Standard Calibration Graph

1. Prepare working standards by pipeting the following volumes of nitrate standard solution into each of five 100-mL volumetric flasks.

Add This Volume of Nitrate Standard Solution to 100-mL Flask	Concentration of NO$_3$-N in mg/L
0.0	0.00
1.0	0.10
2.0	0.20
5.0	0.50
10.0	1.00

Dilute each to 100 mL with distilled water and mix.

2. Determine the amount of nitrate-nitrite as outlined above in the procedure for reduction of nitrate to nitrite.

3. Plot on a sheet of graph paper the absorbance versus concentration.

G. Example

Results from the analyses of samples and working standards for nitrate-nitrite were as follows:

Flask #		Volume	Absorbance
1	Jones St. Well	25 mL	0.440
2	Blank (distilled water)	25 mL	0.00
3	0.10 mg/L NO$_3$-N Standard	25 mL	0.075
4	0.20 mg/L NO$_3$-N Standard	25 mL	0.142
5	0.50 mg/L NO$_3$-N Standard	25 mL	0.355
6	1.00 mg/L NO$_3$-N Standard	25 mL	0.700

H. Calculation

1. Using graph paper, plot the absorbance values of working standards versus their known concentrations. For example, from the above data the following graph can be constructed.

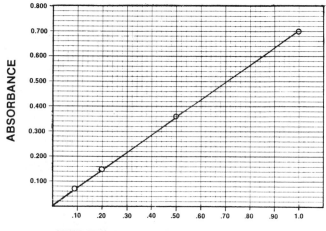

NITRATE & NITRITE-NITROGEN, mg/L

2. Read concentration of NO$_3^-$ + NO$_2^-$ nitrogen from graph shown below.

mg/L nitrate + nitrite nitrogen in sample = 0.62 mg/L

NITRATE & NITRITE-NITROGEN, mg/L at the Jones Street Well

3. Determine concentration of nitrite-nitrogen (NO_2-N) in sample using nitrite procedure.

4. Subtract nitrite from NO_2^- + NO_3^- nitrogen concentration. The result is the amount of nitrate nitrogen in sample.

5. For example, if the sample of Jones St. Well used in the above example contained no nitrite nitrogen then the nitrate nitrogen (NO_3-N) would be 0.62 mg/L.

I. Notes

1. If concentration of nitrate in the sample is greater than 1 mg/L, then the sample must be diluted.

2. Cadmium metal is highly toxic thus caution must be exercised in its use. Rubber gloves should be used whenever it is handled.

J. Reference

See page 4-89, *STANDARD METHODS*, 18th Edition.

12. pH
by Jack Rossum

DISCUSSION

This discussion is presented to give you a better understanding of what a pH value actually represents. Procedures for measuring pH are given in Volume I, Chapter 11, "Laboratory Procedures."

Pure water dissociates according to the following reaction:

$$H_2O = H^+ + OH^-$$

At 25°C and a pH of 7, the activity of the hydrogen ion is equal to the activity of the hydroxyl ion at .000 000 1 moles/liter. "Activity" is a term used by chemists to allow real atoms, molecules, and ions to behave as if they were perfect particles (having zero size). Activity is obtained by multiplying the concentration by an activity coefficient. The value of the activity coefficient depends on the electrical charge on the particle, the temperature, and the other substances dissolved in the water. For hydrogen ion the activity coefficient at 25°C varies from 0.996 in pure water to 0.900 in water containing 400 mg/L of dissolved solids. Activities are expressed in moles per liter which is assumed to be the number of grams per liter since the molecular weight of hydrogen ion is 1.008 (almost 1.0).

When the activities of the hydrogen and hydroxyl ions are equal, the solution is neutral. If hydrogen ions are in excess, the solution is acid and if hydroxyl ions are in excess, the solution is basic. An important property of water is that for any temperature, the product of the activities of these ions is a constant. At 25°C, this constant is .000 000 000 000 01.

In a strong solution of hydrochloric acid, the hydrogen ion activity may be as high as 1 mole per liter, while in a strong solution of lye, the hydroxyl ion concentration may be as high as 1 mole per liter. To avoid the inconvenience of writing these very small numbers, hydrogen ion activities are expressed in terms of pH, with

$$pH = \log_{10} \frac{1}{[H^+]}$$

The relation between pH, H^+, and OH^- at 25°C is shown in Table 21.2.

Most natural waters have pH values between 6.5 and 8.5. The pH of natural waters is controlled by the relative amounts of carbon dioxide, bicarbonate, and carbonate ions. Rainwater usually has a pH of slightly less than 7 because carbon dioxide from the air dissolves to form carbonic acid.

Human blood has a pH of 7.4 and the gastric juices in your stomach have a pH of approximately 0.9 to aid in the digestion of food.

Alum coagulates most effectively at pH values near 6.8.

QUESTIONS

Write your answers in a notebook and then compare your answers with those on page 500.

21.1Q   How is nitrate measured in the nitrate test?

21.1R   If turbidity is interfering with a nitrate analysis, how can turbidity be removed?

21.1S   The pH of natural waters is usually controlled by the relative amounts of what ions?

TABLE 21.2   RELATION BETWEEN pH, H^+, AND OH^- AT 25°C

Activity of H^+ moles/L	Activity of OH^- moles/L	pH
1.	0.000 000 000 000 01	0
0.1	0.000 000 000 000 1	1
0.01	0.000 000 000 001	2
0.001	0.000 000 000 01	3
0.000 1	0.000 000 000 1	4
0.000 01	0.000 000 001	5
0.000 001	0.000 000 01	6
0.000 000 1	0.000 000 1	7
0.000 000 01	0.000 001	8
0.000 000 001	0.000 01	9
0.000 000 000 1	0.000 1	10
0.000 000 000 01	0.001	11
0.000 000 000 001	0.01	12
0.000 000 000 000 1	0.1	13
0.000 000 000 000 01	1.	14

13. Specific Conductance (Conductivity)

A. Discussion

Specific conductance or conductivity is a numerical expression (expressed in micromhos per centimeter) of the ability of a water to conduct an electric current. This number depends on the total concentration of the minerals dissolved in the sample (TDS) and the temperature. Changes in conductivity from normal may indicate changes in mineral composition of the water, seasonal variations in lakes and reservoirs, or

(Sulfate)

intrusion of pollutants. The custom of reporting conductivity values in micromhos/cm at 25°C requires the accurate determination of each sample's temperature at the time of conductivity measurement.

Specific conductance is measured by the use of a conductivity meter.

B. What is Tested?

Sample	Common Range, micromhos/cm
Raw and Treated Surface Waters	30 to 500
Groundwater	100 to 1,000

C. Materials and Procedure

Follow instrument manufacturer's instructions. Also see page 2-43, *STANDARD METHODS*, 18th Edition.

14. Sulfate

A. Discussion

The sulfate ion is one of the major anions occurring in natural waters. Sulfate ions are of importance in water supplies because of the tendency of appreciable amounts to form hard scales in boilers and heat exchangers. EPA is evaluating the need to regulate sulfate in drinking water.

B. What is Tested?

Sample	Common Range, mg/L
Raw or Treated Water Supply	5 to 100

C. Apparatus Required

Turbidimeter *OR* spectrophotometer
Stopwatch or timer
Measuring spoon, 0.3 mL
Magnetic stirrer
Magnetic stir-bar
Pipet, 10 mL
Flasks, Erlenmeyer, 250 mL
Flasks, Volumetric, 100 mL

D. Reagents

NOTE: Standardized solutions are commercially available.

1. Conditioning reagent.

2. Barium chloride, $BaCl_2$, crystals: Sized for turbidimetric work (Baker No. 0974 or equivalent). To ensure uniformity of results, construct a standard curve for each batch of $BaCl_2$ crystals.

3. Standard sulfate solution: Prepare a standard sulfate solution as described in (a) or (b) below; 1.00 mL = 0.10 mg SO_4.

   a. Dilute 10.41 mL standard 0.0200 N H_2SO_4 titrant specified in Alkalinity Test (Chapter 11, Volume I, of this manual) to 100 mL with distilled water.

   b. Dissolve 147.9 mg anhydrous Na_2SO_4 in distilled water and dilute to 1,000 mL.

E. Procedure

1. Place 100 mL of sample or a suitable portion diluted to 100 mL into a clean 250-mL Erlenmeyer flask.

2. Add 5.0 mL of conditioning reagent and mix.

3. While stirring, add a spoonful (0.3 mL) of barium chloride crystals. Stir for exactly 1 minute.

4. Measure turbidity at 30-second intervals for 4 minutes. Consider turbidity to be the maximum reading obtained in the 4-minute interval.

F. Construction of Standard Calibration Curve

1. Using the standard solution prepare the following standards in 100-mL volumetric flasks.

mL of Standard Sulfate Solution Placed in 100-mL Volumetric Flask	Sulfate Concentration, mg/L
5.0	5.0
10.0	10.0
15.0	15.0
20.0	20.0
25.0	25.0

2. Dilute flasks to 100 mL.

3. Transfer to 250-mL Erlenmeyer flask.

4. Determine amount of sulfate as outlined previously.

5. Prepare a standard curve by plotting turbidity values of standards versus the corresponding sulfate concentrations. Set nephelometer (or spectrophotometer) at zero sulfate concentration using distilled water as a control.

G. Example

Results from a series of tests for sulfate were as follows:

Flask	Sample	Volume	Turbidity
1	Distilled Water	100 mL	0
2	Plant Effluent	100 mL	35
3	Jones St. Well	50 mL	45
4	5.0 mg/L SO_4 Standard	100 mL	11
5	10.0 mg/L SO_4 Standard	100 mL	29
6	15.0 mg/L SO_4 Standard	100 mL	40
7	20.0 mg/L SO_4 Standard	100 mL	53

H. Calculation

1. Prepare a standard curve by using data from prepared standards. From the above example:

Concentration Sulfate, mg/L	Turbidity, TU
0.0	0
5.0	11
10.0	29
15.0	40
20.0	53

(Sulfate)

OUTLINE OF PROCEDURE FOR SULFATE

1. Measure 100 mL of sample into clean 250-mL flask.

2. Add 5.0 mL conditioning reagent. Mix.

3. Add barium chloride and stir for 1 minute.

4. Measure turbidity.

The graph below is the result of plotting concentration of standards versus their corresponding turbidity.

2. Obtain concentration of unknown plant and well samples from curve.

(Taste and Odor)

3. Correct (if necessary) for samples of less than 100 mL by using the following formula:

$$\text{Sulfate } (SO_4), \text{ mg}/L = \frac{(\text{Graph Sulfate, mg}/L)(100 \text{ m}L)}{\text{Sample Size, m}L}$$

Using data from example:

	Sample Volume	Turbidity	Concentration from Graph
Plant Effluent	100 mL	35 TU	13 mg/L

Sulfate, mg/L = 13 mg/L

	Sample Volume	Turbidity	Concentration from Graph
Jones St. Well	50 mL	45 TU	17 mg/L

$$\text{Sulfate, mg}/L = \frac{(\text{Sulfate, mg}/L)(100 \text{ m}L)}{\text{Sample Size, m}L}$$

$$= \frac{(17 \text{ mg}/L)(100 \text{ m}L)}{50 \text{ m}L}$$

$$= 34 \text{ mg}/L \text{ } SO_4$$

I. Notes

1. A spectrophotometer can be used to measure absorbance of barium sulfate suspension. Use at 420 nanometer (nm) wavelength.

2. Color or suspended matter will interfere when present in large amounts. Correct for these items by testing blanks from which barium chloride is withheld.

3. Analyze samples and standards with their temperatures in the range of 20 to 25°C.

J. Reference

See page 4-134, *STANDARD METHODS*, 18th Edition.

QUESTIONS

Write your answers in a notebook and then compare your answers with those on pages 500 and 501.

21.1T   What is the meaning of specific conductance or conductivity?

21.1U   Sulfate ions are of concern in drinking water for what reason?

21.1V   A 50-mL sample from a well produced a turbidity reading of 40 TU using a nephelometer (turbidimeter). What was the sulfate concentration in mg/L?

15. Taste and Odor

A. Discussion

Taste and odor are sensory clues that provide the first warning of potential hazards in the environment. Water, in its pure form, cannot produce odor or taste sensations. However, algae, actinomycetes, bacteria, decaying vegetation, metals, and pollutants can cause tastes and odors in drinking water. Corrective measures designed to reduce unpleasant tastes and odors include aeration or the addition of chlorine, chlorine dioxide, potassium permanganate, or activated carbon. (For additional details, see Volume I, Chapter 9, "Taste and Odor Control.")

Odor is considered a quality factor affecting acceptability of drinking water (and foods prepared with it), tainting of fish and other aquatic organisms, and aesthetics of recreational waters. Most organic and some inorganic chemicals contribute to taste and odor. These chemicals may originate from municipal and industrial waste discharges, from natural sources (such as decomposition of vegetable matter), or from associated microbial activity.

Some substances, such as certain inorganic salts, produce taste without odor. Many taste sensations actually are odor sensations, even though the sensation is not noticed until the water is in the mouth.

Taste, like odor, is one of the chemical senses. Taste and odor are different in that odors are sensed high up in our nose and tastes are sensed on our tongue. Taste is simpler than odor because there may be only four true taste sensations: sour, sweet, salty, and bitter. Dissolved inorganic salts of copper, iron, manganese, potassium, sodium, and zinc can be detected by taste.

Operators must remember that a tasteless water is not the most desirable water. Distilled water is considered less pleasant to drink than a high-quality water. The taste test must determine the taste intensity by the threshold test and also evaluate the quality of the drinking water on the basis of desirability for consumers.

B. Apparatus Required

Sample bottles, glass-stoppered or with TFE-lined closures
Constant temperature bath
Odor flasks (500-mL glass-stoppered Erlenmeyer flasks)
Transfer and volumetric pipets or graduated cylinders (200, 100, 50, and 25 mL)
Measuring pipets (10 mL, graduated in 0.1-mL increments)
Thermometer (0 to 110°C)

C. Precautions

Use preliminary tests to select the persons to make taste or odor tests. Use only persons who want to participate in the test. Avoid distracting odors such as those caused by smoking, foods, soaps, perfumes, and shaving lotions. The testers should not have colds or allergies that affect odor response. Do not have the testers perform too many tests and allow frequent rests so the testers won't become tired and lose their sensitivity. Keep the room in which the tests are conducted free from distractions, drafts, and odors.

A panel of five or more testers is recommended for precise work. Do not allow the testers to prepare the samples or to know the dilution concentrations being evaluated. Familiarize testers with the procedure before they participate in a panel test. Present the most dilute sample first to avoid tiring the senses with a concentrated sample. Keep temperature of sample during test within 1°C of the specified temperature. Use opaque or darkly colored flasks to avoid biasing the results due to turbid or colored waters being tested.

D. Procedure

ODOR

1. Determine the approximate range of the threshold odor number by adding 200 mL, 50 mL, 12 mL, and 2.8 mL of sample to 500-mL glass-stoppered Erlenmeyer flasks containing odor-free water[4] to make a total volume of 200 mL. Use a separate flask containing only odor-free water as a reference for comparison. Heat dilutions and reference to desired test temperature (usually 60°C or 140°F).

2. Shake flask containing odor-free water, remove stopper, and sniff vapors. Test sample containing the least amount of odor-bearing water in the same way. If an odor can be detected in this dilution, prepare more dilute samples.

   To prepare more dilute samples, prepare an intermediate dilution consisting of 20-mL sample diluted to 200 mL with odor-free water. Use this dilution for the threshold determination. Multiply the threshold odor number (TON) obtained by 10 to correct for the intermediate dilution.

   If an odor cannot be detected in the first dilution, repeat the above procedure using sample containing the next higher concentration of odor-bearing water and continue this process until odor is detected clearly.

3. Based on the results obtained in the preliminary test, prepare a set of dilutions using Table 21.3 as a guide. Prepare the five dilutions shown in the appropriate column and the three next most concentrated in the next column to the right in Table 21.3. For example, if odor was first noted in the flask containing the 50 mL sample in the preliminary test, prepare flasks containing 50, 35, 25, 17, 12, 8.3, 5.7, and 4.0 mL sample, each diluted to 200 mL with odor-free water. This procedure is necessary to challenge the range of sensitivities of the entire panel of testers.

TABLE 21.3   DILUTIONS FOR VARIOUS ODOR INTENSITIES

PRELIMINARY TEST

Sample Volume in Which Odor First Noted

200 mL	50 mL	12 mL	3.8 mL

FINAL TEST

Volume in mL of Sample to be Diluted to 200 mL

200	50	12	(Intermediate
140	35	8.3	dilution)
100	25	5.7	
70	17	4.0	
50	12	2.8	

Insert two or more blanks near the expected threshold, but avoid any repeated patterns. Do not let the testers know which dilutions are odorous and which are blanks. Instruct each tester to smell each flask in sequence, beginning with the least concentrated sample, until odor is detected with certainty.

4. Record observations by indicating whether odor is noted in each flask. For example,

mL Sample Diluted to 200 mL	12	0	17	25	0	35	50
Response	−	−	−	+	−	+	+

5. Calculate the threshold odor number (TON) as shown in E. Calculations.

TASTE THRESHOLD TEST

1. The taste threshold test is used when the purpose is quantitative measurement of detectable taste. When odor is the predominant sensation, as in the case of chlorophenols, the threshold odor test takes priority.

2. Use the dilution and random blank system described for odor tests when preparing taste samples.

3. Present each dilution and blank to the tester in a clean 50-mL plastic container filled to the 30-mL level. Use high quality clear plastic containers. Discard the plastic container when finished. Do not use glass containers because the soap used to clean the glass could leave a residue which may affect the results.

---

[4] *See STANDARD METHODS, 18th Edition, page 2-11, for directions on how to prepare odor-free water.*

(Taste and Odor)

4. *STANDARD METHODS* recommends maintaining the sample presentation at 40 ± 1°C (104 ± 2°F).

   NOTE: Some operators use normal water temperatures for taste tests or a temperature of 15°C (59°F).

5. Present the series of samples to each tester. Pair each sample with a known blank.

6. Have each tester taste the sample by taking into the mouth whatever volume is comfortable, holding it in the mouth for several seconds, and discharging the sample without swallowing the water.

7. Have the tester compare the sample with the blank and record whether a taste or aftertaste is detectable in the sample.

8. Submit samples in an increasing order of concentration until the tester's taste threshold has been passed.

9. Calculate individual threshold and threshold of the panel as shown in E. Calculations.

TASTE RATING TEST

1. When the purpose of the test is to estimate the taste acceptability, use the "taste rating test" procedure described below.

2. Samples for this test usually represent treated water ready for human consumption. If experimentally treated water is tested, *BE CERTAIN THAT THE WATER IS SAFE TO DRINK* (no pathogens and no toxic chemicals present).

3. Give testers thorough instructions and trial or orientation sessions followed by questions and discussions of procedures.

4. Select panel members on the basis of performance in trial sessions.

5. When testing samples testers work alone.

6. Present samples at a temperature that testers find pleasant for drinking water. Maintain this temperature by the use of a water bath apparatus. A temperature of 15°C (59°F) is recommended, but in any case, do not let the test temperature exceed tap water temperatures that are customary at the time of the test. Specify the test temperature in reporting results.

7. Present each dilution and blank to the tester in a clean 50-mL plastic container filled to the 30-mL level. Use high quality clear plastic containers. Discard the plastic containers when finished. Do not use glass containers because the soap used to clean the glass could leave a residue which may affect the results.

8. Each tester is presented with a list of nine statements about the water ranging on a scale from very favorable to very unfavorable (Table 21.4). The tester's task is to select the statement that best expresses the tester's opin-

ion. The scored rating is the scale number of the statement selected. The panel rating is the arithmetic mean (average) of the scale numbers of all testers.

9. Rating involves the following steps:

   a. Initial tasting of about half the sample by taking water into the mouth, holding it for several seconds, and discharging it without swallowing;

   b. Forming an initial judgment on the rating scale;

   c. A second tasting is made in the same manner as the first;

   d. A final rating is made for the sample and the result is recorded on the appropriate data form;

   e. Rinse mouth with taste- and odor-free water; and

   f. Rest one minute before repeating steps (a) through (e) on the next sample.

10. Independently randomize sample order for each tester. Allow at least 30 minutes rest between repeated rating sessions. Testers should not know the composition or source of samples.

TABLE 21.4   ACTION TENDENCY RATING SCALE FOR TASTE RATING TEST

1. I would be very happy to drink this water as my everyday drinking water.

2. I would be happy to accept this water as my everyday drinking water.

3. I am sure that I could accept this water as my everyday drinking water.

4. I could accept this water as my everyday drinking water.

5. Maybe I could accept this water as my everyday drinking water.

6. I don't think I could accept this water as my everyday drinking water.

7. I could not accept this water as my everyday drinking water.

8. I could never drink this water.

9. I can't stand this water in my mouth and I could never drink it.

E. Calculations

FORMULAS

1. ODOR

The threshold odor number (TON) for an individual tester is calculated using the following formula:

$$TON = \frac{A + B}{A}$$

where:

A = mL sample, and

B = mL odor-free water.

The threshold odor number for a group is presented as the geometric mean of the individual tester thresholds.

Geometric Mean = $(X_1 \times X_2 \times X_3 \ldots X_n)^{1/n}$

where:

X_1 = threshold odor number for tester number 1,

X_2 = threshold odor number for tester number 2,

X_n = threshold odor number for the nth tester, and

n = total number of testers.

2. TASTE THRESHOLD

Calculate the individual tester's threshold taste number and the threshold taste number for a panel using the same formulas that are used for the threshold odor tests.

3. TASTE RATING

Determine the taste rating for a water by calculating the arithmetic mean and *STANDARD DEVIATION*[5] of all ratings given for each sample.

$$\text{Arithmetic Mean, } \overline{X} = \frac{X_1 + X_2 + X_3 + \ldots X_n}{n}$$

where: X_1 = taste rating for tester number 1,

X_2 = taste rating for tester number 2,

X_n = taste rating for nth tester, and

n = total number of testers.

$$\text{Standard Deviation} = \left[\frac{(X_1 - \overline{X})^2 + (X_2 - \overline{X})^2 + \ldots (X_n - \overline{X})^2}{n - 1} \right]^{1/2}$$

$$\text{or} = \left[\frac{(X_1^2 + X_2^2 + \ldots X_n^2) - (X_1 + X_2 + \ldots X_n)^2/n}{n - 1} \right]^{1/2}$$

EXAMPLE 1

Calculate the threshold odor number (TON) for a sample when the first detectable odor occurred when the 25-mL sample was diluted to 200 mL (175 mL of odor-free water was added to the 25-mL sample).

Known		Unknown
A or Sample Size, mL	= 25 mL	TON
B or Odor-Free Water, mL	= 175 mL	

Calculate the threshold odor number (TON).

$$\text{TON} = \frac{A + B}{A}$$

$$= \frac{25 \text{ mL} + 175 \text{ mL}}{25 \text{ mL}}$$

$$= 8$$

EXAMPLE 2

Determine the geometric mean threshold odor number for a panel of five testers given the following results.

Known	Unknown
Tester 1, X_1 = 8	Geometric Mean Threshold Odor Number
Tester 2, X_2 = 6	
Tester 3, X_3 = 12	
Tester 4, X_4 = 8	
Tester 5, X_5 = 4	

Calculate the geometric mean.

$$\text{Geometric Mean TON} = (X_1 \times X_2 \times X_3 \times X_4 \times X_5)^{1/n}$$

$$= (8 \times 6 \times 12 \times 8 \times 4)^{1/5}$$

$$= (18{,}432)^{0.2}$$

$$= 7.1$$

EXAMPLE 3

Calculate the threshold taste number for a sample when the first detectable taste occurred when the 50-mL sample was diluted to 200 mL (150 mL of taste-free water was added to the 50-mL sample).

Known		Unknown
A or Sample Size, mL	= 50 mL	Threshold Taste Number
B or Taste-Free Water, mL	= 150 mL	

Calculate the threshold taste number.

$$\text{Threshold Taste Number} = \frac{A + B}{A}$$

$$= \frac{50 \text{ mL} + 150 \text{ mL}}{50 \text{ mL}}$$

$$= 4$$

EXAMPLE 4

Determine the taste rating for a water by calculating the arithmetic mean and standard deviation for the panel ratings given below.

Known	Unknown
Tester 1, X_1 = 2	1. Arithmetic Mean, $\overline{X}$
Tester 2, X_2 = 5	2. Standard Deviation, S
Tester 3, X_3 = 3	
Tester 4, X_4 = 6	
Tester 5, X_5 = 2	
Tester 6, X_6 = 6	

1. Calculate the arithmetic mean, $\overline{X}$, taste rating.

$$\text{Arithmetic Mean, } \overline{X}, \text{ Taste Rating} = \frac{X_1 + X_2 + X_3 + X_4 + X_5 + X_6}{n}$$

$$= \frac{2 + 5 + 3 + 6 + 2 + 6}{6}$$

$$= \frac{24}{6}$$

$$= 4$$

---

[5] *Standard Deviation. A measure of the spread or dispersion of data.*

(Trihalomethanes)

2. Calculate the standard deviation, S, of the taste rating.

$$\text{Standard Deviation, S} = \left[\frac{(X_1 - \overline{X})^2 + (X_2 - \overline{X})^2 + (X_3 - \overline{X})^2 + (X_4 - \overline{X})^2 + (X_5 - \overline{X})^2 + (X_6 - \overline{X})^2}{n - 1}\right]^{1/2}$$

$$= \left[\frac{(2 - 4)^2 + (5 - 4)^2 + (3 - 4)^2 + (6 - 4)^2 + (2 - 4)^2 + (6 - 4)^2}{6 - 1}\right]^{1/2}$$

$$= \left[\frac{(-2)^2 + 1^2 + (-1)^2 + 2^2 + (-2)^2 + 2^2}{5}\right]^{0.5}$$

$$= \left[\frac{4 + 1 + 1 + 4 + 4 + 4}{5}\right]^{0.5}$$

$$= \left[\frac{18}{5}\right]^{0.5}$$

$$= (3.6)^{0.5}$$

$$= 1.9$$

or

$$\text{Standard Deviation, S} = \left[\frac{(X_1^2 + X_2^2 + X_3^2 + X_4^2 + X_5^2 + X_6^2) - (X_1 + X_2 + X_3 + X_4 + X_5 + X_6)^2/n}{n - 1}\right]^{0.5}$$

$$= \left[\frac{(2^2 + 5^2 + 3^2 + 6^2 + 2^2 + 6^2) - (2 + 5 + 3 + 6 + 2 + 6)^2/6}{6 - 1}\right]^{0.5}$$

$$= \left[\frac{(4 + 25 + 9 + 36 + 4 + 36) - (24)^2/6}{5}\right]^{0.5}$$

$$= \left[\frac{114 - 96}{5}\right]^{0.5}$$

$$= \left[\frac{18}{5}\right]^{0.5}$$

$$= (3.6)^{0.5}$$

$$= 1.9 \text{ (same answer as before)}$$

F. Reference

Odor: See page 2-11, *STANDARD METHODS*, 18th Edition.

Taste: See page 2-15, *STANDARD METHODS*, 18th Edition.

QUESTIONS

Write your answers in a notebook and then compare your answers with those on page 501.

21.1W   List the items that can cause tastes and odors in drinking water.

21.1X   Calculate the threshold odor number (TON) for a sample when the first detectable odor occurred when the 12-mL sample was diluted to 200 mL (188 mL of odor-free water was added to the 12-mL sample).

16. Trihalomethanes

A. Discussion

The trihalomethanes (THMs) are members of the family of organohalogen compounds which are named as derivatives of methane. Current analytical chemistry applied to drinking water has thus far detected chloroform, bromodichloromethane, dibromochloromethane, bromoform, and dichloroiodomethane.

The principal source of chloroform and other trihalomethanes in drinking water is the chemical interaction of chlorine added for disinfection and other purposes with the commonly present natural humic substances and other precursors produced either by normal organic decomposition or by the metabolism of aquatic organisms. Since these natural organic precursors are more commonly found in surface water, water taken from a surface source is more likely to produce high THM levels than most groundwaters.

Generally, the THM-producing reaction is:

Chlorine + Precursors = Chloroform + Other THMs

Chloroform is the most common THM found in drinking water and it is usually present in the highest concentration. The presence in drinking water of chloroform and other THMs and synthetic organic chemicals may have an adverse effect on the health of consumers; therefore, human exposure to these chemicals should be reduced.

B. Reference

For materials and procedures see pages 5-15 and 5-44, *STANDARD METHODS*, 18th Edition.

NOTE: A gas chromatography analyzer is required for this analysis.

17. Total Dissolved Solids

A. Discussion

"Total dissolved solids" (TDS) refers to material that passes through a standard glass-fiber filter disc and remains after evaporation at 180°C. The amount of dissolved solids present in water is a consideration in its suitability for domestic use. In general, waters with a TDS content of less than 50 mg/L are most desirable for such purposes. The higher the TDS concentration, the greater the likelihood of tastes and odors and also scaling problems. As TDS increase, the number of times the water can be recycled and reclaimed before requiring demineralization decreases. In potable waters, TDS consist mainly of inorganic salts, small amounts of organic matter, and dissolved gases.[6]

B. What is Tested?

Sample	Common Range, mg/L
Raw and Treated Surface Waters	20 to 700
Groundwater	100 to 1,000

C. Apparatus Required

Glass-fiber filter discs (Millipore AP40; or Gelman Type A/E)
Flask, suction, 500 mL
Filter holder or Gooch crucible adapter
Gooch crucibles (25 mL if 2.2-cm filter used)
Evaporating dishes, 100 mL (high-silica glass)
Drying oven, 180°C
Steam bath
Vacuum source
Desiccator
Analytical balance
Muffle furnace, 550°C

D. Procedure

Preparation of Dish

1. Ignite a clean evaporating dish at 550 ± 50°C for one hour in muffle furnace.

2. Cool in desiccator then weigh and record weight. Store in desiccator until needed.

Preparation of Glass-Fiber Filter Disc

1. Place the disc on the filter apparatus or insert into the bottom of a suitable Gooch crucible. While vacuum is applied, wash the filter disc with three successive 20-mL volumes of distilled water. Continue the suction to remove all traces of water from the disc and discard the washings.

Sample Analysis

1. Shake the sample vigorously and transfer 100 to 150 mL to the funnel or Gooch crucible by means of a 150-mL graduated cylinder.

2. Filter the sample through the glass-fiber filter and continue to apply vacuum for about three minutes after filtration is complete to remove as much water as possible.

3. Transfer 100 mL of the filtrate to the weighed evaporating dish and evaporate to dryness on a steam bath.

4. Dry the evaporated sample for at least one hour at 180°C. Cool in desiccator and weigh. Repeat drying cycle until constant weight is obtained or until weight loss is less than 0.5 mg.

E. Example

Results from weighings were:

Clean Dish	= 47.0028 grams (47,002.8 mg)
Dissolved Residue + Dish	= 47.0453 grams (47,045.3 mg)
Sample Volume	= 100 mL

---

[6] *Reference.   CHEMISTRY FOR ENVIRONMENTAL ENGINEERS, Fourth Edition, 1994, by Clair N. Sawyer and Perry L. McCarty. Published by McGraw-Hill Publishing Company, 860 Taylor Station Road, Blacklick, OH 43004. Order No. 0070549788. Price, $76.31, plus $8.75 shipping and handling.*

(Total Dissolved Solids)

OUTLINE OF PROCEDURE FOR TOTAL DISSOLVED SOLIDS

1. Ignite dish at 550°C for 1 hour in muffle furnace.

2. Cool.

3. Weigh and store in desiccator.

4. Place glass-fiber disc in crucible.

5. Wash filter crucible with distilled water.

6. Pour 100 mL sample into Gooch crucible.

7. Filter out suspended material. Transfer 100 mL of filtrate into weighed dish.

8. Evaporate to dryness on steam bath.

9. Dry evaporated sample for 1 hour at 180°C.

10. Cool in desiccator.

11. Weigh.

(Total Dissolved Solids)

F. Calculations

1. Total Dissolved Solids, $mg/L = \dfrac{(A - B) \times 1{,}000}{mL \text{ Sample Volume}}$

   where, A = weight of dish and dissolved material in milligrams (mg)

   B = weight of clean dish in milligrams (mg)

2. From example,

   $$\text{Total Dissolved Solids, } mg/L = \dfrac{(A - B) \times 1{,}000}{mL \text{ Sample Volume}}$$

   $$= \dfrac{(47{,}045.3 \text{ mg} - 47{,}002.8 \text{ mg})(1{,}000 \text{ mL}/L)}{100 \text{ mL}}$$

   $$= 425 \text{ mg}/L$$

G. Comments

Because excessive residue in the evaporating dish may form a water-entrapping crust, use a sample that yields no more than 200 mg of residue.

H. Reference

See page 2-55, *STANDARD METHODS*, 18th Edition.

QUESTIONS

Write your answers in a notebook and then compare your answers with those on page 501.

21.1Y   How are trihalomethanes produced?

21.1Z   What are total dissolved solids (TDS)?

End of Lesson 2 of 2 Lessons on ADVANCED LABORATORY PROCEDURES

Please answer the discussion and review questions before continuing with the Objective Test.

DISCUSSION AND REVIEW QUESTIONS

Chapter 21. ADVANCED LABORATORY PROCEDURES

(Lesson 2 of 2 Lessons)

Write the answers to these questions in your notebook before continuing with the Objective Test on page 501. The question numbering continues from Lesson 1.

9. Why is iron undesirable in a domestic water supply?

10. What precautions must be exercised when collecting samples to be analyzed for iron?

11. How would you obtain the manganese concentration in a sample by using a spectrophotometer if turbidity or color was interfering with the results?

12. What is the purpose of the Marble Test?

13. Why is the presence of certain metals in drinking water of serious concern?

14. How would you interpret the results of lab tests which indicate high levels of nitrate in a raw water sample?

15. When performing the nitrate determination, why should caution be exercised when using cadmium and what precautions should be used?

16. How would you interpret the meaning of changes (away from normal) in conductivity in water?

17. Why are sulfate ions of concern in water supplies?

18. How would you attempt to reduce unpleasant tastes and odors in drinking water?

19. Why should exposure to trihalomethanes (THMs) be reduced?

20. Why is the amount of dissolved solids present in water a consideration in its suitability for domestic use?

SUGGESTED ANSWERS

Chapter 21.   ADVANCED LABORATORY PROCEDURES

ANSWERS TO QUESTIONS IN LESSON 1

Answers to questions on page 467.

21.0A   The intensity of a blue color is measured when measuring the concentration of phosphorus in water.

21.0B   The scale on spectrophotometers is usually graduated in two ways:

1. In units of percent transmittance (%T), an arithmetic scale with units graded from 0 to 100%; and
2. In units of absorbance (A), a logarithmic scale of nonequal divisions graduated from 0.0 to 2.0.

21.0C   If an absorbance reading was 0.60, the unknown concentration would be 0.70 mg/L.

Answers to questions on page 471.

21.1A   Yes, the quality of water in any lake, reservoir, or stream has a very direct effect on the abundance and types of aquatic organisms found.

21.1B   Calcium in the form of lime or calcium hydroxide may be used to soften water or to control corrosion through pH adjustment.

21.1C   Titrate sample for calcium immediately after adding sodium hydroxide (NaOH) solution.

21.1D   Chloride concentrations above 250 mg/L are objectionable to many people due to a salty taste.

Answers to questions on page 471.

21.1E   The most common colors which occur in raw water are yellow and brown.

21.1F   True color is normally removed or at least decreased by coagulation and chlorination or ozonation.

21.1G   Stock color standards should be protected against evaporation and contamination when not in use.

Answers to questions on page 478.

21.1H   The presence of dissolved oxygen (DO) in water can contribute to corrosion of piping systems.

21.1I   The common range of fluoride in fluoridated drinking water is 0.8 to 1.2 mg/L.

ANSWERS TO QUESTIONS IN LESSON 2

Answers to questions on pages 483 and 484.

21.1J   Problems that may be caused by iron in a domestic water supply include staining of laundry, concrete, and porcelain. A bitter astringent taste can be detected by some people at levels above 0.3 mg/L.

21.1K   All glassware must be acid washed when analyzing samples for iron to remove deposits of iron oxide which could give false results.

21.1L   Manganese occurs both in suspension and as a soluble complex in surface waters.

21.1M   If the manganese concentration cannot be determined immediately, acidify sample with nitric acid to pH less than 2.

Answers to questions on page 486.

21.1N   Temperature is important in the Marble Test because the solubility of calcium carbonate varies with temperature. Therefore, the test must be performed immediately after the sample is collected and as rapidly as possible.

21.1O   Langelier Index $\cong$ Initial pH − Final pH

$$\cong 8.9 - 8.6$$

$$\cong 0.3$$

Since the Langelier Index is positive, the water is supersaturated with calcium carbonate and not considered corrosive.

21.1P   The concentration of most metals in water is determined by using atomic absorption spectroscopy or colorimetric methods.

Answers to questions on page 489.

21.1Q   In the nitrate test, all nitrate is reduced to nitrite and then measured colorimetrically.

21.1R   Removal of turbidity interfering with nitrate analyses can be accomplished by one of the following methods to remove suspended matter that can clog the reduction column.

1. Filter sample through a glass-fiber filter or a 0.45-micron pore size filter as long as the pH is less than 8, or
2. Add 1 mL zinc solution to 100 mL of sample and mix thoroughly. Add enough sodium hydroxide solution to obtain a pH of 10.5. Let treated sample stand a few minutes to allow the heavy flocculant precipitate to settle. Clarify by filtering through a glass-fiber filter.

21.1S   The pH of natural waters is controlled by the relative amounts of carbon dioxide, bicarbonate, and carbonate ions.

Answers to questions on page 492.

21.1T   Specific conductance or conductivity is a numerical expression (expressed in micromhos per centimeter) of the ability of a water to conduct an electric current. This number depends on the total concentration of the minerals dissolved in the sample (TDS) and the temperature.

21.1U Sulfate ions are of importance in water supplies because of the tendency of appreciable amounts to form hard scales in boilers and heat exchangers.

21.1V A 50-mL sample from a well produced a turbidity reading of 40 TU using a nephelometer. What was the sulfate concentration in mg/L?

Known	Unknown
Sample Size, mL = 50 mL	Sulfate, mg/L
Turbidity, TU = 40 TU	

1. Determine the sulfate concentration from the graph.

   Sulfate Concentration, mg/L = 15 mg/L

2. Calculate the sulfate concentration in mg/L.

$$\text{Sulfate, mg/L} = \frac{(\text{Graph Sulfate, mg/L})(100 \text{ mL})}{\text{Sample Size, mL}}$$

$$= \frac{(15 \text{ mg/L})(100 \text{ mL})}{50 \text{ mL}}$$

$$= 30 \text{ mg/L}$$

Answers to questions on page 496.

21.1W Tastes and odors can be caused in drinking water by algae, actinomycetes, bacteria, decaying vegetation, metals, and pollutants (most organic chemicals and some inorganic chemicals). Dissolved inorganic salts of copper, iron, manganese, potassium, sodium, and zinc can be detected by taste.

21.1X Calculate the threshold odor number (TON) for a sample when the first detectable odor occurred when the 12-mL sample was diluted to 200 mL (188 mL of odor-free water was added to the 12-mL sample).

Known	Unknown
A or Sample Size, mL = 12 mL	TON
B or Odor-Free Water, mL = 188 mL	

Calculate the threshold odor number (TON).

$$\text{TON} = \frac{A + B}{A}$$

$$= \frac{12 \text{ mL} + 188 \text{ mL}}{12 \text{ mL}}$$

$$= 17$$

Answers to questions on page 499.

21.1Y The principal source of chloroform and other trihalomethanes in drinking water is the chemical interaction of chlorine added for disinfection and other purposes with the commonly present natural humic substances and other precursors produced either by normal organic decomposition or by the metabolism of aquatic organisms.

21.1Z Total Dissolved Solids (TDS) refers to material that passes through a standard glass-fiber filter disc and remains after evaporation at 180°C.

OBJECTIVE TEST

Chapter 21. ADVANCED LABORATORY PROCEDURES

Please write your name and mark the correct answers on the answer sheet, as directed at the end of Chapter 1. There may be more than one correct answer to each multiple-choice question.

True-False

1. In the field of water analysis, measuring the intensity of the color enables the concentration of the substance to be determined.
   1. True
   2. False

2. When using a spectrophotometer, a water sample which has a low color intensity will have a low percent transmittance.
   1. True
   2. False

3. If the filters are performing properly, there should be countable algae in the treated water.
   1. True
   2. False

4. Always record the temperature of the water at the time of sampling when measuring dissolved oxygen.
   1. True
   2. False

5. As the temperature of water increases, the DO saturation value increases.
   1. True
   2. False

6. Colloidal ferric hydroxide may persist in small quantities in surface waters that appear clear.
   1. True
   2. False

7. Most groundwaters contain more manganese than iron.
   1. True
   2. False

8. The solubility of calcium carbonate varies with temperature.
   1. True
   2. False

9. During the Marble Test, the water being tested should not be exposed to atmospheric carbon dioxide.

1. True
2. False

10. Taste and odor are sensory clues which provide the first warning of potential hazards in the water environment.

1. True
2. False

11. Water taken from a groundwater source is more likely to produce high THM levels than most surface waters.

1. True
2. False

Best Answer (Select only the closest or best answer.)

12. The quality of water in any lake, reservoir, or stream has a very direct effect on which factor?

1. Abundance and types of aquatic organisms
2. People drinking the water
3. Population living along shore
4. Recreational use of the water

13. What is the principal cation in most natural waters?

1. Calcium
2. Carbon
3. Iron
4. Manganese

14. How is true color normally removed from or at least reduced in drinking water?

1. Chlorination and ozonation
2. Coagulation and chlorination
3. Coagulation and filtration
4. Sedimentation and filtration

15. What is the undesirable taste of iron in water?

1. Bitter astringent
2. Metallic
3. Sour
4. Vegetable

16. What is an undesirable effect of iron in drinking water?

1. Corrosion
2. Precipitate formation
3. Scale formation
4. Staining

17. Which method should be performed if turbidity is present in a sample being tested for manganese?

1. Bleaching
2. Chlorinating
3. Filtering
4. Straining

18. Why are excessive levels of nitrate undesirable in drinking water?

1. Can cause infant methemoglobinemia (blue babies)
2. Can cause tastes and odors
3. Indicates runoff from fertilized areas
4. Stimulates excessive algal growth

19. Specific conductance or conductivity depends on which factors?

1. BOD and TOC
2. COD and temperature
3. COD and TDS
4. TDS and temperature

20. Why is sulfate of concern in drinking water?

1. Cause of tastes and odors
2. Formation of scale on heat exchangers
3. Reactive with soaps and detergents
4. Responsible for staining plumbing fixtures

21. What is a major concern as TDS increase in drinking water?

1. Longevity of soil for agricultural uses increases
2. Number of times water can be recycled before requiring demineralization decreases
3. Number of times water can be used for irrigation increases
4. Rate of scale buildup on boilers decreases

Multiple Choice (Select all correct answers.)

22. What are the units of measurement on a spectrophotometer scale?

1. Absorbance
2. Concentration
3. Galvanic current
4. Percent transmittance
5. Transference

23. Which of the following steps must be taken to construct a spectrophotometer calibration graph?

1. Add developing reagent to standards and blank
2. Add reagent to sample being tested
3. Filter sample to be tested
4. Measure absorbance and transmittance of standards and blank
5. Prepare standards

24. Information from algae counts can serve which of the following purposes?

1. Help document variability in the water quality
2. Help explain the cause of color and turbidity
3. Help explain the clogging of screens or filters
4. Help explain the failure of floc formation
5. Help explain the presence of tastes and odors

25. What are the uses of lime or calcium hydroxide in water treatment plants?

1. Control corrosion through pH adjustment
2. Flocculate turbidity
3. Reduce iron and manganese
4. Remove color
5. Soften water

26. What important facts should an operator know about chloride?

1. Chloride content increases as mineral content of water increases
2. Chloride gives water an objectionable taste
3. Chloride in water is a serious health hazard
4. Chloride occurs in natural waters as a basic salt
5. The maximum allowable concentration is based on taste rather than the physical or health hazards of chloride

27. What are the causes of color in water supplies?

1. Industrial wastes
2. Leachate from groundwater
3. Metallic ions
4. Organic matter of soil origin
5. Organic matter of vegetable origin

28. Why is dissolved oxygen (DO) important to the water treatment plant operator?

    1. Dissolved oxygen must be present in surface waters for survival of fish
    2. Hardness increases with increases in dissolved oxygen
    3. Low dissolved oxygen at bottom of lakes can cause taste and odor problems
    4. Presence of dissolved oxygen can contribute to pipe corrosion
    5. Taste of water is improved by dissolved oxygen

29. Which precautions must be exercised when using a DO probe?

    1. Acidify the sample
    2. Keep the membrane in the tip of the probe moist
    3. Keep the sample iced
    4. Periodically check the calibration of the probe
    5. Turn off aerator diffusers

30. Samples containing excessive amounts of which chemicals must be distilled before being tested for fluoride?

    1. Acids
    2. Aluminum
    3. Hexametaphosphate
    4. Sodium hydroxide
    5. Sulfate

31. What problems can be caused by iron in a domestic water supply?

    1. Bitter tastes
    2. Consumer complaints
    3. Corrosion
    4. Staining of concrete
    5. Staining of laundry

32. Which ions control the pH of natural waters?

    1. Bicarbonate
    2. Carbon dioxide
    3. Carbonate
    4. Chloride
    5. Sodium

33. What do changes in conductivity from normal indicate?

    1. Changes in mineral composition of water
    2. Changes in voltage to conductivity meter
    3. Intrusion of pollutants
    4. Seasonal variations in reservoirs
    5. Variations in sampling techniques

34. Which corrective measures are available to reduce unpleasant tastes and odors in drinking water?

    1. Addition of activated carbon
    2. Addition of chlorine
    3. Addition of potassium permanganate
    4. Aeration
    5. Flocculation

35. Which of these items are recommended procedures for conducting an odor test?

    1. Closely control the temperature of samples
    2. Insert two or more blanks near the expected threshold
    3. Present the most dilute sample first
    4. Select no more than four persons per panel
    5. Use opaque or dark-colored flasks for samples

36. Calculate the threshold odor number (TON) for a sample. The first detectable odor occurred when the 20-mL sample was diluted to 200 mL (180 mL of odor-free water was added to the 20-mL sample).

    1. 5
    2. 8
    3. 10
    4. 13
    5. 15

End of Objective Test

CHAPTER 22

DRINKING WATER REGULATIONS

by

Tim Gannon

Revised by

Jim Sequeira

(1988, 1990, 1991, 1993, 1995, 1997)

NOTICE

EPA rules and regulations are continually changing. State rules and regulations may be stricter. Keep in contact with your state drinking water agency to obtain the rules and regulations that currently apply to your water utility. For current or additional information phone EPA's toll-free Safe Drinking Water Hotline at (800) 426-4791.

TABLE OF CONTENTS

Chapter 22.   DRINKING WATER REGULATIONS

Page

OBJECTIVES 509

WORDS 510

LESSON 1

22.0   HISTORY OF DRINKING WATER LAWS AND STANDARDS 512

22.1   HOW EPA DEVELOPS DRINKING WATER STANDARDS 513

    22.10   Types of Contaminants 513

    22.11   Identifying Contaminants To Be Regulated 513

    22.12   Unregulated Contaminants 514

    22.13   Schedule (1998 Forward) 514

    22.14   Setting Standards 515

    22.15   Types of Water Systems 515

22.2   PRIMARY DRINKING WATER STANDARDS 516

    22.20   Inorganic Chemical Standards 516

        22.200   Antimony 516

        22.201   Arsenic 516

        22.202   Asbestos 516

        22.203   Barium 516

        22.204   Beryllium 516

        22.205   Cadmium 519

        22.206   Chromium 519

        22.207   Copper 519

        22.208   Cyanide 519

        22.209   Fluoride 519

        22.2010   Lead and Copper 519

        22.2011   Mercury 521

        22.2012   Nitrate and Nitrite 521

        22.2013   Selenium 522

        22.2014   Thallium 522

    22.21   Organic Chemical Standards 522

        22.210   Trichloroethylene (TCE) 522

        22.211   1,1-Dichloroethylene 522

22.212   Vinyl Chloride 522

22.213   1,1,1-Trichloroethane 522

22.214   1,2-Dichloroethane 523

22.215   Carbon Tetrachloride 523

22.216   Benzene 523

22.217   Para-Dichlorobenzene (p-Dichlorobenzene) 523

22.22   Microbial Standards 523

22.220   Total Coliform Rule 523

22.2200   Sanitary Survey 524

22.2201   Sampling Plan 524

22.2202   Laboratory Procedures 524

22.2203   Monitoring Frequency 524

22.2204   Determining Compliance 526

22.2205   Reporting and Notification Requirements 526

22.221   Surface Water Treatment Rule (SWTR) 528

22.2210   Criteria for Avoiding Filtration 528

22.2211   Requirements for Filtered Water Systems 529

22.2212   Chlorine Residual Substitution 529

22.2213   Turbidity Requirements 529

22.2214   Monitoring Requirements 530

22.2215   CT Values 531

22.2216   Additional Reading 531

22.23   Disinfectants and Disinfection By-Products (D/DBPs) 531

22.24   Information Collection Rule (ICR) 532

22.240   Final Rule 532

22.241   Purpose of the Rule 532

22.242   Applicability 532

22.243   Types of Data To Be Collected and Why They Are Needed 532

22.2430   Microbial Monitoring 532

22.2431   Disinfection By-Product Monitoring 532

22.2432   Treatment Technology Studies 532

22.244   Schedule 533

22.245   Data Availability 533

22.246   Termination 533

22.247   For More Information 533

22.25   Radiological Standards 533

DISCUSSION AND REVIEW QUESTIONS 534

LESSON 2

22.3   SECONDARY DRINKING WATER STANDARDS 535

    22.30   Enforcement of Regulations 535

    22.31   Secondary Maximum Contaminant Levels 535

    22.32   Monitoring 536

    22.33   Secondary Contaminants 536

        22.330   Aluminum 536

        22.331   Chloride 536

        22.332   Color 536

        22.333   Copper 536

        22.334   Corrosivity 537

        22.335   Fluoride 537

        22.336   Foaming Agents 537

        22.337   Iron and Manganese 537

        22.338   Iron 537

        22.339   Manganese 538

        22.3310 Odor 538

        22.3311 pH 538

        22.3312 Silver 539

        22.3313 Sulfate 539

        22.3314 Total Dissolved Solids (TDS) 539

        22.3315 Zinc 539

22.4   SAMPLING PROCEDURES 540

    22.40   Safe Drinking Water Regulations 540

    22.41   Initial Sampling 540

    22.42   Routine Sampling 540

    22.43   Check and Repeat Sampling 540

    22.44   Sampling Points 540

    22.45   Sampling Point Selection 542

    22.46   Sampling Schedule 542

    22.47   Sampling Route 542

    22.48   Sample Collection 542

22.5   REPORTING PROCEDURES 542

22.6   NOTIFICATION REQUIREMENTS 552

22.7   RECORDKEEPING 552

22.8   CONSUMER CONFIDENCE REPORTS (CCRs) 552

DISCUSSION AND REVIEW QUESTIONS 553

SUGGESTED ANSWERS 554

OBJECTIVE TEST 557

OBJECTIVES

Chapter 22.   DRINKING WATER REGULATIONS

Following completion of Chapter 22, you should be able to:

1. Identify the two basic types of water systems,

2. List the types of primary contaminants,

3. Explain the Total Coliform Rule,

4. Explain the Surface Water Treatment Rule (SWTR),

5. Describe the Primary Drinking Water Standards,

6. Explain the Information Collection Rule (ICR),

7. List the secondary contaminants,

8. Develop and conduct a sampling program,

9. Record and report results,

10. Comply with notification requirements, and

11. Prepare a Consumer Confidence Report (CCR).

WORDS

Chapter 22.   DRINKING WATER REGULATIONS

ACUTE HEALTH EFFECT ACUTE HEALTH EFFECT

An adverse effect on a human or animal body, with symptoms developing rapidly.

CT VALUE CT VALUE

Residual concentration of a given disinfectant in mg/*L* times the disinfectant's contact time in minutes.

CHECK SAMPLING CHECK SAMPLING

Whenever an initial or routine sample analysis indicates that a Maximum Contaminant Level (MCL) has been exceeded, *CHECK SAMPLING* is required to confirm the routine sampling results. Check sampling is in addition to the routine sampling program.

CHLORAMINATION (KLOR-ah-min-NAY-shun) CHLORAMINATION

The application of chlorine and ammonia to water to form chloramines for the purpose of disinfection.

CHRONIC HEALTH EFFECT CHRONIC HEALTH EFFECT

An adverse effect on a human or animal body with symptoms that develop slowly over a long period of time or that recur frequently.

CONSUMER CONFIDENCE REPORTS CONSUMER CONFIDENCE REPORTS

An annual report prepared by a water utility to communicate with its consumers. The report provides consumers with information on the source and quality of their drinking water. The report is an opportunity for positive communication with consumers and to convey the importance of paying for good quality drinking water.

ENTERIC ENTERIC

Of intestinal origin, especially applied to wastes or bacteria.

HETEROTROPHIC (HET-er-o-TROF-ick) HETEROTROPHIC

Describes organisms that use organic matter for energy and growth. Animals, fungi and most bacteria are heterotrophs.

INFORMATION COLLECTION RULE (ICR) INFORMATION COLLECTION RULE (ICR)

The Information Collection Rule (ICR) specifies the requirements for monitoring microbial contaminants and disinfection by-products (DBPs) by large public water systems (PWSs). It also requires large PWSs to conduct either bench- or pilot-scale testing of advanced treatment techniques.

INITIAL SAMPLING INITIAL SAMPLING

The very first sampling conducted under the Safe Drinking Water Act (SDWA) for each of the applicable contaminant categories.

MBAS MBAS

Methylene - **B**lue - **A**ctive **S**ubstances. These substances are used in surfactants or detergents.

MCL MCL

Maximum **C**ontaminant **L**evel. The largest allowable amount. MCLs for various water quality indicators are specified in the National Primary Drinking Water Regulations (NPDWR).

MCLG MCLG

Maximum **C**ontaminant **L**evel **G**oal. MCLGs are health goals based entirely on health effects. They are a preliminary standard set but not enforced by EPA. MCLs consider health effects, but also take into consideration the feasibility and cost of analysis and treatment of the regulated MCL. Although often less stringent than the corresponding MCLG, the MCL is set to protect health.

NTU   NTU

Nephelometric **T**urbidity **U**nits. See TURBIDITY UNITS (TU).

pCi/*L*   pCi/*L*

picoCurie per liter. A picoCurie is a measure of radioactivity. One picoCurie of radioactivity is equivalent to 0.037 nuclear disintegrations per second.

ROUTINE SAMPLING   ROUTINE SAMPLING

Sampling repeated on a regular basis.

SANITARY SURVEY   SANITARY SURVEY

A detailed evaluation and/or inspection of a source of water supply and all conveyances, storage, treatment and distribution facilities to ensure protection of the water supply from all pollution sources.

SURFACTANT (sir-FAC-tent)   SURFACTANT

Abbreviation for surface-active agent. The active agent in detergents that possesses a high cleaning ability.

THM   THM

See **TRI**HALOMETHANES.

THRESHOLD ODOR NUMBER (TON)   THRESHOLD ODOR NUMBER (TON)

The greatest dilution of a sample with odor-free water that still yields a just-detectable odor.

TRIHALOMETHANES (THMs) (tri-HAL-o-METH-hanes)   TRIHALOMETHANES (THMs)

Derivatives of methane, CH_4, in which three halogen atoms (chlorine or bromine) are substituted for three of the hydrogen atoms. Often formed during chlorination by reactions with natural organic materials in the water. The resulting compounds (THMs) are suspected of causing cancer.

TURBIDITY UNITS (TU)   TURBIDITY UNITS (TU)

Turbidity units are a measure of the cloudiness of water. If measured by a nephelometric (deflected light) instrumental procedure, turbidity units are expressed in nephelometric turbidity units (NTU) or simply TU. Those turbidity units obtained by visual methods are expressed in Jackson Turbidity Units (JTU) which are a measure of the cloudiness of water; they are used to indicate the clarity of water. There is no real connection between NTUs and JTUs. The Jackson turbidimeter is a visual method and the nephelometer is an instrumental method based on deflected light.

CHAPTER 22.   DRINKING WATER REGULATIONS

(Lesson 1 of 2 Lessons)

All water treatment plant operators need to be thoroughly familiar with the state and federal laws and standards that apply to domestic water supply systems. These regulations are the goals and guideposts for the water supply industry. Their purpose is to ensure the uniform delivery of safe and aesthetically pleasing drinking water to the public.

This chapter will introduce the major drinking water regulations and explain the monitoring and reporting requirements. For more detailed information, you will need to refer to current copies of your state's regulations and the most recent federal standards. These publications should be made readily available to all operators since operators will only know whether their system is in compliance by comparing monitoring test data with the actual current regulations.

22.0 HISTORY OF DRINKING WATER LAWS AND STANDARDS

Up until shortly after the turn of the century, there were no standards for drinking water. The first standards, established in 1914, were designed in large part to control waterborne bacteria and viruses that cause diseases such as cholera, typhoid, and dysentery. These new standards were overwhelmingly successful in curbing the spread of such diseases. However, with time and technology, other types of contaminants, this time chemicals, again stirred public concern. In 1962 the U.S. Public Health Service (the forerunner of the U.S. Environmental Protection Agency) revised the national drinking water standards to include limits on selected organic chemicals.

In 1972, a series of reports detailing organic contamination in the drinking water supplied to the residents of New Orleans from the Mississippi River triggered profound changes in drinking water regulations. A study by the Environmental Defense Fund found that people drinking treated Mississippi River water in New Orleans had a greater chance of developing certain cancers than those in neighboring areas whose drinking water came from groundwater sources. Heightened public awareness and concern regarding cancer became major factors behind the push for legislative action on the issue of drinking water contamination. The finding of suspected carcinogens in drinking water established a widespread sense of urgency that led to the passage and signing into law of the Safe Drinking Water Act in December, 1974.

The Safe Drinking Water Act (SDWA) gave the federal government, through the U.S. Environmental Protection Agency (EPA), the authority to:

- Set national standards regulating the levels of contaminants in drinking water;

- Require public water systems to monitor and report their levels of identified contaminants; and

- Establish uniform guidelines specifying the acceptable treatment technologies for cleansing drinking water of unsafe levels of pollutants.

While the SDWA gave EPA responsibility for promulgating (passing into law) drinking water regulations, it gave state regulatory agencies the opportunity to assume primary responsibility for enforcing those regulations.

Implementation of the SDWA has greatly improved basic drinking water purity across the nation. However, recent EPA surveys of surface water and groundwater indicate the presence of synthetic organic chemicals in 20 percent of the nation's water sources, with a small percentage at levels of concern. In addition, research studies suggest that some naturally occurring contaminants may pose even greater risks to human health than the synthetic contaminants. Further, there is growing concern about microbial and radon contamination.

In the years following passage of the SDWA, Congress felt that EPA was slow to regulate contaminants and states were lax in enforcing the law. Consequently, in 1986 Congress enacted amendments designed to strengthen the 1974 SDWA. These amendments set deadlines for the establishment of maximum contaminant levels, placed greater emphasis on enforcement, authorized penalties for tampering with drinking water supplies, mandated the complete elimination of lead from drinking water, and placed considerable emphasis on the protection of underground drinking water sources.

The 1986 SDWA amendments set up a timetable under which EPA was required to develop primary standards for 83 contaminants. Other major provisions of the 1986 SDWA amendments required EPA to:

1. Define an approved treatment technique for each regulated contaminant,

2. Specify criteria for filtration of surface water supplies,

3. Specify criteria for disinfection of surface and groundwater supplies, and

4. Prohibit the use of lead products in materials used to convey drinking water.

To comply with the provisions of the 1986 SDWA amendments, the EPA, the states, and the water supply industry undertook significant new programs to clean up the country's water supplies.

On August 6, 1996, the President signed new Safe Drinking Water Act (SDWA) amendments into law as Public Law (PL) 104-182. These amendments made sweeping changes to the existing SDWA, created several new programs, and included a total authorization of more than $12 billion in federal funds for various drinking water programs and activities from fiscal year (FY) 1997 through FY 2003.

Topics covered in the amendments include arsenic research, assistance for water infrastructure and watersheds, assistance to colonias (low-income communities located along the U.S.-Mexico border), backwash water recycling, bottled water, capacity development (technical, financial, and managerial), consumer awareness, contaminant selection and standard-setting authority, definitions of public water system, community water system and noncommunity water system, disinfectants and disinfection by-products, drinking water studies and research, effective date of regulations, enforcement, environmental finance centers and capacity clearinghouse, estrogenic substances screening program, conditions that could qualify a water system for an exemption, groundwater disinfection, groundwater protection programs, lead plumbing and pipes, monitoring and information gathering, monitoring relief, monitoring for unregulated contaminants, occurrence of contaminants in drinking water database, operator certification, primacy, public notification, drinking water regulations for radon, review of NPDWRs (National Primary Drinking Water Regulations), risk assessment application to establishing NPDWRs, small systems (technical assistance, treatment technology, variances), source water quality assessment and petition programs, state revolving loan fund, authorization to promulgate an NPDWR for sulfate, Surface Water Treatment Rule (SWTR) compliance, variance treatment technologies, water conservation and waterborne disease study and training. For additional information and details

see "Overview of the Safe Drinking Water Act Amendments of 1996," by Frederick W. Pontius, *JOURNAL AMERICAN WATER WORKS ASSOCIATION*, October 1996, pages 22-33.

Operators are urged to develop close working relationships with their local regulatory agencies to keep themselves informed of the frequent changes in regulations and requirements.

QUESTIONS

Write your answers in a notebook and then compare your answers with those on page 554.

22.0A What were the first drinking water standards designed to control?

22.0B Why is it important for operators to establish good working relationships with local regulatory agencies?

22.1 HOW EPA DEVELOPS DRINKING WATER STANDARDS

The process by which EPA sets drinking water standards is both long and complicated. It involves deciding which contaminants may endanger public health, conducting studies of the effects of these contaminants, defining the maximum safe level of each contaminant, estimating the costs and benefits of regulation, proposing a standard or limit, listening to and evaluating public reactions to the proposed standard, revising the standard (if needed), proposing the standard in final form, seeking and evaluating additional public input, and finally, publishing the standard. The entire process by which a standard is proposed and promulgated is governed by strict procedural guidelines. It often takes three or more years to produce a standard. The remainder of this section describes the general types of contaminants that are considered public health threats and how EPA decides which contaminants to regulate first, how it approaches the task of regulating contaminants, and how it defines a standard.

22.10 Types of Contaminants

Five types of primary contaminants are considered to be of public health importance:

1. *INORGANIC CONTAMINANTS*, such as lead and mercury;

2. *ORGANIC CONTAMINANTS*, which include pesticides, herbicides, trihalomethanes, solvents, and other synthetic organic compounds;

3. *TURBIDITY*, such as small particles suspended in water which interfere with light penetration and disinfection;

4. *MICROBIAL CONTAMINANTS*, such as bacteria, viruses, and protozoa; and

5. *RADIOLOGICAL CONTAMINANTS*, which include natural and manmade sources of radiation.

22.11 Identifying Contaminants To Be Regulated

The 1986 SDWA required EPA to establish a priority list of contaminants which may have adverse health effects and may require regulation. The 1996 SDWA amendments retained the list of 83 contaminants developed earlier but revised the process by which contaminants are selected for regulation. Before selecting a contaminant for regulation, the EPA must now consult with the scientific community, solicit public comments, and demonstrate that the contaminant actually occurs in public water systems. For this latter purpose, the 1996 amendments require EPA to establish an occurrence database by August 1999. The database will contain information on regulated and unregulated contaminants and the information will be available to the public.

To regulate a substance, EPA must demonstrate that the contaminant meets three criteria:

1. The contaminant has an adverse effect on human health,

2. It occurs or is likely to occur in public water systems at a frequency and concentration of significance to public health, and

3. Regulation of the contaminant offers a meaningful opportunity to reduce health risks for people served by public water systems.

In addition to meeting these three criteria, EPA must also weigh the relative health risks of various contaminants being considered for regulation, the risk reduction that regulation would accomplish, and the costs of implementing the regulations.

By August 2001, EPA must select at least five contaminants from its Drinking Water Contaminant Candidate List (DWCCL) and decide whether to regulate them. The DWCCL currently lists 50 chemicals and 10 microbial contaminants. Of these, 19 chemicals and one microorganism have been rated as high priorities for regulation, and it is from these 20 that EPA will select at least five candidates for regulation.

22.12 Unregulated Contaminants

The SDWA also requires public water supply systems to conduct monitoring for a number of unregulated contaminants (see Table 22.1 and the SDWA poster provided with this manual). The purpose of this monitoring is to assist EPA in identifying the extent of contamination for specific contaminants. These unregulated contaminants are divided into three categories: (1) compounds that can be readily analyzed by the laboratory, (2) contaminants that have a limited localized occurrence and those that require special handling, and (3) compounds that the state feels are important to monitor.

Always keep in mind that EPA's regulatory process is basically just that — a process. No list is permanent; regulations change frequently as new information becomes available. Revisions in the list of unregulated contaminants are expected to be finalized in August 1998. Water treatment plant operators must continually seek opportunities to learn about the regulations that affect the water industry. Also operators should feel free to express their concerns regarding the regulations and the regulatory process to EPA.

TABLE 22.1 UNREGULATED CONTAMINANTS
(April 1998)

Chloroform	Chloromethane
Bromodichloromethane	Bromomethane
Chlorodibromomethane	1,2,3-Trichloropropane
Bromoform	1,1,1,2-Tetrachloroethane
Dibromomethane	Chloroethane
m-Dichlorobenzene	2,2-Dichloropropane
1,1-Dichloropropene	o-Chlorotoluene
1,1-Dichloroethane	p-Chlorotoluene
1,1,2-Tetrachloroethane	Bromobenzene
1,3-Dichloropropane	1,3-Dichloropropene

QUESTIONS

Write your answers in a notebook and then compare your answers with those on page 554.

22.1A List the five types of primary contaminants considered to be of public health importance.

22.1B What criteria must be met before EPA selects a contaminant for regulation?

22.1C Why are water systems required to monitor unregulated contaminants?

22.13 Schedule (1998 Forward)

Compliance with the 1996 SDWA amendments requires EPA to complete the following major activities by the target dates listed.

ARSENIC

The interim standard is 0.05 mg/*L*. A final rule is expected by January 2001.

CONSUMER CONFIDENCE REPORTS (CCRs)

Final rule is expected by August 1998.

DISINFECTANTS/DISINFECTION BY-PRODUCTS RULE (D/DBP RULE)

Final Stage 1 rule is expected in November 1998 and final Stage 2 rule is expected in May 2002. (See Section 22.23 for further information about the D/DBP Rule.)

ENHANCED SURFACE WATER TREATMENT RULE (ESWTR)

Final interim rule is expected in November 1998 and final long-term Stage 1 rule is expected in November 2000.

Final Stage 2 rule is expected by May 2002.

GROUND WATER DISINFECTION RULE (GWDR)

Final rule establishing disinfection requirements for groundwater systems is expected in November 2000.

LEAD AND COPPER RULE

Final rule (revisions of current Lead and Copper Rule) is expected in summer 1998.

PUBLIC NOTIFICATION REGULATIONS

Final rule revising the SDWA public notice requirements is expected in September 1999.

RADIONUCLIDES (other than radon)

By December 2000, EPA will evaluate proposed regulations for radium (including radium 226, radium 228, uranium, alpha emitters, and beta and photon emitters) and issue final rules for radium and uranium or explain why no regulation is necessary for radium.

RADON

Final rule is expected in August 2000.

SULFATE

By August 2001, EPA will decide whether to regulate sulfate. If EPA decides to regulate, a final rule is expected by February 2005.

FILTER BACKWASH RECYCLING

EPA is required to regulate the recycling of filter backwash water no later than August 6, 2000. Present plans are to include the regulation of backwash water prior to that date in the Enhanced Surface Water Treatment Rule.

UNREGULATED CONTAMINANT MONITORING

Final rule revising current unregulated contaminant monitoring requirements is expected in August 1998.

22.14 Setting Standards

A standard is usually the maximum level of a substance that EPA has deemed acceptable in drinking water. The first step in the setting of a standard is to study the human and animal health effects of a given chemical. These studies are normally performed using rats or mice. Based on these studies, EPA establishes a "no observed adverse effect level" (NOAEL). A safety factor is added to the NOAEL and the result is an acceptable daily intake limit of the chemical in question. The limit is adjusted to take into account the average weight and water consumption of the consumer, and the resulting figure is called a maximum contaminant level goal, or MCLG. By policy, the EPA sets MCLGs at zero for known or probable human carcinogens. MCLGs for noncarcinogens are set at a level where no adverse health effects would occur with a margin of safety.

The maximum contaminant level goal represents what EPA believes to be a safe level of consumption based solely on its studies of health effects. It is, however, a goal rather than an immediately achievable constituent limit. To develop more realistic, enforceable limits, EPA further revises the MCLG to take into account existing laboratory detection technology, costs, and reasonableness. After adjusting for these factors, EPA sets the maximum contaminant level (MCL) as close to the MCLG as is realistically feasible. The important difference between the two levels is that the MCLG is a nonenforceable goal and the MCL is an enforceable standard.

EPA has established standards (maximum contaminant levels) for chemicals, pesticides, bacteria and viruses, radioactivity, turbidity, and trihalomethanes. (Refer to the posters included with this manual for a complete listing of current (1998) MCLs.) Most of these substances occur naturally in our environment and in the foods we eat. However, the MCLs apply whether the contaminant is from naturally occurring sources or from manmade pollution. The national drinking water standards set by EPA reflect the levels we can safely consume in our water, taking into account the amounts we are exposed to from these other sources.

Drinking water regulations are sometimes called "interim" regulations because research continues on drinking water contaminants. The existing standards may be strengthened and new standards may be established for other substances based on studies being conducted by the National Academy of Sciences, EPA, and others. The 1996 SDWA amendments gave EPA the authority to issue interim regulations for contaminants which do not appear on the Drinking Water Contaminant Candidate List if the agency determines that the contaminant presents an urgent threat to public health. In making this determination, EPA must consult with the Department of Health and Human Services.

22.15 Types of Water Systems

All of the drinking water regulations apply to all public water systems. It makes no difference whether the water system is publicly or privately owned. A PUBLIC WATER SYSTEM (PWS) is defined as any system which:

1. Has at least 15 service connections, or

2. Regularly serves an average of at least 25 individuals daily at least 60 days out of the year.

Any water system that provides services for fewer connections or persons than this is not covered by the SDWA. Certain other individuals and residences also are excluded, such as those whose water is supplied by an irrigation, mining, or industrial water system. However, regardless of size, all operators must strive to provide consumers with a potable drinking water.

Drinking water regulations also take into account the type of population served by the system and classify water systems as community or noncommunity systems. Therefore, in order to understand what requirements apply to any specific system, it is first necessary to determine whether the system is considered a community system or a noncommunity system. A COMMUNITY WATER SYSTEM is defined as one which:

1. Has at least 15 service connections used by all-year residents, or

2. Regularly serves at least 25 all-year residents.

Any public water system that is not a community water system is classified as a NONCOMMUNITY WATER SYSTEM. Restaurants, campgrounds, and hotels could be considered noncommunity systems for purposes of drinking water regulations.

In addition to distinguishing between community and noncommunity water systems, EPA identifies some small systems as NONTRANSIENT NONCOMMUNITY systems if they regularly serve at least 25 of the same persons over 6 months per year. This classification applies to water systems for facilities such as schools or factories where the consumers served are nearly the same every day but do not actually live at the facility. In general, nontransient noncommunity systems must meet the same requirements as community systems.

A fourth type of system, TRANSIENT NONCOMMUNITY, is a system that does not regularly serve drinking water to at least 25 of the same persons over 6 months per year. This classification is used by EPA only in regulating nitrate levels and total coliform. Examples of a transient noncommunity system might be campgrounds or service stations if those facilities do not meet the definition of a community, noncommunity, or nontransient noncommunity system.

QUESTIONS

Write your answers in a notebook and then compare your answers with those on page 554.

22.1D   What is the MCLG for known or probable human carcinogens?

22.1E   What is the difference between a maximum contaminant level (MCL) and a maximum contaminant level goal (MCLG)?

22.1F   Define a community water system.

22.2   PRIMARY DRINKING WATER STANDARDS

Primary Standards or MCLs are set for substances that are thought to pose a threat to health when present in drinking water at certain levels. Because these substances are of health concern, primary standards are enforceable by law. (In contrast, secondary standards relate to cosmetic factors and are not federally enforceable.) A primary standard is usually expressed as a maximum contaminant level (MCL). Some contaminants, such as pathogenic organisms, are very difficult or expensive to measure so EPA requires the use of specific treatment techniques (disinfection or filtration, for example) which are known to be effective in reducing the health risks of these contaminants. Treatment technique requirements, therefore, are also referred to as primary standards. Table 22.2 lists the current (April 1998) primary standards and health concerns associated with the contaminants.

22.20   Inorganic Chemical Standards

Inorganic chemicals are metals, salts, and other chemical compounds that do not contain carbon. The health concerns about inorganic chemicals are not centered on cancer, but rather on their suspected links to several different human disorders. For example, lead is suspected of contributing to mental retardation in children. The following paragraphs briefly discuss each of the inorganic contaminants regulated by the national drinking water standards. Waters exceeding the MCL for these elements for short periods of time will pose no immediate threat to health. However, studies show that these substances must be controlled because consumption of drinking water that exceeds these standards over long periods of time may prove harmful.

22.200   Antimony

Antimony is used in the production of ceramics, glassware, and pigments. Most exposures to antimony occur in industrial settings where workers may inhale dust containing particles of the metal. Ingestion of antimony can alter cholesterol and glucose levels and may cause chromosome damage in humans. The MCL for antimony is 0.006 mg/L.

22.201   Arsenic

This element occurs naturally in the environment, especially in the western United States, and it is also used in insecticides. Arsenic is found in foods, tobacco, shellfish, drinking water, and in the air in some locations. The national

standard for arsenic is 0.05 milligram per liter of water. Anyone who drinks water that continuously exceeds the national standard by a substantial amount over a lifetime may experience fatigue and loss of energy. Extremely high levels can cause poisoning.

The regulation of arsenic has been vigorously debated for more than ten years. In 1997, EPA released a health effects study plan. Under this plan, EPA will work with the American Water Works Association (AWWA) Research Foundation and the Association of California Water Agencies to assess the health risks from exposure to low levels of arsenic. Based on the results of these studies, EPA must propose an MCL for arsenic by January 1, 2000, and a final rule must be promulgated by January 1, 2001.

22.202   Asbestos

The general term "asbestos" refers to a family of fibrous silicate minerals which have been widely used in the manufacture of commercial products. Asbestos fibers are flexible enough to be woven into fabric that does not conduct electricity, is heat resistant and is chemically inert. Some examples of products containing asbestos include floor and ceiling tiles, paper products, paint and caulking, plastics, brake linings, insulation cement, and filters. Asbestos-cement pipe is a potential source of contamination of drinking water. Deterioration of this pipe material with age and with exposure to corrosive water is thought to release asbestos particles. Mining for asbestos minerals has also contributed to the contamination of some drinking water sources in Canada and the United States.

Scientific evidence on the harmful effects of asbestos consumed in drinking water is less conclusive than the evidence relating to inhaled asbestos. Nonetheless, the MCL of 7 million fibers/liter is presently thought to provide an adequate margin of safety.

22.203   Barium

Although not as widespread as arsenic, this element also occurs naturally in the environment in some areas. Barium can also enter water supplies through industrial waste discharges. Small doses of barium are not harmful. However, it is quite dangerous when consumed in large quantities and will bring on increased blood pressure, nerve damage, and even death. The maximum amount of barium allowed in drinking water by the national standard is 2 milligrams per liter of water.

22.204   Beryllium

The major source of beryllium in the environment is the combustion of coal and oil. Airborne particulates containing

TABLE 22.2 NATIONAL PRIMARY DRINKING WATER STANDARDS

Contaminant	MCL	Health Effects
Inorganics		
Antimony	0.006 mg/L	decreases longevity, alters cholesterol and glucose levels
Arsenic	0.05 mg/L	skin/nervous system toxicity; possible cancer
Asbestos	7 million fibers/L	possible cancer
Barium	2.0 mg/L	circulatory system effects
Beryllium	0.004 mg/L	bone/lung damage; possible cancer
Cadmium	0.005 mg/L	kidney effects
Chromium	0.1 mg/L	skin sensitization; liver/kidney/circulatory/nervous system disorders and respiratory problems
Copper	1.3 mg/L[a]	nervous system/kidney/gastrointestinal effects; toxicity
Cyanide	0.2 mg/L	spleen/liver/brain effects
Fluoride	4.0 mg/L	brown staining and/or pitting of teeth
Lead	0.015 mg/L[a] (at tap)	interference with red blood cell chemistry; developmental delays in children; blood pressure effects in some adults; toxic to infants and pregnant women
Mercury	0.002 mg/L	kidney disorders
Nitrate (as N) and	10.0 mg/L	Methemoglobinemia ("blue-baby"
Nitrite (as N)[b]	1.0 mg/L	syndrome)
Selenium	0.05 mg/L	nervous system damage
Thallium	0.002 mg/L	liver/kidney/intestines/brain effects
Organics		
VOLATILE ORGANICS		
Benzene	0.005 mg/L	possible cancer
Carbon tetrachloride	0.005 mg/L	possible cancer
o-Dichlorobenzene	0.6 mg/L	kidney and liver effects; blood cell damage
p-Dichlorobenzene	0.075 mg/L	kidney and liver effects
1,2-Dichloroethane	0.005 mg/L	possible cancer
1,1-Dichloroethylene	0.007 mg/L	kidney and liver damage
cis-1,2-Dichloroethylene	0.07 mg/L	nervous system/liver/circulatory system damage
trans-1,2-Dichloroethylene	0.1 mg/L	nervous system/liver/circulatory system damage
Dichloromethane	0.005 mg/L	possible cancer
1,2-Dichloropropane	0.005 mg/L	possible cancer
Ethylbenzene	0.7 mg/L	kidney/liver/nervous system damage
Monochlorobenzene	0.1 mg/L	kidney/liver/nervous system damage
Styrene	0.1 mg/L	nervous system/liver damage
Tetrachloroethylene	0.005 mg/L	possible cancer
Toluene	1.0 mg/L	nervous system/kidney/liver damage
1,2,4-Trichlorobenzene	0.07 mg/L	adrenal gland and internal organ damage
1,1,1-Trichloroethane	0.2 mg/L	liver/nervous system/circulatory system damage
1,1,2-Trichloroethane	0.005 mg/L	liver/kidney effects
Trichloroethylene (TCE)	0.005 mg/L	possible cancer
Vinyl chloride	0.002 mg/L	possible cancer
Xylenes (total)	10.0 mg/L	liver/kidney/nervous system damage
PESTICIDES AND SYNTHETIC ORGANICS		
Acrylamide	treatment technique	possible cancer; nervous system effects
Alachlor	0.002 mg/L	possible cancer
Atrazine	0.003 mg/L	cardiac/reproductive system damage
Benzo[a]pyrene	0.0002 mg/L	possible cancer
Carbofuran	0.04 mg/L	nervous system/reproductive system damage
Chlordane	0.002 mg/L	possible cancer
Dalapon	0.2 mg/L	kidney/liver damage
Dibromochloropropane (DBCP)	0.0002 mg/L	possible cancer
Di(2-ethylhexyl)adipate	0.4 mg/L	liver/reproductive system effects
Di(2-ethylhexyl)phthalate	0.006 mg/L	possible cancer
Dinoseb	0.007 mg/L	thyroid/reproductive system damage
Diquat	0.02 mg/L	kidney/gastrointestinal damage; cataract risk
Endothall	0.1 mg/L	liver/kidney/gastrointestinal and reproductive system effects
Endrin	0.002 mg/L	liver/kidney/heart damage
Epichlorohydrin	treatment technique	possible cancer
Ethylene dibromide (EDB)	0.00005 mg/L	possible cancer
Glyphosate	0.7 mg/L	liver/kidney damage
Heptachlor	0.0004 mg/L	possible cancer
Heptachlor epoxide	0.0002 mg/L	possible cancer

TABLE 22.2   NATIONAL PRIMARY DRINKING WATER STANDARDS (continued)

Contaminant	MCL	Health Effects
PESTICIDES AND SYNTHETIC ORGANICS (continued)		
Hexachlorobenzene	0.001 mg/L	possible cancer
Hexachlorocyclopentadiene	0.05 mg/L	stomach/kidney damage
Lindane	0.0002 mg/L	nervous system/immune system/liver/kidney effects
Methoxychlor	0.04 mg/L	nervous system/reproductive system/kidney/liver effects
Oxamyl (Vydate)	0.2 mg/L	kidney damage
PCBs	0.0005 mg/L	possible cancer
Pentachlorophenol	0.001 mg/L	liver/kidney damage
Picloram	0.5 mg/L	liver/kidney damage
Simazine	0.004 mg/L	possible cancer
Toxaphene	0.003 mg/L	possible cancer
2,4-D	0.07 mg/L	liver/kidney/nervous system damage
2,3,7,8-TCDD (Dioxin)	0.00000003 mg/L	possible cancer
2,4,5-TP (Silvex)	0.05 mg/L	liver/kidney damage
Microbial		
Total Coliform	1 per 100 mL	indicators of disease-causing organisms
	<40 samples/mo — no more than 1 positive	
	>40 samples/mo — no more than 5% positive	
Giardia lamblia	3-log (99.9%) removal[c]	Giardiasis; gastrointestinal effects
Legionella	treatment technique[c]	Legionnaire's Disease; affects respiratory system
Enteric viruses	4-log (99.99%) removal[c]	gastrointestinal and other viral infections
Heterotrophic bacteria	treatment technique[c]	gastrointestinal infections
Physical		
Turbidity[c]	0.5 to 5 NTU	interferes with disinfection
Radionuclides		
Gross alpha particles	15 pCi/L	cancer risk
Gross beta particles[d]	4 mrem/yr	cancer risk
Radium 226 & 228	5 pCi/L	bone cancer
Disinfection By-Products		
TTHMs[e]	0.10 mg/L	cancer risk

[a]   Action level for treatment.
[b]   Applies to community, nontransient noncommunity, and transient noncommunity water systems.
[c]   Applies to systems using surface water or groundwater under the influence of surface water.
[d]   Applies to surface water systems serving more than 100,000 persons and any system determined by the state to be vulnerable.
[e]   Applies to systems serving more than 10,000 persons and also to all surface water systems that meet the criteria for avoiding filtration.

beryllium can be inhaled or washed by precipitation into drinking water supplies. Animal studies show that when large doses of beryllium are ingested, it is carried by the bloodstream from the stomach to the liver but it is gradually transferred to the animal's bones. The maximum contaminant level for beryllium is 0.004 mg/*L*.

22.205 Cadmium

Only extremely small amounts of this element are found in natural waters in the United States. Waste discharges from the electroplating, photography, insecticide, and metallurgy industries can increase cadmium levels. The most common source of cadmium in our drinking water is from galvanized pipes and fixtures. The maximum amount of cadmium allowed in drinking water by the national standard is 0.005 milligram per liter of water.

22.206 Chromium

This metal is found in cigarettes, some of our foods, and the air. Some studies suggest that in very small amounts, chromium may be essential to human beings, but this has not been proven. The national standard for chromium is 0.1 milligram per liter of water.

22.207 Copper

Copper in drinking water usually results from the reaction of aggressive water on copper plumbing. Treatment of surface water in storage reservoirs to control algae may also cause high levels of copper. Copper is an essential nutrient; adults require 2 mg daily and children of preschool age require about 0.1 mg daily for normal growth. Excess copper intake can cause Wilson's Disease and exposure over a long period of time can cause liver damage.

The presence of copper in drinking water is also undesirable because of its aesthetic effects. At low levels (0.5 mg/*L* in soft waters) blue or blue-green staining of porcelain occurs. At higher levels (4 mg/*L*), it will stain clothing and blond hair. Concentrations greater than 1 mg/*L* can produce insoluble green curds when reacting with soap.

The primary standard for copper is a treatment technique which requires action to be taken when more than 10 percent of the taps sampled exceed the action level of 1.3 mg/*L*. Treatment technique requirements are contained in the Lead and Copper Rule which is described in Section 22.2010, "Lead and Copper."

22.208 Cyanide

Cyanide is a common ingredient of rat poisons, silver and metal polishes, and photo processing chemicals. Ingestion of even very small amounts of sodium cyanide or potassium cyanide (both readily available to the general public) can cause death within a few minutes to a few hours. Typical symptoms of cyanide poisoning include nausea without vomiting, anxiety, vertigo, lower jaw stiffness, convulsions, paralysis, irregular heartbeat, and coma. The primary standard for cyanide is 0.2 mg/*L*.

22.209 Fluoride

This is a natural mineral and many drinking waters contain some fluoride. Fluoride produces two effects, depending on its concentration, and EPA has set both primary and secondary limits to regulate it. At levels of 6 to 8 mg/*L* fluoride may cause skeletal fluorosis (the bones become brittle) and stiffening of the joints. On the basis of this health hazard, fluoride has been added to the list of primary standards.

At levels of 2 mg/*L* and greater fluoride may cause dental fluorosis, which is discoloration and mottling of the teeth, especially in children. EPA has reclassified dental fluorosis as a cosmetic effect, raised the primary drinking water standard from 1.4 – 2 mg/*L* to 4 mg/*L*, and established a secondary standard of 2 mg/*L* for fluoride.

22.2010 Lead and Copper

Lead is found in the air and in our food. This metal comes from galvanized pipes, solder used with copper pipes, auto exhausts, and other sources. Excessive amounts may cause nervous system disorders or brain or kidney damage and can retard the physical and mental development of children.

Copper is an essential nutrient but excessive amounts can cause Wilson's Disease and liver damage. Corrosion of copper water pipes releases this metal into drinking water. Since corrosive waters are a primary cause of both lead and copper contamination, the EPA has focused its regulatory approach on reducing drinking water corrosivity and removing pipes or solder containing lead from drinking water distribution systems.

EPA promulgated the Lead and Copper Rule on June 7, 1991. Revisions of the rule are expected in 1998. The Rule applies to all community water systems and to nontransient noncommunity systems. Each system was required to begin an initial lead and copper sampling program by July 1993. The Lead and Copper Rule sets action levels for lead and copper and specifies treatment techniques which must be implemented when the action levels are exceeded. The lead level that triggers enforcement of treatment technique requirements is 0.015 mg/*L* and the level for copper is 1.3 mg/*L*. If a water system exceeds the action levels in more than 10 percent of its samples, steps must be taken to control corrosion in the distribution system, educate the public about the harmful effects of lead, and advise the public what steps should be taken to reduce their exposure. Continued failure to meet the action levels after installation of optimum corrosion control measures will usually mean the water system must conduct source water quality studies and implement treatment to reduce source water lead levels. If corrosion control and source water treatment measures fail to bring the contaminant levels below the action levels, water systems will be required to begin a program of replacing lead service lines.

All water systems are required to optimize corrosion control; that is to say, they must do the best they can to control corrosion. Small and medium-sized systems are considered to have optimized corrosion control if they meet the lead and copper action levels during each of two consecutive six-month sampling periods. Large systems have optimized corrosion control if the difference between the source water lead level and the 90th percentile tap water lead level is less than 0.005 mg/L, and the 90th percentile copper concentration is less than or equal to half the copper action level (0.65 mg/L) for two consecutive six-month periods. Any system which is achieving optimal corrosion control (and therefore meeting the action limits) is permitted to reduce monitoring and reporting frequencies.

Large water systems which do not meet the guidelines for optimal corrosion control are required to conduct studies of various types of corrosion control treatment and then submit to the state a plan that would adequately control corrosion in their distribution system. Small and medium-sized systems exceeding the action levels must make a written recommendation to the state for a proposed treatment method, but may also be required to conduct similar studies before the state makes a final determination. Once the state directs a water supplier to install treatment, the agency has 24 months to install the specified treatment and 12 months to collect follow-up samples to determine if the system is working. The state will also determine maximum acceptable levels for pH, alkalinity, calcium (if carbonate stabilization is used), orthophosphate (if an inhibitor with a phosphate compound is used), and silica (if an inhibitor with a silicate compound is used). The system must then continue to operate within these water quality guidelines.

If corrosion control methods fail to reduce lead and copper concentrations below the action levels, the water supplier must collect and analyze source water samples. Data from this sampling is sent to the state along with the water agency's recommended treatment plan for reducing contaminant levels. The state may accept the agency's recommended plan or may require some alternative treatment such as ion exchange, reverse osmosis, lime softening, or coagulation-filtration. When required to install source water treatment, the agency is allowed 24 months for installation and 12 months to collect follow-up samples of specific water quality indicators. Based on the results of the follow-up sampling, the state determines the maximum allowable source water lead and copper concentrations and the water system is required to meet these state limits on an ongoing basis.

Water systems that continue to exceed the lead action level even after installing optimal corrosion control treatment and source water treatment will have to begin a program to replace lead service lines within a maximum of 15 years.

SAMPLING GUIDELINES

The sampling required by the Lead and Copper Rule includes tap water sampling at the consumer's faucet and distribution system sampling. Tap water samples for initial and routine lead and copper monitoring must be collected at high risk locations, which are defined as homes with lead solder installed after 1982, homes with lead pipes, and homes with lead service lines. Tap water samples for water quality indicators (when required) should be taken from representative taps throughout the distribution system. The representative taps can be the same as total coliform sampling sites. These samples will be analyzed for water quality indicator levels to identify optimal treatment and monitor compliance with the Rule.

The Rule calls for first-draw or first-flush samples which are water samples taken after the water stands motionless in the plumbing pipes for at least six hours. This usually means taking a sample early in the day before water is used in the kitchen or bathroom. The Rule permits water utilities to instruct consumers in sampling techniques so that they may collect the samples. One-liter samples are needed.

Distribution system sampling conducted in connection with corrosion control studies requires samples from representative taps throughout the system as well as samples from entry points to the distribution system.

INITIAL AND BASE MONITORING SAMPLING FREQUENCIES

Compliance with the Lead and Copper Rule depends on meeting the action levels during two consecutive six-month monitoring periods. All public water systems are required to collect one sample for lead and copper analysis from the following number of sites during each six-month monitoring period.

System Size (Population)	No. of Sampling Sites (Initial Base Monitoring)	No. of Sampling Sites (Reduced Monitoring)
>100,000	100	50
10,001 to 100,000	60	30
3,301 to 10,000	40	20
501 to 3,300	20	10
101 to 500	10	5
≤100	5	5

If a system meets the lead and copper action levels or maintains optimal corrosion control treatment for two consecutive six-month periods, tap water sampling for lead and copper can be reduced to once per year and half the number of sites (see chart above). After three consecutive years of acceptable performance, tap water sampling can be reduced to once every three years at the reduced number of sites listed above.

WATER QUALITY INDICATOR SAMPLING FREQUENCIES

All large systems (more than 50,000 persons) and any small or medium-sized system that exceeds the lead or copper action level will be required to monitor for the following water quality indicators: pH, alkalinity, calcium, conductivity, orthophosphate, silica, and water temperature. Samples must be taken both from representative taps throughout the system and at entry points to the distribution system. Two tap water samples must be collected for each applicable water quality indicator from the following number of sites during each six-month monitoring period.

System Size (Population)	No. of Sampling Sites (Initial Base Monitoring)	No. of Sampling Sites (Reduced Monitoring)
>100,000	25	10
10,001 to 100,000	10	7
3,301 to 10,000	3	3
501 to 3,300	2	2
101 to 500	1	1
≤100	1	1

In addition to the sampling from representative taps, one sample must be collected every two weeks for each applicable water quality indicator at each entry point to the distribution system.

All large water systems and any small and medium-sized system that exceed the lead or copper action levels after installing optimal corrosion control treatment must continue to collect:

- Two samples for each applicable water quality indicator at each of the sampling sites (taps) every six months, and

- One sample for each applicable water quality indicator at each entry point to the distribution system every two weeks.

- After meeting water quality guidelines for two consecutive six-month monitoring periods, systems may reduce the number of tap samples collected (as indicated in the chart above), and after three consecutive years of acceptable performance they will be permitted to collect annual samples at the reduced number of sampling points.

CALCULATION OF 90TH PERCENTILE

The action levels that trigger implementation of treatment techniques to reduce lead and copper concentrations are based on the principle that no more than 10 percent of the samples should exceed the limit. To determine whether a system meets this test, it is necessary to figure out the lead or copper concentration on the sample that falls at the 90th percentile.

To calculate the 90th percentile value, write down the results from a set of samples arranging them in order of increasing or decreasing concentration. Number each sample beginning with the number 1 for the smallest concentration. Multiply the total number of samples (which will be the same as the number assigned to the highest concentration) by 0.9. Then use the value from this calculation to identify the sample with the same number. The concentration of the sample whose number matches your calculated value is the 90th percentile and is used in determining compliance with the action level. (For systems serving fewer than 100 people, the 90th percentile is the average of the highest concentration and the second highest concentration.)

PUBLIC EDUCATION

A public education program developed by the EPA must be delivered to water system customers within 60 days whenever the system exceeds the lead and/or copper action levels. The information describes the harmful effects of lead in drinking water and tells customers what they can do to reduce their exposure. The education program should continue as long as the system fails to meet the lead and/or copper action levels.

In conjunction with the public education program, the water system must offer to sample a customer's water if asked to do so. However, the water system is not required to pay for the sampling and analysis and is not required to collect and analyze the sample itself.

LEAD SERVICE LINE REPLACEMENT

Any water system that continues to exceed the lead and copper action levels even after optimizing corrosion control and installing source water treatment will be required to replace its lead distribution pipes within a maximum of 15 years. A lead pipeline qualifies for replacement if it contributes more than 15 parts per billion to the total tap water lead levels. Seven percent of the lines meeting this standard must be replaced annually.

22.2011   Mercury

Mercury is found naturally throughout the environment. Large increases in mercury levels in water can be caused by industrial and agricultural use. The health risk from mercury is greater from mercury in fish than simply from waterborne mercury. Mercury poisoning may have an *ACUTE HEALTH EFFECT*[1] in large doses, or a *CHRONIC HEALTH EFFECT*[2] in lower doses taken over an extended time period.

22.2012   Nitrate and Nitrite

Nitrate in drinking water above the national standard of 10 mg/L (as N) poses an immediate threat to children under three months of age. In some infants, excessive levels of nitrate have been known to react with intestinal bacteria that change nitrate to nitrite. Nitrite reacts with hemoglobin in the blood. This reaction will reduce the oxygen-carrying ability of the blood and produce an anemic condition commonly known as "blue baby."

Noncommunity systems *MAY* be allowed to serve water containing up to 20 mg/L nitrate if:

1. The water is not available to infants six months of age and younger;

2. Posting of the potential health hazard is maintained;

3. State and local health authorities are notified annually of nitrate levels that exceed 10 mg/L; and

4. No threat to health will result.

---

[1] *Acute Health Effect. An adverse effect on a human or animal body, with symptoms developing rapidly.*
[2] *Chronic Health Effect. An adverse effect on a human or animal body with symptoms that develop slowly over a long period of time or that recur frequently.*

22.2013 Selenium

This mineral occurs naturally in soil and plants, especially in western states. Selenium is found in meat and other foods. Although it is believed to be essential in the diet, there are indications that excessive amounts of selenium may be toxic. Studies are underway to determine the amount required for good nutrition and the amount that may be harmful.

The national standard for selenium is 0.01 milligram per liter of water. If a person's intake of selenium came only from drinking water, it would take an amount many times greater than the standard to produce any ill effects.

22.2014 Thallium

Thallium is an extremely toxic metal which is used in refining iron, cadmium, and zinc. It is also used for production of optical lenses, jewelry, semiconductors, dyes, and pigments. The most common source of thallium poisoning is ingestion of rat poisons and insecticides. Ingestion of thallium can injure a person's liver, kidneys, and nervous system and may also cause deafness and loss of vision. The primary standard (MCL) for thallium is 0.002 mg/L.

QUESTIONS

Write your answers in a notebook and then compare your answers with those on page 554.

22.2A   Why are primary standards sometimes expressed as treatment techniques rather than MCLs?

22.2B   What are inorganic chemicals?

22.2C   Why is arsenic listed as a primary contaminant?

22.2D   What are two harmful effects of excessive levels of fluoride?

22.2E   What are the sources of lead in drinking water?

22.2F   Why is nitrate considered an immediate threat to public health?

22.21 Organic Chemical Standards

Organic chemicals are either natural or synthetic chemical compounds that contain carbon. Synthetic organic chemicals (SOCs) are manmade compounds and are used throughout the world as pesticides, paints, dyes, solvents, plastics, and food additives. Volatile organic chemicals (VOCs) are a subcategory of organic chemicals. These chemicals are termed "volatile" because they evaporate easily. The most commonly found VOCs are trihalomethanes (THMs), trichloroethylene (TCE), tetrachloroethylene, and 1,1-dichloroethane. THMs were the first regulated VOCs when EPA finalized regulations in 1979.

The most common sources of organic contamination of drinking water are pesticides and herbicides, industrial solvents, and disinfection by-products (trihalomethanes). Millions of pounds of pesticides are used on croplands, forests, lawns, and gardens in the United States each year. They drain off into surface waters or seep into underground water supplies. Spills, poor storage, improper application, and haphazard disposal of organic chemicals have resulted in widespread groundwater contamination. This is a critical problem because once groundwater is contaminated, it may remain that way for a long time.

Many organic chemicals pose health problems if they get into drinking water and the water is not properly treated. The maximum limits for pesticides in drinking water are shown on Table 22.2. The next several paragraphs describe the sources and maximum contaminant levels of some of the most commonly used organic chemical contaminants.

22.210 Trichloroethylene (TCE)

Although the use of trichloroethylene is declining because of stringent regulations, it was, for many years, a common ingredient in household products (spot removers, rug cleaners, air fresheners), dry cleaning agents, industrial metal cleaners and polishes, refrigerants, and even anesthetics. Its wide range of use is perhaps why TCE is the organic contaminant most frequently encountered in groundwater. The MCL for TCE is 0.005 mg/L (5 μg/L).

22.211 1,1-Dichloroethylene

This solvent is used in manufacturing plastics and, more recently, in the production of 1,1,1-trichloroethane. At high doses, 1,1-dichloroethylene causes liver and kidney damage in animals. It also affects the central nervous system and heart of humans. The MCL for this chemical is 0.007 mg/L (7 μg/L).

22.212 Vinyl Chloride

Billions of pounds of this solvent are used annually in the United States to produce polyvinyl chloride (PVC), the most widely used ingredient for manufacturing plastics throughout the world. There is also evidence that vinyl chloride may be a biodegradation end-product of tri- and tetrachloroethylene under certain environmental conditions. There is strong laboratory evidence that vinyl chloride causes cancer in humans. The MCL for vinyl chloride is 0.002 mg/L (2 μg/L).

22.213 1,1,1-Trichloroethane

This chemical has replaced TCE in many industrial and household products. It is the principal solvent in septic tank degreasers, cutting oils, inks, shoe polishes, and many other products. Among the VOCs found in groundwaters, 1,1,1-trichloroethane and TCE are encountered most frequently and in the highest concentrations. It causes depression of the central nervous system and changes in the cardiovascular system and liver in humans and animals but as yet there is not enough evidence to conclude that it causes cancer in humans. The MCL for this contaminant is 0.2 mg/L (200 µg/L).

22.214 1,2-Dichloroethane

1,2-Dichloroethane is used as a solvent for fats, oils, waxes, gums, and resins. This chemical is a probable cause of cancer in humans. The MCL for 1,2-dichloroethane is 0.005 mg/L (5 µg/L).

22.215 Carbon Tetrachloride

Carbon tetrachloride was once a popular household solvent, a frequently used dry cleaning agent, and a charging agent for fire extinguishers. Since 1970, however, carbon tetrachloride has been banned from all use in consumer goods in the United States and in 1978 it was banned as an aerosol propellant. Currently its principal use is in the manufacture of fluorocarbons which are used as refrigerants. Carbon tetrachloride is a probable human carcinogen. The MCL for carbon tetrachloride is 0.005 mg/L (5 µg/L).

22.216 Benzene

Benzene is used primarily in the synthesis of styrene (for plastics), phenol (for resins), and cyclohexane (for nylon). Other uses include the production of detergents, drugs, dyes, and insecticides. Benzene is still being used as a solvent and as a component of gasoline. It is considered a probable human carcinogen. The MCL for benzene is 0.005 mg/L (5 µg/L).

22.217 Para-Dichlorobenzene (p-Dichlorobenzene)

The principal uses of this chemical are in moth control (balls, powders) and as lavatory deodorants. Para-Dichlorobenzene causes liver damage and is suspected of being an animal carcinogen. The MCL is 0.075 mg/L (75 µg/L).

QUESTIONS

Write your answers in a notebook and then compare your answers with those on page 554.

22.2G   What are organic chemicals?

22.2H   What have been the common uses of trichloroethylene (TCE)?

22.22 Microbial Standards

Bacteria, viruses, and other organisms have long been recognized as serious contaminants of drinking water. Organisms such as *Giardia*, *Cryptosporidium*, and *E. coli* (a type of coliform bacteria) cause almost immediate gastrointestinal illness when people consume them in water. Waterborne diseases such as typhoid, cholera, infectious hepatitis, and dysentery have been traced to improperly disinfected drinking water.

Many types of coliform bacteria from human and animal wastes may be found in drinking water if the water is not properly treated. Often the bacteria themselves do not cause diseases transmitted by water, although certain coliforms have been identified as the cause of "traveler's" diarrhea. In general, however, the presence of coliform bacteria indicates that other harmful organisms may be present in the water.

One microbial contaminant that is not currently regulated, *Cryptosporidium*, is being examined for future regulation. The regulations will most likely take the form of mandatory treatment techniques similar to the current regulations for *Giardia* and coliform bacteria. (For more complete information about *Cryptosporidium*, see Chapter 23, Section 23.1016, "*Cryptosporidium*."

Throughout the early 1990s, chemical contaminants in drinking water were the focus of EPA's regulatory efforts. With passage of the 1996 SDWA amendments, Congress directed EPA to focus on microbial contaminants over the next several years and to promulgate a series of new regulations to improve treatment effectiveness. Filtration and disinfection requirements for surface water systems are currently in place, but EPA is working on an Enhanced Surface Water Treatment Rule. Other future regulations include a new Ground Water Disinfection Rule and a Disinfectants/Disinfection By-Products Rule. When complete, these new regulations will significantly affect the water treatment processes of most water suppliers.

22.220 Total Coliform Rule

The primary standards (MCLs) for coliform bacteria have been established to indicate the likely presence of disease-causing bacteria. The Total Coliform Rule uses a presence-absence approach (rather than an estimation of how many coliforms are present) to determine compliance with the standards. The MCLG for coliform is zero.

Compliance under the Total Coliform Rule is determined on a monthly basis. In general, coliform must be absent in at least 95 percent of the samples for those larger systems that collect more than 40 samples per month. Smaller systems that collect fewer than 40 samples cannot have coliform-positive results in more than one sample per month.

Whenever a routine coliform sample is coliform-positive, the regulation calls for determination of the presence of fecal coliform or *E. coli* and for repeat sampling. Whenever fecal coliform or *E. coli* are present in the routine sample and the repeat samples are coliform-positive, there is a violation of the MCL, additional repeat sampling is required, and notification of both the state and the public is required.

22.2200 SANITARY SURVEY

Sanitary surveys are conducted to identify possible health risks that may not be discovered by routine coliform sampling. The Total Coliform Rule required community water systems serving fewer than 4,100 persons to complete an initial sanitary survey by June 1994 and to conduct subsequent surveys every five years. Noncommunity water systems must complete an initial sanitary survey by June 1999 and subsequent surveys every five years with the exception of those systems with protected and disinfected groundwater sources which are allowed ten years for subsequent surveys.

A sanitary survey requires detailed planning, a thorough system survey and reporting of the results. The planning portion involves a review of water quality records for compliance with applicable microbial, inorganic chemical, organic chemical, and radiological contaminant MCLs as well as the records of compliance with the monitoring requirements for those contaminants. The actual field survey is a detailed evaluation and/or inspection of the source of the water supply and all conveyances, storage, treatment, and distribution facilities to ensure protection from all pollution sources. The final report includes the date(s) of the survey, who was present during the survey, the survey findings, the recommended improvements to correct identified problems, and the target dates of completion for any improvements.

22.2201 SAMPLING PLAN

The Total Coliform Rule requires each water supply system to develop and follow a written sampling plan. Each plan must specifically identify sampling points throughout the distribution system. Sampling plans must be approved by the state regulatory agency and it will be necessary to check with your state agency to determine the details of their review process and what documents need to be submitted.

22.2202 LABORATORY PROCEDURES

With regard to coliform testing methodology, EPA will accept any one of five analytical methods for determination of total coliforms:

- Multiple-tube fermentation technique (MTF),
- Membrane filter technique (MF),
- Presence-absence coliform test (P-A),
- Colilert ™ system (ONPG-MUG test), or
- Colisure test.

Regardless of the method used, the standard sample volume for total coliform testing is now 100 mL. This is an increase over the past testing method using 50 mL for the MTF technique.

The multiple-tube fermentation method of testing for coliforms determines the presence or absence of coliforms by the multiple-tube dilution method. This is a process whereby equal portions of a sample (100 mL) are added to tubes containing a culture medium and an inverted vial. Acceptable testing protocols include the use of 10 tubes, 5 tubes, or a single culture tube. If gas accumulates in the inverted vial, it indicates presumptive evidence of coliform organisms and the sample is considered coliform-positive. If no gas forms in any of the vials, the sample is coliform-negative.

The membrane filter method provides for filtering a 100-mL water sample through a thin, porous, cellulose membrane filter under a partial vacuum. The filter is placed in a sterile container and incubated in contact with a special liquid called a "culture medium" which the bacteria use as a food source. Colonies of bacteria then grow on the media. The coliform colonies are visually identified, counted, and recorded as the number of coliform colonies per 100 mL of sample.

The presence-absence (P-A) test for the coliform group is a simple modification of the multiple-tube procedure. Even though this simplified test uses only one large test portion (100 mL) in a single culture bottle, the results still indicate the presence or absence of coliform bacteria and thus meet the testing requirements.

The Colilert ™ system is a privately developed version of the ONPG-MUG test procedure which meets the EPA's laboratory methods requirements. The ONPG-MUG test indicates the presence or absence of coliform bacteria within 24 hours.

The Colisure test is a presence-absence test for coliform bacteria. A sample of water is added to a dehydrated medium and, after 24 to 48 hours, the medium is examined for the presence of coliforms. (The Colisure test is available from IDEX Laboratory, 1 IDEX Drive, Westbrook, ME 04092.)

Water supply systems may contain various other types of bacteria besides coliforms. These are non-pathogenic bacteria and are sometimes referred to as *HETEROTROPHIC*[3] bacteria. During the analyses of water samples for coliforms, heterotrophic bacteria sometimes interfere with the test causing one of the following reactions:

- MTF technique: a turbid culture with no gas production;

- P-A test: a turbid culture in the absence of an acid reaction; or

- MF technique: confluent growth or a coliform colony number "too numerous to count."

The sample being tested can be considered invalid if any of these situations occurs *AND* total coliforms are not detected. A replacement sample must be taken from the same location within 24 hours of receiving the laboratory results. If the replacement sample also shows heterotrophic interference but tests positive for total coliforms, the sample is considered valid.

22.2203 MONITORING FREQUENCY

The routine monitoring frequency for community water systems is based on the population served, as shown in Table 22.3. Routine monitoring frequencies for noncommunity sys-

---

[3] *Heterotrophic (HET-er-o-TROF-ick).   Describes organisms that use organic matter for energy and growth. Animals, fungi and most bacteria are heterotrophs.*

TABLE 22.3   TOTAL COLIFORM MONITORING FREQUENCY FOR COMMUNITY WATER SYSTEMS

Population Served	Minimum Number of Routine Samples Per Month[a]	Population Served	Minimum Number of Routine Samples Per Month
25 to 1,000[b]	1[c]	59,001 to 70,000	70
1,001 to 2,500	2	70,001 to 83,000	80
2,501 to 3,300	3	83,001 to 96,000	90
3,301 to 4,100	4	96,001 to 130,000	100
4,101 to 4,900	5	130,001 to 220,000	120
4,901 to 5,800	6	220,001 to 320,000	150
5,801 to 6,700	7	320,001 to 450,000	180
6,701 to 7,600	8	450,001 to 600,000	210
7,601 to 8,500	9	600,001 to 780,000	240
8,501 to 12,900	10	780,001 to 970,000	270
12,901 to 17,200	15	970,001 to 1,230,000	300
17,201 to 21,500	20	1,230,001 to 1,520,000	330
21,501 to 25,000	25	1,520,001 to 1,850,000	360
25,001 to 33,000	30	1,850,001 to 2,270,000	390
33,001 to 41,000	40	2,270,001 to 3,020,000	420
41,001 to 50,000	50	3,020,001 to 3,960,000	450
50,001 to 59,000	60	3,960,001 or more	480

[a] A noncommunity water system using groundwater and serving 1,000 persons or fewer may monitor at a lesser frequency specified by the state until a sanitary survey is conducted and the state reviews the results. Thereafter, noncommunity water systems using groundwater and serving 1,000 persons or fewer must monitor in each calendar quarter during which the system provides water to the public, unless the state determines that some other frequency is more appropriate and notifies the system (in writing). In all cases, noncommunity water systems using groundwater and serving 1,000 persons or fewer must monitor at least once/year.

A noncommunity water system using surface water, or groundwater under the direct influence of surface water, regardless of the number of persons served, must monitor at the same frequency as a like-sized community public system. A noncommunity water system using groundwater and serving more than 1,000 persons during any month must monitor at the same frequency as a like-sized community water system, except that the state may reduce the monitoring frequency for any month the system serves 1,000 persons or fewer.

[b] Includes public water systems which have at least 15 service connections, but serve fewer than 25 persons.

[c] For a community water system serving 25-1,000 persons, the state may reduce this sampling frequency if a sanitary survey conducted in the last five years indicates that the water system is supplied solely by a protected groundwater source and is free of sanitary defects. However, in no case may the state reduce the sampling frequency to less than once/quarter.

NOTE: These sampling frequencies took effect December 31, 1990.

tems are based on the source of supply and, in some cases, the population served. See Table 22.3, footnote a, for the specific details about monitoring by noncommunity systems.

Whenever a routine sample tests positive for total coliform, two provisions of the Total Coliform Rule take effect: (1) repeat samples (formerly referred to as check samples) must be taken, and (2) the original coliform-positive sample must be tested for the presence of fecal coliform or *E. coli* to determine whether there is an actual or potential violation of the coliform MCL. The second provision above will be discussed in the next section, "Determining Compliance."

The reason repeat samples are required is to investigate whether the original coliform-positive sample was caused by a contamination problem which exists throughout the distribution system or if it is a localized problem which exists only at that one sampling point. With this information, appropriate corrective action can be taken to eliminate the problem as quickly as possible.

The Total Coliform Rule specifies how many repeat samples must be taken, when, and from what locations. It also directs the water utility to collect a specific number of samples the following month, based on the number of routine samples ordinarily collected. Table 22.4 lists the repeat sampling frequencies triggered by a coliform-positive routine sample.

TABLE 22.4   COLIFORM MONITORING — ROUTINE AND REPEAT SAMPLING FREQUENCIES

Number of Routine Samples per Month	Minimum Number of Repeat Samples[a]	Number of Routine Samples Next Month[b]
1 or fewer	4	5
2	3	5
3	3	5
4	3	5
5 or more	3	See Table 22.3

[a] Number of repeat samples in the same month for each total coliform-positive routine sample.

[b] Except where the state has invalidated the original routine sample, substitutes an on-site evaluation of the problem, or waives the requirement on a case-by-case basis.

Noncommunity systems serving more than 1,000 people have the same requirements as community water systems (Table 22.3). Noncommunity systems serving fewer than 1,000 people are required to collect one routine sample per quarter. When the routine sample tests positive, four repeat samples are required in the same quarter and five samples are required the following quarter.

As Table 22.4 indicates, whenever a routine or repeat sample tests positive for total coliform, the water agency must collect a set of either three or four repeat samples within 24 hours of receiving the lab results. At least one of the repeat samples must be taken from the same tap as the original coliform-positive sample; the remaining repeat samples in the set must be collected at nearby taps (within five service connections of the original sampling point), both upstream and downstream of the original. Repeat samples must be taken until no coliforms are detected or until the MCL is exceeded and the state is notified.

For additional information about sampling and compliance procedures, see "Rule Changes Way Systems Will Look at Coliform," *OPFLOW*, Vol. 16, No. 2, December 1990, pages 1, 4, and 5, and "Corrections" *OPFLOW*, Vol. 17, No. 2, February 1991, page 2.

22.2204 DETERMINING COMPLIANCE

As discussed earlier, the MCLG for total coliforms (including fecal coliform and *E. coli*) is zero. The MCL, based on the presence-absence concept, is as follows:

- For water systems analyzing at least 40 samples per month, no more than 5.0 percent of the samples (including routine and repeat samples) may be positive for total coliforms;

- For water systems analyzing fewer than 40 samples per month, no more than one sample per month may be positive for total coliforms.

The Total Coliform Rule makes another significant change in the way compliance is calculated. That is, all valid coliform-positive samples — both routine *AND* repeat samples — must be counted when calculating compliance with the monthly MCL. Under previous regulations, check or repeat samples were not included in the monthly MCL calculation.

On a case-by-case basis, the state may declare a sample invalid for one of several reasons, including interference by heterotrophic bacteria during laboratory analysis, as previously discussed. Total-coliform-positive samples may be invalidated by the state under any of the following conditions:

- The analytical laboratory acknowledges that improper sample analysis caused the positive result;

- The state determines that the contamination is a local plumbing problem; and/or

- The state has substantial grounds to believe that the positive result was unrelated to the quality of drinking water in the distribution system.

A simplified decision tree for determining compliance with the Total Coliform Rule is shown in Figure 22.1. It is strongly

recommended that operators work closely with their state regulatory agencies in implementing this rule.

22.2205 REPORTING AND NOTIFICATION REQUIREMENTS

Reporting frequencies for coliform test results increase in step with the urgency of the problem. A water agency must report the results of monthly coliform testing to the state regulatory agency within the first 10 days of the following month.

Any time a water agency fails to collect a sample as required, the state must be notified within 10 days after the system learns of the violation. An invalid sample result is considered a failure to monitor and must be reported.

If the MCL is exceeded, the state must be notified no later than the end of the next business day and the public within 14 days. This could occur when the water agency exceeds its monthly coliform-positive limit or when test results show the presence of fecal coliforms or *E. coli* in any sample. (See Section 22.6 for further details about public notification procedures.)

The most critical situation exists when either of two situations occurs:

1. A routine sample tests positive for total coliforms and for fecal coliforms or *E. coli*, and any repeat sample tests positive for total coliforms.

2. A routine sample tests positive for total coliforms and negative for fecal coliforms or *E. coli*, and any repeat sample tests positive for fecal coliforms or *E. coli*.

Either of these situations is considered an "acute risk to health." This is an acute Tier 1 violation which requires that the public be notified within 72 hours by broadcast media, as described in Section 22.6, and the regulatory agency must be notified by the end of the next business day following receipt of the lab results.

QUESTIONS

Write your answers in a notebook and then compare your answers with those on pages 554 and 555.

22.2I   Why are microbial contaminants a public health concern?

22.2J   What is the basic approach used to determine compliance with the Total Coliform Rule?

22.2K   List the five analytical methods EPA will accept for coliform testing.

22.2L   What are reasons for collecting repeat coliform samples?

22.2M   What sampling locations are used for repeat coliform samples?

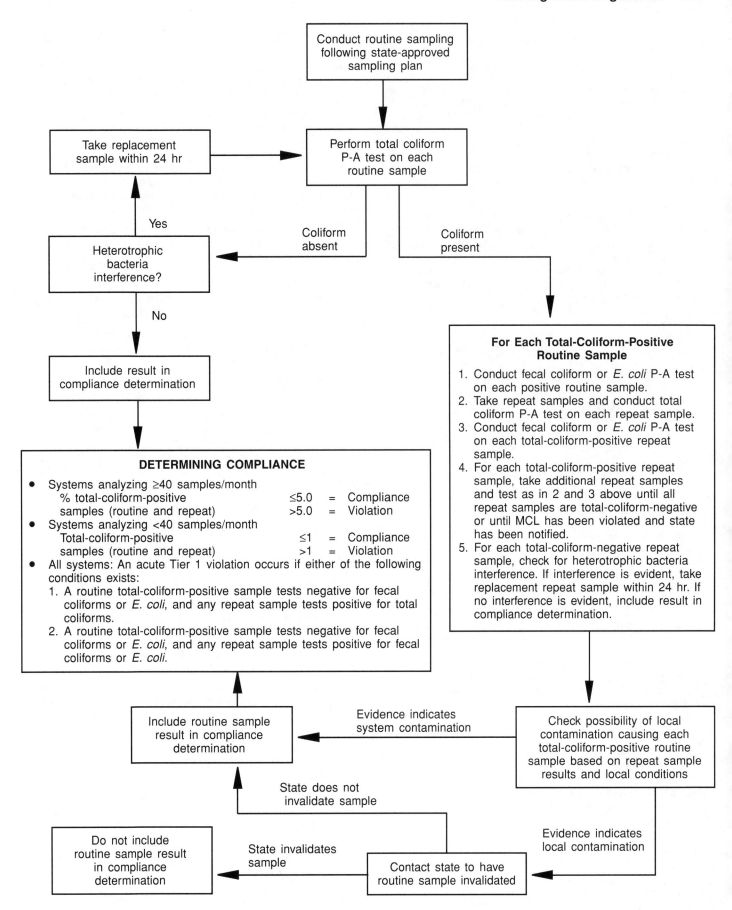

Fig. 22.1   Simplified decision tree for compliance with the Total Coliform Rule

(Reprinted from *OPFLOW*, Vol. 16, No. 12 (December 1990), by permission. Copyright © 1990, American Water Works Association)

22.221 Surface Water Treatment Rule (SWTR)

On June 29, 1989, the EPA promulgated the Surface Water Treatment Rule (SWTR). This regulation sets forth primary drinking water regulations requiring treatment of surface water supplies or groundwater supplies under the direct influence of surface water. These regulations require surface water systems to use a specific water treatment technique (filtration and/or disinfection) rather than meeting maximum contaminant levels (MCLs) for turbidity, *Giardia lamblia*, viruses, *Legionella*, and heterotrophic bacteria. Also the regulations require that all systems must be operated by qualified operators.

The protozoan *Giardia lamblia* is presently the organism most implicated in waterborne disease outbreaks in the United States. These microscopic creatures are found mainly in mountain streams. Once inside the body, they cause a painful and disabling illness. The infection caused by *Giardia* is called Giardiasis. The symptoms of Giardiasis are usually severe diarrhea, gas, cramps, nausea, vomiting, and fatigue.

Giardia and viruses have been added to the traditional coliform and turbidity indicators of microbiological quality. In this case, the Maximum Contaminant Level Goals (MCLGs) are zero because the organisms are pathogens, or indicators of pathogens, and should not be present in drinking water.

The SWTR defines surface water as "all water open to the atmosphere and subject to surface runoff." This would include rivers, lakes, streams, and reservoirs. This surface water definition also includes groundwaters which are directly influenced by surface water. The determination as to whether a supply uses surface water is left up to the state. Generally, if a groundwater source has significant and relatively rapid shifts in water quality such as turbidity, temperature, conductivity, or pH which closely correlate to climatological or nearby surface water conditions, that source can be considered surface water.

At a minimum, the treatment required for surface water would include disinfection systems for very clean and protected source waters. These systems would only be required to disinfect to achieve removal of coliforms to meet the requirements.

Turbidity measurements are a key element in determining compliance with both the filtration and the disinfection requirements of the Surface Water Treatment Rule. The effectiveness of a filtration system in removing particles and organisms is easily obtained by measuring the water's turbidity before and after filtration. High turbidity also reduces the effectiveness of disinfection processes and, therefore, must be controlled and closely monitored.

Water supply systems that are required to filter can use a variety of treatment technologies, including disinfection, to meet the expected performance levels. These technologies include conventional treatment, direct filtration, slow sand filtration, and diatomaceous earth filtration.

The two-pronged treatment technique of the SWTR aims to ensure that harmful microorganisms are either removed by filtration processes or inactivated (and thus made harmless) by disinfection processes. Success, therefore, depends heavily on consistently well-operated filtration and disinfection systems. The general performance standards to be met by all surface water systems and any systems using groundwater under the influence of surface water are:

1. At least 99.9 percent (also called 3 log for the 3 nines) removal and/or inactivation of *Giardia lamblia* cysts, and

2. At least 99.99 percent (4 log) removal and/or inactivation of enteric (intestinal) viruses.

In general, compliance by the surface water purveyor could be through one of the following alternatives:

1. Meeting the criteria for which filtration is not required and providing disinfection according to the specific requirements in the SWTR, or

2. Providing filtration and meeting disinfection criteria required for those supplies that are filtered.

Mandatory filtration affects the small and medium-sized water systems most severely. A few large surface water systems do not filter their water; more than nine million people drink unfiltered water in Seattle, New York City, and Boston alone. However, most of the unfiltered surface water systems serve communities with fewer than 10,000 residents.

The 1996 SDWA amendments imposed deadlines by which EPA must complete work on several major regulations, including promulgation of an Enhanced Surface Water Treatment Rule (ESWTR). Operators are urged to work closely with their state regulatory agencies to stay informed about changes in water regulations as they occur over the next several years. The schedule for promulgation of the ESWTR and related new regulations is as follows:

- November 1998 — Final Stage 1 Disinfectants/Disinfection By-Products Rule (D/DBP Rule),

- November 1998 — Final interim ESWTR (systems serving fewer than 10,000 people),

- November 2000 — Final long-term ESWTR for all systems (expected to include regulations concerning recycling of filter backwash water and possibly will include treatment technique requirements for *Cryptosporidium*),

- November 2000 — Final Ground Water Disinfection Rule (GWDR) establishing disinfection requirements for groundwater systems,

- May 2002 — Final long-term ESWTR for Stage 2 (including Disinfectants/Disinfection By-Products Rule (D/DBP Rule) unless EPA develops a D/DBP Rule separate from the ESWTR), and

- May 2002 — Final Stage 2 Disinfectants/Disinfection By-Products Rule (D/DBP Rule).

22.2210 CRITERIA FOR AVOIDING FILTRATION

To avoid mandatory filtration, a water utility must meet the following requirements to ensure adequate disinfection:

1. The fecal coliform concentration in the water prior to disinfection must not exceed 20/100 mL, or total coliform concentration must not exceed 100/100 mL in more than 10 percent of the samples analyzed in the previous six months;

2. The turbidity of the water prior to disinfection cannot exceed 5 *NTUs*[4] based on grab samples collected every four hours or by continuous monitoring; and

3. Certain site-specific conditions:

   (a) has disinfection that achieves 99.9 percent inactivation of *Giardia* and 99.99 percent inactivation of viruses (CT requirement — see Section 22.2215);

   (b) watershed control or sanitary surveys that satisfy regulatory requirements;

   (c) no history of waterborne disease outbreak without making treatment corrections;

   (d) compliance with long-term coliform maximum contaminant level (MCL);

   (e) compliance with total trihalomethanes MCL, if the system serves more than 10,000 people;

   (f) disinfection system must have an alternative power supply, automatic alarm and start-up to ensure continuous disinfection; and

   (g) ensure that disinfectant residual at entrance to distribution system does not drop below 0.2 mg/L for more than four hours.

If a system cannot meet the source water quality criteria and site-specific conditions listed above, then the system must install and operate appropriate filtration facilities.

22.2211 REQUIREMENTS FOR FILTERED WATER SYSTEMS

For systems that filter, the primary concern is adequate disinfection and filtration performance. The requirements are:

1. For conventional or direct filtration systems, the filtered water turbidity must be less than or equal to 0.5 NTU for at least 95 percent of each month's measurements. For slow sand or diatomaceous earth filtration, the filtered water turbidity must be less than 1 NTU in at least 95 percent of the measurements taken each month.

2. Filtered water turbidity must never exceed 5 NTUs.

3. A disinfectant residual at the entrance to the distribution system of at least 0.2 mg/L.

4. Filtered water supplies must achieve the same disinfection as required for unfiltered systems (that is, 99.9% and 99.99% removal/inactivation of *Giardia lamblia* and viruses) through a combination of filtration and application of a disinfectant.

It is important to remember that this is a two-pronged approach and both elements are considered when determining compliance by systems which are required to install filtration. Filtration alone accomplishes part of the job of removing harmful organisms; disinfection does the rest of the job.

22.2212 CHLORINE RESIDUAL SUBSTITUTION

At the discretion of the state and based on a review of the water system, chlorine residual testing may be substituted for some of the bacteriological testing. Chlorine residual testing could give the operator a quicker indication of the condition of the system. However, the following requirements must be met:

1. Samples must be taken at points which are representative of conditions within the distribution system,

2. Chlorine residual testing can replace only up to 75 percent of the bacteriological testing,

3. At least four chlorine residual tests must be taken to substitute for one bacteriological sample,

4. A free chlorine residual of at least 0.2 mg/L must be maintained throughout the distribution system,

5. If free chlorine residual falls below 0.2 mg/L, check samples must be taken for bacteriological testing and a report must be submitted to the state within 48 hours, and

6. Chlorine residual must be determined daily.

22.2213 TURBIDITY REQUIREMENTS

Turbidity is undesirable in a finished or treated water because it causes cloudiness resulting in an unattractive water. However, the major reason that turbidity is undesirable is because it causes a health hazard by:

1. Interfering with disinfection by reducing the ability of the disinfectant to inactivate or kill disease-causing organisms;

2. Exerting a chlorine demand which makes it difficult to maintain a residual throughout the distribution system;

3. Interfering with the bacteriological examination of the water; and

4. Preventing satisfactory reduction of tastes and odors and asbestos fibers.

The MCLs and monitoring requirements for turbidity (which apply to surface water only) are as follows:

- For unfiltered surface water supplies the turbidity of the raw water prior to disinfection cannot exceed 5 NTU based on grab samples collected every four hours or by continuous turbidity monitoring;

---

[4] *Turbidity Units (TU). Turbidity units are a measure of the cloudiness of water. If measured by a nephelometric (deflected light) instrumental procedure, turbidity units are expressed in nephelometric turbidity units (NTU) or simply TU. Those turbidity units obtained by visual methods are expressed in Jackson Turbidity Units (JTU) which are a measure of the cloudiness of water; they are used to indicate the clarity of water. There is no real connection between NTUs and JTUs. The Jackson turbidimeter is a visual method and the nephelometer is an instrumental method based on deflected light.*

- For surface water supplies using conventional or direct filtration, the process must achieve a turbidity level of less than 5 NTU at all times and not more than 0.5 NTU in more than 5 percent of the samples analyzed during a given month. Turbidity must be sampled every four hours or by continuous monitoring; and

- Those systems using slow sand or diatomaceous earth filtration must achieve a turbidity level of less than 5 NTU at all times and not more than 1 NTU in more than 5 percent of the samples collected each month. Systems using slow sand filtration must sample at least once a day; diatomaceous earth filtration systems must monitor turbidity every four hours or by continuous sampling.

Other filtration technologies may be used if they meet, as a minimum, the turbidity requirements for slow sand filters, the disinfection requirements, and are approved by the state.

Unfiltered systems are required to begin with a clean source water and have a watershed that is protected from human activities that might otherwise have an adverse impact on water quality. Unfiltered systems would have very little, if any, virus contamination. For these systems, the major concern is *Giardia* contamination from animal activities that cannot be prevented by watershed protection. The purpose of the turbidity limit for unfiltered water is to ensure a high probability that turbidity does not interfere with disinfection of *Giardia* cysts. The turbidity limit of 5 NTU serves this purpose.

For filtered water systems, the major burden for *Giardia* removal rests with filtration. With conventional treatment and direct filtration, low turbidity levels (<0.5 NTU) are needed to ensure effective *Giardia* cyst removals. Disinfection of either *Giardia* or viruses will not be hampered at these turbidity levels.

For slow sand filtration and diatomaceous earth filtration, effective *Giardia* removal does not necessarily correlate with low treated water turbidities. However, to ensure effective virus inactivation, a low filtered water turbidity is needed. Viruses are much smaller than *Giardia*, and thus a lower turbidity limit of 1 NTU is needed compared with the turbidity level of 5 NTU for unfiltered supplies to ensure effective disinfection.

22.2214 MONITORING REQUIREMENTS

Unfiltered surface water systems must:

1. Monitor raw water supply for fecal and total coliform. Samples must be collected and analyzed at a minimum frequency based on system size as shown below.

Number of People Served	Samples/Week
<501	1
501 – 3,300	2
3,301 – 10,000	3
10,001 – 25,000	4
>25,000	5

If the fecal coliform concentration in the water prior to disinfection exceeds 10 coliforms/100 mL, or the total coliform concentration exceeds 100 coliforms/100 mL in more than 10 percent of the samples analyzed in a six-month period, the system no longer meets the criteria to avoid filtration.

2. Monitor turbidity every four hours or by continuous measurement.

3. Monitor and control activities on the watershed in order to minimize adverse impacts on water quality. Annual on-site inspections are also required.

4. Continuously monitor the disinfectant residual to ensure a minimum of 0.2 mg/L at the entrance to the distribution system. Systems serving fewer than 3,300 persons may take grab samples at the frequencies shown below.

Number of People Served	Samples/Week
<501	1
501 – 1,000	2
1,001 – 2,500	3
2,501 – 3,300	4

In addition, disinfectant residuals in the distribution system must be monitored at the same frequency and location as total coliform samples.

5. Monitor daily to demonstrate that the level of disinfection achieved is 99.9 percent inactivation of *Giardia* and 99.99 percent inactivation/removal of enteric viruses.

Filtered systems must meet the following requirements:

1. Perform turbidity measurements of representative water every 4 hours (which can be continuous monitoring). For any system using slow sand filtration or any other filtration treatment other than conventional treatment, such as direct filtration or diatomaceous earth filtration, the state may reduce this monitoring to once per day.

2. Continuously monitor the disinfectant residual entering the distribution system to ensure a minimum of 0.2 mg/L at the entrance to the distribution system. Systems serving fewer than 3,300 people may take grab samples at the frequencies shown previously. Disinfectant residuals in the distribution system must be monitored at the same frequency and location as total coliform samples.

3. Monitor daily to demonstrate that a combination of filtration and application of disinfectant achieves 99.9 percent and 99.99 percent removal or inactivation for *Giardia* and viruses, respectively.

4. Measurements for heterotrophic plate count (HPC) bacteria may be substituted for disinfectant residual measurements. If the HPC is less than 500 colonies per m*L*, then the sample is considered equivalent to a detectable disinfectant residual. For systems serving fewer than 500 people, the regulatory agency may determine the adequacy of the disinfectant residual in place of monitoring.

22.2215 CT VALUES

The purpose of the SWTR is to ensure that pathogenic organisms are removed and/or inactivated by the treatment process. To meet this goal, all systems are required to disinfect their water supplies. For some water systems using very clean source water and meeting the other criteria to avoid filtration, disinfection alone can achieve the 3-log (99.9%) *Giardia* and 4-log (99.99%) virus inactivation levels required by the Surface Water Treatment Rule.

Several methods of disinfection are in common use, including free chlorination, chloramination, use of chlorine dioxide, and application of ozone. The concentration of chemical needed and the length of contact time needed to ensure disinfection are different for each disinfectant. Therefore, the effectiveness of the disinfectant is measured by the time (T) in minutes of the disinfectant's contact in the water and the concentration (C) of the disinfectant residual in mg/*L* measured at the end of the contact time. The product of these two factors (C x T) provides a measure of the degree of pathogenic inactivation. The required CT value to achieve inactivation is dependent upon the organism in question, type of disinfectant, pH, and temperature of the water supply.

Time or "T" is measured from point of application to the point where "C" is determined. "T" must be based on peak hour flow rate conditions. In pipelines, "T" is calculated by dividing the volume of the pipeline in gallons by the flow rate in gallons per minute (GPM). In reservoirs and basins, dye tracer tests must be used to determine "T". In this case "T" is the time it takes for 10 percent of the tracer to pass the measuring point.

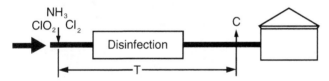

A properly operated filtration system can achieve limited removal or inactivation of microorganisms. Because of this, systems which are required to filter their water are permitted to apply a factor which represents the microorganism removal value of filtration when calculating CT values to meet the disinfection requirements. The factor (removal credit) varies with the type of filtration system. Its purpose is to take into account the combined effect of both disinfection and filtration in meeting the SWTR microbial standards.

Please refer to the Arithmetic Appendix at the end of this manual (Section A.6, "Calculation of CT Values") for instructions on how to perform these calculations for a water treatment plant.

22.2216 ADDITIONAL READING

For more detailed information about the requirements and application of the Surface Water Treatment Rule, you may wish to order a copy of the publication, *GUIDANCE MANUAL OF COMPLIANCE WITH THE FILTRATION AND DISINFECTION REQUIREMENTS FOR PUBLIC WATER SYSTEMS USING SURFACE WATER SOURCES*. It is available from the American Water Works Association, 6666 West Quincy Avenue, Denver, CO 80235. Order No. 20271. Price to members, $43.00; nonmembers, $64.75; price includes cost of shipping and handling.

QUESTIONS

Write your answers in a notebook and then compare your answers with those on page 555.

22.2N What does the Surface Water Treatment Rule (SWTR) specifically require?

22.2O How does the SWTR define surface water?

22.2P How can a water utility avoid mandatory filtration?

22.2Q What are the MCLs for turbidity for surface water?

22.2R How is the effectiveness of a disinfectant measured?

22.23 Disinfectants and Disinfection By-Products (D/DBPs)

Disinfection of drinking water by the addition of chlorine has long been considered a highly effective yet relatively low-cost method of preventing widespread outbreaks of waterborne diseases. In addition to reacting with disease-causing organisms in water, however, chlorine also reacts with many other types of organic materials. There is growing scientific evidence that the by-products of these chemical reactions can produce adverse health effects in humans.

Trihalomethanes (THMs) are an example of a compound formed by the reaction of chlorine with organic matter in water (also see Chapter 15, "Trihalomethanes"). THMs are suspected of being carcinogenic and have been regulated by EPA. The maximum contaminant level (MCL) for total trihalomethanes (TTHMs) is 0.10 milligram per liter or 100 micrograms per liter.

The 1996 SDWA amendments made regulation of disinfectants and disinfection by-products a high priority. Future regulations are expected to set lower permissible levels for trihalomethanes plus limit disinfectants (chlorine, chlorine dioxide, chloramines) and disinfection by-products such as chlorite, bromate, and haloacetic acids (HAAs).

Promulgation of the new D/DBP regulations is linked with completion of the database established by the Information Collection Rule (ICR) described in the following section and with promulgation of several other major new or revised regulations including the Enhanced Surface Water Treatment Rule and the Ground Water Disinfection Rule. The D/DBP Rule (which applies to all systems using a disinfectant) will be phased in by system size and type. Stage 1 of the Rule is expected to be finalized by November 1998 and Stage 2 is expected to be finalized by May 2002.

22.24   Information Collection Rule (ICR)

22.240   Final Rule

The final Information Collection Rule (ICR) was published in the *FEDERAL REGISTER* (FR) in May 1996. This FR notice finalized requirements for monitoring microbial contaminants and disinfection by-products by large public water systems (PWSs). The ICR requires large PWSs to provide operating data and a description of their treatment plant design. It also requires large PWSs to conduct either bench- or pilot-scale testing of advanced treatment techniques.

22.241   Purpose of the Rule

The highest priority health risk concern in the regulation of drinking water is the potential risk-risk tradeoff between the control of microbiological contamination (bacteria, viruses, and protozoa) on the one hand and disinfection by-products on the other hand. This risk-risk tradeoff arises because typically the least expensive way for a public water system to increase microbial control is to increase disinfection (which generally increases by-product formation) and the easiest way to reduce by-products is to decrease disinfection (which generally increases microbial risk). Microbiological contamination often causes flu-like symptoms, but can also cause serious diseases such as hepatitis, giardiasis, cryptosporidiosis, and Legionnaire's Disease. Disinfection by-products may pose the risk of cancer and developmental effects.

In 1992, EPA entered into a Regulatory Negotiation to address this tradeoff. Regulatory Negotiation is a process whereby the agency acts on an equal basis with outside parties to reach consensus on the content of a proposed rule. If the group reaches consensus, the Agency commits to propose the rule with the agreed upon content. In 1993 negotiators reached consensus on a **three-part regulatory approach:**

1. **Interim rules** to reduce levels of disinfection by-products without causing major industry shifts to alternative disinfectants (such as ozone and chlorine dioxide) until the risks from those alternatives are more clearly understood, and to modify the current regulation on microbial contamination to ensure a uniform level of protection, regardless of the quality of the water used as a drinking water source. (The current rule requires a uniform level of contaminant reduction for all public water systems, regardless of the quality of the water used as a drinking water source.)

2. **Intensive data collection and research effort** to learn more about the occurrence of microbial contamination and disinfection by-products, the health risks posed, appropriate analytical methods, and effective forms of treatment.

3. **Longer term rules (as needed)** based on analysis of the data and research.

The Information Collection Rule was negotiated to meet, in part, the second regulatory approach. It requires large public water systems to collect information on the presence and levels of microbial contamination and disinfection by-products and also on the effectiveness of various treatment technologies to reduce those levels. Results from the rule will be used to evaluate how to modify the current regulation on microbial contamination and also to determine the need for, and content of, longer term rules. About 500 utilities are expected to be involved in the data collection effort, for a total cost of $130 million expended over a three-year period beginning in 1997.

22.242   Applicability

The ICR requires large public water systems (PWSs) to generate and report specific monitoring data and other information characterizing their water system. Three classes of PWSs are affected by this rule: (1) PWSs that serve at least 100,000 people and use surface water as their source of supply, (2) PWSs that serve at least 100,000 people and use only groundwater, and (3) PWSs that serve at least 50,000 but fewer than 100,000 people and use groundwater.

22.243   Types of Data To Be Collected and Why They Are Needed

22.2430   MICROBIAL MONITORING

Utilities will monitor for representative bacteria, viruses, and protozoa over an 18-month period. These data are needed to develop national occurrence estimates of the presence and levels of microbial contamination in water entering water treatment plants.

22.2431   DISINFECTION BY-PRODUCT MONITORING

Utilities will monitor for a number of water quality indicators related to disinfection by-products. One category is organic materials which occur in water entering water treatment plants. It is these materials which react with disinfectants to form by-products. A second category is the amount of disinfectant which remains after treatment and is available to react with the organic materials to form by-products. And, finally, the third category is the by-products themselves. These by-products vary depending on the disinfectant being used. These data will provide information on the relationship between the amount and type of organic material in the water, the amount of disinfectant used, the treatment process used, and the degree of by-product formation.

22.2432   TREATMENT TECHNOLOGY STUDIES

Utilities will perform bench- or pilot-scale studies on one of two types of treatment: granular activated carbon or membrane processes. These data will be used to judge the effectiveness of these technologies in reducing the levels of by-product formation and the cost of doing so.

22.244 Schedule

Microbial and disinfection by-product monitoring are to be conducted monthly for 18 months, beginning in early 1997. Treatment technology studies will be conducted over 12 months, beginning in 1998.

22.245 Data Availability

Utilities are responsible for submitting data to EPA on a monthly basis, beginning four months after the initiation of sampling. EPA expects to take about two months to perform quality control checks on the data before entering the data into the data system and having the data available on-line to the public. EPA intends to make the data available on the Internet. Data can be downloaded from the EPA database so that members of the public can analyze the data as they wish.

After eight months of data are entered into the data system, EPA will analyze the data and publish a *FEDERAL REGISTER* notice discussing its analysis. The *FEDERAL REGISTER* notice will also indicate whether EPA believes the current regulation for microbial contamination needs to be modified and, if so, how. EPA will take public comment on the contents of that notice before deciding whether to promulgate revisions to the current Surface Water Treatment Rule. EPA will also await the results of the full 18 months of microbial and disinfection by-product monitoring before promulgating any revisions to the current rule to be sure that the last ten months of data are similar to the results of the first eight months.

Results of the treatment studies will be made available to the public before EPA initiates public dialogue on the need for, and content of, long-term rules.

22.246 Termination

The ICR is scheduled to terminate on December 31, 2000.

22.247 For More Information

Contact the Safe Drinking Water Hotline at (800) 426-4791 for more information. Material in this section came from "Information Collection Rule," US EPA, Office of Water, EPA 811-F-96-001, May 1996.

The following two professional papers provide a very thorough explanation of the Information Collection Rule (ICR).

1. Pontius, Frederick W., "Inside the Information Collection Rule," JAWWA, Vol. 88, No. 8, p. 16, August 1996.

2. Nieminski, Eva C.; Chaudhuri, Sanwat; Flint, Tage I.; Paxman, Scott W.; Reynolds, Florence P.; and Carman, John R., "ICR Survival Guide," JAWWA, Vol. 88, No. 8, p. 50, August 1996.

QUESTIONS

Write your answers in a notebook and then compare your answers with those on page 555.

22.2S   What are trihalomethanes (THMs)?

22.2T   What are the main requirements of the Information Collection Rule (ICR)?

22.25 Radiological Standards

Radioactivity is the only contaminant that has been shown to cause cancer for which standards have been set. Three radioactive elements, radon, radium, and uranium, occur naturally in the ground and dissolve into groundwater supplies. However, the possible exposure to radiation in drinking water is only a fraction of the exposure from all natural sources. The main source of radioactive material in surface water is fallout from nuclear testing. Other sources could be nuclear power plants, nuclear fuel processing plants, and uranium mines. Those sources are monitored constantly and there is no great risk of contamination, barring accidents.

Alpha and radium radioactivity occur naturally in groundwater in parts of the West, Midwest, and Northeast. Standards for those types of radioactivity and for manmade, or beta radiation, have been set at levels of safety comparable to other contaminants.

The MCLs for radiological contaminants are divided into two categories: (1) natural radioactivity which results from well water passing through deposits of naturally occurring radioactive materials, and (2) manmade radioactivity such as might result from industrial wastes, hospitals, or research laboratories. Table 22.5 summarizes the MCLs for radioactivity.

TABLE 22.5 MCLs FOR RADIOACTIVITY

Constituent	Maximum Contaminant Level
Combined Radium 226 and Radium 228	5 pCi/*L*[a]
Gross Alpha Activity (including Radium 226 but excluding Radon and Uranium)	15 pCi/*L*[a]
Gross Beta Particle Activity [b]	4 mrem/yr

[a] pCi/*L*. picoCurie per Liter. A picoCurie is a measure of radioactivity. One picoCurie of radioactivity is equivalent to 0.037 nuclear disintegrations per second.

[b] For surface water systems serving more than 100,000 persons and systems determined by the state to be vulnerable.

Monitoring for natural radioactivity contamination is required every four years for both surface water and groundwater community systems. Routine monitoring procedures to follow are:

1. Test for gross alpha activity; if gross alpha exceeds 5 pCi/*L*, then

2. Test for radium 226; if radium 226 exceeds 3 pCi/*L*, then

3. Test for radium 228.

The MCL for gross beta particle activity is 4 mrem/yr for water systems using surface water and serving more than 100,000 people, and for any other community system determined by the state to be vulnerable to this type of contamination. After the initial monitoring period, beta radiation must be monitored every four years unless the MCL is exceeded or the state determines that more frequent monitoring is appropriate.

Regulation of radon continues to be a source of considerable debate. EPA proposed a maximum contaminant level in

1991 and then withdrew the proposed MCL in 1997 in response to the 1996 SDWA amendments. EPA is now required to promulgate new regulations for radon and uranium as well as revised standards for radium 226 and 228. The final rule for radon is to be completed by August 6, 2000, and final rules for uranium and radium must be completed no later than December 2000. EPA must base its new rules on a scientific risk assessment and an analysis of both the amount of health risk reduction that will be achieved and the cost of implementing the new rules.

QUESTIONS

Write your answers in a notebook and then compare your answers with those on page 555.

22.2U   How does drinking water become contaminated with radioactive elements?

22.2V   The MCLs for radiological contaminants are divided into what two categories?

End of Lesson 1 of 2 Lessons
on
DRINKING WATER REGULATIONS

Please answer the discussion and review questions next.

DISCUSSION AND REVIEW QUESTIONS
Chapter 22.   DRINKING WATER REGULATIONS

(Lesson 1 of 2 Lessons)

At the end of each lesson in this chapter you will find some discussion and review questions. The purpose of these questions is to indicate to you how well you understand the material in the lesson. Write the answers to these questions in your notebook before continuing.

1. What criteria must be met before EPA selects a contaminant for regulation?

2. What are Maximum Contaminant Levels (MCLs)?

3. What is the definition of a public water system?

4. What is a community water system?

5. Inorganic chemicals pose what type of health concerns?

6. What steps must be taken if a water system exceeds the lead and copper action levels in more than ten percent of its samples?

7. What are the most common sources of organic contamination of drinking water?

8. Why are coliform bacteria found in drinking water and what does their presence indicate?

9. What is the purpose of the Surface Water Treatment Rule (SWTR)?

10. Why is turbidity undesirable in a finished or treated water?

11. Why are trihalomethanes (THMs) regulated?

12. What information is being collected under the Information Collection Rule?

13. What are the two categories of MCLs for radiological contaminants?

CHAPTER 22. DRINKING WATER REGULATIONS

(Lesson 2 of 2 Lessons)

22.3 SECONDARY DRINKING WATER STANDARDS

22.30 Enforcement of Regulations

The National Secondary Drinking Water Regulations control contaminants in drinking water that primarily affect the aesthetic qualities relating to the public acceptance of drinking water. At considerably higher concentrations of these contaminants, health implications may also exist as well as aesthetic degradation. These regulations are not federally enforceable; however, some states have passed laws requiring the state health agency to enforce the regulations.

22.31 Secondary Maximum Contaminant Levels

Secondary Maximum Contaminant Levels (SMCLs) apply to public water systems and, in the judgment of the EPA Administrator, are necessary to protect the public welfare or for public acceptance of the drinking water. The SMCL means the maximum permissible level of a contaminant which is delivered to the free-flowing outlet of the ultimate user of a public water system. Contaminants added to the water under circumstances controlled by the user, except those resulting from corrosion of piping and plumbing caused by water quality, are excluded by definition. Currently there are 15 secondary standards (see Table 22.6).

States may establish higher or lower levels depending on local conditions, providing that public health and welfare are adequately protected.

Aesthetic qualities are important factors in public acceptance and confidence in a public water system. States are encouraged to implement SMCLs so that the public will not be driven to obtain drinking water from potentially lower quality, higher risk sources. Many states have chosen to enforce both Primary and Secondary MCLs to ensure that the consumer is provided with the best quality water available.

TABLE 22.6 SECONDARY DRINKING WATER STANDARDS

Contaminant	SMCL	Effect
Aluminum	0.05 to 0.2 mg/L	precipitates cause cloudy looking water
Chloride	250 mg/L	taste and corrosion of water pipes
Color	15 Color Units	aesthetic
Copper	1.0 mg/L	staining
Corrosivity	Noncorrosive	corrosion control
Fluoride	2 mg/L	dental fluorosis (a brownish discoloration of the teeth)
Foaming Agents	0.5 mg/L	aesthetic and taste
Iron	0.3 mg/L	taste and staining
Manganese	0.05 mg/L	taste and staining
Odor	3 Threshold Odor Number[a]	aesthetic and taste
pH	6.5 to 8.5	corrosion control and taste
Silver	0.1 mg/L	blue-gray discoloration of the skin, mucous membranes, and eyes
Sulfate	250 mg/L	taste and laxative effects
Total Dissolved Solids (TDS)	500 mg/L	taste
Zinc	5 mg/L	taste

[a] Threshold Odor Number (TON). The greatest dilution of a sample with odor-free water that still yields a just-detectable odor.

22.32   Monitoring

Collect samples for secondary contaminants at a free flowing outlet of water being delivered to the consumer. Monitor contaminants in these regulations at least as often as the monitoring performed for inorganic chemical contaminants listed in the Primary Drinking Water Regulations as applicable to community water systems. For surface water systems, this means yearly monitoring is required; for groundwater systems, monitor at least once every three years. Collect monthly distribution system physical water quality monitoring samples for color and odors. More frequent monitoring would be appropriate for specific contaminants such as pH, color, odor, or others under certain circumstances as directed by the state.

QUESTIONS

Write your answers in a notebook and then compare your answers with those on page 555.

22.3A   Under what conditions are secondary drinking water regulations enforceable?

22.3B   List the secondary drinking water contaminants.

22.3C   How frequently should the contaminants in the secondary regulations be monitored?

22.33   Secondary Contaminants

22.330   Aluminum

Until relatively recently most environmental aluminum was found in forms which did not greatly affect humans and other animals. Acid rain, however, has caused a significant increase in aluminum exposure. The average daily intake of aluminum in the general population is about 20 milligrams per day; the SMCL is 0.05 to 0.2 mg/L. Although aluminum is regulated as a secondary contaminant because precipitates of the metal can cause cloudy looking water, aluminum compounds may also interfere with absorption of fluoride in the gastrointestinal tract and may decrease the absorption of calcium, iron, and cholesterol. Many over-the-counter antacids contain aluminum and use of these products frequently causes constipation which is thought to be the result of the gastrointestinal effects described above.

22.331   Chloride

The SMCL for chloride is 250 mg/L.

UNDESIRABLE EFFECTS

1. Objectionable salty taste in water.

2. Corrosion of the pipes in hot water systems and other pipelines.

STUDIES ON THE MINERALIZATION OF WATER INDICATE THE FOLLOWING

1. Major taste effects are produced by anions (where TDS was studied).

2. Chloride produces a taste effect somewhere between the milder sulfate and the stronger carbonate.

3. Laxative effects are caused by highly mineralized waters. Mineralized waters often contain chloride as well as high levels of sodium and magnesium sulfate.

CORROSION EFFECT

1. Studies indicate that corrosion depends on concentration of TDS (TDS may contain 50 percent chloride ions).

2. Domestic plumbing, water heaters, and municipal waterworks equipment will deteriorate when high concentrations of chloride ions are present.

EXAMPLE:

Where the TDS = 200 mg/L (Chloride = 100 mg/L), water heater life will range from 10 to 13 years. Water heater life declines uniformly as a function of TDS — 1 year shortened life per 200 mg/L additional TDS.

22.332   Color

The SMCL for color is 15 color units. The level of this water quality indicator is not known to be a measure of the safety of water. However, high color content may indicate:

1. High organic chemical contamination,

2. Inadequate treatment, and

3. High disinfectant demand and the potential for production of excess amounts of disinfection by-products.

Color may be caused by:

1. Natural color-causing solids such as aromatic, polyhydroxy, methoxy, and carboxylic acids,

2. Fluvic and humic acid fractions, and

3. Presence of metals such as copper, iron, and manganese.

Rapid changes in color levels may provoke more citizen complaints than relatively high, constant color levels.

22.333   Copper

The SMCL for copper is 1.0 mg/L. Soft water containing a low level (0.5 mg/L) of copper may cause blue or blue-green staining of porcelain. Higher levels (4 mg/L) of copper will stain clothing and blond hair. When soap is used with water having a copper concentration greater than 1 mg/L, insoluble green curds will form.

22.334 Corrosivity

The corrosivity of water indicates the rate at which water causes the gradual decomposition or destruction of a material (such as a metal or cement lining). The severity and type of corrosivity are dependent on the chemical and physical characteristics of the water and the material.

Corrosivity causes materials to deteriorate and go into solution (be carried by the water). Corrosion of toxic metal pipe materials such as lead can create a serious health hazard. Corrosion of iron may produce a flood of unpleasant telephone calls from consumers complaining about rusty water, stained laundry, and bad tastes.

Corrosivity can cause the reduction of the carrying capacity of a water main. This reduced carrying capacity can cause an increase in pump energy costs and may reduce distribution system pressures. Leaks in water mains due to corrosivity may eventually require replacement of a water main.

22.335 Fluoride

Fluoride produces two effects, depending on its concentration. At levels of 6 to 8 mg/L, fluoride may cause skeletal fluorosis (the bones become brittle) and stiffening of the joints. For this reason fluoride has been added to the list of primary standards (those that have health effects).

At levels of 2 mg/L and greater, fluoride may cause dental fluorosis, which is discoloration and mottling of the teeth, especially in children. EPA has recently reclassified dental fluorosis as a cosmetic effect, raised the primary drinking water standard from 1.4 to 2 mg/L to 4 mg/L, and established a secondary standard of 2 mg/L for fluoride.

22.336 Foaming Agents

The SMCL for foaming agents is 0.5 mg/L.

UNDESIRABLE EFFECTS

1. Causes frothing and foaming which are associated with contamination (greater than 1.0 mg/L).

2. Imparts an unpleasant taste (oily, fishy, perfume-like) (less than 1.0 mg/L).

INFORMATION ITEMS

1. Because no convenient foamability test exists and because *SURFACTANTS*[5] are one major class of substances that cause foaming, this property is determined indirectly by measuring the anionic surfactant (*MBAS*[6]) concentration in the water.

2. Surfactants are synthetic organic chemicals and are the principal ingredient of modern household detergents.

3. The requirement for biodegradability led to the widespread use of Linear Alkylbenzene Sulfonate (LAS), an anionic surfactant.

4. Concentrations of anionic surfactants found in drinking waters range from 0 to 2.6 mg/L in well supplies and 0 to 5 mg/L in surface water supplies.

5. LAS is essentially odorless. The odor and taste characteristics are likely to arise from the degradation of waste products rather than the detergents.

6. If water contains an average concentration of 10 mg/L surfactants, the water is likely to be entirely of wastewater origin.

7. From a toxicological standpoint an MCL of 0.5 mg/L, assuming a daily adult human water intake of 2 liters, would give a safety factor of 15,000.

22.337 Iron and Manganese

1. Iron and manganese are frequently found together in natural waters and produce similar adverse environmental effects and color problems. Excessive amounts of iron and manganese are usually found in groundwater and in surface water contaminated by industrial waste discharges.

2. Prior to 1962, both were covered by a single recommended limit.

3. In 1962, the U.S. Public Health Service recommended separate limits for both iron and manganese to reflect more accurately the levels at which adverse effects occur for each.

4. Both are highly objectionable in large amounts in water supplies for either domestic or industrial use.

5. Both impart color to laundered goods and plumbing fixtures.

6. Taste thresholds in drinking water are considerably higher than the levels which produce staining effects.

7. Both are part of our daily nutritional requirements, but these requirements are not met by the consumption of drinking water.

22.338 Iron

The SMCL for iron is 0.3 mg/L.

UNDESIRABLE EFFECTS

1. At levels greater than 0.05 mg/L some color may develop, staining of fixtures may occur, and precipitates may form.

2. The magnitude of the staining effect is directly proportional to the concentration.

---

[5] Surfactant (sir-FAC-tent). Abbreviation for surface-active agent. The active agent in detergents that possesses a high cleaning ability.
[6] MBAS. **M**ethylene - **B**lue - **A**ctive **S**ubstances. These substances are used in surfactants or detergents.

3. Depending on the sensitivity of taste perception, a bitter, astringent taste can be detected from 0.1 mg/L to 1.0 mg/L.

4. Precipitates that are formed create not only color problems but also lead to bacterial growth of slimes and of the iron-loving bacteria, *Crenothrix*, in wells and distribution piping.

NUTRITIONAL REQUIREMENTS

1. Daily requirement is 1 to 2 mg, but intake of larger quantities is required as a result of poor absorption.

2. The limited amount of iron permitted in water (because of objectionable taste or staining effects) constitutes only a small fraction of the amount normally consumed and does not have toxicologic (poisonous) significance.

22.339   Manganese

The SMCL for manganese is 0.05 mg/L.

UNDESIRABLE EFFECTS

1. A concentration of more than 0.02 mg/L may cause buildup of coatings in distribution piping.

2. If these coatings slough off, they can cause brown blotches in laundry items and black precipitates.

3. Manganese imparts a taste to water above 0.15 mg/L.

4. The application of chlorine, even at low levels, increases the likelihood of precipitation of manganese at low levels.

5. Unless the precipitate is removed, precipitates reaching pipelines will promote bacterial growth.

TOXIC EFFECTS

1. Toxic effects are reported as a result of inhalation of manganese dust or fumes.

2. Liver cirrhosis has arisen in controlled feeding of rats.

3. Neurological effects have been suggested; however, these effects have not been scientifically confirmed.

NUTRITIONAL REQUIREMENTS

1. Daily intake of manganese from a normal diet is about 10 mg.

2. Manganese is essential for proper nutrition.

3. Diets deficient in manganese will interfere with growth, blood and bone formation, and reproduction.

QUESTIONS

Write your answers in a notebook and then compare your answers with those on pages 555 and 556.

22.3D   Why is chloride a secondary contaminant?

22.3E   What are surfactants?

22.3F   What is the impact of chlorine on manganese?

22.3310   Odor

The SMCL for odor is a *THRESHOLD ODOR NUMBER (TON[7])* of 3. Important facts to remember when dealing with odors include:

1. Taste and odor go hand-in-hand.

2. Absence of taste and odor helps to maintain the consumers' confidence in the quality of their water, even though it doesn't guarantee that the water is safe.

3. Research indicates that there are only four true taste sensations: sour, sweet, salty, and bitter.

4. All other sensations ascribed to the sense of taste are actually odors even though the sensation is not noticed until the material is taken into the mouth.

5. Odor tests are less fatiguing to people than taste tests when testing for tastes and odors.

6. Taste and odor tests are useful:

   a. As a check on the quality of raw[8] and treated water, and

   b. To help control odor throughout the plant.

7. Odor is a useful test:

   a. For determining the effectiveness of different kinds of treatment, and

   b. As a means for tracing the source of contaminants.

8. Hydrogen sulfide is included under the odor SMCL.

22.3311   pH

The SMCL for pH is defined as pH values beyond the acceptable range from 6.5 to 8.5. A wide range of pH values in drinking water can be tolerated by consumers.

UNDESIRABLE EFFECTS

1. When the pH increases, the disinfection activity of chlorine falls significantly.

2. High pH may cause increased halogen reactions, which produce chloroform and other trihalomethanes during chlorination.

---

[7] *Threshold Odor Number (TON).   The greatest dilution of a sample with odor-free water that still yields a just-detectable odor.*
[8] *When testing raw water, be sure there are no pathogens or toxic chemicals present.*

3. Both excessively high and low pHs may cause increased corrosivity which can in turn create taste problems, staining problems, and significant health hazards.

4. Metallic piping in contact with low pH water will impart a metallic taste.

5. If the piping is iron or copper, high pH will cause oxide and carbonate compounds to be deposited leaving red or green stains on fixtures and laundry.

6. At a high pH, drinking water acquires a bitter taste.

7. The high degree of mineralization often associated with basic waters results in encrustation of water pipes and water-using appliances.

22.3312 Silver

Silver is a nonessential element, providing no beneficial effects from its ingestion in trace amounts. Chronic toxicity causes an unsightly blue-gray discoloration of the skin, mucous membranes, and eyes. Apparently, beside cosmetic changes, there are no physiologic effects. Ingestion of trace amounts of silver or silver salts results in its accumulation in the body, particularly the skin and eyes. There is some evidence that changes to the kidneys, liver, and spleen can occur. The SMCL for silver is 0.1 mg/L.

22.3313 Sulfate

The SMCL for sulfate is 250 mg/L.

UNDESIRABLE EFFECTS AT HIGH LEVELS

1. Tends to form hard scales in boilers and heat exchangers.

2. Causes taste effects.

3. Causes laxative effect. This effect is commonly noted by newcomers or casual or intermittent users of water high in sulfate. Water containing more than 750 mg/L of sulfate usually produces the laxative effect while water with less than 600 mg/L sulfate usually does not. An individual can adjust to sulfate in drinking water.

4. Sodium sulfate and magnesium sulfate are more active as laxatives, whereas calcium sulfate is less active.

5. When the magnesium sulfate content is 200 mg/L, the most sensitive person will feel the laxative effect; however, magnesium sulfate levels between 500 mg/L and 1,000 mg/L will induce diarrhea in most individuals.

6. Tastes may sometimes be detected at 200 mg/L of sulfate, but generally are detected in the range of 300 to 400 mg/L.

22.3314 Total Dissolved Solids (TDS)

The SMCL for total dissolved solids is 500 mg/L.

UNDESIRABLE EFFECTS

1. TDS imparts adverse taste effects at greater than 500 mg/L.

2. Highly mineralized water influences the deterioration of distribution systems as well as domestic plumbing and appliances (the life of a water heater will decrease one year with each additional 200 mg/L of TDS above a typical 200 mg/L value).

3. Mineralization can also cause precipitates to form in boilers and other heating units, sludge in freezing processes, rings on utensils, and precipitates in food being cooked.

4. There may be a great difference between a detectable concentration and an objectionable concentration of the neutral salts. Many people can become accustomed to high levels.

5. Studies show that the temperature of mineralized waters influences their acceptability to the public.

22.3315 Zinc

The SMCL for zinc is 5 mg/L.

UNDESIRABLE EFFECTS

1. High concentrations of zinc produce adverse physiological effects.

2. Zinc imparts a bitter, astringent taste which is distinguishable at 4 mg/L. Also at 4 mg/L a metallic taste will exist.

3. Zinc will cause a milky appearance in water at 30 mg/L.

4. Zinc may increase lead and cadmium concentrations.

5. The activity of several enzymes is dependent on zinc.

6. Cadmium and lead are common contaminants of zinc used in galvanizing steel pipe.

PHYSIOLOGICAL EFFECTS

1. A concentration of 30 mg/L can cause nausea and fainting.

2. Zinc salts act as gastrointestinal irritants. This symptom of illness is acute and transitory.

3. The vomiting concentration range is 675 to 2,280 mg/L.

4. A wide margin of safety exists between normal food intake and concentrations in water high enough to cause oral toxicity.

DIETARY REQUIREMENTS

1. The daily requirement for preschool children is 0.3 mg Zn/kg of weight.

2. Total zinc in an adult human body averages two grams.

3. Zinc most likely concentrates in the retina of the eye and in the prostate.

4. Zinc deficiency in animals leads to growth retardation.

QUESTIONS

Write your answers in a notebook and then compare your answers with those on page 556.

22.3G   What are the undesirable effects of abnormal pH values?

22.3H   Why are high levels of sulfate undesirable in drinking water?

22.3I   Why are high levels of zinc undesirable in drinking water?

22.4 SAMPLING PROCEDURES

22.40 Safe Drinking Water Regulations

The Safe Drinking Water Act and accompanying regulations require that you must take the following actions to comply:

1. Sampling,

2. Testing,

3. Recordkeeping, and

4. Reporting.

Understanding and implementing each of these steps will help ensure the success of your operation.

The two posters which have been provided with this manual summarize the essential elements of drinking water regulations. The poster titled "Primary Drinking Water Regulations" lists the MCLs, and monitoring, reporting, compliance, and notification procedures for four inorganic chemicals (arsenic, fluoride, lead, and copper) as well as for DBPs, turbidity, microorganisms, and radionuclides. This poster also lists the secondary contaminants, their SMCLs, recommended monitoring frequencies, and reporting procedures.

The second poster, "SDWA Contaminant Monitoring Requirements," focuses on the organic and inorganic chemicals regulated in EPA's Phase II and Phase V proceedings. Also listed are the unregulated contaminants which must be monitored but for which final regulations have not yet been developed. This poster provides detailed information about monitoring, reporting, and notification procedures, and other important information.

When using these posters, you will notice the phrases "State Option" or "State Discretion." This means the state will make the determination about whether a rule or limit or requirement applies. Operators are urged to stay in close contact with their state regulatory agencies and become thoroughly familiar with their state requirements. Although these posters are revised frequently and every effort is made to ensure their accuracy at the time of publication, it is extremely difficult to keep pace with changing regulations. An excellent source of up-to-the-minute information about drinking water regulations is EPA's toll-free Safe Drinking Water Hotline at (800) 426-4791.

22.41 Initial Sampling

"Initial sampling" refers to the very first sampling conducted under the SDWA for each of the applicable contaminant categories. The timing of this sampling depends on:

1. The type of contaminant being monitored,

2. Whether the system is a community or noncommunity water system, and

3. Whether the water source is a surface water or groundwater supply.

22.42 Routine Sampling

Routine sampling refers to sampling repeated on a regular basis. Coliform sampling must be conducted in accordance with a written sampling plan which has been approved by the state regulatory agency. Table 22.7 summarizes the routine sampling requirements for each contaminant category.

22.43 Check and Repeat Sampling

Whenever an initial or routine sample analysis indicates that an MCL has been exceeded, check sampling is required to confirm the routine sampling results. Check sampling is in addition to the routine sampling program. Although check sampling cannot be scheduled in advance, there are specific check sampling procedures to follow. The number of samples, sampling points, and frequency of sampling vary according to the particular contaminant. For example, the regulations specify that wherever coliform bacteria repeat samples are required, at least one of the repeat samples must be taken from the same sampling point as the original and two of the repeat samples must be collected from nearby points upstream and downstream of the original.

22.44 Sampling Points

Some of the samples required to determine compliance with the primary regulations can be taken from the routine sampling points. By coordinating the present sampling points with the sampling program required by the regulations, additional monitoring costs can be minimized. Table 22.7 summarizes what, where, and how often you need to sample for both community and noncommunity water systems. The number of sampling points required will depend on the specific size of the population served and layout of each water system.

As noted in Table 22.7, samples for organics, inorganics, and turbidity must be taken at the points where water enters the distribution system, and samples collected for coliform bacteria must be taken from the consumers' faucets at representative points within the distribution system.

At the very minimum, a small system (with a population of 25 to 1,000) must sample for turbidity and coliform bacteria and also must have two sampling points:

1. One where the water enters the distribution system, and

2. One at a consumer faucet at a representative point in the distribution system.

QUESTIONS

Write your answers in a notebook and then compare your answers with those on page 556.

22.4A   What do the words "Initial Sampling" mean?

22.4B   What is routine sampling?

22.4C   What is check (repeat) sampling?

22.4D   What are the minimum sampling requirements for a small system with a population of 100 people?

**TABLE 22.7 REQUIRED SAMPLING FOR COMMUNITY AND
NONTRANSIENT NONCOMMUNITY WATER SYSTEMS** [a]

Contaminant	Where Samples Are Taken	How Often
Inorganics (except nitrate and nitrite[b])	At entry point(s) to distribution system (from clearwell)	Groundwater systems: one sample every three years Surface water systems: one sample every year
Organics	At entry point(s) to distribution system (from clearwell)	
Volatile		All systems: one sample every year. After three years with no detects, one sample per three-year compliance period.
Pesticides and other synthetics		All systems: four consecutive quarterly samples. If no detects in 1993-1995 sampling period, state may reduce sampling frequency based on system size.
Turbidity	Filtered systems: at entry point(s) to distribution system (from clearwell) Unfiltered systems: immediately prior to point of disinfection	Surface water systems: every four hours or continuously Groundwater systems: state option
Coliform Bacteria	At the consumer's faucet[c]	All systems: sampling based on population served — see Table 22.3
Radioactivity[d]	In the distribution system	
Natural		All systems: average of four consecutive quarterly samples
Manmade		Surface water systems serving more than 100,000 persons and vulnerable systems: average of four consecutive quarterly samples; all other systems: state option

[a] This information is presented in greater detail on the posters included with this manual. Please refer to the posters for sampling requirements for transient noncommunity water systems.
[b] See posters for nitrate and nitrite requirements.
[c] The faucets selected must be representative of conditions within the distribution system.
[d] Applies to community water systems only unless required by the state.

22.45   Sampling Point Selection

The two major considerations in determining the number and location of sampling points are that they should be:

1. Representative of each different surface water source entering the system, and

2. Representative of conditions within the system such as dead ends, loops, storage facilities, and pressure zones.

22.46   Sampling Schedule

A sampling schedule should be prepared which indicates all of the samples that will be collected during a yearly period. The schedule should include the following information:

1. Sampling frequency,

2. Sampling point designation,

3. Location (address),

4. Type of test,

5. Sample volume, and

6. Special handling instructions.

This schedule should be reviewed with your state regulatory agency to determine adequacy to meet the SDWA regulations. A written sampling plan for coliform testing must be approved by the state regulatory agency.

22.47   Sampling Route

After selection of the sampling points and preparation of the sampling schedule, the next step is to select a route. Arrange your route so that samples that must be analyzed immediately are not delayed while other sampling is done. Field data forms must be completed by the person doing the sampling and submitted to the laboratory with the samples.

22.48   Sample Collection

Good sampling techniques are the key to a meaningful and useful sampling program. The following eight steps are necessary to the collection of an acceptable sample:

1. Obtain a sample that is truly representative of the existing conditions;

2. Flush the line before sample collection (except when a first-draw sample is required, such as in testing for lead);

3. Fill the sample bottle without leaving any air pocket;

4. Analyze residual chlorine when the sample is taken;

5. Handle and store the sample so that it does not become contaminated before it reaches the laboratory;

6. Use preservation techniques. These preservation methods are generally:

   a. pH control, and

   b. Refrigeration;

7. Label the sample immediately and keep accurate records of every sample collected including:

   a. Date and time sampled,

   b. Location sampled,

   c. Name of sample collected,

   d. Bottle number,

   e. Type of sample, and

   f. Name of person collecting sample. Any person collecting samples should be required to complete a form providing the above information at the time of sample collection. This form should be supplied by the laboratory; and

8. Keep the time between the collection of the sample and analysis as short as possible.

QUESTIONS

Write your answers in a notebook and then compare your answers with those on page 556.

22.4E   List the information that should be included in a sampling schedule.

22.4F   List the elements necessary to the collection of an acceptable sample.

22.5   REPORTING PROCEDURES

The primary purpose of the SDWA is to protect the public's health. Two general categories of reporting are called for by the Act:

1. Reporting to the public (public notification), and

2. Reporting to the state.

There are four types of reports that must be sent to the state:

1. Initial reports,

2. Routine sampling reports,

3. Check or repeat sampling reports, and

4. Violation reports.

Tables 22.8 through 22.16 outline reporting procedures for various contaminants.

TABLE 22.8   REPORTING PROCEDURES
INORGANIC CHEMICALS (EXCEPT NITRATE) AND ORGANIC CHEMICALS

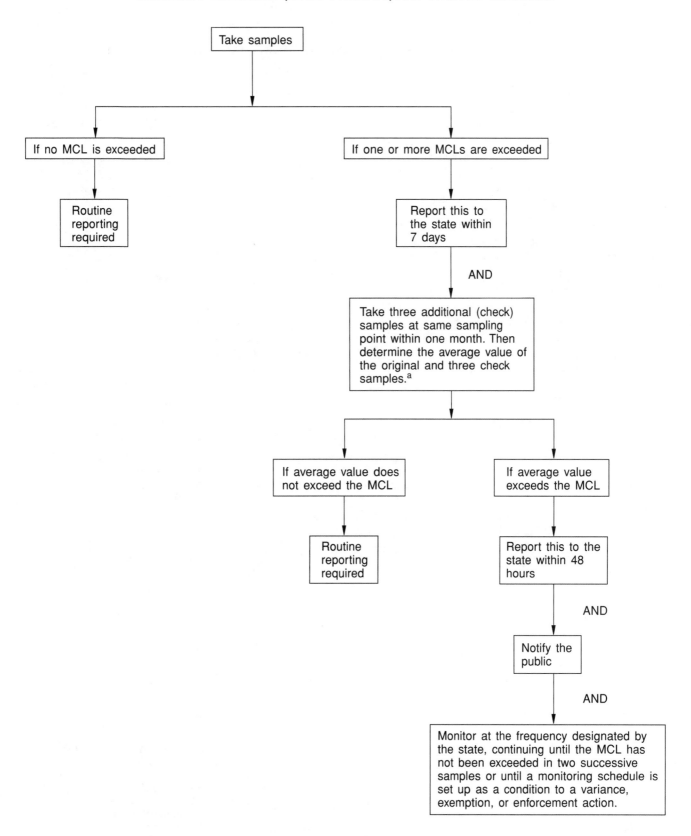

^{a} Average value = $\dfrac{\text{TOTAL of Original Sample + 3 check samples}}{4}$

TABLE 22.9   REPORTING PROCEDURES — NITRATE

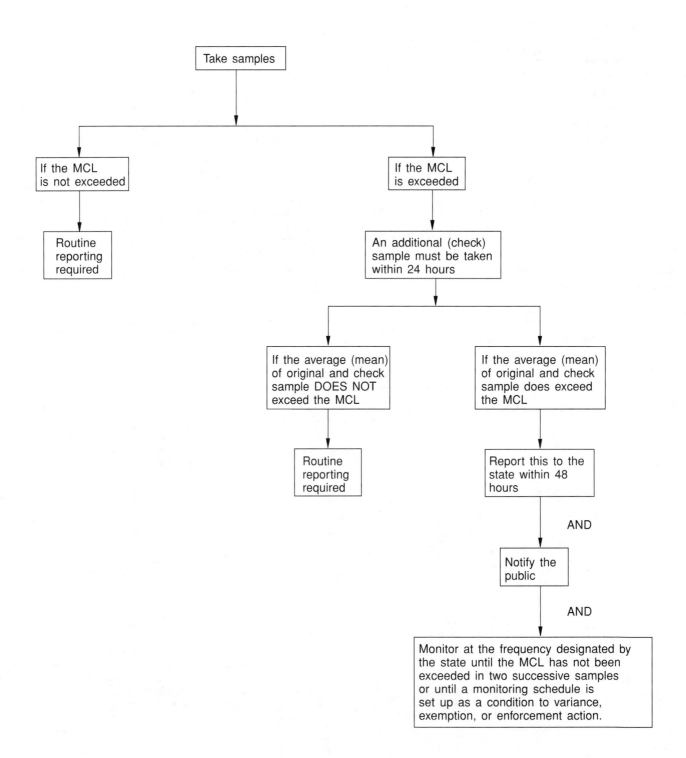

**TABLE 22.10   REPORTING PROCEDURES — TURBIDITY MONITORING
(Surface Water Using Conventional or Direct Filtration)**

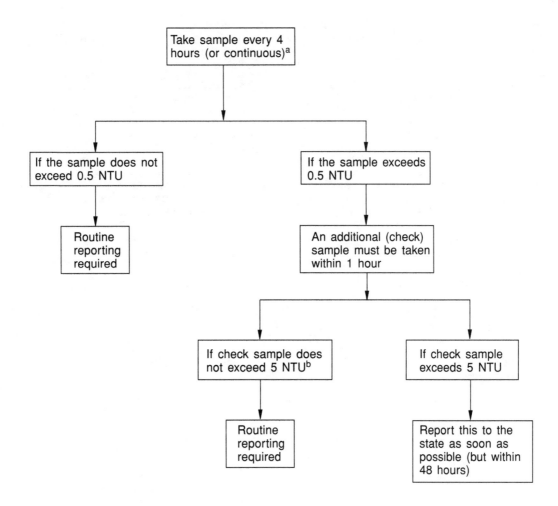

[a] Less frequent sampling may be established at state option.
[b] Filter effluent turbidity must be ≤1 NTU in 95% of samples.

**TABLE 22.11   REPORTING PROCEDURES —
WHEN CALCULATING MONTHLY AVERAGE TURBIDITY VALUE**

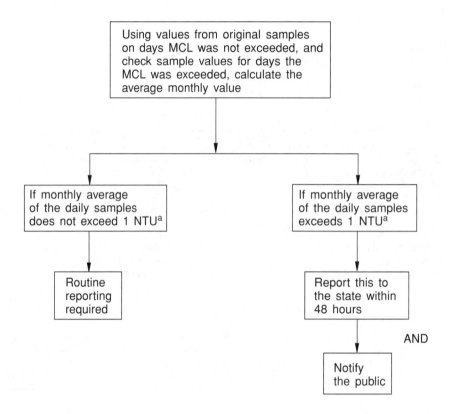

^a MCL of 5 NTU may be established at state option.

TABLE 22.12 REPORTING PROCEDURES
MICROBIAL CONTAMINANTS — TOTAL COLIFORM RULE

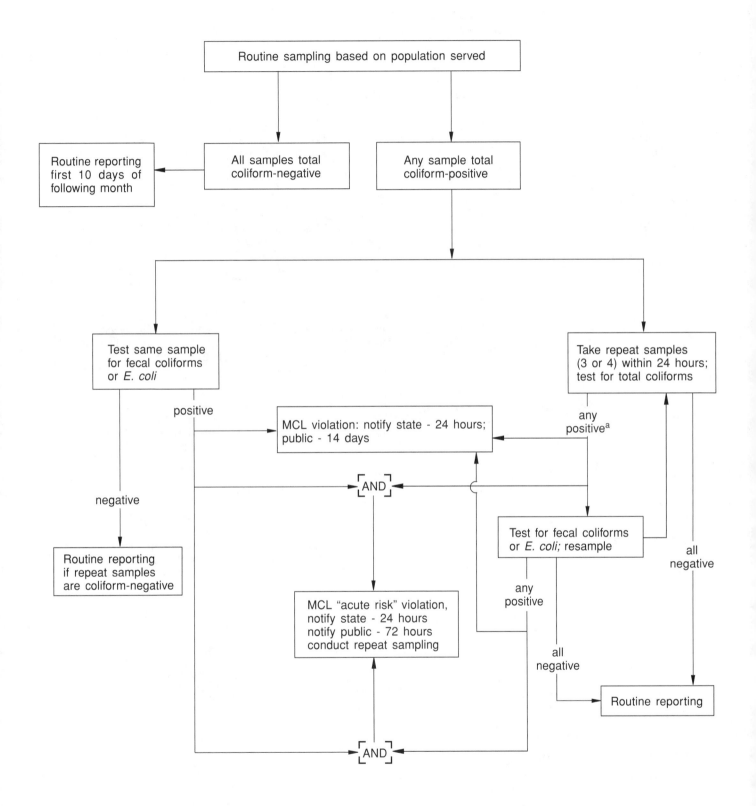

a For systems collecting more than 40 samples per month, MCL is violated when more than 5% are total coliform-positive. For systems collecting fewer than 40 samples per month, MCL is violated when more than one sample is total coliform-positive. Monthly calculations must include repeat samples.

TABLE 22.13 REPORTING PROCEDURES — MICROBIAL CONTAMINANTS — CHLORINE RESIDUAL

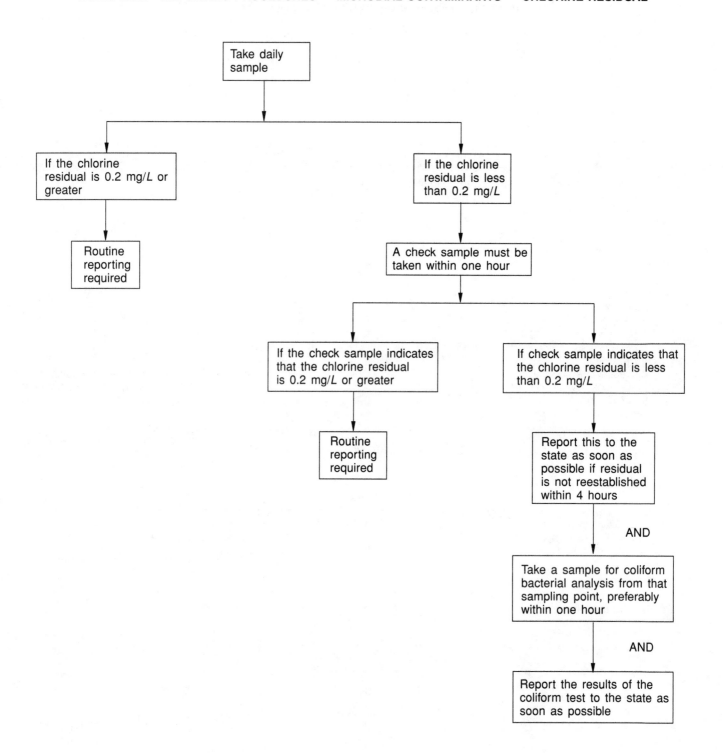

TABLE 22.14 REPORTING PROCEDURES — RADIOLOGICAL CONTAMINANTS — NATURAL
(Test for Gross Alpha Activity)

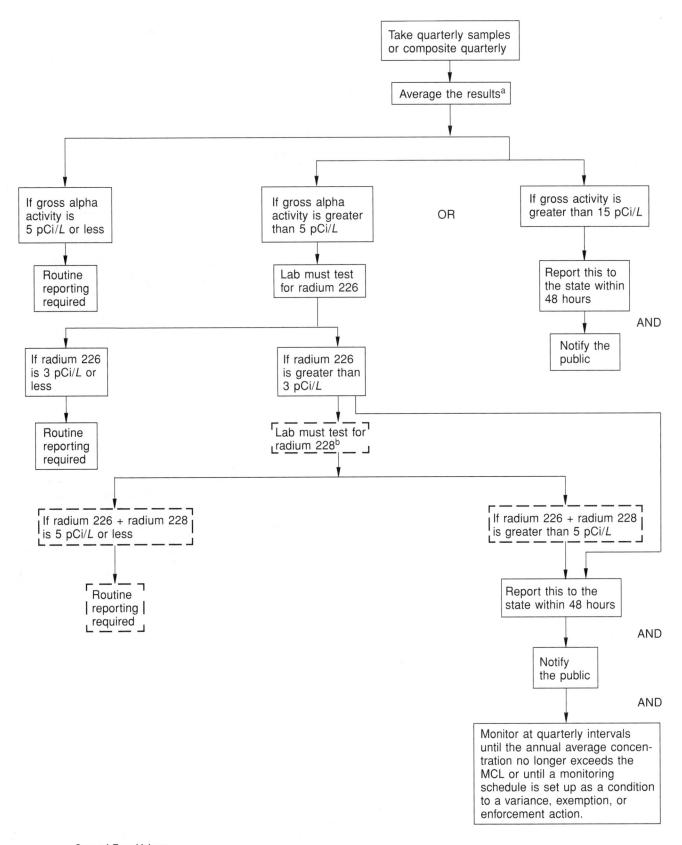

^{a} Average $= \dfrac{\text{Sum of Four Values}}{4}$

No averaging is required if the quarterly samples were composited. In that case, use the results of the single sample.

^{b} This step is required only for the initial monitoring period and not for routine monitoring, *EXCEPT AS REQUIRED BY THE STATE.*

TABLE 22.15   REPORTING PROCEDURES — RADIOLOGICAL CONTAMINANTS — MANMADE[a]

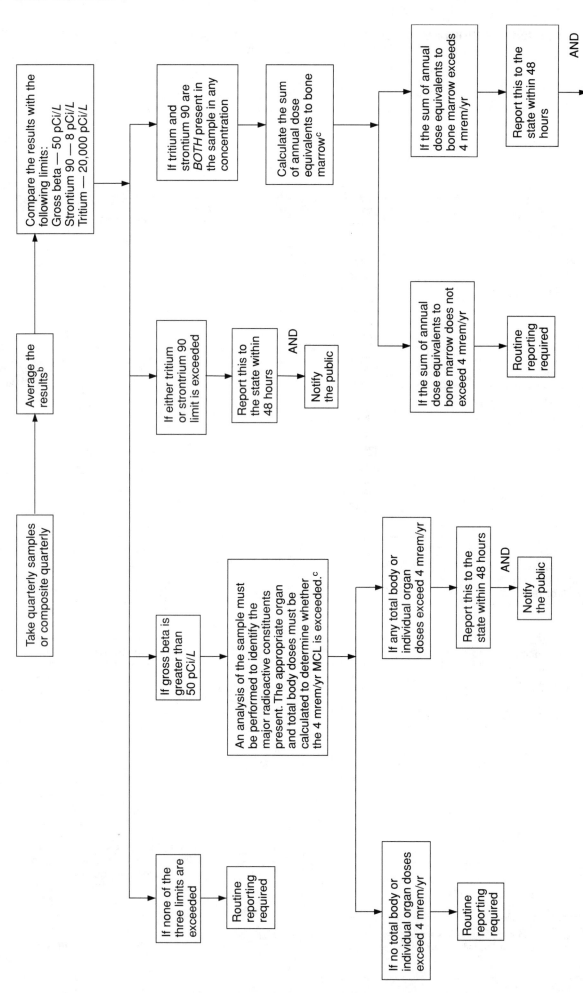

[a] Applies to surface water systems serving populations of 100,000 or more and systems determined by the state to be vulnerable.

[b] Average = $\dfrac{\text{Sum of Four Values}}{4}$

[c] No averaging is required if the quarterly samples were composited. In that case, use the results of the single sample.

It is likely that the laboratory will not make these calculations. You will probably have to get help from state water supply personnel in making these calculations.

TABLE 22.16 REPORTING PROCEDURES — TOTAL TRIHALOMETHANES[a]

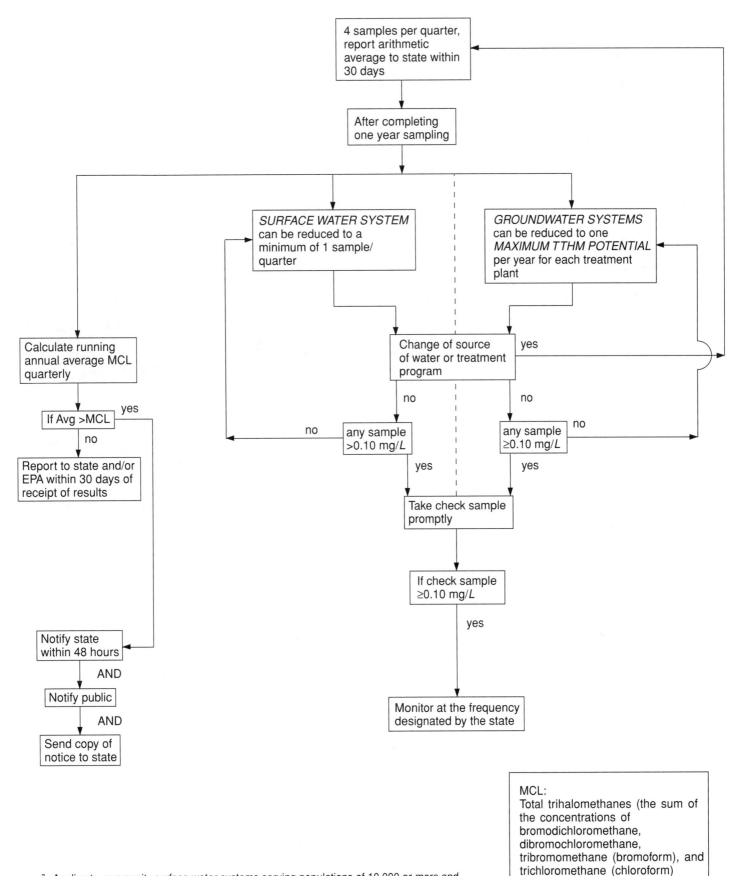

[a] Applies to community surface water systems serving populations of 10,000 or more and all surface water systems that meet the SWTR criteria for avoiding filtration.

22.6 NOTIFICATION REQUIREMENTS

On April 28, 1989, revised regulations took effect concerning how and when the public must be notified of violations of drinking water regulations. All violations are now classified by EPA as either Tier 1 or Tier 2 violations; Tier 1 violations are the more serious ones.

Tier 1 Violations	Tier 2 Violations
Failure to comply with an MCL	Failure to comply with monitoring requirements
Failure to comply with a treatment technique	Failure to comply with a testing procedure
Failure to comply with a variance or exemption schedule	Operating under a variance or exemption

Public notices must include specific information about the health effects of each contaminant. The precise wording, called "mandatory health effects language," must be used in notices for all Tier 1 violations and in notices for operating under a variance or exemption. Contact your regulatory agency for the appropriate wording of any notice you need to issue.

In most cases the public must be advised of Tier 1 violations by newspaper and mail within the time periods listed below. The notices must be repeated every three months as long as the violation exists. Two Tier 1 violations constitute what is known as an "acute risk to health" and the public must be advised of the violation by electronic media (radio and television). These two are: exceeding the nitrate MCL, and receipt of a confirmed coliform-positive sample result.

The prescribed methods for notifying the public of Tier 1 violations and operating under a variance or exemption are as follows:

- Newspaper: As soon as possible, but no later than 14 days after violation

- Hand or mail delivery: no later than 45 days after violation

- Electronic media: no later than 72 hours after violation (radio/television)

If there is no newspaper serving the affected area, notices may be posted in a conspicuous place.

Public notice of Tier 2 violations of monitoring requirements or testing procedures may be issued through newspapers or posting of a notice. In either case, public notices must contain the following information:

1. Explanation of the violation,

2. Potential adverse health effects,

3. Population at risk,

4. Steps system is taking to correct the violation,

5. Need for alternative water supplies, if applicable,

6. What consumers should do, and

7. Water supplier's phone number for further information.

All notices should be written in language that is free of technical jargon, printed in a type size that is easy to read, and published or posted in a conspicuous location. In addition, copies of all public notices must be sent to the state regulatory agency within 10 days after they are issued.

22.7 RECORDKEEPING

Water suppliers are required to keep certain information on file, as follows:

- Bacteriological results — five years

- Chemical results — ten years

- Actions taken to correct violations — three years after the action was taken

- Sanitary survey reports — ten years

- Variance or Exemption records — five years

22.8 CONSUMER CONFIDENCE REPORTS (CCRs)

Consumer confidence reports are an effective means for a water utility to communicate with consumers that their water is safe to drink. These reports also provide an opportunity to inform rate payers of the need for sufficient funds to properly operate and maintain the water supply, treatment, and distribution systems. If higher rates are necessary to fund a capital improvement program, the reports can explain the importance of having sufficient water with adequate pressure and high quality.

EPA has developed regulations requiring every public water system to prepare an annual consumer confidence report. The reports are an opportunity for positive communication with consumers and to convince consumers of the importance of paying for good quality water.

Items that should be covered in consumer confidence reports include:

1. Information on source of drinking water supply,

2. Brief definition of terms,

3. List of contaminants detected including level detected, MCL (maximum contaminant level), and MCLG (maximum contaminant level goal),

4. For MCLs violated, information on health effects, and

5. Information on any unregulated contaminants.

Some utility agencies try to have an article published in the local newspaper explaining the report before it is made available to consumers. This advance information helps the consumers understand the report. Reports should be a short, concise letter report of one or two pages that can be mailed directly to consumers or mailed in the envelope with the utility bill. All utility staff should be familiar with the contents of the report because consumers who know utility personnel frequently will ask personnel questions about the report. Water utilities should emphasize the good job they are doing as guardians of health in these consumer confidence reports.

Contact your local or state drinking water supply agency for suggestions and details on how to prepare a consumer confidence report. Reports probably will be required by the year 2000.

QUESTIONS

Write your answers in a notebook and then compare your answers with those on page 556.

22.5A What are the two general categories of reporting called for by the SDWA?

22.5B What are the four types of reports that must be sent to the state?

22.6A If an MCL is violated, by what means is the public notified?

22.8A Why should all utility staff be familiar with the contents of the consumer confidence report?

End of Lesson 2 of 2 Lessons
on
DRINKING WATER REGULATIONS

Please answer the discussion and review questions before continuing with the Objective Test.

DISCUSSION AND REVIEW QUESTIONS
Chapter 22. DRINKING WATER REGULATIONS
(Lesson 2 of 2 Lessons)

Write the answers to these questions in your notebook before continuing with the Objective Test on page 557. The question numbering continues from Lesson 1.

14. What do secondary drinking water regulations control?

15. Why are secondary drinking water regulations important?

16. How may color be caused in water?

17. Why are iron and manganese undesirable in drinking water?

18. Why is the absence of tastes and odors in drinking water important?

19. Why isn't hydrogen sulfide listed under the Secondary Drinking Water Standards?

20. Why are high levels of total dissolved solids undesirable in drinking water?

21. How is the number of sampling points determined?

22. What are the major considerations in determining the number and location of sampling points?

23. How is a sampling route selected?

24. How can samples be preserved?

25. What items should be covered in a consumer confidence report?

SUGGESTED ANSWERS

Chapter 22.   DRINKING WATER REGULATIONS

ANSWERS TO QUESTIONS IN LESSON 1

Answers to questions on page 513.

22.0A   The first drinking water standards were designed to control waterborne bacteria and viruses that can cause diseases such as cholera, typhoid, and dysentery.

22.0B   Operators should develop good working relationships with their local regulatory agencies in order to keep up to date on the latest changes in regulations that apply to their water treatment system.

Answers to questions on page 514.

22.1A   The five types of primary contaminants considered to be of public health importance are:

1. Inorganic contaminants,
2. Organic contaminants,
3. Turbidity,
4. Microbial contaminants, and
5. Radiological contaminants.

22.1B   To regulate a substance, EPA must demonstrate that the contaminant meets three criteria:

1. The contaminant has an adverse effect on human health,
2. It occurs or is likely to occur in public water systems at a frequency and concentration of significance to public health, and
3. Regulation of the contaminant offers a meaningful opportunity to reduce health risks for people served by public water systems.

22.1C   EPA requires water systems to monitor some unregulated contaminants to assist the agency in determining the extent of contamination by these substances in order to assess whether they need to be regulated.

Answers to questions on page 516.

22.1D   EPA sets MCLGs at zero for known or probable human carcinogens as a matter of policy.

22.1E   A maximum contaminant level goal (MCLG) represents what EPA believes to be a safe level of consumption of a contaminant based solely on health effects, but this is not a legally enforceable standard. The maximum contaminant level (MCL) is a legally enforceable standard which protects public health but takes into account factors such as existing laboratory detection technology, costs, and reasonableness.

22.1F   A community water system is defined as follows:

1. Has at least 15 service connections used by all-year residents, or
2. Regularly serves at least 25 all-year residents.

Answers to questions on page 522.

22.2A   Primary standards for some contaminants are specified as treatment techniques because the contaminants are too difficult or expensive to detect and measure. The specified treatment technique is known to adequately reduce the public health threat of the contaminant.

22.2B   Inorganic chemicals are metals, salts, and other chemical compounds that do not contain carbon.

22.2C   Arsenic is listed as a primary contaminant because anyone who drinks water that continuously exceeds the national standard by a substantial amount over a lifetime may experience fatigue and loss of energy. Extremely high levels can cause poisoning.

22.2D   At levels of 6 to 8 mg/L, fluoride may cause skeletal fluorosis (the bones become brittle) and stiffening of the joints. At levels of 2 mg/L and greater, fluoride may cause dental fluorosis (discoloration and mottling of the teeth), especially in children.

22.2E   Lead may enter drinking water from galvanized pipes, solder used with copper pipes, and through the air from auto exhausts.

22.2F   Nitrate above 10 mg/L in drinking water is considered an immediate threat to public health because it causes a serious disorder called "blue baby" in infants under three months of age. Intestinal bacteria change nitrate to nitrite and the nitrite reduces the oxygen-carrying ability of the blood. This produces a life-threatening anemic condition.

Answers to questions on page 523.

22.2G   Organic chemicals are either natural or synthetic chemical compounds that contain carbon. Synthetic organic chemicals (SOCs) are manmade compounds that are widely used as pesticides, paints, dyes, solvents, plastics, and food additives.

22.2H   Trichloroethylene (TCE) has been widely used as an ingredient in many household products (spot removers, rug cleaners, air fresheners), dry cleaning agents, industrial metal cleaners and polishes, refrigerants, and even anesthetics.

Answers to questions on page 526.

22.2I   Microbial contaminants are a public health concern because they cause almost immediate gastrointestinal illness when people consume them in water. Waterborne diseases such as typhoid, cholera, infectious hepatitis, and dysentery have been traced to improperly disinfected drinking water.

22.2J   The Total Coliform Rule uses a presence-absence approach to determine compliance rather than estimating the number of coliform organisms found in a sample.

22.2K   The five analytical methods EPA will accept for coliform testing include:

1. Multiple-tube fermentation technique (MTF),
2. Membrane filter technique (MF),
3. Presence-absence coliform test (P-A),
4. Colilert™ system (ONPG-MUG test), and
5. Colisure test.

22.2L   Repeat coliform samples are collected to confirm the presence of coliform bacteria and to help determine whether the contamination is a localized or a system-wide problem.

22.2M   When repeat samples must be taken, one must be taken from the same tap as the original coliform-positive sample and at least two must be taken from nearby points (within five service connections) upstream and downstream.

Answers to questions on page 531.

22.2N   The Surface Water Treatment Rule (SWTR) sets forth primary drinking water regulations requiring treatment of surface water supplies or groundwater supplies under the direct influence of surface water. These regulations require a specific water treatment technique (filtration and/or disinfection) in place of the establishment of maximum contaminant levels (MCLs) for turbidity, *Giardia lamblia*, viruses, *Legionella*, and bacteria. Also the regulations require that all systems be operated by qualified operators.

22.2O   The SWTR defines surface water as "all water open to the atmosphere and subject to surface runoff." This would include rivers, lakes, streams, reservoirs, and groundwaters directly influenced by surface water.

22.2P   A water utility can avoid mandatory filtration by meeting the following requirements:

1. The fecal coliform concentration in the water prior to disinfection must not exceed 20/100 mL, or total coliform concentration must not exceed 100/100 mL in more than 10 percent of the samples analyzed in the previous six months;
2. The turbidity of the water prior to disinfection cannot exceed 5 NTUs based on grab samples collected every four hours or by continuous monitoring; and
3. Certain site-specific conditions.

22.2Q   The MCLs for turbidity for surface waters are:

1. For unfiltered surface water supplies the turbidity of the raw water prior to disinfection cannot exceed 5 NTU based on grab samples collected every four hours or by continuous turbidity monitoring;
2. For filtered surface water supplies the filtration process must achieve a turbidity level of less than 5 NTU at all times and not more than 0.5 NTU in more than 5 percent of the samples analyzed during a given month; and
3. Those systems using slow sand or diatomaceous earth filtration must achieve a turbidity level of less than 5 NTU at all times and not more than 1 NTU in more than 5 percent of the samples collected during the month.

22.2R   The effectiveness of a disinfectant is measured by the time (T) in minutes of the disinfectant's contact in water and the concentration (C) of the disinfectant residual in mg/L measured at the end of the contact time. The product of these two factors (C x T) provides a measure of the degree of pathogenic inactivation.

Answers to questions on page 533.

22.2S   Trihalomethanes (THMs) are the product of chlorine combining with organic material in the water; they are suspected carcinogens.

22.2T   The ICR requires large public water systems (PWSs) to monitor microbial contaminants and disinfection by-products, requires large PWSs to provide operating data and a description of their treatment plant design, and requires large PWSs to conduct either bench- or pilot-scale testing of advanced treatment techniques.

Answers to questions on page 534.

22.2U   Drinking water can become contaminated with radioactive elements when these naturally occurring elements dissolve and are carried to groundwater basins as water passes through the soil.

22.2V   The MCLs for radiological contaminants are divided into two categories: (1) natural radioactivity which results from well water passing through deposits of naturally occurring radioactive materials, and (2) manmade radioactivity such as might result from industrial wastes, hospitals, or research laboratories.

ANSWERS TO QUESTIONS IN LESSON 2

Answers to questions on page 536.

22.3A   Secondary drinking water regulations are enforceable after a state has passed a law requiring the state health agency to enforce the regulations.

22.3B   The secondary drinking water contaminants include:

1. Aluminum	9. Manganese
2. Chloride	10. Odor
3. Color	11. pH
4. Copper	12. Silver
5. Corrosivity	13. Sulfate
6. Fluoride	14. Total Dissolved Solids
7. Foaming Agents	(TDS)
8. Iron	15. Zinc

22.3C   Contaminants in the secondary regulations should be monitored at least as often as the monitoring performed for inorganic contaminants listed in the Primary Drinking Water Regulations as applicable to community water systems. More frequent monitoring would be appropriate for specific contaminants such as pH, color, odor, or others under certain circumstances as directed by the state.

Answers to questions on page 538.

22.3D   Chloride is a secondary contaminant because it affects the aesthetic quality of water by imparting an objectionable salty taste in water and because it causes corrosion of the pipes in hot water systems and other pipelines.

22.3E   Surfactants are synthetic organic chemicals and are the principal ingredient of household detergents.

22.3F   The application of chlorine to waters containing manganese increases the likelihood of precipitation at low levels. Unless the precipitate is removed, precipitates reaching pipelines will promote bacterial growth.

Answers to questions on page 540.

22.3G   The undesirable effects of abnormal pH values include:

1. When the pH increases, the disinfection activity of chlorine falls significantly;

2. High pH may cause increased halogen reactions, which produce chloroform and other trihalomethanes during chlorination;

3. Both excessively high and low pHs may cause increased corrosivity which can in turn create taste problems, staining problems, and significant health hazards;

4. Metallic piping in contact with low pH water will impart a metallic taste;

5. If piping is iron or copper, oxide and carbonate compounds will be deposited leaving red or green stains on fixtures and laundry;

6. At high pH, drinking water acquires a bitter taste; and

7. The high degree of mineralization often associated with basic waters results in encrustation of water pipes and water-using appliances.

22.3H   High levels of sulfate are undesirable because they:

1. Tend to form hard scales in boilers and heat exchangers,

2. Cause taste effects, and

3. Cause a laxative effect.

22.3I   High levels of zinc are undesirable in drinking water because they:

1. Produce adverse physiological effects,

2. Impart undesirable tastes,

3. Cause a milky appearance in the water, and

4. May increase lead and cadmium concentrations.

Answers to questions on page 540.

22.4A   "Initial Sampling" refers to the very first sampling conducted under the Safe Drinking Water Act for each of the applicable contaminant categories.

22.4B   Routine sampling refers to sampling repeated on a regular basis.

22.4C   Whenever an initial or routine sample analysis indicates that an MCL has been exceeded, *CHECK OR REPEAT SAMPLING* is required to confirm the routine sampling results. Check sampling is in addition to the routine sampling program.

22.4D   At the very minimum, a small system with a population of 100 people must sample for turbidity and coliform bacteria and also must have two sampling points:

1. One where the water enters the distribution system, and

2. One at a consumer faucet at a point representative of the distribution system.

Answers to questions on page 542.

22.4E   Information that should be specified in a sampling program includes:

1. Sampling frequency,

2. Sampling point designation,

3. Location,

4. Type of test,

5. Sample volume, and

6. Special handling instructions.

22.4F   The following elements are necessary to the collection of an acceptable sample:

1. Obtain a sample that is truly representative of the existing condition,

2. Flush the line before sample collection (except for lead and copper),

3. Fill the sample bottle without leaving any air pocket,

4. Analyze residual chlorine when the sample is taken,

5. Maintain the sample so that it does not become contaminated before it reaches the laboratory,

6. Use preservation techniques (pH control and refrigeration),

7. Keep accurate records of every sample collected (date, time, location, name of sample, bottle number, type of sample, and name of person collecting sample), and

8. Keep the time between the collection of the sample and analysis as short as possible.

Answers to questions on page 553.

22.5A   The two general categories of reporting called for by the SDWA are:

1. Reporting to the public (public notification), and

2. Reporting to the state.

22.5B   The four types of reports that must be sent to the state are:

1. Initial reports,

2. Routine sampling reports,

3. Check or repeat sampling reports, and

4. Violation reports.

22.6A   Required public notification for the violation of a primary MCL includes mail, newspaper, and electronic media (radio and television).

22.8A   All utility staff should be familiar with the contents of the report because consumers who know utility personnel frequently will ask personnel questions about the report.

OBJECTIVE TEST

Chapter 22.   DRINKING WATER REGULATIONS

Please write your name and mark the correct answers on the answer sheet, as directed at the end of Chapter 1. There may be more than one correct answer to each multiple-choice question.

True-False

1. The purpose of drinking water regulations is to ensure the uniform delivery of safe and aesthetically pleasing drinking water to the public.

   1. True
   2. False

2. The important difference between the two levels of drinking water regulations is that the MCLG is an enforceable standard and the MCL is a nonenforceable goal.

   1. True
   2. False

3. MCLs apply only to contaminants from manmade pollution.

   1. True
   2. False

4. A public water system could be publicly or privately owned.

   1. True
   2. False

5. MCLs are set for substances that are thought to pose a threat to health when present in drinking water at certain levels.

   1. True
   2. False

6. The health concerns about inorganic chemicals are centered on cancer.

   1. True
   2. False

7. The Lead and Copper Rule requires all water systems to optimize corrosion control.

   1. True
   2. False

8. Filtered water must have a disinfectant residual at the entrance to the distribution system of at least 0.2 mg/*L*.

   1. True
   2. False

9. When calculating CT values, contact time must be based on peak hour flow conditions.

   1. True
   2. False

10. Samples collected for monitoring of secondary contaminants should be taken at a free-flowing outlet of water being delivered to the consumer.

    1. True
    2. False

11. Secondary maximum contaminant levels are enforceable at the option of the state.

    1. True
    2. False

12. Tier 2 violations are more serious than Tier 1 violations.

    1. True
    2. False

Best Answer (Select only the closest or best answer.)

13. Why is turbidity of importance to public health?

    1. Causes bad tastes
    2. Interferes with disinfection
    3. Looks undesirable
    4. Requires filtration

14. What is a nontransient noncommunity water system?

    1. Consumers served do not live in an incorporated community
    2. Consumers served live at the facility
    3. Does not serve at least 25 of the same persons more than 6 months per year
    4. Serves at least 25 of the same persons more than 6 months per year

15. The Lead and Copper Rule permits water utilities to instruct consumers in which technique?

    1. Boiling water
    2. Evaluating bottled water
    3. Purchasing point of use devices
    4. Sampling

16. Both primary and secondary standards have been set for which one of the following substances?

    1. Asbestos
    2. Fluoride
    3. Lead
    4. Mercury

17. Why are sanitary surveys conducted?

    1. Establish 95th percentile MPN values to meet coliform standards
    2. Identify possible health risks that may not be discovered by routine coliform sampling
    3. Search for alternative sources of water supply
    4. Survey consumers regarding establishment of Coliform Rule standards

18. How does the SWTR define surface water?

    1. All water open to the atmosphere and subject to surface runoff
    2. All water that is not considered groundwater
    3. Any stream, river, reservoir, or lake with surface runoff flow
    4. Water whose surface is exposed to the atmosphere

19. What does the CT value provide a measure of?

    1. Degree of pathogenic inactivation
    2. Intensity of disinfection
    3. Level of disinfection
    4. Strength of disinfectant dose

20. Which disinfection by-product (DBP) is currently (1997) regulated?

    1. Chlorite
    2. Halogenated acids
    3. Halonitriles
    4. Trihalomethanes

21. How will results from the Information Collection Rule (ICR) be used?

    1. Develop a long-term research program
    2. Establish a database on waterborne diseases
    3. Evaluate how to modify the current regulation on microbial contamination
    4. Promote better compliance with regulations

22. How is foamability measured or tested for in a water?

    1. Anionic surfactant (MBAS) concentration
    2. Depth of foam
    3. Diameter of bubbles
    4. Formation of soap curds

23. What do Tier 1 violations for nitrate and coliform bacteria indicate?

    1. Acute risks to health exist
    2. Careless operation
    3. Need for better reporting procedures
    4. Warning that violations must cease

24. What is the purpose of consumer confidence reports (CCRs)?

    1. Document costs of O & M for consumers
    2. Explain to consumers the need for compliance
    3. Opportunity for positive communication with consumers
    4. Provide regulators with operation details

Multiple Choice (Select all correct answers.)

25. Which of the following types of primary contaminants are considered to be of public health importance?

    1. Inorganic contaminants
    2. Microbial contaminants
    3. Organic contaminants
    4. Thermal
    5. Turbidity

26. Who is primarily responsible for enforcing drinking water regulations?

    1. American Water Works Association
    2. Environmental Protection Agency
    3. Federal government
    4. State regulatory primacy agencies
    5. U.S. Congress

27. Which of the following are types of organic contaminants?

    1. Disinfection by-products
    2. Herbicides
    3. Pesticides
    4. Solvents
    5. Trihalomethanes

28. Why are public water systems required to monitor some unregulated contaminants?

    1. Assist EPA in identifying extent of contamination
    2. Ensure that previously regulated contaminants do not reappear in source waters
    3. Evaluate accuracy of proposed laboratory test methods
    4. Measure seasonal variations in contaminant levels
    5. Reassure consumers their water is safe

29. Which of the following treatment methods may be used to control lead and copper?

    1. Aeration
    2. Coagulation-filtration
    3. Ion exchange
    4. Lime softening
    5. Reverse osmosis

30. What are the causes of widespread groundwater contamination by organic chemicals?

    1. Haphazard disposal
    2. Improper application
    3. Poor storage
    4. Spills
    5. Surface water seepage

31. What steps must an agency take when a water system first exceeds the lead or copper action level?

    1. Advise the public about the harmful effects of lead/copper
    2. Begin replacing lead service lines
    3. Conduct source water quality studies
    4. Explain to the public how exposure can be reduced
    5. Take steps to control corrosion in the distribution system

32. Compliance with the Total Coliform Rule is based on which of the following factors?

    1. A presence-absence approach
    2. An estimate of bacterial density
    3. Identification of specific organisms present
    4. Monthly test results
    5. Results of sanitary surveys

33. Which of the following requirements are included in the Total Coliform Rule?

    1. EPA-approved sampling plan
    2. Public notification when a Tier 1 violation occurs
    3. Testing a minimum of 40 samples per month
    4. Use of a 100-mL sample volume
    5. Use of specified lab procedures

34. How does turbidity cause health hazards or aesthetic problems in finished or treated water?

    1. Exerts chlorine demand
    2. Increases nitrate level
    3. Interferes with bacteriological examination
    4. Interferes with disinfection
    5. Prevents satisfactory reduction of tastes and odors

35. Which of the following methods of disinfection are in common use?

   1. Chloramination
   2. Chlorine dioxide
   3. Free chlorination
   4. Iodine
   5. Ozone

36. The required CT value to achieve inactivation of micro-organisms depends on which of the following factors?

   1. Organism being inactivated
   2. Percent dissolved oxygen saturation
   3. pH of water
   4. Temperature of water
   5. Type of disinfectant

37. The Information Collection Rule (ICR) requires utilities to perform treatment technology studies using which types of treatment processes?

   1. Electrodialysis
   2. Granular activated carbon
   3. Ion exchange
   4. Membranes
   5. Reverse osmosis

38. Which of the following are possible sources of radiological contamination of water supplies?

   1. Fallout from nuclear testing
   2. Hospital and research lab wastes
   3. Natural elements in the ground
   4. Nuclear power plants
   5. Uranium mines

39. Which of the following items are monitoring requirements for secondary contaminants?

   1. Collect samples before treated water leaves plant
   2. Groundwater systems must sample once every five years
   3. Sample distribution system for color and odors
   4. Sample from a free-flowing outlet
   5. Surface water systems must sample yearly

40. Which of the following are true taste sensations?

   1. Astringent
   2. Bitter
   3. Salty
   4. Sour
   5. Sweet

41. Which of the following are important facts to remember when dealing with odors?

   1. Absence of taste and odor helps to maintain the consumers' confidence
   2. Hydrogen sulfide is included under the odor SMCL
   3. Odor is a useful test as a means for tracing the source of contaminants
   4. Odor tests are more fatiguing to people than taste tests
   5. Taste and odor go hand-in-hand

42. Which of the following are effects of pH on drinking waters?

   1. At a low pH drinking water acquires a bitter taste
   2. Excessively low pH waters may have increased corrosivity
   3. Low pH may cause decreased production of chloroform and other THMs during chlorination
   4. Metallic piping in contact with low pH water will impart metallic taste
   5. When pH decreases, the disinfection activity of chlorine increases significantly

43. Which of the following are Tier 1 violations? Failure to comply with

   1. MCL.
   2. Monitoring requirements.
   3. Testing procedure.
   4. Treatment technique.
   5. Variance or exemption.

44. Standards have been set for which substances that pose an acute risk to health whenever they are exceeded?

   1. Arsenic
   2. Coliform bacteria
   3. Nitrate
   4. Pesticides
   5. Turbidity

End of Objective Test

CHAPTER 23

ADMINISTRATION

by

Lorene Lindsay

With Portions by

Tim Gannon

and

Jim Sequeira

TABLE OF CONTENTS

Chapter 23.   ADMINISTRATION

Page

OBJECTIVES 565

WORDS 566

LESSON 1

23.0   NEED FOR UTILITY MANAGEMENT 568

23.1   FUNCTIONS OF A MANAGER 568

23.2   PLANNING 570

23.3   ORGANIZING 570

23.4   STAFFING 573

    23.40   The Utility Manager's Responsibilities 573

    23.41   How Many Employees Are Needed? 573

    23.42   Qualifications Profile 574

    23.43   Applications and the Selection Process 575

        23.430   Advertising the Position 575

        23.431   Paper Screening 575

        23.432   Interviewing Applicants 575

        23.433   Selecting the Most Qualified Candidate 575

    23.44   New Employee Orientation 578

    23.45   Employment Policies and Procedures 578

        23.450   Probationary Period 578

        23.451   Compensation 578

        23.452   Training and Certification 578

        23.453   Performance Evaluation 579

        23.454   Dealing With Disciplinary Problems 582

        23.455   Example Policy: Harassment 583

        23.456   Personnel Records 587

    23.46   Unions 587

DISCUSSION AND REVIEW QUESTIONS 588

LESSON 2

23.5   COMMUNICATION 589

    23.50   Oral Communication 589

    23.51   Written Communication 589

23.6   CONDUCTING MEETINGS 591

23.7   PUBLIC RELATIONS 592

    23.70   Establish Objectives 592

    23.71   Utility Operations 592

    23.72   The Mass Media 592

    23.73   Being Interviewed 592

    23.74   Public Speaking 593

    23.75   Telephone Contacts 593

    23.76   Consumer Inquiries 593

    23.77   Plant Tours 593

23.8   FINANCIAL MANAGEMENT 594

    23.80   Financial Stability 594

    23.81   Budgeting 595

    23.82   Equipment Repair/Replacement Fund 596

    23.83   Water Rates 596

    23.84   Capital Improvements and Funding in the Future 596

    23.85   Financial Assistance 597

DISCUSSION AND REVIEW QUESTIONS 598

LESSON 3

23.9   OPERATIONS AND MAINTENANCE 599

    23.90   The Manager's Responsibilities 599

    23.91   Purpose of O & M Programs 599

    23.92   Types of Maintenance 599

    23.93   Benefits of Managing Maintenance 600

    23.94   SCADA Systems 600

        23.940   Description of SCADA (ss-KAY-dah) Systems 600

        23.941   Typical Water Treatment and Distribution SCADA Systems 601

    23.95   Cross Connection Control Program 603

        23.950   Importance of Cross Connection Control 603

        23.951   Program Responsibilities 606

        23.952   Water Supplier Program 606

        23.953   Types of Backflow Prevention Devices 608

        23.954   Devices Required for Various Types of Situations 608

23.10   EMERGENCY RESPONSE 608

    23.100   Planning 608

    23.101   Handling the Threat of Contaminated Water Supplies 611

        23.1010   Importance 611

        23.1011   Toxicity 611

        23.1012   Effective Dosages 611

23.1013 Protective Measures 611

23.1014 Emergency Countermeasures 612

23.1015 In Case of Contamination 612

23.1016 *Cryptosporidium* 612

23.11 SAFETY PROGRAM 614

23.110 Responsibilities 614

23.1100 Everyone Is Responsible for Safety 614

23.1101 Regulatory Agencies 614

23.1102 Managers 614

23.1103 Supervisors 615

23.1104 Operators 616

23.111 First Aid 616

23.112 Hazard Communication Program and Worker Right-To-Know (RTK) Laws 616

23.113 Confined Space Entry Procedures 617

23.114 Reporting 620

23.115 Training 620

23.116 Measuring 625

23.117 Human Factors 626

23.12 RECORDKEEPING 627

23.120 Purpose of Records 627

23.121 Types of Records 627

23.122 Types of Plant Operations Data 627

23.123 Maintenance Records 628

23.124 Procurement Records 628

23.125 Inventory Records 628

23.126 Equipment Records 630

23.127 Disposition of Plant Records 630

23.13 ACKNOWLEDGMENTS 630

23.14 ADDITIONAL READING 630

DISCUSSION AND REVIEW QUESTIONS 631

SUGGESTED ANSWERS 632

OBJECTIVE TEST 636

OBJECTIVES

Chapter 23. ADMINISTRATION

Following completion of Chapter 23, you should be able to:

1. Identify the functions of a manager,

2. Describe the benefits of short-term, long-term, and emergency planning,

3. Define the following terms:

   a. Authority,   d. Accountability, and
   b. Responsibility, e. Unity of command,
   c. Delegation,

4. Read and construct an organizational chart identifying lines of authority and responsibility,

5. Write a job description for a specific position within the utility,

6. Write good interview questions,

7. Conduct employee evaluations,

8. Describe the steps necessary to provide equal and fair treatment to all employees,

9. Prepare a written or oral report on the utility's operations,

10. Communicate effectively within the organization, with media representatives, and with the community,

11. Describe the financial strength of your utility,

12. Calculate your utility's operating ratio, coverage ratio, and simple payback,

13. Prepare a contingency plan for emergencies,

14. Set up a safety program for your utility, and

15. Collect, organize, file, retrieve, use, and dispose of plant records.

WORDS

Chapter 23.   ADMINISTRATION

ACCOUNTABILITY   ACCOUNTABILITY

When a manager gives power/responsibility to an employee, the employee ensures that the manager is informed of results or events.

AUTHORITY   AUTHORITY

The power and resources to do a specific job or to get that job done.

BACK PRESSURE   BACK PRESSURE

A pressure that can cause water to backflow into the water supply when a user's water system is at a higher pressure than the public water system.

BACKFLOW   BACKFLOW

A reverse flow condition, created by a difference in water pressures, which causes water to flow back into the distribution pipes of a potable water supply from any source or sources other than an intended source. Also see BACKSIPHONAGE.

BACKSIPHONAGE   BACKSIPHONAGE

A form of backflow caused by a negative or below atmospheric pressure within a water system. Also see BACKFLOW.

BOND   BOND

(1) A written promise to pay a specified sum of money (called the face value) at a fixed time in the future (called the date of maturity). A bond also carries interest at a fixed rate, payable periodically. The difference between a note and a bond is that a bond usually runs for a longer period of time and requires greater formality. Utility agencies use bonds as a means of obtaining large amounts of money for capital improvements.

(2) A warranty by an underwriting organization, such as an insurance company, guaranteeing honesty, performance, or payment by a contractor.

CALL DATE   CALL DATE

First date a bond can be paid off.

CERTIFICATION EXAMINATION   CERTIFICATION EXAMINATION

An examination administered by a state or professional association that operators take to indicate a level of professional competence. In most states the Chief Operator of a plant must be "certified" (successfully pass a certification examination.) Certification is voluntary in a few states. Current trends indicate that certification of operators will be mandatory in all states and Canadian provinces in the near future.

CODE OF FEDERAL REGULATIONS (CFR)   CODE OF FEDERAL REGULATIONS (CFR)

A publication of the United States Government which contains all of the proposed and finalized federal regulations, including environmental regulations.

CONFINED SPACE   CONFINED SPACE

Confined space means a space that:

A.   Is large enough and so configured that an employee can bodily enter and perform assigned work; and

B.   Has limited or restricted means for entry or exit (for example, tanks, vessels, silos, storage bins, hoppers, vaults, and pits are spaces that may have limited means of entry); and

C.   Is not designed for continuous employee occupancy.

(Definition from the Code of Federal Regulations (CFR) Title 29 Part 1910.146.)

CONFINED SPACE, PERMIT REQUIRED (PERMIT SPACE)

CONFINED SPACE, PERMIT REQUIRED (PERMIT SPACE)

A confined space that has one or more of the following characteristics:

- Contains or has a potential to contain a hazardous atmosphere,
- Contains a material that has the potential for engulfing an entrant,
- Has an internal configuration such that an entrant could be trapped or asphyxiated by inwardly converging walls or by a floor which slopes downward and tapers to a smaller cross section, or
- Contains any other recognized serious safety or health hazard.

(Definition from the Code of Federal Regulations (CFR) Title 29 Part 1910.146.)

COVERAGE RATIO

COVERAGE RATIO

The coverage ratio is a measure of the ability of the utility to pay the principle and interest on loans and bonds (this is known as "debt service") in addition to any unexpected expenses.

DEBT SERVICE

DEBT SERVICE

The amount of money required annually to pay the (1) interest on outstanding debts; or (2) funds due on a maturing bonded debt or the redemption of bonds.

DELEGATION

DELEGATION

The act in which power is given to another person in the organization to accomplish a specific job.

MATERIAL SAFETY DATA SHEET (MSDS)

MATERIAL SAFETY DATA SHEET (MSDS)

A document which provides pertinent information and a profile of a particular hazardous substance or mixture. An MSDS is normally developed by the manufacturer or formulator of the hazardous substance or mixture. The MSDS is required to be made available to employees and operators whenever there is the likelihood of the hazardous substance or mixture being introduced into the workplace. Some manufacturers are preparing MSDSs for products that are not considered to be hazardous to show that the product or substance is *NOT* hazardous.

OSHA (O-shuh)

OSHA

The Williams-Steiger **O**ccupational **S**afety and **H**ealth **A**ct of 1970 (OSHA) is a federal law designed to protect the health and safety of industrial workers and also the operators of water supply systems and treatment plants. The Act regulates the design, construction, operation and maintenance of water supply systems and water treatment plants. OSHA also refers to the federal and state agencies which administer the OSHA regulations.

OPERATING RATIO

OPERATING RATIO

The operating ratio is a measure of the total revenues divided by the total operating expenses.

ORGANIZING

ORGANIZING

Deciding who does what work and delegating authority to the appropriate persons. A utility should have a written organizational plan and written policies.

OUCH PRINCIPLE

OUCH PRINCIPLE

This principle says that as a manager when you delegate job tasks you must be **O**bjective, **U**niform in your treatment of employees, **C**onsistent with utility policies, and **H**ave job relatedness.

PLANNING

PLANNING

Management of utilities to build the resources and financial capability to provide for future needs.

RESPONSIBILITY

RESPONSIBILITY

Answering to those above in the chain of command to explain how and why you have used your authority.

SCADA (ss-KAY-dah) SYSTEM

SCADA SYSTEM

Supervisory **C**ontrol **A**nd **D**ata **A**cquisition system. A computer-monitored alarm, response, control and data acquisition system used by drinking water facilities to monitor their operations.

TAILGATE SAFETY MEETING

TAILGATE SAFETY MEETING

Brief (10 to 20 minutes) safety meetings held every 7 to 10 working days. The term *TAILGATE* comes from the safety meetings regularly held by the construction industry around the tailgate of a truck.

CHAPTER 23. ADMINISTRATION

(Lesson 1 of 3 Lessons)

23.0 NEED FOR UTILITY MANAGEMENT

The management of a public or private utility, large or small, is a complex and challenging job. Communities are concerned about their drinking water and their wastewater. They are aware of past environmental disasters and they want to protect their communities, but they want this protection with a minimum investment of money. In addition to the local community demands, the utility manager must also keep up with increasingly stringent regulations and monitoring from regulatory agencies. While meeting these "external" (outside the utility) concerns, the manager faces the normal challenges from within the organization: personnel, resources, equipment, and preparing for the future. For the successful manager, all of these responsibilities combine to create an exciting and rewarding job.

A brief quiz is given in Table 23.1 that asks some basic management questions. This quiz can be used as a guide to management areas that may need some attention in your utility. You should be able to answer yes to most of the questions; however, all utilities have areas which can be improved.

In the environmental field, as well as other fields, the workforce itself is changing. Minorities, women, and people with disabilities provide new opportunities for growth in the utility. For the employee, however, overcoming employment barriers can be difficult, especially when the workload is demanding and physically challenging. The utility manager must provide adequate support services for these workers and learn to deal with organized worker groups.

Changes in the environmental workplace also are created by advances in technology. The environmental field has exploded with new technologies, such as computer-controlled water treatment processes and distribution systems. The utility manager must keep up with these changes and provide the leadership to keep everyone at the utility up to speed on new ways of doing things. In addition, the utility manager must provide a safer, cleaner work environment while constantly training and retraining employees to understand new technologies.

QUESTIONS

Write your answers in a notebook and then compare your answers with those on page 632.

23.0A What are the local community demands on a utility manager?

23.0B What has created changes in the environmental workplace?

23.1 FUNCTIONS OF A MANAGER

The functions of a utility manager are the same as for the CEO (Chief Executive Officer) of any big company: planning, organizing, staffing, directing, and controlling. In many com-

munities the utility manager may be the only one who has these responsibilities and the community depends on the manager to handle everything.

Planning (see Section 23.2) consists of determining the goals, policies, procedures, and other elements to achieve the goals and objectives of the agency. Planning requires the manager to collect and analyze data, consider alternatives, and then make decisions. Planning must be done before the other managing functions. Planning may be the most difficult in smaller communities, where the future may involve a decline in population instead of growth.

Organizing (see Section 23.3) means that the manager decides who does what work and delegates authority to the appropriate operators. The organizational function in some utilities may be fairly loose while some communities are very tightly controlled.

Staffing (see Section 23.4) is the recruiting of new operators and staff and determining if there are enough qualified operators and staff to fill available positions. The utility manager's staffing responsibilities include selecting and training employees, evaluating their performance, and providing opportunities for advancement for operators and staff in the agency.

Directing includes guiding, teaching, motivating, and supervising operators and utility staff members. Direction includes issuing orders and instructions so that activities at the facilities or in the field are performed safely and are properly completed.

Controlling involves taking the steps necessary to ensure that essential activities are performed so that objectives will be achieved as planned. Controlling means being sure that progress is being made toward objectives and taking corrective action as necessary. The utility manager is directly involved in controlling the treatment process to ensure that water is being properly treated and to make sure that the utility is meeting its short- and long-term goals.

TABLE 23.1   HOW WELL DOES YOUR SYSTEM MANAGE?

The following self-test is designed for small water treatment facilities to provide a guide for identifying areas of concern and for improving small system management.

1. Is the treatment system budget separate from other accounts so that the true cost of treatment can be determined?

2. Are the funds adequate to cover operating costs, debt service, and future capital improvements?

3. Do operational personnel have input into the budget process?

4. Is there a monthly or quarterly review of the actual operating costs compared to the budgeted costs?

5. Does the user charge system adequately reflect the cost of treatment?

6. Are all users properly metered and does the unaccounted for water not exceed 20 percent of the total flow?

7. Are finished water quality tests representative of plant performance?

8. Are operational control decisions based on process control testing within the plant?

9. Are provisions made for continued training for plant personnel?

10. Are qualified personnel available to fill job vacancies and is job turnover relatively low?

11. Are the energy costs for the system not more than 20 to 30 percent of the total operating costs?

12. Is the ratio of corrective (reactive) maintenance to preventive (proactive) maintenance remaining stable and is it less than 1.0?

13. Are maintenance records available for review?

14. Is the spare parts inventory adequate to prevent long delays in equipment repairs?

15. Are old or outdated pieces of equipment replaced as necessary to prevent excessive equipment downtime, inefficient process performance, or unreliability?

16. Are technical resources and tools available for repairing, maintaining, and installing equipment?

17. Is the utility's pump station equipment providing the expected design performance?

18. Are standby units for key equipment available to maintain process performance during breakdowns or during preventive maintenance activities?

19. Are the plant processes adequate to meet the demand for treatment?

20. Does the facility have an adequate emergency response plan including an alternate water source?

QUESTIONS

Write your answers in a notebook and then compare your answers with those on page 632.

23.1A What are the functions of a utility manager?

23.1B In small communities, what does the community depend on the utility manager to do?

23.2 PLANNING[1]

A very large portion of any manager's typical work day will be spent on activities that can be described as planning activities since nearly every area of a manager's responsibilities require some type of planning.

Planning is one of the most important functions of utility management and one of the most difficult. Communities must have good, clean water and the management of water utilities must include building the resources and financial capability to provide for future needs. The utility must plan for future growth, including industrial development, and be ready to provide the water that will be needed as the community grows. The most difficult problem for some small communities is recognizing and planning for a decline in population. The utility manager must develop reliable information to plan for growth or decline. Decisions must be made about goals, both short- and long-term. The manager must prepare plans for the next two years and the next 10 to 20 years. Remember that utility planning should include operational personnel, local officials (decision makers), and the public. Everyone must understand the importance of planning and be willing to contribute to the process.

Operation and maintenance of a utility also involves planning by the utility manager. A preventive maintenance program should be established to keep the system performing as intended and to protect the community's investment in water supply and distribution facilities. (Section 23.9 describes the various types of maintenance and the benefits of establishing maintenance programs.)

The utility also must have an emergency response plan to deal with natural or human disasters. Without adequate planning your utility will be facing system failures, inability to meet compliance regulations, and inadequate service capacity to meet community needs. Plan today and avoid disaster tomorrow. (Section 23.10, "Emergency Response," describes the basic elements of an emergency operations plan.)

23.3 ORGANIZING[2]

A utility should have a written organizational plan and written policies. In some communities the organizational plan and policies are part of the overall community plan. In either case, the utility manager and all plant personnel should have a copy of the organizational plan and written policies of the utility.

The purpose of the organizational plan is to show who reports to whom and to identify the lines of authority. The organizational plan should show each person or job position in the organization with a direct line showing to whom each person reports in the organization. Remember, an employee can serve only one supervisor (unity of command) and each supervisor should ideally manage only six or seven employees. The organizational plan should include a job description for each of the positions on the organizational chart. When the organizational plan is in place, employees know who is their immediate boss and confusion about job tasks is eliminated. A sample organizational plan for a water/wastewater utility is shown in Figure 23.1. The basic job duties for some typical utility positions are described in Table 23.2.

To understand organization and its role in management, we need to understand some other terms including authority, responsibility, delegation, and accountability. AUTHORITY means the power and resources to do a specific job or to get that job done. Authority may be given to an employee due to their position in the organization (this is formal authority) or authority may be given to the employee informally by their co-workers when the employee has earned their respect. RESPONSIBILITY may be described as answering to those above in the chain of command to explain how and why you have used your authority. DELEGATION is the act in which power is given to another person in the organization to accomplish a specific job. Finally when a manager gives power/responsibility to an employee, then the employee is ACCOUNTABLE[3] for the results.

Organization and effective delegation are very important to keep any utility operating well. Effective delegation is uncomfortable for many managers since it requires giving up power and responsibility. Many managers believe that they can do the job better than others, they believe that other employees are not well trained or experienced, and they are afraid of mistakes. The utility manager retains some responsibility even after delegating to another employee and, therefore, the manager is often reluctant to delegate or may delegate the responsibility but not the authority to get the job done. For the utility manager, good organization means that employees are ready to accept responsibility and have the power and resources to make sure that the job gets done.

Employees should not be asked to accept responsibilities for job tasks that are beyond their level of authority in the organizational structure. For example, an operator or lead utility worker should not be asked to accept responsibility for additional lab testing. The responsibility for additional lab testing must be delegated to the lab supervisor. Authority and responsibility must be delegated properly to be effective. When these three components — proper job assignments, authority, and responsibility — are all present, the supervisor has successfully delegated. The success of delegation is dependent upon all three components.

An important and often overlooked part of delegation is *follow-up* by the supervisor. A good manager will delegate and follow up on progress to make sure that the employee has the necessary resources to get the job done. Well-organized managers can delegate effectively and do not try to do all the work themselves, but are responsible for getting good results. The Management Muddle No. 1 that follows describes what can happen when delegation is improperly conducted, and illustrates how an organizational plan can prevent disaster.

---

[1] *Planning.* Management of utilities to build the resources and financial capability to provide for future needs.

[2] *Organizing.* Deciding who does what work and delegating authority to the appropriate persons. A utility should have a written organizational plan and written policies.

[3] *Accountability.* When a manager gives power/responsibility to an employee, the employee ensures that the manager is informed of results or events.

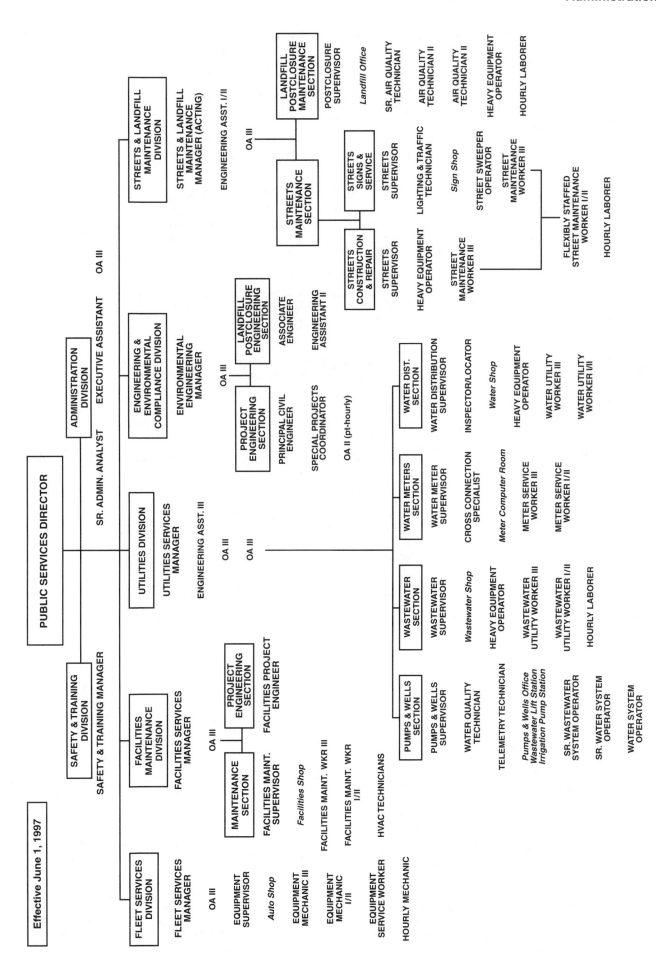

Fig. 23.1 *Organizational chart for medium-sized utility*
(Courtesy of City of Mountain View, California)

TABLE 23.2   JOB DUTIES FOR STAFF OF A MEDIUM-SIZED UTILITY

Job Title	Job Duties
Superintendent	Responsible for administration, operation, and maintenance of entire facility. Exercises direct authority over all plant functions and personnel.
Assistant Superintendent	Assists Superintendent in review of operation and maintenance function, plans special operation and maintenance tasks.
Clerk/Typist	Performs all clerical duties.
Operations Supervisor	Coordinates activities of plant operators and other personnel. Prepares work schedules, inspects plant, and makes note of operational and maintenance requirements.
Lead Utility Worker	Supervises operations and manages all operators.
Utility Worker II (Journey Level)	Controls treatment processes. Collects samples and delivers them to the lab for analysis. Makes operational decisions.
Utility Worker I	Performs assigned job duties.
Maintenance Supervisor	Supervises all maintenance for plant. Plans and schedules all maintenance work. Responsible for all maintenance records.
Maintenance Foreman	Supervises mechanical maintenance crew. Performs inspections and determines repair methods. Schedules all maintenance including preventive maintenance.
Maintenance Mechanic II	Selects proper tools and assigns specific job tasks. Reports any special considerations to Foreman.
Maintenance Mechanic I	Performs assigned job duties.
Electrician II	Schedules and coordinates electrical maintenance with other planned maintenance. Plans and selects specific work methods.
Electrician I	Performs assigned job duties.
Chemist	Directs all laboratory activities and makes operational recommendations to Operations Supervisor. Reports and maintains all required laboratory records. Oversees laboratory quality control.
Laboratory Technician	Performs laboratory tests. Manages day-to-day laboratory operations.

Management Muddle No. 1

The City Manager of Pleasantville calls the Director of Public Works and asks for a report on the need for and cost of a new utility truck to be presented at the September 13 meeting of the City Council. The Director of Public Works calls the Plant Manager and asks for a report on the need and cost for a new utility truck with a deadline of September 12. The Plant Manager calls the Lead Utility Worker, an operator, who has been asking for a new utility truck and has been looking into the details. The Plant Manager requests that the Lead Utility Worker provide a report on September 12 about the purchase of the truck. The Lead Utility Worker gathers all the notes and hand writes a report identifying the need for the truck, the features required, and the cost. The Lead Utility Worker takes the report to City Hall to be typed and leaves it with a secretary on September 12. On September 13, the City Manager is preparing for the City Council meeting and does not have the report. Who is responsible? Who is accountable? How could this situation have been avoided?

Responsibility: The Lead Utility Worker's responsibility has been carried out with the authority and resources made available. Both the Director of Public Works and the Plant Manager failed to follow up on the report on September 12. No one informed the Lead Utility Worker that the report must be presented to the City Council on September 13, nor was the Lead Utility Worker supplied with the resources for getting the report in final form. However, the City Manager is ultimately responsible for reporting to the City Council.

Accountability: Starting with the Lead Utility Worker and working upward, each employee is accountable to his or her supervisor and should have communicated the status of the report.

How to avoid this situation: Good communication and follow-up by each of these supervisors could have prevented this situation completely. The City Manager should have asked to see the report on September 12; the Director of Public Works should have asked the Plant Manager to deliver the report no later than September 11; and the Plant Manager should have asked the Lead Utility Worker to submit the typed report (to the Plant Manager) no later than September 10. When delegating this task, the Plant Manager should have arranged for a secretary or clerk to assist the Lead Utility Worker in typing the report. Providing clerical support enables the Lead Utility Manager to complete the assigned task in a timely manner.

At each step in this chain of delegation, setting an early deadline gives the individual receiving the report an opportunity to review the document and make revisions, if necessary, before forwarding it up the chain of authority and ensures that the report reaches the City Manager no later than September 12.

QUESTIONS

Write your answers in a notebook and then compare your answers with those on page 632.

23.2A Who must be included in utility planning?

23.3A What is the purpose of an organizational plan?

23.3B Why is it sometimes difficult or uncomfortable for supervisors or managers to delegate effectively?

23.3C What is an important and often overlooked part of delegation?

23.4 STAFFING

23.40 The Utility Manager's Responsibilities

The utility manager is also responsible for staffing, which includes hiring new employees, training employees, and evaluating job performance. The utility should have established procedures for job hiring which include requirements for advertising the position, application procedures, and the procedures for conducting interviews.

In the area of staffing, more than any other area of responsibility, a manager must be extremely cautious and consider the consequences before taking action. Personnel management practices have changed dramatically in the past few years and continue to be redefined almost daily by the courts. A manager who violates an employee's or job applicant's rights can be held both personally and professionally liable in court. Throughout this section on staffing you will repeatedly find references to two terms: **job-related** and **documentation**. These are key concepts in personnel management today. Any personnel action you take must be job-related, from the questions you ask during interviews to disciplinary actions or promotions. And while almost no one wants more paperwork, documentation of personnel actions detailing what you did, when you did it, and why you did it (the reasons will be job-related, of course) is absolutely essential. There is no way to predict when you might be called upon to defend your actions in court. Good records not only serve to refresh your memory about past events but can also be used to demonstrate your pattern of lawful behavior over time.

NOTICE

The information provided in this section on staffing should **not** be viewed as **legal advice**. The purpose of this section is simply to identify and describe in general terms the major components of a utility manager's responsibilities in the area of staffing. One issue, harassment, is discussed in somewhat greater detail to illustrate the broad scope of a manager's responsibilities within a single policy area. Personnel administration is affected by many federal and state regulations. Legal requirements of legislation such as the Americans With Disabilities Act (ADA), Equal Employment Opportunity (EEO) Act, Family and Medical Leave Act, and wages and hours laws are complex and beyond the scope of this manual. If your utility does not have established personnel policies and procedures, consider getting help from a labor law attorney to develop appropriate policies. At the very least, you should get help from a recruitment specialist to develop and document hiring procedures which meet the federal guidelines for Equal Employment Opportunity.

23.41 How Many Employees Are Needed?

There is a common tendency for organizations to add personnel in response to changing conditions without first examining how the existing workforce might be reorganized to achieve greater efficiency and meet the new work demands. In water supply and distribution utilities, aging of the system, changes in use, and expansion of the system often mean changes in the operation and maintenance tasks being performed. The manager of a utility should periodically review the agency's work requirements and staffing to ensure that the utility is operating as efficiently as possible. A good time to conduct such a review is during the annual budgeting process or when you are considering hiring a new employee because the workload seems to be greater than the current staff can adequately handle.

The staffing analysis procedure outlined in this section illustrates how to conduct a comprehensive analysis of the type needed for a complete reorganization of the agency. In practice, however, a complete reorganization may not be desirable or even possible. Frequent organizational changes can make employees anxious about their jobs and may interfere with their work performance. Some employees show strong resistance to any change in job responsibilities. Nonetheless, by thoroughly examining the functions and staffing of the utility on a periodic basis, the manager may spot trends (such as an increase in the amount of time spent maintaining certain equipment or portions of the system) or discover inefficiencies that could be corrected over a period of time.

The first step in analyzing the utility's staffing needs is to prepare a detailed list of all the tasks to be performed to operate and maintain the utility. Next, estimate the number of staff hours per year required to perform each task. Be sure to include the time required for supervision and training.

When you have completed the task analysis, prepare a list of the utility's current employees. Assign tasks to each employee based on the person's skills and abilities. To the extent possible, try to minimize the number of different work activities assigned to each person but also keep in mind the need to provide opportunities for career advancement. One full-time staff year equals 260 days, including vacation and holiday time: (52 wk/yr)(5 days/wk) = 260 days/yr.

You can expect to find that this "ideal" staffing arrangement does not exactly match up with your current employees' job assignments. Most likely, you will also find that the number of staff hours required does not exactly equal the number of staff hours available. Your responsibility as a manager is to create the best possible fit between the work to be done and the personnel/skills available to do it. In addition to shifting work assignments between employees, other options you might consider are contracting out some types of work, hiring part-time or seasonal staff, or setting up a second shift (to make fuller use of existing equipment). Of course, you may find that it is time to hire another full- or part-time operator.

23.42 Qualifications Profile

Hiring new employees requires careful planning before the personal interview process. In an effort to limit discriminatory hiring practices, the law and administrative policy have carefully defined the hiring methods and guidelines employers may use. The selection method and examination process used to evaluate applicants must be limited to the applicant's knowledge, skills, and abilities to perform relevant job-related activities. In all but rare cases, factors such as age and level of education may not be used to screen candidates in place of performance testing. A description of the duties and qualifications for the job must be clearly defined in writing. The job description may be used to develop a qualifications profile. This qualifications profile clearly and precisely identifies the required job qualifications. All job qualifications must be relevant to the actual job duties that will be performed in that position. The following list of typical job qualifications may be used to help you develop your own qualifications profiles with advice from a recruitment specialist.

1. General Requirements:

    a. Knowledge of methods, tools, equipment, and materials used in water utilities,

    b. Knowledge of work hazards and applicable safety precautions,

    c. Ability to establish and maintain effective working relations with employees and the general public, and

    d. Possession of a valid state driver's license for the class of equipment the employee is expected to drive.

2. General Educational Development:

    a. Reasoning: Apply common sense understanding to carry out instructions furnished in oral, written, or diagrammatical form,

    b. Mathematical: Use a pocket calculator to make arithmetic calculations relevant to the utility's operation and maintenance processes, and

    c. Language: Communicate with fellow employees and train subordinates in work methods. Fill out maintenance report forms.

3. Specific Vocational Preparation: Three years of experience in water utility operation and maintenance.

4. Interests: May or may not be relevant to knowledge, skills, and ability; for example, an interest in activities concerned with objects and machines, ecology, or business management.

5. Temperament: Must adjust to a variety of tasks requiring frequent change and must routinely use established standards and procedures.

6. Physical Demands: Medium to heavy work involving lifting, climbing, kneeling, crouching, crawling, reaching, hearing, and seeing. Must be able to lift and carry _____ number of pounds for a distance of _____ feet.

7. Working Conditions: The work involves wet conditions, cramped and awkward spaces, noise, risks of bodily injury, and exposure to weather.

QUESTIONS

Write your answers in a notebook and then compare your answers with those on page 632.

23.4A   What do staffing responsibilities include?

23.4B   What are two key personnel management concepts a manager should always keep in mind?

23.4C   List the steps involved in a staffing analysis.

23.4D   What is a qualifications profile?

23.43   Applications and the Selection Process

23.430   Advertising the Position

To advertise a job opening, first prepare a written description of the required job qualifications, compensation, job duties, selection process, and application procedures (with a closing date). The utility should have established procedures about how to advertise the position and conduct the application process. The application procedure may require that the job be posted first within the utility to allow existing personnel first chance at the job opportunity.

23.431   Paper Screening

The next step in the selection process is known as paper screening. The personnel department and the utility manager review each application and eliminate those who are not qualified. The qualified applicants may be given examinations to verify their qualifications. Usually the top three to twelve applicants are selected for an interview, depending on the agency's preference.

23.432   Interviewing Applicants

The purpose of the job interview is to gain additional information about the applicants so that the most qualified person can be selected. The utility manager should prepare for the interview in advance. Review the background information on each applicant. Draw up a list of job-related questions that will be asked of each applicant. During the interviews, briefly note the answers each applicant gives.

It used to be thought that the best way to learn about applicants was to give them plenty of time to talk about themselves because the content and type of information applicants volunteer might provide a deeper insight into the person and what type of employee they will become. Be very careful about open-ended, unstructured conversations with job applicants, even the friendly remarks you make initially to put the applicant at ease during the interview. If the applicant begins to volunteer information which you could not otherwise legally ask for (such as marital status, number of children, religious affiliation, or age), be polite but firm in promptly redirecting the conversation. Even if this information was provided to you voluntarily, an applicant who did not get the job could later allege that you discriminated against them based on age or religion.

The only type of information you may legally request is information about the applicant's job skills, abilities, and experience relating directly to the job for which the person is applying. You must always be sensitive to the civil rights of the applicant and the affirmative action policies of the utility, which is another good reason to prepare a list of questions before the interview process begins. Structure the questions so that you avoid simple yes-and-no answers. Table 23.3 summarizes acceptable and unacceptable pre-employment inquiries to guide you in developing a good list of questions.

If other utility staff members are participating in the interviews, their participation should be confined to the pre-selected questions. Under no circumstances should front line employees conduct interviews in the absence of the manager or another person knowledgeable about personnel policies and practices.

The interview should be conducted in a quiet room without interruptions. Most applicants will be nervous, so start the interview on a positive note with introductions and some general remarks to put the applicant at ease. Explain the details of the job, working conditions, wages, benefits, and potential for advancement. Allow the applicant a chance to ask questions about the job. Ask each applicant the questions you have prepared and jot down brief notes on their responses. Taking notes while interviewing is awkward for some people but it becomes easier with practice. Notes are important because after interviewing several candidates you may not be able to remember what each one said. Also, as mentioned earlier, notes taken at the time of an interview can be valuable evidence in court if an unsuccessful applicant files a lawsuit for unfair hiring practices. At the end of the interview, tell the applicant when a decision will be made and how the applicant will be informed of the decision.

If an applicant's responses during the interview indicate that the person clearly is not qualified for this job but may be qualified for another job, briefly describe the other opportunity and how the person can apply for that position. The applicant may ask to be interviewed immediately for the second position. However, do not violate the utility's hiring procedures for the convenience of a job applicant. The same sequence of hiring procedures should be followed each time a position is filled. Tell this applicant that it will still be necessary to apply for the other position and that another interview may or may not follow, depending on the qualifications of the other applicants for the position.

23.433   Selecting the Most Qualified Candidate

Once the interviews are over, the job of evaluating and selecting the successful candidate begins. Review your interview notes and check the candidates' references. Checking references will verify the job experience of the applicant and may provide insight into the applicant's work habits. Questions you might ask previous employers include: Was the employee reliable and punctual? How well did the employee relate to co-workers? Did the employee consistently practice safe work procedures? Would you rehire this employee?

The rights of certain "protected groups" in the workforce today, such as minorities, women, disabled persons, persons over 40 years of age, and union members, are protected by law. A manager's responsibilities regarding protected groups begins with the hiring process and continues for as long as

TABLE 23.3 ACCEPTABLE AND UNACCEPTABLE PRE-EMPLOYMENT INQUIRIES [a]

Acceptable Pre-Employment Inquiries	Subject	Unacceptable Pre-Employment Inquiries
"Have you ever worked for this agency under a different name?"	NAME	Former name of applicant whose name has been changed by court order or otherwise.
Applicant's place of residence.	ADDRESS OR DURATION OF RESIDENCE	
How long applicant has been resident of this state or city.		
"If hired can you submit a birth certificate or other proof of U.S. citizenship or age?"	BIRTHPLACE	Birthplace of applicant.
		Birthplace of applicant's parents, spouse, or other relatives.
		Requirement that applicant submit a birth certificate, naturalization, or baptismal record.
"If hired, can you furnish proof of age?" /or/ Statement that hire is subject to verification that applicant's age meets legal requirements.	AGE	Questions which tend to identify applicants 40 to 64 years of age.
Statement by employer of regular days, hours, or shift to be worked.	RELIGIOUS	Applicant's religious denomination or affiliation, church, parish, pastor, or religious holidays observed.
		"Do you attend religious services /or/ a house of worship?"
		Applicant may not be told, "This is a Catholic/Protestant/Jewish/atheist organization."
	RACE OR COLOR	Complexion, color of skin, or other questions directly or indirectly indicating race or color.
Statement that photograph may be required after employment.	PHOTOGRAPH	Requirement that applicant affix a photograph to his/her application form.
		Request applicant, at his/her option, to submit photograph.
		Requirement of photograph after interview but before hiring.
Statement by employer that if hired applicant may be required to submit proof of eligibility to work in the United States.	CITIZENSHIP	"Are you a United States citizen?"
		Whether applicant or applicant's parents or spouse are naturalized or native-born U.S. citizens.
		Date when applicant or parents or spouse acquired U.S. citizenship.
		Requirement that applicant produce naturalization papers or first papers.
		Whether applicant's parents or spouse are citizens of the U.S.
Applicant's work experience.	EXPERIENCE	"Are you currently employed?"
Applicant's military experience in armed forces of United States, in a state militia (U.S.), or in a particular branch of the U.S. armed forces.		Applicant's military experience (general).
		Type of military discharge.
Applicant's academic, vocational, or professional education; schools attended.	EDUCATION	Date last attended high school.
Language applicant reads, speaks, or writes fluently.	NATIONAL ORIGIN OR ANCESTRY	Applicant's nationality, lineage, ancestry, national origin, descent, or parentage.
		Date of arrival in United States or port of entry; how long a resident.
		Nationality of applicant's parents or spouse; maiden name of applicant's wife or mother.
		Language commonly used by applicant. "What is your mother tongue?"
		How applicant acquired ability to read, write, or speak a foreign language.
	CHARACTER	"Have you ever been arrested?"

TABLE 23.3 ACCEPTABLE AND UNACCEPTABLE PRE-EMPLOYMENT INQUIRIES (continued)

Acceptable Pre-Employment Inquiries	Subject	Unacceptable Pre-Employment Inquiries
Names of applicant's relatives already employed by the agency.	RELATIVES	Marital status or number of dependents.
		Name or address of relative, spouse, or children of adult applicant.
		"With whom do you reside?"
		"Do you live with your parents?"
Organizations, clubs, professional societies, or other associations of which applicant is a member, excluding any names the character of which indicate the race, religious creed, color, national origin, or ancestry of its members.	ORGANIZATIONS	"List all organizations, clubs, societies, and lodges to which you belong."
"By whom were you referred for a position here?"	REFERENCES	Requirement of submission of a religious reference.
"Do you have any physical condition which may limit your ability to perform the job applied for?"	PHYSICAL CONDITION	"Do you have any physical disabilities?"
		Questions on general medical condition.
Statement by employer that offer may be made contingent on passing a physical examination.		Inquiries as to receipt of Workers' Compensation.
Notice to applicant that any misstatements or omissions of material facts in his/her application may be cause for dismissal.	MISCELLANEOUS	Any inquiry that is not job-related or necessary for determining an applicant's eligibility for employment.

[a] Courtesy of Marion B. McCamey, Affirmative Action Officer, California State University, Sacramento, CA.

the employer/employee relationship lasts. The best principle to deal with protected groups (and all other employees, for that matter) is the "OUCH" principle. The OUCH principle says that when you hire new employees or delegate job tasks to current employees, you must be OBJECTIVE, UNIFORM in your treatment of applicants or employees, CONSISTENT with utility policies, and HAVE JOB RELATEDNESS. If you don't manage with all of these characteristics, you may find yourself in a "hurting" position with regard to protected workers.

Objectivity is the first hurdle. Often the physical characteristics of a person, such as large or small size, may make a person seem more or less job capable. However, many utility agency jobs are done with power tools or other technology which allows all persons, regardless of size, to manage most tasks. Try to remain objective but reasonable in assessing job applicants and making job assignments.

Uniform treatment of job applicants and employees is necessary to protect yourself and other employees. Nothing will destroy morale more quickly than unequal treatment of employees. Your role as a manager is to consistently apply the

policies and procedures that have been adopted by the utility. Often, policies and procedures exist that are not popular and may not even be appropriate. However, the job of the utility manager is to consistently uphold and apply the policies of the utility.

The last part of the OUCH principle is having job relatedness. Any hiring decision must be based on the applicant's qualifications to meet the specific job requirements and any job assignment given to an employee must be related to that employee's job description. Extra assignments, such as buying personal gifts for the boss's family or washing the boss's car, are not appropriate. These types of job assignments will eventually catch up to the manager and can be particularly embarrassing if the public gets involved. So to protect yourself and your utility, remember the OUCH principle as you hire and manage your employees.

Once you have made your selection, the applicant is usually required to pass a medical examination. When this has been successfully completed and the applicant has accepted the position, notify the other applicants that the position has been filled.

23.44   New Employee Orientation

During the first day of work, a new employee should be given all the information available in written and verbal form on the policies and practices of the utility including compensation, benefits, attendance expectations, alcohol and drug testing (if the utility does this), and employer/employee relations. Answer any questions from the new employee at this time and try to explain the overall structure of the utility as well as identify who can answer employee questions when they arise. Introduce the new employee to co-workers and tour the work area. Every utility should have a safety training session for all new employees and specific safety training for some job categories. Provide safety training (see Section 23.11, "Safety Program") for new employees on the first day of employment or as soon thereafter as possible. Establishing safe work practices is a very important function of management.

QUESTIONS

Write your answers in a notebook and then compare your answers with those on page 632.

23.4E   What is the purpose of a job interview?

23.4F   List four "protected groups."

23.4G   What does the "OUCH" principle stand for?

23.4H   When should a new employee's safety training begin?

23.45   Employment Policies and Procedures

23.450   Probationary Period

Many employers now use a probationary period for all new employees. The probationary period is typically three to six months but may be as long as a year. This period begins on the first day of work. Management may reserve the right to terminate employment of the person with or without cause during this probationary period. The employee must be informed of this probationary period and must understand that successful completion of the probationary period is required in order to move into regular employment status.

The probationary period provides a time during which both the employer and employee can assess the "fit" between the job and the person. Normally a performance evaluation is completed near the end of the probationary period. A satisfactory performance evaluation is the mechanism used to move an employee from probationary status into regular employment.

23.451   Compensation

The compensation an employee receives for the work performed includes satisfaction, recognition, security, appropriate pay, and benefits. All are important to keep good employees satisfied. Salaries should be a function of supply and demand. Pay should be high enough to attract and retain qualified employees. Salaries are usually determined by the governing body of the utility in negotiation with employee groups, when appropriate. The salary structure should meet all state and federal regulations and accurately reflect the level of service given by the employee. A survey of salaries

from other utilities in the area may provide valuable information in the development of a salary structure.

The benefits supplied by the employer are an important part of the compensation package. Benefits generally include the following: retirement, health insurance, life insurance, employer's portion of social security, holiday and vacation pay, sick leave, personal leave, parental leave, worker's compensation, and protective clothing. Many employers now provide dental and/or vision insurance, long-term disability insurance, educational bonus or costs and leave, bereavement leave, and release time for jury duty. Some employers also include in their benefit package cash bonus programs and longevity pay. The value of an employee's entire benefit package is often computed and printed on the pay stub as a reminder that salary alone is not the only compensation being provided.

23.452   Training and Certification[4]

Training has become an ongoing process in the workplace. The utility manager must provide new employee training as well as ongoing training for all employees. Safety training is particularly important for all utility operators and staff members and is discussed in detail later in Section 23.11. Certified water supply system and treatment plant operators earn their certificates by knowing how to do their jobs safely. Preparing for certification examinations is one means by which operators learn to identify safety hazards and to follow safe procedures at all times under all circumstances.

Although it is extremely important, safety is not the sole benefit to be derived from a certification program. Other benefits include protection of the public's investment in water supply and treatment facilities and employee pride and recognition.

Vast sums of public funds have been invested in the construction of water supply and treatment facilities. Certification of operators assures utilities that these facilities will be operated and maintained by qualified operators who possess a certain level of competence. These operators should have the knowledge and skills not only to prevent unnecessary deterioration and failure of the facilities, but also to improve operation and maintenance techniques.

Achievement of a level of certification is a public acknowledgment of a water supply system or treatment plant operator's skills and knowledge. Presentation of certificates at an official meeting of the governing body will place the operators in a position to receive recognition for their efforts and may even get press coverage and public opinion that is favorable. An improved public image will give the certified operator more credibility in discussions with property owners.

Recognition for their personal efforts will raise the self-esteem of all certified operators. Certification will also give water supply system and treatment plant operators an upgraded image that has been too long denied them. If properly publicized, certification ceremonies will give the public a more

---

[4] *Certification Examination.   An examination administered by a state or professional association that operators take to indicate a level of professional competence. In most states the Chief Operator of a plant must be "certified" (successfully pass a certification examination). Certification is voluntary in a few states. Current trends indicate that certification of operators will be mandatory in all states and Canadian provinces in the near future.*

accurate image of the many dedicated, well-qualified operators working for them. Certification provides a measurable goal that operators can strive for by preparing themselves to do a better job. Passing a certification exam should be recognized by an increase in salary and other employee benefits.

Most states and Canadian provinces now require that water treatment plant operators be certified. To maintain current certification, these operators must complete additional training classes every one to five years. In the environmental field, new technologies and regulations require operators to attend training to keep up with their field. The utility manager has the responsibility to provide employees with high-quality training opportunities. Many types of training are available to meet the different training needs of utility operators, for example, in-house training, training conducted by training centers, professional organizations, engineering firms, or regulatory agencies, and correspondence courses such as this one by the Office of Water Programs.

ABC stands for the Association of Boards of Certification for Operating Personnel in Water Utilities and Pollution Control Systems. If you wish to find out how operators can become certified in your state or province, contact:

Executive Director, ABC
208 Fifth Street
Ames, IA 50010-6259
Phone: (515) 232-3623

ABC will provide you with the name and address of the appropriate contact person.

One area of training that is frequently overlooked is training for supervisors. Managing people requires a different set of skills than performing the day-to-day work of operating and maintaining a water treatment facility. Supervisors need to know how to communicate effectively and how to motivate others, as well as how to delegate responsibility and hold people accountable for their performance. Supervisors share management's responsibility for fair and equitable treatment of all workers and are required to act in accordance with applicable state and federal personnel regulations. Making the transition from operator to supervisor also requires a change in attitude. A supervisor is part of the management team and is therefore obliged to promote the best interests of the utility at all times. When the interests of the utility conflict with the desires of one or more employees, the supervisor must support management's decisions and policies regardless of the supervisor's own personal opinion about the issue. It is the responsibility of the utility manager to ensure that supervisors receive appropriate training in all of these areas.

Training on how to motivate people, deal with co-workers, and supervise or manage people working for you has become a very highly specialized field of training. These are complex topics that are beyond the scope of this manual. If you have

a need for or wish to learn more about how to deal with people, consider enrolling in courses or reading books on supervision or personnel management.

QUESTIONS

Write your answers in a notebook and then compare your answers with those on page 632.

23.4I What is the purpose of a probationary period for new employees?

23.4J What kind of compensation does an employee receive for work performed?

23.4K Why should utility managers provide training opportunities for employees?

23.453 Performance Evaluation

Most organizations conduct some type of performance evaluation, usually on an annual basis. The evaluation may be written and/or oral; however, a written evaluation is strongly recommended because it will provide a record of the employee's performance. Documentation of this type may be needed in the future to support taking disciplinary action if the employee's performance consistently fails to meet expectations. The evaluation of employee performance can be a challenging task, especially when performance has not been acceptable. However, evaluations are also an opportunity to provide employees with positive feedback and let them know their contributions to the organization have been noticed and appreciated.

A formal performance evaluation typically begins with an employee's immediate supervisor filling out the performance evaluation form (a sample evaluation form is shown in Figure 23.2). Complete the entire form and be specific about the employee's achievements as well as areas needing improvement. Next, schedule a private meeting with the employee to discuss the evaluation. Give the employee frequent opportunities to be heard and listen carefully. If some of the employee's accomplishments were overlooked, note them on the evaluation form and consider whether this new information changes your overall rating of performance in one or more categories.

After reviewing the employee's performance for the past year, set performance goals for the next year. Be sure to document the goals you have agreed upon. Setting performance goals is particularly important if an employee's performance has been poor and improvement is needed. If appropriate, develop a written performance improvement plan which includes specific dates when you will again review the employee's progress in meeting the performance goals. Some supervisors find it helpful to schedule an informal mid-year meeting with each employee to review their progress and to avoid surprises during the next performance evaluation.

Many employees and managers dread even the thought of a performance evaluation and see it as an ordeal to be endured. When properly conducted, however, a performance review can strengthen the lines of communication and increase trust between the employee and the manager. Use this opportunity to acknowledge the employee's unique contributions and to seek solutions to any problems the employee may be having in completing work assignments. Ask the employee how you can be of assistance in removing any obstacles to getting the job done. If necessary, provide coaching to help the employee understand both how and why certain tasks are performed. Be generous (but sincere) with praise for the good work the employee does well every day

EMPLOYEE EVALUATION FORM

Employee Name _____ Date _____

Job Title _____ Department _____

Evaluate the employee on the job now being performed. Circle the number which most nearly expresses your overall judgment. In the space for comments, consider the employee's performance since their last evaluation and make notes about the progress or specific concerns in that area. The care and accuracy of this appraisal will determine its value to you, the employee, and your employer.

JOB KNOWLEDGE: (Consider knowledge of the job gained through experience, education, and special training)

5. Well informed on all phases of work
4. Knowledge thorough enough to perform well without assistance
3. Adequate grasp of essentials, some assistance required
2. Requires considerable assistance to perform
1. Inadequate knowledge

Comments: _____

_____

_____

QUALITY OF WORK: (Consider accuracy and dependability of the results)

5. Exceptionally accurate, practically no mistakes
4. Usually accurate, seldom necessary to check results
3. Acceptable, occasional errors
2. Often unacceptable, frequent errors, needs supervision
1. Unacceptable, too many errors

Comments: _____

_____

_____

INITIATIVE: (Consider the speed with which the employee grasps new job skills)

5. Excellent, grasps new ideas and suggests improvements, is a leader with others
4. Very resourceful, can work unsupervised, manages time well, is reliable
3. Shows initiative on occasion, is reliable
2. Lacks initiative, must be reminded to complete tasks
1. Needs constant prodding to complete job tasks, is unreliable

Comments: _____

_____

_____

Fig. 23.2   Employee evaluation form

COOPERATION AND RELATIONSHIPS: (Consider manner of handling relationships with co-workers, superiors, and the public)

5. Excellent cooperation and communication with co-workers, supervisors, and others, takes and gives instructions well
4. Gets along well with co-workers
3. Acceptable, usually gets along well, occasionally complains
2. Shows a reluctance to cooperate, complains
1. Very poor cooperation, does not follow instruction, dislikes fellow employees

Comments: _____

_____

_____

ATTENDANCE: (Consider frequency of absences, reasons for absences or tardiness, and promptness in giving notice about absences)

5. Excellent, absent only for emergencies, illness, civic duties, always on time, gives notice when absent
4. Rarely absent or late, always gives notice and good reason
3. Occasionally absent, less important reasons, usually gives notice, but not always in time
2. Often absent, lack of adequate notice or reasons for absenteeism
1. Unexcusable absenteeism, does not give notice, reasons are unacceptable, cannot be depended upon

Comments: _____

_____

_____

OVERALL EVALUATION: Superior _____ Good _____ Satisfactory _____ Unsatisfactory _____

Comments: _____

_____

_____

I hereby certify that this appraisal is my best judgment of the service value of this employee and is based on personal observation and knowledge of the employee's work.

Supervisor's Signature _____ Date _____

I hereby certify that I have personally reviewed this report.

Employee's Signature _____ Date _____

Fig. 23.2   Employee evaluation form (continued)

and try to keep the employee's shortcomings in perspective. If the person is doing a good job 95 percent of the time, don't let the entire discussion consist of criticism about the remaining 5 percent of the person's job assignments.

At the end of the meeting, ask the employee to sign the evaluation form to acknowledge having seen and discussed it. Give the employee a copy of the evaluation. If the employee disagrees with any part of the evaluation, invite the person to submit a written statement describing the reasons for their disagreement. The written statement should be filed with the completed performance evaluation form.

23.454 Dealing With Disciplinary Problems

Handling employee discipline problems is difficult, even for an experienced manager. But remember, **no discipline problem ever solves itself and the sooner you deal with the problem, the better the outcome will be**. If problem behavior is not corrected, then other employees will become dissatisfied and the problems will increase.

Every utility, no matter how small, should have written employment policies enabling the manager to deal effectively with employee problems. It should also provide a formal complaint or grievance procedure by which employees can have their complaint heard and resolved without fear of retaliation by the supervisor.

Dealing with employee discipline requires tact and skill. You will have to find your own style and then try to stay FLEXIBLE, CALM, and OPEN-MINDED when the situation gets really tough. If you repeatedly find yourself unable to deal successfully with disciplinary problems, consult with the utility's personnel office (if available) or consider enrolling in a management training course designed specifically around strategies and techniques for disciplining employees.

A commonly accepted method for dealing with job-related employee problems is to first discuss the problem with the employee in private. Most employers will give a person two or three verbal warnings; then the warnings should be written with copies given to the employee. Finally, if the written warnings do not produce positive results, the employee may have to be suspended or dismissed. Your job is to make sure that all warnings are documented with specific descriptions of unsatisfactory behaviors and to make sure that all employees are treated fairly.

Start the disciplinary discussion with a positive comment about the employee. Then identify the problem but keep emotion and blame out of the discussion. The best approach is to state the problem and then ask the employee to suggest a solution. If they respond inappropriately, you must restate the problem and explain that you are trying to find a positive solution that is acceptable to everyone.

Try to keep the discussion focused on solving the problems and do not permit the employee to heap on general com-

plaints, report on what other employees do, or wander from the topic. The following is an example of how you might start the discussion for an employee who is tardy every day. "Joe, you have done a good job in keeping that north side pump station running. You are an asset to this operation. Your tardiness every morning, however, is causing problems. Is there some reason for you to be tardy? We need to find a solution to this problem because your being late creates a bad situation for the night shift. What do you suggest?"

Always remain calm and do not allow yourself to become angry when dealing with an employee about performance issues. If you begin to feel angry and are about to lose control, or if the employee becomes combative or abusive, suggest that the meeting is not producing positive results and schedule an alternative meeting time. Do not let the emotions of the moment carry you into a rage in front of employees. If either you or one of your employees expresses extreme emotions, then the discussion should be postponed until everyone cools down. The following steps may serve as a guide to dealing with confrontation; they apply equally to the employee and the supervisor.

- Maintain an adult approach — positive criticism should be taken/given to improve job skills.

- Create a private environment — job performance issues should be discussed in private between the employee and supervisor.

- Listen very carefully — be sure that both you and the employee understand the situation in the same way. If not, you need to keep talking until both parties are in agreement about the problem and the solution.

- Keep your language appropriate — anger and bad language will cause the situation to escalate. Keep your cool and hold your tongue.

- Stay focused in the present — let go of all the past slights, misunderstandings, and dissatisfaction. Problems must be solved one at a time.

- Aim for a permanent solution — changes in job performance need to be permanent to be effective.

Reports of violence in the workplace appear regularly in newspapers and on television. Managers and supervisors should be alert for signs that an employee might become violent and should take any threat of violence seriously.

Violence in the workplace may take the form of physical harm, psychological harm, and/or property damage. Common warning signs include abusive language, threatening or confrontational behavior, and brandishing a weapon. Some examples of physical harm include pushing, hitting, shoving, or any other form of physical assault. Threats and harassment are forms of psychological harm, and property damage can range from theft or destruction of equipment to sabotage of the employer's computer systems.

The utility's safe workplace policy should be a "zero tolerance" policy. Any employee who is the target of violent behavior or who witnesses such behavior should be encouraged to immediately report the behavior to a supervisor and the incident should be investigated promptly. If necessary for the immediate safety of other employees, the offending employee should be placed on administrative leave, escorted from the work environment, and permitted to return to work only after the investigation has been completed.

Management Muddle No. 2

Sue has been working for five years as a laboratory technician and was recently passed over for promotion. A lab director who has more college experience than Sue was hired from another plant. Since then Sue's work has not been very good, she has come to work late, and she does not always get all of the lab tests done during her workday. What should be done about Sue? If you were the supervisor, how would you handle this problem with Sue?

Actions: As the supervisor, you should ask Sue to come by your office. In private, you should discuss with Sue why the new lab director was hired. Discuss with her the good work record she has maintained over the past five years, and explain the changes you have seen in her work recently. At this point you might ask her to evaluate her own performance or what she would do if she were in your situation. She might need to express her resentment about the new lab director. If she does, let her ramble and rave just for a few minutes, then stop her. You might say, "OK, you're unhappy, but what are we going to do to change this situation? How can I help you to regain your motivation and improve your work habits?" If possible you might help her figure out a way to continue her college education, go to additional training classes, or reorganize the lab so that her job duties change somewhat. There are many other possibilities for helping Sue to become motivated again but she should be part of the process. It is important to communicate clearly that her job performance must improve.

QUESTIONS

Write your answers in a notebook and then compare your answers with those on page 632.

23.4L Who is the appropriate person to conduct an employee's performance evaluation?

23.4M What should be the attitude of a supervisor or manager when dealing with disciplinary problems?

23.4N What are some common warning signs that an employee could become violent?

23.455 Example Policy: Harassment

Harassment is any behavior that is offensive, annoying, or humiliating to an individual and that interferes with a person's ability to do a job. This behavior is uninvited, often repeated, and creates an uncomfortable or even hostile environment in the workplace. Harassment is not limited to physical behavior but also may be verbal or involve the display of offensive pictures or other images. Sexual harassment is legally defined as unwanted sexual advances, or visual, verbal, or physical conduct of a sexual nature. Any type is harassment is inappropriate in the workplace. A manager's responsibilities with regard to harassment include:

- Establish a written policy (such as the one shown in Figure 23.3) that clearly defines and prohibits harassment of any type,

- Distribute copies of the harassment policy to all employees and take whatever steps are necessary (small group discussions, general staff meetings, training sessions) to ensure that all employees understand the policy,

- Encourage employees to report incidents of harassment to their immediate supervisor, a manager, or the personnel department,

- Investigate every reported case of harassment, and

- Document all aspects of the complaint investigation, including the procedures followed, statements by witnesses, the complainant, and the accused person, the conclusions reached in the case, and the actions taken (if any).

How do you know when offensive behavior could be considered sexual harassment? Unwelcome sexual advances or other verbal or physical conduct of a sexual nature could be interpreted by an employee as sexual harassment under the following conditions:

- A person is required, or feels they are required, to accept unwelcome sexual conduct in order to get a job or keep a job,

- Decisions about an employee's job or work status are made based upon either the employee's acceptance or rejection of unwelcome sexual conduct, or

- The conduct interferes with the employee's work performance or creates an intimidating, hostile, or offensive working environment.

The following is a list of examples of the kind of behavior that is unacceptable and illegal. It is only a partial list to give you an idea of the scope of the requirements.

- Unwanted hugging, patting, kissing, brushing up against someone's body, or other inappropriate sexual touching,

- Subtle or open pressure for sexual activity,

- Persistent sexually explicit or sexist statements, jokes, or stories,

- Repeated leering or staring at a person's body,

- Suggestive or obscene notes or phone calls, and/or

- Display of sexually explicit pictures or cartoons.

The best way to prevent harassment is to set an example by your own behavior and to keep communication open between employees. In most cases an open discussion with employees about harassment can help everyone understand that innuendo and slurs about a person's race, religion, sex, appearance, or any other personal belief or characteristic are

---

SUBJECT: HARASSMENT POLICY AND   NO: _____
COMPLAINT PROCEDURE

PURPOSE:

To establish a strong commitment to prohibit harassment in employment, to define discrimination harassment and to set forth a procedure for investigating and resolving internal complaints of harassment.

POLICY:

Harassment of an applicant or employee by a supervisor, management employee, or co-worker on the basis of race, religion, color, national origin, ancestry, handicap, disability, medical condition, marital status, familial status, sex, sexual orientation, or age will not be tolerated. This policy applies to all terms and conditions of employment, including, but not limited to, hiring, placement, promotion, disciplinary action, layoff, recall, transfer, leave of absence, compensation, and training.

Disciplinary action up to and including termination will be instituted for behavior described in the definition of harassment set forth below:

- Any retaliation against a person for filing a harassment charge or making a harassment complaint is prohibited. Employees found to be retaliating against another employee shall be subject to disciplinary action up to and including termination.

DEFINITION:

Harassment includes, but is not limited to:

A. Verbal Harassment — For example, epithets, derogatory comments or slurs on the basis of race, religious creed, color, national origin, ancestry, handicap, disability, medical condition, marital status, familial status, sex, sexual orientation, or age. This might include inappropriate sex-oriented comments on appearance, including dress or physical features or race-oriented stories.

B. Physical Harassment — For example, assault, impeding or blocking movement, with a physical interference with normal work or movement when directed at an individual on the basis of race, religion, color, national origin, ancestry, handicap, disability, medical condition, marital status, familial status, age, sex, or sexual orientation. This could be conduct in the form of pinching, grabbing, patting, propositioning, leering, or making explicit or implied job threats or promises in return for submission to physical acts.

C. Visual Forms of Harassment — For example, derogatory posters, notices, bulletins, cartoons, or drawings on the basis of race, religious creed, color, national origin, ancestry, handicap, disability, medical conditions, marital status, familial status, sex, sexual orientation, or age.

D. Sexual Favors — Unwelcome sexual advances, requests for sexual favors, and other verbal or physical conduct of a sexual nature which is conditioned upon an employment benefit, unreasonably interferes with an individual's work performance, or creates an offensive work environment.

Fig. 23.3 Sexual harassment policy
(Courtesy of City of Mountain View, California)

SUBJECT: HARASSMENT POLICY AND COMPLAINT PROCEDURE (continued)

COMPLAINT PROCEDURE:

A. Filing:

An employee who believes he or she has been harassed may make a complaint orally or in writing with any of the following:

1. Immediate supervisor.
2. Any supervisor or manager within or outside of the department.
3. Department head.
4. Employee Services Director (or his/her designee).

Any supervisor or department head who receives a harassment complaint should notify the Employee Services Director immediately.

B. Upon notification of the harassment complaint, the Employee Services Director shall:

1. Authorize the investigation of the complaint and supervise and/or investigate the complaint. The investigation will include interviews with:

   (a) The complainant;
   (b) The accused harasser; and
   (c) Any other persons the Employee Services Director has reasons to believe has relevant knowledge concerning the complaint. This may include victims of similar conduct.

2. Review factual information gathered through the investigation to determine whether the alleged conduct constitutes harassment; giving consideration to all factual information, the totality of the circumstances, including the nature of the verbal, physical, visual, or sexual conduct and the context in which the alleged incidents occurred.

3. Report the results of the investigation and the determination as to whether harassment occurred to appropriate persons, including to the complainant, the alleged harasser, the supervisor, and the department head. If discipline is imposed, the discipline may or may not be communicated to the complainant.

4. If harassment occurred, take and/or recommend to the appropriate department head or other appropriate authority prompt and effective remedial action against the harasser. The action will be commensurate with the severity of the offense.

5. Take reasonable steps to protect the victim and other potential victims from further harassment.

6. Take reasonable steps to protect the victim from any retaliation as a result of communicating the complaint.

DISSEMINATION OF POLICY:

All employees, supervisors, and managers shall be sent copies of this policy.

Effective Date:	May, 1992	_____
Revision Date:	March 1, 1993	City Manager

Fig. 23.3 Sexual harassment policy (continued)
(Courtesy of City of Mountain View, California)

humiliating. The most productive way to control such behavior is by enlisting the help of all employees to feel that they have the right and the responsibility to stop harassment. When you get employees to think about their behavior and how their behavior makes others feel, they will usually realize they should speak up to prevent harassment.

Here is an example of how employees handled a problem of harassment. A group of operators often had coffee in the office of the utility during their morning break. One of the operators often used foul language, which was embarrassing and offensive to one of the operator's co-workers. The manager sent a memo to all employees that mentioned respect for fellow workers and included a reminder about inappropriate language. The next day all of the other operators had taped their copy of the memo to the mailbox of the one operator who was most vocal. These operators found a way to send their message loud and clear — no one wants to work in an environment that is unpleasant to others. As a manager, you must establish an atmosphere that is open, congenial, and harmonious for all employees.

Occasional flirting, innuendo, or jokes may not meet the legal definition of sexual harassment. Nevertheless, they may be offensive or intimidating to others. Every employee has a right to a workplace free of discrimination and harassment, and every employee has a responsibility to respect the rights of others.

Managers need to **be aware of** and **take action to prevent** any type of harassment in the workplace. It is not enough to simply distribute copies of the utility's harassment policy. If legal action is taken against the utility due to harassment or the existence of a hostile work environment, the utility manager may face both personal and professional liability if it can be shown that the manager *should have known* harassment was occurring or that the manager permitted a hostile environment to continue to exist.

Management Muddle No. 3

The maintenance crew is a group of five men who have been with the utility for many years and are well respected for their work habits. However, in the maintenance shed the walls are covered by calendars of scantily clad women and the language used out in the shed is sometimes pretty rough. One of your operators is a woman; she is well respected by her co-workers and is a very good operator. She comes to

your office to complain about the situation in the maintenance shed and demands that you remove the pictures from the walls in the shed. She goes on to report that when she went out to the shed and requested assistance to check on a pump, which was noisy and running hot, she was told "Kiss my _____, toots!" As the manager, what should you do? Should you immediately go to the maintenance shed and rip down the pictures? What should you say to the female operator in your office?

Actions: Your first response should be to reassure your operator that you understand her anger and frustration. Let her know that you will investigate the matter immediately and take action to correct any problems you find. Ask her to write out a complete statement of the facts, including her concerns about the pump, when and how her request for assistance was made, to whom the request was made, who made the offensive remark, the names of any witnesses, and what responses she has gotten from the maintenance crew in the past. Try to establish if this is a one-time response or if this problem has been going on for some time.

Begin your investigation with a trip to the maintenance shed to observe and evaluate what is hanging on the walls. Discuss the situation with the crew. Try to make this an open discussion so that everybody understands how the pictures affect the atmosphere and the image of professionalism of the utility. The best solution is to get the crew to understand how this type of behavior looks to persons outside their own small group and then let them take down the pictures. (Be sure to follow up later to confirm that the calendars or other offensive material has not reappeared.)

Next, set up private interviews with the person accused of making the offensive remark and each of the witnesses. Ask each person to describe the encounter in the maintenance shed and make detailed notes of their responses. (Depending on the complexity of the situation, it may sometimes be appropriate to have each person involved submit a written statement describing what occurred.)

After you have thoroughly investigated the incident, discuss with the crew the use of acceptable language in response to other employees. An open discussion and increased awareness of sexual harassment should be all that is necessary to change this situation. If it is not, arrange for a training program in sexual harassment awareness, if one is available. Be sure to establish a policy on the consequences of inappropriate behavior and be prepared to enforce the policy when needed.

Retaliation against an employee for filing a complaint about harassment or a hostile work environment is also illegal. Some examples of retaliation are demotion, suspension, failure to hire or consider for hire, failure to make impartial employment recommendations or decisions, adversely changing working conditions, spreading rumors, or denying any employment benefit. Retaliation could be the basis for a lawsuit involving not only the person who is accused of retaliation, but also the immediate supervisor, the manager, and the utility.

Most areas of personnel management, including harassment and retaliation issues, are complex and have significant legal consequences for everyone involved. The discussion in this section is *NOT* a complete explanation of harassment or retaliation. If your utility is large enough to employ a personnel specialist or a labor law attorney, ask them to review your staffing policies and procedures and consult with them whenever you have questions about personnel matters. If you manage a small utility and have no in-house sources for technical or legal advice, enroll in appropriate training courses or consider working with an attorney on a contract basis.

23.456 Personnel Records

A personnel file should be maintained for each utility employee. This file should contain all documents related to the employee's hiring, performance reviews, promotions, disciplinary actions, and any other records of employment-related matters. Since these records often contain sensitive, confidential information, access to personnel records should be closely controlled. (Also see Section 23.12, "Recordkeeping," for more information about what records should be kept and how long they should be kept.)

QUESTIONS

Write your answers in a notebook and then compare your answers with those on pages 632 and 633.

23.4O What is harassment?

23.4P List three types of behavior that could be considered sexual harassment.

23.4Q What is the best way to prevent harassment?

23.46 Unions

Whether your utility operators belong to a union now or may join one in the future, a good employee-management relationship is crucial to keeping an agency functioning properly. Managers, supervisors, crew leaders, and operators all have to work together to develop this relationship.

Most of a manager's union contacts are with a shop steward. The shop steward is elected by the union employees and is their official representative to management and the local union. The steward is in an awkward position because the steward is an employee who is expected to do a full-time job like other employees, while also representing all of the employees. The steward must create an effective link between the utility manager and/or supervisors and the employees.

During contract negotiations between management and the employees' union representatives, management should be in constant consultation with the supervisors. Many employee demands regarding working conditions originate from the supervisor's daily dealings with the employees. An effective supervisor can minimize unreasonable demands. Also any demands that are agreed upon must be implemented and carried out by a supervisor. A supervisor can help both sides reach an acceptable contractual agreement.

Once a contract has been agreed upon by both the union and the utility, the utility manager and the other supervisors must manage the organization within the framework of the contract. Do not attempt to ignore or "get around" the contract even if you disagree with some aspects of it. If you do not

understand certain contract provisions, ask for clarification before you begin implementation of those provisions.

Contracts do not change the supervisor's delegated authority or responsibility. Operators must carry out the supervisor's orders and get the work done properly, safely, and within a reasonable amount of time. As a supervisor, you have the right and even the duty to make decisions. However, a contract gives a union the right to protest or challenge your decision. When an operator requires discipline, disciplinary action is a management responsibility.

Handling employee grievances within the framework of a union contract can be a very time-consuming job for the supervisor and the steward. Union contracts usually spell out in great detail the steps and procedures the steward and the supervisor must follow to settle differences. Grievances can develop over disciplinary action, distribution of overtime, transfers, promotions, demotions, and interpretation of labor contracts. The shop steward must communicate complaints and grievances from operators to the supervisor. Then the supervisor and the steward must work together to settle complaints and adjust grievances. When a shop steward and supervisor can work together, the steward can help the supervisor to be an effective manager.

An effective manager lets everyone know they are available to discuss problems. ***Dealing with grievances as quickly as possible*** often prevents small problems from growing into large problems. When a shop steward presents a grievance to you, listen carefully and sympathetically to the steward. Discuss the problem with the employee directly with the help of the shop steward. Try to identify the facts and cause of the problem and keep a written record of your findings. Focus on the problem and do not get caught up in irrelevant issues. Make every effort to settle the grievance quickly and to everyone's satisfaction.

The consequences of any solution to a grievance must be considered and solutions must be consistent and fair to other operators. The solution or settlement should be clear and understandable to everyone involved. Once a solution has been agreed upon, prepare a written summary of the agreement. Review this final report with the shop steward to be sure the intent of the solution is understood and properly documented. The entire grievance procedure must be documented and properly filed, from initial presentation to final solution and settlement.

Union activities are governed by the National Labor Relations Act. When a union attempts to organize the utility's employees, your rights and actions as a manager are also governed by this Act. Be sure to seek competent legal assistance if your experience in dealing with a union is limited or if you have no such experience.

QUESTIONS

Write your answers in a notebook and then compare your answers with those on page 633.

23.4R What is the role of a shop steward?

23.4S How does a union contract affect a supervisor's authority?

END OF LESSON 1 OF 3 LESSONS

ON

ADMINISTRATION

Please answer the discussion and review questions next.

DISCUSSION AND REVIEW QUESTIONS

Chapter 23.   ADMINISTRATION

(Lesson 1 of 3 Lessons)

At the end of each lesson in this chapter you will find some discussion and review questions. The purpose of these questions is to indicate to you how well you understand the material in the lesson. Write the answers to these questions in your notebook before continuing.

1. What are the different types of demands on a utility manager?

2. List the basic functions of a manager.

3. What can happen without adequate utility planning?

4. What is the purpose of an organizational plan?

5. Define the following terms:

    1. Authority,

    2. Responsibility,

    3. Delegation, and

    4. Accountability.

6. When has a supervisor successfully delegated?

7. What two concepts should a manager keep in mind to avoid violating the rights of an employee or job applicant?

8. Why should a manager thoroughly examine the functions and staffing of the utility on a periodic basis?

9. When hiring new employees, the selection method and examination process used to evaluate applicants must be based on what criteria?

10. Why should you make notes of applicants' responses during job interviews?

11. What information should be provided to a new employee during orientation?

12. What type of training should be provided for supervisors?

13. Why is it important to formally document each employee's performance on a regular basis?

14. How should discipline problems be solved?

15. What steps can you take to help reach a successful resolution to a confrontation with an employee?

16. What is a manager's responsibility for preventing harassment in the workplace?

17. How are employee grievances usually handled under a union contract?

CHAPTER 23.   ADMINISTRATION

(Lesson 2 of 3 Lessons)

23.5   COMMUNICATION

Good communication is an essential part of good management skills. Both written and oral communication skills are needed to effectively organize and direct the operation of a treatment facility. Remember that communication is a two-part process; information must be given and it must be understood. Good listening skills are as important in communication as the information you need to communicate. As the manager of a water utility, you will need to communicate with employees, with your governing body, and with the public. Your communication style will be slightly different with each of these groups but you should be able to adjust easily to your audience.

23.50   Oral Communication

Oral communication may be informal, such as talking with employees, or it may be formal, such as giving a technical presentation. In both cases your words should be appropriate to the audience, for example, avoid technical jargon when talking with nontechnical audiences. As you talk, you should be observing your audience to be sure that what you are saying is getting across. If you are talking with an employee, it is a good idea to ask for feedback from the employee, especially if you are giving instructions. When the employee is talking, watch and listen carefully and clarify areas that seem unclear. Likewise, in a more formal presentation, watching your audience will give you feedback about how well your message is being received. Some tips for preparing a formal speech are given in Table 23.4.

23.51   Written Communication

Written communication is more demanding than oral communication and requires more careful preparation. Again, keep your audience in mind and use language that will be understood. Written communication requires more organization since you cannot clarify and explain ideas in response to your audience. Before you begin you should have a clear idea of exactly what you wish to communicate, then keep your language as concise as possible. Extra words and phrases tend to confuse and clutter your message. Good writing skills develop slowly, but you should be able to find good writing

classes in your community if you need help improving your skills. In addition, many publications and computer software programs are available which assist you in writing the most commonly needed documents such as memos, letters, press releases, resumes, monitoring reports, and the annual report.

Before you can write a report you must first organize your thoughts. Ask yourself, what is the objective of this report? Am I trying to persuade someone of something? What information is important to communicate in this report? For whom is the report being written? How can I make it interesting? What does the reader want to learn from this report?

After you have answered the above questions, the next step is to prepare a general outline of how you intend to proceed with the preparation of the report. List not only key topics, but try to list all of the related topics. Then arrange the key topics in sequence so there is a workable, smooth flow from one topic to the next. Do not attempt to make your outline perfect. It is just a guide. It should be flexible. As you write you will find that you need to remove nonessential points and expand on more important points.

You might, for example, outline the following points in preparation for writing a report on a polymer testing program.

- A problem condition of high turbidity was discovered

- Polymer testing offered the best means of reducing turbidity

- Funds, equipment, and material were acquired

- Operators were trained

- Tests were conducted

- Results and conclusions were reached

- Corrective actions were planned and taken

- Conclusion, the tests did or did not produce the anticipated results or correct the problem

Once you are fairly sure you have included all the major topics you will want to discuss, go through the outline and write down facts you want to include on each topic. As you work through it, you may decide to move material from one topic to another. The outline will help you organize your ideas and facts.

TABLE 23.4   TIPS FOR GIVING AN ORAL PRESENTATION

1. Arrive early. Give yourself plenty of time to become familiar with the room, practice using your audiovisuals, and make any necessary changes in room setup.

2. Be ready for mistakes. Number the pages in your presentation and your audiovisuals. Check the order of the pages before the meeting begins.

3. Pace yourself. Don't speak too quickly, speak slowly and carefully. Keep a careful eye on audience reaction to be sure that you are speaking at a pace which can be understood.

4. Project yourself. Speak loudly and look at the audience. Do not talk with your back to the audience. Check that those in the back can hear you.

5. Be natural. Try not to read your presentation. Practice ahead of time so that you can speak normally and keep eye contact with your audience.

6. Connect with the audience. Try to smile and make eye contact with audience.

7. Involve the audience. Allow for audience questions and invite their comments.

8. Repeat audience questions. Always repeat the question so everyone can hear and to be sure that you hear the question correctly.

9. Know when to stop. Keep your remarks within the time allocated for your presentation and be aware that long, rambling speeches create a negative impression on the audience.

10. Use readable audiovisuals. Audiovisuals should enhance and reinforce your words. Be sure that all members of the audience can see and read your audiovisuals. Normal typewritten text is not readable on overheads; use large type so everyone can see. Use no more than five to seven key ideas per overhead.

11. Organize your presentation. Prepare an introduction, body of the speech, and conclusion. "Tell them what you're going to say, say it, and then tell them what you said." The presentation should have three to five main points presented in some logical order, for example, chronologically or from simple to complex.

When your outline is complete, you will have the essentials of your report. Now you need to tailor it to the audience that will be reading it. Take a few minutes to think about your audience. What information do they want? What aspects of the topics will they be most interested in reading? Each of the following groups may be interested in specific topics in the report. Consider these interests as you write.

1. Management

Management will have specific interests that relate to the cost effectiveness of the program. A report to management should include a summary that presents the essential information, procedures used, an analysis of the data (including trends), and conclusions. Be sure to include complete cost information. Did the benefits warrant the costs? As a result of the tests, can future expenses be reduced? Backup information and field data can be included in an appendix for those who want more information.

2. Other Utilities

Other utilities will be interested in costs but will also want more detailed information about how the program was performed. They will also be interested in the results and benefits of the program. Explain how the tests were done, the procedures, size of the crew, equipment used, source and availability of materials, difficulties encountered and how they were overcome.

3. Citizen Groups

Citizens' interest will be more general. What is a polymer test and why is it needed? Is the polymer harmless? Will it injure fish or birds? How does the polymer test work? Who pays for the test? How much will it cost to implement results and will they be effective?

Your report may be written to include all of these groups. Adjust the outline to include the topics of interest to each group and identify the topics so readers can find the information most interesting to them. Keep the following information in mind as you write your report:

- Drafts. Good reports are not perfect the first time. Re-read and improve your report several times.

- Facts. Confine your writing to the facts and events that occurred. Include figures and statistics only when they make the report more effective. Include only the relevant facts. Large amounts of data should be put in the appendix. Do not clutter the report with unimportant data.

- Continuity. To be interesting and understood, a report must have continuity. It must make sense to the reader and be organized logically. In the report on the polymer testing, the report should be organized to show you had a problem, you had to find a way to identify where the problem existed, you did the testing, you identified the problems and the corrective actions.

- Effective. To be effective, a report should achieve the objective for which it was written. In this example we wanted to justify the costs for the program to management, help other utilities in conducting a similar program, and help citizens to understand what we were doing and why.

- Candid. A good report should be frank and straightforward. Keep the language appropriate for the audience. Do not try to impress your readers with technical terms they do not understand. Your purpose is to communicate information. Keep the information accurate and easy to understand.

The annual report is an important part of the management of the utility. It is one of the most involved writing projects that the utility must put together. The annual report should be a review of what and how the utility operated during the past year and it should also include the goals for the next year. In many small communities the annual report may be presented orally to the city council rather than written. If this report is well written, it can be used to highlight accomplishments and provide support for future planning.

The first step to organizing the report is to make a list of three or four major accomplishments of the last year, then make a list of the top three goals for next year. These accomplishments and goals should be the focus of the report. The annual report should be a summary of the expenses, treatment services provided, and revenues generated over the last year. As you organize this information, keep those accomplishments in mind and let the data tell the story of how the utility accomplished last year's tasks. The data by itself may seem boring but as you organize the data it becomes a meaningful description of the year's accomplishments. Conclude with projections for next year. The facts and figures should tell the audience how you plan to accomplish your goals for the next year. The annual report may be simple or complex depending on your community needs. A sample Table of Contents for a medium-sized utility is given in Table 23.5. When you are finished the annual report will be a valuable planning tool for the utility and can be used to build support for new projects.

TABLE 23.5 EXAMPLE OF TABLE OF CONTENTS FOR THE ANNUAL REPORT OF A UTILITY

TABLE OF CONTENTS

Executive Summary

Summary of the Treatment Process Including Flows and Costs

Review of Goals and Objectives for the Year

Special Projects Completed

Professional Awards or Recognition for the Utility or Its Staff

General Operating Conditions Including Regulatory Requirements

Expectations for the Next Year — Goals and Objectives

Recommended Changes for the Utility in Organizing, Staffing, Equipment, or Resources Summary

Appendixes: Operating Data
             Budget
             Information on Special Projects

QUESTIONS

Write your answers in a notebook and then compare your answers with those on page 633.

23.5A What kinds of communication skills are needed by a manager?

23.5B What are the most common written documents that a utility manager must write?

23.5C What should be included in the annual report?

23.6 CONDUCTING MEETINGS

As a utility manager you will be asked to conduct meetings. These meetings may be with employees, your governing board, the public, or with other professionals in your field. Many new managers fail to prepare for these meetings and the meetings end up as a terrible waste of time. As a manager you need to learn to conduct meetings in a way that is productive and guides the participants into an active role. The following steps should be taken to conduct a productive meeting.

Before the meeting:

- Prepare an agenda and distribute it to all participants.

- Find an adequate meeting room.

- Set a beginning and ending time for the meeting.

During the meeting:

- Start the meeting on time.

- Clearly state the purpose and objectives of the meeting.

- Involve all the participants.

- Do not let one or two individuals dominate the meeting.

- Keep the discussion on track and on time with the agenda.

- When the group makes a decision or reaches consensus, restate your understanding of the results.

- Make clear assignments for participants and review them with everyone during the meeting.

After the meeting:

- Send out minutes of the meeting.

- Send out reminders, when appropriate, about any assignments made for participants, and the next meeting time.

QUESTIONS

Write your answers in a notebook and then compare your answers with those on page 633.

23.6A   With whom may a utility manager be asked to conduct meetings?

23.6B   What should be done before a meeting?

23.7 PUBLIC RELATIONS

23.70 Establish Objectives

The first step in organizing an effective public relations campaign is to establish objectives. The only way to know whether your program is a success is to have a clear idea of what you expect to achieve — for example, better customer relations, greater water conservation, and enhanced organizational credibility. Each objective must be specific, achievable, and measurable. It is also important to know your audience and tailor various elements of your public relations effort to specific groups you wish to reach, such as community leaders, school children, or the average customer. Your objective may be the same in each case, but what you say and how you say it will depend upon your target audience.

23.71 Utility Operations

Good public relations begin at home. Dedicated, service-oriented employees provide for better public relations than paid advertising or complicated public relations campaigns. For most people, contact with an agency employee establishes their first impression of the competence of the organization, and those initial opinions are difficult to change.

In addition to ensuring that employees are adequately trained to do their jobs and knowledgeable about the utility's operations, management has the responsibility to keep employees informed about the organization's plans, practices, and goals. Newsletters, bulletin boards, and regular, open communication between supervisors and subordinates will help build understanding and contribute to a team spirit.

Despite the old adage to the contrary, the customer is not always right. Management should try to instill among its employees the attitude that while the customer may be confused or unclear about the situation, everyone is entitled to courteous treatment and a factual explanation. Whenever possible, employees should phrase responses as positively, or neutrally, as possible, avoiding negative language. For example, "Your complaint" is better stated as "Your question." "You should have ..." is likely to make the customer defensive, while "Will you please ..." is courteous and respectful. "You made a mistake" emphasizes the negative, "What we'll do..." is a positive, problem-solving approach.

23.72 The Mass Media

We live in the age of communications, and one of the most effective and least expensive ways to reach people is through the mass media — radio, television, and newspapers. Each medium has different needs and deadlines, and obtaining coverage for your issue or event is easier if you are aware of these constraints. Television must have strong visuals, for example. When scheduling a press conference, provide an interesting setting and be prepared to suggest good shots to the reporter. Radio's main advantage over television and newspapers is immediacy, so have a spokesperson available and prepared to give the interview over the telephone if necessary. Newspapers give more thorough, in-depth coverage to stories than do the broadcast media, so be prepared to spend extra time with print reporters and provide written backup information and additional contacts.

It is not difficult to get press coverage for your event or press conference if a few simple guidelines are followed:

1. Demonstrate that your story is newsworthy, that it involves something unusual or interesting.

2. Make sure your story will fit the targeted format (television, radio, or newspaper).

3. Provide a spokesperson who is interesting, articulate, and well prepared.

23.73 Being Interviewed

Whether you are preparing for a scheduled interview or are simply contacted by the press on a breaking news story, here are some key hints to keep in mind when being interviewed.

1. Speak in personal terms, free of institutional jargon.

2. Do not argue or show anger if the reporter appears to be rude or overly aggressive.

3. If you don't know an answer, say so and offer to find out. Don't bluff.

4. If you say you will call back by a certain time, do so. Reporters face tight deadlines.

5. State your key points early in the interview, concisely and clearly. If the reporter wants more information, he or she will ask for it.

6. If a question contains language or concepts with which you disagree, don't repeat them, even to deny them.

7. Know your facts.

8. Never ask to see a story before it is printed or broadcast. Doing so indicates that you doubt the reporter's ability and professionalism.

23.74 Public Speaking

Direct contact with people in your community is another effective tool in promoting your utility. Though the audiences tend to be small, a personal, face-to-face presentation generally leaves a strong and long-lasting impact on the listener.

Depending upon the size of the organization, your utility may wish to establish a speaker's bureau and send a list of topics to service clubs in the area. Visits to high schools and college campuses can also be beneficial, and educators are often looking for new and interesting topics to supplement their curriculum.

Effective public speaking takes practice. It is important to be well prepared while retaining a personal, informal style. Find out how long your talk is expected to be, and don't exceed that time frame. Have a definite beginning, middle, and end to your presentation. Visual aids such as charts, slides, or models can assist in conveying your message. The use of humor and anecdotes can help to warm up the audience and build rapport between the speaker and the listener. Just be sure the humor is natural, not forced, and that the point of your story is accessible to the particular audience. Try to keep in mind that audiences only expect you to do your best. They are interested in learning about their water supply and will appreciate that you are making a sincere effort to inform them about an important subject.

23.75 Telephone Contacts

First impressions are extremely important, and frequently a person's first contact with your water utility is over the telephone. A person who answers the phone in a courteous, pleasant, and helpful manner goes a long way toward establishing a friendly, cooperative atmosphere. Be sure anyone answering telephone inquiries receives appropriate training and conveys a positive image for the utility.

Following a few simple guidelines will help to start your utility off on the right note with your customers:

1. ANSWER CALLS PROMPTLY. Your conversation will get off to a better start if the phone is answered by the third or fourth ring.

2. IDENTIFY YOURSELF. This adds a personal note and lets the caller know whom he or she is talking to.

3. PAY ATTENTION. Don't conduct side conversations. Minimize distractions so you can give the caller your full attention, avoiding repetitions of names, addresses, and other pertinent facts.

4. MINIMIZE TRANSFERS. Nobody likes to get the runaround. Few things are more frustrating to a caller than being transferred from office to office, repeating the situation, problem, or concern over and over again. Transfer only those calls that must be transferred, and make certain you are referring the caller to the right person. Then, explain why you are transferring the call. This lets the caller know you are referring him or her to a co-worker for a reason and reassures the customer that the problem or question will be dealt with. In some cases, it may be better to take a message and have someone return the call than to keep transferring the customer's call.

23.76 Consumer Inquiries

No single set of rules can possibly apply to all types of consumer questions or complaints about water quality and service. There are, however, basic principles to follow in responding to inquiries and concerns.

1. BE PREPARED. Your employees should be familiar enough with your utility's organization, services, and policies to either respond to the question or complaint or locate the person who can.

2. LISTEN. Ask the customer to describe the problem and listen carefully to the explanation. Take written notes of the facts and addresses.

3. DON'T ARGUE. Callers often express a great deal of pent-up frustration in their contacts with a utility. Give the caller your full attention. Once you've heard them out, most people will calm down and state their problems in more reasonable terms.

4. AVOID JARGON. The average consumer lacks the technical knowledge to understand the complexities of water quality. Use plain, nontechnical language and avoid telling the consumer more than he or she needs to know.

5. SUMMARIZE THE PROBLEM. Repeat your understanding of the situation back to the caller. This will assure the customer that you understand the problem and offer the opportunity to clear up any confusion or missed communication.

6. PROMISE SPECIFIC ACTION. Make an effort to give the customer an immediate, clear, and accurate answer to the problem. Be as specific as possible without promising something you can't deliver.

In some cases, you may wish to have a representative of the utility visit the customer and observe the problem first hand. If the complaint involves water quality, take samples if necessary and report back to the customer to be sure the problem has been resolved.

Complaints can be a valuable asset in determining consumer acceptance and pinpointing water quality problems. Customer calls are frequently your first indication that something may be wrong. Responding to complaints and inquiries promptly can save the utility money and staff resources, and minimize the number of customers who are inconvenienced. Still, education can greatly reduce complaints about water quality. Information brochures, utility bill inserts, and other educational tools help to inform customers and avoid future complaints.

23.77 Plant Tours

Tours of water treatment plants can be an excellent way to inform the public about your utility's efforts to provide a safe, high quality water supply. Political leaders, such as the City

Council and members of the Board of Supervisors, should be invited and encouraged to tour the facilities, as should school groups and service clubs.

A brochure describing your utility's goals, accomplishments, operations, and processes can be a good supplement to the tour and should be handed out at the end of the visit. The more visually interesting the brochure is, the more likely that it will be read, and the use of color, photographs, graphics, or other design features is encouraged. If you have access to the necessary equipment, production of a videotape program about the utility can also add interest to the facility tour.

The tour itself should be conducted by an employee who is very familiar with plant operations and can answer the types of questions that are likely to arise. Consider including:

1. A description of the sources of water supply,

2. History of the plant, the years of operation, modifications and innovations over the years,

3. Major plant design features, including plant capacity and safety features,

4. Observation of the treatment processes, including filtration, sedimentation, flocculation, and disinfection,

5. A visit to the laboratory, including information on the quality of water distributed to consumers, and

6. Anticipated improvements, expansions, and long-range plans for meeting future service needs.

Plant tours can contribute to a water utility's overall program to gain financing for capital improvements. If the City Council or other governing board has seen the treatment process first hand, it is more likely to understand the need for enhancement and support future funding.

QUESTIONS

Write your answers in a notebook and then compare your answers with those on page 633.

23.7A   What is the first step in organizing a public relations campaign?

23.7B   How can employees be kept informed of the utility's plans, practices, and goals?

23.7C   Which news medium is more likely to give a story thorough, in-depth coverage?

23.7D   What is the key to effective public speaking?

23.7E   How do customer complaints help a utility?

23.8   FINANCIAL MANAGEMENT

Financial management for a utility should include providing financial stability for the utility, careful budgeting, and providing capital improvement funds for future utility expansion. These three areas must be examined on a routine basis to ensure the continued operation of the utility. They may be formally reviewed on an annual basis or more frequently when the utility is changing rapidly. The utility manager should understand what is required for each of the three areas and be able to develop record systems that keep the utility on track and financially prepared for the future.

23.80   Financial Stability

How do you measure financial stability for a utility? Two very simple calculations can be used to help you determine how healthy and stable the finances are for the utility. These two calculations are the OPERATING RATIO and the COVERAGE RATIO. The operating ratio is a measure of the total revenues divided by the total operating expenses. The coverage ratio is a measure of the ability of the utility to pay the principal and interest on loans and bonds (this is known as *DEBT SERVICE*[5]) in addition to any unexpected expenses. A utility that is in good financial shape will have an operating ratio and coverage ratio above 1.0. In fact, most bonds and loans require the utility to have a coverage ratio of at least 1.25. As state and federal funds for utility improvements have become much more difficult to obtain, these financial indicators have become more important for utilities. Being able to show and document the financial stability of the utility is an important part of getting funding for more capital improvements.

The operating ratio is perhaps the simplest measure of a utility's financial stability. In essence, the utility must be generating enough revenue to pay its operating expenses. The actual ratio is usually computed on a yearly basis, since many utilities may have monthly variations that do not reflect the overall performance. The total revenue is calculated by adding up all revenue generated by user fees, hook-up charges, taxes or assessments, interest income, and special income. Next determine the total operating expenses by adding up the expenses of the utility, including administrative costs, salaries, benefits, energy costs, chemicals, supplies, fuel, equipment costs, equipment replacement fund, principal and interest payments, and other miscellaneous expenses.

EXAMPLE 1

The total revenues for a utility are $1,686,000 and the operating expenses for the utility are $1,278,899. The debt service expenses are $560,000. What is the operating ratio? What is the coverage ratio?

Known		Unknown
Total Revenue, $	= $1,686,000	Operating Ratio
Operating Expenses, $	= $1,278,899	Coverage Ratio
Debt Service Expenses, $	= $560,000	

---

[5] *Debt Service.   The amount of money required annually to pay the (1) interest on outstanding debts; or (2) funds due on a maturing bonded debt or the redemption of bonds.*

1. Calculate operating ratio.

$$\text{Operating Ratio} = \frac{\text{Total Revenue, \$}}{\text{Operating Expenses, \$}}$$

$$= \frac{\$1,686,000}{\$1,278,899}$$

$$= 1.32$$

2. Calculate non-debt expenses.

Non-Debt Expenses, \$ = Operating Exp, \$ − Debt Service Exp, \$

$$= \$1,278,899 - \$560,000$$

$$= \$718,899$$

3. Calculate coverage ratio.

$$\text{Coverage Ratio} = \frac{\text{Total Revenue, \$} - \text{Non-Debt Expenses, \$}}{\text{Debt Service Expenses, \$}}$$

$$= \frac{\$1,686,000 - \$718,899}{\$560,000}$$

$$= 1.73$$

These calculations provide a good starting point for looking at the financial strength of the utility. Both of these calculations use the total revenue for the utility, which is an important component for any utility budgeting. As managers we often focus on the expense side and forget to look carefully at the revenue side of utility management. The fees collected by the utility, including hook-up fees and user fees, must accurately reflect the cost of providing service. These fees must be reviewed annually and they must be increased as expenses rise to maintain financial stability. Some other areas to examine on the revenue side include how often and how well user fees are collected, the number of delinquent accounts, and the accuracy of meters. Some small communities have found they can cut their administrative costs significantly by switching to a quarterly billing cycle. The utility must have the support of the community to determine and collect user fees, and the utility must keep track of revenue generation as carefully as resource spending.

23.81 Budgeting

Budgeting for the utility is perhaps the most unpleasant task of the year for many managers. The list of needs usually is much larger than the possible revenue for the utility. The only way for the manager to prepare a good budget is to have good records from the year before. A system of recording or filing purchase orders (see Section 23.124, "Procurement Records") or a requisition records system must be in place to keep track of expenses and prevent spending money that is not in the budget.

To budget effectively, a manager needs to understand how the money has been spent over the last year, the needs of the utility, and how the needs should be prioritized. The manager also must take into account cost increases that cannot be controlled while trying to minimize the expenses as much as possible. The following problem is an example of the types of decisions a manager must make to keep the budget in line while also improving service from the utility.

EXAMPLE 2

A pump which has been in operation for 25 years pumps a constant 600 GPM through 47 feet of dynamic head. The pump uses 6,071 kilowatt-hours of electricity per month, at a cost of \$0.085 per kilowatt-hr. The old pump efficiency has dropped to 63 percent. Assuming a new pump that operates at 86 percent efficiency is available for \$9,730.00, how long would it take to pay for replacing the old pump?

Known		Unknown
Electricity, kW-hr/mo	= 6,071 kW-hr/mo	New Pump Payback Time, yr
Electricity Cost, \$/kW-hr	= \$0.085/kW-hr	
Old Pump Efficiency, %	= 63%	
New Pump Efficiency, %	= 86%	
New Pump Cost, \$	= \$9,730	

1. Calculate old pump operating costs in dollars per month.

$$\text{Old Pump Operating Costs, \$/mo} = (\text{Electricity, kW-hr/mo})(\text{Electricity Cost, \$/kW-hr})$$

$$= (6,071 \text{ kW-hr/mo})(\$0.085/\text{kW-hr})$$

$$= \$516.04/\text{mo}$$

2. Calculate new pump operating electricity requirements.

$$\text{New Pump Electricity, kW-hr/mo} = (\text{Old Pump Electricity, kW-hr/mo}) \frac{(\text{Old Pump Eff, \%})}{(\text{New Pump Eff, \%})}$$

$$= (6,071 \text{ kW-hr/mo}) \frac{(63\%)}{(86\%)}$$

$$= 4,447 \text{ kW-hr/mo}$$

3. Calculate new pump operating costs in dollars per month.

$$\text{New Pump Operating Costs, \$/mo} = (\text{Electricity, kW-hr/mo})(\text{Electricity Cost, \$/kW-hr})$$

$$= (4,447 \text{ kW-hr/mo})(\$0.085/\text{kW-hr})$$

$$= \$378.03/\text{mo}$$

4. Calculate annual cost savings of new pump.

Cost Savings, \$/yr = (Old Costs, \$/mo − New Costs, \$/mo)(12 mo/yr)

$$= (\$516.04/\text{mo} - \$378.03/\text{mo})(12 \text{ mo/yr})$$

$$= \$1,656.12/\text{yr}$$

5. Calculate the new pump payback time in years.

$$\text{Payback Time, yr} = \frac{\text{Initial Cost, \$}}{\text{Savings, \$/yr}}$$

$$= \frac{\$9,730.00}{\$1,656.12/\text{yr}}$$

$$= 5.9 \text{ years}$$

In this example a payback time of 5.9 years is acceptable and would probably justify the expense for a new pump. This calculation was a simple payback calculation which did not take into account the maintenance on each pump, depreciation, and inflation. Many excellent references are available from EPA to help utility managers make more complex decisions about purchasing new equipment.

The annual report should be used to help develop the budget so that long-term planning will have its place in the budgeting process. The utility manager must track revenue generation and expenses with adequate records to budget effectively. The manager must also get input from other personnel in the utility as well as community leaders as the budgeting process proceeds. This input from others is invaluable to gain support for the budget and to keep the budget on track once adopted.

23.82   Equipment Repair/Replacement Fund

To adequately plan for the future, every utility must have a repair/replacement fund. The purpose of this fund is to generate additional revenue to pay for the repair and replacement of capital equipment as the equipment wears out. To prepare adequately for this repair/replacement, the manager should make a list of all capital equipment (this is called an asset inventory) and estimate the replacement cost for each item. The expected life span of the equipment must be used to determine how much money should be collected over time. When a treatment plant is new, the balance in repair/replacement fund should be increasing each year. As the plant gets older, the funds will have to be used and the balance may get dangerously low as equipment breakdowns occur. Perhaps the hardest job for the utility manager is to maintain a positive balance in this account with the understanding that this account is not meant to generate a "profit" for the utility but rather to plan for future equipment needs. In water treatment facilities construction, providing an adequate repair/replacement fund is very important, but if this repair/replacement fund hasn't been reviewed annually, it must be updated.

To set up a repair/replacement fund for your utility, you should first put together a list of the equipment required for each process in your utility. Once you have this list, you need to estimate the life expectancy of the equipment and the replacement cost. From this list you can predict the amount of money you should set aside each year so that when each piece of equipment wears out, you will have enough money to replace that piece of equipment. Several EPA publications listed in Section 23.14, "Additional Reading," at the end of this chapter are excellent references for utility planning.

23.83   Water Rates

The process of determining the cost of water and establishing a water rate schedule for customers is a subject of much controversy. There is no single set of rules for determining water rates. The establishment of a rate schedule involves many factors including the form of ownership (investor or publicly owned), differences in regulatory control over the water utility (state commission or local authority), and differences in individual viewpoints and preferences concerning

the appropriate philosophy to be followed to meet local conditions and requirements.

Generally, the development of water rate schedules involves the following procedures:

- A determination of the total revenue requirements for the period that the rates are to be effective (usually one year).

- A determination of all the cost components of system operations. That is, how much does it cost to treat the water? How much does it cost to distribute? How much does it cost to install a water service to a customer? How much are administrative costs?

- Distribution of the various component costs to the various customer classes in accordance with their requirements for service.

- The design of water rates that will recover from each class of customers, within practical limits, the cost to serve that class of customers.

Sales of water to customers may be metered or unmetered. In the case of metered sales, the charge to the customer is based on a rate schedule applied to the amount of water used through each water meter. If meters are not used, the charge per customer is based on a flat rate per period of time per fixture, foot of frontage, number of rooms, or other measurable unit. Although the flat rate basis still is fairly common, meter-based rates are more widely used.

See *SMALL WATER SYSTEM OPERATION AND MAINTENANCE*, Chapter 8, "Setting Water Rates for Small Water Utilities," for an explanation and examples of how to determine and set water rates. This publication is available from Ken Kerri, Office of Water Programs, California State University, Sacramento, 6000 J Street, Sacramento, CA 95819-6025. Price, $20.00.

23.84   Capital Improvements and Funding in the Future

A capital improvements fund must be a part of the utility budget and included in the operating ratio. Your responsibility as the utility manager is to be sure that everyone, your governing body and the public, understands the capital improvement fund is not a profit for the utility but a replacement fund to keep the utility operating in the future.

Capital planning starts with a look at changes in the community. Where are the areas of growth in the community, where are the areas of decline, and what are the anticipated changes in industry within the community? After identifying the changing needs in the community, you should examine the existing utility structure. Identify your weak spots (in the distribution system or with in-plant processes). Make a list of the areas that will be experiencing growth, weak spots in the system, and anticipated new regulatory requirements. The list should include expected capital improvements that will need to be made over the next year, two years, five years, and ten years. You can use the information in your annual reports and other operational logs to help compile the list.

Once you have compiled this information, prioritize the list and make a timetable for improving each of the areas. Starting at the top of the priority list, estimate the costs for improvements and incorporate these costs into your capital improvement budget. The calculations you have made previously, including corrective to preventive maintenance ratios, operating ratio, coverage ratio, and payback time will all be useful in prioritizing and streamlining your list of needs. Remember to involve all of your local officials and the public in this capital improvement budget so they understand what will be needed.

Long-term capital improvements such as a new plant or a new treatment process are usually anticipated in your 10-year or 20-year projection. These long-term capital improvements usually require some additional financing. The basic ways for a utility to finance capital improvements are through general obligation bonds, revenue bonds, or loan funding programs.

General obligation bonds or *ad valorem* (based on value) taxes are assessed based on property taxes. These bonds usually have a lower interest rate and longer payback time, but the total bond limit is determined for the entire community. This means that the water utility will have available only a portion of the total bond capacity of the community. These bonds are not often used for funding water utility improvements today.

The second type of bond, the revenue bond, is commonly used to fund utility improvements. This bond has no limit on the amount of funds available and the user charges provide repayment on the bond. To qualify for these bonds, the utility must show sound financial management and the ability to repay the bond. As the utility manager you should be aware of the provisions of the bond. Be sure the bond has a call date, which is the first date when you can pay off the bond. The common practice is for a 20-year bond to have a 10-year call date and for a 15-year bond to have an 8-year call date. The bond will also have a call premium, which is the amount of extra funds needed to pay off the debt on the call date. You should try to get your bonds a call premium of no more than 102 percent par. This means that for a debt of $200,000 on the call date, the total payoff would be $204,000, which includes the extra two percent for the call premium. You will need to get help from a financial advisor to prepare for and issue the bonds. These advisors will help you negotiate the best bond structure for your community.

Special assessment bonds may be used to extend services into specific areas. The direct users pay the capital costs and the assessment is usually based on frontage or area of real estate. These special assessments carry a greater risk to investors but may be the best way to extend service to some areas.

The most common way to finance water supply system improvements in the past has been federal and state grant programs. The Block Grants from HUD are still available for some projects and Rural Utilities Service (RUS) loans may also be used as a funding source. In addition, state revolving fund (SRF) programs provide loans (but not direct grants) for improvements. The SRF program has already been implemented with wastewater improvements and the new Safe Drinking Water Regulations include an SRF program for funding water treatment improvements. These SRF programs will be very competitive and utilities must provide evidence of sound financial management to qualify for these loans. You should contact your state regulatory agency to find out more about the SRF program in your state.

23.85 Financial Assistance

Many small water treatment and distribution systems need additional funds to repair and upgrade their systems. Potential funding sources include loans and grants from federal and state agencies, banks, foundations, and other sources. Some of the federal funding programs for small public utility systems include:

- Appalachian Regional Commission (ARC),

- Department of Housing and Urban Development (HUD) (provides Community Development Block Grants),

- Economic Development Administration (EDA),

- Indian Health Service (IHS), and

- Rural Utilities Service (RUS)(formerly Farmer's Home Administration (FmHA) and Rural Development Administration (RDA)).

For additional information see, "Financing Assistance Available for Small Public Water Systems," by Susan Campbell, Benjamin W. Lykins, Jr., and James A. Goodrich, *Journal American Water Works Association*, June 1993, pages 47-53.

Another valuable contact is the Environmental Financing Information Network which provides information on financing alternatives for state and local environmental programs and projects in the form of abstracts of publications, case studies, and contacts. Contact Environmental Financing Information Network, U.S. Environmental Protection Agency (EPA), EFIN (mail code 2731R), 401 M Street, SW, Washington, DC 20460. Phone (202) 564-4994 and FAX (202) 565-2587.

Also many states have one or more special financing mechanisms for small public utility systems. These funds may be in the form of grants, loans, bonds, or revolving loan funds. Contact your state drinking water agency for more information.

QUESTIONS

Write your answers in a notebook and then compare your answers with those on page 633.

23.8A   List the three main areas of financial management for a utility.

23.8B   How is a utility's operating ratio calculated?

23.8C   Why is it important for a manager to consult with other utility personnel and with community leaders during the budget process?

23.8D   How can long-term capital improvements be financed?

23.8E   What is a revenue bond?

**END OF LESSON 2 OF 3 LESSONS
ON
ADMINISTRATION**

Please answer the discussion and review questions next.

DISCUSSION AND REVIEW QUESTIONS

Chapter 23.   ADMINISTRATION

(Lesson 2 of 3 Lessons)

Write the answers to these questions in your notebook before continuing. The question numbering continues from Lesson 1.

18. With whom do managers need to communicate?

19. What information should be included in the utility's annual report?

20. List four steps that can be taken during a meeting to make sure it is a productive meeting.

21. What happens any time you or a member of your utility comes in contact with the public?

22. What attitude should management try to develop among its employees regarding the consumer?

23. What is the value of consumer complaints?

24. How do you measure financial stability for a utility?

25. How can a manager prepare a good budget?

CHAPTER 23.   ADMINISTRATION

(Lesson 3 of 3 Lessons)

23.9   OPERATIONS AND MAINTENANCE

23.90   The Manager's Responsibilities

A utility manager's specific operation and maintenance (O & M) responsibilities vary depending on the size of the utility. At a small utility, the manager may oversee all utility operations while also serving as chief operator and supervising a small staff of operations and maintenance personnel. In larger utility agencies, the manager may have no direct, day-to-day responsibility for operations and maintenance but is ultimately responsible for efficient, cost-effective operation of the entire utility. Whether large or small, every utility needs an effective operations and maintenance program.

23.91   Purpose of O & M Programs

The purpose of O & M programs is to maintain design functionality (capacity) and/or to restore the system components to their original condition and thus functionality. Stated another way, does the system perform as designed and intended? The ability to effectively operate and maintain a water supply utility so it performs as intended depends greatly on proper design (including selection of appropriate materials and equipment), construction and inspection, acceptance, and system start-up. Permanent system deficiencies that affect O & M of the system are frequently the result of these phases. O & M staff should be involved at the beginning of each project, including planning, design, construction, acceptance, and start-up. When a utility system is designed with future O & M considerations in mind, the result is a more effective O & M program in terms of O & M cost and performance.

Effective O & M programs are based on knowing what components make up the system, where they are located, and the condition of the components. With that information, proactive maintenance can be planned and scheduled, rehabilitation needs identified, and long-term Capital Improvement Programs (CIP) planned and budgeted. High-performing agencies have all developed performance measurements of their O & M program and track the information necessary to evaluate performance.

23.92   Types of Maintenance

Water supply and distribution system maintenance can be either a proactive or a reactive activity. Commonly accepted types of maintenance include three classifications: corrective maintenance, preventive maintenance, and predictive maintenance.

Corrective maintenance, including emergency maintenance, is reactive. For example, a piece of equipment or a system is allowed to operate until it fails, with little or no scheduled maintenance occurring prior to the failure. Only when the equipment or system fails is maintenance performed. Reliance on reactive maintenance will always result in poor system performance, especially as the system ages. Utility agencies taking a corrective maintenance approach are characterized by:

- The inability to plan and schedule work,
- The inability to budget adequately,
- Poor use of resources, and
- A high incidence of equipment and system failures.

Emergency maintenance involves two types of emergencies: normal emergencies and extraordinary emergencies. Public utilities are faced with normal emergencies such as water main breaks on a daily basis. Normal emergencies can be reduced by an effective maintenance program. Extraordinary emergencies, such as high-intensity rainstorms, hurricanes, floods, and earthquakes, will always be unpredictable occurrences. However, the effects of extraordinary emergencies on the utility's performance can be minimized by implementation of a planned maintenance program and development of a comprehensive emergency response plan (see Section 23.10).

Preventive maintenance is proactive and is defined as a programmed, systematic approach to maintenance activities. This type of maintenance will always result in improved system performance except in the case where major chronic problems are the result of design and/or construction flaws that cannot be corrected by O & M activities. Proactive maintenance is performed on a periodic (preventive) basis or an as-needed (predictive) basis. Preventive maintenance can be scheduled on the basis of specific criteria such as equipment operating time since the last maintenance was performed, or passage of a certain amount of time (calendar period). Lubrication of motors, for example, is frequently based on running time.

The major elements of a good preventive maintenance program include the following:

1. Planning and scheduling,

2. Records management,

3. Spare parts management,

4. Cost and budget control,

5. Emergency repair procedures, and

6. Training program.

Some benefits of taking a preventive maintenance approach are:

1. Maintenance can be planned and scheduled,

2. Work backlog can be identified,

3. Adequate resources necessary to support the maintenance program can be budgeted,

4. Capital Improvement Program (CIP) items can be identified and budgeted for, and

5. Human and material resources can be used effectively.

Predictive maintenance, which is also proactive, is a method of establishing baseline performance data, monitoring performance criteria over a period of time, and observing changes in performance so that failure can be predicted and maintenance can be performed on a planned, scheduled basis. Knowing the condition of the system makes it possible to plan and schedule maintenance on an "as required" basis and thus avoid unnecessary maintenance.

In reality, every agency operates their system with corrective and emergency maintenance, preventive maintenance, and predictive maintenance methods. The goal, however, is to reduce the corrective and emergency maintenance efforts by performing preventive maintenance which will minimize system failures that result in stoppages and overflows.

System performance is frequently a reliable indicator of how the system is operated and maintained. Agencies that rely primarily on corrective maintenance as their method of operating and maintaining the system are never able to focus on preventive and predictive maintenance since most of their resources are directed at corrective maintenance activities and it is difficult to free up these resources to begin developing preventive maintenance programs. For an agency to develop an effective proactive maintenance program, they must add initial resources over and above those currently existing in order to establish preventive and predictive maintenance programs.

23.93   Benefits of Managing Maintenance

The goal of managing maintenance is to minimize investments of labor, materials, money, and equipment. In other words, we want to manage our human and material resources as effectively as possible, while delivering a high level of service to our customers. The benefits of an effective operation and maintenance program are as follows:

● Ensuring the availability of facilities and equipment as intended.

● Maintaining the reliability of the equipment and facilities as designed. Utility systems are required to operate 24 hours per day, 7 days per week, 365 days per year. Reliability is a critical component of the operation and maintenance program. If equipment and facilities are not reliable, then

the ability of the system to perform as designed is impaired.

● Maintaining the value of the investment. Water supply and distribution systems represent major capital investments for communities and are major capital assets of the community. If maintenance of the system is not managed, equipment and facilities will deteriorate through normal use and age. Maintaining the value of the capital asset is one of the utility manager's major responsibilities. Accomplishing this goal requires ongoing investment to maintain existing facilities and equipment, extend the life of the system, and establish a comprehensive O & M program.

● Obtaining full use of the system throughout its design life.

● Collecting accurate information and data on which to base the operation and maintenance of the system and justify requests for the financial resources necessary to support it.

QUESTIONS

Write your answers in a notebook and then compare your answers with those on page 633.

23.9A   What is the purpose of an operation and maintenance (O & M) program?

23.9B   What are the three common types of maintenance?

23.9C   List the major elements of a good preventive maintenance program.

23.94   SCADA Systems

23.940   Description of SCADA (ss-KAY-dah) Systems

SCADA stands for **S**upervisory **C**ontrol **A**nd **D**ata **A**cquisition system. This is a computer-monitored alarm, response, control, and data acquisition system used by operators to monitor and adjust their treatment processes and facilities.

A SCADA system collects, stores, and analyzes information about all aspects of operation and maintenance, transmits alarm signals when necessary, and allows fingertip control of alarms, equipment, and processes. SCADA provides the information that operators need to solve minor problems before they become major incidents. As the nerve center of a water utility, the system allows operators to enhance the efficiency of their water facility by keeping them fully informed and fully in control.

A typical SCADA system is made up of basically four groups of components:

1. Field-mounted sensors, instrumentation, and controlled or monitored equipment. These devices sense system variables and generate input signals to the SCADA system for monitoring. These devices also receive the command output signals from the SCADA system.

2. Remote Terminal Units (RTUs). These devices gather the data from the field-mounted instruments and provide the control signals to the field equipment.

3. Communications medium. This is the link between the SCADA RTUs and the main control location. There are many communications mediums available for transmitting signals between the RTUs and the supervisory control station. Some of the options presently available include:

   • FM (VHF/UHF) radio,

   • Dedicated leased telephone circuits,

   • Privately owned metallic signal lines,

   • Conventional dial telephone lines (pulse or tone/DTMF),

   • Coaxial cable networks,

   • Spread spectrum radio,

   • Fiber-optic cable,

   • Microwave,

   • 900 MHz radio,

   • Cellular telephone, and

   • Ground station satellites.

4. Supervisory control and monitoring equipment. There are three basic categories of supervisory equipment:

   a. Hardware-based systems include graphic displays, annunciator lamp boxes, chart recorders, and similar equipment.

   b. Software-based systems include all computer-based systems such as microcomputers, workstations, mini and mainframes. Software-based systems sometimes offer more flexibility and capabilities than hardware-based systems and are often less expensive.

   c. Hybrid systems are a combination of hardware and software systems; for example, a PC (microcomputer) with a graphic display panel.

Applications for SCADA systems include water distribution system control and monitoring, water treatment plant control monitoring, and other related applications. SCADA systems can vary from merely data collection and storage to total data analysis, interpretation, and process control.

In water applications, SCADA systems monitor levels, pressures, and flows and also operate pumps, valves, and alarms. They monitor temperatures, speeds, motor currents, pH, dissolved oxygen levels, and other operating guidelines, and provide control as necessary. SCADA also logs event and analog signal trends and monitors equipment operating time for maintenance purposes.

A SCADA system might include liquid level, pressure, and flow sensors. The measured (sensed) information could be transmitted by one of the communications systems listed earlier to a computer system which stores, analyzes, and presents the information. The information may be read by an operator on dials or as digital readouts or analyzed and plotted by the computer as trend charts.

Most SCADA systems present a graphical picture of the overall system on the screen of a computer monitor. In addition, detailed pictures of specific portions of the system can be examined by the operator following a request and instructions to the computer. The graphical displays on a TV or computer screen can include current operating information. The operator can observe this information, analyze it for trends, or determine if it is within acceptable operating ranges, and then decide if any adjustments or changes are necessary.

SCADA systems are capable of analyzing data and providing operating, maintenance, regulatory, and annual reports. In some plants operators rely on a SCADA system to help them prepare daily, weekly, and monthly maintenance schedules, monitor the spare parts inventory status, order additional spare parts when necessary, print out work orders and record completed work assignments.

SCADA systems can also be used to enhance energy conservation programs. For example, operators can develop energy management routines that allow for both maximum energy savings and maximum water storage prior to entering "on-peak" periods. In this type of system, power meters are used to accurately measure and record power consumption and the information can then be reviewed by operators to watch for changes that may indicate equipment problems.

Emergency response procedures can be programmed into a SCADA system. Operator responses can be provided for different operational scenarios that could be encountered as a result of adverse weather changes, fires, or earthquakes.

QUESTIONS

Write your answers in a notebook and then compare your answers with those on page 633.

23.9D What does SCADA stand for?

23.9E What does a SCADA system do?

23.9F How could measured (sensed) information be transmitted?

23.941 Typical Water Treatment and Distribution SCADA Systems

Water treatment and water distribution SCADA systems are usually linked together with the controls located at the water treatment plant. Information that historically was recorded on paper strip charts is now being recorded and stored (archived) by computers. This information can be easily retrieved and reviewed by a SCADA system, rather than examining years of strip chart records to find needed information. Therefore,

SCADA systems quickly provide operators with the information they need to make informed decisions.

SCADA systems can be used at water treatment plants to provide a constant flow for treatment for long periods of time. The raw water can be monitored continuously for turbidity, pH, and temperature. If these water quality indicators change significantly or exceed predetermined levels, the SCADA system will alert the operator to the change. The operator must then determine if a change in chemical doses or operating procedures is necessary.

Filtration systems are commonly monitored by SCADA systems. Influent and effluent turbidity levels, head losses through the filter, filter flows, and filter valve settings (70 percent open, for example) are all measured, recorded, and stored for future reference. If the flow needs to be increased, the operator has "fingertip control" of each filter valve and can open each filter valve as much as desired from the control room. This procedure is much easier, faster, and more accurate than manually turning each valve.

Filter backwashing is another function which a SCADA system can be programmed to control using any of three basic approaches: (1) SCADA monitors filter head loss and automatically starts backwashing after an elapsed time; (2) the SCADA system initiates backwashing when a target head loss is exceeded; or (3) the operator can start the backwash on the basis of an analysis of a head loss and/or filtered water turbidity trend chart drawn by the SCADA system over a time period since the last backwash. Also, by analyzing filtered water turbidity, the operator can decide to reduce the flow to the filter or make adjustments to the coagulant chemical and/or the prefilter polymer.

Clear well water levels and fluctuations, as well as expected consumer demands, can be studied by operators to determine if the raw water flows to the treatment plant need to be increased or decreased.

Historical operating data stored in a SCADA system is readily available at any time. The SCADA system can be asked to identify all days during the last two years when the temperature exceeded 10°F (38°C) or the demand was greater than 50 MGD. The system demands and plant performance under these conditions can be recalled by the SCADA system, analyzed by the operators, and the results used to operate the plant under these conditions (100°F or 38°C or demand greater than 50 MGD).

Distribution system service storage tank levels, system demands, and system pressures are all recorded and plotted by SCADA systems. Operators study this information and decide if adjustments are necessary in booster pump operation and/or target levels in service storage tanks. SCADA systems can plot system pressures over time against flow demands. A steady pressure in spite of fluctuating flows shows that the operators are in control of the system. If a customer phones and complains about a loss of water pressure, a review of system pressures can indicate if a problem exists or if the problem might be in the customer's home.

Hand-held computers are being used to assign work orders to field crews. Crews could be instructed to perform routine preventive maintenance on hydrants and valves or to investigate a drinking water taste or odor complaint. The field crew uses the computer to record standard tasks performed and also to record special comments. The standardized comments allow for field information to be retrieved and analyzed (queried).

Electrical energy consumption can be optimized by the use of SCADA systems. Time-power management describes procedures used to minimize power costs and meet consumer water and pressure demands. Most power companies are anxious to work with operators to try to increase water treatment and distribution power consumption during periods when electrical system power demands are low and also to decrease water power consumption during periods of peak demands on electrical power supplies. SCADA systems also monitor power consumption and conduct a diagnostic performance of pumps. Operators can review this information and then identify potential pump problems before they become serious.

SCADA systems are continually improving and helping operators do a better job. Today operators can create their own screens, their own graphics, and show whatever operating characteristics they wish to display on the screen. The main screen could be a flow diagram of the supply, treatment, or distribution system. Critical operating information could be displayed for each pumping station or each treatment process and detailed screens could be easily reached for each piece of equipment.

Information on the screen should be color coded with the colors of red, yellow, green, blue, white, and any other necessary colors. Colors could be used to indicate if a pump is running, ready, unavailable, or failed and/or if a valve is open, closed, moving, unavailable, or failed. A "failed" signal is used by the computer to inform the operator that something is wrong with the information or signal the computer is receiving or is being instructed to display. The signal is not logical with the rest of the information available to the computer. For example, if there is no power to a motor, then the motor can't be running even though the computer is receiving a signal that indicates it is running. Therefore the computer would send a "failed" signal.

The operator can request a computer to display a summary of all alarm conditions in a plant, a particular plant area, or a segment of the distribution system. A blinking alarm signal indicates that the alarm condition has not yet been acknowledged by the operator. On the other hand, a steady alarm signal, one that is not blinking, indicates that the alarm has been acknowledged but the alarm indicator will stay on until the condition causing it is fixed. Also the screen could be set up to automatically designate certain alarm conditions as *PRIORITY* alarms, which means they require immediate operator attention.

Current laptop computers allow operators to plug into a telephone at home or on vacation, access their plant SCADA system, and help operators on duty solve operational problems. Computer networking systems allow operators at terminals in offices, in plants, and in the field to work together and use the same information or whatever information they need from one central file service (computer database).

A drawback of some SCADA systems is that when the system fails ("goes down") due to a power failure, the system will often display the numbers that were registered immediately before the failure and not display the current numbers. The operator may therefore experience a period of time when accurate, current information about the system is not immediately available.

Customer satisfaction with the performance of a water utility can be enhanced by the use of an effective SCADA system. Historically when a booster pump failed or "tripped out," the first a utility learned of this problem was when an irate consumer phoned the water agency and complained about being out of water. The utility then had to contact the operators and send a crew into the field to correct the problem. Today, SCADA systems often alert operators to a booster pump failure or "trip out" immediately. The operator may be able to correct or "override" the failure or "trip out" from the office without ever having to travel to the problem booster pump in the field. Thus, the problem is corrected without the customers ever being aware that a problem occurred and was corrected almost immediately.

When operators decide to initiate or expand the SCADA system for their plant or distribution system, the first step is to decide what the SCADA system should do to make the operators' jobs easier, more efficient, and safer and to make their facilities' performance more reliable and cost effective. Cost savings associated with the use of a SCADA system frequently include reduced labor costs for operation, maintenance, and monitoring functions that were formerly performed manually. Precise control of chemical feed rates by a SCADA system eliminates wasteful overdosing. Preventive maintenance monitoring can save on equipment and repair costs and, as previously noted, energy savings may result from use of off-peak electrical power rates. Operators should visit facilities with SCADA systems and talk to the operators about what they find beneficial and also detrimental with regard to SCADA systems and how the systems contribute to their performance as operators.

The greatest challenge for operators using SCADA systems is to realize that just because a computer says something (a pump is operating as expected), *THIS DOES NOT MEAN*

THAT THE COMPUTER IS ALWAYS CORRECT. Also when the system fails due to a power failure or for any other reason (natural disaster), operators will be required to operate the plant manually and without critical information. Could you do this?

Operators will always be needed to question and analyze the results from SCADA systems. They will be needed to *SEE* if the floc looks OK, to *LISTEN* to a pump to be sure it sounds proper, and to *SMELL* the water and the equipment to determine if unexpected or unidentified changes are occurring. Water treatment plants and distribution systems will always need alert, knowledgeable, and experienced operators who have a "feel" for their plant and their distribution system.

QUESTIONS

Write your answers in a notebook and then compare your answers with those on page 634.

23.9G   What do SCADA systems do with information that was formerly recorded on paper strip charts?

23.9H   What water quality indicators can be easily monitored by a SCADA system?

23.9I   What can an operator do when a customer phones and complains about a loss of water pressure?

23.9J   What are the greatest challenges for operators using SCADA systems?

23.95   Cross Connection Control Program

23.950   *Importance of Cross Connection Control*

BACKFLOW[6] of contaminated water through cross connections into community water systems is not just a theoretical problem. Contamination through cross connections has consistently caused more waterborne disease outbreaks in the United States than any other reported factor. Inspections have often disclosed numerous unprotected cross connections between public water systems and other piped systems on consumers' premises which might contain wastewater, stormwater, processed waters (containing a wide variety of chemicals), and untreated supplies from private wells, streams, and ocean waters. Therefore, an effective cross connection control program is essential.

Backflow results from either *BACK PRESSURE*[7] or *BACK-SIPHONAGE*[8] situations in the distribution system. Back pressure occurs when the user's water supply is at a higher pressure than the public water supply system (Figure 23.4). Typical locations where back pressure problems could develop include services to premises where wastewater or toxic chemicals are handled under pressure or where there are unapproved auxiliary water supplies such as a private well or the use of surface water or seawater for firefighting. Backsiphonage is caused by the development of negative or below atmospheric pressures in the water supply piping (Figure 23.5). This condition can occur when there are extremely high water demands (firefighting), water main breaks, or the use of on-line booster pumps.

---

[6] *Backflow.   A reverse flow condition, created by a difference in water pressures, which causes water to flow back into the distribution pipes of a potable water supply from any source or sources other than an intended source. Also see BACKSIPHONAGE.*
[7] *Back Pressure.   A pressure that can cause water to backflow into the water supply when a user's water system is at a higher pressure than the public water system.*
[8] *Backsiphonage.   A form of backflow caused by a negative or below atmospheric pressure within a water system. Also see BACKFLOW.*

HYDRAULIC GRADIENT

Fig. 23.4   Backflow due to back pressure

(Source: *MANUAL OF CROSS-CONNECTION CONTROL PRACTICES AND PROCEDURES*,
Sanitary Engineering Branch, California Department of Health Services, Berkeley, CA)

DISTRIBUTION SYSTEM

HYDRAULIC GRADIENT

Fig. 23.5   Backsiphonage due to extremely high water demand
(Source: *MANUAL OF CROSS-CONNECTION CONTROL PRACTICES AND PROCEDURES,*
Sanitary Engineering Branch, California Department of Health Services, Berkeley, CA)

The best way to prevent backflow is to permanently eliminate the hazard. Back pressure hazards can be eliminated by severing (eliminating) any direct connection at the pump causing the back pressure with the domestic water supply system. Another solution to the problem is to require an air gap separation device (Figure 23.6) where the water supply service line connects to the private system under pressure from the pump. To eliminate or minimize backsiphonage problems, proper enforcement of plumbing codes and improved water distribution and storage facilities will be helpful. As an additional safety factor for certain selected conditions, a double check valve (Figure 23.7) may be required at the meter.

23.951 Program Responsibilities

Responsibilities in the implementation of cross connection control programs are shared by water suppliers, water users (businesses and industries), health agencies, and plumbing officials.

The water supplier is responsible for preventing contamination of the public water system by backflow. This responsibility begins at the source, includes the entire distribution system, and ends at the user's connection. To meet this responsibility, the water supplier must issue (promulgate) and enforce needed laws, rules, regulations, and policies. Water service should not be provided to premises where the strong possibility of an unprotected cross connection exists. The essential elements of a water supplier cross connection control program are discussed in the next section.

The water user is responsible for keeping contaminants out of the potable water system on the user's premises. When backflow prevention devices are required by the health agency or water supplier, the water user must pay for the installation, testing, and maintenance of the approved devices. The user is also responsible for preventing the creation of cross connections through modifications of the plumbing system on the premises. The health agency or water supplier may, when necessary, require a water user to designate a water supervisor or foreman to be responsible for the cross connection control program within the water user's premises.

The local or state health agency is responsible for issuing and enforcing laws, rules, regulations, and policies needed to control cross connections. Also this agency must have a program that assures maintenance of an adequate cross connection control program. Protection of the system on the user's premises is provided where needed by the water utilities.

The plumbing agency (building inspectors) is responsible for the enforcement of building regulations relating to prevention of cross connections on the user's premises.

QUESTIONS

Write your answers in a notebook and then compare your answers with those on page 634.

23.9K   What has caused more waterborne disease outbreaks in the United States than any other reported factor?

23.9L   Who is usually responsible for the implementation of cross connection control programs?

23.9M   What is the water user's cross connection control responsibility?

23.952 Water Supplier Program

The following elements should be included in each water supplier's cross connection control program:

1. Enactment of an ordinance providing enforcement authority if the supplier is a government agency, or enactment of appropriate rules of service if the system is investor-owned.[9]

2. Training of personnel on the causes of and hazards from cross connections and procedures to follow for effective cross connection control.

3. Listing and inspection or re-inspection on a priority basis of all existing facilities where cross connections are of concern.

4. Review and screening of all applications for new services or modification of existing services for cross connection hazards to determine if backflow protection is needed.

5. Obtaining a list of approved backflow prevention devices and a list of certified testers, if available.

6. Acceptable installation of the proper type of device needed for the specific hazard on the premises.

7. Routine testing of installed backflow prevention devices as required by the health agency or the water supplier. Contact the health agency for approved procedures.

8. Maintenance of adequate records for each backflow prevention device installed, including records of inspection and testing.

---

[9] *A typical ordinance is available in CROSS-CONNECTION CONTROL MANUAL, available from ERIC/CSMEE, 1929 Kenny Road, Columbus, OH 43210-1080. Order No. G110. Price $7.25 plus $2.00 shipping and handling. Also available at no charge from ORD Publications, 26 West Martin Luther King Drive, Cincinnati, OH 45268. Order No. 570989007.*

TANK SHOULD BE OF SUBSTANTIAL CONSTRUCTION AND
OF A KIND AND SIZE TO SUIT CONSUMER'S NEEDS.
TANK MAY BE SITUATED AT GROUND LEVEL (WITH A
PUMP TO PROVIDE ADEQUATE PRESSURE HEAD) OR
BE ELEVATED ABOVE THE GROUND.

Fig. 23.6   Typical air gap separation

(From *MANUAL OF CROSS-CONNECTION CONTROL PRACTICES AND PROCEDURES*, Sanitary Engineering Branch, California Department of Health Services, Berkeley, CA)

Fig. 23.7   Typical double check valve backflow prevention device

(From *MANUAL OF CROSS-CONNECTION CONTROL PRACTICES AND PROCEDURES*, Sanitary Engineering Branch, California Department of Health Services, Berkeley, CA)

9. Notification of each water user when a backflow prevention device has to be tested. This should be done after installation or repair of the device and at least once a year.

10. Maintenance of adequate pressures throughout the distribution system at all times to minimize the hazards from any undetected cross connections which may exist.

All field personnel should be constantly alert for situations where cross connections are likely to exist, whether protection has been installed or not. An example is a contractor using a fire hose from a hydrant to fill a tank truck for dust control or the jetting (for compaction) of pipe trenches. Operators should especially be on the lookout for illegal bypassing of installed backflow prevention devices.

23.953 Types of Backflow Prevention Devices

Different types of backflow prevention devices are available. The particular type of device most suitable for a given situation depends on the degree of health hazard, the probability of backflow occurring, the complexity of the piping on the premises, and the probability of the piping being modified. The higher the assessed risk due to these factors, the more reliable and positive the type of device needed. The types of devices normally approved are listed below according to the degree of assessed risk, with the type of device providing the greatest protection listed first. Only the first three devices are approved for use at service connections.

1. Air gap separation.

2. Reduced pressure principle (RPP) device.

3. Double check valve.

4. Pressure vacuum breaker (only used for internal protection on the premises).

5. Atmospheric (non-pressure) vacuum breaker.

Figure 23.6 shows a typical air gap separation device and its recommended location. Figure 23.7 shows the installation of a typical double check valve backflow prevention device. These devices are normally installed on the water user's side of the connection to the utility's system and as close to the connection as practical. Figure 23.8 shows a typical installation of pressure vacuum breakers.

Only backflow prevention devices that have passed both laboratory and field evaluations by a recognized testing agency and that have been accepted by the health agency and the water supplier should be used.

23.954 Devices Required for Various Types of Situations

The state or local health agency should be contacted to determine the actual types of devices acceptable for various situations inside the consumer's premises. However, the types of devices generally acceptable for particular situations can be mentioned.

An air gap or a reduced pressure principle (RPP) device is normally required at services to wastewater treatment plants, wastewater pumping stations, reclaimed water reuse areas, areas where toxic substances in toxic concentrations are handled under pressure, and premises having an auxiliary water supply which is or may be contaminated. The ultimate degree of protection is also needed in cases where fertilizer, herbicides, or pesticides are injected into a sprinkler system.

A double check valve device should be required when a moderate hazard exists on the premises or where an auxiliary supply exists, but adequate protection on the premises is provided.

Atmospheric and pressure vacuum breakers are usually required for irrigation systems; however, they are not adequate in situations where they may be subject to back pressure. If there is a possibility of back pressure, a reduced pressure principle device is needed.

QUESTIONS

Write your answers in a notebook and then compare your answers with those on page 634.

23.9N   What factors should be considered when selecting a backflow prevention device?

23.9O   Air gap or reduced pressure principle backflow prevention devices are installed under what conditions?

23.10   EMERGENCY RESPONSE

23.100   Planning

Contingency planning is an essential facet of utility management and one that is often overlooked. Although utilities in various locations will be vulnerable to somewhat different kinds of natural disasters, the effects of these disasters in many cases will be quite similar. As a first step toward an effective contingency plan, each utility should make an assessment of its own vulnerability and then develop and implement a comprehensive plan of action.

All utilities suffer from common problems such as equipment breakdowns and leaking pipes. During the past few years there has also been an increasing amount of vandalism, civil disorder, toxic spills, and employee strikes which have threatened to disrupt utility operations. In observing today's international tension and the potential for nuclear war or the effects of terrorist-induced chemical or biological warfare, water utilities must seriously consider how to respond. Natural disasters such as floods, earthquakes, hurricanes, forest fires, avalanches, and blizzards are a more or less routine occurrence for some utilities. When such catastrophic emergencies occur, the utility must be prepared to minimize the effects of the event and have a plan for rapid recovery. Such preparation should be a specific obligation of every utility manager.

Start by assessing the vulnerability of the utility during various types of emergency situations. If the extent of damage can be estimated for a series of most probable events, the

MINIMUM OF 6" ABOVE
HIGHEST OUTLET

FLOW

ABSOLUTELY NO MEANS OF SHUT-OFF
ON THE DISCHARGE SIDE OF THE
VACUUM BREAKER

MINIMUM OF 12" ABOVE
HIGHEST OUTLET

FLOW

DOWNSTREAM SIDE OF VACUUM BREAKER MAY
BE MAINTAINED UNDER PRESSURE BY A VALVE.
BUT, THERE MAY BE ABSOLUTELY NO MEANS OF
IMPOSING PRESSURE BY PUMP OR OTHER
MEANS

Fig. 23.8   Typical installations of atmospheric (top) and pressure (bottom) vacuum breakers
(From *MANUAL OF CROSS-CONNECTION CONTROL PRACTICES AND PROCEDURES*, Sanitary Engineering Branch, California Department of Health Services, Berkeley, CA)

weak elements can be studied and protection and recovery operations can center on these elements. Although all elements are important for the utility to function, experience with disasters points out elements that are most subject to disruption. These elements are:

1. The absence of trained personnel to make critical decisions and carry out orders,

2. The loss of power to the utility's facilities,

3. An inadequate amount of supplies and materials, and

4. Inadequate communication equipment.

The following steps should be taken in assessing the vulnerability of a system:

1. Identify and describe the system components,

2. Assign assumed disaster characteristics,

3. Estimate disaster effects on system components,

4. Estimate customer demand for service following a potential disaster, and

5. Identify key system components that would be primarily responsible for system failure.

If the assessment shows a system is unable to meet estimated requirements because of the failure of one or more critical components, the vulnerable elements have been identified. Repeating this procedure using several "typical" disasters will usually point out system weaknesses. Frequently the same vulnerable element appears for a variety of assumed disaster events.

You might consider, for example, the case of the addition of toxic pollutants to water supplies. The list of toxic agents that may have a harmful effect on humans is almost endless. However, it is recognized that there is a relationship between the quantity of toxic agents added to the treatment provided for the supply. Adequate chlorination is effective against most biological agents. Other considerations are the amount of dilution water and the solubility of the chemical agents. There is the possibility that during normal detention times many of the biological agents will die off with adequate chlorination.

Although the drafting of an emergency plan for a water system may be a difficult job, the existence of such a plan can be of critical importance during an emergency situation.

An emergency operations plan need not be too detailed, since all types of emergencies cannot be anticipated and a complex response program can be more confusing than helpful. Supervisory personnel must have a detailed description of their responsibilities during emergencies. They will need information, supplies, equipment, and the assistance of trained personnel. All these can be provided through a properly constructed emergency operations plan that is not extremely detailed.

The following outline can be used as the basis for developing an emergency operations plan:

1. Make a vulnerability assessment,

2. Inventory organizational personnel,

3. Provide for a recovery operation (plan),

4. Provide training programs for operators in carrying out the plan,

5. Coordinate with local and regional agencies such as the health, police, and fire departments to develop procedures for carrying out the plan,

6. Establish a communications procedure, and

7. Provide protection for personnel, plant equipment, records, and maps.

By following these steps, an emergency plan can be developed and maintained even though changes in personnel may occur. "Emergency Simulation" training sessions, including the use of standby power, equipment, and field test equipment will ensure that equipment and personnel are ready at times of emergency.

A list of phone numbers for operators to call in an emergency should be prepared and posted by a phone for emergency use. The list should include:

1. Plant supervisor,

2. Director of public works or head of utility agency,

3. Police,

4. Fire,

5. Doctor (2 or more),

6. Ambulance (2 or more),

7. Hospital (2 or more),

If appropriate for your utility, also include the following phone numbers on the emergency list:

8. Chlorine supplier and manufacturer,

9. CHEMTREC (800-424-9300) for the hazardous chemical spills; sponsored by the Manufacturing Chemists Association,

10. U.S. Coast Guard's National Response Center (800-424-8802),

11. Local and state poison control centers, and

12. Local hazardous materials spill response team.

You should prepare a list for your plant *NOW*, if you have not already done so.

For additional information on emergencies, see Chapter 7, "Disinfection," Section 7.52, "Chlorine Leaks"; Chapter 10, "Plant Operation," Section 10.9, "Emergency Conditions and Procedures"; and Chapter 18, "Maintenance," Section 18.02, "Emergencies."

QUESTIONS

Write your answers in a notebook and then compare your answers with those on page 634.

23.10A What is the first step toward an effective contingency plan for emergencies?

23.10B Why is too detailed an emergency operations plan not needed or even desirable?

23.10C An emergency operations plan should include what specific information?

23.101 Handling the Threat of Contaminated Water Supplies[10]

23.1010 Importance

More than 50 water utilities in southern Louisiana were threatened with cyanide poisoning in their water supplies in one year. Such threats can occur anywhere, and every water utility should be prepared to handle this type of emergency.

23.1011 Toxicity

The term toxicity is often used when discussing contamination of a water supply with the intention of creating a serious health hazard. Toxicity is the ability of a contaminant (chemical or biological) to cause injury when introduced into the body. The degree of toxicity varies with the concentration of contaminant required to cause injury, the speed with which the injury takes place, and the severity of the injury.

The effect of a toxic contaminant, once added to a water supply, depends on several things. First the amount of contaminant added can vary, as can the size of the water supply. In general, it takes larger quantities of a contaminant to be toxic in a larger water supply. Second, the solubility of the contaminant can vary. The more soluble the substance is in water, the more likely it is to cause problems. Finally the detention time of the contaminant in the water can vary. For example, many biological agents will die before they can cause a problem in the water supply.

Generally, the terms acute and chronic are used to describe toxic agents and their effects. An acute toxic agent causes injury quickly. When the contaminant causes illness in seconds, minutes, or hours after a single exposure or a single dose, it is considered an acute toxic agent. A chronic agent causes injury to occur over an extended period of exposure. Generally, the contaminant is ingested in repeated doses over a period of days, months, or years.

23.1012 Effective Dosages (See Table 23.6)

When determining the effective dosage of a contaminant (the amount of that contaminant necessary to cause injury) the following facts must be considered:

1. Quantity or concentration of the contaminant,

2. Duration of exposure to the contaminant,

3. Physical form of the contaminant (size of particle; physical state — solid, liquid, gas),

4. Attraction of the contaminant to the organism being contaminated,

5. Solubility of the contaminant in the organism, and

6. Sensitivity of the organism to the contaminant.

Concentration of a contaminant can be expressed in two ways. The maximum allowable concentration (MAC) is the maximum concentration of the contaminant allowed in drinking water. Table 23.6 lists several contaminants and their MACs, specifically for short-term emergencies ranging up to three days. The MACs should not be confused with concentration required to have an acute effect on the population. Lethal dose 50 (LD 50) is used to express the concentration of a contaminant that will produce 50 percent fatalities from an average exposure.

TABLE 23.6 EMERGENCY LIMITS OF SOME CHEMICAL POLLUTANTS IN DRINKING WATER[a]

Chemical	Concentration Limits, mg/L	
	Emergency Short Term (Three days)	Long Term
Cyanide (CN)	5.0	0.01
Aldrin	0.05	0.032
Chlordane	0.06	0.003
DDT	1.4	0.042
Dieldrin	0.05	0.017
Endrin	0.01	0.001
Heptachlor	0.1	0.018
Heptachlor epoxide	0.05	0.018
Lindane	2.0	0.056
Methoxychlor	2.8	0.035
Toxaphene	1.4	0.005
Beryllium	0.1	0.000
Boron	25.0	1.000
2,4-D	2.0	0.1
Ethylene chlorohydrin	2.0	
Organophosphorus and carbamate pesticides	2.0	0.100
Trinitrotoluene $(NO_2)(C_6H_2CH_3)$	0.75	0.005

[a] These limits, based on current knowledge and informed judgment, have been recommended by knowledgeable persons in the field of toxicology. They are subject to change should new information indicate the need. Additional information on some of the chemicals listed can be found in "Report of the Secretary's Commission on Pesticides and Their Relationship to Environmental Health," Parts I and II, USDHEW, Washington, DC, Dec. 1969.

23.1013 Protective Measures

A utility can take three approaches to protect its water supply from contamination. First, the utility can isolate those reservoirs that offer easy access to the general public. These reservoirs can be fenced off and patrolled, or they can be covered. If access to on-line reservoirs is limited, persons attempting to contaminate the water supply will generally be forced to look to larger bodies of water. Contamination of these large water bodies requires larger quantities of contaminant, increases the detention time of the contaminant, and increases the likelihood of its detection.

As a second means of protection, the water utility can develop an extensive detection and monitoring program. Detecting any contaminant that might be added to a water

---

[10] *This section was reprinted from OPFLOW, Vol. No. 3, March 1983, by permission. Copyright 1983, the American Water Works Association.*

supply is difficult and expensive. However, because most contaminants cause secondary effects in a water supply, such as taste, color, odor, or chlorine demand, detection is easier.

Because utility operators "know" their water supply (they know its characteristics), any subtle changes in taste, odor, color, and chlorine demand are instantly recognized. Once it has been determined that the water supply may be contaminated, water samples can be tested. Tests can either be done at the utility's laboratory, if it is a large utility, or the samples can be sent to the state health department.

Finally, the utility can maintain a high chlorine residual. Generally, chlorine residuals of one mg/L or higher effectively oxidize or destroy most contaminants. For example, infectious hepatitis virus will not survive a free residual chlorine level of 0.7 mg/L.

23.1014 Emergency Countermeasures

Following is a list of emergency countermeasures that, when used over a short time period, can increase protection of a water supply:

1. Maintaining a high chlorine residual in the system,

2. Having engineers, chemists, and medical personnel on 24-hour alert,

3. Continuously monitoring key points in the distribution system (monitoring chlorine residual is mandatory),

4. Increasing security around exposed on-line reservoirs,

5. Sealing off access to manholes within a three- to six-block radius of highly populated areas,

6. Setting up emergency crews who can isolate sections of the distribution system, and

7. Staffing the treatment facility on a 24-hour basis.

23.1015 In Case of Contamination

If contamination of the water supply is discovered, the immediate concern must be the safety of the public. If the contaminated water has entered the distribution system, immediate public notification is the highest priority. The local police chief, sheriff, or other responsible governmental authority will help to spread the word. Alternative sources of water may need to be provided.

If the contaminated water has not entered the distribution system, it may be possible to isolate the contaminated source and continue to supply water from other, unaffected sources. If the contaminated water is the only source for the community, treatment measures may be available that will remove the contaminant or reduce its toxicity.

Table 23.7 lists a series of emergency treatment steps that can be taken when identified chemicals are added to the system. These emergency treatment methods are effective only if the contaminant has been identified.

QUESTIONS

Write your answers in a notebook and then compare your answers with those on page 634.

23.10D What does the word toxicity mean?

23.10E The degree of toxicity varies with what factors?

23.10F List possible secondary effects in a water supply which may allow detection of a contaminant without specific testing.

23.1016 Cryptosporidium

Cryptosporidium is a parasite that has become a significant public health concern for drinking water utilities. Even when drinking water meets or exceeds all current state and federal standards, it may contain sufficient *Cryptosporidia* to cause serious illness in sensitive individuals. This section contains suggestions that operators should consider to protect consumers from "crypto."

Operators need to develop a strategy for protecting their source water supplies and optimizing the operation of their water treatment plant to protect the public health. *Cryptosporidium* oocyst contamination is widespread in the water environment. Potential sources of the parasite in the watersheds of your water supply need to be identified and controlled. The most serious threat to a public water supply occurs during periods of heavy rains or snow melts that flush areas which are sources of high concentrations of oocysts into waters upstream of a plant intake. In the watershed, these potentially contaminated areas include wastewater treatment plants, cattle feedlots, and pastures where livestock graze.

Conventional water treatment plants using coagulation, flocculation, sedimentation, filtration, and disinfection can provide effective treatment to protect drinking water from *Cryptosporidium*. Be especially alert during periods when the intake water has high turbidity levels resulting from storm water runoff, snow melt runoff, and/or lake overturns. During these periods all treatment processes must operate effectively. Try to achieve turbidity levels of 0.1 NTU or lower at all times. Run frequent jar tests to determine or simply to verify that you are using the optimum coagulant doses as intake turbidity and other water quality indicators change (pH, temperature, alkalinity). Also monitor your filtration processes continuously to avoid any increases in turbidity in the treated water. If the water used for backwashing filters is routinely returned to the headworks for conservation purposes, avoid recycling the backwash water during periods of high intake water turbidity. Recycling backwash water may tend to concentrate oocysts in the filter media. Instead, consider wasting the backwash water until the high turbidity levels drop back to normal levels.

Chemical inactivation of *Cryptosporidium* oocysts by disinfection is influenced by several factors. The effectiveness of chemical disinfectants such as chlorine, chlorine dioxide, and ozone is reduced by the presence of high levels of total organic carbon (TOC)(caused by color and turbidity), lower water temperatures, and shorter disinfection contact times. Therefore, effective disinfection can be difficult during periods of high turbidity caused by high storm water or snow melt runoff flows.

The best approach to evaluating the potential threat of the drinking water to the public is the analysis for *Cryptosporidium* oocysts in the treated drinking water. However, current sampling and analytical methods make it difficult for operators to

TABLE 23.7   EMERGENCY TREATMENT FOR REDUCING CONCENTRATION OF SPECIFIC CHEMICALS IN COMMUNITY WATER SUPPLIES [a]

Concentration	Treatment	Concentration	Treatment
Arsenicals Unknown organic and inorganic arsenicals in groundwater at concentrations of 100 mg/*L*	Precipitation with ferric sulfate and liming to pH 6.8, followed by sedimentation and filtration.	*Nerve Agents* (Organophosphorus compounds)	Superchlorination at pH 7 to provide at least 40 mg/*L* residual after 30-min chlorine contact time, followed by dechlorination and conventional clarification processes.
Cyanides Hydrogen cyanide	Prechlorination to free residual with pH 7, followed by coagulation, sedimentation, and filtration. *Caution:* housed facilities must be adequately ventilated.	*Pesticides* 2,4-DCP (2,4-Dichlorophenol) an impurity in commercial 2,4-D herbicides	Adsorption on activated carbon followed by coagulation, sedimentation, and filtration.
	Precipitation with ferrous or ferric salts to form Prussian blue (iron ferric cyanide) followed by coagulation, sedimentation, and clarification. As long as an excess of iron coagulant is applied, the filtered water should be nontoxic even though it is blue.	DDT (dichloro-diphenyltrichloroethane), concentrations of 10 gm/*L*	Chemical coagulation, sedimentation, and filtration.
		Dieldrin, concentrations of 10 gm/*L*	Chemical coagulation, sedimentation, and filtration. Supplemental treatment with activated carbon may be necessary.
Acetone cyanohydrin	Same as for hydrogen cyanide.	Endrin, concentrations of 10 gm/*L*	Chemical coagulation, sedimentation, and filtration. Supplemental treatment with activated carbon may be necessary.
Cyanogen chloride	Same as for hydrogen cyanide.		
Hydrocarbons Kerosene, peak concentrations of 140 mg/*L*	Preapplications of bleaching clay and activated carbon, plus some increase in normal dosages of alum, chlorine dioxide, lime, and carbon, to provide treatment enabling continued production of water.	Lindane, concentrations of 10 gm/*L*	Application of activated carbon followed by chemical coagulation, sedimentation, and filtration.
Miscellaneous Organic Chemicals LSD (lysergic acid derivative)	Chlorination in alkaline water, or water made alkaline by addition of lime or soda ash, to provide a free chlorine residual. Two parts free chlorine are required to react with each part LSD.	Parathion, concentrations of 10 gm/*L*	Chemical coagulation, sedimentation, and filtration. Supplemental treatment with activated carbon may be necessary. Omit prechlorination as chlorine reacts with parathion to form paraoxon, which is more toxic than parathion.

[a] Source: Graham Walton, Chief, Technical Services, National Water Supply Research Laboratory, USSR Program, Oct. 24, 1968.

use the detection of *Cryptosporidium* oocysts for determining the efficiency and effectiveness of filtration and chemical inactivation treatment processes. Today operators are using turbidity and particle counting measurements as a means of determining the treatment processes' ability to remove and/or inactivate oocysts. Test methods for identifying the presence or potential presence of *Cryptosporidium* are evolving and should be used to analyze both source and treated (finished) waters for "crypto."

Keeping the public informed is another good strategy for preventing outbreaks of disease due to *Cryptosporidium.* Operators need to educate the media and consumers regarding the sources of the parasite, possible health risks, monitoring efforts, and treatment processes. Sensitive populations must be informed that even properly treated municipal drinking water, bottled water, and water treated by a home water treatment device still may not be free of *Cryptosporidia.* The Centers for Disease Control and Prevention suggests,

"Immunocompromised persons who wish to take independent action to reduce the risk of waterborne *Cryptosporidium* may choose to take precautions similar to those recommended during outbreaks (such as boiling tap water for one minute). Such decisions should be made in conjunction with their health care provider."

There are alternatives to boiling water that may be effective when used with proper precautions. Point-of-use filters that remove particles one micrometer (1 μm) in diameter or smaller are effective. One-micrometer filters for cyst removal and reverse osmosis units are also acceptable. Bottled water from protected springs and wells may be a safe drinking water, especially if treated by reverse osmosis or distillation to remove *Cryptosporidium* before bottling.

Operators must stay current with the efforts of our profession to prevent outbreaks of waterborne *Cryptosporidium.*

QUESTIONS

Write your answers in a notebook and then compare your answers with those on page 634.

23.10G Why is *Cryptosporidium* a significant public health concern for drinking water utilities?

23.10H When does the most serious threat of *Cryptosporidium* occur to a public water supply?

23.10I How can a water treatment plant be operated to protect the public from *Cryptosporidium*?

23.11 SAFETY PROGRAM

23.110 Responsibilities

23.1100 Everyone Is Responsible for Safety

Waterworks utilities, regardless of size, must have a safety program if they are to realize a low frequency of accident occurrence. A safety program also provides a means of comparing frequency, disability, and severity of injuries with other utilities. The utility should identify the causes of accidents and injuries, provide safety training, implement an accident reporting system, and hold supervisors responsible for implementing the safety program. Each utility should have a safety officer or supervisor evaluate every accident, offer recommendations, and keep and apply statistics.

The effectiveness of any safety program will depend upon how the utility holds its supervisors responsible. If the utility holds only the safety officer or the employees responsible, the program will fail. The supervisors are key in any organization. If they disregard safety measures, essential parts of the program will not work. The results will be an overall poor safety record. After all, the first line supervisor is where the work is being performed, and some may take advantage of an unsafe situation in order to get the job completed. The organization must discipline such supervisors and make them aware of their responsibility for their own and their operators' safety.

Safety is good business both for the operator and the agency. For a good safety record to be accomplished, all individuals must be educated and must believe in the program. All individuals involved must have the conviction that accidents can be prevented. The operations should be studied to determine the safe way of performing each job. Safety pays, both in monetary savings and in the health and well-being of the operating staff.

23.1101 Regulatory Agencies

Many state and federal agencies are involved in ensuring safe working conditions. The one law that has had the greatest impact has been the *OCCUPATIONAL SAFETY AND HEALTH ACT OF 1970 (OSHA)*,[11] Public Law 91-596, which took effect on December 29, 1970. This legislation affects more than 75,000,000 employees and has been the basis for most of the current state laws covering employees. Also, many state regulatory agencies enforce the OSHA requirements.

The OSHA regulations provide for safety inspections, penalties, recordkeeping, and variances. Managers and supervisors must understand the OSHA Act and must furnish each operator with the rules of conduct in order to comply with occupational safety and health standards. The intent of the regulations is to create a place of employment which is free from recognized hazards that could cause serious physical harm or death to an operator.

Civil and criminal penalties are allowed under the OSHA Law, depending upon the size of the business and the seriousness of the violation. A routine violation could cost an employer or supervisor up to $1,000 for each violation. A serious, willful, or repeated violation could cause the employer or supervisor to be assessed a penalty of not more than $10,000 for each violation. Penalties are assessed against the supervisor responsible for the injured operator. Operators should become familiar with the OSHA regulations as they apply to their organizations. Managers and supervisors must correct violations and prevent others from occurring.

23.1102 Managers

The utility manager is responsible for the safety of the agency's personnel and the public exposed to the water utility's operations. Therefore, the manager must develop and administer an effective safety program and must provide new employee safety training as well as ongoing training for all employees. The basic elements of a safety program include a safety policy statement, safety training and promotion, and accident investigation and reporting.

A safety policy statement should be prepared by the top management of the utility. The purpose of the statement is to let employees know that the safety program has the full support of the agency and its management. The statement should:

1. Define the goals and objectives of the program,

---

[11] *OSHA (O-shuh). The Williams-Steiger Occupational Safety and Health Act of 1970 (OSHA) is a federal law designed to protect the health and safety of industrial workers and also the operators of water supply systems and treatment plants. The Act regulates the design, construction, operation and maintenance of water supply systems and water treatment plants. OSHA also refers to the federal and state agencies which administer the OSHA regulations.*

2. Identify the persons responsible for each element of the program,

3. Affirm management's intent to enforce safety regulations, and

4. Describe the disciplinary actions that will be taken to enforce safe work practices.

Give a copy of the safety policy statement to every current employee and each new employee during orientation. Figure 23.9 is an example of a safety policy statement for a water supply utility.

The following list of responsibilities for safety is from the *PLANT MANAGER'S HANDBOOK*.[12] These responsibilities represent a typical list but may be incomplete if your agency is subject to stricter local, state, and/or federal regulations than what is shown here. Check with your safety professional.

Management has the responsibility to:

1. Formulate a written safety policy,

2. Provide a safe workplace,

3. Set achievable safety goals,

4. Provide adequate training, and

5. Delegate authority to ensure that the program is properly implemented.

The manager is the key to any safety program. Implementation and enforcement of the program is the responsibility of the manager. The manager also has the responsibility to:

1. Ensure that all employees are trained and periodically retrained in proper safe work practices,

2. Ensure that proper safety practices are implemented and continued as long as the policy is in effect,

3. Investigate all accidents and injuries to determine their cause,

4. Institute corrective measures where unsafe conditions or work methods exist, and

5. Ensure that equipment, tools, and the work are maintained to comply with established safety standards.

QUESTIONS

Write your answers in a notebook and then compare your answers with those on page 634.

23.11A What should be the duties of a safety officer?

23.11B Who should be responsible for the implementation of a safety program?

23.11C Who enforces the OSHA requirements?

23.11D What are the utility manager's responsibilities with regard to safety?

23.11E What should be included in a utility's policy statement on safety?

23.1103 Supervisors

The success of any safety program will depend upon how the supervisors of the utility view their responsibility. The supervisor who has the responsibility for directing work activities must be safety conscious. This supervisor controls the operators' general environment and work habits and influences whether or not the operators comply with safety regulations. The supervisor is in the best position to counsel, instruct, and review the operators' working methods and thereby effectively ensure compliance with all aspects of the utility's safety program.

SAFETY POLICY STATEMENT

It is the policy of the Las Vegas Valley Water District that every employee shall have a safe and healthy place to work. It is the District's responsibility; its greatest asset, the employees and their safety.

When a person enters the employ of the District, he or she has a right to expect to be provided a proper work environment, as well as proper equipment and tools, so that they will be able to devote their energies to the work without undue danger. Only under such circumstances can the association between employer and employee be mutually profitable and harmonious. It is the District's desire and intention to provide a safe workplace, safe equipment, proper materials, and to establish and insist on safe work methods and practices at all times. It is a basic responsibility of all District employees to make the SAFETY of human beings a matter for their daily and hourly concern. This responsibility must be accepted by everyone who works at the District, regardless of whether he or she functions in a management, supervisory, staff, or the operative capacity. Employees must use the SAFETY equipment provided; Rules of Conduct and SAFETY shall be observed; and, SAFETY equipment must not be destroyed or abused. Further, it is the policy of the Water District to be concerned with the safety of the general public. Accordingly, District employees have the responsibility of performing their duties in such a manner that the public's safety will not be jeopardized.

The joint cooperation of employees and management in the implementation and continuing observance of this policy will provide safe working conditions and relatively accident-free performance to the mutual benefit of all involved. The Water District considers the SAFETY of its personnel to be of primary importance, and asks each employee's full cooperation in making this policy effective.

Fig. 23.9 Safety policy statement
(Permission of Las Vegas Valley Water District)

---

[12] *PLANT MANAGER'S HANDBOOK (MOP SM-4).* Available from Water Environment Federation, 601 Wythe Street, Alexandria, VA 22314-1994. Order No. MSM4GK. Price to members, $32.50; nonmembers, $41.50; price includes cost of shipping and handling.

The problem, however, is one of the supervisor accepting this responsibility. The supervisor who wishes to complete the job and go on to the next one without taking time to be concerned about working conditions, the welfare of operators, or considering any aspects of safety is a poor supervisor. Only after an accident occurs will a careless supervisor question the need for a work program based on safety. At this point, however, it is too late, and the supervisor may be tempted to simply cover up past mistakes. As sometimes happens, the supervisor may even be partially or fully responsible for the accident by causing unsafe acts to take place, by requiring work to be performed in haste, by disregarding an unsafe work environment, or by overlooking or failing to consider any number of safety hazards. This negligent supervisor could be fined, sentenced to a jail term, or even be barred from working in the profession.

All utilities should make their supervisors bear the greatest responsibility for safety and hold them accountable for planning, implementing, and controlling the safety program. If most accidents are caused and do not just happen, then it is the supervisor who can help prevent most accidents.

Equally important are the officials above the supervisor. These officials include commissioners, managers, public works directors, chief engineers, superintendents, and chief operators. The person in responsible charge for the entire agency or operation must believe in the safety program. This person must budget, promote, support, and enforce the safety program by vocal and visible examples and actions. The top person's support is absolutely essential for an effective safety program.

23.1104   Operators

Each operator also shares in the responsibility for an effective safety program. After all, operators have the most to gain since they are the most likely victims of accidents. A review of accident causes shows that the accident victim often has not acted responsibly. In some way the victim has not complied with the safety regulations, has not been fully aware of the working conditions, has not been concerned about fellow employees, or just has not accepted any responsibility for the utility's safety program.

Each operator must accept, at least in part, responsibility for fellow operators, for the utility's equipment, for the operator's own welfare, and even for seeing that the supervisor complies with established safety regulations. As pointed out above, the operator has the most to gain. If the operator accepts and uses unsafe equipment, it is the operator who is in danger if something goes wrong. If the operator fails to protect the other operators, it is the operator who must make up the work lost because of injury. If operators fail to consider their own welfare, it is they who suffer the pain of any injury, the loss of income, and maybe even the loss of life.

The operator must accept responsibility for an active role in the safety program by becoming aware of the utility's safety policy and conforming to established regulations. *THE OPERATOR SHOULD ALWAYS CALL TO THE SUPERVISOR'S ATTENTION UNSAFE CONDITIONS*, environment, equipment, or other concerns operators may have about the work they are performing. Safety should be an essential part of the operator's responsibility.

23.111   First Aid

By definition, first-aid means emergency treatment for injury or sudden illness, before regular medical treatment is available. Everyone in an organization should be able to give some degree of prompt treatment and attention to an injury.

First-aid training in the basic principles and practices of life-saving steps that can be taken in the early stages of an injury are available through the local Red Cross, Heart Association, local fire departments, and other organizations. Such training should periodically be reinforced so that the operator has a complete understanding of water safety, cardiopulmonary resuscitation (CPR), and other life-saving techniques. All operators need training in first aid, but it is especially important for those who regularly work with electrical equipment or must handle chlorine and other dangerous chemicals. (Chapter 20, "Safety," lists specific first-aid procedures for exposure to a variety of water treatment chemicals.)

First aid has little to do with preventing accidents, but it has an important bearing upon the survival of the injured patient. A well-equipped first-aid chest or kit is essential for proper treatment. The kit should be inspected regularly by the safety officer to ensure that supplies are available when needed. First-aid kits should be prominently displayed throughout the treatment plant and in company vehicles. Special consideration must be given to the most hazardous areas of the plant such as shops, laboratories, and chemical handling facilities.

Regardless of size, each utility should establish standard operating procedures (SOP) for first-aid treatment of injured personnel. All new operators should be instructed in the utility's first-aid program.

QUESTIONS

Write your answers in a notebook and then compare your answers with those on page 635.

23.11F   How could a supervisor be responsible for an accident?

23.11G   What types of safety-related responsibilities must each operator accept?

23.11H   What is first aid?

23.11I   First-aid training is most important for operators involved in what types of activities?

23.112   Hazard Communication Program and Worker Right-To-Know (RTK) Laws

In the past few years there has been an increased emphasis nationally on hazardous materials and wastes. Much of this attention has focused on hazardous and toxic waste dumps and the efforts to clean them up after the long-term effects on human health were recognized. Each year thousands of new chemical compounds are produced for industrial, commercial, and household use. Frequently, the long-term effects of these chemicals are unknown. As a result, federal and state laws have been enacted to control all aspects of hazardous materials handling and use. These laws are more commonly known as Worker Right-To-Know (RTK) laws which are enforced by OSHA.

As noted earlier, the intent of the OSHA regulations is to create a place of employment which is free from recognized hazards that could cause serious physical harm or death to an operator (or other employee). In many cases, the individual states have the authority under the OSHA Standard to develop their own state RTK laws and most states have adopted their own laws. The Federal OSHA Standard 29 *CFR*[13] 1910.1200 — Hazard Communication forms the basis of most of these state RTK laws. Unfortunately, state laws vary significantly from state to state. The state laws that have been passed are at least as stringent as the federal standard and, in most cases, are even more stringent. State laws are also under continuous revision and, because a strong emphasis is being placed on hazardous materials and worker exposure, state laws can be expected to be amended in the future to apply to virtually everybody in the workplace. Managers should become familiar with both the state and federal OSHA regulations that apply to their organizations.

The basic elements of a hazard communication program are described in the following paragraphs.

1. Identify Hazardous Materials — While there are thousands of chemical compounds which could be considered hazardous, focus on the ones to which operators and other personnel in your utility are most likely to be exposed.

2. Obtain Chemical Information and Define Hazardous Conditions — Once the inventory of hazardous chemicals is complete, the next step is to obtain specific information on each of the chemicals. This information is generally incorporated into a standard format form called the *MATERIAL SAFETY DATA SHEET (MSDS)*.[14] This information is commonly available from manufacturers. Many agencies request an MSDS when the purchase order is generated and will refuse to accept delivery of the shipment if the MSDS is not included. Figure 23.10 shows OSHA's standard MSDS form, but other forms are also acceptable provided they contain all of the required information.

The purpose of the MSDS is to have a readily available reference document that includes complete information on common names, safe exposure level, effects of exposure, symptoms of exposure, flammability rating, type of first-aid procedures, and other information about each hazardous substance. Operators should be trained to read and understand the MSDS forms. The forms themselves should be stored in a convenient location where they are readily available for reference.

3. Properly Label Hazards — Once the physical, chemical, and health hazards have been identified and listed, a labeling and training program must be implemented. To meet labeling requirements on hazardous materials, specialized labeling is available from a number of sources, including commercial label manufacturers. Exemptions to labeling requirements do exist, so consult your local safety regulatory agency for specific details.

4. Train Operators — The last element in the hazard communication program is training and making information available to utility personnel. A common-sense approach eliminates the confusing issue of which of the thousands of substances operators should be trained for, and concentrates on those that they will be exposed to or use in everyday maintenance routines.

The Hazard Communication Standard and the individual state requirements are obviously a very complex set of regulations. Remember, however, that the ultimate goal of these regulations is to provide additional operator protection. These standards and regulations, once the intent is understood, are relatively easy to implement.

23.113 Confined Space Entry Procedures

CONFINED SPACES[15, 16] pose significant risks for a large number of workers, including many utility operators. OSHA has therefore defined very specific procedures to protect the health and safety of operators whose jobs require them to enter or work in a confined space. The regulations (which can be found in the Code of Federal Regulations at 29 CFR 1910.146) require conditions in the confined space to be tested and evaluated before anyone enters the space. If conditions exceed OSHA's limits for safe exposure, additional

---

[13] *Code of Federal Regulations (CFR). A publication of the United States Government which contains all of the proposed and finalized federal regulations, including environmental regulations.*

[14] *Material Safety Data Sheet (MSDS). A document which provides pertinent information and a profile of a particular hazardous substance or mixture. An MSDS is normally developed by the manufacturer or formulator of the hazardous substance or mixture. The MSDS is required to be made available to employees and operators whenever there is the likelihood of the hazardous substance or mixture being introduced into the workplace. Some manufacturers are preparing MSDSs for products that are not considered to be hazardous to show that the product or substance is NOT hazardous.*

[15] *Confined Space. Confined space means a space that:*
 A. Is large enough and so configured that an employee can bodily enter and perform assigned work; and
 B. Has limited or restricted means for entry or exit (for example, tanks, vessels, silos, storage bins, hoppers, vaults, and pits are spaces that may have limited means of entry); and
 C. Is not designed for continuous employee occupancy.
 (Definition from the Code of Federal Regulations (CFR) Title 29 Part 1910.146.)

[16] *Confined Space, Permit-Required (Permit Space). A confined space that has one or more of the following characteristics:*
 • Contains or has a potential to contain a hazardous atmosphere,
 • Contains a material that has the potential for engulfing an entrant,
 • Has an internal configuration such that an entrant could be trapped or asphyxiated by inwardly converging walls or by a floor which slopes downward and tapers to a smaller cross section, or
 • Contains any other recognized serious safety or health hazard.
 (Definition from the Code of Federal Regulations (CFR) Title 29 Part 1910.146.)

Material Safety Data Sheet	U.S. Department of Labor	
May be used to comply with OSHA's Hazard Communication Standard, 29 CFR 1910.1200 Standard must be consulted for specific requirements.	Occupational Safety and Health Administration (Non-Mandatory Form) Form Approved OMB No. 1218-0072	

IDENTITY *(As Used on Label and List)*	Note: Blank spaces are not permitted. If any item is not applicable, or no information is available, the space must be marked to indicate that.

Section I

Manufacturer's Name	Emergency Telephone Number
Address *(Number, Street, City, State, and ZIP Code)*	Telephone Number for Information
	Date Prepared
	Signature of Preparer *(optional)*

Section II — Hazardous Ingredients/Identity Information

Hazardous Components (Specific Chemical Identity: Common Name(s))	OSHA PEL	ACGIH TLV	Other Limits Recommended	%(optional)

Section III — Physical/Chemical Characteristics

Boiling Point		Specific Gravity (H_2O = 1)	
Vapor Pressure (mm Hg.)		Melting Point	
Vapor Density (Air = 1)		Evaporation Rate (Butyl Acetate = 1)	
Solubility in Water			
Appearance and Odor			

Section IV — Fire and Explosion Hazard Data

Flash Point (Method Used)		Flammable Limits	LEL	UEL
Extinguishing Media				
Special Fire Fighting Procedures				
Unusual Fire and Explosion Hazards				

(Reproduce locally)	OSHA 174, Sept. 1985

Fig. 23.10   Material Safety Data Sheet

Section V — Reactivity Data

Stability	Unstable		Conditions to Avoid
	Stable		

Incompatibility *(Materials to Avoid)*

Hazardous Decomposition or Byproducts

Hazardous Polymerization	May Occur		Condition to Avoid
	Will Not Occur		

Section VI — Health Hazard Data

Route(s) of Entry: Inhalation?   Skin?   Ingestion?

Health Hazards *(Acute and Chronic)*

Carcinogenicity   NTP?   IARC Monographs?   OSHA Regulated?

Signs and Symptoms of Exposure

Medical Conditions
Generally Aggravated by Exposure

Emergency and First Aid Procedures

Section VII — Precautions for Safe Handling and Use

Steps to Be Taken in Case Material is Released or Spilled

Waste Disposal Method

Precautions to be Taken in Handling and Storing

Other Precautions

Section VIII — Control Measures

Respiratory Protection (Specify Type)

Ventilation	Local Exhaust		Special
	Mechanical *(General)*		Other

Protective Gloves	Eye Protection

Other Protective Clothing or Equipment

Work/Hygienic Practices

* USGPO 1986-491-529/45775

Fig. 23.10   Material Safety Data Sheet (continued)

safety precautions must be taken and a confined space entry permit (Figure 23.11) must be approved by the appropriate authorities prior to anyone entering the space.

The managers of water utilities may or may not be involved in the day-to-day details of enforcing the agency's confined space policy and procedures. However, every utility manager should be aware of the current OSHA requirements and should ensure that the utility's policies not only comply with current regulations, but that the agency's policies are vigorously enforced for the safety of all operators.

QUESTIONS

Write your answers in a notebook and then compare your answers with those on page 635.

23.11J   List the basic elements of a hazard communication program.

23.11K   What are a manager's responsibilities for ensuring the safety of operators entering or working in confined spaces?

23.114   Reporting

The mainstay of a safety program is the method of reporting and keeping of statistics. These records are needed regardless of the size of the utility because they provide a means of identifying accident frequencies and causes as well as the personnel involved. The records can be looked upon as the operator's safety report card. Therefore, it becomes the responsibility of each injured operator to fill out the utility's accident report.

All injuries should be reported, even if they are minor in nature, so as to establish a record in case the injury develops into a serious injury. It may be difficult at a later date to prove the accident did occur on the job and have the utility accept the responsibility for costs. The responsibility for reporting accidents affects several levels of personnel. First, of course, is the injured person. Next, it is the responsibility of the supervisor, and finally, the

Responsibility of Management to review the causes and take steps to prevent such accidents from happening in the future.

Accident report forms may be very simple. However, they must record all details required by law and all data needed for statistical purposes. The forms shown in Figures 23.12 and 23.13 are examples for you to consider for use in your plant. The report must show the name of the injured, employee number, division, time of accident, nature of injury, cause of accident, first aid administered, and remarks for items not covered elsewhere. There should be a review process by foreman, supervisor, safety officer, and management. *RECOMMENDATIONS ARE NEEDED AS WELL AS A FOLLOW-UP REVIEW TO BE SURE THAT PROPER ACTION HAS BEEN TAKEN TO PREVENT RECURRENCE.*

In addition to reports needed by the utility, other reports may be required by state or federal agencies. For example, vehicle accident reports must be submitted to local police departments. If a member of the public is injured, additional forms are needed because of possible subsequent claims for damages. If the accident is one of occupational injury, causing lost time, other reports may be required. Follow-up investigations to identify causes and responsibility may require the development of other specific types of record forms.

In the preparation of accident reports, it is the operator's responsibility to correctly fill out each form, giving complete details. The supervisor must be sure no information is overlooked which may be helpful in preventing recurrence.

The Safety Officer must review the reports and determine corrective actions and make recommendations.

In day-to-day actions, operators, supervisors, and management often overlook opportunities to counsel individual operators in safety matters. Then, when an accident occurs, they are not inclined to look too closely at accident reports. First, the accident is a series of embarrassments, to the injured person, to the supervisor, and to management. Therefore, there is a reluctance to give detailed consideration to accident reports. However, if a safety program is to function well, it will require a thorough effort on the part of the operator, supervisor, and management in accepting their responsibility for the accident and making a greater effort through good reporting to prevent future similar accidents. Accident reports must be analyzed, discussed, and the real cause of the accident identified and corrected.

Emphasis on the prevention of future accidents cannot be overstressed. We must identify the causes of accidents and implement whatever measures are necessary to protect operators from becoming injured.

23.115   Training

If a safety program is to work well, management will have to accept responsibility for the following three components of training:

1. Safety education of all employees,

2. Reinforced education in safety, and

3. Safety education in the use of tools and equipment.

Or to put it another way, the three most important controlling factors in safety are education, education, and more education.

Confined Space Pre-Entry Checklist/Confined Space Entry Permit

Date and Time Issued: _____ Date and Time Expires: _____ Job Site/Space I.D.: _____

Job Supervisor: _____ Equipment to be worked on: _____ Work to be performed: _____

Attendant personnel: _____   _____   _____

1. Atmospheric Checks: Time _____   Oxygen _____ %   Toxic _____ ppm

   Explosive _____ % LFL   Carbon Monoxide _____ ppm

2. Tester's signature: _____

3. Source isolation: (No Entry)   N/A   Yes   No

   Pumps or lines blinded,
   disconnected, or blocked   ( )   ( )   ( )

4. Ventilation Modification: N/A   Yes   No

   Mechanical   ( )   ( )   ( )

   Natural ventilation only   ( )   ( )   ( )

5. Atmospheric check after isolation and ventilation:

   Oxygen _____ %   [19.5 – 23.5%]

   Explosive _____ % LFL   [<10%]

   Toxic _____ ppm   [<10 ppm H_2S]

   Carbon Monoxide _____ ppm   [<35 ppm CO]

   Tester's signature: _____

   Time: _____

6. Communication procedures: _____

7. Rescue procedures: _____

8. Entry, attendant, and backup persons   Yes   No   Yes   No

   Successfully completed required training? ( )   ( )   Is training current? ( )   ( )

9. Equipment: N/A   Yes   No

   Direct reading gas monitor tested   ( )   ( )   ( )

   Safety harnesses and lifelines for entry and attendant persons   ( )   ( )   ( )

   Hoisting equipment   ( )   ( )   ( )

   Powered communications   ( )   ( )   ( )

   SCBAs for entry and attendant persons   ( )   ( )   ( )

   Protective clothing   ( )   ( )   ( )

   All electric equipment listed for Class I, Division I, Group D
   and nonsparking tools   ( )   ( )   ( )

10. Periodic atmospheric tests:

    Oxygen: ____% Time ____; ____% Time ____; ____% Time ____; ____% Time ____;

    Explosive: ____% Time ____; ____% Time ____; ____% Time ____; ____% Time ____;

    Toxic: ____% Time ____; ____% Time ____; ____% Time ____; ____% Time ____;

    Carbon Monoxide: ____% Time ____; ____% Time ____; ____% Time ____; ____% Time ____;

We have reviewed the work authorized by this permit and the information contained herein. Written instructions and safety procedures have been received and are understood. Entry cannot be approved if any brackets ( ) are marked in the "No" column. This permit is not valid unless all appropriate items are completed.

	Name	Signature
Permit Prepared By: (Supervisor)	_____	_____
Approved By: (Unit Supervisor)	_____	_____
Reviewed By: (Authorized Entrant(s))	_____	_____
(Attendant(s))	_____	_____
(Entry Supervisor)	_____	_____

This permit to be kept at job site. Return job site copy to Safety Office following job completion.

Fig. 23.11   Confined space pre-entry checklist/permit

Date _____

Name of injured employee _____ Employee # _____ Area _____

Date of accident _____ Time _____ Employee's Occupation _____

Location of accident _____ Nature of injury _____

Name of doctor _____ Address _____

Name of hospital _____ Address _____

Witnesses (name & address) _____

PHYSICAL CAUSES

Indicate below by an "X" whether, in your opinion, the accident was caused by:

_____ Improper guarding   _____ No mechanical cause

_____ Defective substances or equipment   _____ Working methods

_____ Hazardous arrangement   _____ Lack of knowledge or skill

_____ Improper illumination   _____ Wrong attitude

_____ Improper dress or apparel   _____ Physical defect

_____ Not listed (describe briefly) _____

UNSAFE ACTS

Sometimes the injured person is not directly associated with the causes of an accident. Using an "X" to represent the injured worker and an "O" to represent any other person involved, indicate whether, in your opinion, the accident was caused by:

_____ Operating without authority   _____ Unsafe loading, placement & etc.

_____ Failure to secure or warn   _____ Took unsafe position

_____ Working at unsafe speed   _____ Worked on moving equipment

_____ Made safety device inoperative   _____ Teased, abused, distracted & etc.

_____ Unsafe equipment or hands instead of equipment _____ Did not use safe clothing or personal protective equipment

_____ No unsafe act

_____ Not listed (describe briefly) _____

What job was the employee doing? _____

What specific action caused the accident? _____

What steps will be taken to prevent recurrence? _____

_____

_____

Date of Report _____ Immediate Supervisor _____

REVIEWING AUTHORITY

Comments: | Comments:

Safety Officer   Date | Department Director   Date

Fig. 23.12 Supervisor's accident report

INJURED: COMPLETE THIS SECTION

Name _____ Age _____ Sex _____

Address _____

Title _____ Dept. Assigned _____

Place of Accident _____

Street or Intersection _____

Date _____ Hour _____ A.M. _____ P.M. _____

Type of Job You Were Doing When Injured

_____

Object Which Directly Injured You   Part of Body Injured

_____

How Did Accident Happen? (Be specific and give details; use back of sheet if necessary.)

	Yes	No
Did You Report Accident or Exposure at Once? (Explain "No")	☐	☐
Did You Report Accident or Exposure to Supervisor? Give Name	☐	☐
Were There Witnesses to Accident or Exposure? Give Names	☐	☐
Did You See a Doctor? (If Yes, Give Name)	☐	☐
Are You Going to See a Doctor? (Give Name)	☐	☐

_____   _____
                Date   Signature

SUPERVISOR: COMPLETE THIS SECTION — (Return to Personnel as Soon as Possible)

	Yes	No
Was an Investigation of Unsafe Conditions and/or Unsafe Acts Made? If Yes, Please Submit Copy.	☐	☐
Was Injured Intoxicated or Behaving Inappropriately at Time of Accident? (Explain "Yes")	☐	☐

Date Disability   Last Day   Date Back
Commenced _____   Wages Earned _____   on Job _____

Date Report Completed _____ 19____ Signed By _____

                                                  Title _____

Distribution: Canary - Department Head, Pink - Supervisor, White - Personnel

Fig. 23.13   Accident report

Responsibility for overall training must be that of upper management. A program that will educate operators and then reinforce this education in safety must be planned systematically and promoted on a continuous basis. There are many avenues to achieving this goal.

The safety education program should start with the new operator. Even before employment, verify the operator's past record and qualifications and review the pre-employment physical examination. In the new operator's orientation, include instruction in the importance of safety at your utility or plant. Also discuss the matter of proper reporting of accidents as well as the organization's policies and practices. Give new operators copies of all safety SOPs and direct their attention to parts that directly involve them. Ask the safety officer to give a talk about utility policy, safety reports, and past accidents, and to orient the new operator toward the importance of safety to operators and to the organization.

The next consideration must be one of training the new operator in how to perform assigned work. Most supervisors think in terms of On-the-Job Training (OJT). However, OJT is not a good way of preventing accidents with an inexperienced operator. The idea is all right if the operator comes to the organization trained in how to perform the work, such as a treatment operator from another plant. Then you only need to explain your safety program and how your policies affect the new operator. For a new operator who is inexperienced in water treatment or in utility operation, the supervisor must give detailed consideration to the operator's welfare. In this instance, the training should include not only a safety talk, but the foreman (supervisor) must train the inexperienced operator in all aspects of treatment plant safety. This training includes instruction in the handling of chemicals, the dangers of electrical apparatus, fire hazards, and proper maintenance of equipment to prevent accidents. Special instructions will also be needed for specific work environments such as manholes, gases (chlorine and hydrogen sulfide (H_2S)), water safety, and any specific hazards that are unique to your facility. The new operator must be checked out on any equipment personnel may operate such as vehicles, forklifts, valve operators, and radios. All new operators should be required to participate in a safety orientation program during the first few days of their employment, and an overall training program in the first few months.

The next step in safety education is reinforcement. Even if the operator is well trained, mistakes can occur; therefore, the education must be continual. Many organizations use the *TAILGATE*[17] method as a means of maintaining the operator's interest in safety. The program should be conducted by the first line supervisor. Schedule the informal tailgate meeting for a suitable location, keep it short, avoid distractions, and be sure that everyone can hear. Hand out literature, if available. Tailgate talks should communicate to the operator specific considerations, new problems, and accident information. These topics should be published. One resource for such meetings can be those operators who have been involved in an accident. Although it is sometimes embarrassing to the injured, the victim is now the expert on how the accident occurred, what could have been done to prevent it, and how it felt to have the injury. Encourage all operators, new and old, to participate in tailgate safety sessions.

Use safety posters to reinforce safety training and to make operators aware of the location of dangerous areas or show the importance of good work habits. Such posters are available through the National Safety Council's catalog.[18]

Awards for good safety records are another means of keeping operators aware of the importance of safety. The awards could be given to individuals in recognition of a good safety record. Publicity about the awards may provide an incentive to the operators and demonstrates the organization's determination to maintain a good safety record. The awards may include: AWWA's water drop pins, certificates, and/or plaques showing number of years without an accident. Consider publishing a utility newsletter on safety tips or giving details concerning accidents that may be helpful to other operators in the organization. Awards may be given to the organization in recognition of its effort in preventing accidents or for its overall safety program. A suggestion program concerning safety will promote and reinforce the program and give recognition to the best suggestions. The goal of all these efforts is to reinforce concerns for the safety of all operators. If safety, as an idea, is present, then accidents can be prevented.

Education of the operator in the use of tools and equipment is necessary. As pointed out above, OJT is not the answer to a good safety record. A good safety record will be achieved only with good work habits and safe equipment. If the operator is trained in the proper use of equipment (hand tools or vehicles), the operator is less likely to misuse them. However, if the supervisor finds an operator misusing tools or equipment, then it is the supervisor's responsibility to reprimand the operator as a means of reinforcing utility policies. The careless operator who misuses equipment is a hazard to other operators. Careless operators will also be the cause of a poor safety record in the operator's division or department.

An important part of every job should be the consideration of its safety aspects by the supervisor. The supervisor should instruct the foreman or operators about any dangers involved in job assignments. If a job is particularly dangerous, then the supervisor must bring that fact to everyone's attention and clarify utility policy in regard to unsafe acts and conditions.

If the operator is unsure of how to perform a job, then it is the operator's responsibility to ask for the training needed. Each operator must think, act, and promote safety if the organization is to achieve a good safety record. Training is the key to achieving this objective and training is everyone's responsibility — management, the supervisors, foremen, and operators.

QUESTIONS

Write your answers in a notebook and then compare your answers with those on page 635.

23.11L What is the mainstay of a safety program?

23.11M Why should you report even a minor injury?

23.11N Why should a safety officer review an accident report form?

23.11O A new, inexperienced operator must receive instruction on what aspects of treatment plant safety?

23.11P What should an operator do if unsure of how to perform a job?

23.116 Measuring

To be complete, a safety program must also include some means of identifying, measuring, and analyzing the effects of the program. The systematic classification of accidents, injuries, and lost time is the responsibility of the safety officer. This person should use an analytical method which would refer to types and classes of accidents. Reports should be prepared using statistics showing lost time, costs, type of injuries, and other data, based on a specific time interval.

Such data call attention to the effectiveness of the program and promote awareness of the types of accidents that are happening. Management can use this information to decide where the emphasis should be placed to avoid accidents. However, statistical data are of little value if a report is prepared and then set on the bookshelf or placed in a supervisor's desk drawer. The data must be distributed and read by all operating and maintenance personnel.

As an example, injuries can be classified as fractures, burns, bites, eye injuries, cuts, and bruises. Causes can be referred to as heat, machinery, falling, handling objects, chemicals, unsafe acts, and miscellaneous. Cost can be con-

sidered as lost time, lost dollars, lost production, contaminated water, or any other means of showing the effects of the accidents.

Good analytical reporting will provide a great deal of detail without a lot of paper to read and comprehend. Keep the method of reporting simple and easy to understand by all operators, so they can identify with the causes and be aware of how to prevent the accident happening to themselves and/or other operators. Table 23.8 gives one method of summarizing the causes of various types of injuries.

TABLE 23.8 SUMMARY OF TYPES AND CAUSES OF INJURIES

Type of Injury	PRIMARY CAUSE OF INJURY										
	Unsafe Act	Chemical	Falls	Handling Objects	Heat	Machinery	Falling Objects	Stepping	Striking	Miscellaneous	TOTAL
Fractures											
Sprains											
Eye Injuries											
Bites											
Cuts											
Bruises											
Burns											
Miscellaneous											

There are many other methods of compiling data. Table 23.8 could reflect cost in dollars or in work hours lost. Not all accidents mean time lost, but there can be other cost factors. The data analysis should also indicate if the accidents involve vehicles, company personnel, the public, company equipment, loss of chemical, or other factors. Results also should show direct cost and indirect cost to the agency, operator, and the public.

Once the statistical data have been compiled, someone must be responsible for reviewing it in order to take preventive actions. Frequently such responsibility rests with the safety committee. In fact, safety committees may operate at several levels, for example management committee, working committee, or an accident review board. In any event, the committee must be active, be serious, and be fully supported by management.

Another means of measuring safety is by calculating the injury frequency rate for an indication of the effectiveness of your safety program. Multiply the number of disabling injuries by one million and divide by the total number of employee-hours worked. The number of injuries per year is multiplied by one million in order to obtain injury frequency rate values or numbers which are easy to use. In our example problems, we obtained numbers between one and one thousand.

$$\text{Injury Frequency Rate} = \frac{(\text{Number of Disabling Injuries/year})(1,000,000)}{\text{Number of Hours Worked/year}}$$

These calculations indicate a frequency rate per year, which is the usual means of showing such data. Note that this calculation accounts only for disabling injuries. You may wish to show all injuries, but the calculations are much the same.

EXAMPLE 3

A rural water company employs 36 operators who work in many small towns throughout a three-state area. The operators suffered four injuries in one year while working 74,880 hours. Calculate the injury frequency rate.

Known		Unknown
Number of Operators	= 36	Injury Frequency Rate
Number of Injuries	= 4 injuries/yr	
Number of Hours Worked	= 74,880 hr/yr	

Calculate the injury frequency rate.

$$\text{Injury Frequency Rate} = \frac{(\text{Number of Injuries/year})(1{,}000{,}000)}{\text{Number of Hours Worked/year}}$$

$$= \frac{(4 \text{ Injuries/yr})(1{,}000{,}000)}{74{,}880 \text{ hr/yr}}$$

$$= 53.4$$

EXAMPLE 4

Of the four injuries suffered by the operators in Example 3, one was a disabling injury. Calculate the injury frequency rate for the disabling injuries.

Known		Unknown
Number of Disabling Injuries	= 1 injury/yr	Injury Frequency Rate
Number of Hours Worked	= 74,880 hr/yr	

Calculate the injury frequency rate.

$$\text{Injury Frequency Rate (Disabling Injuries)} = \frac{(\text{Number of Disabling Injuries/yr})(1{,}000{,}000)}{\text{Number of Hours Worked/yr}}$$

$$= \frac{(1 \text{ injury/yr})(1{,}000{,}000)}{74{,}880 \text{ hr/yr}}$$

$$= 13.4$$

Yet another consideration may be lost-time accidents. The safety officer's analysis may take into account many other considerations, but in any event, the method given here will provide a means of recording and measuring injuries in the treatment plant. In measuring lost-time injuries, a severity rate can be considered.

A severity rate is based on one lost hour for every million operator hours worked. The rate is found by multiplying the number of hours lost by one million and dividing by the total of operator-hours worked.

$$\text{Injury Severity Rate} = \frac{(\text{Number of Hours Lost/yr})(1{,}000{,}000)}{\text{Number of Hours Worked/yr}}$$

EXAMPLE 5

The water company described in Examples 3 and 4 experienced 40 operator-hours lost due to injuries while the operators worked 74,880 hours. Calculate the injury severity rate.

Known		Unknown
Number of Hours Lost	= 40 hr/yr	Injury Severity Rate
Number of Hours Worked	= 74,880 hr/yr	

Calculate the injury severity rate.

$$\text{Injury Severity Rate} = \frac{(\text{Number of Hours Lost/yr})(1{,}000{,}000)}{\text{Number of Hours Worked/yr}}$$

$$= \frac{(40 \text{ hr/yr})(1{,}000{,}000)}{74{,}880 \text{ hr/yr}}$$

$$= 534$$

Notice that all these data points are based on a one-year time interval which makes them suitable for use by the safety officer in preparing an annual report.

23.117   Human Factors

First, you may ask, what is a human factor? Well, it is not too often that a safety text considers human factors as part of the safety program. However, if these factors are understood and emphasis is given to their practical application, then many accidents can be prevented. Human Factors Engineering is the specialized study of technology relating to the design of operator-machine interface. That is to say, it examines ways in which machinery might be designed or altered to make it easier to use, safer, and more efficient for the operator. We hear a lot about making computers more user friendly, but human factors engineering is just as important to everyday operation of other machinery in the everyday plant.

Many accidents occur because the operator forgets the human factors. The ultimate responsibility for accidents due to human factors belongs to the management group. However, this does not relieve the operator of the responsibility to point out the human factors as they relate to safety. After all, it is the operator using the equipment who can best tell if it meets all the needs for an interrelationship between operator and machine.

The first step in the prevention of accidents takes place in the plant design. Even with excellent designs, accidents can and do happen. However, every step possible must be taken during design to ensure a maximum effort of providing a safe plant environment. Most often the operator has little to do with design, and therefore needs to understand human factors engineering so as to be able to evaluate these factors as the plant is being operated. As newer plants become automated, this type of understanding may even be more important.

Other contributing human factors are the operator's mental and physical characteristics. The operator's decision-making abilities and general behavior (response time, sense of alarm, and perception of problems and danger) are all important factors. Ideally, tools and machines should function as intuitive extensions of the operator's natural senses and actions. Any factors disrupting this flow of action can cause an accident. Therefore, be on the lookout for such factors. When you find a system that cannot be operated in a smooth, logical sequence of steps, change it. You may prevent an accident. If the everyday behavior of an operator is inappropriate with regard to a specific job, reconsider the assignment to prevent an accident.

The human factor in safety is the responsibility of design engineers, supervisors, and operators. However, the operator who is doing the work will have a greater understanding of the operator-machine interface. For this reason, the operator is the appropriate person to evaluate the means of reducing the human factor's contribution to the cause of accidents, thereby improving the plant's safety record.

QUESTIONS

Write your answers in a notebook and then compare your answers with those on page 635.

23.11Q Statistical accident reports should contain what types of accident data?

23.11R How can injuries be classified?

23.11S How can causes of injuries be classified?

23.11T How can costs of accidents be classified?

23.12 RECORDKEEPING

23.120 Purpose of Records

Accurate records are a very important part of effective operation of a water treatment plant and distribution system facilities. Records are a valuable source of information. They can save time when trouble develops and provide proof that problems were identified and solved. Pertinent and complete records should be used as a basis for plant operation, interpreting results of water treatment, preparing preventive maintenance programs, and preparation of budget requests. When accurately kept, records provide an essential basis for design of future changes or expansions of the treatment plant, and also can be used to aid in the design of other water treatment plants where similar water may be treated and similar problems may develop.

If legal questions or problems occur in connection with the treatment of the water or the operation of the plant, accurate and complete records will provide evidence of what actually occurred and what procedures were followed.

Records are essential for effective management of water treatment facilities and to satisfy legal requirements. Some of the important uses of records include:

1. Aiding operators in solving treatment and water quality problems,

2. Providing a method of alerting operators to changes in source water quality,

3. Showing that the treated water is acceptable to the consumer,

4. Documenting that the final product meets plant performance standards, as well as the standards of the regulatory agencies,

5. Determining performance of treatment processes, equipment, and the plant,

6. Satisfying legal requirements,

7. Aiding in answering complaints,

8. Anticipating routine maintenance,

9. Providing data for cost analysis and preparation of budgets,

10. Providing data for future engineering designs, and

11. Providing information for monthly and annual reports.

23.121 Types of Records

There are many different types of records that are required for effective management and operation of water supply, treatment, and distribution system facilities. Below is a listing of some essential records:

1. Source of supply,

2. Operation,

3. Laboratory,

4. Maintenance,

5. Chemical inventory and usage,

6. Purchases,

7. Chlorination station,

8. Main disinfection,

9. Cross connection control,

10. Personnel,

11. Accidents, and

12. Customer complaints.

23.122 Types of Plant Operations Data[19]

Plant operations logs can be as different as the plants and water systems whose information they record. The differences in amount, nature, and format of data are so significant that any attempt to prepare a "typical" log would be very difficult.

---

[19] *Also see Volume I, Chapter 10, "Plant Operation," Section 10.6, "Operating Records and Reports," for additional details and recordkeeping forms.*

This section will outline the kinds of data that are usually required to help you develop a useful log for your facilities.

Treatment plant data such as total flows, chemical use, chemical doses, filter performance, reservoir levels, quality control tests, and rainfall and runoff information represent the bulk of the data required for proper plant operation. Frequently, however, source and distribution system data such as reservoir storage and water quality data are included because of the impact of this information on plant operation and operator responsibilities. Typical plant operations data include:

1. Plant title, agency, and location;

2. Date;

3. Names of operators and supervisors on duty;

4. Source of supply,

   a. Reservoir elevation and volume of storage,
   b. Reservoir inflow and outflow,
   c. Evaporation and precipitation,
   d. Apparent runoff, seepage loss, or infiltration gain, and
   e. Production figures from wells;

5. Water treatment plant,

   a. Plant inflow,
   b. Treated water flow,
   c. Plant operating water (backwash), and
   d. Clear well level;

6. Distribution system,

   a. Flows to system (system demand),
   b. Distribution system reservoir levels and changes, and
   c. Comparison of production with deliveries (unaccounted for water);

7. Chemical inventory and usage,

   a. Chemical inventory/storage (measured use and deliveries),
   b. Metered or estimated plant usages, and
   c. Calculated usage of chemicals (compare with actual use);

8. Quality control tests,

   a. Turbidity,
   b. Chlorine residual,
   c. Coliforms,
   d. Odor,
   e. Color, and
   f. Other;

9. Filter performance,

   a. Operation,

      (1) Total hours, all units,
      (2) Filtered water turbidities,
      (3) Head losses,
      (4) Levels, and
      (5) Flow rates;

   b. Backwash,

      (1) Total hours,
      (2) Head losses,
      (3) Total washwater used, and
      (4) Duration and rate of back/surface wash;

10. Meteorologic,

    a. Rainfall, evaporation, and temperature of both water and air, and
    b. Weather (clear, cloudy, windy); and

11. Remarks.

    Space should be provided to describe or explain unusual data or events. Extensive notes should be entered on a daily worksheet or diary.

23.123 Maintenance Records

A good plant maintenance effort depends heavily upon good recordkeeping. There are several areas where proper records and documentation can definitely improve overall plant performance.

23.124 Procurement Records

Ordering repair parts and supplies usually is done when the on-hand quantity of a stocked part or chemical falls below the reorder point, a new item is added to stock, or an item has been requested that is not stocked. Most organizations require employees to submit a requisition (similar to the one shown in Figure 23.14) when they need to purchase equipment or supplies. When the requisition has been approved by the authorized person (a supervisor or purchasing agent, in most cases) the items are ordered using a form called a purchase order. A purchase order contains a number of important items. These items include: (1) the date, (2) a complete description of each item and quantity needed, (3) prices, (4) the name of the vendor, and (5) a purchase order number.

A copy of the purchase order should be retained in a suspense file or on a clipboard until the ordered items arrive. This procedure helps keep track of the items that have been ordered but have not yet been received.

All supplies should be processed through the storeroom immediately upon arrival. When an item is received it should be so recorded on an inventory card. The inventory card will keep track of the numbers of an item in stock, when last ordered, cost, and other information. Furthermore, by always logging in supplies immediately upon receipt, you are in a position to reject defective or damaged shipments and control shortages or errors in billing. Some utilities use personal computers to keep track of orders and deliveries.

23.125 Inventory Records

An inventory consists of the supplies the treatment plant needs to keep on hand to operate the facility. These maintenance supplies may include repair parts, spare valves, electrical supplies, tools, and lubricants. The purpose of maintain-

Fig. 23.14 Requisition/purchase order form

ing an inventory is to provide needed parts and supplies quickly, thereby reducing equipment downtime and work delays.

In deciding what supplies to stock, keep in mind the economics involved in buying and stocking an item as opposed to depending upon outside availability to provide needed supplies. Is the item critical to continued plant or process operation? Should certain frequently used repair parts be kept on hand? Does the item have a shelf life?

Inventory costs can be held to a minimum by keeping on hand only those parts and supplies for which a definite need exists or which would take too long to obtain from an outside vendor. A "definite need" for an item is usually demonstrated by a history of regular use. Some items may be infrequently used but may be vital in the event of an emergency; these items should also be stocked. Take care to exclude any parts and supplies that may become obsolete, and do not stock parts for equipment scheduled for replacement.

Tools should be inventoried. Tools that are used by operators on a daily basis should be permanently signed out to them. More expensive tools and tools that are only occasionally used, however, should be kept in a storeroom. These tools should be signed out only when needed and signed back in immediately after use.

23.126 Equipment Records

You will need to keep accurate records to monitor the operation and maintenance of plant equipment. Equipment control cards and work orders can be used to:

* Record important equipment data such as make, model, serial number, and date purchased,

* Record maintenance and repair work performed to date,

* Anticipate preventive maintenance needs, and

* Schedule future maintenance work.

See Chapter 18, Section 18.00, "Preventive Maintenance Records," for additional information.

23.127 Disposition of Plant Records

Good recordkeeping is very important because records indicate potential problems, adequate operation, and are a good waterworks practice. Usually the only record required by the health agency is the summary of the daily turbidity of the treated surface water as it enters the distribution system. Chlorine residual and bacterial counts are often required. Other records that may also be required include:

1. Total trihalomethane (TTHM) data (frequency of this report is based on the number of people served),

2. The daily log and records of the analyses to control the treatment process may be required when there are chronic treatment problems,

3. Chlorination, constituent removal, and sequestering records may be required from small systems (especially those demonstrating little understanding of the processes), and

4. Records showing the quantity of water from each source in use may be required from systems with sources producing water not meeting state and/or local health department water quality standards.

An important question is how long records should be kept. Records should be kept as long as they may be useful. Some

information will become useless after a short time, while other data may be valuable for many years. Data that might be used for future design or expansion should be kept indefinitely. Laboratory data will always be useful and should be kept indefinitely. Regulatory agencies may require you to keep certain water quality analyses (bacteriological test results) and customer complaint records on file for specified time periods (10 years for chemical analyses and bacteriological tests).

Even if old records are not consulted every day, this does not lessen their potential value. For orderly records handling and storage, set up a schedule to periodically review old records and to dispose of those records that are no longer needed. A decision can be made when a record is established regarding the time period for which it must be retained.

QUESTIONS

Write your answers in a notebook and then compare your answers with those on page 635.

23.12A   List some of the important uses of records.

23.12B   What is "unaccounted for water"?

23.12C   What chemical inventory and usage records should be kept?

23.12D   List the important items usually contained on a purchase order.

23.13 ACKNOWLEDGMENTS

During the writing of this material, Lynne Scarpa, Phil Scott, Chris Smith, and Rich von Langen, all members of California Water Environment Association (CWEA), provided many excellent materials and suggestions for improvement. Their generous contributions are greatly appreciated.

23.14 ADDITIONAL READING

1. *WATER UTILITY MANAGEMENT PRACTICES* (M5). Obtain from Customer Services, AWWA, 6666 West Quincy Avenue, Denver, CO 80235. Order No. 30005. Price to members, $34.00; nonmembers, $49.00. Price includes cost of shipping and handling.

2. *A WATER AND WASTEWATER MANAGER'S GUIDE FOR STAYING FINANCIALLY HEALTHY*, US EPA 430-09-89-004, July 1989. Order from National Technical Information Service (NTIS), 5285 Port Royal Road, Springfield, VA 22161. Order No. PB90114455. Price, $24.50, plus $4.00 shipping and handling.

3. *WASTEWATER UTILITY RECORDKEEPING, REPORTING AND MANAGEMENT INFORMATION SYSTEMS*, US EPA 430-9-82-006, July 1982. Order from National Technical Information Service (NTIS), 5285 Port Royal Road, Springfield, VA 22161. Order No. PB83109348. Price, $27.00, plus $4.00 shipping and handling.

4. *SUPERVISION: CONCEPTS AND PRACTICES OF MANAGEMENT*, Seventh Edition, 1998, Hilgert, Raymond L., and Edwin Leonard, Jr. Order from International Thomson Publishing (ITP), 7625 Empire Drive, Florence, KY 41042-0668. ISBN No. 0538863536. Price, $55.95, plus 10 percent of price for shipping and handling.

5. *THE POPULAR PLANT MANAGER — HOW TO WIN PUBLIC SUPPORT*, Manual of Practice No. SM-6, 1986. Order from Water Environment Federation, 601 Wythe Street, Alexandria, VA 22314-1994. Order No. MSM6GK. Price to members, $21.30; nonmembers, $28.30. Price includes cost of shipping and handling.

6. *TEXAS MANUAL*, Chapter 18*, "Effective Public Relations in Water Works Operations," and Chapter 19*, "Planning and Financing."

7. *WATER RATES* (M1). Obtain from Customer Services, AWWA, 6666 West Quincy Avenue, Denver, CO 80235.

Order No. 30001. Price to members, $28.00; nonmembers, $44.00; price includes cost of shipping and handling.

8. *EMERGENCY PLANNING FOR WATER UTILITY MANAGEMENT* (M19). Obtain from Customer Services, AWWA, 6666 West Quincy Avenue, Denver, CO 80235. Order No. 30019. Price to members, $34.00; nonmembers, $49.00; price includes cost of shipping and handling.

* Depends on addition.

END OF LESSON 3 OF 3 LESSONS
ON
ADMINISTRATION

Please answer the discussion and review questions before continuing with the Objective Test.

DISCUSSION AND REVIEW QUESTIONS

Chapter 23. ADMINISTRATION

(Lesson 3 of 3 Lessons)

Write the answers to these questions in your notebook before continuing with the Objective Test on page 636. The question numbering continues from Lesson 2.

26. What can happen when agencies rely primarily on corrective maintenance to keep the system running?

27. What does a SCADA system do?

28. What items should be included in a water supplier's cross connection control program?

29. What factors should be considered when selecting a backflow prevention device for a particular situation?

30. How would you assess the vulnerability of a water supply system?

31. How can a utility protect its water supply from contamination?

32. What would you do if you discovered that contaminated water has entered your distribution system?

33. Why must waterworks utilities have a safety program?

34. How can a good safety record be accomplished?

35. What is the intent of the OSHA regulations?

36. What are the four main elements of a hazard communication program?

37. What topics should be included in a safety officer's talk to new operators?

38. Why are records important?

SUGGESTED ANSWERS

Chapter 23.   ADMINISTRATION

ANSWERS TO QUESTIONS IN LESSON 1

Answers to questions on page 568.

23.0A   Local utility demands on a utility manager include protection from environmental disasters with a minimum investment of money.

23.0B   Changes in the environmental workplace are created by changes in the workforce and advances in technology.

Answers to questions on page 570.

23.1A   The functions of a utility manager include planning, organizing, staffing, directing, and controlling.

23.1B   In small communities the community depends on the manager to handle everything.

Answers to questions on page 573.

23.2A   Utility planning must include operational personnel, local officials (decision makers), and the public.

23.3A   The purpose of an organizational plan is to show who reports to whom and to identify the lines of authority.

23.3B   Effective delegation is uncomfortable for many managers since it requires giving up power and responsibility. Many managers believe that they can do the job better than others, they believe that other employees are not well trained or experienced, and they are afraid of mistakes. The utility manager retains some responsibility even after delegating to another employee and, therefore, the manager is often reluctant to delegate or may delegate the responsibility but not the authority to get the job done.

23.3C   An important and often overlooked part of delegation is follow-up by the supervisor.

Answers to questions on page 575.

23.4A   Staffing responsibilities include hiring new employees, training employees, and evaluating job performance.

23.4B   The two personnel management concepts a manager should always keep in mind are "job-related" and "documentation."

23.4C   The steps involved in a staffing analysis include:

1. List the tasks to be performed,
2. Estimate the number of staff hours per year required to perform each task,
3. List the utility's current employees,
4. Assign tasks based on each employee's skills and abilities, and
5. Adjust the work assignments as necessary to achieve the best possible fit between the work to be done and the personnel/skills available to do it.

23.4D   A qualifications profile is a clear statement of the knowledge, skills, and abilities a person must possess to perform the essential job duties of a particular position.

Answers to questions on page 578.

23.4E   The purpose of a job interview is to gain additional information about the applicants so that the most qualified person can be selected to fill a job opening.

23.4F   Protected groups include minorities, women, disabled persons, persons over 40 years of age, and union members.

23.4G   The "OUCH" principle stands for:
Objectivity,
Uniform treatment of employees,
Consistency, and
Having job relatedness.

23.4H   A new employee's safety training should begin on the first day of employment or as soon thereafter as possible.

Answers to questions on page 579.

23.4I   The purpose of a probationary period for new employees is to provide a time during which both the employer and employee can assess the "fit" between the job and the person.

23.4J   The compensation an employee receives for the work performed includes satisfaction, recognition, security, appropriate pay, and benefits.

23.4K   Utility managers should provide training opportunities for employees so they can keep informed of new technologies and regulations. Training for supervisors is also important to ensure that supervisors have the knowledge, skills, and attitude that will enable them to be effective supervisors.

Answers to questions on page 583.

23.4L   An employee's immediate supervisor should conduct the employee's performance evaluation.

23.4M   Dealing with employee discipline requires tact and skill. The manager or supervisor should stay flexible, calm, and open-minded.

23.4N   Common warning signs of potential violence include abusive language, threatening or confrontational behavior, and brandishing a weapon.

Answers to questions on page 587.

23.4O   Harassment is any behavior that is offensive, annoying, or humiliating to an individual and that interferes with a person's ability to do a job. This behavior is uninvited, often repeated, and creates an uncomfortable or even hostile environment in the workplace.

23.4P Types of behavior that could be considered sexual harassment include:

- Unwanted hugging, patting, kissing, brushing up against someone's body, or other inappropriate sexual touching,
- Subtle or open pressure for sexual activity,
- Persistent sexually explicit or sexist statements, jokes, or stories,
- Repeated leering or staring at a person's body,
- Suggestive or obscene notes or phone calls, and/or
- Display of sexually explicit pictures or cartoons.

23.4Q The best way to prevent harassment is to set an example by your own behavior and to keep communication open between employees. A manager must also be aware of and take action to prevent any type of harassment in the workplace.

Answers to questions on page 587.

23.4R The shop steward is elected by the union employees and is their official representative to management and the local union.

23.4S Union contracts do not change the supervisor's delegated authority or responsibility. Operators must carry out the supervisor's orders and get the work done properly, safely, and within a reasonable amount of time. However, a contract gives a union the right to protest or challenge a supervisor's decision.

ANSWERS TO QUESTIONS IN LESSON 2

Answers to questions on page 591.

23.5A A manager needs both written and oral communication skills.

23.5B The most common written documents that a utility manager must write include memos, business letters, press releases, monitoring reports, and the annual report.

23.5C The annual report should be a review of what and how the utility operated during the past year and also the goals for the next year.

Answers to questions on page 592.

23.6A A utility manager may be asked to conduct meetings with employees, the governing board, the public, and with other professionals in your field.

23.6B Before a meeting (1) prepare an agenda and distribute, (2) find an adequate meeting room, and (3) set a beginning and ending time.

Answers to questions on page 594.

23.7A The first step in organizing a public relations campaign is to establish objectives so you will have a clear idea of what you expect to achieve.

23.7B Employees can be informed about the utility's plans, practices, and goals through newsletters, bulletin boards, and regular, open communication between supervisors and subordinates.

23.7C Newspapers give more thorough, in-depth coverage to stories than do the broadcast media.

23.7D Practice is the key to effective public speaking.

23.7E Complaints can be a valuable asset in determining consumer acceptance and pinpointing water quality problems. Customer calls are frequently the first indication that something may be wrong. Responding to complaints and inquiries promptly can save the utility money and staff resources, and minimize customer inconvenience.

Answers to questions on page 598.

23.8A The three main areas of financial management for a utility include providing financial stability for the utility, careful budgeting, and providing capital improvement funds for future utility expansion.

23.8B The operating ratio for a utility is calculated by dividing total revenues by total operating expenses.

23.8C It is important for a manager to get input from other personnel in the utility as well as community leaders as the budgeting process proceeds in order to gain support for the budget and to keep the budget on track once adopted.

23.8D The basic ways for a utility to finance capital improvements are through general obligation bonds, revenue bonds, or loan funding programs.

23.8E A revenue bond is a debt incurred by the community, often to finance utility improvements. User charges provide repayment on the bond.

ANSWERS TO QUESTIONS IN LESSON 3

Answers to questions on page 600.

23.9A The purpose of an O & M program is to maintain design functionality and/or to restore the system components to their original condition and thus functionality. That is, to ensure that the system performs as designed and intended.

23.9B Commonly accepted types of maintenance include corrective maintenance, preventive maintenance, and predictive maintenance.

23.9C The major elements of a good preventive maintenance program include the following:

1. Planning and scheduling,
2. Records management,
3. Spare parts management,
4. Cost and budget control,
5. Emergency repair procedures, and
6. Training program.

Answers to questions on page 601.

23.9D SCADA stands for **S**upervisory **C**ontrol **A**nd **D**ata **A**cquisition system.

23.9E A SCADA system collects, stores, and analyzes information about all aspects of operation and maintenance, transmits alarm signals when necessary, and allows fingertip control of alarms, equipment, and processes.

23.9F Measured (sensed) information could be transmitted by FM radio, leased telephone circuits, private signal lines, dial telephone lines, coaxial cable networks, spread spectrum radio, fiber-optic cable, microwave, 900 MHz radio, cellular telephone, or satellite communications systems.

Answers to questions on page 603.

23.9G   SCADA systems record and store (archive) data in computers for easy retrieval and analysis.

23.9H   Water quality indicators that can be easily monitored by a SCADA system include turbidity, pH, and temperature.

23.9I   When a customer phones and complains about a loss of water pressure, the operator can determine the recorded system pressures near the customer's residence. If there is a loss of water pressure the operator can try to determine the cause (if the water pressure was below an acceptable minimum (30 psi), the SCADA system should have alerted the operators immediately). If there is not a system loss of water pressure, the operator can suggest how the customer can try to locate the cause of the problem on the customer's property.

23.9J   The greatest challenges for operators using SCADA systems are to realize that computers may not be correct and to have the ability to operate when the SCADA system fails.

Answers to questions on page 606.

23.9K   Contamination through cross connections has consistently caused more waterborne disease outbreaks in the United States than any other reported factor.

23.9L   Responsibilities in the implementation of cross connection control programs are shared by water suppliers, water users, health agencies, and plumbing officials.

23.9M   The water user's cross connection control responsibility is to keep contaminants out of the potable water system on the user's premises. The user also has the responsibility to prevent the creation of cross connections through modifications of the plumbing system on the premises.

Answers to questions on page 608.

23.9N   Factors that should be considered when selecting a backflow prevention device include the (1) degree of hazard, (2) probability of backflow occurring, and (3) complexity of the piping on the premises and the probability of its modification.

23.9O   Air gap or reduced pressure principle backflow prevention devices are installed at wastewater treatment plants, wastewater pumping stations, reclaimed water reuse areas, areas where toxic substances in toxic concentrations are handled under pressure, premises having an auxiliary water supply which is or may be contaminated, and in locations where fertilizer, herbicides, or pesticides are injected into a sprinkler system.

Answers to questions on page 611.

23.10A   The first step toward an effective contingency plan for emergencies is to make an assessment of vulnerability. Then a comprehensive plan of action can be developed and implemented.

23.10B   A detailed emergency operations plan is not needed since all types of emergencies cannot be anticipated and a complex response program can be more confusing than helpful.

23.10C   An emergency operations plan should include:

1. Vulnerability assessment,
2. Inventory of personnel,
3. Provisions for a recovery operation,
4. Provisions for training programs for operators in carrying out the plan,
5. Inclusion of coordination plans with health, police, and fire departments,
6. Establishment of a communications procedure, and
7. Provisions for protection of personnel, plant equipment, records, and maps.

Answers to questions on page 612.

23.10D   Toxicity is the ability of a contaminant (chemical or biological) to cause injury when introduced into the body.

23.10E   The degree of toxicity varies with the concentration of contaminant required to cause injury, the speed with which the injury takes place, and the severity of the injury.

23.10F   Possible secondary effects in a water supply which may allow detection of a contaminant without specific testing include taste, odor, color, and chlorine demand.

Answers to questions on page 614.

23.10G   *Cryptosporidium* is a significant public health concern because sensitive populations may become seriously ill even when the drinking water meets or exceeds all current state and federal standards.

23.10H   The most serious threat of *Cryptosporidium* to a public water supply occurs during periods of heavy rains or snow melts that flush areas which are sources of high concentrations of oocysts into waters upstream of a plant intake.

23.10I   A water treatment plant can be operated to protect the public from *Cryptosporidium* by optimizing the treatment processes. The operator must continually verify optimum coagulant doses, be sure filtered water turbidity levels are low, and provide adequate disinfection chemicals and contact times.

Answers to questions on page 615.

23.11A   A safety officer should evaluate every accident, offer recommendations, and keep and apply statistics.

23.11B   The supervisors should be responsible for the implementation of a safety program.

23.11C   Both state and federal regulatory agencies enforce the OSHA requirements.

23.11D   The utility manager is responsible for the safety of the agency's personnel and the public exposed to the water utility's operations. Therefore, the manager must develop and administer an effective safety program and must provide new employee safety training as well as ongoing training for all employees.

23.11E   A safety policy statement should:

1. Define the goals and objectives of the program,
2. Identify the persons responsible for each element of the program,
3. Affirm management's intent to enforce safety regulations, and
4. Describe the disciplinary actions that will be taken to enforce safe work practices.

Answers to questions on page 616.

23.11F A supervisor may be responsible, in part of completely, for an accident by causing unsafe acts to take place, by requiring that work be performed in haste, by disregarding an unsafe environment of the workplace, or by failing to consider any number of safety hazards.

23.11G Each operator must accept, at least in part, responsibility for fellow operators, for the utility's equipment, for the operator's own welfare, and even for seeing that the supervisor complies with established safety regulations.

23.11H First aid means emergency treatment for injury or sudden illness, before regular medical treatment is available.

23.11I First-aid training is most important for operators who regularly work with electrical equipment and those who must handle chlorine and other dangerous chemicals.

Answers to questions on page 620.

23.11J The basic elements of a hazard communication program include the following:

1. Identify hazardous materials,
2. Obtain chemical information and define hazardous conditions,
3. Properly label hazards, and
4. Train operators.

23.11K A utility manager may or may not be involved in the day-to-day details of enforcing the agency's confined space policy and procedures. However, every utility manager should be aware of the current OSHA requirements and should ensure that the utility's policies not only comply with current regulations, but that the agency's policies are vigorously enforced for the safety of all operators.

Answers to questions on page 625.

23.11L The mainstay of a safety program is the method of reporting and keeping statistics.

23.11M All injuries should be reported, even if they are minor in nature, so as to establish a record in case the injury develops into a serious injury. It may be difficult at a later date to prove whether the accident occurred on or off the job and this information may determine who is responsible for the costs.

23.11N A safety officer should review an accident report form to (1) determine corrective actions, and (2) make recommendations.

23.11O A new, inexperienced operator must receive instruction on all aspects of plant safety. This training includes instruction in the handling of chemicals, the dangers of electrical apparatus, fire hazards, and proper maintenance of equipment to prevent accidents. Special instructions are required for specific work environments such as manholes, gases (chlorine and hydrogen sulfide (H_2S)), water safety, and any specific hazards that are unique to your facility. All new operators should be required to participate in a safety orientation program during the first few days of employment, and an overall training program in the first few months.

23.11P If an operator is unsure of how to perform a job, then it is the operator's responsibility to ask for the training needed.

Answers to questions on page 627.

23.11Q Statistical accident reports should contain accident statistics showing lost time, costs, type of injuries, and other data, based on some time interval.

23.11R Injuries can be classified as fractures, burns, bites, eye injuries, cuts, and bruises.

23.11S Causes of injuries can be classified as heat, machinery, falling, handling objects, chemicals, unsafe acts, and miscellaneous.

23.11T Costs of accidents can be classified as lost time, lost dollars, lost production, contaminated water, or any other means of showing the effects of the accidents.

Answers to questions on page 630.

23.12A Some of the important uses of records include:

1. Aiding operators in solving treatment and water quality problems,
2. Providing a method of alerting operators to changes in source water quality,
3. Showing that the treated water is acceptable to the consumer,
4. Documenting that the final product meets plant performance standards, as well as the standards of the regulatory agencies,
5. Determining performance of treatment processes, equipment, and the plant,
6. Satisfying legal requirements,
7. Aiding in answering complaints,
8. Anticipating routine maintenance,
9. Providing data for cost analysis and preparation of budgets,
10. Providing data for future engineering designs, and
11. Providing information for monthly and annual reports.

23.12B "Unaccounted for water" is the difference between the amount of treated water that enters the distribution system and water that is delivered to consumers.

23.12C Chemical inventory and usage records that should be kept include:

1. Chemical inventory/storage (measured use and deliveries),
2. Metered or estimated plant usages, and
3. Calculated usage of chemicals (compare with actual use).

23.12D Important items usually contained on a purchase order include: (1) the date, (2) a complete description of each item and quantity needed, (3) prices, (4) the name of the vender, and (5) a purchase order number.

OBJECTIVE TEST

Chapter 23.   ADMINISTRATION

Please write your name and mark the correct answers on the answer sheet, as directed at the end of Chapter 1. There may be more than one correct answer to each multiple-choice question.

True-False

1. Communities expect utility management to protect the environment and their communities with a minimum investment of money.

   1. True
   2. False

2. The workforce in the environmental field is fairly stable.

   1. True
   2. False

3. Advances in technology are creating changes in the environmental workplace.

   1. True
   2. False

4. The functions of a utility manager are different from those of a CEO, Chief Executive Officer, of a big company.

   1. True
   2. False

5. An operator can serve two or more supervisors.

   1. True
   2. False

6. Delegation requires giving up power and responsibility.

   1. True
   2. False

7. A good manager will delegate and follow up on progress to make sure that the operator has the necessary resources to get the job done.

   1. True
   2. False

8. Most states require certified operators to complete additional training to maintain certification.

   1. True
   2. False

9. Every utility agency should have a complaint or grievance procedure for unhappy employees.

   1. True
   2. False

10. Nothing will destroy morale more quickly than equal treatment of employees.

    1. True
    2. False

11. In many small communities the annual report may be given orally to the city council rather than written.

    1. True
    2. False

12. Every utility worker should be part of the utility team acting to project a good public image.

    1. True
    2. False

13. Being able to show and document the financial stability of the utility is an important part of getting funding for capital improvements.

    1. True
    2. False

14. When a treatment plant is new, the balance in the equipment repair/replacement fund should be decreasing each year.

    1. True
    2. False

15. An emergency operations plan should be as detailed as possible.

    1. True
    2. False

Best Answer (Select only the closest or best answer.)

16. Which problem makes planning most difficult in smaller communities?

    1. Decline in population
    2. Lack of revenue
    3. Stringent regulations
    4. Untrained operators

17. What task is performed by a utility manager when directing?

    1. Evaluating job performance
    2. Hiring staff
    3. Issuing orders and instructions
    4. Training operators

18. Ideally, how many operators should each supervisor manage?

    1. 3 operators
    2. 5 operators
    3. 6 operators
    4. 10 operators

19. What does authority mean?

    1. Authority means an act in which power is given to another person.
    2. Authority means answering to those above in the chain of command.
    3. Authority means being accountable for results.
    4. Authority means the power and resources to do a job.

20. Which one of the following questions is an acceptable interview question?

    1. Do you prefer to work with others or by yourself?
    2. What is the name of your pastor or religious leader?
    3. What is the nationality of your parents or spouse?
    4. What is your age?

21. What is the main purpose of a probationary period for new employees?

    1. Allow time for operator to become certified
    2. Assess the "fit" between the job and the person
    3. Inform employee of utility policies and procedures
    4. Provide safety training

22. Who should conduct an employee's performance evaluation?

    1. Employee of equal rank
    2. Employee's immediate supervisor
    3. Shop steward
    4. Utility manager

23. What is the best way to start a disciplinary meeting with an employee?

    1. Explaining that you want a response that is acceptable to everyone
    2. Identifying the problem
    3. Indicating you are looking for a positive solution
    4. Making a positive comment about the employee

24. What is the name of the federal legislation that governs union activities?

    1. Code of Federal Regulations
    2. Equal Employment Opportunity Act
    3. National Labor Relations Act
    4. Occupational Safety and Health Act

25. What should be the concluding section in an annual report?

    1. Highlights of accomplishments
    2. Projections for next year
    3. Review of how utility operated last year
    4. Summary of expenses

26. What is the first step for developing a public relations plan?

    1. Contact news media
    2. Establish objectives
    3. Identify target audience
    4. Prepare promotional material

27. What must a utility manager have to prepare a good budget?

    1. A method of disregarding uncontrolled increases in costs
    2. A system which prevents spending money not in budget
    3. Good records from previous year
    4. Sufficient revenue

28. What must every treatment facility have to adequately plan for the future?

    1. Compliance with regulations
    2. Maintenance records
    3. Management support
    4. Repair/replacement fund

29. What should a manager look at as a first step in capital planning?

    1. Changes in the community
    2. Current sources of revenue
    3. Existing utility structure
    4. New regulatory requirements

30. What is the main intent of the OSHA regulations?

    1. Create a safe work environment
    2. Identify hazards in the workplace
    3. Protect the public from hazardous chemicals
    4. Train operators in safe procedures

Multiple Choice (Select all correct answers.)

31. What kinds of demands are utility managers expected to meet?

    1. Compliance with regulations
    2. Perform with a minimum investment of money
    3. Population forecasts
    4. Preparation of utility for future
    5. Protection of environment

32. What are the functions of a utility manager?

    1. Controlling
    2. Directing
    3. Organizing
    4. Planning
    5. Staffing

33. Which items are areas of concern for improving water supply system management?

    1. Input to budget process by management only
    2. Monitoring tests are unrepresentative of plant performance
    3. Relatively high job turnover
    4. Treatment system budget combined with other accounts
    5. User charge system inadequately reflects cost of service

34. Who should be involved with utility planning?

    1. Federal officials
    2. Local officials
    3. Operational personnel
    4. Public
    5. Regulators

35. What problems will a utility face without adequate planning?

    1. Adequate staff
    2. Budget surpluses
    3. Inability to meet compliance regulations
    4. Inadequate service capacity
    5. System failures

36. What are the purposes of a utility organizational plan?

    1. Control activities of operators
    2. Identify the lines of authority
    3. Organize plant activities
    4. Provide a means for emergency planning
    5. Show who reports to whom

37. What steps should a supervisor take in conducting a performance evaluation?

    1. Ask employee to sign completed evaluation form
    2. Compare employee's performance against others' performance
    3. Fill out evaluation form
    4. Schedule general staff meeting
    5. Set performance goals for next year

38. Which of the following topics are acceptable on an employee evaluation form?

    1. Attendance
    2. Cooperation and relationships
    3. Initiative
    4. Job knowledge
    5. Quality of work

39. Which of the following groups are considered protected groups in the workforce today?

    1. Disabled persons
    2. Minorities
    3. OUCH groups
    4. Union members
    5. Women

40. What kinds of behavior are considered sexual harassment? Behavior of a sexual nature that is

    1. Annoying.
    2. Hostile.
    3. Humiliating.
    4. Offensive.
    5. Uninvited.

41. What are the essential elements of good written and oral communications?

    1. Audience must understand technical terms
    2. Complete details must be presented
    3. Individual's style of presentation must be consistent
    4. Information must be given
    5. Information must be understood

42. What should be done before a successful meeting?

    1. Find an adequate meeting room
    2. Involve all participants
    3. Prepare an agenda and distribute to participants
    4. Restate your understanding of results
    5. Set a beginning and ending time

43. What are some guidelines for a successful news interview?

    1. Ask to approve a draft of the story
    2. Give as much detail as possible
    3. If you don't know an answer, bluff
    4. Know your facts
    5. State key points early in the interview

44. What are a manager's responsibilities for financial management of a utility?

    1. Careful budgeting
    2. Collecting unpaid bills
    3. Providing capital improvement funds
    4. Providing financial stability
    5. Stopping services for delinquent accounts

45. What is debt service?

    1. Debts owed contractors for work completed
    2. Funds due on a maturing bonded debt
    3. Funds due on redemption of bonds
    4. Interest on outstanding debts
    5. Unpaid debts owed by customers

46. How can the financial stability of a utility be measured?

    1. Consumer Price Index
    2. Coverage ratio
    3. Depreciation expenses
    4. Operating ratio
    5. Payback time

47. What is the purpose of a capital improvement (CIP) fund?

    1. A fund to attract low interest bonds
    2. A method of reducing utility service charges
    3. A profit for the utility
    4. A replacement fund to keep the utility operating in the future
    5. A requirement for obtaining state revolving funds (SRF)

48. Effective O & M (operation and maintenance) programs are based on what types of information?

    1. Condition of system components
    2. Location of system components
    3. Replacement costs of components
    4. Types of components that make up the system
    5. Vulnerability of components in a disaster

49. What are the major elements of a good preventive maintenance program?

    1. Cost and budget control
    2. Large work backlog
    3. Planning and scheduling
    4. Spare parts management
    5. Training program

50. Who is responsible for preventing cross connections which might endanger public water supplies?

    1. Building inspectors
    2. Consumers
    3. Plumbers
    4. Public health agencies
    5. Water suppliers

51. Which types of backflow prevention devices are approved for use at water service connections?

    1. Air gap separation devices
    2. Corporation stop devices
    3. Curb stop devices
    4. Double check valve devices
    5. Reduced pressure principle devices

52. What factors influence the impact of a toxic contaminant in a water supply?

    1. Amount of contaminant
    2. Detention time
    3. Size of water supply
    4. Solubility of contaminant
    5. Type of water distribution system

53. What are the basic elements of a safety program?

    1. Accident investigation
    2. Insurance coverage
    3. Recordkeeping
    4. Safety training for operators
    5. Written safety policy

54. What steps can be taken by management to signal the agency's support for a safety program?

    1. Develop a written safety policy statement
    2. Develop budgets and schedules based on safe practices
    3. Hold the safety officer accountable for any accidents
    4. Provide all employees with appropriate safety equipment
    5. Provide all employees with safety training

55. What are important characteristics of successful tailgate safety meetings?

    1. Held in an auditorium
    2. Held where distractions can be avoided
    3. Held where everyone can hear
    4. Kept short
    5. Scheduled in a suitable location

56. What are important uses or purposes of accident reports?

    1. Correcting hazardous conditions
    2. Deciding what first aid should be administered
    3. Determining if the employer should pay the injured worker's medical costs
    4. Embarrassing supervisors into greater safety awareness
    5. Preventing similar accidents in the future

57. What are some ways safety training can be delivered or reinforced?

    1. Articles in a company newsletter
    2. Awards for good safety records
    3. On-the-job training
    4. Prompt disciplinary action for carelessness
    5. Tailgate sessions

58. What do complete and accurate plant records enable a water utility to do?

    1. Convince customers the water is safe and pleasant to drink
    2. Document compliance with regulatory requirements
    3. Hire only highly qualified operators
    4. Prepare realistic budgets
    5. Solve treatment and water quality problems

End of Objective Test

APPENDIX

WATER TREATMENT PLANT OPERATION

(VOLUME II)

Final Examination and
Suggested Answers

How to Solve Water Treatment Plant
Arithmetic Problems

Water Abbreviations

Water Words

Subject Index

FINAL EXAMINATION

VOLUME II

This final examination was prepared *TO HELP YOU RE-VIEW* the material in this manual. The questions are divided into five types:

1. True-False,

2. Best Answer,

3. Multiple Choice,

4. Short Answer, and

5. Problems.

To work this examination:

1. Write the answers to each question in your notebook,

2. After you have worked a group of questions (you decide how many), check your answers with the suggested answers at the end of this exam, and

3. If you missed a question and don't understand why, reread the material in the manual.

You may wish to use this examination for review purposes when preparing for civil service and certification examinations.

Since you have already completed this course, you do not have to send your answers to California State University, Sacramento.

True-False

1. Iron or manganese is most frequently found in water systems supplied by surface waters.

    1. True
    2. False

2. Iron and manganese ion exchange units are similar to an upflow pressure filter.

    1. True
    2. False

3. The dose of potassium permanganate to control iron and manganese must be exact.

    1. True
    2. False

4. Hydrofluosilicic acid is easier to feed than other powdered fluoridation chemicals because it is more soluble in water.

    1. True
    2. False

5. Both volumetric and gravimetric feeders measure volume of chemical delivered during a specific time period.

    1. True
    2. False

6. Fluoridation must be a continuous operation.

    1. True
    2. False

7. A positive Langelier Index indicates that water is corrosive.

    1. True
    2. False

8. Alkalinity is the capacity of water to neutralize bases.

    1. True
    2. False

9. Carbonate hardness can be removed by soda only.

    1. True
    2. False

10. The use of packing on brine pumps is recommended over mechanical seals.

    1. True
    2. False

11. The MCL for TTHMs was established on the basis of the health effects data.

    1. True
    2. False

12. For many systems, a large part of the production of THMs will take place after the water leaves the treatment plant.

    1. True
    2. False

13. Removing free chlorine from the chlorine/bromide/precursor reaction will stop the formation of any significant amount of THMs.

    1. True
    2. False

14. Demineralization is the process which removes dissolved minerals (salts) from water.

    1. True
    2. False

15. The mineral flux through a membrane depends on pressure.

    1. True
    2. False

16. Oxidizing agents, such as chlorine, should be removed by pretreatment before RO units to prevent membrane degradation.

    1. True
    2. False

17. Alum may sometimes be used instead of organic polymers to reduce the quantity of sludge produced.
    1. True
    2. False

18. Polymer sludges are suitable as a soil conditioner.
    1. True
    2. False

19. Electricity will flow through a circuit when a switch is open.
    1. True
    2. False

20. Electrical problems result from some type of mechanical failure.
    1. True
    2. False

21. Too much grease in antifriction type bearings (ball or roller) promotes friction and heat.
    1. True
    2. False

22. Never operate a piston pump against a closed discharge valve.
    1. True
    2. False

23. Replace only damaged V-belts on a multiple-drive unit.
    1. True
    2. False

24. Flowmeters are calibrated to read out flows in velocity units.
    1. True
    2. False

25. When water is forced to go faster in a pipe, the pressure in the pipe increases.
    1. True
    2. False

26. An analog display is a direct numerical readout.
    1. True
    2. False

27. The most common reason for an inoperable instrument is an unnoticed failure of the instrument air supply.
    1. True
    2. False

28. Always pour acid into water, never the reverse.
    1. True
    2. False

29. From the standpoint of safety, both weak and strong bases must be given the same consideration when being handled.
    1. True
    2. False

30. Liquid alum is acidic and very corrosive.
    1. True
    2. False

31. Once a lockout device is installed, it is not removed until repairs are complete unless removal is authorized by an appropriate official.
    1. True
    2. False

32. When using a spectrophotometer, a water sample which has a low color intensity will have a low percent transmittance.
    1. True
    2. False

33. Always record the temperature of the water at the time of sampling when measuring dissolved oxygen.
    1. True
    2. False

34. The solubility of calcium carbonate varies with temperature.
    1. True
    2. False

35. MCLs apply only to contaminants from manmade pollution.
    1. True
    2. False

36. The health concerns about inorganic chemicals are centered on cancer.
    1. True
    2. False

37. Filtered water must have a disinfectant residual at the entrance to the distribution system of at least 0.2 mg/L.
    1. True
    2. False

38. An operator can serve two or more supervisors.
    1. True
    2. False

39. Delegation requires giving up power and responsibility.
    1. True
    2. False

40. When a treatment plant is new, the balance in the equipment repair/replacement fund should be decreasing each year.
    1. True
    2. False

Best Answer (Select only the closest or best answer.)

1. How can the growth of iron bacteria be controlled?
    1. Chlorination
    2. Coagulation
    3. Filtration
    4. Sedimentation

2. Why should chlorine never be fed ahead of the polyphosphate when controlling iron and manganese?
    1. Chlorine after polyphosphate lowers chlorine doses
    2. Chlorine after polyphosphate reduces THMs
    3. Chlorine will cause insoluble precipitates to form too soon
    4. Wrong, chlorine should be fed ahead to increase CT value

3. How can the greensand filter media be kept in a free, loose, fluid condition?

   1. Agitate media with an air wash or air-water wash
   2. Backwash with treated water
   3. Cleanse media with a detergent solution
   4. Reverse flows and use a chlorine wash

4. What problems are caused by hard water in systems using saturators?

   1. Excessive fluoride doses
   2. Irregular fluoride doses
   3. pH fluctuations
   4. Scaling

5. Where should fluoride be added to drinking water?

   1. After addition of coagulant chemical
   2. At intake to maximize contact time
   3. Before filtration
   4. Where least possible removal of fluoride occurs

6. Why must any potable water line connected to a chemical feeder unit be provided with a vacuum breaker or an air gap? To prevent

   1. Cross connection.
   2. Overfeeding.
   3. Suction of chemicals.
   4. Water hammer.

7. What does water hardness measure?

   1. Concentration of anions in water
   2. Concentration of cations in water
   3. Incompressibility of water
   4. Soap- and detergent-consuming power of water

8. What is a limitation of the lime-soda softening process?

   1. Color removal may be complicated
   2. Inactivation of bacteria
   3. Removal of excess fluoride
   4. Removal of iron and manganese

9. What happens if quicklime accidentally gets wet?

   1. Considerable heat will be generated
   2. Hardness will not be removed
   3. Quicklime will not dissolve in water
   4. Storage time will be increased

10. What is ion exchange softening?

    1. Exchanging hard water for soft water
    2. Exchanging hardness-causing ions for alkalinity ions
    3. Exchanging hardness-causing ions for sodium ions
    4. Exchanging softening chemicals for resins

11. Where should representative samples be collected to determine the extent of a THM problem?

    1. Clear well of treatment plant
    2. Distribution system
    3. Intake of treatment plant
    4. Source watershed

12. Why is removing THMs after they are formed NOT a strategy of choice?

    1. Effectiveness of disinfecting chemical will be reduced
    2. Removal of high concentrations of THMs cannot be achieved
    3. Strategy will allow for a continued chlorine demand
    4. THMs will continue to form in distribution systems

13. What happens to the water flux through the membrane as the mineral content of the feed decreases?

    1. Decreases
    2. Fluctuates
    3. Increases
    4. Stays constant

14. How does an increase in feedwater temperature affect membrane performance?

    1. Flux decreases
    2. Flux increases
    3. Mineral rejection capacity increases
    4. Rate of hydrolysis is decreased

15. What is a disinfection option other than chlorination for a reverse osmosis (RO) process?

    1. Brine solution
    2. Permanganate
    3. pH adjustment
    4. Ultraviolet

16. How often should sedimentation tanks be drained and cleaned?

    1. When adequate sludge density is achieved
    2. When sludge buildup interferes with the treatment processes
    3. When the designer/manufacturer recommends
    4. When the operator has the time

17. What is a key to speedy sludge drying?

    1. Dewater sludge using a filter press.
    2. Rake up dried sludge.
    3. Regularly remove water on top of sludge.
    4. Remove sludge during day to a drying bed.

18. How can the efficiency of the sand drying bed dewatering process be improved?

    1. Apply greater depths of wet sludge.
    2. Precondition process sludge with chemical coagulants.
    3. Prevent formation of cracks in drying sludge.
    4. Treat sludge using a centrifuge.

19. What should you do when maintenance tasks are beyond your capabilities or repair facilities?

    1. Read manufacturer's literature
    2. Request assistance
    3. Substitute alternative procedures
    4. Try to perform maintenance task

20. What could happen if battery cables are not properly connected?

    1. An arc of electricity across the battery could cause an explosion
    2. The battery will be "dead" again
    3. The engine will consume too much gas
    4. The vehicle will run too fast

21. What does electrical voltage measure?

    1. Electrical pressure available to cause a flow of current
    2. Indication of work being done
    3. Rate at which power is being used
    4. Resistance to the flow of current

22. What should be done if a centrifugal pump is vibrating excessively after start-up?

    1. Lower pump speed
    2. Reduce discharge pressure head
    3. Reduce flows
    4. Shut unit down and isolate pump

23. What is the primary use of a butterfly valve?

    1. Control flow
    2. Measure flow
    3. Regulate flow pressure
    4. Stop flow

24. What is a snubber?

    1. Air cushion chamber
    2. Mechanical pressure element
    3. Primary element
    4. Surge protection device

25. What is a problem encountered when using probes to measure water levels?

    1. Accumulation of scum on probe
    2. Measuring entire range of depth readings
    3. Rods move up and down
    4. Signals can't be transmitted electronically

26. What is the most precise method of measuring liquid level?

    1. Bubbler
    2. Float
    3. Probe
    4. Target pointer

27. How are bases neutralized?

    1. Dilute acids
    2. Dilute bases
    3. Salts
    4. Strong acids

28. What is the first safety measure an operator should take when entering a chlorination room?

    1. Determine location of self-contained breathing apparatus
    2. Look for chlorine leaks
    3. Make sure ventilating system is working
    4. Measure chlorine concentration in atmosphere

29. According to OSHA law, what type of paperwork must be completed before entering a confined space?

    1. Entry permit
    2. NPDES permit
    3. Safety and health permit
    4. Sewer-use permit

30. What type of gloves would provide suitable protection against sparks, chips, rough material, and moderate heat?

    1. Aluminized
    2. Leather
    3. Neoprene or cork-dipped
    4. Rubber

31. What is an undesirable effect of iron in drinking water?

    1. Corrosion
    2. Precipitate formation
    3. Scale formation
    4. Staining

32. Which method should be performed if turbidity is present in a sample being tested for manganese?

    1. Bleaching
    2. Chlorinating
    3. Filtering
    4. Straining

33. Why is sulfate of concern in drinking water?

    1. Cause of tastes and odors
    2. Formation of scale on heat exchangers
    3. Reactive with soaps and detergents
    4. Responsible for staining plumbing fixtures

34. Why is turbidity of importance to public health?

    1. Causes bad tastes
    2. Interferes with disinfection
    3. Looks undesirable
    4. Requires filtration

35. Why are sanitary surveys conducted?

    1. Establish 95th percentile MPN values to meet coliform standards
    2. Identify possible health risks that may not be discovered by routine coliform sampling
    3. Search for alternative sources of water supply
    4. Survey consumers regarding establishment of Coliform Rule standards

36. How does the SWTR define surface water?

    1. All water open to the atmosphere and subject to surface runoff
    2. All water that is not considered groundwater
    3. Any stream, river, reservoir, or lake with surface runoff flow
    4. Water whose surface is exposed to the atmosphere

37. Ideally, how many operators should each supervisor manage?

    1. 3 operators
    2. 5 operators
    3. 6 operators
    4. 10 operators

38. What is the main purpose of a probationary period for new employees?

    1. Allow time for operator to become certified
    2. Assess the "fit" between the job and the person
    3. Inform employee of utility policies and procedures
    4. Provide safety training

39. What should a manager look at as a first step in capital planning?

    1. Changes in the community
    2. Current sources of revenue
    3. Existing utility structure
    4. New regulatory requirements

Multiple Choice (Select all correct answers.)

1. How can iron and manganese be easily detected in water?

    1. Color of filter media
    2. Color of filter walls
    3. Color of raw water
    4. Odor of raw water
    5. Taste of raw water

2. What are the most common treatment processes used to control iron and manganese?

   1. Ion exchange
   2. Oxidation with chlorine
   3. Oxidation with permanganate
   4. Phosphate treatment
   5. Reduction by aeration

3. What should be done if a dose of chlorine added to treated water produces a brown- or rust-colored floc?

   1. Adjust pH
   2. Decrease chemical dose
   3. Increase chemical dose
   4. Increase flows
   5. Reduce flows

4. What could be the cause of excessive pressure drop across a greensand filter bed immediately after backwashing?

   1. Accumulation of greensand fines at surface of bed
   2. Backwash rate too low
   3. Channeling through filters
   4. Filter bed cemented as evidenced by mounding around periphery of vessel
   5. Well throwing fine sand, silt, and colloidal clay

5. What types of pumps are used to add fluoride ions to water?

   1. Centrifugal pumps
   2. Diaphragm pumps
   3. Electronic pumps
   4. Peristaltic pumps
   5. Propeller pumps

6. What items should be included in a checklist for shutting down a fluoride chemical system?

   1. Drain and clean the mix and feed tanks
   2. Flush out the chemical supply lines with water
   3. Flush out the solution lines with water
   4. Leave the water supply to the chemical system on
   5. Shut off and lock out the electrical power

7. What sanitary defects could develop in a fluoridation system?

   1. Fluoridation chemical not meeting AWWA specifications
   2. Inadequate feed rate control equipment
   3. Inadequate free chlorine residual in treated water
   4. Lack of backflow safeguards
   5. No analyzer to measure fluoride ion levels in treated water

8. What are some of the benefits of softening in addition to the removal of hardness?

   1. Control of corrosion with proper stabilization
   2. Lack of process wastes for ultimate disposal
   3. Removal of iron and manganese
   4. Removal of radioactivity
   5. Sometimes a reduction in tastes and odors

9. Which water treatment chemical(s) lowers the pH of the water being treated?

   1. Aluminum sulfate (alum)
   2. Caustic soda
   3. Hydrated lime
   4. Soda ash
   5. Sodium hypochlorite

10. What are the advantages of using caustic soda instead of soda ash for softening?

    1. Ease of handling and storage
    2. Less safety hazard
    3. Less sludge is formed
    4. Protective clothing need not be worn when handling
    5. Stability in storage

11. What are the common stages of operation of an ion exchange softener?

    1. Backwash
    2. Brine
    3. Maintenance
    4. Rinse
    5. Service

12. Where should samples be collected for THMs?

    1. Faucets with aerators
    2. Faucets with hoses
    3. Hose bibs
    4. Sampling taps
    5. Swivel faucets

13. What types of treatment processes are available to remove THMs after they are formed?

    1. Adsorption
    2. Aeration
    3. Clarification
    4. Filtration
    5. Oxidation

14. What treatment processes can be used to remove THM precursors?

    1. Adsorption
    2. Aeration
    3. Clarification
    4. Ion exchange
    5. Oxidation

15. What types of semipermeable membranes are used most often for demineralization?

    1. Cellulose acetate
    2. Geosynthetics
    3. Permeable rubber
    4. Porous plastic
    5. Thin film composites

16. What factors influence the piping material used for reverse osmosis units?

    1. Water compressibility
    2. Water flow rate
    3. Water pressure
    4. Water salinity
    5. Water temperature

17. What are the symptoms of membrane fouling?

    1. High pressure difference
    2. Higher product water flow rate
    3. Higher salt rejection
    4. Lower product water flow rate
    5. Lower salt rejection

18. What are the advantages of the electrodialysis process for demineralization?

    1. Efficient removal of most inorganic constituents
    2. Low cost of operation
    3. Minimal operator knowledge required
    4. Waste brine contains only salts removed
    5. Well-developed technology

19. What chemical solutions are used in electrodialysis cleaning?

    1. Caustic soda
    2. Chelating agents
    3. Citric acid
    4. Detergents
    5. Hydrochloric acid

20. What are the advantages of polymer sludge over alum sludge?

    1. Denser
    2. Easier to dewater
    3. Less costly
    4. Removes hardness
    5. Treats all waters

21. What sludge treatment processes are used by plants that produce large volumes of sludge to reduce the volume of sludge that must be handled and ultimately disposed of?

    1. Coagulation
    2. Conditioning
    3. Dewatering
    4. Elutriation
    5. Thickening

22. What sludge treatment processes are used to dewater sludges?

    1. Belt filter presses
    2. Centrifuges
    3. Sand drying beds
    4. Screw pumps
    5. Solar lagoons

23. What information should be included on an equipment service card?

    1. Date each maintenance task was completed
    2. Description of each required maintenance service
    3. Frequency of required services
    4. References that provide instructions for each task
    5. Signature of the person who performed the task

24. What are fuses installed to protect?

    1. Circuits
    2. Electrical equipment
    3. Heaters
    4. Motors
    5. Operators

25. What are possible causes of bearing failures?

    1. Entry of water into bearing housing
    2. Frequent starts and stops
    3. Lack of or improper lubricant
    4. Mechanical unbalance of rotating parts
    5. Misalignment of coupling

26. What special precautions must be followed when handling or storing oils and greases?

    1. Avoid creating a fire hazard
    2. Keep any spills wiped up
    3. Keep materials and containers clean
    4. Make sure lids are tight on containers
    5. Post "NO SMOKING" signs in area

27. What are some unusual conditions for electric motors?

    1. Bearings smelling hot
    2. Excessive humming
    3. Excessive sparking at brushes
    4. Rapid knocking
    5. Vibration

28. Which of the following are level sensing devices?

    1. Capacitance probe
    2. Direct pressure
    3. Float
    4. Pneumatic bubbler
    5. Sonar

29. Which process variables are usually monitored closely and continuously in a water treatment plant?

    1. Chlorine residual
    2. Coliforms
    3. Nitrate
    4. pH
    5. Turbidity

30. What are the causes of erratic instrument operation?

    1. Fluctuating process variable
    2. Low temperature
    3. Oil in air supply
    4. Water in air supply
    5. Windy conditions

31. What are an operator's general responsibilities for safety?

    1. Develop a safety program
    2. Investigate accidents
    3. Report all injuries
    4. Report observed hazards
    5. Use safe work procedures

32. What steps should be taken immediately if one of the fusible plugs melts on a one-ton chlorine tank?

    1. If working alone, call for assistance
    2. Insert a new plug
    3. Position the tank with the leak on top
    4. Turn on the ventilation system
    5. Use an ammonia-soaked swab to check for leaking chlorine

33. Salts may be sources of what types of safety hazards?

    1. Burns
    2. Explosions
    3. Illness
    4. Loss of eyesight
    5. Violent chemical reactions

34. Which of the following are procedures for safely handling and storing activated carbon?

    1. Increase the humidity in storage areas to control dust
    2. Install fire hoses with water jet nozzles to extinguish fires
    3. Store bags of activated carbon in single rows
    4. Use explosion-proof equipment and wiring in storage areas
    5. Warn operators to use caution when smoking near activated carbon

35. What atmospheric conditions must be tested for in a confined space?

    1. Explosive gases
    2. Inert gases
    3. Nitrogen gases
    4. Oxygen deficiency
    5. Toxic gases

36. Information from algae counts can serve which of the following purposes?

    1. Help document variability in the water quality
    2. Help explain the cause of color and turbidity
    3. Help explain the clogging of screens or filters
    4. Help explain the failure of floc formation
    5. Help explain the presence of tastes and odors

37. What important facts should an operator know about chloride?

    1. Chloride content increases as mineral content of water increases
    2. Chloride gives water an objectionable taste
    3. Chloride in water is a serious health hazard
    4. Chloride occurs in natural waters as a basic salt
    5. The maximum allowable concentration is based on taste rather than the physical or health hazards of chloride

38. Why is dissolved oxygen (DO) important to the water treatment plant operator?

    1. Dissolved oxygen must be present in surface waters for survival of fish
    2. Hardness increases with increases in dissolved oxygen
    3. Low dissolved oxygen at bottom of lakes can cause taste and odor problems
    4. Presence of dissolved oxygen can contribute to pipe corrosion
    5. Taste of water is improved by dissolved oxygen

39. Which of the following are types of organic contaminants?

    1. Disinfection by-products
    2. Herbicides
    3. Pesticides
    4. Solvents
    5. Trihalomethanes

40. Which of the following treatment methods may be used to control lead and copper?

    1. Aeration
    2. Coagulation-filtration
    3. Ion exchange
    4. Lime softening
    5. Reverse osmosis

41. The required CT value to achieve inactivation of microorganisms depends on which of the following factors?

    1. Organism being inactivated
    2. Percent dissolved oxygen saturation
    3. pH of water
    4. Temperature of water
    5. Type of disinfectant

42. Which of the following are Tier 1 violations? Failure to comply with

    1. MCL.
    2. Monitoring requirements.
    3. Testing procedure.
    4. Treatment technique.
    5. Variance or exemption.

43. What kinds of demands are utility managers expected to meet?

    1. Compliance with regulations
    2. Perform with a minimum investment of money
    3. Population forecasts
    4. Preparation of utility for future
    5. Protection of environment

44. What problems will a utility face without adequate planning?

    1. Adequate staff
    2. Budget surpluses
    3. Inability to meet compliance regulations
    4. Inadequate service capacity
    5. System failures

45. Which of the following groups are considered protected groups in the workforce today?

    1. Disabled persons
    2. Minorities
    3. OUCH groups
    4. Union members
    5. Women

46. What are a manager's responsibilities for financial management of a utility?

    1. Careful budgeting
    2. Collecting unpaid bills
    3. Providing capital improvement funds
    4. Providing financial stability
    5. Stopping services for delinquent accounts

47. What are the major elements of a good preventive maintenance program?

    1. Cost and budget control
    2. Large work backlog
    3. Planning and scheduling
    4. Spare parts management
    5. Training program

Short Answer

1. What problems are caused by iron and manganese in drinking water?

2. Where should a sample for iron and manganese testing be collected?

3. How do polyphosphates control manganese?

4. How does the pH of the water influence the rate of oxidation or iron to insoluble ferric hydroxide?

5. What happens when an ion exchange resin becomes fouled with iron rust or manganese dioxide?

6. What is the purpose of a reaction basin following the aeration process?

7. How does an operator decide when to backwash a manganese greensand filter?

8. Why are drinking waters fluoridated?

9. List the three compounds most commonly used to fluoridate water.

10. What is a saturator?

11. Why must overfeeding of fluoridation chemicals be prevented?

12. List the safety equipment that should be available near a fluoridation system.

13. Why should water be softened?

14. What causes hardness in water?

15. What is recarbonation?

16. What compounds are formed when calcium and magnesium are precipitated out of water in the lime softening process?

17. What types of chemical feeders are used to apply dry lime?

18. What test is used to determine if water is stable?

19. When running jar tests, how would you determine the optimum dosage for a coagulant, lime, and soda ash for softening water?

20. How would you determine if an ion exchange softener rinse stage has been successful?

21. How are trihalomethanes formed?

22. What important factors influence the production of trihalomethanes?

23. What is the influence of higher temperatures and pH on the production of trihalomethanes (THMs)?

24. What items must be considered before an alternative disinfectant is applied to any water system?

25. List the common membrane demineralizing processes.

26. What usually happens to water flux with time? Explain.

27. How does fouling develop on membranes?

28. How will an increase in feedwater temperature influence the water flux?

29. How does the operator of a reverse osmosis plant avoid possible damage to the membrane from scaling?

30. How is the operating pressure on a reverse osmosis unit regulated?

31. When should the reverse osmosis elements be cleaned?

32. What must be removed by pretreatment of the feedwater supply to an electrodialysis unit?

33. What items must be considered to prevent biological fouling of the cation and anion membranes in an electrodialysis unit?

34. Why are strict laws needed regarding the disposal of process wastes?

35. The amount of sludge produced by a conventional water filtration plant depends on what factors?

36. What precautions must be taken before draining a tank?

37. Describe a typical sludge drying bed.

38. Why should sludge be disposed of as close as possible to the water treatment plant?

39. What is the purpose of monitoring and reporting for a sludge disposal program?

40. Why should operators thoroughly read and understand manufacturers' literature before attempting to maintain plant equipment?

41. What protective devices are used to protect operators and equipment from being harmed by electricity?

42. What is cavitation?

43. Why is cleanliness important in the storage and use of lubricants?

44. What is a cross connection?

45. How would you determine if a motor is running unusually hot?

46. What happens when couplings are not in proper alignment?

47. List five common types of valves found in water treatment facilities?

48. List some possible uses of gasoline engines in water treatment plants.

49. How would you search for chlorine leaks?

50. What is an advantage of instruments over our human senses?

51. What is the difference between precision and accuracy?

52. What is the purpose of an electrical lockout device?

53. What is a sensor?

54. How does a bubbler measure the level of a liquid?

55. How are flows measured with Venturi meters?

56. How are charts driven in remote locations where electricity is not available?

57. What basic principle should guide you in programming the frequency of operation of an ON/OFF control?

58. Why is it poor practice to ignore many of the lamps that are "lit up" (alarm conditions) on an annunciator panel?

59. What problems are created by oil and moisture in instrument air, and how can these contaminants be removed?

60. How could you tell if a float might be stuck and how would you determine if it was actually stuck?

61. Who is responsible for safety?

62. What are the causes of most accidents?

63. How can ammonia leaks be detected?

64. Where are chlorine leaks most often found?

65. What is the first-aid treatment for lime burns?

66. How can an operator detect an activated carbon fire?

67. How can an operator prevent fires in a water treatment plant?

68. What precautions should be taken when operating power tools in a wet or damp location?

69. List four examples of stored energy that could be hazardous to operators.

70. Where should respiratory apparatus be stored?

71. What is the most common reason safety equipment falls into disrepair?

72. What are the units of measurements for spectrophotometers?

73. What are the two general types of color found in water and what is the cause of each type?

74. What is the purpose of the Marble Test?

75. How would you interpret the meaning of changes (away from normal) in conductivity in water?

76. What are Maximum Contaminant Levels (MCLs)?

77. What is a community water system?

78. Why are coliform bacteria found in drinking water and what does their presence indicate?

79. Why are secondary drinking water regulations important?

80. What items should be covered in a consumer confidence report?

81. Why should a manager thoroughly examine the functions and staffing of the utility on a periodic basis?

82. What type of training should be provided for supervisors?

83. What is a manager's responsibility for preventing harassment in the workplace?

84. What factors should be considered when selecting a backflow prevention device for a particular situation?

85. How can a good safety record be accomplished?

Problems

1. What is the setting on a potassium permanganate chemical feeder in pounds per day if the required chemical dose is 2.4 mg/L and the flow is 0.48 MGD?

1. 1.2 lbs/day
2. 4.0 lbs/day
3. 9.6 lbs/day
4. 13.5 lbs/day
5. 20.0 lbs/day

2. A flow of 1.2 MGD is to be treated with an 18-percent solution of hydrofluosilicic acid (H_2SiF_6). The water to be treated contains no fluoride and the desired fluoride concentration is 1.4 mg/L. Assume the hydrofluosilicic acid weighs 9.5 pounds per gallon and 79.2 percent fluoride purity of the acid. Calculate the hydrofluosilicic acid feed rate in gallons per day. Select the closest answer.

1. 5.8 GPD
2. 10.3 GPD
3. 11.6 GPD
4. 12.9 GPD
5. 14.5 GPD

3. The feed solution from a saturator containing 1.8 percent fluoride ion is used to treat a flow of 550,000 gallons per day. The desired dose is 1.3 mg/L of fluoride ion and the raw water does not have any fluoride. Calculate the feed rate of the saturator solution in gallons per day. Select the closest answer.

1. 27.8 gal/day
2. 39.7 gal/day
3. 46.9 gal/day
4. 65.0 gal/day
5. 84.4 gal/day

4. How many gallons of water with a hardness of 16 grains per gallon may be treated with an ion exchange softener with an exchange capacity of 12,000 kilograins?

1. 0.31 M gal
2. 0.53 M gal
3. 0.58 M gal
4. 0.64 M gal
5. 0.75 M gal

5. Results of the quarterly average TTHM measurements for five quarters are given below. What is the running annual average of quarterly TTHM measurements at the end of the period?

Quarter	1	2	3	4	5
Avg Quarterly TTHM, µg/L	77	61	87	58	74

1. 56 µg/L
2. 70 µg/L
3. 71 µg/L
4. 89 µg/L
5. 95 µg/L

6. Estimate the ability of a reverse osmosis plant to reject minerals by calculating the mineral rejection as a percent. The feedwater contains 1,800 mg/L TDS and the product water TDS is 130 mg/L.

1. 88%
2. 90%
3. 92%
4. 93%
5. 94%

7. Estimate the pumping capacity of a pump in gallons per minute if it takes 14 minutes for the water level in a tank to drop 3 feet. The tank is 8 feet in diameter.

1. 14 GPM
2. 31 GPM
3. 72 GPM
4. 80 GPM
5. 90 GPM

8. Calculate the feed rate of a dry chemical feeder in pounds per day if 4.0 pounds of chemical are caught in a weighing tin during 14 minutes.

   1. 180 lbs/day
   2. 206 lbs/day
   3. 310 lbs/day
   4. 410 lbs/day
   5. 1,440 lbs/day

9. Calculate the threshold odor number (TON) for a sample. The first detectable odor occurred when the 20-mL sample was diluted to 200 mL (180 mL of odor-free water was added to the 20-mL sample).

   1. 5
   2. 8
   3. 10
   4. 13
   5. 15

SUGGESTED ANSWERS FOR FINAL EXAMINATION
VOLUME II

True-False

1. False   Water systems supplied by wells and springs most frequently have iron and manganese.

2. False   Iron and manganese ion exchange units are similar to a downflow pressure filter.

3. True   The dose of potassium permanganate for iron and manganese must be exact.

4. False   Hydrofluosilicic acid is a liquid, *NOT* a powdered fluoridation chemical.

5. False   Gravimetric feeders measure the weight of chemical delivered.

6. False   Fluoridation does *NOT* have to be a continuous operation.

7. False   A negative Langelier Index indicates that water is corrosive; a positive Langelier Index indicates a scale-forming tendency in the water.

8. False   Alkalinity is the capacity of water to neutralize acids.

9. False   Carbonate hardness can be removed by lime only.

10. True   Packing is recommended over mechanical seals on brine pumps.

11. False   The MCL for TTHMs was *NOT* established on basis of health effects data, but was set as a feasible level for compliance.

12. True   Production of THMs will take place after water leaves the treatment plant.

13. True   Removing free chlorine from the chlorine/bromide/precursor reaction will stop the formation of THMs.

14. True   Demineralization is a process which removes dissolved minerals from water.

15. False   The mineral flux through a membrane does *NOT* depend on pressure.

16. True   Remove oxidizing agents before RO units to prevent membrane degradation.

17. False   Organic polymers may be used instead of alum to reduce the quantity of sludge.

18. True   Polymer sludges are suitable as a soil conditioner.

19. False   Electricity will flow through a circuit when a switch is closed.

20. True   Electrical problems result from some type of mechanical failure.

21. True   Too much grease in antifriction bearings promotes friction and heat.

22. True   Never operate a piston pump against a closed discharge valve.

23. False   Replace the complete set with a set of matched belts.

24. False   Flowmeters read out flows in an appropriate unit of flow rate.

25. False   Pressure in a pipe decreases when the water goes faster.

26. False A digital display is a direct numerical readout.

27. True   Inoperable instruments commonly result from failure of the air supply.

28. True   Always pour acid into water, never the reverse.

29. True   Give both weak and strong bases the same safety considerations.

30. True   Liquid alum is acidic and very corrosive.

31. True   Once a lockout device is installed, it is not removed until repairs are complete.

32. False A sample which has low color intensity will have high percent transmittance.

33. True   Always record temperature of water when measuring dissolved oxygen.

34. True   The solubility of calcium carbonate varies with temperature.

35. False MCLs apply to naturally occurring contaminants and manmade pollution.

36. False Health concerns for inorganic chemicals center on human disorders but *NOT* cancer.

37. True   The disinfectant residual must be at least 0.2 mg/*L*.

38. False An operator can serve only one supervisor.

39. True   Delegation requires giving up power and responsibility.

40. False When plant is new, balance in fund should be increasing each year.

Best Answer

1. 1 Chlorination can control the growth of iron bacteria.

2. 3 Chlorine should never be fed ahead of the polyphosphate when controlling iron and manganese due to formation of insoluble precipitates.

3. 1 Agitation with an air wash or air-water wash will keep greensand filter media free and loose.

4. 4 Scaling problems are caused by hard water in systems using saturators.

5. 4 Add fluoride where the least possible removal of fluoride occurs.

6. 1 A vacuum breaker or air gap prevents a cross connection.

7. 4 Hardness measures the soap- and detergent-consuming power of water.

8. 1 Color removal may be complicated by lime-soda softening.

9. 1 Considerable heat will be generated if quicklime accidentally gets wet.

10. 3 Ion exchange softening exchanges hardness-causing ions for sodium ions.

11. 2 Collect samples from the distribution system to determine the extent of a THM problem.

12. 4 Removing THMs after they are formed is not a good strategy because they will continue to form in distribution systems.

13. 3 Water flux increases through the membrane as the mineral content of the feed decreases.

14. 2 An increase in feedwater temperature causes an increase in flux.

15. 4 Ultraviolet light is a disinfection option other than chlorination for a reverse osmosis (RO) process.

16. 2 Sedimentation tanks should be drained and cleaned when sludge buildup interferes with the treatment processes.

17. 3 The key to speedy sludge drying is regular removal of water on top of the sludge.

18. 2 The efficiency of the sand drying bed dewatering process can be improved by preconditioning the process sludge with chemical coagulants.

19. 2 When maintenance tasks are beyond your capabilities or repair facilities, request assistance.

20. 1 If battery cables are not properly connected, an arc of electricity across the battery could cause an explosion.

21. 1 Electrical voltage measures the electrical pressure available to cause a flow of current.

22. 4 When a centrifugal pump is vibrating excessively after start-up, shut the unit down and isolate the pump.

23. 1 The primary use of a butterfly valve is to control flow.

24. 4 A snubber is a surge protection device.

25. 1 Scum accumulation on probes is a problem when using probes to measure water levels.

26. 1 The most precise method of measuring liquid level is the bubbler.

27. 1 Bases are neutralized with dilute acids.

28. 3 When entering a chlorination room, make sure the ventilating system is working.

29. 1 OSHA law requires that a confined space entry permit be obtained before entering the confined space.

30. 2 Leather gloves protect well against sparks, chips, rough materials, and moderate heat.

31. 4 An undesirable effect of iron in drinking water is staining.

32. 1 The bleaching method should be used if turbidity is present in a sample being tested for manganese.

33. 2 Sulfate is a concern in drinking water because it forms scale on heat exchangers.

34. 2 Turbidity is of public health importance because it interferes with disinfection.

35. 2 Sanitary surveys are conducted to identify possible health risks not discovered by routine coliform sampling.

36. 1 The SWTR defines surface water as all water that is open to the atmosphere and subject to surface runoff.

37. 3 Ideally, each supervisor should only manage 6 or 7 operators.

38. 2   The main purpose of a probationary period for new employees is to assess the "fit" between the job and the person.

39. 1   Capital planning begins with looking at changes in the community.

Multiple Choice

1. 1, 2   Iron and manganese can easily be detected by a brown or black color of the filter media or a brown or black stain on the filter walls.

2. 1, 2, 3, 4   The most common treatment processes used to control iron and manganese are ion exchange, oxidation with chlorine or permanganate, and phosphate treatment.

3. 3, 5   If a brown- or rust-colored floc is produced when a dose of chlorine is added to treated water, increase the chemical dose or reduce flows.

4. 1, 2, 4, 5   Excessive pressure drop across a greensand filter bed immediately after backwashing could be caused by an accumulation of greensand fines at the surface of the bed, too low a backwash rate, cementing (hardening) of the filter bed, or an excess of fine sand, silt, and colloidal clay from the water supply well.

5. 2, 3, 4   Diaphragm pumps, electronic pumps, and peristaltic pumps are used to add fluoride ions to water.

6. 1, 2, 3, 5   Items that should be included on a checklist for shutting down a fluoride chemical system include draining and cleaning the mix and feed tanks, flushing the chemical supply lines and the solution lines with water, and shutting off and locking out electrical power.

7. 1, 2, 3, 4, 5   Sanitary defects that could develop in a fluoridation system include chemical not meeting AWWA specifications, inadequate feed rate control equipment, inadequate free chlorine residual, lack of backflow safeguards, and lack of an analyzer to measure fluoride ion levels in the treated water.

8. 1, 3, 4, 5   In addition to removing hardness, some benefits of softening include control of corrosion with proper stabilization, removal of iron, manganese, and radioactivity, and (sometimes) a reduction in tastes and odors.

9. 1   Aluminum sulfate (alum) lowers the pH of water being treated.

10. 1, 3, 5   Caustic soda is easier to handle and store, forms less sludge, and is more stable in storage than soda ash.

11. 1, 2, 4, 5   The common stages of operation of an ion exchange softener include backwash, brine, rinse, and service stages.

12. 4   Collect samples for THMs from sampling taps.

13. 1, 2, 5   THMs can be removed after they are formed by the processes of adsorption, aeration, and oxidation.

14. 1, 3, 4, 5   Adsorption, clarification, ion exchange, and oxidation are processes that can be used to remove THM precursors.

15. 1, 5   Cellulose acetate and thin film composite membranes are the types of semipermeable membranes most often used for demineralization.

16. 3, 4   Water pressure and salinity influence the type of piping material used for reverse osmosis units.

17. 1, 4, 5   Symptoms of membrane fouling include a high pressure difference across the membrane, a lower product water flow rate, and/or a lower salt rejection rate.

18. 1, 4, 5   Some advantages of the electrodialysis process for demineralization include its efficient removal of most inorganic constituents, the fact that the waste brine contains only salts removed, and the fact that electrodialysis is a well-developed technology.

19. 1, 5   Caustic soda is used to remove organic fouling or slime and hydrochloric acid is used to remove scale when cleaning an electrodialysis unit.

20. 1, 2   When compared with alum sludges, polymer sludges have the advantages of being denser and easier to dewater.

21. 2, 3, 5   Conditioning, dewatering, and thickening are processes used to reduce sludge volumes.

22. 1, 2, 3, 5   Sludges can be dewatered by the use of belt filter presses, centrifuges, sand drying beds, and solar lagoons.

23. 2, 3, 4   An equipment service card should describe each required maintenance task, the frequency of required services (most frequent first), and references where instructions for each task can be found.

24. 1, 2, 3, 4, 5   Fuses are installed to protect circuits, electrical equipment, heaters, motors, and operators.

25. 1, 3, 4, 5   Bearing failure could be caused by water getting into the bearing housing, lack of lubricant or use of the wrong type of lubricant, mechanical unbalance of rotating parts, or misalignment of a coupling.

26. 1, 2, 3, 4, 5   When storing oils and greases, avoid creating a fire hazard, keep any spills wiped up, keep materials and containers clean, make sure lids are tight on containers, and post "NO SMOKING" signs in areas where oils and greases are being used or stored.

27. 1, 2, 3, 4, 5   Bearings smelling hot, excessive humming, excessive sparking at the brushes, rapid knocking, and vibration are all unusual conditions for electric motors.

28. 1, 2, 3, 4, 5 Level sensing devices include capacitance probes, direct pressure, floats, pneumatic bubblers, and sonar devices.

29. 1, 4, 5 Chlorine, pH, and turbidity are process variables which are usually monitored closely and continuously in a water treatment plant.

30. 3, 4 Oil or water in the air supply to instruments can cause erratic instrument operation.

31. 3, 4, 5 An operator's general responsibilities for safety include reporting all injuries, reporting any observed hazards, and using safe work procedures at all times.

32. 1, 3 If one of the fusible plugs melts on a chlorine tank, immediately call for assistance if you are working alone and position the tank with the leak on top so gas escapes, not liquid.

33. 1, 2, 3, 4, 5 Salts may be the sources of burns, explosions, illness, loss of eyesight, and violent chemical reactions.

34. 3, 4 Procedures for safely handling and storing activated carbon include storing bags of activated carbon in single rows and using explosion-proof equipment and wiring around activated carbon.

35. 1, 4, 5 Confined spaces must be tested for the presence of explosive or toxic gases and for oxygen deficiency.

36. 1, 2, 3, 5 Information from algae counts helps document variability in the water quality. It also helps to explain the cause of color and turbidity, the cause of clogging of screens or filters, and the presence of tastes and odors.

37. 1, 2, 5 Important facts an operator should know about chloride are that as the mineral content of water increases, so does the chloride content; chloride gives water an objectionable salty taste; and the maximum allowable concentration is based on taste rather than chloride's physical or health hazards.

38. 1, 3, 4, 5 Dissolved oxygen (DO) is important to the water treatment plant operator because DO must be present in surface waters for fish to survive, low DO at the bottom of lakes can cause taste and odor problems, the presence of dissolved oxygen can contribute to pipe corrosion, and the taste of water is improved by dissolved oxygen.

39. 1, 2, 3, 4, 5 Types of organic contaminants include disinfection by-products (which may be organic or inorganic), herbicides, pesticides, solvents, and trihalomethanes.

40. 2, 3, 4, 5 Treatment methods that may be used to control lead and copper include coagulation-filtration, ion exchange, lime softening, and reverse osmosis.

41. 1, 3, 4, 5 The required CT value to achieve inactivation of microorganisms depends on the type of organism being inactivated, the pH and temperature of the water, and the type of disinfectant being used.

42. 1, 4, 5 The following are Tier 1 violations: failure to comply with the MCL, failure to comply with a treatment technique, and/or failure to comply with a variance or exemption.

43. 1, 2, 4, 5 Utility managers are expected to be in compliance with regulations, to perform with a minimum investment of money, to prepare the utility for the future, and to protect the environment.

44. 3, 4, 5 Without adequate planning, a utility will be unable to meet compliance regulations, will have an inadequate service capacity, and will experience system failures.

45. 1, 2, 4, 5 Groups that are considered protected in the workforce today include disabled persons, minorities, unions, and women.

46. 1, 3, 4 A manager's responsibilities in the financial management of a utility include careful budgeting, providing capital improvement funds, and providing financial stability.

47. 1, 3, 4, 5 The major elements of a good preventive maintenance program include cost and budget control, planning and scheduling, spare parts management, and a training program.

Short Answer

1. When clothes are washed in water containing iron and manganese, they will come out stained. Excessive iron and manganese in water can also stain plumbing fixtures. Iron bacteria will cause thick slimes to form on the walls of water mains. These slimes are rust colored from iron and black from manganese. Variations in flow cause these slimes to slough which results in dirty water. Furthermore, these slimes will impart foul tastes and odors to the water.

2. Samples for iron and manganese testing should be collected as close to the well or source of water as possible.

3. Polyphosphates control manganese by delaying the precipitation of oxidized manganese for a few days so that the scale that builds up on the pipe walls is greatly reduced.

4. The higher the pH, the faster the rate of oxidation of iron to insoluble ferric hydroxide.

5. If an ion exchange resin becomes fouled with iron rust or manganese dioxide, the exchange capacity of the resin is reduced and the resin must be cleaned.

6. The purpose of the reaction basin is to allow time for the oxidation reactions to take place. The aeration process should produce sufficient dissolved oxygen for the iron to be oxidized to insoluble ferric hydroxide.

7. Typically a manganese greensand filter should be backwashed when head loss reaches 10 psi or after treating a predetermined number of gallons of water.

8. Drinking waters are fluoridated to reduce the incidence (number) of dental caries (tooth decay) in children.

9. The three compounds most commonly used to fluoridate water are hydrofluosilicic acid, sodium fluoride, and sodium silicofluoride.

10. A saturator is a device which produces a fluoride solution for the fluoridation process. The device is usually a cylindrical container with granular sodium fluoride on the bottom. Water flows either upward or downward through the sodium fluoride to produce the fluoride solution.

11. Overfeeding of fluoridation chemicals must be prevented to avoid illness and bad public relations.

12. Safety equipment that should be available near a fluoridation system include an eyewash, drench showers, dust masks, face shields, gloves, and vent fans.

13. Hard waters cause difficulties in doing the laundry and in dishwashing in the household. There is also a coating that forms inside the hot water heater. Many industrial processes are adversely affected by hard water.

14. Hardness is caused mainly by the calcium and magnesium ions in water.

15. Recarbonation is a process in which carbon dioxide is bubbled into the water being treated to convert carbonate ions to bicarbonate ions to stabilize the solution against the precipitation of carbonate compounds. The pH may also be lowered by the addition of acid.

16. In the lime softening process, calcium is precipitated out as calcium carbonate and magnesium as magnesium hydroxide.

17. Lime may be applied by dry feeding techniques using volumetric or gravimetric feeders.

18. The marble test is used to determine if a water is stable. The Langelier Index is also used to determine the corrosivity of water.

19. The optimum coagulant dose is selected based on the best looking sample from the settling properties of the floc. The optimum dosages for lime and soda ash are determined from the results of the carbon dioxide, magnesium, alkalinity, and hardness tests run on the source and softened waters.

20. To determine if an ion exchange softener rinse stage has been successful, taste the waste effluent near the end of the rinse stage. If water does not have a salty taste, the rinse stage has been successful. The chloride or conductivity tests may also be used.

21. Trihalomethanes are formed by the reactions of natural organic compounds with halogens (such as chlorine).

22. Important factors that influence the production of trihalomethanes include the effects of time, temperature, pH, and the types and concentrations of chemicals.

23. The higher the temperature and the higher the pH, the faster the production of trihalomethanes (THMs).

24. Before an alternative disinfectant is applied to any system, the source of the water supply, water quality, and treatment effectiveness for bacteriological control must be evaluated.

25. The common membrane demineralizing processes are reverse osmosis and electrodialysis.

26. Even under ideal conditions (pure feedwater and no fouling of the membrane surface), there is a decline in water flux with time. This decrease in flux is due to membrane compaction. Flux decline also results from foulants and bacterial growth.

27. Fouling results from impurities in the feedwater such as suspended solids, dissolved organics and inorganics, and other potential foulants. These impurities can be deposited or grow on the membrane surface, thus hindering the flow of water through the membrane.

28. An increase in feedwater temperature will increase the water flux.

29. The operator of a reverse osmosis plant must properly maintain and control all flows and recovery rates to avoid possible damage to the membranes from scaling.

30. Operating pressure on a reverse osmosis unit is regulated by a control valve on the influent manifold.

31. The reverse osmosis elements should be cleaned when the operator observes (1) lower product water flow rate, (2) lower salt rejection, (3) higher differential pressure (ΔP), and (4) higher operating pressure.

32. Iron, manganese, and chlorine residual must be removed from the feedwater supply to the electrodialysis unit.

33. To prevent biological fouling of the cation and anion membranes, the operator must control feedwater pH, biological quality, and bacteriological quality.

34. Strict laws are needed regarding the disposal of process wastes to prevent rivers and streams from becoming more polluted. These laws are designed to prevent any waste discharge that could discolor, pollute, or generally be harmful to aquatic or plant life or the environment.

35. The amount of sludge produced by a conventional water filtration plant depends on:

1. The turbidity of raw water,
2. Use of a source water stabilizing reservoir, and
3. Type of coagulant.

36. Before draining a tank, always determine the level of the water table. If the water table is high, an empty tank could float like a cork on the water surface and cause considerable damage to the tank and piping.

37. Sludge drying beds are made with underdrains covered with gradations of aggregate and sand. The drains terminate into a sump where recovery pumps can return the water drained from the sludge back to the plant to be reprocessed.

38. Sludge should be disposed of as close as possible to the water treatment plant to reduce hauling costs.

39. The purpose of monitoring and reporting for a sludge disposal program is to prove that your processes are not creating any adverse environmental impacts.

40. The operator should thoroughly read and understand manufacturers' literature before attempting to maintain plant equipment so that the job required to keep the equipment operating can be done properly.

41. Protective or safety devices used to protect operators and equipment from being harmed by electricity include fuses, circuit breakers, and grounds.

42. Cavitation is the formation and collapse of a gas pocket or bubble on the blade of an impeller. The collapse of this gas pocket or bubble drives water into the impeller with a terrific force that can cause pitting on the impeller surface.

43. When storing lubricants, cleanliness is of utmost importance. Contaminated lubricants will ruin the equipment you are trying to protect.

44. A cross connection is a connection between two piping systems where an undesirable water (water from water seal) could enter a domestic water supply.

45. To check the temperature of a motor, a thermometer should be placed on the casing near the bearing and held in place with putty or clay.

46. When couplings are not in proper alignment, breaking or excessive wear results in either or both the driven machinery and the driver.

47. Five common types of valves found in water treatment facilities include gate valves, globe valves, eccentric valves, butterfly valves, and check valves.

48. Gasoline engines may be used in water treatment plants to drive pumps, generators, tractors, and vehicles.

49. Large chlorine leaks can be detected by smell. Small leaks are detected by soaking a cloth with ammonia water and holding the cloth near areas where leaks might develop. A white cloud will indicate the presence of a leak.

50. An advantage of instruments over our senses is that instruments provide quantities or measurable information, whereas only qualitative information is available from our senses.

51. Precision refers to the *repeatability* of a measurement (to measure something over and over and get the same answer) and accuracy refers to the *closeness* of a measurement to the actual value.

52. The purpose of an electrical lockout device is to positively prevent the operation of an electrical circuit, or to de-energize the circuit temporarily.

53. A sensor is the primary element that measures a variable. The sensor is often a transducer of some type that converts energy of one kind into some other form to produce a readout or signal.

54. A bubbler measures the level of a liquid by sensing (measuring) air pressure necessary to cause bubbles to just flow out the end of the tube.

55. Flows are measured with Venturi meters by sensing the pressure differential between the water pressure before the restriction in the meter or tube, and the pressure within the restriction.

56. In remote locations where no electricity is available, charts are driven by hand-wound drives or batteries.

57. ON/OFF controls should be programmed to operate or cycle associated equipment on and off no more often than actually necessary for plant or system operation.

58. Ignoring alarm conditions in an annunciator panel is poor practice because a *true* alarm condition requiring immediate operator attention may be lost due to a resulting general indifference to the alarm system.

59. Oil and moisture in instrument air cause instrument operational problems. Moisture can be removed from instrument air by the use of desiccators and air dryers. Oil introduced into compressor air can be removed by filtration through special oil-absorbent elements.

60. A float suspected of being stuck would be indicated by a very constant level indication. To determine if the float is actually stuck, try jiggling its cable to free the float or take other measures to cause a slight fluctuation in the reading.

61. Safety is the responsibility of everyone, from top management to all employees.

62. Operator negligence and carelessness are the causes of most accidents.

63. Ammonia leaks can be detected by odor or by using a cloth swab soaked with hydrochloric acid. This will form a white cloud of ammonium chloride.

64. Chlorine leaks are most often found in the control valve.

65. Lime burns, which are like burns from other caustics, should be treated by alternately washing with water and a mild acetic acid solution. One may also use large amounts of soap and water. For eye contact, wash immediately with large amounts of warm water and rinse with a boric acid solution.

66. Activated carbon fires can be detected by the smell of charred paper, burned paint, or other similar odors, before seeing any evidence of flames.

67. Fires can be prevented by good housekeeping. This means a well-kept, neat, and orderly plant.

68. When operating power tools in a wet or damp location, some consideration should be given to the use of rubber mats or insulated platforms. Use only grounded tools.

69. Examples of stored energy that could be hazardous to operators include electrical power; air, gas, or steam pressure; water (hydraulic) pressure; spring tension; rotational forces in flywheels; and the energy in elevated machine parts if they suddenly swing free.

70. Respiratory apparatus must be stored outside of chlorinating, sulfur dioxide, carbon dioxide, ozone, and ammonia rooms in an unlocked cabinet. The storage cabinets must have a controlled environment to prevent deterioration of the equipment.

71. Safety equipment may fall into disrepair because it is only used occasionally and may deteriorate due to heat, time, and other environmental factors.

72. The scale on spectrophotometers is usually graduated in two ways:

    1. In units of percent transmittance (%T), an arithmetic scale with units graded from 0 to 100%; and
    2. In units of absorbance (A), a logarithmic scale of nonequal divisions graduated from 0.0 to 2.0.

73. The two general types of color found in water are true color and apparent color. True color results from the presence of dissolved organic substances or from certain minerals such as copper sulfate dissolved in the water. Apparent color is caused by suspended materials (including colloidal substances).

74. The Marble Test is used to determine the degree to which a sample of water is saturated with calcium carbonate. The Marble Test results are used in the lime-soda softening process and to control corrosion.

75. Changes in conductivity from normal levels may indicate changes in mineral composition of the water, seasonal variations in lakes and reservoirs, or intrusion of pollutants.

76. Maximum Contaminant Levels (MCLs) are enforceable drinking water standards that reflect the levels of contaminants we can safely consume in our water, taking into account the amounts we are exposed to from all sources. MCLs represent the highest permissible concentrations of particular substances in drinking water.

77. A community water system

    1. Has at least 15 service connections used by all-year residents, or
    2. Regularly serves at least 25 all-year residents.

78. Many types of coliform bacteria from human and animal wastes may be found in drinking water if the water is not properly treated. Often the bacteria themselves do not cause diseases transmitted by water, although certain coliforms have been identified as the cause of "traveler's" diarrhea. In general, however, the presence of coliform bacteria indicates that other harmful organisms may be present in the water.

79. Secondary drinking water regulations are important because aesthetic qualities are important factors in public acceptance and confidence in a public water system. SMCLs are important so that the public will not be driven to obtain drinking water from potentially lower quality, higher risk sources.

80. Items that should be covered in consumer confidence reports include:

    1. Information on source of drinking water supply,
    2. Brief definition of terms,
    3. List of contaminants detected including level detected, MCL (maximum contaminant level), and MCLG (maximum contaminant level goal),
    4. For MCLs violated, information on health effects, and
    5. Information on any unregulated contaminants.

81. By thoroughly examining the functions and staffing of the utility on a periodic basis, the manager may spot trends or discover inefficiencies that could be corrected over a period of time.

82. Supervisors should be trained to communicate effectively, motivate others, delegate responsibility, and hold people accountable for their performance. Supervisors also need to be familiar with applicable state and federal personnel regulations, and should receive training on their role and responsibilities as part of the management team.

83. A manager's responsibility for preventing harassment in the workplace includes *being aware of* and *taking action to prevent* any type of harassment from occurring.

84. The particular type of backflow prevention device most suitable for a given situation depends on the degree of health hazard, the probability of backflow occurring, the complexity of the piping on the premises, and the probability of the piping being modified. The higher the assessed risk due to these factors, the more reliable and positive the type of device needed.

85. To achieve a good safety record, all individuals must be educated about safety and must believe in the safety program. All individuals involved must have the conviction that accidents can be prevented.

Problems

1. What is the setting on a potassium permanganate chemical feeder in pounds per day if the required chemical dose is 2.4 mg/L and the flow is 0.48 MGD?

Known	Unknown
Flow, MGD = 0.48 MGD	Chemical Feeder, lbs/day
Dose, mg/L = 2.4 mg/L	

Determine the chemical feeder setting in pounds per day.

$$\text{Chemical Feeder, lbs/day} = (\text{Flow, MGD})(\text{Dose, mg/}L)(8.34 \text{ lbs/gal})$$
$$= (0.48 \text{ MGD})(2.4 \text{ mg/}L)(8.34 \text{ lbs/gal})$$
$$= 9.6 \text{ lbs/day}$$

2. A flow of 1.2 MGD is to be treated with an 18-percent solution of hydrofluosilicic acid (H_2SiF_6). The water to be treated contains no fluoride and the desired fluoride concentration is 1.4 mg/L. Assume the hydrofluosilicic acid weighs 9.5 pounds per gallon and 79.2 percent fluoride purity of the acid. Calculate the hydrofluosilicic acid feed rate in gallons per day. Select the closest answer.

Known	Unknown
Flow, MGD = 1.2 MGD	Feed Rate, gal/day
Acid Solution, % = 18%	
Fluoride Purity, % = 79.2%	
Acid, lbs/gal = 9.5 lbs/gal	
Desired F, mg/L = 1.4 mg/L	

1. Calculate the hydrofluosilicic acid feed rate in pounds per day.

$$\text{Feed Rate, lbs/day} = \frac{(\text{Flow, MGD})(\text{Desired F, mg/}L)(8.34 \text{ lbs/gal})(100\%)(100\%)}{(\text{Acid Solution, \%})(\text{Fluoride Purity, \%})}$$

$$= \frac{(1.2 \text{ MGD})(1.4 \text{ mg/}L)(8.34 \text{ lbs/gal})(100\%)(100\%)}{(18\%)(79.2\%)}$$

$$= 98 \text{ lbs acid/day}$$

2. Determine the feed rate of the acid in gallons per day.

$$\text{Feed Rate, gal/day} = \frac{\text{Feed Rate, lbs/day}}{\text{Acid, lbs/gal}}$$

$$= \frac{98 \text{ lbs acid/day}}{9.5 \text{ lbs acid/gal}}$$

$$= 10.3 \text{ gal acid/day}$$

3. The feed solution from a saturator containing 1.8 percent fluoride ion is used to treat a flow of 550,000 gallons per day. The desired dose is 1.3 mg/L of fluoride ion and the raw water does not have any fluoride. Calculate the feed rate of the saturator solution in gallons per day. Select the closest answer.

Known	Unknown
Flow, gal/day = 550,000 GPD	Feed Rate, gal/day
Desired F, mg/L = 1.3 mg/L	
Feed Solution, % F = 1.8% F	

1. Convert the feed solution from a percentage fluoride ion to milligrams fluoride ion per liter of water.

$$\text{Feed Solution, mg/}L = \frac{(\text{Feed Solution, \%})(10{,}000 \text{ mg/}L)}{1\%}$$

$$= \frac{(1.8\%)(10{,}000 \text{ mg/}L)}{1\%}$$

$$= 18{,}000 \text{ mg/}L$$

2. Calculate the feed rate of the solution in gallons per day.

$$\text{Feed Rate, gal/day} = \frac{(\text{Flow, gal/day})(\text{Feed Dose, mg/}L)}{\text{Feed Solution, mg/}L}$$

$$= \frac{(550{,}000 \text{ gal/day})(1.3 \text{ mg/}L)}{18{,}000 \text{ mg/}L}$$

$$= 39.7 \text{ gal/day}$$

4. How many gallons of water with a hardness of 16 grains per gallon may be treated with an ion exchange softener with an exchange capacity of 12,000 kilograins?

Known	Unknown
Hardness, grains/gal = 16 grains/gal	Water Treated, gallons
Exchange Capacity, grains = 12,000,000 grains	

Calculate the gallons of water that may be treated.

$$\text{Water Treated, gal} = \frac{\text{Exchange Capacity, grains}}{\text{Hardness, grains/gal}}$$

$$= \frac{12{,}000{,}000 \text{ grains}}{16 \text{ grains/gal}}$$

$$= 750{,}000 \text{ gal}$$

Or

$$= 0.75 \text{ M gal}$$

5. Results of the quarterly average TTHM measurements for five quarters are given below. What is the running annual average of quarterly TTHM measurements at the end of the period?

Quarter	1	2	3	4	5
Avg Quarterly TTHM, µg/L	77	61	87	58	74

Known	Unknown
Results from analyses of 5 quarters of TTHM sampling	Final running annual average of quarterly TTHM measurements

Calculate the final running annual average of the quarterly TTHM measurements.

$$\text{Annual Running TTHM Average, µg/}L = \frac{\text{Sum of Avg TTHM for Last Four Quarters}}{\text{Number of Quarters}}$$

$$= \frac{61 \text{ µg/}L + 87 \text{ µg/}L + 58 \text{ µg/}L + 74 \text{ µg/}L}{4}$$

$$= \frac{280 \text{ µg/}L}{4}$$

$$= 70 \text{ µg/}L$$

6. Estimate the ability of a reverse osmosis plant to reject minerals by calculating the mineral rejection as a percent. The feedwater contains 1,800 mg/L TDS and the product water TDS is 130 mg/L.

Known	Unknown
Feedwater TDS, mg/L = 1,800 mg/L	Mineral Rejection, %
Product Water TDS, mg/L = 130 mg/L	

Calculate the mineral rejection as a percent.

$$\text{Mineral Rejection, \%} = \left(1 - \frac{\text{Product TDS, mg/}L}{\text{Feed TDS, mg/}L}\right)(100\%)$$

$$= \left(1 - \frac{130 \text{ mg/}L}{1{,}800 \text{ mg/}L}\right)(100\%)$$

$$= (1 - 0.07)(100\%)$$

$$= 93\%$$

7. Estimate the pumping capacity of a pump in gallons per minute if it takes 14 minutes for the water level in a tank to drop 3 feet. The tank is 8 feet in diameter.

Known	Unknown
Drop, ft = 3 ft	Pumping Capacity, GPM
Diameter, ft = 8 ft	
Pumping Time, min = 14 min	

1. Calculate the volume pumped in gallons.

$$\text{Volume, gal} = (0.785)(\text{Diameter, ft})^2(\text{Drop, ft})(7.48 \text{ gal/cu ft})$$

$$= (0.785)(8 \text{ ft})^2(3 \text{ ft})(7.48 \text{ gal/cu ft})$$

$$= 1{,}127 \text{ gallons pumped}$$

2. Estimate the pumping capacity in gallons per minute.

$$\text{Pumping Capacity, GPM} = \frac{\text{Volume Pumped, gal}}{\text{Pumping Time, min}}$$

$$= \frac{1{,}127 \text{ gal}}{14 \text{ min}}$$

$$= 80 \text{ GPM}$$

8. Calculate the feed rate of a dry chemical feeder in pounds per day if 4.0 pounds of chemical are caught in a weighing tin during 14 minutes.

Known	Unknown
Chemical, lbs = 4.0 lbs	Chemical Feed, lbs/day
Time, min = 14 min	

Calculate the chemical feed rate in pounds of chemical per day.

$$\text{Chemical Feed, lbs/day} = \frac{(\text{Chemical, lbs})(60 \text{ min/hr})(24 \text{ hr/day})}{\text{Time, min}}$$

$$= \frac{(4.0 \text{ lbs})(60 \text{ min/hr})(24 \text{ hr/day})}{14 \text{ min}}$$

$$= 410 \text{ lbs/day}$$

9. Calculate the threshold odor number (TON) for a sample. The first detectable odor occurred when the 20-mL sample was diluted to 200 mL (180 mL of odor-free water was added to the 20-mL sample).

Known	Unknown
A or Sample Size, mL = 20 mL	TON
B or Odor-Free Water, mL = 180 mL	

Calculate the threshold odor number (TON).

$$\text{TON} = \frac{A + B}{A}$$

$$= \frac{20 \text{ mL} + 180 \text{ mL}}{20 \text{ mL}}$$

$$= 10$$

APPENDIX

HOW TO SOLVE WATER TREATMENT PLANT ARITHMETIC PROBLEMS

(VOLUME II)

by

Ken Kerri

TABLE OF CONTENTS

HOW TO SOLVE WATER TREATMENT PLANT ARITHMETIC PROBLEMS

			Page
A.1	BASIC CONVERSION FACTORS (ENGLISH SYSTEM)		663
A.2	BASIC FORMULAS		663
A.3	TYPICAL WATER TREATMENT PLANT PROBLEMS (ENGLISH SYSTEM)		667
	A.30	Iron and Manganese Control	667
	A.31	Fluoridation	668
	A.32	Softening	669
	A.33	Trihalomethanes	673
	A.34	Demineralization	673
	A.35	Maintenance	674
	A.36	Advanced Laboratory Procedures	675
	A.37	Administration, Safety	677
A.4	BASIC CONVERSION FACTORS (METRIC SYSTEM)		677
A.5	TYPICAL WATER TREATMENT PLANT PROBLEMS (METRIC SYSTEM)		677
	A.50	Iron and Manganese Control	677
	A.51	Fluoridation	678
	A.52	Softening	680
	A.53	Trihalomethanes	684
	A.54	Demineralization	684
	A.55	Maintenance	685
	A.56	Advanced Laboratory Procedures	686
	A.57	Administration, Safety	688
A.6	CALCULATION OF CT VALUES		688
A.7	CALCULATION OF LOG REMOVALS		690

HOW TO SOLVE WATER TREATMENT PLANT ARITHMETIC PROBLEMS

(VOLUME II)

A.1 BASIC CONVERSION FACTORS (ENGLISH SYSTEM)

UNITS

    1,000,000 = 1 Million   1,000,000/1 Million

LENGTH

12 in = 1 ft	12 in/ft
3 ft = 1 yd	3 ft/yd
5,280 ft = 1 mi	5,280 ft/mi

AREA

144 sq in = 1 sq ft	144 sq in/sq ft
43,560 sq ft = 1 acre	43,560 sq ft/ac

VOLUME

7.48 gal = 1 cu ft	7.48 gal/cu ft
1,000 mL = 1 liter	1,000 mL/L
3.785 L = 1 gal	3.785 L/gal
231 cu in = 1 gal	231 cu in/gal

WEIGHT

1,000 mg = 1 gm	1,000 mg/gm
1,000 gm = 1 kg	1,000 gm/kg
454 gm = 1 lb	454 gm/lb
2.2 lbs = 1 kg	2.2 lbs/kg

POWER

    0.746 kW = 1 HP   0.746 kW/HP

DENSITY

8.34 lbs = 1 gal	8.34 lbs/gal
62.4 lbs = 1 cu ft	62.4 lbs/cu ft

DOSAGE

17.1 mg/L = 1 grain/gal	17.1 mg/L/gpg
64.7 grains = 1 mg	64.7 grains/mg

PRESSURE

2.31 ft water = 1 psi	2.31 ft/psi
0.433 psi = 1 ft water	0.433 psi/ft
1.133 ft water = 1 in Mercury	1.133 ft water/in Mercury

FLOW

694 GPM = 1 MGD	694 GPM/MGD
1.55 CFS = 1 MGD	1.55 CFS/MGD

TIME

60 sec = 1 min	60 sec/min
60 min = 1 hr	60 min/hr
24 hr = 1 day	24 hr/day

NOTE: In our conversion factors the values in the right hand column may be written either as 24 hr/day or 1 day/ 24 hours depending on which units we wish to convert to our desired results.

A.2 BASIC FORMULAS

IRON AND MANGANESE CONTROL

1a. Stock Solution, mg/mL $= \dfrac{(\text{Polyphosphate, grams})(1{,}000 \text{ mg/gm})}{(\text{Solution, liter})(1{,}000 \text{ mL/L})}$

1b. Dose, mg/L $= \dfrac{(\text{Stock Solution, mg/mL})(\text{Volume Added, mL})}{\text{Sample Volume, L}}$

1c. Dose, lbs/MG $= \dfrac{(\text{Dose, mg/L})(3.785 \text{ L/gal})(1{,}000{,}000/\text{Million})}{(1{,}000 \text{ mg/gm})(454 \text{ gm/lb})}$

2. Chemical Feeder, lbs/day $= (\text{Flow, MGD})(\text{Dose, mg/L})(8.34 \text{ lbs/gal})$

3. Detention Time, min $= \dfrac{(\text{Basin Vol, gal})(24 \text{ hr/day})(60 \text{ min/hr})}{\text{Flow, gal/day}}$

4. $KMnO_4$ Dose, mg/L $= 0.2(\text{Iron, mg/L}) + 2.0(\text{Manganese, mg/L})$

FLUORIDATION

5. Feed Rate,
    gal/day
    $$= \frac{(\text{Feed Rate, lbs F/day})(100\%)}{(\text{NaF Solution, lbs F/gal})(\text{Purity}, \%)}$$

6. Feed Solution,
    gal/day
    $$= \frac{(\text{Flow, gal/day})(\text{Feed Dose, mg/}L)}{\text{Feed Solution, mg/}L}$$

7. Fluoride Ion
    Purity, %
    $$= \frac{(\text{Molecular Weight of Fluoride})(100\%)}{\text{Molecular Weight of Chemical}}$$

8a. Feed Dose, mg/L = Desired Dose, mg/L – Actual Conc, mg/L

8b. Feed Rate,
    lbs/day
    $$= \frac{\text{Feed Rate, lbs F/day}}{\text{lbs F/lb Commercial Na}_2\text{SiF}_6}$$

9. Feed Solution,
    gal
    $$= \frac{(\text{Flow Vol, gal})(\text{Feed Dose, mg/}L)}{\text{Feed Solution, mg/}L}$$

10. Mixture
    Strength, %
    $$= \frac{(\text{Tank, gal})(\text{Tank, }\%) + (\text{Vendor, gal})(\text{Vendor, }\%)}{\text{Tank, gal + Vendor, gal}}$$

SOFTENING

11. Total Hardness,
    mg/L as $CaCO_3$
    $$= \frac{\text{Calcium Hardness,}}{\text{mg/}L \text{ as CaCO}_3} + \frac{\text{Magnesium Hardness,}}{\text{mg/}L \text{ as CaCO}_3}$$

12. If alkalinity is greater than total hardness,

    Carbonate Hardness,
    mg/L as $CaCO_3$
    $$= \frac{\text{Total Hardness,}}{\text{mg/}L \text{ as CaCO}_3}$$

    and

    Noncarbonate Hardness,
    mg/L as $CaCO_3$
    $$= 0$$

13. If alkalinity is less than total hardness,

    Carbonate Hardness,
    mg/L as $CaCO_3$
    $$= \text{Alkalinity, mg/}L \text{ as CaCO}_3$$

    and

    Noncarbonate Hardness,
    mg/L as $CaCO_3$
    $$= \frac{\text{Total Hardness,}}{\text{mg/}L \text{ as CaCO}_3} - \frac{\text{Alkalinity,}}{\text{mg/}L \text{ as CaCO}_3}$$

14a. Phenolphthalein
     Alkalinity,
     mg/L as $CaCO_3$
     $$= \frac{A \times N \times 50{,}000}{\text{m}L \text{ of sample}}$$

14b. Total Alkalinity,
     mg/L as $CaCO_3$
     $$= \frac{B \times N \times 50{,}000}{\text{m}L \text{ of sample}}$$

15a. Hydrated Lime
     ($Ca(OH)_2$) Feed, mg/L
     $$= \frac{(A + B + C + D)1.15}{\text{Purity of Lime, as a decimal}}$$

15b. Soda Ash (Na_2CO_3)
     Feed, mg/L
     $$= \left(\begin{array}{c}\text{Noncarbonate Hardness,} \\ \text{mg/}L \text{ as CaCO}_3\end{array}\right)(106/100)$$

15c. Total CO_2 Feed,
     mg/L
     $$= \frac{(\text{Ca(OH)}_2 \text{ excess, mg/}L)(44/74)}{+ (\text{Mg}^{2+} \text{ residual, mg/}L)(44/24.3)}$$

16. Feeder Setting,
    lbs/day
    $$= (\text{Flow, MGD})(\text{Conc, mg/}L)(8.34 \text{ lbs/gal})$$

17. Feed Rate, lbs/min
    $$= \frac{\text{Feeder Setting, lbs/day}}{(60 \text{ min/hr})(24 \text{ hr/day})}$$

18. Hardness, mg/L
    $$= \frac{(\text{Hardness, grains/gal})(17.1 \text{ mg/}L)}{1 \text{ grain/gal}}$$

19. Exchange Capacity,
    grains
    $$= (\text{Resin Vol, cu ft})\left(\begin{array}{c}\text{Removal Capacity,} \\ \text{grains/cu ft}\end{array}\right)$$

20. Water Treated, gal $= \dfrac{\text{Exchange Capacity, grains}}{\text{Hardness, grains/gal}}$

21. Operating Time, hr $= \dfrac{\text{Water Treated, gal}}{(\text{Avg Daily Flow, gal/min})(60 \text{ min/hr})}$

22. Salt Needed, lbs $= \left(\dfrac{\text{Salt Required,}}{\text{lbs/1,000 gr}}\right)(\text{Hardness Removed, gr})$

23. Bypass Flow, GPD $= \dfrac{(\text{Total Flow, GPD})(\text{Plant Effl Hardness, gpg})}{\text{Raw Water Hardness, gpg}}$

TRIHALOMETHANES

24. Avg TTHM, µg/L $= \dfrac{\text{Sum of Measurements, µg/}L}{\text{Number of Measurements}}$

25. Annual Running TTHM Average, µg/L $= \dfrac{\text{Sum of Avg TTHM for Four Quarters}}{\text{Number of Quarters}}$

DEMINERALIZATION

26. Flow, GPD/sq ft $= \dfrac{(\text{Flux, gm/sq cm-sec})(2.54 \text{ cm/in})^2(12 \text{ in/ft})^2(60 \text{ sec/min})(60 \text{ min/hr})(24 \text{ hr/day})}{(1,000 \text{ gm/}L)(3.785 \ L\text{/gal})}$

27. Mineral Rejection, % $= \left(1 - \dfrac{\text{Product TDS, mg/}L}{\text{Feed TDS, mg/}L}\right)(100\%)$

28. Recovery, % $= \dfrac{(\text{Product Flow, MGD})(100\%)}{\text{Feed Flow, MGD}}$

MAINTENANCE

29. Pump Capacity, GPM $= \dfrac{\text{Tank Volume, gal}}{\text{Pumping Time, min}}$

30. Flow, GPD $= \dfrac{(\text{Volume Pumped, gal})(24 \text{ hr/day})}{\text{Time, hr}}$

31. Polymer Feed, lbs/day $= \dfrac{(\text{Poly Conc, mg/}L)(\text{Vol Pumped, m}L)(60 \text{ min/hr})(24 \text{ hr/day})}{(\text{Time Pumped, min})(1,000 \text{ m}L\text{/}L)(1,000 \text{ mg/gm})(454 \text{ gm/lb})}$

32. Chemical Feed, lbs/day $= \dfrac{(\text{Chemical, gm})(60 \text{ min/hr})(24 \text{ hr/day})}{(454 \text{ gm/lb})(\text{Time, min})}$

ADVANCED LABORATORY PROCEDURES

33. Threshold Odor Number (TON) $= \dfrac{\text{Size of Sample, m}L + \text{Odor-Free Water, m}L}{\text{Size of Sample, m}L}$

34. Geometric Mean $= (X_1 \times X_2 \times X_3 \times \ldots X_n)^{1/n}$

35. Threshold Taste Number $= \dfrac{\text{Size of Sample, m}L + \text{Taste-Free Water, m}L}{\text{Size of Sample, m}L}$

36a. Arithmetic Mean, $\overline{X}$ Taste Rating $= \dfrac{X_1 + X_2 + X_3 + \ldots X_n}{n}$

36b. Standard Deviation, S Taste Rating $= \left[\dfrac{(X_1 - \overline{X})^2 + (X_2 - \overline{X})^2 + \ldots (X_n - \overline{X})^2}{n-1}\right]^{0.5}$

or $= \left[\dfrac{(X_1^2 + X_2^2 + \ldots X_n^2) - (X_1 + X_2 + \ldots X_n)^2/n}{n-1}\right]^{0.5}$

REGULATIONS

37. Portions Positive, %/mo $= \dfrac{(\text{Number Positive/mo})(100\%)}{\text{Total Portions Tested}}$

ADMINISTRATION, SAFETY

38.   Injury Freq Rate $= \dfrac{(\text{Injuries, number/yr})(1{,}000{,}000)}{\text{Hours Worked, number/yr}}$

39.   Injury Severity Rate $= \dfrac{(\text{Number of Hours Lost/yr})(1{,}000{,}000)}{\text{Number of Hours Worked/yr}}$

LOG REMOVALS

45a. Log Removal $= \text{Log Influent, particles/m}L - \text{Log Effluent, particles/m}L$

45b. Log Removal $= \text{Log}\left[\dfrac{\text{Influent, particles/m}L}{\text{Effluent, particles/m}L}\right]$

A.3 TYPICAL WATER TREATMENT PLANT PROBLEMS (ENGLISH SYSTEM)

A.30 Iron and Manganese Control

EXAMPLE 1

A standard polyphosphate solution is prepared by mixing and dissolving 1.0 gram of polyphosphate in a container and adding distilled water to the one-liter mark. Determine the concentration of the stock solution in milligrams per milliliter. If 6.0 milliliters of the stock solution are added to a one-liter sample, what is the polyphosphate dose in milligrams per liter and pounds per million gallons?

Known	Unknown
Polyphosphate, gm = 1.0 gm	1. Stock Solution, mg/mL
Solution, L = 1.0 L	2. Dose, mg/L
Stock Solution, mL = 6 mL	3. Dose, lbs/MG
Sample, L = 1 L	

1. Calculate the concentration of the stock solution in milligrams per milliliter.

$$\text{Stock Solution, mg/m}L = \frac{(\text{Polyphosphate, gm})(1,000 \text{ mg/gm})}{(\text{Solution, }L)(1,000 \text{ m}L/L)}$$

$$= \frac{(1.0 \text{ gm})(1,000 \text{ mg/gm})}{(1 \text{ }L)(1,000 \text{ m}L/L)}$$

$$= 1.0 \text{ mg/m}L$$

2. Determine the polyphosphate dose in the sample in milligrams per liter.

$$\text{Dose, mg/}L = \frac{(\text{Stock Solution, mg/m}L)(\text{Vol Added, m}L)}{\text{Sample Volume, }L}$$

$$= \frac{(1.0 \text{ mg/m}L)(6 \text{ m}L)}{1 L}$$

$$= 6.0 \text{ mg/}L$$

3. Determine the polyphosphate dose in the sample in pounds of phosphate per million gallons of water.

$$\text{Dose, lbs/MG} = \frac{(\text{Dose, mg/}L)(3.785 \text{ }L/\text{gal})(1,000,000/\text{Mil})}{(1,000 \text{ mg/gm})(454 \text{ gm/lb})}$$

$$= \frac{(6.0 \text{ mg/}L)(3.785 \text{ }L/\text{gal})(1,000,000/\text{Mil})}{(1,000 \text{ mg/gm})(454 \text{ gm/lb})}$$

$$= 50 \text{ lbs/MG}$$

EXAMPLE 2

Determine the chemical feeder setting in pounds of polyphosphate per day if 0.62 MGD is treated with a dose of 6 mg/L.

Known	Unknown
Flow, MGD = 0.62 MGD	Chemical Feeder, lbs/day
Dose, mg/L = 6 mg/L	

Determine the chemical feeder setting in pounds per day.

$$\text{Chemical Feeder, lbs/day} = (\text{Flow, MGD})(\text{Dose, mg/}L)(8.34 \text{ lbs/gal})$$

$$= (0.62 \text{ MGD})(6 \text{ mg/}L)(8.34 \text{ lbs/gal})$$

$$= 31 \text{ lbs/day}$$

EXAMPLE 3

A reaction basin 14 feet in diameter and 4 feet deep treats a flow of 240,000 gallons per day. What is the average detention time in minutes?

Known	Unknown
Diameter, ft = 14 ft	Detention Time, min
Depth, ft = 4 ft	
Flow, GPD = 240,000 GPD	

1. Calculate the basin volume in cubic feet.

$$\text{Basin Vol, cu ft} = (0.785)(\text{Diameter, ft})^2(\text{Depth, ft})$$

$$= (0.785)(14 \text{ ft})^2(4 \text{ ft})$$

$$= 615 \text{ cu ft}$$

2. Convert the basin volume from cubic feet to gallons.

$$\text{Basin Vol, gal} = (\text{Basin Vol, cu ft})(7.48 \text{ gal/cu ft})$$

$$= (615 \text{ cu ft})(7.48 \text{ gal/cu ft})$$

$$= 4,600 \text{ gal}$$

3. Determine the average detention time in minutes for the reaction basin.

$$\text{Detention Time, min} = \frac{(\text{Basin Vol, gal})(24 \text{ hr/day})(60 \text{ min/hr})}{\text{Flow, gal/day}}$$

$$= \frac{(4,600 \text{ gal})(24 \text{ hr/day})(60 \text{ min/hr})}{240,000 \text{ gal/day}}$$

$$= 28 \text{ minutes}$$

EXAMPLE 4

Calculate the potassium permanganate dose in milligrams per liter for a well water with 2.4 mg/L iron before aeration and 0.3 mg/L after aeration. The manganese concentration is 0.8 mg/L both before and after aeration.

Known	Unknown
Iron, mg/L = 0.3 mg/L	KMnO$_4$ Dose, mg/L
Manganese, mg/L = 0.8 mg/L	

Calculate the potassium permanganate dose in milligrams per liter.

$$\text{KMnO}_4 \text{ Dose, mg/}L = 0.2(\text{Iron, mg/}L) + 2.0(\text{Manganese, mg/}L)$$

$$= 0.2(0.3 \text{ mg/}L) + 2.0(0.8 \text{ mg/}L)$$

$$= 1.66 \text{ mg/}L$$

NOTE: If there are any oxidizable compounds (organic color, bacteria, or hydrogen sulfide) in the water, the dose will have to be increased.

A.31   Fluoridation

EXAMPLE 5

Determine the setting for a chemical feed pump in gallons per day when the desired fluoride dose is 1.8 pounds of fluoride per day. The sodium fluoride solution contains 0.2 pounds of fluoride per gallon and the fluoride purity is 43.4 percent.

Known		Unknown
Feed Rate, lbs F/day	= 1.8 lbs F/day	Feed Rate, gal/day
NaF Solution, lbs F/gal	= 0.2 lbs F/gal	
Purity, %	= 43.4%	

Determine the setting on the chemical feed pump in gallons per day.

$$\text{Feed Rate, gal/day} = \frac{(\text{Feed Rate, lbs F/day})(100\%)}{(\text{NaF Solution, lbs F/gal})(\text{Purity, \%})}$$

$$= \frac{(1.8 \text{ lbs F/day})(100\%)}{(0.2 \text{ lb F/gal})(43.4\%)}$$

$$= 20.7 \text{ gal/day}$$

$$\text{or } = 21 \text{ gal/day}$$

EXAMPLE 6

Determine the setting on a chemical feed pump in gallons per day if 500,000 gallons per day of water must be treated with 0.9 mg/L of fluoride. The fluoride feed solution contains 18,000 mg/L of fluoride.

Known		Unknown
Flow, gal/day	= 500,000 gal/day	Feed Pump, gal/day
Fluoride, mg/L	= 0.9 mg/L	
Feed Solution, mg/L	= 18,000 mg/L	

Determine the setting on the chemical feed pump in gallons per day.

$$\text{Feed Pump, gal/day} = \frac{(\text{Flow, gal/day})(\text{Feed Dose, mg/}L)}{\text{Feed Solution, mg/}L}$$

$$= \frac{(500,000 \text{ gal/day})(0.9 \text{ mg/}L)}{18,000 \text{ mg/}L}$$

$$= 25 \text{ gal/day}$$

EXAMPLE 7

Determine the fluoride ion purity of Na_2SiF_6 as a percent.

Known	Unknown
Fluoride Chemical, Na_2SiF_6	Fluoride Ion Purity, %

Determine the molecular weight of fluoride and Na_2SiF_6.

Symbol	(No. Atoms)	(Atomic Wt)	=	Molecular Wt
Na_2	(2)	(22.99)	=	45.98
Si	(1)	(28.09)	=	28.09
F_6	(6)	(19.00)	=	114.00
	Molecular Weight of Chemical		=	188.07

Calculate the fluoride ion purity as a percent.

$$\text{Fluoride Ion Purity, \%} = \frac{(\text{Molecular Weight of Fluoride})(100\%)}{\text{Molecular Weight of Chemical}}$$

$$= \frac{(114.00)(100\%)}{188.07}$$

$$= 60.62\%$$

EXAMPLE 8

A flow of 1.7 MGD is treated with sodium silicofluoride. The raw water contains 0.2 mg/L of fluoride ion and the desired fluoride concentration is 1.1 mg/L. What should be the chemical feed rate in pounds per day? Assume each pound of commercial sodium silicofluoride (Na_2SiF_6) contains 0.6 pound of fluoride ion.

Known		Unknown
Flow, MGD	= 1.7 MGD	Feed Rate, lbs/day
Raw Water F, mg/L	= 0.2 mg/L	
Desired F, mg/L	= 1.1 mg/L	
Chemical, lbs F/lb	= 0.6 lb F/lb	

1. Determine the fluoride feed dose in milligrams per liter.

   $$\text{Feed Dose, mg/}L = \text{Desired Dose, mg/}L - \text{Actual Conc, mg/}L$$

   $$= 1.1 \text{ mg/}L - 0.2 \text{ mg/}L$$

   $$= 0.9 \text{ mg/}L$$

2. Calculate the fluoride feed rate in pounds per day.

   $$\text{Feed Rate, lbs F/day} = (\text{Flow, MGD})(\text{Feed Dose, mg/}L)(8.34 \text{ lbs/gal})$$

   $$= (1.7 \text{ MGD})(0.9 \text{ mg/}L)(8.34 \text{ lbs/gal})$$

   $$= 12.8 \text{ lbs F/day}$$

3. Determine the chemical feed rate in pounds of commercial sodium silicofluoride per day.

   $$\text{Feed Rate, lbs/day} = \frac{\text{Feed Rate, lbs F/day}}{\text{lbs F/lb Commercial } Na_2SiF_6}$$

   $$= \frac{12.8 \text{ lbs F/day}}{0.6 \text{ lb F/lb Commercial } Na_2SiF_6}$$

   $$= 21.3 \text{ lbs/day Commercial } Na_2SiF_6$$

EXAMPLE 9

The feed solution from a saturator containing 1.8 percent fluoride ion is used to treat a total flow of 250,000 gallons of water. The raw water has a fluoride ion content of 0.2 mg/L and the desired fluoride level in the treated water is 0.9 mg/L. How many gallons of feed solution are needed?

Known	Unknown
Flow Vol, gal = 250,000 gal	Feed Solution, gal
Raw Water F, mg/L = 0.2 mg/L	
Desired F, mg/L = 0.9 mg/L	
Feed Solution, % F = 1.8% F	

1. Convert the feed solution from a percentage fluoride ion to milligrams fluoride ion per liter of water.

$$1.0\% \text{ F} = 10,000 \text{ mg F}/L$$

$$\text{Feed Solution, mg}/L = \frac{(\text{Feed Solution, \%})(10,000 \text{ mg}/L)}{1.0\%}$$

$$= \frac{(1.8\% \text{ F})(10,000 \text{ mg}/L)}{1.0\%}$$

$$= 18,000 \text{ mg}/L$$

2. Determine the fluoride feed dose in milligrams per liter.

$$\text{Feed Dose, mg}/L = \text{Desired Dose, mg}/L - \text{Raw Water F, mg}/L$$

$$= 0.9 \text{ mg}/L - 0.2 \text{ mg}/L$$

$$= 0.7 \text{ mg}/L$$

3. Calculate the gallons of feed solution needed.

$$\text{Feed Solution, gal} = \frac{(\text{Flow Vol, gal})(\text{Feed Dose, mg}/L)}{\text{Feed Solution, mg}/L}$$

$$= \frac{(250,000 \text{ gal})(0.7 \text{ mg}/L)}{18,000 \text{ mg}/L}$$

$$= 9.7 \text{ gallons}$$

EXAMPLE 10

A hydrofluosilicic acid (H_2SiF_6) tank contains 350 gallons of acid with a strength of 19.3 percent. A commercial vendor delivers 2,500 gallons of acid with a strength of 18.1 percent to the tank. What is the resulting strength of the mixture as a percentage?

Known	Unknown
Tank Contents, gal = 350 gal	Mixture Strength, %
Tank Strength, % = 19.3%	
Vendor, gal = 2,500 gal	
Vendor Strength, % = 18.1%	

Calculate the strength of the mixture as a percentage.

$$\text{Mixture Strength, \%} = \frac{(\text{Tank, gal})(\text{Tank, \%}) + (\text{Vendor, gal})(\text{Vendor, \%})}{\text{Tank, gal} + \text{Vendor, gal}}$$

$$= \frac{(350 \text{ gal})(19.3\%) + (2,500 \text{ gal})(18.1\%)}{350 \text{ gal} + 2,500 \text{ gal}}$$

$$= \frac{6,755 + 45,250}{2,850}$$

$$= 18.2\%$$

A.32 Softening

EXAMPLE 11

Determine the total hardness as $CaCO_3$ for a sample of water with a calcium content of 33 mg/L and a magnesium content of 6 mg/L.

Known	Unknown
Calcium, mg/L = 33 mg/L	Total Hardness, mg/L as $CaCO_3$
Magnesium, mg/L = 6 mg/L	

Calculate the total hardness as milligrams per liter of calcium carbonate equivalent.

$$\text{Total Hardness, mg}/L \text{ as } CaCO_3 = \text{Calcium Hardness, mg}/L \text{ as } CaCO_3 + \text{Magnesium Hardness, mg}/L \text{ as } CaCO_3$$

$$= 2.5(\text{Ca, mg}/L) + 4.12(\text{Mg, mg}/L)$$

$$= 2.5(33 \text{ mg}/L) + 4.12(6 \text{ mg}/L)$$

$$= 82 \text{ mg}/L + 25 \text{ mg}/L$$

$$= 107 \text{ mg}/L \text{ as } CaCO_3$$

EXAMPLE 12

The alkalinity of a water is 120 mg/L as $CaCO_3$ and the total hardness is 105 mg/L as $CaCO_3$. What is the carbonate and noncarbonate hardness in mg/L as $CaCO_3$?

Known	Unknown
Alkalinity, mg/L = 120 mg/L as $CaCO_3$	1. Carbonate Hardness, mg/L as $CaCO_3$
Total Hardness, mg/L = 105 mg/L as $CaCO_3$	2. Noncarbonate Hardness, mg/L as $CaCO_3$

1. Determine the carbonate hardness in mg/L as $CaCO_3$.

Since the alkalinity is greater than the total hardness (120 mg/L > 105 mg/L),

$$\text{Carbonate Hardness, mg}/L \text{ as } CaCO_3 = \text{Total Hardness, mg}/L \text{ as } CaCO_3$$

$$= 105 \text{ mg}/L \text{ as } CaCO_3$$

2. Determine the noncarbonate hardness in mg/L as $CaCO_3$.

Since the alkalinity is greater than the total hardness,

$$\text{Noncarbonate Hardness, mg}/L \text{ as } CaCO_3 = 0$$

In other words, all of the hardness is in the carbonate form.

EXAMPLE 13

The alkalinity of a water is 92 mg/L as $CaCO_3$ and the total hardness is 105 mg/L. What is the carbonate and noncarbonate hardness in mg/L as $CaCO_3$?

Known	Unknown
Alkalinity, mg/L = 92 mg/L as $CaCO_3$	1. Carbonate Hardness, mg/L as $CaCO_3$
Total Hardness, mg/L = 105 mg/L as $CaCO_3$	2. Noncarbonate Hardness, mg/L as $CaCO_3$

1. Determine the carbonate hardness in mg/L as $CaCO_3$.

Since the alkalinity is less than the total hardness (92 mg/L < 105 mg/L),

$$\text{Carbonate Hardness, mg/L as } CaCO_3 = \text{Alkalinity, mg/L as } CaCO_3$$

$$= 92 \text{ mg/L as } CaCO_3$$

2. Determine the noncarbonate hardness in mg/L as $CaCO_3$.

Since the alkalinity is less than the total hardness (92 mg/L < 105 mg/L),

$$\text{Noncarbonate Hardness, mg/L as } CaCO_3 = \text{Total Hardness, mg/as } CaCO_3 - \text{Alkalinity, mg/L as } CaCO_3$$

$$= 105 \text{ mg/L} - 92 \text{ mg/L}$$

$$= 13 \text{ mg/L as } CaCO_3$$

EXAMPLE 14

Results from alkalinity titrations on a water sample were as follows:

Known

Sample Size, mL	= 100 mL
mL Titrant Used to pH 8.3, A	= 1.1 mL
Total mL of Titrant Used, B	= 12.4 mL
Acid Normality, N	= 0.02 N H_2SO_4

Unknown

1. Total Alkalinity, mg/L as $CaCO_3$
2. Bicarbonate Alkalinity, mg/L as $CaCO_3$
3. Carbonate Alkalinity, mg/L as $CaCO_3$
4. Hydroxide Alkalinity, mg/L as $CaCO_3$

See Table 14.4, page 82, for alkalinity relationships among constituents.

1. Calculate the phenolphthalein alkalinity in mg/L as $CaCO_3$.

$$\text{Phenolphthalein Alkalinity, mg/L as } CaCO_3 = \frac{A \times N \times 50{,}000}{\text{mL of sample}}$$

$$= \frac{(1.1 \text{ mL})(0.02 \ N)(50{,}000)}{100 \text{ mL}}$$

$$= 11 \text{ mg/L as } CaCO_3$$

2. Calculate the total alkalinity in mg/L as $CaCO_3$.

$$\text{Total Alkalinity, mg/L as } CaCO_3 = \frac{B \times N \times 50{,}000}{\text{mL of sample}}$$

$$= \frac{(12.4 \text{ mL})(0.02 \ N)(50{,}000)}{100 \text{ mL}}$$

$$= 124 \text{ mg/L as } CaCO_3$$

3. Refer to Table 14.4 for alkalinity constituents. The second row indicates that since P is less than ½T (11 mg/L < ½(124 mg/L)), bicarbonate alkalinity is T – 2P and carbonate alkalinity is 2P.

$$\text{Bicarbonate Alkalinity, mg/L as } CaCO_3 = T - 2P$$

$$= 124 \text{ mg/L} - 2(11 \text{ mg/L})$$

$$= 102 \text{ mg/L as } CaCO_3$$

$$\text{Carbonate Alkalinity, mg/L as } CaCO_3 = 2P$$

$$= 2(11 \text{ mg/L})$$

$$= 22 \text{ mg/L as } CaCO_3$$

$$\text{Hydroxide Alkalinity, mg/L as } CaCO_3 = 0 \text{ mg/L as } CaCO_3$$

EXAMPLE 15

Calculate the hydrated lime ($Ca(OH)_2$) with 90 percent purity, soda ash, and carbon dioxide requirements in milligrams per liter for the water shown below.

Known

Constituents	Source Water	Softened Water After Recarbonation and Filtration
CO_2, mg/L	= 7 mg/L	= 0 mg/L
Total Alkalinity, mg/L	= 125 mg/L as $CaCO_3$	= 22 mg/L as $CaCO_3$
Total Hardness, mg/L	= 240 mg/L as $CaCO_3$	= 35 mg/L as $CaCO_3$
Mg^{2+}, mg/L	= 38 mg/L	= 8 mg/L
pH	= 7.6	= 8.8
Lime Purity, %	= 90%	

Unknown

1. Hydrated Lime, mg/L
2. Soda Ash, mg/L
3. Carbon Dioxide, mg/L

1. Calculate the hydrated lime ($Ca(OH)_2$) required in milligrams per liter.

$$A = (CO_2, \text{ mg/L})(74/44)$$

$$= (7 \text{ mg/L})(74/44)$$

$$= 12 \text{ mg/L}$$

$$B = (\text{Alkalinity, mg/L})(74/100)$$

$$= (125 \text{ mg/L})(74/100)$$

$$= 93 \text{ mg/L}$$

$$C = (\text{Hydroxide, mg/L})(74/100)$$

$$= 0$$

$D = (Mg^{2+}, mg/L)(74/24.3)$

$= (38\ mg/L)(74/24.3)$

$= 116\ mg/L$

Hydrated Lime $(Ca(OH)_2)$ Feed, mg/L $= \dfrac{(A + B + C + D)1.15}{\text{Purity of Lime, as a decimal}}$

$= \dfrac{(12\ mg/L + 93\ mg/L + 0 + 116\ mg/L)1.15}{0.90}$

$= \dfrac{(221\ mg/L)(1.15)}{0.90}$

$= 282\ mg/L$

2. Calculate the soda ash required in milligrams per liter.

Total Hardness Removed, mg/L as $CaCO_3$ $=$ Total Hardness, mg/L as $CaCO_3$ $-$ Total Hardness Remaining, mg/L as $CaCO_3$

$= 240\ mg/L - 35\ mg/L$

$= 205\ mg/L$

Noncarbonate Hardness, mg/L as $CaCO_3$ $=$ Total Hardness Removed, mg/L as $CaCO_3$ $-$ Carbonate Hardness, mg/L as $CaCO_3$

$= 205\ mg/L - 125\ mg/L$

$= 80\ mg/L$ as $CaCO_3$

Soda Ash (Na_2CO_3) Feed, mg/L $= \left(\begin{array}{c}\text{Noncarbonate Hardness,}\\ mg/L \text{ as } CaCO_3\end{array}\right)(106/100)$

$= (80\ mg/L)(106/100)$

$= 85\ mg/L$

3. Calculate the dosage of carbon dioxide required for recarbonation.

Excess Lime, $mg/L = (A + B + C + D)(0.15)$

$= (12\ mg/L + 93\ mg/L + 0 + 116\ mg/L)(0.15)$

$= (221\ mg/L)(0.15)$

$= 33\ mg/L$

Total CO_2 Feed, mg/L $= \begin{array}{l}(Ca(OH)_2 \text{ excess}, mg/L)(44/74)\\ + (Mg^{2+} \text{ residual}, mg/L)(44/24.3)\end{array}$

$= (33\ mg/L)(44/74) + (8\ mg/L)(44/24.3)$

$= 20\ mg/L + 15\ mg/L$

$= 35\ mg/L$

EXAMPLE 16

The optimum lime dosage from the jar tests is 180 mg/L. If the flow to be treated is 1.7 MGD, what is the feeder setting in pounds per day and the feed rate in pounds per minute?

Known	Unknown
Lime Dose, mg/L = 180 mg/L	1. Feeder Setting, lbs/day
Flow, MGD = 1.7 MGD	2. Feed Rate, lbs/min

1. Calculate the feeder setting in pounds per day.

Feeder Setting, lbs/day $=$ (Flow, MGD)(Lime, mg/L)(8.34 lbs/gal)

$= (1.7\ MGD)(180\ mg/L)(8.34\ lbs/gal)$

$= 2,550\ lbs/day$

2. Calculate the feed rate in pounds per minute.

Feed Rate, lbs/min $= \dfrac{\text{Feeder Setting, lbs/day}}{(60\ min/hr)(24\ hr/day)}$

$= \dfrac{2,550\ lbs/day}{(60\ min/hr)(24\ hr/day)}$

$= 1.8\ lbs/min$

EXAMPLE 17

How much soda ash is required (pounds per day and pounds per minute) to remove 40 mg/L noncarbonate hardness as $CaCO_3$ from a flow of 1.7 MGD?

Known	Unknown
Noncarbonate Hardness Removed, mg/L as $CaCO_3$ = 40 mg/L	1. Feeder Setting, lbs/day
Flow, MGD = 1.7 MGD	2. Feed Rate, lbs/min

1. Calculate the soda ash dose in milligrams per liter. See Section 14.316, "Calculation of Chemical Dosages," page 86, for the following formula.

Soda Ash, mg/L $= \left(\begin{array}{c}\text{Noncarbonate Hardness,}\\ mg/L \text{ as } CaCO_3\end{array}\right)(106/100)$

$= (40\ mg/L)(106/100)$

$= 43\ mg/L$

2. Determine the feeder setting in pounds per day.

Feeder Setting, lbs/day $=$ (Flow, MGD)(Soda Ash, mg/L)(8.34 lbs/gal)

$= (1.7\ MGD)(43\ mg/L)(8.34\ lbs/gal)$

$= 610\ lbs/day$

3. Calculate the soda ash feed rate in pounds per minute.

$$\text{Feed Rate, lbs/min} = \frac{\text{Feeder Setting, lbs/day}}{(60 \text{ min/hr})(24 \text{ hr/day})}$$

$$= \frac{610 \text{ lbs/day}}{(60 \text{ min/hr})(24 \text{ hr/day})}$$

$$= 0.43 \text{ lbs/min}$$

EXAMPLE 18

What is the hardness in milligrams per liter for a water with a hardness of 12 grains per gallon?

Known	Unknown
Hardness, gpg = 12 grains/gallon	Hardness, mg/L

Calculate the hardness in milligrams per liter.

$$\text{Hardness, mg/}L = \frac{(\text{Hardness, grains/gal})(17.1 \text{ mg/}L)}{1 \text{ grain/gal}}$$

$$= \frac{(12 \text{ grains/gal})(17.1 \text{ mg/}L)}{1 \text{ grain/gal}}$$

$$= 205 \text{ mg/}L$$

EXAMPLE 19

Estimate the exchange capacity in grains of hardness for an ion exchange unit which contains 600 cubic feet of resin with a removal capacity of 25,000 grains per cubic foot.

Known	Unknown
Resin Vol, cu ft = 600 cu ft	Exchange Capacity, grains
Removal Cap, gr/cu ft = 25,000 gr/cu ft	

Estimate the exchange capacity in grains of hardness.

$$\text{Exchange Capacity, grains} = (\text{Resin Vol, cu ft})(\text{Removal Capacity, gr/cu ft})$$

$$= (600 \text{ cu ft})(25,000 \text{ gr/cu ft})$$

$$= 15,000,000 \text{ grains of hardness}$$

EXAMPLE 20

How many gallons of water with a hardness of 12 grains per gallon may be treated by an ion exchange softener with an exchange capacity of 15,000,000 grains?

Known	Unknown
Hardness, grains/gal = 12 grains/gal	Water Treated, gallons
Exchange Capacity, grains = 15,000,000 grains	

Calculate the gallons of water that may be treated.

$$\text{Water Treated, gal} = \frac{\text{Exchange Capacity, grains}}{\text{Hardness, grains/gal}}$$

$$= \frac{15,000,000 \text{ grains}}{12 \text{ grains/gal}}$$

$$= 1,250,000 \text{ gal}$$

EXAMPLE 21

How many hours will an ion exchange softening unit operate when treating an average daily flow of 750 GPM? The unit is capable of softening 1,250,000 gallons of water before requiring regeneration.

Known	Unknown
Avg Daily Flow, GPM = 750 GPM	Operating Time, hr
Water Treated, gal = 1,250,000 gal	

Estimate how many hours the softening unit can operate before requiring regeneration.

$$\text{Operating Time, hr} = \frac{\text{Water Treated, gal}}{(\text{Avg Daily Flow, gal/min})(60 \text{ min/hr})}$$

$$= \frac{1,250,000 \text{ gal}}{(750 \text{ gal/min})(60 \text{ min/hr})}$$

$$= 27.8 \text{ hours}$$

EXAMPLE 22

Determine the pounds of salt needed to regenerate an ion exchange softening unit capable of removing 15,000,000 grains of hardness if 0.25 pound of salt are required for every 1,000 grains of hardness removed.

Known	Unknown
Hardness Removed, gr = 15,000,000 grains	Salt Needed, lbs
Salt Required, lbs/1,000 gr = 0.25 lb salt/1,000 gr	

Calculate the pounds of salt needed to regenerate the ion exchange softening unit.

$$\text{Salt Needed, lbs} = (\text{Salt Required, lbs/1,000 gr})(\text{Hardness Removed, gr})$$

$$= \left(\frac{0.25 \text{ lb salt}}{1,000 \text{ grains}}\right)(15,000,000 \text{ grains})$$

$$= 3,750 \text{ lbs of salt}$$

EXAMPLE 23

Estimate the bypass flow in gallons per day around an ion exchange softener if the plant treats 250,000 gallons per day with a source water hardness of 20 grains per gallon if the desired product water hardness is 5 grains per gallon.

Known	Unknown
Total Flow, GPD = 250,000 GPD	Bypass Flow, GPD
Source Water Hardness, gpg = 20 grains/gal	
Plant Effl Hardness, gpg = 5 grains/gal	

Estimate the bypass flow in gallons per day.

$$\text{Bypass Flow, GPD} = \frac{(\text{Total Flow, GPD})(\text{Plant Effl Hardness, gpg})}{\text{Source Water Hardness, gpg}}$$

$$= \frac{(250,000 \text{ GPD})(5 \text{ gpg})}{20 \text{ gpg}}$$

$$= 62,500 \text{ GPD}$$

A.33   Trihalomethanes

EXAMPLE 24

A water utility collected and analyzed eight samples from a water distribution system on the same day for TTHMs. The results are shown below.

Sample No.	1	2	3	4	5	6	7	8
TTHM, $\mu g/L$	80	90	100	90	110	100	100	90

What was the average TTHM for the day?

Known	**Unknown**
Results from analyses of 8 TTHM samples	Average TTHM level for the day

Calculate the average TTHM level in micrograms per liter.

$$\text{Avg TTHM,} \atop \mu g/L = \frac{\text{Sum of Measurements, } \mu g/L}{\text{Number of Measurements}}$$

$$= \frac{80\,\mu g/L + 90\,\mu g/L + 100\,\mu g/L + 90\,\mu g/L + 110\,\mu g/L + 100\,\mu g/L + 100\,\mu g/L + 90\,\mu g/L}{8}$$

$$= \frac{760\,\mu g/L}{8}$$

$$= 95\,\mu g/L$$

EXAMPLE 25

The results of the quarterly average TTHM measurements for two years are given below. Calculate the running annual average of the four quarterly measurements in micrograms per liter.

Quarter	1	2	3	4	1	2	3	4
Avg Quarterly TTHM, $\mu g/L$	77	88	112	95	83	87	109	89

Known	**Unknown**
Results from analyses of two years of TTHM sampling	Running Annual Average of quarterly TTHM measurements

Calculate the running annual average of the quarterly TTHM measurements.

$$\text{Annual Running TTHM} \atop \text{Average, } \mu g/L = \frac{\text{Sum of Avg TTHM for Four Quarters}}{\text{Number of Quarters}}$$

QUARTERS 1, 2, 3, AND 4

$$\text{Annual Running TTHM} \atop \text{Average, } \mu g/L = \frac{77\,\mu g/L + 88\,\mu g/L + 112\,\mu g/L + 95\,\mu g/L}{4}$$

$$= \frac{372\,\mu g/L}{4}$$

$$= 93\,\mu g/L$$

QUARTERS 2, 3, 4, AND 1

$$\text{Annual Running TTHM} \atop \text{Average, } \mu g/L = \frac{88\,\mu g/L + 112\,\mu g/L + 95\,\mu g/L + 83\,\mu g/L}{4}$$

$$= \frac{378\,\mu g/L}{4}$$

$$= 95\,\mu g/L$$

QUARTERS 3, 4, 1, AND 2

$$\text{Annual Running TTHM} \atop \text{Average, } \mu g/L = \frac{112\,\mu g/L + 95\,\mu g/L + 83\,\mu g/L + 87\,\mu g/L}{4}$$

$$= \frac{377\,\mu g/L}{4}$$

$$= 94\,\mu g/L$$

QUARTERS 4, 1, 2, AND 3

$$\text{Annual Running TTHM} \atop \text{Average, } \mu g/L = \frac{95\,\mu g/L + 83\,\mu g/L + 87\,\mu g/L + 109\,\mu g/L}{4}$$

$$= \frac{374\,\mu g/L}{4}$$

$$= 94\,\mu g/L$$

QUARTERS 1, 2, 3, AND 4

$$\text{Annual Running TTHM} \atop \text{Average, } \mu g/L = \frac{83\,\mu g/L + 87\,\mu g/L + 109\,\mu g/L + 89\,\mu g/L}{4}$$

$$= \frac{368\,\mu g/L}{4}$$

$$= 92\,\mu g/L$$

SUMMARY OF RESULTS

Quarter	1	2	3	4	1	2	3	4
Avg Quarterly TTHM, $\mu g/L$	77	88	112	95	83	87	109	89
Annual Running TTHM Avg, $\mu g/L$				93	95	94	94	92

A.34   Demineralization

EXAMPLE 26

Convert a water flux of 12 x 10^{-4} gm/sq cm-sec to gallons per day per square foot.

Known	**Unknown**
Water Flux, gm/sq cm-sec = 12 x 10^{-4} gm/sq cm-sec	Flow, GPD/sq ft

Convert the water flux from gm/sq cm-sec to flow in GPD/sq ft.

$$\text{Flow,} \atop \text{GPD/sq ft} = \frac{(\text{Flux, gm/sq cm-sec})(2.54\text{ cm/in})^2(12\text{ in/ft})^2(60\text{ sec/min})(60\text{ min/hr})(24\text{ hr/day})}{(1{,}000\text{ gm/L})(3.785\ L/\text{gal})}$$

$$= \frac{(0.0012\text{ gm/sq cm-sec})(2.54\text{ cm/in})^2(12\text{ in/ft})^2(60\text{ sec/min})(60\text{ min/hr})(24\text{ hr/day})}{(1{,}000\text{ gm/L})(3.785\ L/\text{gal})}$$

$$= 25.5\text{ GPD/sq ft}$$

EXAMPLE 27

Estimate the ability of a reverse osmosis plant to reject minerals by calculating the mineral rejection as a percent. The feedwater contains 1,800 mg/L TDS and the product water TDS is 120 mg/L.

Known	Unknown
Feedwater TDS, mg/L	= 1,800 mg/L	Mineral Rejection, %
Product Water TDS, mg/L	= 120 mg/L	

Calculate the mineral rejection as a percent.

$$\text{Mineral Rejection, \%} = \left(1 - \frac{\text{Product TDS, mg/}L}{\text{Feed TDS, mg/}L}\right)(100\%)$$

$$= \left(1 - \frac{120 \text{ mg/}L}{1,800 \text{ mg/}L}\right)(100\%)$$

$$= (1 - 0.067)(100\%)$$

$$= 93.3\%$$

EXAMPLE 28

Estimate the percent recovery of a reverse osmosis unit with a 4-2-1 arrangement if the feed flow is 2.0 MGD and the product flow is 1.75 MGD.

Known	Unknown
Product Flow, MGD = 1.75 MGD	Recovery, %
Feed Flow, MGD = 2.0 MGD	

Calculate the recovery as a percent.

$$\text{Recovery, \%} = \frac{(\text{Product Flow, MGD})(100\%)}{\text{Feed Flow, MGD}}$$

$$= \frac{(1.75 \text{ MGD})(100\%)}{2.0 \text{ MGD}}$$

$$= 87.5\%$$

A.35 Maintenance

EXAMPLE 29

Calculate the pumping capacity of a pump in gallons per minute when 12 minutes are required for the water to rise 3 feet in an 8-foot by 6-foot rectangular tank.

Known	Unknown
Length, ft = 8 ft	Pump Capacity, GPM
Width, ft = 6 ft	
Depth, ft = 3 ft	
Time, min = 12 min	

1. Calculate the volume pumped in cubic feet.

Volume Pumped, cu ft = (Length, ft)(Width, ft)(Depth, ft)

$$= (8 \text{ ft})(6 \text{ ft})(3 \text{ ft})$$

$$= 144 \text{ cu ft}$$

2. Convert the volume pumped from cubic feet to gallons.

Volume Pumped, gal = (Volume Pumped, cu ft)(7.48 gal/cu ft)

$$= (144 \text{ cu ft})(7.48 \text{ gal/cu ft})$$

$$= 1,077 \text{ gal}$$

3. Calculate the pump capacity in gallons per minute.

$$\text{Pump Capacity, GPM} = \frac{\text{Volume Pumped, gal}}{\text{Pumping Time, min}}$$

$$= \frac{1,077 \text{ gal}}{12 \text{ min}}$$

$$= 90 \text{ GPM}$$

EXAMPLE 30

A small chemical feed pump lowered the chemical solution in a 2.5-foot diameter tank 2.25 feet during seven hours. Estimate the flow delivered by the pump in gallons per minute and gallons per day.

Known	Unknown
Tank Diameter, ft = 2.5 ft	Flow, GPM
Chemical Drop, ft = 2.25 ft	Flow, GPD
Time, hr = 7.0 hr	

1. Determine the gallons of chemical solution pumped.

Volume, gal = (0.785)(Diameter, ft)^2(Drop, ft)(7.48 gal/cu ft)

$$= (0.785)(2.5 \text{ ft})^2(2.25 \text{ ft})(7.48 \text{ gal/cu ft})$$

$$= 83 \text{ gallons}$$

2. Estimate the flow delivered by the pump in gallons per minute and gallons per day.

$$\text{Flow, GPM} = \frac{\text{Volume Pumped, gal}}{(\text{Time, hr})(60 \text{ min/hr})}$$

$$= \frac{83 \text{ gallons}}{(7 \text{ hr})(60 \text{ min/hr})}$$

$$= 0.2 \text{ GPM}$$

or

$$\text{Flow, GPD} = \frac{(\text{Volume Pumped, gal})(24 \text{ hr/day})}{\text{Time, hr}}$$

$$= \frac{(83 \text{ gallons})(24 \text{ hr/day})}{7 \text{ hr}}$$

$$= 285 \text{ GPD}$$

EXAMPLE 31

Determine the chemical feed in pounds of polymer per day from a chemical feed pump. The polymer solution is 1.8 percent or 18,000 mg polymer per liter. Assume a specific gravity of the polymer solution of 1.0. During a test run the chemical feed pump delivered 650 mL of polymer solution in 4.5 minutes.

Known	Unknown
Polymer Solution, % = 1.8%	Polymer Feed, lbs/day
Polymer Conc, mg/L = 18,000 mg/L	
Polymer Sp Gr = 1.0	
Volume Pumped, mL = 650 mL	
Time Pumped, min = 4.5 min	

Calculate the polymer fed by the chemical feed pump in pounds of polymer per day.

$$\text{Polymer Feed, lbs/day} = \frac{(\text{Poly Conc, mg/L})(\text{Vol Pumped, mL})(60 \text{ min/hr})(24 \text{ hr/day})}{(\text{Time Pumped, min})(1,000 \text{ mL/L})(1,000 \text{ mg/gm})(454 \text{ gm/lb})}$$

$$= \frac{(18,000 \text{ mg/L})(650 \text{ mL})(60 \text{ min/hr})(24 \text{ hr/day})}{(4.5 \text{ min})(1,000 \text{ mL/L})(1,000 \text{ mg/gm})(454 \text{ gm/lb})}$$

$$= 8.2 \text{ lbs/day}$$

EXAMPLE 32

Determine the actual chemical feed in pounds per day from a dry chemical feeder. A pie tin placed under the chemical feeder caught 824 grams of chemical during five minutes.

Known	Unknown
Chemical, gm = 824 gm	Chemical Feed, lbs/day
Time, min = 5 min	

Determine the chemical feed in pounds per day.

$$\text{Chemical Feed, lbs/day} = \frac{(\text{Chemical, gm})(60 \text{ min/hr})(24 \text{ hr/day})}{(454 \text{ gm/lb})(\text{Time, min})}$$

$$= \frac{(824 \text{ gm})(60 \text{ min/hr})(24 \text{ hr/day})}{(454 \text{ gm/lb})(5 \text{ min})}$$

$$= 523 \text{ lbs/day}$$

A.36 Advanced Laboratory Procedures

EXAMPLE 33

Calculate the threshold odor number (TON) for a sample when the first detectable odor occurred when the 70-mL sample was diluted to 200 mL (130 mL of odor-free water was added to the 70-mL sample).

Known	Unknown
Size of Sample, mL = 70 mL	TON
Odor-Free Water, mL = 130 mL	

Calculate the threshold odor number (TON).

$$\text{TON} = \frac{\text{Size of Sample, mL} + \text{Odor-Free Water, mL}}{\text{Size of Sample, mL}}$$

$$= \frac{70 \text{ mL} + 130 \text{ mL}}{70 \text{ mL}}$$

$$= 3$$

EXAMPLE 34

Determine the geometric mean threshold odor number for a panel of six testers given the results shown below.

Known	Unknown
Tester 1, X_1 = 2	Geometric Mean Threshold Odor Number
Tester 2, X_2 = 4	
Tester 3, X_3 = 3	
Tester 4, X_4 = 8	
Tester 5, X_5 = 6	
Tester 6, X_6 = 2	

Calculate the geometric mean.

$$\text{Geometric Mean TON} = (X_1 \times X_2 \times X_3 \times X_4 \times X_5 \times X_6)^{1/n}$$

$$= (2 \times 4 \times 3 \times 8 \times 6 \times 2)^{1/6}$$

$$= (2,304)^{0.167}$$

$$= 3.6$$

EXAMPLE 35

Calculate the threshold taste number for a sample when the first detectable taste occurred when the 8.3-mL sample was diluted to 200 mL (191.7 mL of taste-free water was added to the 8.3-mL sample).

Known	Unknown
Sample Size, mL = 8.3 mL	Threshold Taste Number
Taste-Free Water, mL = 191.7 mL	

Calculate the threshold taste number.

$$\text{Threshold Taste Number} = \frac{\text{Sample Size, mL} + \text{Taste-Free Water, mL}}{\text{Sample Size, mL}}$$

$$= \frac{8.3 \text{ mL} + 191.7 \text{ mL}}{8.3 \text{ mL}}$$

$$= 24$$

EXAMPLE 36

Determine the taste rating for a water by calculating the arithmetic mean and standard deviation for the panel ratings given below.

Known	Unknown
Tester 1, $X_1 = 2$	1. Arithmetic Mean, $\overline{X}$
Tester 2, $X_2 = 5$	2. Standard Deviation, S
Tester 3, $X_3 = 3$	
Tester 4, $X_4 = 6$	
Tester 5, $X_5 = 2$	
Tester 6, $X_6 = 6$	

1. Calculate the arithmetic mean, $\overline{X}$, taste rating.

$$\begin{aligned}\text{Arithmetic Mean, } \overline{X} \atop \text{Taste Rating} &= \frac{X_1 + X_2 + X_3 + X_4 + X_5 + X_6}{n} \\[2mm] &= \frac{2 + 5 + 3 + 6 + 2 + 6}{6} \\[2mm] &= \frac{24}{6} \\[2mm] &= 4\end{aligned}$$

2. Calculate the standard deviation, S, of the taste rating.

$$\begin{aligned}\text{Standard} \atop \text{Deviation, S} &= \left[\frac{(X_1 - \overline{X})^2 + (X_2 - \overline{X})^2 + (X_3 - \overline{X})^2 + (X_4 - \overline{X})^2 + (X_5 - \overline{X})^2 + (X_6 - \overline{X})^2}{n - 1}\right]^{0.5} \\[2mm] &= \left[\frac{(2 - 4)^2 + (5 - 4)^2 + (3 - 4)^2 + (6 - 4)^2 + (2 - 4)^2 + (6 - 4)^2}{6 - 1}\right]^{0.5} \\[2mm] &= \left[\frac{(-2)^2 + (1)^2 + (-1)^2 + (2)^2 + (-2)^2 + (2)^2}{5}\right]^{0.5} \\[2mm] &= \left[\frac{4 + 1 + 1 + 4 + 4 + 4}{5}\right]^{0.5} \\[2mm] &= \left[\frac{18}{5}\right]^{0.5} \\[2mm] &= (3.6)^{0.5} \\[2mm] &= 1.9\end{aligned}$$

or

$$\begin{aligned}\text{Standard} \atop \text{Deviation, S} &= \left[\frac{(X_1^2 + X_2^2 + X_3^2 + X_4^2 + X_5^2 + X_6^2) - (X_1 + X_2 + X_3 + X_4 + X_5 + X_6)^2/n}{n - 1}\right]^{0.5} \\[2mm] &= \left[\frac{(2^2 + 5^2 + 3^2 + 6^2 + 2^2 + 6^2) - (2 + 5 + 3 + 6 + 2 + 6)^2/6}{6 - 1}\right]^{0.5} \\[2mm] &= \left[\frac{(4 + 25 + 9 + 36 + 4 + 36) - (24)^2/6}{5}\right]^{0.5} \\[2mm] &= \left[\frac{114 - 96}{5}\right]^{0.5} \\[2mm] &= \left[\frac{18}{5}\right]^{0.5} \\[2mm] &= (3.6)^{0.5} \\[2mm] &= 1.9\end{aligned}$$

EXAMPLE 37

A small water system collected 14 samples during one month. After each sample was collected, 10 mL of each sample was placed in each of 5 fermentation tubes. At the end of the month, the results indicated that 2 out of a total of 70 fermentation tubes were positive. What percent of the portions tested during the month were positive?

Known	Unknown
Number Positive/mo = 2 positive/mo	Portions Positive, %/mo
Total Portions Tested = 70 portions	

Calculate the percent of the portions tested during the month which were positive.

$$\text{Portions Positive, \%/mo} = \frac{(\text{Number Positive/mo})(100\%)}{\text{Total Portions Tested}}$$

$$= \frac{(2 \text{ positive/mo})(100\%)}{70 \text{ portions}}$$

$$= 3\%/\text{mo}$$

A.37 Administration, Safety

EXAMPLE 38

Calculate the injury frequency rate for a water utility where there were four injuries in one year and the operators worked 97,120 hours.

Known	Unknown
Injuries, number/yr = 4 injuries/yr	Injury Frequency Rate
Hours Worked, number/yr = 97,120 hr/yr	

Calculate the injury frequency rate.

$$\text{Injury Freq Rate} = \frac{(\text{Injuries, number/yr})(1,000,000)}{\text{Hours Worked, number/yr}}$$

$$= \frac{(4 \text{ injuries/yr})(1,000,000)}{97,120 \text{ hr/yr}}$$

$$= 41.2$$

EXAMPLE 39

Calculate the injury severity rate for a water company which experienced 57 operator-hours lost due to injuries while the operators worked 97,120 hours during the year.

Known	Unknown
Number of Hours Lost/yr = 57 hr/yr	Injury Severity Rate
Number of Hours Worked/yr = 97,120 hr/yr	

Calculate the injury severity rate.

$$\text{Injury Severity Rate} = \frac{(\text{Number of Hours Lost/yr})(1,000,000)}{\text{Number of Hours Worked/yr}}$$

$$= \frac{(57 \text{ hr/yr})(1,000,000)}{97,120 \text{ hr/yr}}$$

$$= 587$$

A.4 BASIC CONVERSION FACTORS (METRIC SYSTEM)

LENGTH

100 cm = 1 m	100 cm/m
3.281 ft = 1 m	3.281 ft/m

AREA

2.4711 ac = 1 ha*	2.4711 ac/ha
10,000 sq m = 1 ha	10,000 sq m/ha

VOLUME

1,000 mL = 1 liter	1,000 mL/L
1,000 L = 1 cu m	1,000 L/cu m
3.785 L = 1 gal	3.785 L/gal

WEIGHT

1,000 mg = 1 gm	1,000 mg/gm
1,000 gm = 1 kg	1,000 gm/kg

DENSITY

1 kg = 1 liter	1 kg/L

PRESSURE

10.015 m = 1 kg/sq cm	10.015 m/kg/sq cm
1 Pascal = 1 N/sq m	1 Pa/N/sq m
1 psi = 6,895 Pa	1 psi/6,895 Pa

FLOW

3,785 cu m/day = 1 MGD	3,785 cu m/day/MGD
3.785 ML/day = 1 MGD	3.785 ML/day/MGD

* hectare

A.5 TYPICAL WATER TREATMENT PLANT PROBLEMS (METRIC SYSTEM)

A.50 Iron and Manganese Control

EXAMPLE 1

A standard polyphosphate solution is prepared by mixing and dissolving 1.0 gram of polyphosphate in a container and adding distilled water to the one-liter mark. Determine the concentration of the stock solution in milligrams per milliliter. If 6.0 milliliters of the stock solution are added to a one-liter sample, what is the polyphosphate dose in milligrams per liter and milligrams per kilogram?

Known	Unknown
Polyphosphate, gm = 1.0 gm	1. Stock Solution, mg/mL
Solution, L = 1.0 L	2. Dose, mg/L
Stock Solution, mL = 6 mL	3. Dose, mg/kg
Sample, L = 1 L	

1. Calculate the concentration of the stock solution in milligrams per milliliter.

$$\text{Stock Solution, mg/m}L = \frac{(\text{Polyphosphate, gm})(1,000 \text{ mg/gm})}{(\text{Solution, }L)(1,000 \text{ m}L/L)}$$

$$= \frac{(1.0 \text{ gm})(1,000 \text{ mg/gm})}{(1 \text{ }L)(1,000 \text{ m}L/L)}$$

$$= 1.0 \text{ mg/m}L$$

2. Determine the polyphosphate dose in the sample in milligrams per liter.

$$\text{Dose, mg/}L = \frac{(\text{Stock Solution, mg/m}L)(\text{Vol Added, m}L)}{\text{Sample Volume, }L}$$

$$= \frac{(1.0 \text{ mg/m}L)(6 \text{ m}L)}{1 \text{ }L}$$

$$= 6.0 \text{ mg/}L$$

3. Determine the polyphosphate dose in the sample in milligrams of phosphate per kilogram of water.

$$\text{Dose, mg/kg} = \frac{(\text{Stock Solution, mg/}L)(\text{Vol Added, m}L)}{(\text{Sample Volume, }L)(1 \text{ kg/}L)}$$

$$= \frac{(1.0 \text{ mg/m}L)(6 \text{ m}L)}{(1 \text{ }L)(1 \text{ kg/}L)}$$

$$= 6.0 \text{ mg/kg}$$

EXAMPLE 2

Determine the chemical feeder setting in grams per second and kilograms per day if 2.4 MLD (mega or million liters per day) are treated with a dose of 5 mg/L.

Known	Unknown
Flow, MLD = 2.4 MLD	1. Chemical Feeder, gm/sec
Dose, mg/L = 5 mg/L	2. Chemical Feeder, kg/day

1. Determine the chemical feeder setting in grams per second.

$$\text{Chemical Feeder,} \atop \text{gm/sec} = \frac{(\text{Flow, M}L\text{D})(\text{Dose, mg/}L)(1{,}000{,}000/\text{M})}{(24 \text{ hr/day})(60 \text{ min/hr})(60 \text{ sec/min})(1{,}000 \text{ mg/gm})}$$

$$= \frac{(2.4 \text{ M}L\text{D})(5 \text{ mg/}L)(1{,}000{,}000/\text{M})}{(24 \text{ hr/day})(60 \text{ min/hr})(60 \text{ sec/min})(1{,}000 \text{ mg/gm})}$$

$$= 0.139 \text{ gm/sec}$$

$$\text{or} = 139 \text{ mg/sec}$$

2. Determine the chemical feeder setting in kilograms per day.

$$\text{Chemical Feeder,} \atop \text{kg/day} = \frac{(\text{Flow, M}L\text{D})(\text{Dose, mg/}L)(1{,}000{,}000/\text{M})}{(1{,}000 \text{ mg/gm})(1{,}000 \text{ gm/kg})}$$

$$= \frac{(2.4 \text{ M}L\text{D})(5 \text{ mg/}L)(1{,}000{,}000/\text{M})}{(1{,}000 \text{ mg/gm})(1{,}000 \text{ gm/kg})}$$

$$= 12 \text{ kg/day}$$

EXAMPLE 3

A reaction basin 4 meters in diameter and 1.2 meters deep treats a flow of 0.9 MLD. What is the average detention time in minutes?

Known	Unknown
Diameter, m = 4 m	Detention Time, min
Depth, m = 1.2 m	
Flow, MLD = 0.9 MLD	

1. Calculate the basin volume in cubic meters.

$$\text{Basin Vol, cu m} = (0.785)(\text{Diameter, m})^2(\text{Depth, m})$$

$$= (0.785)(4 \text{ m})^2(1.2 \text{ m})$$

$$= 15.1 \text{ cu m}$$

2. Determine the average detention time in minutes for the reaction basin.

$$\text{Detention Time,} \atop \text{min} = \frac{(\text{Basin Vol, cu m})(24 \text{ hr/day})(60 \text{ min/hr})(1{,}000 \text{ }L/\text{cu m})}{(\text{Flow, M}L\text{D})(1{,}000{,}000/\text{M})}$$

$$= \frac{(15.1 \text{ cu m})(24 \text{ hr/day})(60 \text{ min/hr})(1{,}000 \text{ }L/\text{cu m})}{(0.9 \text{ M}L\text{D})(1{,}000{,}000/\text{M})}$$

$$= 24 \text{ minutes}$$

EXAMPLE 4

Calculate the potassium permanganate dose in milligrams per liter for a well water with 2.4 mg/L iron before aeration and 0.3 mg/L after aeration. The manganese concentration is 0.8 mg/L both before and after aeration.

Known	Unknown
Iron, mg/L = 0.3 mg/L	KMnO$_4$ Dose, mg/L
Manganese, mg/L = 0.8 mg/L	

Calculate the potassium permanganate dose in milligrams per liter.

$$\text{KMnO}_4 \text{ Dose, mg/}L = 0.2(\text{Iron, mg/}L) + 2.0(\text{Manganese, mg/}L)$$

$$= 0.2(0.3 \text{ mg/}L) + 2.0(0.8 \text{ mg/}L)$$

$$= 1.66 \text{ mg/}L$$

NOTE: If there are any oxidizable compounds (organic color, bacteria, or hydrogen sulfide) in the water, the dose will have to be increased.

A.51 Fluoridation

EXAMPLE 5

Determine the setting for a chemical feed pump in liters per day and milliliters per second when the desired fluoride dose is 0.9 kilogram of fluoride per day. The sodium fluoride solution contains 0.025 kilogram of fluoride per liter and fluoride purity is 43.4 percent.

Known	Unknown
Feed Rate, kg F/day = 0.9 kg F/day	1. Feed Rate, liters/day
NaF Solution, kg F/L = 0.025 kg F/L	2. Feed Rate, mL/sec
Purity, % = 43.4%	

1. Determine the setting on the chemical feed pump in liters per day.

$$\text{Feed Rate,} \atop L/\text{day} = \frac{(\text{Feed Rate, kg F/day})(100\%)}{(\text{NaF Solution, kg F/}L)(\text{Purity, }\%)}$$

$$= \frac{(0.9 \text{ kg F/day})(100\%)}{(0.025 \text{ kg F/}L)(43.4\%)}$$

$$= 83 \text{ liters/day}$$

2. Convert the feed rate from kilograms per day to grams per second.

$$\text{Feed Rate,} \atop \text{gm/sec} = \frac{(\text{Feed Rate, kg/day})(1{,}000 \text{ gm/kg})}{(24 \text{ hr/day})(60 \text{ min/hr})(60 \text{ sec/min})}$$

$$= \frac{(0.9 \text{ kg/day})(1{,}000 \text{ gm/kg})}{(24 \text{ hr/day})(60 \text{ min/hr})(60 \text{ sec/min})}$$

$$= 0.010 \text{ gm/sec}$$

$$\text{or } = 10 \text{ mg/sec}$$

3. Determine the setting on the chemical feed pump in milliliters per second.

$$\text{Feed Rate,} \atop \text{m}L\text{/sec} = \frac{(\text{Feed Rate, gm/sec})(100\%)(1{,}000 \text{ m}L/L)}{(\text{Na}F \text{ Solution, kg } F/L)(\text{Purity, }\%)(1{,}000 \text{ gm/kg})}$$

$$= \frac{(0.010 \text{ gm/sec})(100\%)(1{,}000 \text{ m}L/L)}{(0.025 \text{ kg } F/L)(43.4\%)(1{,}000 \text{ gm/kg})}$$

$$= 0.92 \text{ m}L\text{/sec}$$

EXAMPLE 6

Determine the setting on a chemical feed pump in liters per day and milliliters per second if 2 megaliters per day of water must be treated with 0.9 mg/L of fluoride. The fluoride feed solution contains 18,000 mg/L of fluoride.

Known		Unknown
Flow, MLD	= 2 MLD	1. Feed Pump, liters/day
Fluoride, mg/L	= 0.9 mg/L	2. Feed Pump, mL/sec
Feed Solution, mg/L	= 18,000 mg/L	

1. Determine the setting on the chemical feed pump in liters per day.

$$\text{Feed Pump,} \atop \text{liters/day} = \frac{(\text{Flow, M}L\text{D})(\text{Feed Dose, mg/}L)(1{,}000{,}000/\text{M})}{\text{Feed Solution, mg/}L}$$

$$= \frac{(2.0 \text{ M}L\text{D})(0.9 \text{ mg/}L)(1{,}000{,}000/\text{M})}{18{,}000 \text{ mg/}L}$$

$$= 100 \text{ liters/day}$$

2. Determine the setting on the chemical feed pump in milliliters per second.

$$\text{Feed Pump,} \atop \text{m}L\text{/sec} = \frac{(\text{Flow, M}L\text{D})(\text{Feed Dose, mg/}L)(1{,}000{,}000/\text{M})}{(\text{Feed Solution, mg/}L)(24 \text{ hr/day})(60 \text{ min/hr})(60 \text{ sec/min})}$$

$$= \frac{(2 \text{ M}L\text{D})(0.9 \text{ mg/}L)(1{,}000{,}000/\text{M})}{(18{,}000 \text{ mg/}L)(24 \text{ hr/day})(60 \text{ min/hr})(60 \text{ sec/min})}$$

$$= 1.16 \text{ m}L\text{/sec}$$

EXAMPLE 7

Determine the fluoride ion purity of Na$_2$SiF$_6$ as a percent.

Known	Unknown
Fluoride Chemical, Na$_2$SiF$_6$	Fluoride Ion Purity, %

Determine the molecular weight of fluoride and Na$_2$SiF$_6$.

Symbol	(No. Atoms)	(Atomic Wt)	=	Molecular Wt
Na$_2$	(2)	(22.99)	=	45.98
Si	(1)	(28.09)	=	28.09
F$_6$	(6)	(19.00)	=	114.00
	Molecular Weight of Chemical		=	188.07

Calculate the fluoride ion purity as a percent.

$$\text{Fluoride Ion} \atop \text{Purity, }\% = \frac{(\text{Molecular Weight of Fluoride})(100\%)}{\text{Molecular Weight of Chemical}}$$

$$= \frac{(114.00)(100\%)}{188.07}$$

$$= 60.62\%$$

EXAMPLE 8

A flow of 6.5 MLD is treated with sodium silicofluoride. The raw water contains 0.2 mg/L of fluoride ion and the desired fluoride concentration is 1.1 mg/L. What should be the chemical feed rate in kilograms per day and milligrams per second? Assume each gram of commercial sodium silicofluoride (Na$_2$SiF$_6$) contains 0.6 gram of fluoride ion.

Known		Unknown
Flow, MLD	= 6.5 MLD	1. Feed Rate, kg/day
Raw Water F, mg/L	= 0.2 mg/L	2. Feed Rate, mg/sec
Desired F, mg/L	= 1.1 mg/L	
Chemical, gm F/gm	= 0.6 gm F/gm	

1. Determine the fluoride feed dose in milligrams per liter.

$$\text{Feed Dose, mg/}L = \text{Desired Dose, mg/}L - \text{Actual Conc, mg/}L$$

$$= 1.1 \text{ mg/}L - 0.2 \text{ mg/}L$$

$$= 0.9 \text{ mg/}L$$

2. Calculate the chemical feed rate in kilograms per day.

$$\text{Feed Rate,} \atop \text{kg/day} = \frac{(\text{Flow, M}L\text{D})(\text{Feed Dose, mg/}L)(1{,}000{,}000/\text{M})}{(\text{Purity, gm F/gm chemical})(1{,}000 \text{ mg/gm})(1{,}000 \text{ gm/kg})}$$

$$= \frac{(6.5 \text{ M}L\text{D})(0.9 \text{ mg/}L)(1{,}000{,}000/\text{M})}{(0.6 \text{ gm F/gm chemical})(1{,}000 \text{ mg/gm})(1{,}000 \text{ gm/kg})}$$

$$= 9.75 \text{ kg/day}$$

3. Calculate the chemical feed rate in milligrams per second.

$$\text{Feed Rate,} \atop \text{mg/sec} = \frac{(\text{Flow, M}L\text{D})(\text{Dose, mg/}L)(1{,}000{,}000/\text{M})}{(\text{Purity, gm F/gm chemical})(24 \text{ hr/day})(60 \text{ min/hr})(60 \text{ sec/min})}$$

$$= \frac{(6.5 \text{ M}L\text{D})(0.9 \text{ mg/}L)(1{,}000{,}000/\text{M})}{(0.6 \text{ gm F/gm chemical})(24 \text{ hr/day})(60 \text{ min/hr})(60 \text{ sec/min})}$$

$$= 113 \text{ mg/sec}$$

EXAMPLE 9

The feed solution from a saturator containing 1.8 percent fluoride ion is used to treat a total flow of 0.95 megaliter (ML) of water. The raw water has a fluoride ion content of 0.2 mg/L and the desired fluoride level in the treated water is 0.9 mg/L. How many liters of feed solution are needed?

Known	Unknown
Flow Vol, ML = 0.95 ML	Feed Solution, liters
Raw Water F, mg/L = 0.2 mg/L	
Desired F, mg/L = 0.9 mg/L	
Feed Solution, % F = 1.8% F	

1. Convert the feed solution from a percentage fluoride ion to milligrams fluoride ion per liter of water.

   1.0% F = 10,000 mg F/L

   $$\text{Feed Solution, mg/L} = \frac{(\text{Feed Solution, \%})(10,000 \text{ mg/L})}{1.0\%}$$

   $$= \frac{(1.8\% \text{ F})(10,000 \text{ mg/L})}{1.0\%}$$

   $$= 18,000 \text{ mg/L}$$

2. Determine the fluoride feed dose in milligrams per liter.

   Feed Dose, mg/L = Desired Dose, mg/L − Raw Water F, mg/L

   $$= 0.9 \text{ mg/L} - 0.2 \text{ mg/L}$$

   $$= 0.7 \text{ mg/L}$$

3. Calculate the liters of feed solution needed.

   $$\text{Feed Solution, } L = \frac{(\text{Flow Vol, ML})(\text{Feed Dose, mg/L})(1,000,000/M)}{\text{Feed Solution, mg/L}}$$

   $$= \frac{(0.95 \text{ ML})(0.7 \text{ mg/L})(1,000,000/M)}{18,000 \text{ mg/L}}$$

   $$= 37 \text{ liters}$$

EXAMPLE 10

A hydrofluosilicic acid (H_2SiF_6) tank contains 1,300 liters of acid with a strength of 19.3 percent. A commercial vendor delivers 10,000 liters of acid with a strength of 18.1 percent to the tank. What is the resulting strength of the mixture as a percentage?

Known	Unknown
Tank Contents, liters = 1,300 L	Mixture Strength, %
Tank Strength, % = 19.3%	
Vendor, L = 10,000 L	
Vendor Strength, % = 18.1%	

Calculate the strength of the mixture as a percentage.

$$\text{Mixture Strength, \%} = \frac{(\text{Tank, } L)(\text{Tank, \%}) + (\text{Vendor, } L)(\text{Vendor, \%})}{(\text{Tank, } L + \text{Vendor, } L)}$$

$$= \frac{(1,300 \text{ } L)(19.3\%) + (10,000 \text{ } L)(18.1\%)}{(1,300 \text{ } L + 10,000 \text{ } L)}$$

$$= \frac{25,090 + 181,000}{11,300}$$

$$= 18.2\%$$

A.52   Softening

EXAMPLE 11

Determine the total hardness as $CaCO_3$ for a sample of water with a calcium content of 33 mg/L and a magnesium content of 6 mg/L.

Known	Unknown
Calcium, mg/L = 33 mg/L	Total Hardness, mg/L as $CaCO_3$
Magnesium, mg/L = 6 mg/L	

Calculate the total hardness as milligrams per liter of calcium carbonate equivalent.

$$\text{Total Hardness, mg/L as } CaCO_3 = \text{Calcium Hardness, mg/L as } CaCO_3 + \text{Magnesium Hardness, mg/L as } CaCO_3$$

$$= 2.5(\text{Ca, mg/L}) + 4.12(\text{Mg, mg/L})$$

$$= 2.5(33 \text{ mg/L}) + 4.12(6 \text{ mg/L})$$

$$= 82 \text{ mg/L} + 25 \text{ mg/L}$$

$$= 107 \text{ mg/L as } CaCO_3$$

EXAMPLE 12

The alkalinity of a water is 120 mg/L as $CaCO_3$ and the total hardness is 105 mg/L as $CaCO_3$. What is the carbonate and noncarbonate hardness in mg/L as $CaCO_3$?

Known	Unknown
Alkalinity, mg/L = 120 mg/L as $CaCO_3$	1. Carbonate Hardness, mg/L as $CaCO_3$
Total Hardness, mg/L = 105 mg/L as $CaCO_3$	2. Noncarbonate Hardness, mg/L as $CaCO_3$

1. Determine the carbonate hardness in mg/L as $CaCO_3$.

   Since the alkalinity is greater than the total hardness (120 mg/L > 105 mg/L),

   $$\text{Carbonate Hardness, mg/L as } CaCO_3 = \text{Total Hardness, mg/L as } CaCO_3$$

   $$= 105 \text{ mg/L as } CaCO_3$$

2. Determine the noncarbonate hardness in mg/L as $CaCO_3$.

   Since the alkalinity is greater than the total hardness,

   Noncarbonate Hardness, mg/L as $CaCO_3$ = 0

   In other words, all of the hardness is in the carbonate form.

EXAMPLE 13

The alkalinity of a water is 92 mg/L as $CaCO_3$ and the total hardness is 105 mg/L. What is the carbonate and noncarbonate hardness in mg/L as $CaCO_3$?

Known	Unknown
Alkalinity, mg/L = 92 mg/L as $CaCO_3$	1. Carbonate Hardness, mg/L as $CaCO_3$
Total Hardness, mg/L = 105 mg/L as $CaCO_3$	2. Noncarbonate Hardness, mg/L as $CaCO_3$

1. Determine the carbonate hardness in mg/L as $CaCO_3$.

   Since the alkalinity is less than the total hardness (92 mg/L < 105 mg/L),

   Carbonate Hardness, mg/L as $CaCO_3$ = Alkalinity, mg/L as $CaCO_3$

   = 92 mg/L as $CaCO_3$

2. Determine the noncarbonate hardness in mg/L as $CaCO_3$.

   Since the alkalinity is less than the total hardness (92 mg/L < 105 mg/L),

   Noncarbonate Hardness, mg/L as $CaCO_3$ = Total Hardness, mg/L as $CaCO_3$ − Alkalinity, mg/L as $CaCO_3$

   = 105 mg/L − 92 mg/L

   = 13 mg/L as $CaCO_3$

EXAMPLE 14

Results from alkalinity titrations on a water sample were as follows:

Known

Sample Size, mL	= 100 mL
mL Titrant Used to pH 8.3, A	= 1.1 mL
Total mL of Titrant Used, B	= 12.4 mL
Acid Normality, N	= 0.02 N H_2SO_4

Unknown

1. Total Alkalinity, mg/L as $CaCO_3$
2. Bicarbonate Alkalinity, mg/L as $CaCO_3$
3. Carbonate Alkalinity, mg/L as $CaCO_3$
4. Hydroxide Alkalinity, mg/L as $CaCO_3$

See Table 14.4, page 82, for alkalinity relationships among constituents.

1. Calculate the phenolphthalein alkalinity in mg/L as $CaCO_3$.

   Phenolphthalein Alkalinity, mg/L as $CaCO_3$ = $\dfrac{A \times N \times 50{,}000}{mL\ of\ sample}$

   = $\dfrac{(1.1\ mL)(0.02\ N)(50{,}000)}{100\ mL}$

   = 11 mg/L as $CaCO_3$

2. Calculate the total alkalinity in mg/L as $CaCO_3$.

   Total Alkalinity, mg/L as $CaCO_3$ = $\dfrac{B \times N \times 50{,}000}{mL\ of\ sample}$

   = $\dfrac{(12.4\ mL)(0.02\ N)(50{,}000)}{100\ mL}$

   = 124 mg/L as $CaCO_3$

3. Refer to Table 14.4 for alkalinity constituents. The second row indicates that since P is less than ½T (11 mg/L < ½ (124 mg/L), bicarbonate alkalinity is T − 2P and carbonate alkalinity is 2P.

   Bicarbonate Alkalinity, mg/L as $CaCO_3$ = T − 2P

   = 124 mg/L − 2(11 mg/L)

   = 102 mg/L as $CaCO_3$

   Carbonate Alkalinity, mg/L as $CaCO_3$ = 2P

   = 2(11 mg/L)

   = 22 mg/L as $CaCO_3$

   Hydroxide Alkalinity, mg/L as $CaCO_3$ = 0 mg/L as $CaCO_3$

EXAMPLE 15

Calculate the hydrated lime ($Ca(OH)_2$) with 90 percent purity, soda ash, and carbon dioxide requirements in milligrams per liter for the water shown below.

Known

Constituents	Source Water	Softened Water After Recarbonation and Filtration
CO_2, mg/L	= 7 mg/L	= 0 mg/L
Total Alkalinity, mg/L	= 125 mg/L as $CaCO_3$	= 22 mg/L as $CaCO_3$
Total Hardness, mg/L	= 240 mg/L as $CaCO_3$	= 35 mg/L as $CaCO_3$
Mg^{2+}, mg/L	= 38 mg/L	= 8 mg/L
pH	= 7.6	= 8.8
Lime Purity, %	= 90%	

Unknown

1. Hydrated Lime, mg/L
2. Soda Ash, mg/L
3. Carbon Dioxide, mg/L

1. Calculate the hydrated lime ($Ca(OH)_2$) required in milligrams per liter.

   A = (CO_2, mg/L)(74/44)

   = (7 mg/L)(74/44)

   = 12 mg/L

   B = (Alkalinity, mg/L)(74/100)

   = (125 mg/L)(74/100)

   = 93 mg/L

   C = (Hydroxide, mg/L)(74/100)

   = 0

   D = (Mg^{2+}, mg/L)(74/24.3)

   = (38 mg/L)(74/24.3)

   = 116 mg/L

$$\text{Hydrated Lime } (Ca(OH)_2) \text{ Feed, mg/}L = \frac{(A + B + C + D)1.15}{\text{Purity of Lime, as a decimal}}$$

$$= \frac{(12 \text{ mg/}L + 93 \text{ mg/}L + 0 + 116 \text{ mg/}L)1.15}{0.90}$$

$$= \frac{(221 \text{ mg/}L)(1.15)}{0.90}$$

$$= 282 \text{ mg/}L$$

2. Calculate the soda ash required in milligrams per liter.

$$\text{Total Hardness Removed, mg/}L \text{ as } CaCO_3 = \text{Total Hardness, mg/}L \text{ as } CaCO_3 - \text{Total Hardness Remaining, mg/}L \text{ as } CaCO_3$$

$$= 240 \text{ mg/}L - 35 \text{ mg/}L$$

$$= 205 \text{ mg/}L$$

$$\text{Noncarbonate Hardness, mg/}L \text{ as } CaCO_3 = \text{Total Hardness Removed, mg/}L \text{ as } CaCO_3 - \text{Carbonate Hardness, mg/}L \text{ as } CaCO_3$$

$$= 205 \text{ mg/}L - 125 \text{ mg/}L$$

$$= 80 \text{ mg/}L \text{ as } CaCO_3$$

$$\text{Soda Ash } (Na_2CO_3) \text{ Feed, mg/}L = \left(\frac{\text{Noncarbonate Hardness,}}{\text{mg/}L \text{ as } CaCO_3}\right)(106/100)$$

$$= (80 \text{ mg/}L)(106/100)$$

$$= 85 \text{ mg/}L$$

3. Calculate the dosage of carbon dioxide required for recarbonation.

   Excess Lime, mg/L = (A + B + C + D)(0.15)

   = (12 mg/L + 93 mg/L + 0 + 116 mg/L)(0.15)

   = (221 mg/L)(0.15)

   = 33 mg/L

$$\text{Total } CO_2 \text{ Feed, mg/}L = (Ca(OH)_2 \text{ excess, mg/}L)(44/74) + (Mg^{2+} \text{ residual, mg/}L)(44/24.3)$$

$$= (33 \text{ mg/}L)(44/74) + (8 \text{ mg/}L)(44/24.3)$$

$$= 20 \text{ mg/}L + 15 \text{ mg/}L$$

$$= 35 \text{ mg/}L$$

EXAMPLE 16

The optimum lime dosage from the jar tests is 180 mg/L. If the flow to be treated is 6.5 MLD, what is the feeder setting in kilograms per day and the feed rate in grams per second?

Known	Unknown
Lime Dose, mg/L = 180 mg/L	1. Feeder Setting, kg/day
Flow, MLD = 6.5 MLD	2. Feed Rate, gm/sec

1. Calculate the feeder setting in kilograms per day.

$$\text{Feeder Setting, kg/day} = \frac{(\text{Flow, M}LD)(\text{Lime, mg/}L)(1,000,000/\text{M})}{(1,000 \text{ mg/gm})(1,000 \text{ gm/kg})}$$

$$= \frac{(6.5 \text{ M}LD)(180 \text{ mg/}L)(1,000,000/\text{M})}{(1,000 \text{ mg/gm})(1,000 \text{ gm/kg})}$$

$$= 1,170 \text{ kg/day}$$

2. Calculate the feed rate in grams per second.

$$\text{Feed Rate, gm/sec} = \frac{(\text{Flow, M}LD)(\text{Lime, mg/}L)(1,000,000/\text{M})}{(1,000 \text{ mg/gm})(24 \text{ hr/day})(60 \text{ min/hr})(60 \text{ sec/min})}$$

$$= \frac{(6.5 \text{ M}LD)(180 \text{ mg/}L)(1,000,000/\text{M})}{(1,000 \text{ mg/gm})(24 \text{ hr/day})(60 \text{ min/hr})(60 \text{ sec/min})}$$

$$= 13.5 \text{ gm/sec}$$

EXAMPLE 17

How much soda ash is required (kilograms per day and grams per second) to remove 40 mg/L noncarbonate hardness as $CaCO_3$ from a flow of 6.5 MLD?

Known	Unknown
Noncarbonate Hardness Removed, mg/L as $CaCO_3$ = 40 mg/L	1. Feeder Setting, kg/day
Flow, MLD = 6.5 MLD	2. Feed Rate, gm/sec

1. Calculate the soda ash dose in milligrams per liter. See Section 14.316, "Calculation of Chemical Dosages," page 86, for the following formula.

$$\text{Soda Ash, mg/}L = \left(\frac{\text{Noncarbonate Hardness,}}{\text{mg/}L \text{ as } CaCO_3}\right)(106/100)$$

$$= (40 \text{ mg/}L)(106/100)$$

$$= 43 \text{ mg/}L$$

2. Determine the feeder setting in kilograms per day.

$$\text{Feeder Setting, kg/day} = \frac{(\text{Flow, M}LD)(\text{Soda Ash, mg/}L)(1,000,000/\text{M})}{(1,000 \text{ mg/gm})(1,000 \text{ gm/kg})}$$

$$= \frac{(6.5 \text{ M}LD)(40 \text{ mg/}L)(1,000,000/\text{M})}{(1,000 \text{ mg/gm})(1,000 \text{ gm/kg})}$$

$$= 260 \text{ kg/day}$$

3. Calculate the soda ash feed rate in grams per second.

$$\text{Feed Rate, gm/sec} = \frac{(\text{Flow, M}LD)(\text{Soda Ash, mg/}L)(1,000,000/\text{M})}{(1,000 \text{ mg/gm})(24 \text{ hr/day})(60 \text{ min/hr})(60 \text{ sec/min})}$$

$$= \frac{(6.5 \text{ M}LD)(40 \text{ mg/}L)(1,000,000/\text{M})}{(1,000 \text{ mg/gm})(24 \text{ hr/day})(60 \text{ min/hr})(60 \text{ sec/min})}$$

$$= 3.0 \text{ gm/sec}$$

EXAMPLE 18

What is the hardness in grains per gallon for a water with a hardness of 200 mg/L?

Known	Unknown
Hardness, mg/L = 200 mg/L	Hardness, grains/gal

Calculate the hardness in grains per gallon.

$$\text{Hardness, grains/gal} = \frac{(\text{Hardness, mg/}L)(1 \text{ grain/gal})}{17.1 \text{ mg/}L}$$

$$= \frac{(200 \text{ mg/}L)(1 \text{ grain/gal})}{17.1 \text{ mg/}L}$$

$$= 11.7 \text{ grains/gal}$$

EXAMPLE 19

Estimate the exchange capacity in milligrams of hardness for an ion exchange unit which contains 20 cubic meters of resin with a removal capacity of 14,000 milligrams per cubic meter.

Known	Unknown
Resin Vol, cu m = 20 cu m	Exchange Capacity, milligrams
Removal Cap, mg/cu m = 14,000 mg/cu m	

Estimate the exchange capacity in milligrams of hardness.

$$\text{Exchange Capacity, mg} = (\text{Resin Vol, cu m})(\text{Removal Capacity, mg/cu m})$$

$$= (20 \text{ cu m})(14,000 \text{ mg/cu m})$$

$$= 280,000 \text{ mg of hardness}$$

EXAMPLE 20

How many liters of water with a hardness of 200 mg/L may be treated by an ion exchange softener with an exchange capacity of 280,000 milligrams?

Known	Unknown
Hardness, mg/L = 200 mg/L	Water Treated, liters
Exchange Capacity, mg = 280,000 mg	

Calculate the liters of water that may be treated.

$$\text{Water Treated, liters} = \frac{\text{Exchange Capacity, mg}}{\text{Hardness, mg/}L}$$

$$= \frac{280,000 \text{ mg}}{200 \text{ mg/}L}$$

$$= 1,400 \text{ liters}$$

EXAMPLE 21

How many hours will an ion exchange softening unit operate when treating an average daily flow of 50 liters per second. The unit is capable of softening 4,500,000 liters of water before requiring regeneration.

Known	Unknown
Avg Daily Flow, L/sec = 50 L/sec	Operating Time, hr
Water Treated, L = 4,500,000 L	

Estimate how many hours the softening unit can operate before requiring regeneration.

$$\text{Operating Time, hr} = \frac{\text{Water Treated, } L}{(\text{Avg Daily Flow, } L\text{/sec})(60 \text{ sec/min})(60 \text{ min/hr})}$$

$$= \frac{4,500,000 \ L}{(50 \ L\text{/sec})(60 \text{ sec/min})(60 \text{ min/hr})}$$

$$= 25 \text{ hours}$$

EXAMPLE 22

Determine the kilograms of salt needed to regenerate an ion exchange softening unit capable of removing 225,000 milligrams of hardness if 7 kilograms of salt are required for every 1,000 milligrams of hardness removed.

Known	Unknown
Hardness Removed, mg = 225,000 mg	Salt Needed, kg
Salt Required, kg/1,000 mg = 7 kg salt/1,000 mg	

Calculate the kilograms of salt needed to regenerate the ion exchange softening unit.

$$\text{Salt Needed, kg} = (\text{Salt Required, kg/1,000 mg})(\text{Hardness Removed, mg})$$

$$= \frac{(7 \text{ kg salt})(225,000 \text{ mg})}{1,000 \text{ mg}}$$

$$= 1,575 \text{ kilograms of salt}$$

EXAMPLE 23

Estimate the bypass flow in cubic meters per day and megaliters per day around an ion exchange softener in a plant that treats 1,000 cubic meters per day with a source water hardness of 350 mg/L if the desired product water hardness is 80 mg/L.

Known	Unknown
Total Flow, cu m/day = 1,000 cu m/day	1. Bypass Flow, cu m/day
Source Water Hardness, mg/L = 350 mg/L	2. Bypass Flow, MLD
Plant Effl Hardness, mg/L = 80 mg/L	

1. Estimate the bypass flow in cubic meters per day.

$$\text{Bypass Flow, cu m/day} = \frac{(\text{Total Flow, cu m/day})(\text{Plant Effl Hardness, mg/}L)}{\text{Source Water Hardness, mg/}L}$$

$$= \frac{(1,000 \text{ cu m/day})(80 \text{ mg/}L)}{350 \text{ mg/}L}$$

$$= 229 \text{ cu m/day}$$

2. Estimate the bypass flow in megaliters per day.

$$\text{Bypass Flow, MLD} = \frac{(\text{Total Flow, cu m/day})(\text{Plant Effl Hardness, mg/}L)(1,000 \ L\text{/cu m})}{(\text{Source Water Hardness, mg/}L)(1,000,000/M)}$$

$$= \frac{(1,000 \text{ cu m/day})(80 \text{ mg/}L)(1,000 \ L\text{/cu m})}{(350 \text{ mg/}L)(1,000,000/M)}$$

$$= 0.229 \text{ M}LD$$

A.53   Trihalomethanes

EXAMPLE 24

A water utility collected and analyzed eight samples from a water distribution system on the same day for TTHMs. The results are shown below.

Sample No.	1	2	3	4	5	6	7	8
TTHM, μg/L	80	90	100	90	110	100	100	90

What was the average TTHM for the day?

Known	Unknown
Results from analyses of 8 TTHM samples	Average TTHM level for the day

Calculate the average TTHM level in micrograms per liter.

$$\text{Avg TTHM, μg/L} = \frac{\text{Sum of Measurements, μg/L}}{\text{Number of Measurements}}$$

$$= \frac{80\ \text{μg/L} + 90\ \text{μg/L} + 100\ \text{μg/L} + 90\ \text{μg/L} + 110\ \text{μg/L} + 100\ \text{μg/L} + 100\ \text{μg/L} + 90\ \text{μg/L}}{8}$$

$$= \frac{760\ \text{μg/L}}{8}$$

$$= 95\ \text{μg/L}$$

EXAMPLE 25

The results of the quarterly average TTHM measurements for two years are given below. Calculate the running annual average of the four quarterly measurements in micrograms per liter.

Quarter	1	2	3	4	1	2	3	4
Avg Quarterly TTHM, μg/L	77	88	112	95	83	87	109	89

Known	Unknown
Results from analyses of two years of TTHM sampling	Running Annual Average of quarterly TTHM measurements

Calculate the running annual average of the quarterly TTHM measurements.

$$\text{Annual Running TTHM Avg, μg/L} = \frac{\text{Sum of Avg TTHM for Four Quarters}}{\text{Number of Quarters}}$$

QUARTERS 1, 2, 3, AND 4

$$\text{Annual Running TTHM Avg, μg/L} = \frac{77\ \text{μg/L} + 88\ \text{μg/L} + 112\ \text{μg/L} + 95\ \text{μg/L}}{4}$$

$$= \frac{372\ \text{μg/L}}{4}$$

$$= 93\ \text{μg/L}$$

QUARTERS 2, 3, 4, AND 1

$$\text{Annual Running TTHM Avg, μg/L} = \frac{88\ \text{μg/L} + 112\ \text{μg/L} + 95\ \text{μg/L} + 83\ \text{μg/L}}{4}$$

$$= \frac{378\ \text{μg/L}}{4}$$

$$= 95\ \text{μg/L}$$

QUARTERS 3, 4, 1, AND 2

$$\text{Annual Running TTHM Avg, μg/L} = \frac{112\ \text{μg/L} + 95\ \text{μg/L} + 83\ \text{μg/L} + 87\ \text{μg/L}}{4}$$

$$= \frac{377\ \text{μg/L}}{4}$$

$$= 94\ \text{μg/L}$$

QUARTERS 4, 1, 2, AND 3

$$\text{Annual Running TTHM Avg, μg/L} = \frac{95\ \text{μg/L} + 83\ \text{μg/L} + 87\ \text{μg/L} + 109\ \text{μg/L}}{4}$$

$$= \frac{374\ \text{μg/L}}{4}$$

$$= 94\ \text{μg/L}$$

QUARTERS 1, 2, 3, AND 4

$$\text{Annual Running TTHM Avg, μg/L} = \frac{83\ \text{μg/L} + 87\ \text{μg/L} + 109\ \text{μg/L} + 89\ \text{μg/L}}{4}$$

$$= \frac{368\ \text{μg/L}}{4}$$

$$= 92\ \text{μg/L}$$

SUMMARY OF RESULTS

Quarter	1	2	3	4	1	2	3	4
Avg Quarterly TTHM, μg/L	77	88	112	95	83	87	109	89
Annual Running TTHM Avg, μg/L				93	95	94	94	92

A.54   Demineralization

EXAMPLE 26

Convert a water flux of 12 x 10^{-4} gm/sq cm-sec to liters per second per square centimeter and liters per day per square centimeter.

Known	Unknown
Water Flux, gm/sq cm-sec = 12 x 10^{-4} gm/sq cm-sec	1. Flow, liters per sq cm-sec 2. Flow, liters per sq cm-day

1. Convert the water flux from gm/sq cm-sec to flow in liters per second per square centimeter.

$$\text{Flow, } L/\text{sq cm-sec} = \frac{\text{Flux, gm/sq cm-sec}}{1,000 \text{ gm}/L}$$

$$= \frac{12 \times 10^{-4} \text{ gm/sq cm-sec}}{1,000 \text{ m}L}$$

$$= 12 \times 10^{-7} \text{ } L/\text{sq cm-sec}$$

2. Convert the water flux from gm/sq cm-sec to flow in liters per day per square centimeter.

$$\text{Flow, } \frac{L/\text{sq}}{\text{cm-day}} = \frac{(\text{Flux, gm/sq cm-sec})(60 \text{ sec/min})(60 \text{ min/hr})(24 \text{ hr/day})}{1,000 \text{ gm}/L}$$

$$= \frac{(0.0012 \text{ gm/sq cm-sec})(60 \text{ sec/min})(60 \text{ min/hr})(24 \text{ hr/day})}{1,000 \text{ gm}/L}$$

$$= 0.10 \text{ } L/\text{sq cm-day}$$

EXAMPLE 27

Estimate the ability of a reverse osmosis plant to reject minerals by calculating the mineral rejection as a percent. The feedwater contains 1,800 mg/L TDS and the product water TDS is 120 mg/L.

Known	Unknown
Feedwater TDS, mg/L = 1,800 mg/L	Mineral Rejection, %
Product Water TDS, mg/L = 120 mg/L	

Calculate the mineral rejection as a percent.

$$\text{Mineral Rejection, \%} = \left(1 - \frac{\text{Product TDS, mg}/L}{\text{Feed TDS, mg}/L}\right)(100\%)$$

$$= \left(1 - \frac{120 \text{ mg}/L}{1,800 \text{ mg}/L}\right)(100\%)$$

$$= (1 - 0.067)(100\%)$$

$$= 93.3\%$$

EXAMPLE 28

Estimate the percent recovery of a reverse osmosis unit with a 4-2-1 arrangement if the feed flow is 8.0 MLD and the product flow is 7.0 MLD.

Known	Unknown
Product Flow, MLD = 7.0 MLD	Recovery, %
Feed Flow, MLD = 8.0 MLD	

Calculate the recovery as a percent.

$$\text{Recovery, \%} = \frac{(\text{Product Flow, MLD})(100\%)}{\text{Feed Flow, MLD}}$$

$$= \frac{(7.0 \text{ MLD})(100\%)}{8.0 \text{ MLD}}$$

$$= 87.5\%$$

A.55 Maintenance

EXAMPLE 29

Calculate the pumping capacity of a pump in liters per second when 12 minutes are required for the water to rise 1.0 meters in a 2.5-meter by 2.0-meter rectangular tank.

Known	Unknown
Length, m = 2.5 m	Pump Capacity, L/sec
Width, m = 2.0 m	
Depth, m = 1.0 m	
Time, min = 12 min	

1. Calculate the volume pumped in cubic meters.

$$\text{Volume Pumped, cu m} = (\text{Length, m})(\text{Width, m})(\text{Depth, m})$$

$$= (2.5 \text{ m})(2.0 \text{ m})(1.0 \text{ m})$$

$$= 5.0 \text{ cu m}$$

2. Calculate the pump capacity in liters per second.

$$\text{Pump Capacity, liters/sec} = \frac{(\text{Volume Pumped, cu m})(1,000 \text{ } L/\text{cu m})}{(\text{Pumping Time, min})(60 \text{ sec/min})}$$

$$= \frac{(5.0 \text{ cu m})(1,000 \text{ } L/\text{cu m})}{(12 \text{ min})(60 \text{ sec/min})}$$

$$= 417 \text{ } L/\text{sec}$$

EXAMPLE 30

A small chemical feed pump lowered the chemical solution in a 0.8-meter diameter tank 0.7 meter during 7.0 hours. Estimate the flow delivered by the pump in liters per second and milliliters per second.

Known	Unknown
Tank Diameter, m = 0.8 m	1. Flow, L/sec
Chemical Drop, m = 0.7 m	2. Flow, mL/sec
Time, hr = 7.0 hr	

1. Determine the liters of chemical solution pumped.

$$\text{Volume, liters} = (0.785)(\text{Diameter, m})^2(\text{Drop, m})(1,000 \text{ } L/\text{cu m})$$

$$= (0.785)(0.8 \text{ m})^2(0.7 \text{ m})(1,000 \text{ } L/\text{cu m})$$

$$= 352 \text{ liters}$$

2. Estimate the flow delivered by the pump in liters per second.

$$\text{Flow, } L/\text{sec} = \frac{\text{Volume Pumped, } L}{(\text{Pumping Time, hr})(60 \text{ min/hr})(60 \text{ sec/min})}$$

$$= \frac{352 \text{ } L}{(7.0 \text{ hr})(60 \text{ min/hr})(60 \text{ sec/min})}$$

$$= 0.014 \text{ } L/\text{sec}$$

3. Estimate the flow delivered by the pump in milliliters per second.

$$\text{Flow, m}L/\text{sec} = \frac{(\text{Volume Pumped, } L)(1,000 \text{ m}L/L)}{(\text{Pumping Time, hr})(60 \text{ min/hr})(60 \text{ sec/min})}$$

$$= \frac{(352 \text{ } L)(1,000 \text{ m}L/L)}{(7.0 \text{ hr})(60 \text{ min/hr})(60 \text{ sec/min})}$$

$$= 14 \text{ m}L/\text{sec}$$

EXAMPLE 31

Determine the chemical feed in kilograms of polymer per day and grams per second from a chemical feed pump. The polymer solution is 1.8 percent or 18,000 mg polymer per liter. Assume a specific gravity of the polymer solution of 1.0. During a test run the chemical feed pump delivered 650 mL of polymer solution in 4.5 minutes.

Known	Unknown
Polymer Solution, % = 1.8%	1. Polymer Feed, kg/day
Polymer Conc, mg/L = 18,000 mg/L	2. Polymer Feed, gm/sec
Polymer Sp Gr = 1.0	
Volume Pumped, mL = 650 mL	
Time Pumped, min = 4.5 min	

1. Calculate the polymer fed by the chemical feed pump in kilograms of polymer per day.

$$\text{Polymer Feed, kg/day} = \frac{(\text{Vol Pumped, mL})(\text{Poly Conc, mg/L})(60 \text{ min/hr})(24 \text{ hr/day})}{(\text{Time Pumped, min})(1,000 \text{ mL/L})(1,000 \text{ mg/gm})(1,000 \text{ gm/kg})}$$

$$= \frac{(650 \text{ mL})(18,000 \text{ mg/L})(60 \text{ min/hr})(24 \text{ hr/day})}{(4.5 \text{ min})(1,000 \text{ mL/L})(1,000 \text{ mg/gm})(1,000 \text{ gm/kg})}$$

$$= 3.7 \text{ kg/day}$$

2. Calculate the polymer fed by the chemical feed pump in grams of polymer per second.

$$\text{Polymer Feed, gm/sec} = \frac{(\text{Vol Pumped, mL})(\text{Poly Conc, mg/L})}{(\text{Time Pumped, min})(1,000 \text{ mL/L})(60 \text{ sec/min})(1,000 \text{ mg/gm})}$$

$$= \frac{(650 \text{ mL})(18,000 \text{ mg/L})}{(4.5 \text{ min})(1,000 \text{ mL/L})(60 \text{ sec/min})(1,000 \text{ mg/gm})}$$

$$= 0.043 \text{ gm/sec}$$

$$\text{or} = 43 \text{ mg/sec}$$

EXAMPLE 32

Determine the actual chemical feed in kilograms per day and grams per second from a dry chemical feeder. A pie tin placed under the chemical feeder caught 824 grams of chemical during five minutes.

Known	Unknown
Chemical, gm = 824 gm	1. Chemical Feed, kg/day
Time, min = 5 min	2. Chemical Feed, gm/sec

1. Determine the chemical feed in kilograms per day.

$$\text{Chemical Feed, kg/day} = \frac{(\text{Chemical, gm})(60 \text{ min/hr})(24 \text{ hr/day})}{(\text{Time, min})(1,000 \text{ gm/kg})}$$

$$= \frac{(824 \text{ gm})(60 \text{ min/hr})(24 \text{ hr/day})}{(5 \text{ min})(1,000 \text{ gm/kg})}$$

$$= 237 \text{ kg/day}$$

2. Determine the chemical feed in grams per second.

$$\text{Chemical Feed, gm/sec} = \frac{\text{Chemical, gm}}{(\text{Time, min})(60 \text{ sec/min})}$$

$$= \frac{824 \text{ gm}}{(5 \text{ min})(60 \text{ sec/min})}$$

$$= 2.75 \text{ gm/sec}$$

A.56 Advanced Laboratory Procedures

EXAMPLE 33

Calculate the threshold odor number (TON) for a sample when the first detectable odor occurred when the 70-mL sample was diluted to 200 mL (130 mL of odor-free water was added to the 70-mL sample).

Known	Unknown
Size of Sample, mL = 70 mL	TON
Odor-Free Water, mL = 130 mL	

Calculate the threshold odor number (TON).

$$\text{TON} = \frac{\text{Size of Sample, mL} + \text{Odor-Free Water, mL}}{\text{Size of Sample, mL}}$$

$$= \frac{70 \text{ mL} + 130 \text{ mL}}{70 \text{ mL}}$$

$$= 3$$

EXAMPLE 34

Determine the geometric mean threshold odor number for a panel of six testers given the results shown below.

Known	Unknown
Tester 1, X_1 = 2	Geometric Mean Threshold Odor Number
Tester 2, X_2 = 4	
Tester 3, X_3 = 3	
Tester 4, X_4 = 8	
Tester 5, X_5 = 6	
Tester 6, X_6 = 2	

Calculate the geometric mean.

$$\text{Geometric Mean TON} = (X_1 \times X_2 \times X_3 \times X_4 \times X_5 \times X_6)^{1/n}$$

$$= (2 \times 4 \times 3 \times 8 \times 6 \times 2)^{1/6}$$

$$= (2,304)^{0.167}$$

$$= 3.6$$

EXAMPLE 35

Calculate the threshold taste number for a sample when the first detectable taste occurred when the 8.3-mL sample was diluted to 200 mL (191.7 mL of taste-free water was added to the 8.3-mL sample).

Known	Unknown
Sample Size, mL = 8.3 mL	Threshold Taste Number
Taste-Free Water, mL = 191.7 mL	

Calculate the threshold taste number.

$$\text{Threshold Taste Number} = \frac{\text{Sample Size, mL} + \text{Taste-Free Water, mL}}{\text{Sample Size, mL}}$$

$$= \frac{8.3 \text{ mL} + 191.7 \text{ mL}}{8.3 \text{ mL}}$$

$$= 24$$

EXAMPLE 36

Determine the taste rating for a water by calculating the arithmetic mean and standard deviation for the panel ratings given below.

Known	**Unknown**
Tester 1, $X_1 = 2$	1. Arithmetic Mean, $\overline{X}$
Tester 2, $X_2 = 5$	2. Standard Deviation, S
Tester 3, $X_3 = 3$	
Tester 4, $X_4 = 6$	
Tester 5, $X_5 = 2$	
Tester 6, $X_6 = 6$	

1. Calculate the arithmetic mean, $\overline{X}$, taste rating.

$$\text{Arithmetic Mean, } \overline{X} \atop \text{Taste Rating} = \frac{X_1 + X_2 + X_3 + X_4 + X_5 + X_6}{n}$$

$$= \frac{2 + 5 + 3 + 6 + 2 + 6}{6}$$

$$= \frac{24}{6}$$

$$= 4$$

2. Calculate the standard deviation, S, of the taste rating.

$$\text{Standard Deviation, } S = \left[\frac{(X_1 - \overline{X})^2 + (X_2 - \overline{X})^2 + (X_3 - \overline{X})^2 + (X_4 - \overline{X})^2 + (X_5 - \overline{X})^2 + (X_6 - \overline{X})^2}{n - 1} \right]^{0.5}$$

$$= \left[\frac{(2 - 4)^2 + (5 - 4)^2 + (3 - 4)^2 + (6 - 4)^2 + (2 - 4)^2 + (6 - 4)^2}{6 - 1} \right]^{0.5}$$

$$= \left[\frac{(-2)^2 + (1)^2 + (-1)^2 + (2)^2 + (-2)^2 + (2)^2}{5} \right]^{0.5}$$

$$= \left[\frac{4 + 1 + 1 + 4 + 4 + 4}{5} \right]^{0.5}$$

$$= \left[\frac{18}{5} \right]^{0.5}$$

$$= (3.6)^{0.5}$$

$$= 1.9$$

or

$$\text{Standard Deviation, } S = \left[\frac{(X_1^2 + X_2^2 + X_3^2 + X_4^2 + X_5^2 + X_6^2) - (X_1 + X_2 + X_3 + X_4 + X_5 + X_6)^2/n}{n - 1} \right]^{0.5}$$

$$= \left[\frac{(2^2 + 5^2 + 3^2 + 6^2 + 2^2 + 6^2) - (2 + 5 + 3 + 6 + 2 + 6)^2/6}{6 - 1} \right]^{0.5}$$

$$= \left[\frac{(4 + 25 + 9 + 36 + 4 + 36) - (24)^2/6}{5} \right]^{0.5}$$

$$= \left[\frac{114 - 96}{5} \right]^{0.5}$$

$$= \left[\frac{18}{5} \right]^{0.5}$$

$$= (3.6)^{0.5}$$

$$= 1.9$$

EXAMPLE 37

A small water system collected 14 samples during one month. After each sample was collected, 10 mL of each sample was placed in each of 5 fermentation tubes. At the end of the month, the results indicated that 2 out of a total of 70 fermentation tubes were positive. What percent of the portions tested during the month were positive?

Known	Unknown
Number Positive/mo = 2 positive/mo	Portions Positive, %/mo
Total Portions Tested = 70 portions	

Calculate the percent of the portions tested during the month which were positive.

$$\text{Portions Positive, \%/mo} = \frac{(\text{Number Positive/mo})(100\%)}{\text{Total Portions Tested}}$$

$$= \frac{(2 \text{ positive/mo})(100\%)}{70 \text{ portions}}$$

$$= 3\%/\text{mo}$$

A.57 Administration, Safety

EXAMPLE 38

Calculate the injury frequency rate for a water utility where there were four injuries in one year and the operators worked 97,120 hours.

Known	Unknown
Injuries, number/yr = 4 injuries/yr	Injury Frequency Rate
Hours Worked, number/yr = 97,120 hr/yr	

Calculate the injury frequency rate.

$$\text{Injury Freq Rate} = \frac{(\text{Injuries, number/yr})(1,000,000)}{\text{Hours Worked, number/yr}}$$

$$= \frac{(4 \text{ injuries/yr})(1,000,000)}{97,120 \text{ hr/yr}}$$

$$= 41.2$$

EXAMPLE 39

Calculate the injury severity rate for a water company which experienced 57 operator-hours lost due to injuries while the operators worked 97,120 hours during the year.

Known	Unknown
Number of Hours Lost/yr = 57 hr/yr	Injury Severity Rate
Number of Hours Worked/yr = 97,120 hr/yr	

Calculate the injury severity rate.

$$\text{Injury Severity Rate} = \frac{(\text{Number of Hours Lost/yr})(1,000,000)}{\text{Number of Hours Worked/yr}}$$

$$= \frac{(57 \text{ hr/yr})(1,000,000)}{97,120 \text{ hr/yr}}$$

$$= 587$$

A.6 CALCULATION OF CT VALUES

The Surface Water Treatment Rule requires all surface water systems and all systems using groundwater under the influence of surface water to achieve 3-log removal of *Giardia* and 4-log removal or inactivation of viruses. This level of treatment can be accomplished by disinfection alone if the source water is relatively free of turbidity and the system meets other specific conditions. Or, the treatment requirements can be met by a combination of filtration and disinfection.

When both filtration and disinfection are used, it is first necessary to know the effectiveness of filtration in removing *Giardia* and viruses before it will be possible to determine the level of disinfection needed to reach the 3-log and 4-log treatment levels. Research studies of conventional, direct, slow sand, and diatomaceous earth filtration have measured the ability of each of these systems to remove *Giardia* cysts. For example, a well-operated conventional filtration system should be able to achieve 2.5-log removal of *Giardia* and 2.0-log removal/inactivation of viruses. Table A.1 lists the treatment removal efficiencies of each of these four types of filtration systems. Using the example above, if filtration achieves 2.5-log removal, disinfection processes will need to achieve at least 0.5-log *Giardia* removal to meet the SWTR requirement of 3-log *Giardia* removal.[1]

TABLE A.1 LOG REMOVAL EFFICIENCY

Type of Filtration	Treatment Removal Credit (Log Removals)		Required Disinfection (Log Inactivations*)	
	Giardia	Viruses	*Giardia*	Viruses
Conventional	2.5	2.0	0.5	2.0
Direct	2.0	1.0	1.0	3.0
Slow Sand	2.0	2.0	1.0	2.0
Diatomaceous Earth	2.0	1.0	1.0	3.0

* Assumed 3-log *Giardia* and 4-log virus removal and/or inactivation (can be increased based on sanitary hazards in watershed).

Not all disinfectants are equally effective at inactivating *Giardia* and viruses. Research has shown that a free chlorination system that achieves 3-log *Giardia* inactivation also achieves 4-log virus inactivation. On the other hand, a system using chloramination must disinfect to the 4-log level for virus inactivation before the water will be considered safe and free of harmful organisms.

---

[1] *The 1996 amendments to the Safe Drinking Water Act require EPA to develop additional regulations to provide greater protection of the public from microorganisms such as Cryptosporidium in drinking water. Log removal levels listed in this section are current as of publication of this manual (April 1998) but may change in the next few years as new rules are promulgated. Please refer to Chapter 22, "Drinking Water Regulations," for additional information about the types of regulations being developed and EPA's schedule for completion. Also, drinking water supply and distribution utilities and operators are strongly urged to stay in close contact with their state and federal regulatory agencies to keep informed of new regulations such as the Enhanced Surface Water Treatment Rule (ESWTR), the Disinfectants/Disinfection By-Products (D/DBP) Rule, and new filter backwash recycling rules.*

The effectiveness of disinfection by free chlorination also depends on pH and temperature. The required CT value for any given free chlorine residual increases with increasing pH and decreasing temperature. Tables A.2 through A.7 (pages 691-696) provide the CT values for inactivation of *Giardia* cysts by free chlorine, and the remainder of this section provides examples of how to calculate disinfection CT (concentration x contact time) values using free chlorination.

EXAMPLE 40

A 10-MGD direct filtration plant applies free chlorine as a disinfectant. The disinfectant has a contact time of 26 minutes under peak flow conditions. The pH of the water is 7.5 and the temperature is 10°C. The free chlorine residual is 2.0 mg/*L*. Table A.1 above indicates that direct filtration is capable of achieving 2-log (99-percent) removal of *Giardia* cysts. Therefore 1-log (90-percent or CT-90) *Giardia* inactivation must be achieved by disinfection.

SOLUTION

1. Using Table A.4 with a pH of 7.5, a temperature of 10°C, 1.0-log inactivation, and a free chlorine residual of 2.0 mg/*L*, find the required CT value of 50 mg/*L*-min.

2. Calculate the CT provided.

$$CT \text{ Provided, mg/}L\text{-min} = (C, \text{mg/}L)(T, \text{min})$$
$$= (2 \text{ mg/}L)(26 \text{ min})$$
$$= 52 \text{ mg/}L\text{-min}$$

   Since 52 mg/*L*-min is greater than the required 50 mg/*L*-min, the free chlorine residual is adequate for the peak flow conditions.

3. Using the above procedure, assume appropriate free chlorine residuals for lower flows and determine if the CT values provided are greater than the required CT-90 (1-log) values.

Flow, MGD	Contact Time, min	Free Chlorine Residual (assumed), mg/*L*	CT Provided, mg/*L*-min	CT-90 Required,* mg/*L*-min
10	26	2	52	50
7.5	39	1.4	55	47
5	52	1	52	45
2.5	104	0.5	52	43

* From Table A.4 (CT-90 = 1-log inactivation).

Changing the disinfectant dose to meet the required CT values as the flow changes is not a practical operational procedure. The suggested operational procedure is to adjust the disinfectant dose to meet the highest flow requirement with various flow ranges.

Flow Range, MGD	Free Chlorine Residual, mg/*L*
7.5 - 10	2.0
5.0 - 7.5	1.4
2.5 - 5.0	1.0

EXAMPLE 41

The 10-MGD plant in Example 40 is a conventional filtration plant and only needs to achieve 0.5-log *Giardia* inactivation (CT-70). Rework Example 40 for 0.5-log *Giardia* inactivation assuming a free chlorine residual of 1.0 mg/*L* for peak flow conditions.

Flow, MGD	Contact Time, min	Free Chlorine Residual (assumed), mg/*L*	CT Provided, mg/*L*-min	CT-70 Required, mg/*L*-min
10	26	1.0	26	22
7.5	39	0.7	27	22
5	52	0.5	26	21
2.5	104	0.4	42	21

EXAMPLE 42

A conventional water treatment plant consists of flocculation, sedimentation, filtration, and a clear well. Prechlorination is applied before flocculation and postchlorination after the clear well. A dye tracer study has been done to determine the chlorine contact times (T_{10}, time for 10 percent of the tracer to pass through a tank). Assume a water temperature of 15°C and a pH of 7.5. The plant needs to achieve 0.5-log inactivation of *Giardia* cysts. Determine the fraction of the CT value (CTF) the plant provides the first customer in the distribution system given the following information:

Process	Cl$_2$ Free Residual, mg/*L*	T_{10}, min
Flocculation	0.8	15
Sedimentation	0.4	75
Filtration	0.2	15
Clear Well	0.6	120
Pipe to Customer	0.4	20

SOLUTION

Calculate the actual CT value for each process, determine the CT required from Table A.5, calculate the CT actual/CT required ratio and sum the ratios. The sum of the ratios is the CTF value and should be greater than 1.0.

Process	Cl Conc., mg/*L*	T_{10}, min	CT Actual	CT Required*	CT Ratio
Floc.	0.8 mg/*L*	15 min	12	15	0.80
Sed.	0.4 mg/*L*	75 min	30	14	2.14
Filt.	0.2 mg/*L*	15 min	3	14	0.21
CW	0.6 mg/*L*	120 min	72	14	5.14
Pipe	0.4 mg/*L*	20 min	8	14	0.57
					8.86

* From Table A.5.

EXAMPLE 43

If the sum of the CT actual/CT required ratios for the flocculation, sedimentation, and filtration processes for Example 42 was 0.72, determine the free chlorine residual from the clear well necessary to achieve a total CTF (CT fraction) value greater than 1.0 for the plant only (neglect pipe CT). Assume the T_{10} value (actual detention time for the clear well) is 30 minutes.

SOLUTION

Determine the minimum CT ratio for the clear well that will produce a total CTF value greater than 1.0 for the plant.

$$\begin{aligned} \text{Min. Clear Well CT Ratio Needed} &= \text{Min. CTF} - \text{CTF Provided} \\ &= 1.0 - 0.72 \\ &= 0.28 \end{aligned}$$

Determine the CT ratios (CT actual/CT required) for various chlorine residuals in the clear well. Start with the minimum free chlorine residual for the clear well.

Cl₂ Free Residual, mg/L	T₁₀, min	CT Actual	CT Required	CT Ratio
0.2 mg/L	30 min	6	14	0.43
0.4 mg/L	30 min	12	14	0.86
0.6 mg/L	30 min	18	14	1.29
0.8 mg/L	30 min	24	15	1.60

Since the free chlorine residual of 0.2 mg/L produces a CT ratio of 0.43, which is greater than 0.28, the free chlorine residual of 0.2 mg/L will be adequate according to these calculations.

EXAMPLE 44

If prechlorination were not practiced in Example 43, what free chlorine residual would be necessary for the clear well alone to provide adequate disinfection?

SOLUTION

The required CT value is 14 mg/L-min.

$$\text{Free Chlorine Residual, mg/L} = \frac{CT,\ mg/L\text{-min}}{T_{10},\ min}$$

$$= \frac{14\ mg/L\text{-min}}{30\ min}$$

$$= 0.5\ mg/L\ or\ greater$$

A.7 CALCULATION OF LOG REMOVALS

Regulations may require the calculation of log removals for inactivation of *Giardia* cysts, viruses, or particle counts. How are log removals calculated? The following example illustrates two methods of calculating log removals.

EXAMPLE 45

Calculate the log removal of 5- to 15-micron particles per milliliter if the influent particle count to a water treatment filter reported 2,100 particles in the 5- to 15-microns range per milliliter of water and the filter effluent reported 30 particles in the 5- to 15-microns range per milliliter of filtered water.

Known	Unknown
Influent, particles/mL = 2,100 particles/mL	Log Removal
Effluent, particles/mL = 30 particles/mL	

Calculate the log removal of particles in the 5- to 15-microns range per mL by the filter.

PROCEDURE 1

$$\text{Log Removal} = \frac{\text{Log Influent,}}{\text{particles/mL}} - \frac{\text{Log Effluent,}}{\text{particles/mL}}$$

$$= \text{Log 2,100 particles/mL} - \text{Log 30 particles/mL}$$

$$= 3.30 - 1.5$$

$$= 1.8$$

PROCEDURE 2

$$\text{Log Removal} = \text{Log}\left[\frac{\text{Influent, particles/mL}}{\text{Effluent, particles/mL}}\right]$$

$$= \text{Log}\left[\frac{2,100\ particles/mL}{30\ particles/mL}\right]$$

$$= \text{Log 70}$$

$$= 1.8$$

TABLE A.2   CT VALUES FOR INACTIVATION OF *GIARDIA* CYSTS BY FREE CHLORINE AT 0.5° C OR LOWER (1)

CHLORINE CONCENTRATION (mg/L)	pH<=6						pH=6.5						pH=7.0						pH=7.5					
	Log Inactivations						Log Inactivations						Log Inactivations						Log Inactivations					
	0.5	1.0	1.5	2.0	2.5	3.0	0.5	1.0	1.5	2.0	2.5	3.0	0.5	1.0	1.5	2.0	2.5	3.0	0.5	1.0	1.5	2.0	2.5	3.0
<=0.4	23	46	69	91	114	137	27	54	82	109	136	163	33	65	98	130	163	195	40	79	119	158	198	237
0.6	24	47	71	94	118	141	28	56	84	112	140	168	33	67	100	133	167	200	40	80	120	159	199	239
0.8	24	48	73	97	121	145	29	57	86	115	143	172	34	68	103	137	171	205	41	82	123	164	205	246
1	25	49	74	99	123	148	29	59	88	117	147	176	35	70	105	140	175	210	42	84	127	169	211	253
1.2	25	51	76	101	127	152	30	60	90	120	150	180	36	72	108	143	179	215	43	86	130	173	216	259
1.4	26	52	78	103	129	155	31	61	92	123	153	184	37	74	111	147	184	221	44	89	133	177	222	266
1.6	26	52	79	105	131	157	32	63	95	126	158	189	38	75	113	151	188	226	46	91	137	182	228	273
1.8	27	54	81	108	135	162	32	64	97	129	161	193	39	77	116	154	193	231	47	93	140	186	233	279
2	28	55	83	110	138	165	33	66	99	131	164	197	39	79	118	157	197	236	48	95	143	191	238	286
2.2	28	56	85	113	141	169	34	67	101	134	168	201	40	81	121	161	202	242	50	99	149	198	248	297
2.4	29	57	86	115	143	172	34	68	103	137	171	205	41	82	124	165	206	247	50	99	149	199	248	298
2.6	29	58	88	117	146	175	35	70	105	139	174	209	42	84	126	168	210	252	51	101	152	203	253	304
2.8	30	59	89	119	148	178	36	71	107	142	178	213	43	86	129	171	214	257	52	103	155	207	258	310
3	30	60	91	121	151	181	36	72	109	145	181	217	44	87	131	174	218	261	53	105	158	211	263	316

CHLORINE CONCENTRATION (mg/L)	pH=8.0						pH=8.5						pH<=9.0					
	Log Inactivations						Log Inactivations						Log Inactivations					
	0.5	1.0	1.5	2.0	2.5	3.0	0.5	1.0	1.5	2.0	2.5	3.0	0.5	1.0	1.5	2.0	2.5	3.0
<=0.4	46	92	139	185	231	277	55	110	165	219	274	329	65	130	195	260	325	390
0.6	48	95	143	191	238	286	57	114	171	228	285	342	68	136	204	271	339	407
0.8	49	98	148	197	246	295	59	118	177	236	295	354	70	141	211	281	352	422
1	51	101	152	203	253	304	61	122	183	243	304	365	73	146	219	291	364	437
1.2	52	104	157	209	261	313	63	125	188	251	313	376	75	150	226	301	376	451
1.4	54	107	161	214	268	321	65	129	194	258	323	387	77	155	232	309	387	464
1.6	55	110	165	219	274	329	66	132	199	265	331	397	80	159	239	318	398	477
1.8	56	113	169	225	282	338	68	136	204	271	339	407	82	163	245	326	408	489
2	58	115	173	231	288	346	70	139	209	278	348	417	83	167	250	333	417	500
2.2	59	118	177	235	294	353	71	142	213	284	355	426	85	170	256	341	426	511
2.4	60	120	181	241	301	361	73	145	218	290	363	435	87	174	261	348	435	522
2.6	61	123	184	245	307	368	74	148	222	296	370	444	89	178	267	355	444	533
2.8	63	125	188	250	313	375	75	151	226	301	377	452	91	181	272	362	453	543
3	64	127	191	255	318	382	77	153	230	307	383	460	92	184	276	368	460	552

Notes:

(1) CT = CT for 3-log inactivation
99.9

Reprinted from *GUIDANCE MANUAL FOR COMPLIANCE WITH THE FILTRATION AND DISINFECTION REQUIREMENTS FOR PUBLIC WATER SYSTEMS USING SURFACE WATER SOURCES*, a publication of the American Water Works Association. Reproduced with permission. Copyright © 1991 by American Water Works Association.

TABLE A.3   CT VALUES FOR INACTIVATION OF *GIARDIA* CYSTS BY FREE CHLORINE AT 0.5° C (1)

CHLORINE CONCENTRATION (mg/L)	pH≤6 Log Inactivations						pH=6.5 Log Inactivations						pH=7.0 Log Inactivations						pH=7.5 Log Inactivations					
	0.5	1.0	1.5	2.0	2.5	3.0	0.5	1.0	1.5	2.0	2.5	3.0	0.5	1.0	1.5	2.0	2.5	3.0	0.5	1.0	1.5	2.0	2.5	3.0
<=0.4	16	32	49	65	81	97	20	39	59	78	98	117	23	46	70	93	116	139	28	55	83	111	138	166
0.6	17	33	50	67	83	100	20	40	60	80	100	120	24	48	72	95	119	143	29	57	86	114	143	171
0.8	17	34	52	69	86	103	20	41	61	81	102	122	24	49	73	97	122	146	29	58	88	117	146	175
1	18	35	53	70	88	105	21	42	63	83	104	125	25	50	75	99	124	149	30	60	90	119	149	179
1.2	18	36	54	71	89	107	21	42	64	85	106	127	25	51	76	101	127	152	31	61	92	122	153	183
1.4	18	36	55	73	91	109	22	43	65	87	108	130	26	52	78	103	129	155	31	62	94	125	156	187
1.6	19	37	56	74	93	111	22	44	66	88	110	132	26	53	79	105	132	158	32	64	96	128	160	192
1.8	19	38	57	76	95	114	22	45	68	90	113	135	27	54	81	108	135	162	33	65	98	131	163	196
2	19	39	58	77	97	116	23	46	69	92	115	138	28	55	83	110	138	165	33	67	100	133	167	200
2.2	20	39	59	79	98	118	23	47	70	93	117	140	28	56	85	113	141	169	34	68	102	136	170	204
2.4	20	40	60	80	100	120	24	48	72	95	119	143	29	57	86	115	143	172	35	70	105	139	174	209
2.6	20	41	61	81	102	122	24	49	73	97	122	146	29	58	88	117	146	175	36	71	107	142	178	213
2.8	21	41	62	83	103	124	25	49	74	99	123	148	30	59	89	119	148	178	36	72	109	145	181	217
3	21	42	63	84	105	126	25	50	76	101	126	151	30	61	91	121	152	182	37	74	111	147	184	221

CHLORINE CONCENTRATION (mg/L)	pH=8.0 Log Inactivations						pH=8.5 Log Inactivations						pH≤9.0 Log Inactivations					
	0.5	1.0	1.5	2.0	2.5	3.0	0.5	1.0	1.5	2.0	2.5	3.0	0.5	1.0	1.5	2.0	2.5	3.0
<=0.4	33	66	99	132	165	198	39	79	118	157	197	236	47	93	140	186	233	279
0.6	34	68	102	136	170	204	41	81	122	163	203	244	49	97	146	194	243	291
0.8	35	70	105	140	175	210	42	84	126	168	210	252	50	100	151	201	251	301
1	36	72	108	144	180	216	43	87	130	173	217	260	52	104	156	208	260	312
1.2	37	74	111	147	184	221	45	89	134	178	223	267	53	107	160	213	267	320
1.4	38	76	114	151	189	227	46	91	137	183	228	274	55	110	165	219	274	329
1.6	39	77	116	155	193	232	47	94	141	187	234	281	56	112	169	225	281	337
1.8	40	79	119	159	198	238	48	96	144	191	239	287	58	115	173	230	288	345
2	41	81	122	162	203	243	49	98	147	196	245	294	59	118	177	235	294	353
2.2	41	83	124	165	207	248	50	100	150	200	250	300	60	120	181	241	301	361
2.4	42	84	127	169	211	253	51	102	153	204	255	306	61	123	184	245	307	368
2.6	43	86	129	172	215	258	52	104	156	208	260	312	63	125	188	250	313	375
2.8	44	88	132	175	219	263	53	106	159	212	265	318	64	127	191	255	318	382
3	45	89	134	179	223	268	54	108	162	216	270	324	65	130	195	259	324	389

Notes:

(1) CT = CT for 3-log inactivation

99.9

Reprinted from *GUIDANCE MANUAL FOR COMPLIANCE WITH THE FILTRATION AND DISINFECTION REQUIREMENTS FOR PUBLIC WATER SYSTEMS USING SURFACE WATER SOURCES*, a publication of the American Water Works Association. Reproduced with permission. Copyright © 1991 by American Water Works Association.

TABLE A.4 CT VALUES FOR INACTIVATION OF *GIARDIA* CYSTS BY FREE CHLORINE AT 10° C (1)

CHLORINE CONCENTRATION (mg/L)	pH ≤ 6 Log Inactivations						pH = 6.5 Log Inactivations						pH = 7.0 Log Inactivations						pH = 7.5 Log Inactivations					
	0.5	1.0	1.5	2.0	2.5	3.0	0.5	1.0	1.5	2.0	2.5	3.0	0.5	1.0	1.5	2.0	2.5	3.0	0.5	1.0	1.5	2.0	2.5	3.0
≤0.4	12	24	37	49	61	73	15	29	44	59	73	88	17	35	52	69	87	104	21	42	63	83	104	125
0.6	13	25	38	50	63	75	15	30	45	60	75	90	18	36	54	71	89	107	21	43	64	85	107	128
0.8	13	26	39	52	65	78	15	31	46	61	77	92	18	37	55	73	92	110	22	44	66	87	109	131
1	13	26	40	53	66	79	16	31	47	63	78	94	19	37	56	75	93	112	22	45	67	89	112	134
1.2	13	27	40	53	67	80	16	32	48	63	79	95	19	38	57	76	95	114	23	46	69	91	114	137
1.4	14	27	41	55	68	82	16	33	49	65	82	98	19	39	58	77	97	116	23	47	70	93	117	140
1.6	14	28	42	55	69	83	17	33	50	66	83	99	20	40	60	79	99	119	24	48	72	96	120	144
1.8	14	29	43	57	72	86	17	34	51	67	84	101	20	41	61	81	102	122	25	49	74	98	123	147
2	15	29	44	58	73	87	17	35	52	69	87	104	21	41	62	83	103	124	25	50	75	100	125	150
2.2	15	30	45	59	74	89	18	35	53	70	88	105	21	42	64	85	106	127	26	51	77	102	128	153
2.4	15	30	45	60	75	90	18	36	54	71	89	107	22	43	65	86	108	129	26	52	79	105	131	157
2.6	15	31	46	61	77	92	18	37	55	73	92	110	22	44	66	87	109	131	27	53	80	107	133	160
2.8	16	31	47	62	78	93	19	37	56	74	93	111	22	45	67	89	112	134	27	54	82	109	136	163
3	16	32	48	63	79	95	19	38	57	75	94	113	23	46	69	91	114	137	28	55	83	111	138	166

CHLORINE CONCENTRATION (mg/L)	pH = 8.0 Log Inactivations						pH = 8.5 Log Inactivations						pH ≤ 9.0 Log Inactivations					
	0.5	1.0	1.5	2.0	2.5	3.0	0.5	1.0	1.5	2.0	2.5	3.0	0.5	1.0	1.5	2.0	2.5	3.0
≤0.4	25	50	75	99	124	149	30	59	89	118	148	177	35	70	105	139	174	209
0.6	26	51	77	102	128	153	31	61	92	122	153	183	36	73	109	145	182	218
0.8	26	53	79	105	132	158	32	63	95	126	158	189	38	75	113	151	188	226
1	27	54	81	108	135	162	33	65	98	130	163	195	39	78	117	156	195	234
1.2	28	55	83	111	138	166	33	67	100	133	167	200	40	80	120	160	200	240
1.4	28	57	85	113	142	170	34	69	103	137	172	206	41	82	124	165	206	247
1.6	29	58	87	116	145	174	35	70	106	141	176	211	42	84	127	169	211	253
1.8	30	60	90	119	149	179	36	72	108	143	179	215	43	86	130	173	216	259
2	30	61	91	121	152	182	37	74	111	147	184	221	44	88	133	177	221	265
2.2	31	62	93	124	155	186	38	75	113	150	188	225	45	90	136	181	226	271
2.4	32	63	95	127	158	190	38	77	115	153	192	230	46	92	138	184	230	276
2.6	32	65	97	129	162	194	39	78	117	156	195	234	47	94	141	187	234	281
2.8	33	66	99	131	164	197	40	80	120	159	199	239	48	96	144	191	239	287
3	34	67	101	134	168	201	41	81	122	162	203	243	49	97	146	195	243	292

Notes:

(1) CT = CT for 3-log inactivation
99.9

TABLE A.5 CT VALUES FOR INACTIVATION OF *GIARDIA* CYSTS BY FREE CHLORINE AT 15° C (1)

CHLORINE CONCENTRATION (mg/L)	pH ≤ 6 Log Inactivations						pH = 6.5 Log Inactivations						pH = 7.0 Log Inactivations						pH = 7.5 Log Inactivations					
	0.5	1.0	1.5	2.0	2.5	3.0	0.5	1.0	1.5	2.0	2.5	3.0	0.5	1.0	1.5	2.0	2.5	3.0	0.5	1.0	1.5	2.0	2.5	3.0
≤0.4	8	16	25	33	41	49	10	20	30	39	49	59	12	23	35	47	58	70	14	28	42	55	69	83
0.6	8	17	25	33	42	50	10	20	30	40	50	60	12	24	36	48	60	72	14	29	43	57	72	86
0.8	9	17	26	35	43	52	10	20	31	41	51	61	12	24	37	49	61	73	15	29	44	59	73	88
1	9	18	27	35	44	53	11	21	32	42	53	63	13	25	38	50	63	75	15	30	45	60	75	90
1.2	9	18	27	36	45	54	11	21	32	43	53	64	13	25	38	51	63	76	15	31	46	61	77	92
1.4	9	18	28	37	46	55	11	22	33	43	54	65	13	26	39	52	65	78	16	31	47	63	78	94
1.6	9	19	28	37	47	56	11	22	33	44	55	66	13	26	40	53	66	79	16	32	48	64	80	96
1.8	10	19	29	38	48	57	11	23	34	45	57	68	14	27	41	54	68	81	16	33	49	65	82	98
2	10	19	29	39	48	58	12	23	35	46	58	69	14	28	42	55	69	83	17	33	50	67	83	100
2.2	10	20	30	39	49	59	12	23	35	47	58	70	14	28	43	57	71	85	17	34	51	68	85	102
2.4	10	20	30	40	50	60	12	24	36	48	60	72	14	29	43	57	72	86	18	35	53	70	88	105
2.6	10	20	31	41	51	61	12	24	37	49	61	73	15	29	44	59	73	88	18	36	54	71	89	107
2.8	10	21	31	41	52	62	12	25	37	49	62	74	15	30	45	59	74	89	18	36	55	73	91	109
3	11	21	32	42	53	63	13	25	38	51	63	76	15	30	46	61	76	91	19	37	56	74	93	111

CHLORINE CONCENTRATION (mg/L)	pH = 8.0 Log Inactivations						pH = 8.5 Log Inactivations						pH ≤ 9.0 Log Inactivations					
	0.5	1.0	1.5	2.0	2.5	3.0	0.5	1.0	1.5	2.0	2.5	3.0	0.5	1.0	1.5	2.0	2.5	3.0
≤0.4	17	33	50	66	83	99	20	39	59	79	98	118	23	47	70	93	117	140
0.6	17	34	51	68	85	102	20	41	61	81	102	122	24	49	73	97	122	146
0.8	18	35	53	70	88	105	21	42	63	84	105	126	25	50	76	101	126	151
1	18	36	54	72	90	108	22	43	65	87	108	130	26	52	78	104	130	156
1.2	19	37	56	74	93	111	22	45	67	89	112	134	27	53	80	107	133	160
1.4	19	38	57	76	95	114	23	46	69	91	114	137	28	55	83	110	138	165
1.6	19	39	58	77	97	116	24	47	71	94	118	141	28	56	85	113	141	169
1.8	20	40	60	79	99	119	24	48	72	96	120	144	29	58	87	115	144	173
2	20	41	61	81	102	122	25	49	74	98	123	147	30	59	89	118	148	177
2.2	21	41	62	83	103	124	25	50	75	100	125	150	30	60	91	121	151	181
2.4	21	42	64	85	106	127	26	51	77	102	128	153	31	61	92	123	153	184
2.6	22	43	65	86	108	129	27	52	78	104	130	156	31	63	94	125	157	188
2.8	22	44	66	88	110	132	27	53	80	106	133	159	32	64	96	127	159	191
3	22	45	67	89	112	134	27	54	81	108	135	162	33	65	98	130	163	195

Notes:
(1) CT$_{99.9}$ = CT for 3-log inactivation

TABLE A.6 CT VALUES FOR INACTIVATION OF *GIARDIA* CYSTS BY FREE CHLORINE AT 20° C (1)

CHLORINE CONCENTRATION (mg/L)	pH ≤ 6 Log Inactivations						pH = 6.5 Log Inactivations						pH = 7.0 Log Inactivations						pH = 7.5 Log Inactivations					
	0.5	1.0	1.5	2.0	2.5	3.0	0.5	1.0	1.5	2.0	2.5	3.0	0.5	1.0	1.5	2.0	2.5	3.0	0.5	1.0	1.5	2.0	2.5	3.0
≤0.4	6	12	18	24	30	36	7	15	22	29	37	44	9	17	26	35	43	52	10	21	31	41	52	62
0.6	6	13	19	25	32	38	8	15	23	30	38	45	9	18	27	36	45	54	11	21	32	43	53	64
0.8	7	13	20	26	33	39	8	15	23	31	38	46	9	18	28	37	46	55	11	22	33	44	55	66
1	7	13	20	26	33	39	8	16	24	31	39	47	9	19	28	37	47	56	11	22	34	45	56	67
1.2	7	13	20	27	33	40	8	16	24	32	40	48	10	19	29	38	48	57	12	23	35	46	58	69
1.4	7	14	21	27	34	41	8	16	25	33	41	49	10	19	29	39	48	58	12	23	35	47	58	70
1.6	7	14	21	28	35	42	8	17	25	33	42	50	10	20	30	39	49	59	12	24	36	48	60	72
1.8	7	14	22	29	36	43	9	17	26	34	43	51	10	20	31	41	51	61	12	25	37	49	62	74
2	7	15	22	29	37	44	9	17	26	35	43	52	10	21	31	41	52	62	13	25	38	50	63	75
2.2	7	15	22	29	37	44	9	18	27	35	44	53	11	21	32	42	53	63	13	26	39	51	64	77
2.4	8	15	23	30	38	45	9	18	27	36	45	54	11	22	33	43	54	65	13	26	39	52	65	78
2.6	8	15	23	31	38	46	9	18	28	37	46	55	11	22	33	44	55	66	13	27	40	53	67	80
2.8	8	16	24	31	39	47	9	19	28	37	47	56	11	22	34	45	56	67	14	27	41	54	68	81
3	8	16	24	31	39	47	10	19	29	38	48	57	11	23	34	45	57	68	14	28	42	55	69	83

CHLORINE CONCENTRATION (mg/L)	pH = 8.0 Log Inactivations						pH = 8.5 Log Inactivations						pH < 9.0 Log Inactivations					
	0.5	1.0	1.5	2.0	2.5	3.0	0.5	1.0	1.5	2.0	2.5	3.0	0.5	1.0	1.5	2.0	2.5	3.0
≤0.4	12	25	37	49	62	74	15	30	45	59	74	89	18	35	53	70	88	105
0.6	13	26	39	51	64	77	15	31	46	61	77	92	18	36	55	73	91	109
0.8	13	26	40	53	66	79	16	32	48	63	79	95	19	38	57	75	94	113
1	14	27	41	54	68	81	16	33	49	65	82	98	20	39	59	78	98	117
1.2	14	28	42	55	69	83	17	33	50	67	83	100	20	40	60	80	100	120
1.4	14	28	43	57	71	85	17	34	52	69	86	103	21	41	62	82	103	123
1.6	15	29	44	58	73	87	18	35	53	70	88	105	21	42	63	84	105	126
1.8	15	30	45	59	74	89	18	36	54	72	90	108	22	43	65	86	108	129
2	15	30	46	61	76	91	18	37	55	73	92	110	22	44	66	88	110	132
2.2	16	31	47	62	78	93	19	38	57	75	94	113	23	45	68	90	113	135
2.4	16	32	48	63	79	95	19	38	58	77	96	115	23	46	69	92	115	138
2.6	16	32	49	65	81	97	20	39	59	78	98	117	24	47	71	94	118	141
2.8	17	33	50	66	83	99	20	40	60	79	99	119	24	48	72	95	119	143
3	17	34	51	67	84	101	20	41	61	81	102	122	24	49	73	97	122	146

Notes:
(1) CT = CT for 3-log inactivation
         99.9

TABLE A.7   CT VALUES FOR INACTIVATION OF *GIARDIA* CYSTS BY FREE CHLORINE AT 25° C (1)

CHLORINE CONCENTRATION (mg/L)	pH <= 6 Log Inactivations						pH = 6.5 Log Inactivations						pH = 7.0 Log Inactivations						pH = 7.5 Log Inactivations					
	0.5	1.0	1.5	2.0	2.5	3.0	0.5	1.0	1.5	2.0	2.5	3.0	0.5	1.0	1.5	2.0	2.5	3.0	0.5	1.0	1.5	2.0	2.5	3.0
<=0.4	4	8	12	16	20	24	5	10	15	19	24	29	6	12	18	23	29	35	7	14	21	28	35	42
0.6	4	8	13	17	21	25	5	10	15	20	25	30	6	12	18	24	30	36	7	14	22	29	36	43
0.8	4	9	13	17	22	26	5	10	16	21	26	31	6	12	19	25	31	37	7	15	22	29	37	44
1	4	9	13	17	22	26	5	10	16	21	26	31	6	12	19	25	31	37	8	15	23	30	38	45
1.2	5	9	14	18	23	27	5	11	16	21	27	32	6	13	19	25	32	38	8	15	23	31	38	46
1.4	5	9	14	18	23	27	6	11	17	22	28	33	7	13	20	26	33	39	8	16	24	31	39	47
1.6	5	9	14	19	23	28	6	11	17	22	28	33	7	13	20	27	33	40	8	16	24	32	40	48
1.8	5	10	15	19	24	29	6	11	17	23	28	34	7	14	21	27	34	41	8	16	25	33	41	49
2	5	10	15	19	24	29	6	12	18	23	29	35	7	14	21	27	34	41	8	17	25	33	42	50
2.2	5	10	15	20	25	30	6	12	18	23	29	35	7	14	21	28	35	42	9	17	26	34	43	51
2.4	5	10	15	20	25	30	6	12	18	24	30	36	7	14	22	29	36	43	9	17	26	35	43	52
2.6	5	10	16	21	26	31	6	12	19	25	31	37	7	15	22	29	37	44	9	18	27	35	44	53
2.8	5	10	16	21	26	31	6	12	19	25	31	37	8	15	23	30	38	45	9	18	27	36	45	54
3	5	11	16	21	27	32	6	13	19	25	32	38	8	15	23	31	38	46	9	18	28	37	46	55

CHLORINE CONCENTRATION (mg/L)	pH = 8.0 Log Inactivations						pH = 8.5 Log Inactivations						pH <= 9.0 Log Inactivations					
	0.5	1.0	1.5	2.0	2.5	3.0	0.5	1.0	1.5	2.0	2.5	3.0	0.5	1.0	1.5	2.0	2.5	3.0
<=0.4	8	17	25	33	42	50	10	20	30	39	49	59	12	23	35	47	58	70
0.6	9	17	26	34	43	51	10	20	31	41	51	61	12	24	37	49	61	73
0.8	9	18	27	35	44	53	11	21	32	42	53	63	13	25	38	50	63	75
1	9	18	27	36	45	54	11	22	33	43	54	65	13	26	39	52	65	78
1.2	9	18	28	37	46	55	11	22	34	45	56	67	13	27	40	53	67	80
1.4	10	19	29	38	48	57	12	23	35	46	58	69	14	27	41	55	68	82
1.6	10	19	29	39	48	58	12	23	35	47	58	70	14	28	42	56	70	84
1.8	10	20	30	40	50	60	12	24	36	48	60	72	14	29	43	57	72	86
2	10	20	31	41	51	61	12	25	37	49	62	74	15	29	44	59	73	88
2.2	10	21	31	41	52	62	13	25	38	50	63	75	15	30	45	60	75	90
2.4	11	21	32	42	53	63	13	26	39	51	64	77	15	31	46	61	77	92
2.6	11	22	33	43	54	65	13	26	39	52	65	78	16	31	47	63	78	94
2.8	11	22	33	44	55	66	13	27	40	53	67	80	16	32	48	64	80	96
3	11	22	34	45	56	67	14	27	41	54	68	81	16	32	49	65	81	97

Notes:

(1)   CT = CT for 3-log inactivation
        99.9

Reprinted from *GUIDANCE MANUAL FOR COMPLIANCE WITH THE FILTRATION AND DISINFECTION REQUIREMENTS FOR PUBLIC WATER SYSTEMS USING SURFACE WATER SOURCES*, a publication of the American Water Works Association. Reproduced with permission. Copyright © 1991 by American Water Works Association.

WATER ABBREVIATIONS

ac	acre		kg	kilogram
ac-ft	acre-feet		km	kilometer
af	acre feet		kN	kilonewton
amp	ampere		kW	kilowatt
°C	degrees Celsius		kWh	kilowatt-hour
CFM	cubic feet per minute		L	liter
CFS	cubic feet per second		lb	pound
Ci	Curie		lbs/sq in	pounds per square inch
cm	centimeter		m	meter
cu ft	cubic feet		M	Mega
cu in	cubic inch		M	million
cu m	cubic meter		mg	milligram
cu yd	cubic yard		MGD	million gallons per day
°F	degrees Fahrenheit		mg/L	milligram per liter
ft	feet or foot		min	minute
ft-lb/min	foot-pounds per minute		mL	milliliter
g	gravity		mm	millimeter
gal	gallon		N	Newton
gal/day	gallons per day		ohm	ohm
GFD	gallons of flux per square foot per day		Pa	Pascal
gm	gram		pCi	picoCurie
GPD	gallons per day		ppb	parts per billion
gpg	grains per gallon		ppm	parts per million
GPM	gallons per minute		psf	pounds per square foot
gr	grain		psi	pounds per square inch
ha	hectare		psig	pounds per square inch gage
HP	horsepower		sec	second
hr	hour		sq ft	square feet or foot
in	inch		sq in	square inches
k	kilo		W	watt

WATER WORDS

A Summary of the Words Defined

in

WATER TREATMENT PLANT OPERATION,

SMALL WATER SYSTEM OPERATION AND MAINTENANCE,

and

WATER DISTRIBUTION SYSTEM OPERATION AND MAINTENANCE

PROJECT PRONUNCIATION KEY

by Warren L. Prentice

The Project Pronunciation Key is designed to aid you in the pronunciation of new words. While this key is based primarily on familiar sounds, it does not attempt to follow any particular pronunciation guide. This key is designed solely to aid operators in this program.

You may find it helpful to refer to other available sources for pronunciation help. Each current standard dictionary contains a guide to its own pronunciation key. Each key will be different from each other and from this key. Examples of the differences between the key used in this program and the *WEBSTER'S NEW WORLD COLLEGE DICTIONARY* [1] "Key" are shown below.

In using this key, you should accent (say louder) the syllable which appears in capital letters. The following chart is presented to give examples of how to pronounce words using the Project Key.

WORD	SYLLABLE				
	1st	2nd	3rd	4th	5th
acid	AS	id			
coagulant	co	AGG	you	lent	
biological	BUY	o	LODGE	ik	cull

The first word, *ACID*, has its first syllable accented. The second word, *COAGULANT*, has its second syllable accented. The third word, *BIOLOGICAL*, has its first and third syllables accented.

We hope you will find the key useful in unlocking the pronunciation of any new word.

Term	Project Key	Webster Key
acid	AS-id	aś id
coagulant	co-AGG-you-lent	kō ag' yoo lənt
biological	BUY-o-LODGE-ik-cull	bī ə läj' i kəl

---

[1] The *WEBSTER'S NEW WORLD COLLEGE DICTIONARY*, Third Edition, 1996, was chosen rather than an unabridged dictionary because of its availability to the operator. Other editions may be slightly different.

WATER WORDS

A

ABC   ABC

See **A**SSOCIATION OF **B**OARDS OF **C**ERTIFICATION.

atm   atm

The abbreviation for atmosphere. One atmosphere is equal to 14.7 psi or 100 kPa.

AWWA   AWWA

See **A**MERICAN **W**ATER **W**ORKS **A**SSOCIATION.

ABSORPTION (ab-SORP-shun)   ABSORPTION

The taking in or soaking up of one substance into the body of another by molecular or chemical action (as tree roots absorb dissolved nutrients in the soil).

ACCOUNTABILITY   ACCOUNTABILITY

When a manager gives power/responsibility to an employee, the employee ensures that the manager is informed of results or events.

ACCURACY   ACCURACY

How closely an instrument measures the true or actual value of the process variable being measured or sensed.

ACID RAIN   ACID RAIN

Precipitation which has been rendered (made) acidic by airborne pollutants.

ACIDIC (uh-SID-ick)   ACIDIC

The condition of water or soil which contains a sufficient amount of acid substances to lower the pH below 7.0.

ACIDIFIED (uh-SID-uh-FIE-d)   ACIDIFIED

The addition of an acid (usually nitric or sulfuric) to a sample to lower the pH below 2.0. The purpose of acidification is to "fix" a sample so it won't change until it is analyzed.

ACRE-FOOT   ACRE-FOOT

A volume of water that covers one acre to a depth of one foot, or 43,560 cubic feet (1,233.5 cubic meters).

ACTIVATED CARBON   ACTIVATED CARBON

Adsorptive particles or granules of carbon usually obtained by heating carbon (such as wood). These particles or granules have a high capacity to selectively remove certain trace and soluble materials from water.

ACUTE HEALTH EFFECT   ACUTE HEALTH EFFECT

An adverse effect on a human or animal body, with symptoms developing rapidly.

ADSORBATE (add-SORE-bait)   ADSORBATE

The material being removed by the adsorption process.

ADSORBENT (add-SORE-bent)   ADSORBENT

The material (activated carbon) that is responsible for removing the undesirable substance in the adsorption process.

ADSORPTION (add-SORP-shun)   ADSORPTION

The gathering of a gas, liquid, or dissolved substance on the surface or interface zone of another material.

AERATION (air-A-shun)   AERATION

The process of adding air to water. Air can be added to water by either passing air through water or passing water through air.

AEROBIC (AIR-O-bick)   AEROBIC

A condition in which atmospheric or dissolved molecular oxygen is present in the aquatic (water) environment.

AESTHETIC (es-THET-ick)   AESTHETIC

Attractive or appealing.

AGE TANK   AGE TANK

A tank used to store a known concentration of chemical solution for feed to a chemical feeder. Also called a DAY TANK.

AIR BINDING   AIR BINDING

The clogging of a filter, pipe or pump due to the presence of air released from water. Air entering the filter media is harmful to both the filtration and backwash processes. Air can prevent the passage of water during the filtration process and can cause the loss of filter media during the backwash process.

AIR GAP   AIR GAP

An open vertical drop, or vertical empty space, that separates a drinking (potable) water supply to be protected from another water system in a water treatment plant or other location. This open gap prevents the contamination of drinking water by backsiphonage or backflow because there is no way raw water or any other water can reach the drinking water.

AIR PADDING   AIR PADDING

Pumping dry air (dew point −40°F) into a container to assist with the withdrawal of a liquid or to force a liquified gas such as chlorine out of a container.

AIR STRIPPING   AIR STRIPPING

A treatment process used to remove dissolved gases and volatile substances from water. Large volumes of air are bubbled through the water being treated to remove (strip out) the dissolved gases and volatile substances.

ALARM CONTACT   ALARM CONTACT

A switch that operates when some preset low, high or abnormal condition exists.

ALGAE (AL-gee)   ALGAE

Microscopic plants which contain chlorophyll and live floating or suspended in water. They also may be attached to structures, rocks or other submerged surfaces. Excess algal growths can impart tastes and odors to potable water. Algae produce oxygen during sunlight hours and use oxygen during the night hours. Their biological activities appreciably affect the pH, alkalinity, and dissolved oxygen of the water.

ALGAL (AL-gull) BLOOM   ALGAL BLOOM

Sudden, massive growths of microscopic and macroscopic plant life, such as green or blue-green algae, which develop in lakes and reservoirs.

ALGICIDE (AL-juh-SIDE)   ALGICIDE

Any substance or chemical specifically formulated to kill or control algae.

ALIPHATIC (AL-uh-FAT-ick) HYDROXY ACIDS   ALIPHATIC HYDROXY ACIDS

Organic acids with carbon atoms arranged in branched or unbranched open chains rather than in rings.

ALIQUOT (AL-li-kwot)   ALIQUOT

Portion of a sample. Often an equally divided portion of a sample.

ALKALI (AL-ka-lie)

ALKALI

Any of certain soluble salts, principally of sodium, potassium, magnesium, and calcium, that have the property of combining with acids to form neutral salts and may be used in chemical water treatment processes.

ALKALINE (AL-ka-LINE)

ALKALINE

The condition of water or soil which contains a sufficient amount of alkali substances to raise the pH above 7.0.

ALKALINITY (AL-ka-LIN-it-tee)

ALKALINITY

The capacity of water to neutralize acids. This capacity is caused by the water's content of carbonate, bicarbonate, hydroxide, and occasionally borate, silicate, and phosphate. Alkalinity is expressed in milligrams per liter of equivalent calcium carbonate. Alkalinity is not the same as pH because water does not have to be strongly basic (high pH) to have a high alkalinity. Alkalinity is a measure of how much acid must be added to a liquid to lower the pH to 4.5.

ALLUVIAL (uh-LOU-vee-ul)

ALLUVIAL

Relating to mud and/or sand deposited by flowing water. Alluvial deposits may occur after a heavy rainstorm.

ALTERNATING CURRENT (A.C.)

ALTERNATING CURRENT (A.C.)

An electric current that reverses its direction (positive/negative values) at regular intervals.

ALTITUDE VALVE

ALTITUDE VALVE

A valve that automatically shuts off the flow into an elevated tank when the water level in the tank reaches a predetermined level. The valve automatically opens when the pressure in the distribution system drops below the pressure in the tank.

AMBIENT (AM-bee-ent) TEMPERATURE

AMBIENT TEMPERATURE

Temperature of the surrounding air (or other medium). For example, temperature of the room where a gas chlorinator is installed.

AMERICAN WATER WORKS ASSOCIATION

AMERICAN WATER WORKS ASSOCIATION

A professional organization for all persons working in the water utility field. This organization develops and recommends goals, procedures and standards for water utility agencies to help them improve their performance and effectiveness. For information on AWWA membership and publications, contact AWWA, 6666 W. Quincy Avenue, Denver, CO 80235. Phone (303) 794-7711.

AMPERAGE (AM-purr-age)

AMPERAGE

The strength of an electric current measured in amperes. The amount of electric current flow, similar to the flow of water in gallons per minute.

AMPERE (AM-peer)

AMPERE

The unit used to measure current strength. The current produced by an electromotive force of one volt acting through a resistance of one ohm.

AMPEROMETRIC (am-PURR-o-MET-rick)

AMPEROMETRIC

A method of measurement that records electric current flowing or generated, rather than recording voltage. Amperometric titration is a means of measuring concentrations of certain substances in water.

AMPEROMETRIC (am-PURR-o-MET-rick) TITRATION

AMPEROMETRIC TITRATION

A means of measuring concentrations of certain substances in water (such as strong oxidizers) based on the electric current that flows during a chemical reaction. Also see TITRATE.

AMPLITUDE

AMPLITUDE

The maximum strength of an alternating current during its cycle, as distinguished from the mean or effective strength.

ANAEROBIC (AN-air-O-bick)

ANAEROBIC

A condition in which atmospheric or dissolved molecular oxygen is *NOT* present in the aquatic (water) environment.

ANALOG

ANALOG

The readout of an instrument by a pointer (or other indicating means) against a dial or scale.

ANALYZER

ANALYZER

A device which conducts periodic or continuous measurement of some factor such as chlorine, fluoride or turbidity. Analyzers operate by any of several methods including photocells, conductivity or complex instrumentation.

ANGSTROM (ANG-strem)   ANGSTROM

A unit of length equal to one-tenth of a nanometer or one-tenbillionth of a meter (1 Angstrom = 0.000 000 000 1 meter). One Angstrom is the approximate diameter of an atom.

ANION (AN-EYE-en)   ANION

A negatively charged ion in an electrolyte solution, attracted to the anode under the influence of a difference in electrical potential. Chloride ion (Cl^-) is an anion.

ANIONIC (AN-eye-ON-ick) POLYMER   ANIONIC POLYMER

A polymer having negatively charged groups of ions; often used as a filter aid and for dewatering sludges.

ANNULAR (AN-you-ler) SPACE   ANNULAR SPACE

A ring-shaped space located between two circular objects, such as two pipes.

ANODE (an-O-d)   ANODE

The positive pole or electrode of an electrolytic system, such as a battery. The anode attracts negatively charged particles or ions (anions).

APPARENT COLOR   APPARENT COLOR

Color of the water that includes not only the color due to substances in the water but suspended matter as well.

APPROPRIATIVE   APPROPRIATIVE

Water rights to or ownership of a water supply which is acquired for the beneficial use of water by following a specific legal procedure.

APPURTENANCE (uh-PURR-ten-nans)   APPURTENANCE

Machinery, appliances, structures and other parts of the main structure necessary to allow it to operate as intended, but not considered part of the main structure.

AQUEOUS (A-kwee-us)   AQUEOUS

Something made up of, similar to, or containing water; watery.

AQUIFER (ACK-wi-fer)   AQUIFER

A natural underground layer of porous, water-bearing materials (sand, gravel) usually capable of yielding a large amount or supply of water.

ARCH   ARCH

(1) The curved top of a sewer pipe or conduit.
(2) A bridge or arch of hardened or caked chemical which will prevent the flow of the chemical.

ARTESIAN (are-TEE-zhun)   ARTESIAN

Pertaining to groundwater, a well, or underground basin where the water is under a pressure greater than atmospheric and will rise above the level of its upper confining surface if given an opportunity to do so.

ASEPTIC (a-SEP-tick)   ASEPTIC

Free from the living germs of disease, fermentation, or putrefaction. Sterile.

ASSOCIATION OF BOARDS OF CERTIFICATION (ABC)   ASSOCIATION OF BOARDS OF CERTIFICATION (ABC)

An international organization representing over 150 boards which certify the operators of waterworks and wastewater facilities. For information on ABC publications regarding the preparation of and how to study for operator certification examinations, contact ABC, 208 Fifth Street, Ames, IA 50010-6259. Phone (515) 232-3623.

ASYMMETRIC (A-see-MET-rick)   ASYMMETRIC

Not similar in size, shape, form or arrangement of parts on opposite sides of a line, point or plane.

ATOM   ATOM

The smallest unit of a chemical element; composed of protons, neutrons and electrons.

AUDIT, WATER   AUDIT, WATER

A thorough examination of the accuracy of water agency records or accounts (volumes of water) and system control equipment. Water managers can use audits to determine their water distribution system efficiency. The overall goal is to identify and verify water and revenue losses in a water system.

AUTHORITY   AUTHORITY

The power and resources to do a specific job or to get that job done.

AVAILABLE CHLORINE   AVAILABLE CHLORINE

A measure of the amount of chlorine available in chlorinated lime, hypochlorite compounds, and other materials that are used as a source of chlorine when compared with that of elemental (liquid or gaseous) chlorine.

AVAILABLE EXPANSION   AVAILABLE EXPANSION

The vertical distance from the sand surface to the underside of a trough in a sand filter. This distance is also called FREEBOARD.

AVERAGE   AVERAGE

A number obtained by adding quantities or measurements and dividing the sum or total by the number of quantities or measurements. Also called the arithmetic mean.

$$\text{Average} = \frac{\text{Sum of Measurements}}{\text{Number of Measurements}}$$

AVERAGE DEMAND   AVERAGE DEMAND

The total demand for water during a period of time divided by the number of days in that time period. This is also called the average daily demand.

AXIAL TO IMPELLER   AXIAL TO IMPELLER

The direction in which material being pumped flows around the impeller or flows parallel to the impeller shaft.

AXIS OF IMPELLER   AXIS OF IMPELLER

An imaginary line running along the center of a shaft (such as an impeller shaft).

B

BOD (pronounce as separate letters)   BOD

Biochemical **O**xygen **D**emand. The rate at which organisms use the oxygen in water while stabilizing decomposable organic matter under aerobic conditions. In decomposition, organic matter serves as food for the bacteria and energy results from its oxidation. BOD measurements are used as a measure of the organic strength of wastes in water.

BACK PRESSURE   BACK PRESSURE

A pressure that can cause water to backflow into the water supply when a user's water system is at a higher pressure than the public water system.

BACKFLOW   BACKFLOW

A reverse flow condition, created by a difference in water pressures, which causes water to flow back into the distribution pipes of a potable water supply from any source or sources other than an intended source. Also see BACKSIPHONAGE.

BACKSIPHONAGE   BACKSIPHONAGE

A form of backflow caused by a negative or below atmospheric pressure within a water system. Also see BACKFLOW.

BACKWASHING   BACKWASHING

The process of reversing the flow of water back through the filter media to remove the entrapped solids.

BACTERIA (back-TEAR-e-ah)   BACTERIA

Bacteria are living organisms, microscopic in size, which usually consist of a single cell. Most bacteria use organic matter for their food and produce waste products as a result of their life processes.

BAFFLE   BAFFLE

A flat board or plate, deflector, guide or similar device constructed or placed in flowing water or slurry systems to cause more uniform flow velocities, to absorb energy, and to divert, guide, or agitate liquids (water, chemical solutions, slurry).

BAILER (BAY-ler)   BAILER

A 10- to 20-foot-long pipe equipped with a valve at the lower end. A bailer is used to remove slurry from the bottom or the side of a well as it is being drilled.

BASE-EXTRA CAPACITY METHOD   BASE-EXTRA CAPACITY METHOD

A cost allocation method used by water utilities to determine water rates for various water user groups. This method considers base costs (O & M expenses and capital costs), extra capacity costs (additional costs for maximum day and maximum hour demands), customer costs (meter maintenance and reading, billing, collection, accounting) and fire protection costs.

BASE METAL   BASE METAL

A metal (such as iron) which reacts with dilute hydrochloric acid to form hydrogen. Also see NOBLE METAL.

BATCH PROCESS   BATCH PROCESS

A treatment process in which a tank or reactor is filled, the water is treated or a chemical solution is prepared, and the tank is emptied. The tank may then be filled and the process repeated.

BENCH SCALE TESTS   BENCH SCALE TESTS

A method of studying different ways or chemical doses for treating water on a small scale in a laboratory.

BIOCHEMICAL OXYGEN DEMAND (BOD)   BIOCHEMICAL OXYGEN DEMAND (BOD)

The rate at which organisms use the oxygen in water while stabilizing decomposable organic matter under aerobic conditions. In decomposition, organic matter serves as food for the bacteria and energy results from its oxidation. BOD measurements are used as a measure of the organic strength of wastes in water.

BIOLOGICAL GROWTH   BIOLOGICAL GROWTH

The activity and growth of any and all living organisms.

BLANK   BLANK

A bottle containing only dilution water or distilled water; the sample being tested is not added. Tests are frequently run on a *SAMPLE* and a *BLANK* and the differences are compared.

BOND   BOND

(1) A written promise to pay a specified sum of money (called the face value) at a fixed time in the future (called the date of maturity). A bond also carries interest at a fixed rate, payable periodically. The difference between a note and a bond is that a bond usually runs for a longer period of time and requires greater formality. Utility agencies use bonds as a means of obtaining large amounts of money for capital improvements.

(2) A warranty by an underwriting organization, such as an insurance company, guaranteeing honesty, performance, or payment by a contractor.

BONNET (BON-it)   BONNET

The cover on a gate valve.

BOWL, PUMP   BOWL, PUMP

The submerged pumping unit in a well, including the shaft, impellers and housing.

BRAKE HORSEPOWER   BRAKE HORSEPOWER

(1) The horsepower required at the top or end of a pump shaft (input to a pump).

(2) The energy provided by a motor or other power source.

BREAKPOINT CHLORINATION   BREAKPOINT CHLORINATION

Addition of chlorine to water until the chlorine demand has been satisfied. At this point, further additions of chlorine will result in a free chlorine residual that is directly proportional to the amount of chlorine added beyond the breakpoint.

BREAKTHROUGH   BREAKTHROUGH

A crack or break in a filter bed allowing the passage of floc or particulate matter through a filter. This will cause an increase in filter effluent turbidity. A breakthrough can occur (1) when a filter is first placed in service, (2) when the effluent valve suddenly opens or closes, and (3) during periods of excessive head loss through the filter (including when the filter is exposed to negative heads).

BRINELLING (bruh-NEL-ing)   BRINELLING

Tiny indentations (dents) high on the shoulder of the bearing race or bearing. A type of bearing failure.

BUFFER   BUFFER

A solution or liquid whose chemical makeup neutralizes acids or bases without a great change in pH.

BUFFER CAPACITY   BUFFER CAPACITY

A measure of the capacity of a solution or liquid to neutralize acids or bases. This is a measure of the capacity of water for offering a resistance to changes in pH.

C

C FACTOR   C FACTOR

A factor or value used to indicate the smoothness of the interior of a pipe. The higher the C Factor, the smoother the pipe, the greater the carrying capacity, and the smaller the friction or energy losses from water flowing in the pipe. To calculate the C Factor, measure the flow, pipe diameter, distance between two pressure gages, and the friction or energy loss of the water between the gages.

$$\text{C Factor} = \frac{\text{Flow, GPM}}{193.75(\text{Diameter, ft})^{2.63}(\text{Slope})^{0.54}}$$

CT VALUE   CT VALUE

Residual concentration of a given disinfectant in mg/L times the disinfectant's contact time in minutes.

CAISSON (KAY-sawn)   CAISSON

A structure or chamber which is usually sunk or lowered by digging from the inside. Used to gain access to the bottom of a stream or other body of water.

CALCIUM CARBONATE EQUILIBRIUM   CALCIUM CARBONATE EQUILIBRIUM

A water is considered stable when it is just saturated with calcium carbonate. In this condition the water will neither dissolve nor deposit calcium carbonate. Thus, in this water the calcium carbonate is in equilibrium with the hydrogen ion concentration.

CALCIUM CARBONATE ($CaCO_3$) EQUIVALENT   CALCIUM CARBONATE ($CaCO_3$) EQUIVALENT

An expression of the concentration of specified constituents in water in terms of their equivalent value to calcium carbonate. For example, the hardness in water which is caused by calcium, magnesium and other ions is usually described as calcium carbonate equivalent. Alkalinity test results are usually reported as mg/L $CaCO_3$ equivalents. To convert chloride to $CaCO_3$ equivalents, multiply the concentration of chloride ions in mg/L by 1.41, and for sulfate, multiply by 1.04.

CALIBRATION   CALIBRATION

A procedure which checks or adjusts an instrument's accuracy by comparison with a standard or reference.

CALL DATE   CALL DATE

First date a bond can be paid off.

CAPILLARY ACTION   CAPILLARY ACTION

The movement of water through very small spaces due to molecular forces.

CAPILLARY FORCES   CAPILLARY FORCES

The molecular forces which cause the movement of water through very small spaces.

CAPILLARY FRINGE   CAPILLARY FRINGE

The porous material just above the water table which may hold water by capillarity (a property of surface tension that draws water upward) in the smaller void spaces.

CARCINOGEN (CAR-sin-o-JEN)

Any substance which tends to produce cancer in an organism.

CARCINOGEN

CATALYST (CAT-uh-LIST)

A substance that changes the speed or yield of a chemical reaction without being consumed or chemically changed by the chemical reaction.

CATALYST

CATALYZE (CAT-uh-LIZE)

To act as a catalyst. Or, to speed up a chemical reaction.

CATALYZE

CATALYZED (CAT-uh-LIZED)

To be acted upon by a catalyst.

CATALYZED

CATHODE (KA-thow-d)

The negative pole or electrode of an electrolytic cell or system. The cathode attracts positively charged particles or ions (cations).

CATHODE

CATHODIC (ca-THOD-ick) PROTECTION

An electrical system for prevention of rust, corrosion, and pitting of metal surfaces which are in contact with water or soil. A low-voltage current is made to flow through a liquid (water) or a soil in contact with the metal in such a manner that the external electromotive force renders the metal structure cathodic. This concentrates corrosion on auxiliary anodic parts which are deliberately allowed to corrode instead of letting the structure corrode.

CATHODIC PROTECTION

CATION (CAT-EYE-en)

A positively charged ion in an electrolyte solution, attracted to the cathode under the influence of a difference in electrical potential. Sodium ion (Na^+) is a cation.

CATION

CATIONIC POLYMER

A polymer having positively charged groups of ions; often used as a coagulant aid.

CATIONIC POLYMER

CAUTION

This word warns against potential hazards or cautions against unsafe practices. Also see DANGER, NOTICE, and WARNING.

CAUTION

CAVITATION (CAV-uh-TAY-shun)

The formation and collapse of a gas pocket or bubble on the blade of an impeller or the gate of a valve. The collapse of this gas pocket or bubble drives water into the impeller or gate with a terrific force that can cause pitting on the impeller or gate surface. Cavitation is accompanied by loud noises that sound like someone is pounding on the impeller or gate with a hammer.

CAVITATION

CENTRATE

The water leaving a centrifuge after most of the solids have been removed.

CENTRATE

CENTRIFUGAL (sen-TRIF-uh-gull) PUMP

A pump consisting of an impeller fixed on a rotating shaft that is enclosed in a casing, and having an inlet and discharge connection. As the rotating impeller whirls the liquid around, centrifugal force builds up enough pressure to force the water through the discharge outlet.

CENTRIFUGAL PUMP

CENTRIFUGE

A mechanical device that uses centrifugal or rotational forces to separate solids from liquids.

CENTRIFUGE

CERTIFICATION EXAMINATION

An examination administered by a state or professional association that operators take to indicate a level of professional competence. In most states the Chief Operator of a plant must be "certified" (successfully pass a certification examination). Certification is voluntary in a few states. Current trends indicate that certification of operators will be mandatory in all states and Canadian provinces in the near future.

CERTIFICATION EXAMINATION

CHARGE CHEMISTRY

A branch of chemistry in which the destabilization and neutralization reactions occur between stable negatively charged and stable positively charged particles.

CHARGE CHEMISTRY

CHECK SAMPLING CHECK SAMPLING

Whenever an initial or routine sample analysis indicates that a Maximum Contaminant Level (MCL) has been exceeded, *CHECK SAMPLING* is required to confirm the routine sampling results. Check sampling is in addition to the routine sampling program.

CHECK VALVE CHECK VALVE

A special valve with a hinged disc or flap that opens in the direction of normal flow and is forced shut when flows attempt to go in the reverse or opposite direction of normal flows.

CHELATING (key-LAY-ting) AGENT CHELATING AGENT

A chemical used to prevent the precipitation of metals (such as copper).

CHELATION (key-LAY-shun) CHELATION

A chemical complexing (forming or joining together) of metallic cations (such as copper) with certain organic compounds, such as EDTA (ethylene diamine tetracetic acid). Chelation is used to prevent the precipitation of metals (copper). Also see SEQUESTRATION.

CHLORAMINATION (KLOR-ah-min-NAY-shun) CHLORAMINATION

The application of chlorine and ammonia to water to form chloramines for the purpose of disinfection.

CHLORAMINES (KLOR-uh-means) CHLORAMINES

Compounds formed by the reaction of hypochlorous acid (or aqueous chlorine) with ammonia.

CHLORINATION (KLOR-uh-NAY-shun) CHLORINATION

The application of chlorine to water, generally for the purpose of disinfection, but frequently for accomplishing other biological or chemical results (aiding coagulation and controlling tastes and odors).

CHLORINATOR (KLOR-uh-NAY-ter) CHLORINATOR

A metering device which is used to add chlorine to water.

CHLORINE DEMAND CHLORINE DEMAND

Chlorine demand is the difference between the amount of chlorine added to water and the amount of residual chlorine remaining after a given contact time. Chlorine demand may change with dosage, time, temperature, pH, and nature and amount of the impurities in the water.

Chlorine Demand, mg/*L* = Chlorine Applied, mg/*L* – Chlorine Residual, mg/*L*

CHLORINE REQUIREMENT CHLORINE REQUIREMENT

The amount of chlorine which is needed for a particular purpose. Some reasons for adding chlorine are reducing the number of coliform bacteria (Most Probable Number), obtaining a particular chlorine residual, or oxidizing some substance in the water. In each case a definite dosage of chlorine will be necessary. This dosage is the chlorine requirement.

CHLOROPHENOLIC (klor-o-FEE-NO-lick) CHLOROPHENOLIC

Chlorophenolic compounds are phenolic compounds (carbolic acid) combined with chlorine.

CHLOROPHENOXY (KLOR-o-fuh-KNOX-ee) CHLOROPHENOXY

A class of herbicides that may be found in domestic water supplies and cause adverse health effects. Two widely used chlorophenoxy herbicides are 2,4-D (2,4-Dichlorophenoxy acetic acid) and 2,4,5-TP (2,4,5-Trichlorophenoxy propionic acid (silvex)).

CHLORORGANIC (klor-or-GAN-ick) CHLORORGANIC

Organic compounds combined with chlorine. These compounds generally originate from, or are associated with, life processes such as those of algae in water.

CHRONIC HEALTH EFFECT CHRONIC HEALTH EFFECT

An adverse effect on a human or animal body with symptoms that develop slowly over a long period of time or that recur frequently.

CIRCLE OF INFLUENCE CIRCLE OF INFLUENCE

The circular outer edge of a depression produced in the water table by the pumping of water from a well. Also see CONE OF INFLUENCE and CONE OF DEPRESSION.

[SEE DRAWING ON PAGE 709]

TOP OR PLAN VIEW

SIDE OR ELEVATION VIEW

CIRCLE OF INFLUENCE and CONE OF DEPRESSION/CONE OF INFLUENCE

CIRCUIT

The complete path of an electric current, including the generating apparatus or other source; or, a specific segment or section of the complete path.

CIRCUIT BREAKER

A safety device in an electric circuit that automatically shuts off the circuit when it becomes overloaded. The device can be manually reset.

CISTERN (SIS-turn)

A small tank (usually covered) or a storage facility used to store water for a home or farm. Often used to store rainwater.

CLARIFIER (KLAIR-uh-fire)

A large circular or rectangular tank or basin in which water is held for a period of time during which the heavier suspended solids settle to the bottom. Clarifiers are also called settling basins and sedimentation basins.

CLASS, PIPE AND FITTINGS

The working pressure rating, including allowances for surges, of a specific pipe for use in water distribution systems. The term is used for cast iron, ductile iron, asbestos cement and some plastic pipe.

CLEAR WELL

A reservoir for the storage of filtered water of sufficient capacity to prevent the need to vary the filtration rate with variations in demand. Also used to provide chlorine contact time for disinfection.

COAGULANT AID

Any chemical or substance used to assist or modify coagulation.

COAGULANTS (co-AGG-you-lents)

Chemicals that cause very fine particles to clump (floc) together into larger particles. This makes it easier to separate the solids from the water by settling, skimming, draining or filtering.

COAGULATION (co-AGG-you-LAY-shun)

The clumping together of very fine particles into larger particles (floc) caused by the use of chemicals (coagulants). The chemicals neutralize the electrical charges of the fine particles, allowing them to come closer and form larger clumps. This clumping together makes it easier to separate the solids from the water by settling, skimming, draining or filtering.

CODE OF FEDERAL REGULATIONS (CFR)

A publication of the United States Government which contains all of the proposed and finalized federal regulations, including environmental regulations.

COLIFORM (COAL-i-form)

A group of bacteria found in the intestines of warm-blooded animals (including humans) and also in plants, soil, air and water. Fecal coliforms are a specific class of bacteria which only inhabit the intestines of warm-blooded animals. The presence of coliform bacteria is an indication that the water is polluted and may contain pathogenic (disease-causing) organisms.

COLLOIDS (CALL-loids)

Very small, finely divided solids (particles that do not dissolve) that remain dispersed in a liquid for a long time due to their small size and electrical charge. When most of the particles in water have a negative electrical charge, they tend to repel each other. This repulsion prevents the particles from clumping together, becoming heavier, and settling out.

COLOR

The substances in water that impart a yellowish-brown color to the water. These substances are the result of iron and manganese ions, humus and peat materials, plankton, aquatic weeds, and industrial waste present in the water. Also see TRUE COLOR.

COLORIMETRIC MEASUREMENT

A means of measuring unknown chemical concentrations in water by measuring a sample's color intensity. The specific color of the sample, developed by addition of chemical reagents, is measured with a photoelectric colorimeter or is compared with "color standards" using, or corresponding with, known concentrations of the chemical.

COMBINED AVAILABLE RESIDUAL CHLORINE
COMBINED AVAILABLE RESIDUAL CHLORINE

The concentration of residual chlorine which is combined with ammonia (NH_3) and/or organic nitrogen in water as a chloramine (or other chloro derivative) yet is still available to oxidize organic matter and use its bactericidal properties.

COMBINED RESIDUAL CHLORINATION
COMBINED RESIDUAL CHLORINATION

The application of chlorine to water to produce combined available chlorine residual. This residual can be made up of monochloramines, dichloramines, and nitrogen trichloride.

COMMODITY-DEMAND METHOD
COMMODITY-DEMAND METHOD

A cost allocation method used by water utilities to determine water rates for the various water user groups. This method considers the commodity costs (water, chemicals, power, amount of water use), demand costs (treatment, storage, distribution), customer costs (meter maintenance and reading, billing, collection, accounting) and fire protection costs.

COMPLETE TREATMENT
COMPLETE TREATMENT

A method of treating water which consists of the addition of coagulant chemicals, flash mixing, coagulation-flocculation, sedimentation and filtration. Also called CONVENTIONAL FILTRATION.

COMPOSITE (come-PAH-zit) (PROPORTIONAL) SAMPLE
COMPOSITE (PROPORTIONAL) SAMPLE

A composite sample is a collection of individual samples obtained at regular intervals, usually every one or two hours during a 24-hour time span. Each individual sample is combined with the others in proportion to the rate of flow when the sample was collected. The resulting mixture (composite sample) forms a representative sample and is analyzed to determine the average conditions during the sampling period.

COMPOUND
COMPOUND

A pure substance composed of two or more elements whose composition is constant. For example, table salt (sodium chloride, NaCl) is a compound.

CONCENTRATION POLARIZATION
CONCENTRATION POLARIZATION

(1) A buildup of retained particles on the membrane surface due to dewatering of the feed closest to the membrane. The thickness of the concentration polarization layer is controlled by the flow velocity across the membrane.

(2) Used in corrosion studies to indicate a depletion of ions near an electrode.

(3) The basis for chemical analysis by a polarograph.

CONDITIONING
CONDITIONING

Pretreatment of sludge to facilitate removal of water in subsequent treatment processes.

CONDUCTANCE
CONDUCTANCE

A rapid method of estimating the dissolved solids content of a water supply. The measurement indicates the capacity of a sample of water to carry an electric current, which is related to the concentration of ionized substances in the water. Also called SPECIFIC CONDUCTANCE.

CONDUCTIVITY
CONDUCTIVITY

A measure of the ability of a solution (water) to carry an electric current.

CONDUCTOR
CONDUCTOR

A substance, body, device or wire that readily conducts or carries electric current.

CONDUCTOR CASING
CONDUCTOR CASING

The outer casing of a well. The purpose of this casing is to prevent contaminants from surface waters or shallow groundwaters from entering a well.

CONE OF DEPRESSION
CONE OF DEPRESSION

The depression, roughly conical in shape, produced in the water table by the pumping of water from a well. Also called the CONE OF INFLUENCE. Also see CIRCLE OF INFLUENCE.

[SEE DRAWING ON PAGE 709]

CONE OF INFLUENCE
CONE OF INFLUENCE

The depression, roughly conical in shape, produced in the water table by the pumping of water from a well. Also called the CONE OF DEPRESSION. Also see CIRCLE OF INFLUENCE.

[SEE DRAWING ON PAGE 709]

CONFINED SPACE

Confined space means a space that:

A. Is large enough and so configured that an employee can bodily enter and perform assigned work; and

B. Has limited or restricted means for entry or exit (for example, tanks, vessels, silos, storage bins, hoppers, vaults, and pits are spaces that may have limited means of entry); and

C. Is not designed for continuous employee occupancy.

(Definition from the Code of Federal Regulations (CFR) Title 29 Part 1910.146.)

CONFINED SPACE, CLASS "A"

A confined space that presents a situation that is immediately dangerous to life or health (IDLH). These include but are not limited to oxygen deficiency, explosive or flammable atmospheres, and/or concentrations of toxic substances.

(Definition from NIOSH, "Criteria for a Recommended Standard: Working in Confined Spaces.")

CONFINED SPACE, CLASS "B"

A confined space that has the potential for causing injury and illness, if preventive measures are not used, but not immediately dangerous to life and health.

(Definition from NIOSH, "Criteria for a Recommended Standard: Working in Confined Spaces.")

CONFINED SPACE, CLASS "C"

A confined space in which the potential hazard would not require any special modification of the work procedure.

(Definition from NIOSH, "Criteria for a Recommended Standard: Working in Confined Spaces.")

CONFINED SPACE, PERMIT-REQUIRED (PERMIT SPACE)

A confined space that has one or more of the following characteristics:

- Contains or has a potential to contain a hazardous atmosphere,
- Contains a material that has the potential for engulfing an entrant,
- Has an internal configuration such that an entrant could be trapped or asphyxiated by inwardly converging walls or by a floor which slopes downward and tapers to a smaller cross section, or
- Contains any other recognized serious safety or health hazard.

(Definition from the Code of Federal Regulations (CFR) Title 29 Part 1910.146.)

CONSOLIDATED FORMATION

A geologic material whose particles are stratified (layered), cemented or firmly packed together (hard rock); usually occurring at a depth below the ground surface. Also see UNCONSOLIDATED FORMATION.

CONSUMER CONFIDENCE REPORTS

An annual report prepared by a water utility to communicate with its consumers. The report provides consumers with information on the source and quality of their drinking water. The report is an opportunity for positive communication with consumers and to convey the importance of paying for good quality drinking water.

CONTACTOR

An electric switch, usually magnetically operated.

CONTAMINATION

The introduction into water of microorganisms, chemicals, toxic substances, wastes, or wastewater in a concentration that makes the water unfit for its next intended use.

CONTINUOUS SAMPLE

A flow of water from a particular place in a plant to the location where samples are collected for testing. This continuous stream may be used to obtain grab or composite samples. Frequently, several taps (faucets) will flow continuously in the laboratory to provide test samples from various places in a water treatment plant.

CONTROL LOOP

The path through the control system between the sensor, which measures a process variable, and the controller, which controls or adjusts the process variable.

CONTROL SYSTEM

CONTROL SYSTEM

An instrumentation system which senses and controls its own operation on a close, continuous basis in what is called proportional (or modulating) control.

CONTROLLER

CONTROLLER

A device which controls the starting, stopping, or operation of a device or piece of equipment.

CONVENTIONAL FILTRATION

CONVENTIONAL FILTRATION

A method of treating water which consists of the addition of coagulant chemicals, flash mixing, coagulation-flocculation, sedimentation and filtration. Also called COMPLETE TREATMENT. Also see DIRECT FILTRATION and IN-LINE FILTRATION.

CONVENTIONAL TREATMENT

CONVENTIONAL TREATMENT

See CONVENTIONAL FILTRATION. Also called COMPLETE TREATMENT.

CORPORATION STOP

CORPORATION STOP

A water service shutoff valve located at a street water main. This valve cannot be operated from the ground surface because it is buried and there is no valve box. Also called a corporation cock.

CORROSION

CORROSION

The gradual decomposition or destruction of a material by chemical action, often due to an electrochemical reaction. Corrosion may be caused by (1) stray current electrolysis, (2) galvanic corrosion caused by dissimilar metals, or (3) differential-concentration cells. Corrosion starts at the surface of a material and moves inward.

CORROSION INHIBITORS

CORROSION INHIBITORS

Substances that slow the rate of corrosion.

CORROSIVE GASES

CORROSIVE GASES

In water, dissolved oxygen reacts readily with metals at the anode of a corrosion cell, accelerating the rate of corrosion until a film of oxidation products such as rust forms. At the cathode where hydrogen gas may form a coating on the cathode and slow the corrosion rate, oxygen reacts rapidly with hydrogen gas forming water, and again increases the rate of corrosion.

CORROSIVITY

CORROSIVITY

An indication of the corrosiveness of a water. The corrosiveness of a water is described by the water's pH, alkalinity, hardness, temperature, total dissolved solids, dissolved oxygen concentration, and the Langelier Index.

COULOMB (COO-lahm)

COULOMB

A measurement of the amount of electrical charge carried by an electric current of one ampere in one second. One coulomb equals about 6.25×10^{18} electrons (6,250,000,000,000,000,000 electrons).

COUPON

COUPON

A steel specimen inserted into water to measure the corrosiveness of water. The rate of corrosion is measured as the loss of weight of the coupon (in milligrams) per surface area (in square decimeters) exposed to the water per day. 10 decimeters = 1 meter = 100 centimeters.

COVERAGE RATIO

COVERAGE RATIO

The coverage ratio is a measure of the ability of the utility to pay the principle and interest on loans and bonds (this is known as "debt service") in addition to any unexpected expenses.

CROSS CONNECTION

CROSS CONNECTION

A connection between a drinking (potable) water system and an unapproved water supply. For example, if you have a pump moving nonpotable water and hook into the drinking water system to supply water for the pump seal, a cross connection or mixing between the two water systems can occur. This mixing may lead to contamination of the drinking water.

CURB STOP

CURB STOP

A water service shutoff valve located in a water service pipe near the curb and between the water main and the building. This valve is usually operated by a wrench or valve key and is used to start or stop flows in the water service line to a building. Also called a curb cock.

CURIE

CURIE

A measure of radioactivity. One Curie of radioactivity is equivalent to 3.7×10^{10} or 37,000,000,000 nuclear disintegrations per second.

CURRENT

CURRENT

A movement or flow of electricity. Water flowing in a pipe is measured in gallons per second past a certain point, not by the number of water molecules going past a point. Electric current is measured by the number of coulombs per second flowing past a certain point in a conductor. A coulomb is equal to about 6.25×10^{18} electrons (6,250,000,000,000,000,000 electrons). A flow of one coulomb per second is called one ampere, the unit of the rate of flow of current.

CYCLE

CYCLE

A complete alternation of voltage and/or current in an alternating current (A.C.) circuit.

D

DBP

DBP

See **D**ISINFECTION **B**Y-**P**RODUCT.

DPD (pronounce as separate letters)

DPD

A method of measuring the chlorine residual in water. The residual may be determined by either titrating or comparing a developed color with color standards. DPD stands for N,N-diethyl-p-phenylene-diamine.

DANGER

DANGER

The word *DANGER* is used where an immediate hazard presents a threat of death or serious injury to employees. Also see CAUTION, NOTICE, and WARNING.

DANGEROUS AIR CONTAMINATION

DANGEROUS AIR CONTAMINATION

An atmosphere presenting a threat of causing death, injury, acute illness, or disablement due to the presence of flammable and/or explosive, toxic or otherwise injurious or incapacitating substances.

A. Dangerous air contamination due to the flammability of a gas or vapor is defined as an atmosphere containing the gas or vapor at a concentration greater than 10 percent of its lower explosive (lower flammable) limit.

B. Dangerous air contamination due to a combustible particulate is defined as a concentration greater than 10 percent of the minimum explosive concentration of the particulate.

C. Dangerous air contamination due to the toxicity of a substance is defined as the atmospheric concentration immediately hazardous to life or health.

DATEOMETER (day-TOM-uh-ter)

DATEOMETER

A small calendar disc attached to motors and equipment to indicate the year in which the last maintenance service was performed.

DATUM LINE

DATUM LINE

A line from which heights and depths are calculated or measured. Also called a datum plane or a datum level.

DAY TANK

DAY TANK

A tank used to store a chemical solution of known concentration for feed to a chemical feeder. A day tank usually stores sufficient chemical solution to properly treat the water being treated for at least one day. Also called an AGE TANK.

DEAD END

DEAD END

The end of a water main which is not connected to other parts of the distribution system by means of a connecting loop of pipe.

DEBT SERVICE

DEBT SERVICE

The amount of money required annually to pay the (1) interest on outstanding debts; or (2) funds due on a maturing bonded debt or the redemption of bonds.

DECANT

DECANT

To draw off the upper layer of liquid (water) after the heavier material (a solid or another liquid) has settled.

DECANT WATER

DECANT WATER

Water that has separated from sludge and is removed from the layer of water above the sludge.

DECHLORINATION (dee-KLOR-uh-NAY-shun) DECHLORINATION

The deliberate removal of chlorine from water. The partial or complete reduction of residual chlorine by any chemical or physical process.

DECIBEL (DES-uh-bull) DECIBEL

A unit for expressing the relative intensity of sounds on a scale from zero for the average least perceptible sound to about 130 for the average level at which sound causes pain to humans. Abbreviated dB.

DECOMPOSITION, DECAY DECOMPOSITION, DECAY

The conversion of chemically unstable materials to more stable forms by chemical or biological action. If organic matter decays when there is no oxygen present (anaerobic conditions or putrefaction), undesirable tastes and odors are produced. Decay of organic matter when oxygen is present (aerobic conditions) tends to produce much less objectionable tastes and odors.

DEFLUORIDATION (de-FLOOR-uh-DAY-shun) DEFLUORIDATION

The removal of excess fluoride in drinking water to prevent the mottling (brown stains) of teeth.

DEGASIFICATION (DEE-GAS-if-uh-KAY-shun) DEGASIFICATION

A water treatment process which removes dissolved gases from the water. The gases may be removed by either mechanical or chemical treatment methods or a combination of both.

DELEGATION DELEGATION

The act in which power is given to another person in the organization to accomplish a specific job.

DEMINERALIZATION (DEE-MIN-er-al-uh-ZAY-shun) DEMINERALIZATION

A treatment process which removes dissolved minerals (salts) from water.

DENSITY (DEN-sit-tee) DENSITY

A measure of how heavy a substance (solid, liquid or gas) is for its size. Density is expressed in terms of weight per unit volume, that is, grams per cubic centimeter or pounds per cubic foot. The density of water (at 4°C or 39°F) is 1.0 gram per cubic centimeter or about 62.4 pounds per cubic foot.

DEPOLARIZATION DEPOLARIZATION

The removal or depletion of ions in the thin boundary layer adjacent to a membrane or pipe wall.

DEPRECIATION DEPRECIATION

The gradual loss in service value of a facility or piece of equipment due to all the factors causing the ultimate retirement of the facility or equipment. This loss can be caused by sudden physical damage, wearing out due to age, obsolescence, inadequacy or availability of a newer, more efficient facility or equipment. The value cannot be restored by maintenance.

DESALINIZATION (DEE-SAY-leen-uh-ZAY-shun) DESALINIZATION

The removal of dissolved salts (such as sodium chloride, NaCl) from water by natural means (leaching) or by specific water treatment processes.

DESICCANT (DESS-uh-kant) DESICCANT

A drying agent which is capable of removing or absorbing moisture from the atmosphere in a small enclosure.

DESICCATION (DESS-uh-KAY-shun) DESICCATION

A process used to thoroughly dry air; to remove virtually all moisture from air.

DESICCATOR (DESS-uh-KAY-tor) DESICCATOR

A closed container into which heated weighing or drying dishes are placed to cool in a dry environment in preparation for weighing. The dishes may be empty or they may contain a sample. Desiccators contain a substance, such as anhydrous calcium chloride, which absorbs moisture and keeps the relative humidity near zero so that the dish or sample will not gain weight from absorbed moisture.

DESTRATIFICATION (de-STRAT-uh-fuh-KAY-shun) DESTRATIFICATION

The development of vertical mixing within a lake or reservoir to eliminate (either totally or partially) separate layers of temperature, plant, or animal life. This vertical mixing can be caused by mechanical means (pumps) or through the use of forced air diffusers which release air into the lower layers of the reservoir.

DETECTION LAG

DETECTION LAG

The time period between the moment a process change is made and the moment when such a change is finally sensed by the associated measuring instrument.

DETENTION TIME

DETENTION TIME

(1) The theoretical (calculated) time required for a small amount of water to pass through a tank at a given rate of flow.

(2) The actual time in hours, minutes or seconds that a small amount of water is in a settling basin, flocculating basin or rapid-mix chamber. In storage reservoirs, detention time is the length of time entering water will be held before being drafted for use (several weeks to years, several months being typical).

$$\text{Detention Time, hr} = \frac{(\text{Basin Volume, gal})(24 \text{ hr/day})}{\text{Flow, gal/day}}$$

DEW POINT

DEW POINT

The temperature to which air with a given quantity of water vapor must be cooled to cause condensation of the vapor in the air.

DEWATER

DEWATER

(1) To remove or separate a portion of the water present in a sludge or slurry. To dry sludge so it can be handled and disposed of.

(2) To remove or drain the water from a tank or a trench.

DIATOMACEOUS (DYE-uh-toe-MAY-shus) EARTH

DIATOMACEOUS EARTH

A fine, siliceous (made of silica) "earth" composed mainly of the skeletal remains of diatoms.

DIATOMS (DYE-uh-toms)

DIATOMS

Unicellular (single cell), microscopic algae with a rigid (box-like) internal structure consisting mainly of silica.

DIELECTRIC (DIE-ee-LECK-trick)

DIELECTRIC

Does not conduct an electric current. An insulator or nonconducting substance.

DIGITAL READOUT

DIGITAL READOUT

Use of numbers to indicate the value or measurement of a variable. The readout of an instrument by a direct, numerical reading of the measured value. The signal sent to such readouts is usually an analog signal.

DILUTE SOLUTION

DILUTE SOLUTION

A solution that has been made weaker, usually by the addition of water.

DIMICTIC (die-MICK-tick)

DIMICTIC

Lakes and reservoirs which freeze over and normally go through two stratification and two mixing cycles within a year.

DIRECT CURRENT (D.C.)

DIRECT CURRENT (D.C.)

Electric current flowing in one direction only and essentially free from pulsation.

DIRECT FILTRATION

DIRECT FILTRATION

A method of treating water which consists of the addition of coagulant chemicals, flash mixing, coagulation, minimal flocculation, and filtration. The flocculation facilities may be omitted, but the physical-chemical reactions will occur to some extent. The sedimentation process is omitted. Also see CONVENTIONAL FILTRATION and IN-LINE FILTRATION.

DIRECT RUNOFF

DIRECT RUNOFF

Water that flows over the ground surface or through the ground directly into streams, rivers, or lakes.

DISCHARGE HEAD

DISCHARGE HEAD

The pressure (in pounds per square inch or psi) measured at the centerline of a pump discharge and very close to the discharge flange, converted into feet. The pressure is measured from the centerline of the pump to the hydraulic grade line of the water in the discharge pipe.

$$\text{Discharge Head, ft} = (\text{Discharge Pressure, psi})(2.31 \text{ ft/psi})$$

DISINFECTION (dis-in-FECT-shun)   DISINFECTION

The process designed to kill or inactivate most microorganisms in water, including essentially all pathogenic (disease-causing) bacteria. There are several ways to disinfect, with chlorination being the most frequently used in water treatment. Compare with STERILIZATION.

DISINFECTION BY-PRODUCT (DBP)   DISINFECTION BY-PRODUCT (DBP)

A contaminant formed by the reaction of disinfection chemicals (such as chlorine) with other substances in the water being disinfected.

DISTILLATE (DIS-tuh-late)   DISTILLATE

In the distillation of a sample, a portion is evaporated; the part that is condensed afterward is the distillate.

DIVALENT (die-VAY-lent)   DIVALENT

Having a valence of two, such as the ferrous ion, Fe^{2+}. Also called bivalent.

DIVERSION   DIVERSION

Use of part of a stream flow as a water supply.

DRAFT   DRAFT

(1) The act of drawing or removing water from a tank or reservoir.

(2) The water which is drawn or removed from a tank or reservoir.

DRAWDOWN   DRAWDOWN

(1) The drop in the water table or level of water in the ground when water is being pumped from a well.

(2) The amount of water used from a tank or reservoir.

(3) The drop in the water level of a tank or reservoir.

DRIFT   DRIFT

The difference between the actual value and the desired value (or set point); characteristic of proportional controllers that do not incorporate reset action. Also called OFFSET.

DYNAMIC PRESSURE   DYNAMIC PRESSURE

When a pump is operating, the vertical distance (in feet) from a reference point (such as a pump centerline) to the hydraulic grade line is the dynamic head. Also see ENERGY GRADE LINE, STATIC HEAD, STATIC PRESSURE, and TOTAL DYNAMIC HEAD.

Dynamic Pressure, psi = (Dynamic Head, ft)(0.433 psi/ft)

E

EPA   EPA

United States **E**nvironmental **P**rotection **A**gency. A regulatory agency established by the U.S. Congress to administer the nation's environmental laws. Also called the U.S. EPA.

EDUCTOR (e-DUCK-ter)   EDUCTOR

A hydraulic device used to create a negative pressure (suction) by forcing a liquid through a restriction, such as a Venturi. An eductor or aspirator (the hydraulic device) may be used in the laboratory in place of a vacuum pump. As an injector, it is used to produce vacuum for chlorinators. Sometimes used instead of a suction pump.

EFFECTIVE RANGE   EFFECTIVE RANGE

That portion of the design range (usually from 10 to 90+ percent) in which an instrument has acceptable accuracy. Also see RANGE and SPAN.

EFFECTIVE SIZE (E.S.)   EFFECTIVE SIZE (E.S.)

The diameter of the particles in a granular sample (filter media) for which 10 percent of the total grains are smaller and 90 percent larger on a weight basis. Effective size is obtained by passing granular material through sieves with varying dimensions of mesh and weighing the material retained by each sieve. The effective size is also approximately the average size of the grains.

EFFLUENT   EFFLUENT

Water or other liquid — raw (untreated), partially or completely treated — flowing *FROM* a reservoir, basin, treatment process, or treatment plant.

EJECTOR   EJECTOR

A device used to disperse a chemical solution into water being treated.

ELECTROCHEMICAL REACTION   ELECTROCHEMICAL REACTION

Chemical changes produced by electricity (electrolysis) or the production of electricity by chemical changes (galvanic action). In corrosion, a chemical reaction is accompanied by the flow of electrons through a metallic path. The electron flow may come from an external source and cause the reaction, such as electrolysis caused by a D.C. (direct current) electric railway or the electron flow may be caused by a chemical reaction as in the galvanic action of a flashlight dry cell.

ELECTROCHEMICAL SERIES   ELECTROCHEMICAL SERIES

A list of metals with the standard electrode potentials given in volts. The size and sign of the electrode potential indicates how easily these elements will take on or give up electrons, or corrode. Hydrogen is conventionally assigned a value of zero.

ELECTROLYSIS (ee-leck-TRAWL-uh-sis)   ELECTROLYSIS

The decomposition of material by an outside electric current.

ELECTROLYTE (ee-LECK-tro-LITE)   ELECTROLYTE

A substance which dissociates (separates) into two or more ions when it is dissolved in water.

ELECTROLYTIC (ee-LECK-tro-LIT-ick) CELL   ELECTROLYTIC CELL

A device in which the chemical decomposition of material causes an electric current to flow. Also, a device in which a chemical reaction occurs as a result of the flow of electric current. Chlorine and caustic (NaOH) are made from salt (NaCl) in electrolytic cells.

ELECTROMOTIVE FORCE (E.M.F.)   ELECTROMOTIVE FORCE (E.M.F.)

The electrical pressure available to cause a flow of current (amperage) when an electric circuit is closed. Also called VOLTAGE.

ELECTROMOTIVE SERIES   ELECTROMOTIVE SERIES

A list of metals and alloys presented in the order of their tendency to corrode (or go into solution). Also called the GALVANIC SERIES. This is a practical application of the theoretical ELECTROCHEMICAL SERIES.

ELECTRON   ELECTRON

(1) A very small, negatively charged particle which is practically weightless. According to the electron theory, all electrical and electronic effects are caused either by the movement of electrons from place to place or because there is an excess or lack of electrons at a particular place.

(2) The part of an atom that determines its chemical properties.

ELEMENT   ELEMENT

A substance which cannot be separated into its constituent parts and still retain its chemical identity. For example, sodium (Na) is an element.

END BELLS   END BELLS

Devices used to hold the rotor and stator of a motor in position.

END POINT   END POINT

Samples are titrated to the end point. This means that a chemical is added, drop by drop, to a sample until a certain color change (blue to clear, for example) occurs. This is called the *END POINT* of the titration. In addition to a color change, an end point may be reached by the formation of a precipitate or the reaching of a specified pH. An end point may be detected by the use of an electronic device such as a pH meter. The completion of a desired chemical reaction.

ENDEMIC (en-DEM-ick)   ENDEMIC

Something peculiar to a particular people or locality, such as a disease which is always present in the population.

ENDRIN (EN-drin)   ENDRIN

A pesticide toxic to freshwater and marine aquatic life that produces adverse health effects in domestic water supplies.

ENERGY GRADE LINE (EGL)   ENERGY GRADE LINE (EGL)

A line that represents the elevation of energy head (in feet) of water flowing in a pipe, conduit or channel. The line is drawn above the hydraulic grade line (gradient) a distance equal to the velocity head ($V^2/2g$) of the water flowing at each section or point along the pipe or channel. Also see HYDRAULIC GRADE LINE.

[SEE DRAWING ON PAGE 720]

ENTERIC   ENTERIC

Of intestinal origin, especially applied to wastes or bacteria.

ENTRAIN   ENTRAIN

To trap bubbles in water either mechanically through turbulence or chemically through a reaction.

ENZYMES (EN-zimes)   ENZYMES

Organic substances (produced by living organisms) which cause or speed up chemical reactions. Organic catalysts and/or bio-chemical catalysts.

EPIDEMIC (EP-uh-DEM-ick)   EPIDEMIC

A disease that occurs in a large number of people in a locality at the same time and spreads from person to person.

EPIDEMIOLOGY (EP-uh-DE-me-ALL-o-gee)   EPIDEMIOLOGY

A branch of medicine which studies epidemics (diseases which affect significant numbers of people during the same time period in the same locality). The objective of epidemiology is to determine the factors that cause epidemic diseases and how to prevent them.

EPILIMNION (EP-uh-LIM-knee-on)   EPILIMNION

The upper layer of water in a thermally stratified lake or reservoir. This layer consists of the warmest water and has a fairly uniform (constant) temperature. The layer is readily mixed by wind action.

EQUILIBRIUM, CALCIUM CARBONATE   EQUILIBRIUM, CALCIUM CARBONATE

A water is considered stable when it is just saturated with calcium carbonate. In this condition the water will neither dissolve nor deposit calcium carbonate. Thus, in this water the calcium carbonate is in equilibrium with the hydrogen ion concentration.

EQUITY   EQUITY

The value of an investment in a facility.

EQUIVALENT WEIGHT   EQUIVALENT WEIGHT

That weight which will react with, displace or is equivalent to one gram atom of hydrogen.

ESTER   ESTER

A compound formed by the reaction between an acid and an alcohol with the elimination of a molecule of water.

EUTROPHIC (you-TRO-fick)   EUTROPHIC

Reservoirs and lakes which are rich in nutrients and very productive in terms of aquatic animal and plant life.

EUTROPHICATION (you-TRO-fi-KAY-shun)   EUTROPHICATION

The increase in the nutrient levels of a lake or other body of water; this usually causes an increase in the growth of aquatic animal and plant life.

EVAPORATION   EVAPORATION

The process by which water or other liquid becomes a gas (water vapor or ammonia vapor).

EVAPOTRANSPIRATION (ee-VAP-o-TRANS-purr-A-shun)   EVAPOTRANSPIRATION

(1) The process by which water vapor passes into the atmosphere from living plants. Also called TRANSPIRATION.

(2) The total water removed from an area by transpiration (plants) and by evaporation from soil, snow and water surfaces.

PIPE

CANAL OR OPEN CHANNEL

WATER SURFACE

ENERGY GRADE LINE

HYDRAULIC GRADE LINE

$V^2/2g$

FLOW

$V^2/2g$ = VELOCITY HEAD

ENERGY GRADE LINE and HYDRAULIC GRADE LINE

F

FACULTATIVE (FACK-ul-TAY-tive)   FACULTATIVE

Facultative bacteria can use either dissolved molecular oxygen or oxygen obtained from food materials such as sulfate or nitrate ions. In other words, facultative bacteria can live under aerobic or anaerobic conditions.

FEEDBACK   FEEDBACK

The circulating action between a sensor measuring a process variable and the controller which controls or adjusts the process variable.

FEEDWATER   FEEDWATER

The water that is fed to a treatment process; the water that is going to be treated.

FINISHED WATER   FINISHED WATER

Water that has passed through a water treatment plant; all the treatment processes are completed or "finished." This water is ready to be delivered to consumers. Also called PRODUCT WATER.

FIX, SAMPLE   FIX, SAMPLE

A sample is "fixed" in the field by adding chemicals that prevent the water quality indicators of interest in the sample from changing before final measurements are performed later in the lab.

FIXED COSTS   FIXED COSTS

Costs that a utility must cover or pay even if there is no demand for water or no water to sell to customers. Also see VARIABLE COSTS.

FLAGELLATES (FLAJ-el-LATES)   FLAGELLATES

Microorganisms that move by the action of tail-like projections.

FLAME POLISHED   FLAME POLISHED

Melted by a flame to smooth out irregularities. Sharp or broken edges of glass (such as the end of a glass tube) are rotated in a flame until the edge melts slightly and becomes smooth.

FLOAT ON SYSTEM   FLOAT ON SYSTEM

A method of operating a water storage facility. Daily flow into the facility is approximately equal to the average daily demand for water. When consumer demands for water are low, the storage facility will be filling. During periods of high demand, the facility will be emptying.

FLOC   FLOC

Clumps of bacteria and particulate impurities that have come together and formed a cluster. Found in flocculation tanks and settling or sedimentation basins.

FLOCCULATION (FLOCK-you-LAY-shun)   FLOCCULATION

The gathering together of fine particles after coagulation to form larger particles by a process of gentle mixing.

FLUIDIZED (FLEW-id-I-zd)   FLUIDIZED

A mass of solid particles that is made to flow like a liquid by injection of water or gas is said to have been fluidized. In water treatment, a bed of filter media is fluidized by backwashing water through the filter.

FLUORIDATION (FLOOR-uh-DAY-shun)   FLUORIDATION

The addition of a chemical to increase the concentration of fluoride ions in drinking water to a predetermined optimum limit to reduce the incidence (number) of dental caries (tooth decay) in children. Defluoridation is the removal of excess fluoride in drinking water to prevent the mottling (brown stains) of teeth.

FLUSHING   FLUSHING

A method used to clean water distribution lines. Hydrants are opened and water with a high velocity flows through the pipes, removes deposits from the pipes, and flows out the hydrants.

FLUX   FLUX

A flowing or flow.

FOOT VALVE

FOOT VALVE

A special type of check valve located at the bottom end of the suction pipe on a pump. This valve opens when the pump operates to allow water to enter the suction pipe but closes when the pump shuts off to prevent water from flowing out of the suction pipe.

FREE AVAILABLE RESIDUAL CHLORINE

FREE AVAILABLE RESIDUAL CHLORINE

That portion of the total available residual chlorine composed of dissolved chlorine gas (Cl_2), hypochlorous acid (HOCl), and/or hypochlorite ion (OCl^-) remaining in water after chlorination. This does not include chlorine that has combined with ammonia, nitrogen, or other compounds.

FREE RESIDUAL CHLORINATION

FREE RESIDUAL CHLORINATION

The application of chlorine to water to produce a free available chlorine residual equal to at least 80 percent of the total residual chlorine (sum of free and combined available chlorine residual).

FREEBOARD

FREEBOARD

(1) The vertical distance from the normal water surface to the top of the confining wall.

(2) The vertical distance from the sand surface to the underside of a trough in a sand filter. This distance is also called AVAILABLE EXPANSION.

FRICTION LOSSES

FRICTION LOSSES

The head, pressure or energy (they are the same) lost by water flowing in a pipe or channel as a result of turbulence caused by the velocity of the flowing water and the roughness of the pipe, channel walls, or restrictions caused by fittings. Water flowing in a pipe loses head, pressure or energy as a result of friction losses. Also see HEAD LOSS.

FUNGI (FUN-ji)

FUNGI

Mushrooms, molds, mildews, rusts, and smuts that are small non-chlorophyll-bearing plants lacking roots, stems and leaves. They occur in natural waters and grow best in the absence of light. Their decomposition may cause objectionable tastes and odors in water.

FUSE

FUSE

A protective device having a strip or wire of fusible metal which, when placed in a circuit, will melt and break the electric circuit if heated too much. High temperatures will develop in the fuse when a current flows through the fuse in excess of that which the circuit will carry safely.

G

GAGE PRESSURE

GAGE PRESSURE

The pressure within a closed container or pipe as measured with a gage. In contrast, absolute pressure is the sum of atmospheric pressure (14.7 lbs/sq in) *PLUS* pressure within a vessel (as measured with a gage). Most pressure gages read in "gage pressure" or psig (**p**ounds per **s**quare **i**nch **g**age pressure).

GALVANIC CELL

GALVANIC CELL

An electrolytic cell capable of producing electric energy by electrochemical action. The decomposition of materials in the cell causes an electric (electron) current to flow from cathode to anode.

GALVANIC SERIES

GALVANIC SERIES

A list of metals and alloys presented in the order of their tendency to corrode (or go into solution). Also called the ELECTROMO-TIVE SERIES. This is a practical application of the theoretical ELECTROCHEMICAL SERIES.

GALVANIZE

GALVANIZE

To coat a metal (especially iron or steel) with zinc. Galvanization is the process of coating a metal with zinc.

GARNET

GARNET

A group of hard, reddish, glassy, mineral sands made up of silicates of base metals (calcium, magnesium, iron and manganese). Garnet has a higher density than sand.

GAUGE, PIPE

GAUGE, PIPE

A number that defines the thickness of the sheet used to make steel pipe. The larger the number, the thinner the pipe wall.

GEOLOGICAL LOG GEOLOGICAL LOG

A detailed description of all underground features discovered during the drilling of a well (depth, thickness and type of formations).

GEOPHYSICAL LOG GEOPHYSICAL LOG

A record of the structure and composition of the earth encountered when drilling a well or similar type of test hole or boring.

GERMICIDE (GERM-uh-SIDE) GERMICIDE

A substance formulated to kill germs or microorganisms. The germicidal properties of chlorine make it an effective disinfectant.

GIARDIASIS (gee-are-DYE-uh-sis) GIARDIASIS

Intestinal disease caused by an infestation of *Giardia* flagellates.

GRAB SAMPLE GRAB SAMPLE

A single sample of water collected at a particular time and place which represents the composition of the water only at that time and place.

GRADE GRADE

(1) The elevation of the invert (or bottom) of a pipeline, canal, culvert, or similar conduit.

(2) The inclination or slope of a pipeline, conduit, stream channel, or natural ground surface; usually expressed in terms of the ratio or percentage of number of units of vertical rise or fall per unit of horizontal distance. A 0.5 percent grade would be a drop of one-half foot per hundred feet of pipe.

GRAVIMETRIC GRAVIMETRIC

A means of measuring unknown concentrations of water quality indicators in a sample by *WEIGHING* a precipitate or residue of the sample.

GRAVIMETRIC FEEDER GRAVIMETRIC FEEDER

A dry chemical feeder which delivers a measured weight of chemical during a specific time period.

GREENSAND GREENSAND

A mineral (glauconite) material that looks like ordinary filter sand except that it is green in color. Greensand is a natural ion exchange material which is capable of softening water. Greensand which has been treated with potassium permanganate ($KMnO_4$) is called manganese greensand; this product is used to remove iron, manganese and hydrogen sulfide from groundwaters.

GROUND GROUND

An expression representing an electrical connection to earth or a large conductor which is at the earth's potential or neutral voltage.

H

HTH (pronounce as separate letters) HTH

High **T**est **H**ypochlorite. Calcium hypochlorite or $Ca(OCl)_2$.

HARD WATER HARD WATER

Water having a high concentration of calcium and magnesium ions. A water may be considered hard if it has a hardness greater than the typical hardness of water from the region. Some textbooks define hard water as water with a hardness of more than 100 mg/L as calcium carbonate.

HARDNESS, WATER HARDNESS, WATER

A characteristic of water caused mainly by the salts of calcium and magnesium, such as bicarbonate, carbonate, sulfate, chloride and nitrate. Excessive hardness in water is undesirable because it causes the formation of soap curds, increased use of soap, deposition of scale in boilers, damage in some industrial processes, and sometimes causes objectionable tastes in drinking water.

HEAD HEAD

The vertical distance (in feet) equal to the pressure (in psi) at a specific point. The pressure head is equal to the pressure in psi times 2.31 ft/psi.

HEAD LOSS

The head, pressure or energy (they are the same) lost by water flowing in a pipe or channel as a result of turbulence caused by the velocity of the flowing water and the roughness of the pipe, channel walls, or restrictions caused by fittings. Water flowing in a pipe loses head, pressure or energy as a result of friction losses. The head loss through a filter is due to friction losses caused by material building up on the surface or in the top part of a filter. Also see FRICTION LOSSES.

HEADER

A large pipe to which a series of smaller pipes are connected. Also called a MANIFOLD.

HEAT SENSOR

A device that opens and closes a switch in response to changes in the temperature. This device might be a metal contact, or a thermocouple which generates a minute electric current proportional to the difference in heat, or a variable resistor whose value changes in response to changes in temperature. Also called a TEMPERATURE SENSOR.

HECTARE (HECK-tar)

A measure of area in the metric system similar to an acre. One hectare is equal to 10,000 square meters and 2.4711 acres.

HEPATITIS (HEP-uh-TIE-tis)

Hepatitis is an inflammation of the liver usually caused by an acute viral infection. Yellow jaundice is one symptom of hepatitis.

HERBICIDE (HERB-uh-SIDE)

A compound, usually a manmade organic chemical, used to kill or control plant growth.

HERTZ

The number of complete electromagnetic cycles or waves in one second of an electric or electronic circuit. Also called the frequency of the current. Abbreviated Hz.

HETEROTROPHIC (HET-er-o-TROF-ick)

Describes organisms that use organic matter for energy and growth. Animals, fungi and most bacteria are heterotrophs

HIGH-LINE JUMPERS

Pipes or hoses connected to fire hydrants and laid on top of the ground to provide emergency water service for an isolated portion of a distribution system.

HOSE BIB

Faucet. A location in a water line where a hose is connected.

HYDRATED LIME

Limestone that has been "burned" and treated with water under controlled conditions until the calcium oxide portion has been converted to calcium hydroxide ($Ca(OH)_2$). Hydrated lime is quicklime combined with water. $CaO + H_2O \rightarrow Ca(OH)_2$. Also called slaked lime. Also see QUICKLIME.

HYDRAULIC GRADE LINE (HGL)

The surface or profile of water flowing in an open channel or a pipe flowing partially full. If a pipe is under pressure, the hydraulic grade line is at the level water would rise to in a small vertical tube connected to the pipe. Also see ENERGY GRADE LINE.

[SEE DRAWING ON PAGE 720]

HYDRAULIC GRADIENT

The slope of the hydraulic grade line. This is the slope of the water surface in an open channel, the slope of the water surface of the groundwater table, or the slope of the water pressure for pipes under pressure.

HYDROGEOLOGIST (HI-dro-gee-ALL-uh-gist)

A person who studies and works with groundwater.

HYDROLOGIC (HI-dro-LOJ-ick) CYCLE

The process of evaporation of water into the air and its return to earth by precipitation (rain or snow). This process also includes transpiration from plants, groundwater movement, and runoff into rivers, streams and the ocean. Also called the water cycle.

HYDROLYSIS (hi-DROLL-uh-sis)

(1) A chemical reaction in which a compound is converted into another compound by taking up water.

(2) Usually a chemical degradation of organic matter.

HYDROLYSIS

HYDROPHILIC (HI-dro-FILL-ick)

Having a strong affinity (liking) for water. The opposite of HYDROPHOBIC.

HYDROPHILIC

HYDROPHOBIC (HI-dro-FOE-bick)

Having a strong aversion (dislike) for water. The opposite of HYDROPHILIC.

HYDROPHOBIC

HYDROPNEUMATIC (HI-dro-new-MAT-ick)

A water system, usually small, in which a water pump is automatically controlled (started and stopped) by the air pressure in a compressed-air tank.

HYDROPNEUMATIC

HYDROSTATIC (HI-dro-STAT-ick) PRESSURE

(1) The pressure at a specific elevation exerted by a body of water at rest, or

(2) In the case of groundwater, the pressure at a specific elevation due to the weight of water at higher levels in the same zone of saturation.

HYDROSTATIC PRESSURE

HYGROSCOPIC (HI-grow-SKOP-ick)

Absorbing or attracting moisture from the air.

HYGROSCOPIC

HYPOCHLORINATION (HI-poe-KLOR-uh-NAY-shun)

The application of hypochlorite compounds to water for the purpose of disinfection.

HYPOCHLORINATION

HYPOCHLORINATORS (HI-poe-KLOR-uh-NAY-tors)

Chlorine pumps, chemical feed pumps or devices used to dispense chlorine solutions made from hypochlorites such as bleach (sodium hypochlorite) or calcium hypochlorite into the water being treated.

HYPOCHLORINATORS

HYPOCHLORITE (HI-poe-KLOR-ite)

Chemical compounds containing available chlorine; used for disinfection. They are available as liquids (bleach) or solids (powder, granules, and pellets) in barrels, drums, and cans. Salts of hypochlorous acid.

HYPOCHLORITE

HYPOLIMNION (HI-poe-LIM-knee-on)

The lowest layer in a thermally stratified lake or reservoir. This layer consists of colder, more dense water, has a constant temperature and no mixing occurs.

HYPOLIMNION

I

ICR

The **I**nformation **C**ollection **R**ule (ICR) specifies the requirements for monitoring microbial contaminants and disinfection by-products (DBPs) by large public water systems (PWSs). It also requires large PWSs to conduct either bench- or pilot-scale testing of advanced treatment techniques.

ICR

IDLH

Immediately **D**angerous to **L**ife or **H**ealth. The IDLH concentration of a gas represents a maximum level from which one could escape within 30 minutes without any escape-impairing symptoms or any irreversible health effects.

IDLH

IMHOFF CONE

A clear, cone-shaped container marked with graduations. The cone is used to measure the volume of settleable solids in a specific volume (usually one liter) of water.

IMHOFF CONE

IMPELLER

A rotating set of vanes in a pump or compressor designed to pump or move water or air.

IMPELLER

IMPERMEABLE (im-PURR-me-uh-BULL) IMPERMEABLE

Not easily penetrated. The property of a material or soil that does not allow, or allows only with great difficulty, the movement or passage of water.

INDICATOR (CHEMICAL) INDICATOR (CHEMICAL)

A substance that gives a visible change, usually of color, at a desired point in a chemical reaction, generally at a specified end point.

INDICATOR (INSTRUMENT) INDICATOR (INSTRUMENT)

A device which indicates the result of a measurement. Most indicators in the water utility field use either a fixed scale and movable indicator (pointer) such as a pressure gage or a movable scale and movable indicator like those used on a circular flow-recording chart. Also called a RECEIVER.

INFILTRATION (IN-fill-TRAY-shun) INFILTRATION

The seepage of groundwater into a sewer system, including service connections. Seepage frequently occurs through defective or cracked pipes, pipe joints, connections or manhole walls.

INFLUENT INFLUENT

Water or other liquid — raw (untreated) or partially treated — flowing *INTO* a reservoir, basin, treatment process, or treatment plant.

INFORMATION COLLECTION RULE (ICR) INFORMATION COLLECTION RULE (ICR)

The Information Collection Rule (ICR) specifies the requirements for monitoring microbial contaminants and disinfection by-products (DBPs) by large public water systems (PWSs). It also requires large PWSs to conduct either bench- or pilot-scale testing of advanced treatment techniques.

INITIAL SAMPLING INITIAL SAMPLING

The very first sampling conducted under the Safe Drinking Water Act (SDWA) for each of the applicable contaminant categories.

INJECTOR WATER INJECTOR WATER

Service water in which chlorine is added (injected) to form a chlorine solution.

IN-LINE FILTRATION IN-LINE FILTRATION

The addition of chemical coagulants directly to the filter inlet pipe. The chemicals are mixed by the flowing water. Flocculation and sedimentation facilities are eliminated. This pretreatment method is commonly used in pressure filter installations. Also see CONVENTIONAL FILTRATION and DIRECT FILTRATION.

INORGANIC INORGANIC

Material such as sand, salt, iron, calcium salts and other mineral materials. Inorganic substances are of mineral origin, whereas organic substances are usually of animal or plant origin. Also see ORGANIC.

INORGANIC WASTE INORGANIC WASTE

Waste material such as sand, salt, iron, calcium, and other mineral materials which are only slightly affected by the action of organisms. Inorganic wastes are chemical substances of mineral origin; whereas organic wastes are chemical substances of an animal or plant origin.

INPUT HORSEPOWER INPUT HORSEPOWER

The total power used in operating a pump and motor.

$$\text{Input Horsepower, HP} = \frac{(\text{Brake Horsepower, HP})(100\%)}{\text{Motor Efficiency, \%}}$$

INSECTICIDE INSECTICIDE

Any substance or chemical formulated to kill or control insects.

INSOLUBLE (in-SAWL-you-bull) INSOLUBLE

Something that cannot be dissolved.

INTEGRATOR INTEGRATOR

A device or meter that continuously measures and calculates (adds) a process rate variable in cumulative fashion; for example, total flows displayed in gallons, million gallons, cubic feet, or some other unit of volume measurement. Also called a TOTALIZER.

INTERFACE

The common boundary layer between two substances such as water and a solid (metal); or between two fluids such as water and a gas (air); or between a liquid (water) and another liquid (oil).

INTERLOCK

An electric switch, usually magnetically operated. Used to interrupt all (local) power to a panel or device when the door is opened or the circuit is exposed to service.

INTERNAL FRICTION

Friction within a fluid (water) due to cohesive forces.

INTERSTICE (in-TUR-stuhz)

A very small open space in a rock or granular material. Also called a PORE, VOID, or void space. Also see VOID.

INVERT (IN-vert)

The lowest point of the channel inside a pipe, conduit, or canal.

ION

An electrically charged atom, radical (such as SO_4^{2-}), or molecule formed by the loss or gain of one or more electrons.

ION EXCHANGE

A water treatment process involving the reversible interchange (switching) of ions between the water being treated and the solid resin. Undesirable ions in the water are switched with acceptable ions on the resin.

ION EXCHANGE RESINS

Insoluble polymers, used in water treatment, that are capable of exchanging (switching or giving) acceptable cations or anions to the water being treated for less desirable ions.

IONIC CONCENTRATION

The concentration of any ion in solution, usually expressed in moles per liter.

IONIZATION (EYE-on-uh-ZAY-shun)

The splitting or dissociation (separation) of molecules into negatively and positively charged ions.

J

JAR TEST

A laboratory procedure that simulates a water treatment plant's coagulation/flocculation units with differing chemical doses and also energy of rapid mix, energy of slow mix, and settling time. The purpose of this procedure is to *ESTIMATE* the minimum or ideal coagulant dose required to achieve certain water quality goals. Samples of water to be treated are commonly placed in six jars. Various amounts of chemicals are added to each jar, stirred and the settling of solids is observed. The dose of chemicals that provides satisfactory settling, removal of turbidity and/or color is the dose used to treat the water being taken into the plant at that time. When evaluating the results of a jar test, the operator should also consider the floc quality in the flocculation area and the floc loading on the filter.

JOGGING

The frequent starting and stopping of an electric motor.

JOULE (jewel)

A measure of energy, work or quantity of heat. One joule is the work done when the point of application of a force of one newton is displaced a distance of one meter in the direction of the force. Approximately equal to 0.7375 ft-lbs.

K

KELLY

The square section of a rod which causes the rotation of the drill bit. Torque from a drive table is applied to the square rod to cause the rotary motion. The drive table is chain or gear driven by an engine.

KILO KILO

(1) Kilogram.

(2) Kilometer.

(3) A prefix meaning "thousand" used in the metric system and other scientific systems of measurement.

KINETIC ENERGY KINETIC ENERGY

Energy possessed by a moving body of matter, such as water, as a result of its motion.

KJELDAHL (KELL-doll) NITROGEN KJELDAHL NITROGEN

Nitrogen in the form of organic proteins or their decomposition product ammonia, as measured by the Kjeldahl Method.

L

LANGELIER INDEX (L.I.) LANGELIER INDEX (L.I.)

An index reflecting the equilibrium pH of a water with respect to calcium and alkalinity. This index is used in stabilizing water to control both corrosion and the deposition of scale.

$$\text{Langelier Index} = pH - pH_s$$

where pH = actual pH of the water, and

pH_s = pH at which water having the same alkalinity and calcium content is just saturated with calcium carbonate.

LAUNDERING WEIR (LAWN-der-ing weer) LAUNDERING WEIR

Sedimentation basin overflow weir. A plate with V-notches along the top to ensure a uniform flow rate and avoid short-circuiting.

LAUNDERS (LAWN-ders) LAUNDERS

Sedimentation basin and filter discharge channels consisting of overflow weir plates (in sedimentation basins) and conveying troughs.

LEAD (LEE-d) LEAD

A wire or conductor that can carry electric current.

LEATHERS LEATHERS

O-rings or gaskets used with piston pumps to provide a seal between the piston and the side wall.

LEVEL CONTROL LEVEL CONTROL

A float device (or pressure switch) which senses changes in a measured variable and opens or closes a switch in response to that change. In its simplest form, this control might be a floating ball connected mechanically to a switch or valve such as is used to stop water flow into a toilet when the tank is full.

LINDANE (LYNN-dane) LINDANE

A pesticide that causes adverse health effects in domestic water supplies and also is toxic to freshwater and marine aquatic life.

LINEARITY (LYNN-ee-AIR-it-ee) LINEARITY

How closely an instrument measures actual values of a variable through its effective range; a measure used to determine the accuracy of an instrument.

LITTORAL (LIT-or-al) ZONE LITTORAL ZONE

(1) That portion of a body of fresh water extending from the shoreline lakeward to the limit of occupancy of rooted plants.

(2) The strip of land along the shoreline between the high and low water levels.

LOGARITHM (LOG-a-rith-m) LOGARITHM

The exponent that indicates the power to which a number must be raised to produce a given number. For example: if $B^2 = N$, the 2 is the logarithm of N (to the base B), or $10^2 = 100$ and $\log_{10} 100 = 2$. Also abbreviated to "log."

LOGGING, ELECTRICAL LOGGING, ELECTRICAL

A procedure used to determine the porosity (spaces or voids) of formations in search of water-bearing formations (aquifers). Electrical probes are lowered into wells, an electric current is induced at various depths, and the resistance measured of various formations indicates the porosity of the material.

LOWER EXPLOSIVE LIMIT (LEL)

LOWER EXPLOSIVE LIMIT (LEL)

The lowest concentration of gas or vapor (percent by volume in air) that explodes if an ignition source is present at ambient temperature. At temperatures above 250°F the LEL decreases because explosibility increases with higher temperature.

M

M or MOLAR

M or MOLAR

A molar solution consists of one gram molecular weight of a compound dissolved in enough water to make one liter of solution. A gram molecular weight is the molecular weight of a compound in grams. For example, the molecular weight of sulfuric acid (H_2SO_4) is 98. A one *M* solution of sulfuric acid would consist of 98 grams of H_2SO_4 dissolved in enough distilled water to make one liter of solution.

MBAS

MBAS

Methylene - **B**lue - **A**ctive **S**ubstances. These substances are used in surfactants or detergents.

MCL

MCL

Maximum **C**ontaminant **L**evel. The largest allowable amount. MCLs for various water quality indicators are specified in the National Primary Drinking Water Regulations (NPDWR).

MCLG

MCLG

Maximum **C**ontaminant **L**evel **G**oal. MCLGs are health goals based entirely on health effects. They are a preliminary standard set but not enforced by EPA. MCLs consider health effects, but also take into consideration the feasibility and cost of analysis and treatment of the regulated MCL. Although often less stringent than the corresponding MCLG, the MCL is set to protect health.

mg/*L*

mg/*L*

See MILLIGRAMS PER LITER, mg/*L*.

MPN (pronounce as separate letters)

MPN

MPN is the **M**ost **P**robable **N**umber of coliform-group organisms per unit volume of sample water. Expressed as a density or population of organisms per 100 m*L* of sample water.

MSDS

MSDS

See **M**ATERIAL **S**AFETY **D**ATA **S**HEET.

MACROSCOPIC (MACK-row-SKAWP-ick) ORGANISMS

MACROSCOPIC ORGANISMS

Organisms big enough to be seen by the eye without the aid of a microscope.

MANDREL (MAN-drill)

MANDREL

A special tool used to push bearings in or to pull sleeves out.

MANIFOLD

MANIFOLD

A large pipe to which a series of smaller pipes are connected. Also called a HEADER.

MANOMETER (man-NAH-mut-ter)

MANOMETER

An instrument for measuring pressure. Usually, a manometer is a glass tube filled with a liquid that is used to measure the difference in pressure across a flow measuring device such as an orifice or a Venturi meter. The instrument used to measure blood pressure is a type of manometer.

VENTURI METER

MANOMETER

MATERIAL SAFETY DATA SHEET (MSDS)

MATERIAL SAFETY DATA SHEET (MSDS)

A document which provides pertinent information and a profile of a particular hazardous substance or mixture. An MSDS is normally developed by the manufacturer or formulator of the hazardous substance or mixture. The MSDS is required to be made available to employees and operators whenever there is the likelihood of the hazardous substance or mixture being introduced into the workplace. Some manufacturers are preparing MSDSs for products that are not considered to be hazardous to show that the product or substance is *NOT* hazardous.

MAXIMUM CONTAMINANT LEVEL (MCL)

MAXIMUM CONTAMINANT LEVEL (MCL)

See MCL.

MEASURED VARIABLE

MEASURED VARIABLE

A characteristic or component part that is sensed and quantified (reduced to a reading of some kind) by a primary element or sensor.

MECHANICAL JOINT

MECHANICAL JOINT

A flexible device that joins pipes or fittings together by the use of lugs and bolts.

MEG

MEG

A procedure used for checking the insulation resistance on motors, feeders, bus bar systems, grounds, and branch circuit wiring. Also see MEGGER.

MEGGER (from megohm)

MEGGER

An instrument used for checking the insulation resistance on motors, feeders, bus bar systems, grounds, and branch circuit wiring. Also see MEG.

MEGOHM

MEGOHM

Meg means one million, so 5 megohms means 5 million ohms. A megger reads in millions of ohms.

MENISCUS (meh-NIS-cuss)

MENISCUS

The curved surface of a column of liquid (water, oil, mercury) in a small tube. When the liquid wets the sides of the container (as with water), the curve forms a valley. When the confining sides are not wetted (as with mercury), the curve forms a hill or upward bulge.

MESH

MESH

One of the openings or spaces in a screen or woven fabric. The value of the mesh is usually given as the number of openings per inch. This value does not consider the diameter of the wire or fabric; therefore, the mesh number does not always have a definite relationship to the size of the hole.

MESOTROPHIC (MESS-o-TRO-fick)

MESOTROPHIC

Reservoirs and lakes which contain moderate quantities of nutrients and are moderately productive in terms of aquatic animal and plant life.

METABOLISM (meh-TAB-uh-LIZ-um)

METABOLISM

(1) The biochemical processes in which food is used and wastes are formed by living organisms.

(2) All biochemical reactions involved in cell formation and growth.

METALIMNION (MET-uh-LIM-knee-on)

METALIMNION

The middle layer in a thermally stratified lake or reservoir. In this layer there is a rapid decrease in temperature with depth. Also called the THERMOCLINE.

METHOXYCHLOR (meth-OXY-klor)

METHOXYCHLOR

A pesticide which causes adverse health effects in domestic water supplies and is also toxic to freshwater and marine aquatic life. The chemical name for methoxychlor is 2,2-bis(p-methoxyphenol)-1,1,1-trichloroethane.

METHYL ORANGE ALKALINITY METHYL ORANGE ALKALINITY

A measure of the total alkalinity in a water sample. The alkalinity is measured by the amount of standard sulfuric acid required to lower the pH of the water to a pH level of 4.5, as indicated by the change in color of methyl orange from orange to pink. Methyl orange alkalinity is expressed as milligrams per liter equivalent calcium carbonate.

MICROBIAL (my-KROW-bee-ul) GROWTH MICROBIAL GROWTH

The activity and growth of microorganisms such as bacteria, algae, diatoms, plankton and fungi.

MICRON (MY-kron) MICRON

A unit of length. One millionth of a meter or one thousandth of a millimeter. One micron equals 0.00004 of an inch.

MICROORGANISMS (MY-crow-OR-gan-IS-zums) MICROORGANISMS

Living organisms that can be seen individually only with the aid of a microscope.

MIL MIL

A unit of length equal to 0.001 of an inch. The diameter of wires and tubing is measured in mils, as is the thickness of plastic sheeting.

MILLIGRAMS PER LITER, mg/*L* MILLIGRAMS PER LITER, mg/*L*

A measure of the concentration by weight of a substance per unit volume. For practical purposes, one mg/*L* of a substance in fresh water is equal to one part per million parts (ppm). Thus a liter of water with a specific gravity of 1.0 weighs one million milligrams. If it contains 10 milligrams of calcium, the concentration is 10 milligrams per million milligrams, or 10 milligrams per liter (10 mg/*L*), or 10 parts of calcium per million parts of water, or 10 parts per million (10 ppm).

MILLIMICRON (MILL-uh-MY-kron) MILLIMICRON

A unit of length equal to $10^{-3}\mu$ (one thousandth of a micron), 10^{-6} millimeters, or 10^{-9} meters; correctly called a nanometer, nm.

MOLAR MOLAR

See *M* for MOLAR.

MOLE MOLE

The molecular weight of a substance, usually expressed in grams.

MOLECULAR WEIGHT MOLECULAR WEIGHT

The molecular weight of a compound in grams is the sum of the atomic weights of the elements in the compound. The molecular weight of sulfuric acid (H_2SO_4) in grams is 98.

Element	Atomic Weight	Number of Atoms	Molecular Weight
H	1	2	2
S	32	1	32
O	16	4	64
			98

MOLECULE (MOLL-uh-KULE) MOLECULE

The smallest division of a compound that still retains or exhibits all the properties of the substance.

MONOMER (MON-o-MER) MONOMER

A molecule of low molecular weight capable of reacting with identical or different monomers to form polymers.

MONOMICTIC (mo-no-MICK-tick) MONOMICTIC

Lakes and reservoirs which are relatively deep, do not freeze over during the winter months, and undergo a single stratification and mixing cycle during the year. These lakes and reservoirs usually become destratified during the mixing cycle, usually in the fall of the year.

MONOVALENT MONOVALENT

Having a valence of one, such as the cuprous (copper) ion, Cu^+.

MOST PROBABLE NUMBER (MPN) MOST PROBABLE NUMBER (MPN)

See MPN.

MOTILE (MO-till) MOTILE

Capable of self-propelled movement. A term that is sometimes used to distinguish between certain types of organisms found in water.

MOTOR EFFICIENCY MOTOR EFFICIENCY

The ratio of energy delivered by a motor to the energy supplied to it during a fixed period or cycle. Motor efficiency ratings will vary depending upon motor manufacturer and usually will be near 90.0 percent.

MUDBALLS MUDBALLS

Material that is approximately round in shape and varies from pea-sized up to two or more inches in diameter. This material forms in filters and gradually increases in size when not removed by the backwashing process.

MULTI-STAGE PUMP MULTI-STAGE PUMP

A pump that has more than one impeller. A single-stage pump has one impeller.

N

N or NORMAL *N* or NORMAL

A normal solution contains one gram equivalent weight of reactant (compound) per liter of solution. The equivalent weight of an acid is that weight which contains one gram atom of ionizable hydrogen or its chemical equivalent. For example, the equivalent weight of sulfuric acid (H_2SO_4) is 49 (98 divided by 2 because there are two replaceable hydrogen ions). A one *N* solution of sulfuric acid would consist of 49 grams of H_2SO_4 dissolved in enough water to make one liter of solution.

NETA NETA

See **N**ATIONAL **E**NVIRONMENTAL **T**RAINING **A**SSOCIATION.

NIOSH (NYE-osh) NIOSH

The **N**ational **I**nstitute of **O**ccupational **S**afety and **H**ealth is an organization that tests and approves safety equipment for particular applications. NIOSH is the primary federal agency engaged in research in the national effort to eliminate on-the-job hazards to the health and safety of working people. The NIOSH Publications Catalog contains a listing of NIOSH publications concerning industrial hygiene and occupational health. To obtain a copy of the catalog, write to National Technical Information Service (NTIS), 5285 Port Royal Road, Springfield, VA 22161. NTIS Stock No. PB-86-116-787, price $84.00.

NOM (NATURAL ORGANIC MATTER) NOM (NATURAL ORGANIC MATTER)

Humic substances composed of humic and fulvic acids that come from decayed vegetation.

NPDES PERMIT NPDES PERMIT

National **P**ollutant **D**ischarge **E**limination **S**ystem permit is the regulatory agency document issued by either a federal or state agency which is designed to control all discharges of pollutants from point sources and storm water runoff into U.S. waterways. NPDES permits regulate discharges into navigable waters from all point sources of pollution, including industries, municipal wastewater treatment plants, sanitary landfills, large agricultural feedlots and return irrigation flows.

NPDWR NPDWR

National **P**rimary **D**rinking **W**ater **R**egulations.

NSDWR NSDWR

National **S**econdary **D**rinking **W**ater **R**egulations.

NTU NTU

Nephelometric **T**urbidity **U**nits. See TURBIDITY UNITS (TU).

NAMEPLATE NAMEPLATE

A durable metal plate found on equipment which lists critical installation and operating conditions for the equipment.

NATIONAL ENVIRONMENTAL TRAINING ASSOCIATION (NETA) NATIONAL ENVIRONMENTAL TRAINING ASSOCIATION (NETA)

A professional organization devoted to serving the environmental trainer and promoting better operation of waterworks and pollution control facilities. For information on NETA membership and publications, contact NETA, 2930 E. Camelback Road, Phoenix, AZ 85016. Phone (602) 956-6099.

NATIONAL INSTITUTE OF
OCCUPATIONAL SAFETY AND HEALTH

NATIONAL INSTITUTE OF
OCCUPATIONAL SAFETY AND HEALTH

See NIOSH.

NATIONAL PRIMARY DRINKING WATER
REGULATIONS

NATIONAL PRIMARY DRINKING WATER
REGULATIONS

Commonly referred to as NPDWR.

NATIONAL SECONDARY DRINKING WATER
REGULATIONS

NATIONAL SECONDARY DRINKING WATER
REGULATIONS

Commonly referred to as NSDWR.

NEPHELOMETRIC (NEFF-el-o-MET-rick)

NEPHELOMETRIC

A means of measuring turbidity in a sample by using an instrument called a nephelometer. A nephelometer passes light through a sample and the amount of light deflected (usually at a 90-degree angle) is then measured.

NEWTON

NEWTON

A force which, when applied to a body having a mass of one kilogram, gives it an acceleration of one meter per second per second.

NITRIFICATION (NYE-truh-fuh-KAY-shun)

NITRIFICATION

An aerobic process in which bacteria change the ammonia and organic nitrogen in water into oxidized nitrogen (usually nitrate).

NITROGENOUS (nye-TRAH-jen-us)

NITROGENOUS

A term used to describe chemical compounds (usually organic) containing nitrogen in combined forms. Proteins and nitrates are nitrogenous compounds.

NOBLE METAL

NOBLE METAL

A chemically inactive metal (such as gold). A metal that does not corrode easily and is much scarcer (and more valuable) than the so-called useful or base metals. Also see BASE METAL.

NOMINAL DIAMETER

NOMINAL DIAMETER

An approximate measurement of the diameter of a pipe. Although the nominal diameter is used to describe the size or diameter of a pipe, it is usually not the exact inside diameter of the pipe.

NONIONIC (NON-eye-ON-ick) POLYMER

NONIONIC POLYMER

A polymer that has no net electrical charge.

NONPOINT SOURCE

NONPOINT SOURCE

A runoff or discharge from a field or similar source. A point source refers to a discharge that comes out the end of a pipe.

NONPOTABLE (non-POE-tuh-bull)

NONPOTABLE

Water that may contain objectionable pollution, contamination, minerals, or infective agents and is considered unsafe and/or unpalatable for drinking.

NONVOLATILE MATTER

NONVOLATILE MATTER

Material such as sand, salt, iron, calcium, and other mineral materials which are only slightly affected by the actions of organisms and are not lost on ignition of the dry solids at 550°C. Volatile materials are chemical substances usually of animal or plant origin. Also see INORGANIC WASTE and VOLATILE MATTER or VOLATILE SOLIDS.

NORMAL

NORMAL

See *N* for NORMAL.

NOTICE

NOTICE

This word calls attention to information that is especially significant in understanding and operating equipment or processes safely. Also see CAUTION, DANGER, and WARNING.

NUTRIENT

NUTRIENT

Any substance that is assimilated (taken in) by organisms and promotes growth. Nitrogen and phosphorus are nutrients which promote the growth of algae. There are other essential and trace elements which are also considered nutrients.

O

ORP (pronounce as separate letters)   ORP

Oxidation-**R**eduction **P**otential. The electrical potential required to transfer electrons from one compound or element (the oxidant) to another compound or element (the reductant); used as a qualitative measure of the state of oxidation in water treatment systems. ORP is measured in millivolts, with negative values indicating a tendency to reduce compounds or elements and positive values indicating a tendency to oxidize compounds or elements.

OSHA (O-shuh)   OSHA

The Williams-Steiger **O**ccupational **S**afety and **H**ealth **A**ct of 1970 (OSHA) is a federal law designed to protect the health and safety of industrial workers and also the operators of water supply systems and treatment plants. The Act regulates the design, construction, operation and maintenance of water supply systems and water treatment plants. OSHA also refers to the federal and state agencies which administer the OSHA regulations.

OCCUPATIONAL SAFETY AND HEALTH ACT OF 1970   OCCUPATIONAL SAFETY AND HEALTH ACT OF 1970

See OSHA.

ODOR THRESHOLD   ODOR THRESHOLD

The minimum odor of a water sample that can just be detected after successive dilutions with odorless water. Also called THRESHOLD ODOR.

OFFSET   OFFSET

The difference between the actual value and the desired value (or set point); characteristic of proportional controllers that do not incorporate reset action. Also called DRIFT.

OHM   OHM

The unit of electrical resistance. The resistance of a conductor in which one volt produces a current of one ampere.

OLFACTORY (ol-FAK-tore-ee) FATIGUE   OLFACTORY FATIGUE

A condition in which a person's nose, after exposure to certain odors, is no longer able to detect the odor.

OLIGOTROPHIC (AH-lig-o-TRO-fick)   OLIGOTROPHIC

Reservoirs and lakes which are nutrient poor and contain little aquatic plant or animal life.

OPERATING PRESSURE DIFFERENTIAL   OPERATING PRESSURE DIFFERENTIAL

The operating pressure range for a hydropneumatic system. For example, when the pressure drops below 40 psi the pump will come on and stay on until the pressure builds up to 60 psi. When the pressure reaches 60 psi the pump will shut off.

OPERATING RATIO   OPERATING RATIO

The operating ratio is a measure of the total revenues divided by the total operating expenses.

ORGANIC   ORGANIC

Substances that come from animal or plant sources. Organic substances always contain carbon. (Inorganic materials are chemical substances of mineral origin.) Also see INORGANIC.

ORGANICS   ORGANICS

(1) A term used to refer to chemical compounds made from carbon molecules. These compounds may be natural materials (such as animal or plant sources) or manmade materials (such as synthetic organics). Also see ORGANIC.

(2) Any form of animal or plant life. Also see BACTERIA.

ORGANISM   ORGANISM

Any form of animal or plant life. Also see BACTERIA.

ORGANIZING   ORGANIZING

Deciding who does what work and delegating authority to the appropriate persons. A utility should have a written organizational plan and written policies.

ORIFICE (OR-uh-fiss)

An opening (hole) in a plate, wall, or partition. An orifice flange or plate placed in a pipe consists of a slot or a calibrated circular hole smaller than the pipe diameter. The difference in pressure in the pipe above and at the orifice may be used to determine the flow in the pipe.

ORTHOTOLIDINE (or-tho-TOL-uh-dine)

Orthotolidine is a colorimetric indicator of chlorine residual. If chlorine is present, a yellow-colored compound is produced. This reagent is no longer approved for chemical analysis to determine chlorine residual.

OSMOSIS (oz-MOE-sis)

The passage of a liquid from a weak solution to a more concentrated solution across a semipermeable membrane. The membrane allows the passage of the water (solvent) but not the dissolved solids (solutes). This process tends to equalize the conditions on either side of the membrane.

OUCH PRINCIPLE

This principle says that as a manager when you delegate job tasks you must be **O**bjective, **U**niform in your treatment of employees, **C**onsistent with utility policies, and **H**ave job relatedness.

OVERALL EFFICIENCY, PUMP

The combined efficiency of a pump and motor together. Also called the WIRE-TO-WATER EFFICIENCY.

OVERDRAFT

The pumping of water from a groundwater basin or aquifer in excess of the supply flowing into the basin. This pumping results in a depletion or "mining" of the groundwater in the basin.

OVERFLOW RATE

One of the guidelines for the design of settling tanks and clarifiers in treatment plants. Used by operators to determine if tanks and clarifiers are hydraulically (flow) over- or underloaded. Also called SURFACE LOADING.

$$\text{Overflow Rate, GPD/sq ft} = \frac{\text{Flow, gallons/day}}{\text{Surface Area, sq ft}}$$

OVERHEAD

Indirect costs necessary for a water utility to function properly. These costs are not related to the actual production and delivery of water to consumers, but include the costs of rent, lights, office supplies, management and administration.

OVERTURN

The almost spontaneous mixing of all layers of water in a reservoir or lake when the water temperature becomes similar from top to bottom. This may occur in the fall/winter when the surface waters cool to the same temperature as the bottom waters and also in the spring when the surface waters warm after the ice melts.

OXIDATION (ox-uh-DAY-shun)

Oxidation is the addition of oxygen, removal of hydrogen, or the removal of electrons from an element or compound. In the environment, organic matter is oxidized to more stable substances. The opposite of REDUCTION.

OXIDATION-REDUCTION POTENTIAL (ORP)

The electrical potential required to transfer electrons from one compound or element (the oxidant) to another compound or element (the reductant); used as a qualitative measure of the state of oxidation in water treatment systems. ORP is measured in millivolts, with negative values indicating a tendency to reduce compounds or elements and positive values indicating a tendency to oxidize compounds or elements.

OXIDIZING AGENT

Any substance, such as oxygen (O_2) or chlorine (Cl_2), that will readily add (take on) electrons. The opposite is a REDUCING AGENT.

OXYGEN DEFICIENCY

An atmosphere containing oxygen at a concentration of less than 19.5 percent by volume.

OZONATION (O-zoe-NAY-shun)

The application of ozone to water for disinfection or for taste and odor control.

P

PCBs
PCBs

See **PO**LY**CH**LORINATED **BI**PHENYLS.

pCi/*L*
pCi/*L*

picoCurie per liter. A picoCurie is a measure of radioactivity. One picoCurie of radioactivity is equivalent to 0.037 nuclear disintegrations per second.

pcu (PLATINUM COBALT UNITS)
pcu (PLATINUM COBALT UNITS)

Platinum cobalt units are a measure of color using platinum cobalt standards by visual comparison.

PMCL
PMCL

Primary **M**aximum **C**ontaminant **L**evel. Primary MCLs for various water quality indicators are established to protect public health.

PPM
PPM

See **PARTS PER MILLION**.

PSIG
PSIG

Pounds per **S**quare **I**nch **G**age pressure. The pressure within a closed container or pipe measured with a gage in pounds per square inch. See GAGE PRESSURE.

PACKER ASSEMBLY
PACKER ASSEMBLY

An inflatable device used to seal the tremie pipe inside the well casing to prevent the grout from entering the inside of the conductor casing.

PALATABLE (PAL-uh-tuh-bull)
PALATABLE

Water at a desirable temperature that is free from objectionable tastes, odors, colors, and turbidity. Pleasing to the senses.

PARSHALL FLUME
PARSHALL FLUME

A device used to measure the flow in an open channel. The flume narrows to a throat of fixed dimensions and then expands again. The rate of flow can be calculated by measuring the difference in head (pressure) before and at the throat of the flume.

PARTICLE COUNT
PARTICLE COUNT

The results of a microscopic examination of treated water with a special particle counter which classifies suspended particles by number and size.

PARTICULATE (par-TICK-you-let)
PARTICULATE

A very small solid suspended in water which can vary widely in size, shape, density, and electrical charge. Colloidal and dispersed particulates are artificially gathered together by the processes of coagulation and flocculation.

PARTS PER MILLION (PPM)
PARTS PER MILLION (PPM)

Parts per million parts, a measurement of concentration on a weight or volume basis. This term is equivalent to milligrams per liter (mg/*L*) which is the preferred term.

PASCAL
PASCAL

The pressure or stress of one newton per square meter. Abbreviated Pa.

$$1 \text{ psi} = 6{,}895 \text{ Pa} = 6.895 \text{ kN/sq m} = 0.0703 \text{ kg/sq cm}$$

PATHOGENIC (PATH-o-JEN-ick) ORGANISMS

PATHOGENIC ORGANISMS

Organisms, including bacteria, viruses or cysts, capable of causing diseases (typhoid, cholera, dysentery) in a host (such as a person). There are many types of organisms which do *NOT* cause disease. These organisms are called non-pathogenic.

PATHOGENS (PATH-o-jens)

PATHOGENS

Pathogenic or disease-causing organisms.

PEAK DEMAND

PEAK DEMAND

The maximum momentary load placed on a water treatment plant, pumping station or distribution system. This demand is usually the maximum average load in one hour or less, but may be specified as the instantaneous load or the load during some other short time period.

PERCENT SATURATION

PERCENT SATURATION

The amount of a substance that is dissolved in a solution compared with the amount dissolved in the solution at saturation, expressed as a percent.

$$\text{Percent Saturation, \%} = \frac{\text{Amount of Substance That Is Dissolved} \times 100\%}{\text{Amount Dissolved in Solution at Saturation}}$$

PERCOLATING (PURR-co-LAY-ting) WATER

PERCOLATING WATER

Water that passes through soil or rocks under the force of gravity.

PERCOLATION (PURR-co-LAY-shun)

PERCOLATION

The slow passage of water through a filter medium; or, the gradual penetration of soil and rocks by water.

PERIPHYTON (pair-e-FI-tawn)

PERIPHYTON

Microscopic plants and animals that are firmly attached to solid surfaces under water such as rocks, logs, pilings and other structures.

PERMEABILITY (PURR-me-uh-BILL-uh-tee)

PERMEABILITY

The property of a material or soil that permits considerable movement of water through it when it is saturated.

PERMEATE (PURR-me-ate)

PERMEATE

(1) To penetrate and pass through, as water penetrates and passes through soil and other porous materials.

(2) The liquid (demineralized water) produced from the reverse osmosis process that contains a *LOW* concentration of dissolved solids.

PERMIT-REQUIRED CONFINED SPACE
 (PERMIT SPACE)

PERMIT-REQUIRED CONFINED SPACE
(PERMIT SPACE)

See CONFINED SPACE, PERMIT-REQUIRED (PERMIT SPACE).

PESTICIDE

PESTICIDE

Any substance or chemical designed or formulated to kill or control weeds or animal pests. Also see ALGICIDE, HERBICIDE, INSECTICIDE, and RODENTICIDE.

PET COCK

PET COCK

A small valve or faucet used to drain a cylinder or fitting.

pH (pronounce as separate letters)

pH

pH is an expression of the intensity of the basic or acidic condition of a liquid. Mathematically, pH is the logarithm (base 10) of the reciprocal of the hydrogen ion activity.

$$pH = \text{Log} \ \frac{1}{[H^+]}$$

The pH may range from 0 to 14, where 0 is most acidic, 14 most basic, and 7 neutral. Natural waters usually have a pH between 6.5 and 8.5.

PHENOLIC (fee-NO-lick) COMPOUNDS

PHENOLIC COMPOUNDS

Organic compounds that are derivatives of benzene.

PHENOLPHTHALEIN (FEE-nol-THAY-leen) ALKALINITY

The alkalinity in a water sample measured by the amount of standard acid required to lower the pH to a level of 8.3, as indicated by the change in color of phenolphthalein from pink to clear. Phenolphthalein alkalinity is expressed as milligrams per liter of equivalent calcium carbonate.

PHOTOSYNTHESIS (foe-toe-SIN-thuh-sis)

A process in which organisms, with the aid of chlorophyll (green plant enzyme), convert carbon dioxide and inorganic substances into oxygen and additional plant material, using sunlight for energy. All green plants grow by this process.

PHYTOPLANKTON (FI-tow-PLANK-ton)

Small, usually microscopic plants (such as algae), found in lakes, reservoirs, and other bodies of water.

PICO

A prefix used in the metric system and other scientific systems of measurement which means 10^{-12} or 0.000 000 000 001.

PICOCURIE

A measure of radioactivity. One picoCurie of radioactivity is equivalent to 0.037 nuclear disintegrations per second.

PITLESS ADAPTER

A fitting which allows the well casing to be extended above ground while having a discharge connection located below the frost line. Advantages of using a pitless adapter include the elimination of the need for a pit or pump house and it is a watertight design, which helps maintain a sanitary water supply.

PLAN VIEW

A diagram or photo showing a facility as it would appear when looking down on top of it.

PLANKTON

(1) Small, usually microscopic, plants (phytoplankton) and animals (zooplankton) in aquatic systems.
(2) All of the smaller floating, suspended or self-propelled organisms in a body of water.

PLANNING

Management of utilities to build the resources and financial capability to provide for future needs.

PLUG FLOW

A type of flow that occurs in tanks, basins or reactors when a slug of water moves through a tank without ever dispersing or mixing with the rest of the water flowing through the tank.

POINT SOURCE

A discharge that comes out the end of a pipe. A nonpoint source refers to runoff or a discharge from a field or similar source.

POLARIZATION

The concentration of ions in the thin boundary layer adjacent to a membrane or pipe wall.

POLE SHADER

A copper bar circling the laminated iron core inside the coil of a magnetic starter.

POLLUTION

The impairment (reduction) of water quality by agricultural, domestic, or industrial wastes (including thermal and radioactive wastes) to a degree that has an adverse effect on any beneficial use of water.

POLYANIONIC (poly-AN-eye-ON-ick)

Characterized by many active negative charges especially active on the surface of particles.

POLYCHLORINATED BIPHENYLS

A class of organic compounds that cause adverse health effects in domestic water supplies.

POLYELECTROLYTE (POLY-ee-LECK-tro-lite)

POLYELECTROLYTE

A high-molecular-weight (relatively heavy) substance having points of positive or negative electrical charges that is formed by either natural or manmade processes. Natural polyelectrolytes may be of biological origin or derived from starch products and cellulose derivatives. Manmade polyelectrolytes consist of simple substances that have been made into complex, high-molecular-weight substances. Used with other chemical coagulants to aid in binding small suspended particles to larger chemical flocs for their removal from water. Often called a POLYMER.

POLYMER (POLY-mer)

POLYMER

A long chain molecule formed by the union of many monomers (molecules of lower molecular weight). Polymers are used with other chemical coagulants to aid in binding small suspended particles to larger chemical flocs for their removal from water.

PORE

PORE

A very small open space in a rock or granular material. Also called an INTERSTICE, VOID, or void space. Also see VOID.

POROSITY

POROSITY

(1) A measure of the spaces or voids in a material or aquifer.

(2) The ratio of the volume of spaces in a rock or soil to the total volume. This ratio is usually expressed as a percentage.

$$\text{Porosity, \%} = \frac{(\text{Volume of Spaces})(100\%)}{\text{Total Volume}}$$

POSITIVE BACTERIOLOGICAL SAMPLE

POSITIVE BACTERIOLOGICAL SAMPLE

A water sample in which gas is produced by coliform organisms during incubation in the multiple tube fermentation test. See Chapter 11, Laboratory Procedures, "Coliform Bacteria," in *WATER TREATMENT PLANT OPERATION,* Volume I, for details.

POSITIVE DISPLACEMENT PUMP

POSITIVE DISPLACEMENT PUMP

A type of piston, diaphragm, gear or screw pump that delivers a constant volume with each stroke. Positive displacement pumps are used as chemical solution feeders.

POSTCHLORINATION

POSTCHLORINATION

The addition of chlorine to the plant effluent, *FOLLOWING* plant treatment, for disinfection purposes.

POTABLE (POE-tuh-bull) WATER

POTABLE WATER

Water that does not contain objectionable pollution, contamination, minerals, or infective agents and is considered satisfactory for drinking.

POWER FACTOR

POWER FACTOR

The ratio of the true power passing through an electric circuit to the product of the voltage and amperage in the circuit. This is a measure of the lag or lead of the current with respect to the voltage. In alternating current the voltage and amperes are not always in phase; therefore, the true power may be slightly less than that determined by the direct product.

PRECHLORINATION

PRECHLORINATION

The addition of chlorine at the headworks of the plant *PRIOR TO* other treatment processes mainly for disinfection and control of tastes, odors, and aquatic growths. Also applied to aid in coagulation and settling.

PRECIPITATE (pre-SIP-uh-TATE)

PRECIPITATE

(1) An insoluble, finely divided substance which is a product of a chemical reaction within a liquid.

(2) The separation from solution of an insoluble substance.

PRECIPITATION (pre-SIP-uh-TAY-shun)

PRECIPITATION

(1) The process by which atmospheric moisture falls onto a land or water surface as rain, snow, hail, or other forms of moisture.

(2) The chemical transformation of a substance in solution into an insoluble form (precipitate).

PRECISION

PRECISION

The ability of an instrument to measure a process variable and repeatedly obtain the same result. The ability of an instrument to reproduce the same results.

PRECURSOR, THM (pre-CURSE-or)

PRECURSOR, THM

Natural organic compounds found in all surface and groundwaters. These compounds *MAY* react with halogens (such as chlorine) to form trihalomethanes (tri-HAL-o-METH-hanes) (THMs); they *MUST* be present in order for THMs to form.

PRESCRIPTIVE (pre-SKRIP-tive)   PRESCRIPTIVE

Water rights which are acquired by diverting water and putting it to use in accordance with specified procedures. These procedures include filing a request (with a state agency) to use unused water in a stream, river or lake.

PRESSURE CONTROL   PRESSURE CONTROL

A switch which operates on changes in pressure. Usually this is a diaphragm pressing against a spring. When the force on the diaphragm overcomes the spring pressure, the switch is actuated (activated).

PRESSURE HEAD   PRESSURE HEAD

The vertical distance (in feet) equal to the pressure (in psi) at a specific point. The pressure head is equal to the pressure in psi times 2.31 ft/psi.

PRESTRESSED   PRESTRESSED

A prestressed pipe has been reinforced with wire strands (which are under tension) to give the pipe an active resistance to loads or pressures on it.

PREVENTIVE MAINTENANCE UNITS   PREVENTIVE MAINTENANCE UNITS

Crews assigned the task of cleaning sewers (for example, balling or high-velocity cleaning crews) to prevent stoppages and odor complaints. Preventive maintenance is performing the most effective cleaning procedure, in the area where it is most needed, at the proper time in order to prevent failures and emergency situations.

PRIMARY ELEMENT   PRIMARY ELEMENT

The hydraulic structure used to measure flows. In open channels, weirs and flumes are primary elements or devices. Venturi meters and orifice plates are the primary elements in pipes or pressure conduits.

PRIME   PRIME

The action of filling a pump casing with water to remove the air. Most pumps must be primed before start-up or they will not pump any water.

PROCESS VARIABLE   PROCESS VARIABLE

A physical or chemical quantity which is usually measured and controlled in the operation of a water treatment plant or an industrial plant.

PRODUCT WATER   PRODUCT WATER

Water that has passed through a water treatment plant. All the treatment processes are completed or finished. This water is the product from the water treatment plant and is ready to be delivered to the consumers. Also called FINISHED WATER.

PROFILE   PROFILE

A drawing showing elevation plotted against distance, such as the vertical section or *SIDE* view of a pipeline.

PRUSSIAN BLUE   PRUSSIAN BLUE

A blue paste or liquid (often on a paper like carbon paper) used to show a contact area. Used to determine if gate valve seats fit properly.

PUMP BOWL   PUMP BOWL

The submerged pumping unit in a well, including the shaft, impellers and housing.

PUMPING WATER LEVEL   PUMPING WATER LEVEL

The vertical distance in feet from the centerline of the pump discharge to the level of the free pool while water is being drawn from the pool.

PURVEYOR (purr-VAY-or), WATER   PURVEYOR, WATER

An agency or person that supplies water (usually potable water).

PUTREFACTION (PEW-truh-FACK-shun)   PUTREFACTION

Biological decomposition of organic matter, with the production of foul-smelling and -tasting products, associated with anaerobic (no oxygen present) conditions.

Q

QUICKLIME

A material that is mostly calcium oxide (CaO) or calcium oxide in natural association with a lesser amount of magnesium oxide. Quicklime is capable of combining with water, that is, becoming slaked. Also see HYDRATED LIME.

R

RADIAL TO IMPELLER

Perpendicular to the impeller shaft. Material being pumped flows at a right angle to the impeller.

RADICAL

A group of atoms that is capable of remaining unchanged during a series of chemical reactions. Such combinations (radicals) exist in the molecules of many organic compounds; sulfate (SO_4^{2-}) is an inorganic radical.

RANGE

The spread from minimum to maximum values that an instrument is designed to measure. Also see EFFECTIVE RANGE and SPAN.

RANNEY COLLECTOR

This water collector is constructed as a dug well from 12 to 16 feet (3.5 to 5 m) in diameter that has been sunk as a caisson near the bank of a river or lake. Screens are driven radially and approximately horizontally from this well into the sand and the gravel deposits underlying the river.

[SEE DRAWING ON PAGE 742]

RATE OF RETURN

A value which indicates the return of funds received on the basis of the total equity capital used to finance physical facilities. Similar to the interest rate on savings accounts or loans.

RAW WATER

(1) Water in its natural state, prior to any treatment.

(2) Usually the water entering the first treatment process of a water treatment plant.

REAERATION (RE-air-A-shun)

The introduction of air through forced air diffusers into the lower layers of the reservoir. As the air bubbles form and rise through the water, oxygen from the air dissolves into the water and replenishes the dissolved oxygen. The rising bubbles also cause the lower waters to rise to the surface where oxygen from the atmosphere is transferred to the water. This is sometimes called surface reaeration.

REAGENT (re-A-gent)

A pure chemical substance that is used to make new products or is used in chemical tests to measure, detect, or examine other substances.

RECARBONATION (re-CAR-bun-NAY-shun)

A process in which carbon dioxide is bubbled into the water being treated to lower the pH. The pH may also be lowered by the addition of acid. Recarbonation is the final stage in the lime-soda ash softening process. This process converts carbonate ions to bicarbonate ions and stabilizes the solution against the precipitation of carbonate compounds.

RECEIVER

A device which indicates the result of a measurement. Most receivers in the water utility field use either a fixed scale and movable indicator (pointer) such as a pressure gage or a movable scale and movable indicator like those used on a circular flow-recording chart. Also called an INDICATOR.

RECORDER

A device that creates a permanent record, on a paper chart or magnetic tape, of the changes in a measured variable.

PLAN VIEW OF COLLECTOR PIPES

ELEVATION VIEW

RANNEY COLLECTOR

REDUCING AGENT

Any substance, such as base metal (iron) or the sulfide ion (S^{2-}), that will readily donate (give up) electrons. The opposite is an OXIDIZING AGENT.

REDUCTION (re-DUCK-shun)

Reduction is the addition of hydrogen, removal of oxygen, or the addition of electrons to an element or compound. Under anaerobic conditions (no dissolved oxygen present), sulfur compounds are reduced to odor-producing hydrogen sulfide (H_2S) and other compounds. The opposite of OXIDATION.

REFERENCE

A physical or chemical quantity whose value is known exactly, and thus is used to calibrate instruments or standardize measurements. Also called a STANDARD.

REGULATORY NEGOTIATION

A process whereby the U.S. Environmental Protection Agency acts on an equal basis with outside parties to reach consensus on the content of a proposed rule. If the group reaches consensus, the US EPA commits to propose the rule with the agreed upon content.

RELIQUEFACTION (re-LICK-we-FACK-shun)

The return of a gas to the liquid state; for example, a condensation of chlorine gas to return it to its liquid form by cooling.

REPRESENTATIVE SAMPLE

A sample portion of material or water that is as nearly identical in content and consistency as possible to that in the larger body of material or water being sampled.

RESIDUAL CHLORINE

The amount of free and/or available chlorine remaining after a given contact time under specified conditions.

RESIDUE

The dry solids remaining after the evaporation of a sample of water or sludge. Also see TOTAL DISSOLVED SOLIDS.

RESINS

See ION EXCHANGE RESINS.

RESISTANCE

That property of a conductor or wire that opposes the passage of a current, thus causing electric energy to be transformed into heat.

RESPIRATION

The process in which an organism uses oxygen for its life processes and gives off carbon dioxide.

RESPONSIBILITY

Answering to those above in the chain of command to explain how and why you have used your authority.

REVERSE OSMOSIS (oz-MOE-sis)

The application of pressure to a concentrated solution which causes the passage of a liquid from the concentrated solution to a weaker solution across a semipermeable membrane. The membrane allows the passage of the water (solvent) but not the dissolved solids (solutes). The liquid produced is a demineralized water. Also see OSMOSIS.

RIPARIAN (ri-PAIR-ee-an)

Water rights which are acquired together with title to the land bordering a source of surface water. The right to put to beneficial use surface water adjacent to your land.

RODENTICIDE (row-DENT-uh-SIDE)

Any substance or chemical used to kill or control rodents.

ROTAMETER (RODE-uh-ME-ter)   ROTAMETER

A device used to measure the flow rate of gases and liquids. The gas or liquid being measured flows vertically up a tapered, calibrated tube. Inside the tube is a small ball or bullet-shaped float (it may rotate) that rises or falls depending on the flow rate. The flow rate may be read on a scale behind or on the tube by looking at the middle of the ball or at the widest part or top of the float.

ROTOR   ROTOR

The rotating part of a machine. The rotor is surrounded by the stationary (non-moving) parts (stator) of the machine.

ROUTINE SAMPLING   ROUTINE SAMPLING

Sampling repeated on a regular basis.

S

SCADA (ss-KAY-dah) SYSTEM   SCADA SYSTEM

Supervisory **C**ontrol **A**nd **D**ata **A**cquisition system. A computer-monitored alarm, response, control and data acquisition system used by drinking water facilities to monitor their operations.

SCFM   SCFM

Cubic **F**eet of air per **M**inute at **S**tandard conditions of temperature, pressure, and humidity (0°C, 14.7 psia, and 50% relative humidity).

SDWA   SDWA

See **S**AFE **D**RINKING **W**ATER **A**CT.

SMCL   SMCL

Secondary **M**aximum **C**ontaminant **L**evel. Secondary MCLs for various water quality indicators are established to protect public welfare.

SNARL   SNARL

Suggested **N**o **A**dverse **R**esponse **L**evel. The concentration of a chemical in water that is expected not to cause an adverse health effect.

SACRIFICIAL ANODE   SACRIFICIAL ANODE

An easily corroded material deliberately installed in a pipe or tank. The intent of such an installation is to give up (sacrifice) this anode to corrosion while the water supply facilities remain relatively corrosion free.

SAFE DRINKING WATER ACT   SAFE DRINKING WATER ACT

Commonly referred to as SDWA. An Act passed by the U.S. Congress in 1974. The Act establishes a cooperative program among local, state and federal agencies to ensure safe drinking water for consumers. The Act has been amended several times, including the 1980 and 1986 Amendments.

SAFE WATER   SAFE WATER

Water that does not contain harmful bacteria, or toxic materials or chemicals. Water may have taste and odor problems, color and certain mineral problems and still be considered safe for drinking.

SAFE YIELD   SAFE YIELD

The annual quantity of water that can be taken from a source of supply over a period of years without depleting the source permanently (beyond its ability to be replenished naturally in "wet years").

SALINITY   SALINITY

(1) The relative concentration of dissolved salts, usually sodium chloride, in a given water.

(2) A measure of the concentration of dissolved mineral substances in water.

SANITARY SURVEY   SANITARY SURVEY

A detailed evaluation and/or inspection of a source of water supply and all conveyances, storage, treatment and distribution facilities to ensure protection of the water supply from all pollution sources.

SAPROPHYTES (SAP-row-FIGHTS)   SAPROPHYTES

Organisms living on dead or decaying organic matter. They help natural decomposition of organic matter in water.

SATURATION   SATURATION

The condition of a liquid (water) when it has taken into solution the maximum possible quantity of a given substance at a given temperature and pressure.

SATURATOR (SAT-you-RAY-tore)   SATURATOR

A device which produces a fluoride solution for the fluoridation process. The device is usually a cylindrical container with granular sodium fluoride on the bottom. Water flows either upward or downward through the sodium fluoride to produce the fluoride solution.

SCHEDULE, PIPE   SCHEDULE, PIPE

A sizing system of numbers that specifies the I.D. (inside diameter) and O.D. (outside diameter) for each diameter pipe. The schedule number is the ratio of internal pressure in psi divided by the allowable fiber stress multiplied by 1,000. Typical schedules of iron and steel pipe are schedules 40, 80, and 160. Other forms of piping are divided into various classes with their own schedule schemes.

SCHMUTZDECKE (sh-moots-DECK-ee)   SCHMUTZDECKE

A layer of trapped matter at the surface of a slow sand filter in which a dense population of microorganisms develops. These microorganisms within the film or mat feed on and break down incoming organic material trapped in the mat. In doing so the microorganisms both remove organic matter and add mass to the mat, further developing the mat and increasing the physical straining action of the mat.

SECCHI (SECK-key) DISC   SECCHI DISC

A flat, white disc lowered into the water by a rope until it is just barely visible. At this point, the depth of the disc from the water surface is the recorded Secchi disc transparency.

SEDIMENTATION (SED-uh-men-TAY-shun)   SEDIMENTATION

A water treatment process in which solid particles settle out of the water being treated in a large clarifier or sedimentation basin.

SEIZE UP   SEIZE UP

Seize up occurs when an engine overheats and a part expands to the point where the engine will not run. Also called "freezing."

SENSOR   SENSOR

A device that measures (senses) a physical condition or variable of interest. Floats and thermocouples are examples of sensors. Also called a PRIMARY ELEMENT.

SEPTIC (SEP-tick)   SEPTIC

A condition produced by bacteria when all oxygen supplies are depleted. If severe, the bottom deposits produce hydrogen sulfide, the deposits and water turn black, give off foul odors, and the water has a greatly increased chlorine demand.

SEQUESTRATION (SEE-kwes-TRAY-shun)   SEQUESTRATION

A chemical complexing (forming or joining together) of metallic cations (such as iron) with certain inorganic compounds, such as phosphate. Sequestration prevents the precipitation of the metals (iron). Also see CHELATION.

SERVICE PIPE   SERVICE PIPE

The pipeline extending from the water main to the building served or to the consumer's system.

SET POINT   SET POINT

The position at which the control or controller is set. This is the same as the desired value of the process variable.

SEWAGE   SEWAGE

The used household water and water-carried solids that flow in sewers to a wastewater treatment plant. The preferred term is WASTEWATER.

SHEAVE (SHE-v)   SHEAVE

V-belt drive pulley which is commonly made of cast iron or steel.

SHIM   SHIM

Thin metal sheets which are inserted between two surfaces to align or space the surfaces correctly. Shims can be used anywhere a spacer is needed. Usually shims are 0.001 to 0.020 inch thick.

SHOCK LOAD   SHOCK LOAD

The arrival at a water treatment plant of raw water containing unusual amounts of algae, colloidal matter, color, suspended solids, turbidity, or other pollutants.

SHORT-CIRCUITING   SHORT-CIRCUITING

A condition that occurs in tanks or basins when some of the water travels faster than the rest of the flowing water. This is usually undesirable since it may result in shorter contact, reaction, or settling times in comparison with the theoretical (calculated) or presumed detention times.

SIMULATE   SIMULATE

To reproduce the action of some process, usually on a smaller scale.

SINGLE-STAGE PUMP   SINGLE-STAGE PUMP

A pump that has only one impeller. A multi-stage pump has more than one impeller.

SLAKE   SLAKE

To mix with water so that a true chemical combination (hydration) takes place, such as in the slaking of lime.

SLAKED LIME   SLAKED LIME
See HYDRATED LIME.

SLOPE   SLOPE

The slope or inclination of a trench bottom or a trench side wall is the ratio of the vertical distance to the horizontal distance or "rise over run." Also see GRADE (2).

2 VERTICAL

1 HORIZONTAL

2:1 SLOPE

SLUDGE (sluj)   SLUDGE
The settleable solids separated from water during processing.

SLURRY (SLUR-e)   SLURRY

A watery mixture or suspension of insoluble (not dissolved) matter; a thin, watery mud or any substance resembling it (such as a grit slurry or a lime slurry).

SOFT WATER   SOFT WATER

Water having a low concentration of calcium and magnesium ions. According to U.S. Geological Survey guidelines, soft water is water having a hardness of 60 milligrams per liter or less.

SOFTWARE PROGRAMS   SOFTWARE PROGRAMS

Computer programs; the list of instructions that tell a computer how to perform a given task or tasks. Some software programs are designed and written to monitor and control water distribution systems and treament processes.

SOLENOID (SO-luh-noid)   SOLENOID

A magnetically (electric coil) operated mechanical device. Solenoids can operate small valves or electric switches.

SOLUTION   SOLUTION

A liquid mixture of dissolved substances. In a solution it is impossible to see all the separate parts.

SOUNDING TUBE   SOUNDING TUBE

A pipe or tube used for measuring the depths of water.

SPAN   SPAN

The scale or range of values an instrument is designed to measure. Also see RANGE.

SPECIFIC CONDUCTANCE SPECIFIC CONDUCTANCE

A rapid method of estimating the dissolved solids content of a water supply. The measurement indicates the capacity of a sample of water to carry an electric current, which is related to the concentration of ionized substances in the water. Also called CONDUCTANCE.

SPECIFIC GRAVITY SPECIFIC GRAVITY

(1) Weight of a particle, substance, or chemical solution in relation to the weight of an equal volume of water. Water has a specific gravity of 1.000 at 4°C (39°F). Particulates in raw water may have a specific gravity of 1.005 to 2.5.

(2) Weight of a particular gas in relation to the weight of an equal volume of air at the same temperature and pressure (air has a specific gravity of 1.0). Chlorine has a specific gravity of 2.5 as a gas.

SPECIFIC YIELD SPECIFIC YIELD

The quantity of water that a unit volume of saturated permeable rock or soil will yield when drained by gravity. Specific yield may be expressed as a ratio or as a percentage by volume.

SPOIL SPOIL

Excavated material such as soil from the trench of a water main.

SPORE SPORE

The reproductive body of an organism which is capable of giving rise to a new organism either directly or indirectly. A viable (able to live and grow) body regarded as the resting stage of an organism. A spore is usually more resistant to disinfectants and heat than most organisms.

SPRING LINE SPRING LINE

Theoretical center of a pipeline. Also, the guideline for laying a course of bricks.

STALE WATER STALE WATER

Water which has not flowed recently and may have picked up tastes and odors from distribution lines or storage facilities.

STANDARD STANDARD

A physical or chemical quantity whose value is known exactly, and thus is used to calibrate instruments or standardize measurements. Also called a REFERENCE.

STANDARD DEVIATION STANDARD DEVIATION

A measure of the spread or dispersion of data.

STANDARD METHODS STANDARD METHODS

STANDARD METHODS FOR THE EXAMINATION OF WATER AND WASTEWATER. A joint publication of the American Public Health Association, American Water Works Association, and the Water Environment Federation which outlines the procedures used to analyze the impurities in water and wastewater.

STANDARD SOLUTION STANDARD SOLUTION

A solution in which the exact concentration of a chemical or compound is known.

STANDARDIZE STANDARDIZE

To compare with a standard.

(1) In wet chemistry, to find out the exact strength of a solution by comparing it with a standard of known strength. This information is used to adjust the strength by adding more water or more of the substance dissolved.

(2) To set up an instrument or device to read a standard. This allows you to adjust the instrument so that it reads accurately, or enables you to apply a correction factor to the readings.

STARTERS (MOTOR) STARTERS (MOTOR)

Devices used to start up large motors gradually to avoid severe mechanical shock to a driven machine and to prevent disturbance to the electrical lines (causing dimming and flickering of lights).

STATIC HEAD STATIC HEAD

When water is not moving, the vertical distance (in feet) from a specific point to the water surface is the static head. (The static pressure in psi is the static head in feet times 0.433 psi/ft.) Also see DYNAMIC PRESSURE and STATIC PRESSURE.

STATIC PRESSURE STATIC PRESSURE

When water is not moving, the vertical distance (in feet) from a specific point to the water surface is the static head. The static pressure in psi is the static head in feet times 0.433 psi/ft. Also see DYNAMIC PRESSURE and STATIC HEAD.

STATIC WATER DEPTH STATIC WATER DEPTH

The vertical distance in feet from the centerline of the pump discharge down to the surface level of the free pool while no water is being drawn from the pool or water table.

STATIC WATER LEVEL STATIC WATER LEVEL

(1) The elevation or level of the water table in a well when the pump is not operating.

(2) The level or elevation to which water would rise in a tube connected to an artesian aquifer, basin, or conduit under pressure.

STATOR STATOR

That portion of a machine which contains the stationary (non-moving) parts that surround the moving parts (rotor).

STERILIZATION (STARE-uh-luh-ZAY-shun) STERILIZATION

The removal or destruction of all microorganisms, including pathogenic and other bacteria, vegetative forms and spores. Compare with DISINFECTION.

STETHOSCOPE STETHOSCOPE

An instrument used to magnify sounds and convey them to the ear.

STRATIFICATION (STRAT-uh-fuh-KAY-shun) STRATIFICATION

The formation of separate layers (of temperature, plant, or animal life) in a lake or reservoir. Each layer has similar characteristics such as all water in the layer has the same temperature. Also see THERMAL STRATIFICATION.

STRAY CURRENT CORROSION STRAY CURRENT CORROSION

A corrosion activity resulting from stray electric current originating from some source outside the plumbing system such as D.C. grounding on phone systems.

SUBMERGENCE SUBMERGENCE

The distance between the water surface and the media surface in a filter.

SUBSIDENCE (sub-SIDE-ence) SUBSIDENCE

The dropping or lowering of the ground surface as a result of removing excess water (overdraft or overpumping) from an aquifer. After excess water has been removed, the soil will settle, become compacted and the ground surface will drop and can cause the settling of underground utilities.

SUCTION LIFT SUCTION LIFT

The *NEGATIVE* pressure [in feet (meters) of water or inches (centimeters) of mercury vacuum] on the suction side of the pump. The pressure can be measured from the centerline of the pump *DOWN TO* (lift) the elevation of the hydraulic grade line on the suction side of the pump.

SUPERCHLORINATION (SUE-per-KLOR-uh-NAY-shun) SUPERCHLORINATION

Chlorination with doses that are deliberately selected to produce free or combined residuals so large as to require dechlorination.

SUPERNATANT (sue-per-NAY-tent) SUPERNATANT

Liquid removed from settled sludge. Supernatant commonly refers to the liquid between the sludge on the bottom and the scum on the water surface of a basin or container.

SUPERSATURATED SUPERSATURATED

An unstable condition of a solution (water) in which the solution contains a substance at a concentration greater than the saturation concentration for the substance.

SURFACE LOADING SURFACE LOADING

One of the guidelines for the design of settling tanks and clarifiers in treatment plants. Used by operators to determine if tanks and clarifiers are hydraulically (flow) over- or underloaded. Also called OVERFLOW RATE.

$$\text{Surface Loading, GPD/sq ft} = \frac{\text{Flow, gallons/day}}{\text{Surface Area, sq ft}}$$

SURFACTANT (sir-FAC-tent)   SURFACTANT

Abbreviation for surface-active agent. The active agent in detergents that possesses a high cleaning ability.

SURGE CHAMBER   SURGE CHAMBER

A chamber or tank connected to a pipe and located at or near a valve that may quickly open or close or a pump that may suddenly start or stop. When the flow of water in a pipe starts or stops quickly, the surge chamber allows water to flow into or out of the pipe and minimize any sudden positive or negative pressure waves or surges in the pipe.

[SEE DRAWING ON PAGE 750]

SUSPENDED SOLIDS   SUSPENDED SOLIDS

(1) Solids that either float on the surface or are suspended in water, wastewater, or other liquids, and which are largely removable by laboratory filtering.

(2) The quantity of material removed from water in a laboratory test, as prescribed in *STANDARD METHODS FOR THE EXAMINATION OF WATER AND WASTEWATER*, and referred to as Total Suspended Solids Dried at 103–105°C.

T

TCE   TCE

See **TRICHLOROETHANE**.

TDS   TDS

See **TOTAL DISSOLVED SOLIDS**.

THM   THM

See **TRIHALOMETHANES**.

THM PRECURSOR   THM PRECURSOR

See PRECURSOR, THM.

TAILGATE SAFETY MEETING   TAILGATE SAFETY MEETING

Brief (10 to 20 minutes) safety meetings held every 7 to 10 working days. The term *TAILGATE* comes from the safety meetings regularly held by the construction industry around the tailgate of a truck.

TELEMETRY (tel-LEM-uh-tree)   TELEMETRY

The electrical link between the transmitter and the receiver. Telephone lines are commonly used to serve as the electrical line.

TEMPERATURE SENSOR   TEMPERATURE SENSOR

A device that opens and closes a switch in response to changes in the temperature. This device might be a metal contact, or a thermocouple that generates minute electric current proportional to the difference in heat, or a variable resistor whose value changes in response to changes in temperature. Also called a HEAT SENSOR.

THERMAL STRATIFICATION (STRAT-uh-fuh-KAY-shun)   THERMAL STRATIFICATION

The formation of layers of different temperatures in a lake or reservoir. Also see STRATIFICATION.

THERMOCLINE (THUR-moe-KLINE)   THERMOCLINE

The middle layer in a thermally stratified lake or reservoir. In this layer there is a rapid decrease in temperature with depth. Also called the METALIMNION.

THERMOCOUPLE   THERMOCOUPLE

A heat-sensing device made of two conductors of different metals joined at their ends. An electric current is produced when there is a difference in temperature between the ends.

THICKENING   THICKENING

Treatment to remove water from the sludge mass to reduce the volume that must be handled.

TYPES OF SURGE CHAMBERS

THRESHOLD ODOR

THRESHOLD ODOR

The minimum odor of a water sample that can just be detected after successive dilutions with odorless water. Also called ODOR THRESHOLD.

THRESHOLD ODOR NUMBER (TON)

THRESHOLD ODOR NUMBER (TON)

The greatest dilution of a sample with odor-free water that still yields a just-detectable odor.

THRUST BLOCK

THRUST BLOCK

A mass of concrete or similar material appropriately placed around a pipe to prevent movement when the pipe is carrying water. Usually placed at bends and valve structures.

TIME LAG

TIME LAG

The time required for processes and control systems to respond to a signal or to reach a desired level.

TIMER

TIMER

A device for automatically starting or stopping a machine or other device at a given time.

TITRATE (TIE-trate)

TITRATE

To *TITRATE* a sample, a chemical solution of known strength is added drop by drop until a certain color change, precipitate, or pH change in the sample is observed (end point). Titration is the process of adding the chemical reagent in increments until completion of the reaction, as signaled by the end point.

TOPOGRAPHY (toe-PAH-gruh-fee)

TOPOGRAPHY

The arrangement of hills and valleys in a geographic area.

TOTAL DISSOLVED SOLIDS (TDS)

TOTAL DISSOLVED SOLIDS (TDS)

All of the dissolved solids in a water. TDS is measured on a sample of water that has passed through a very fine mesh filter to remove suspended solids. The water passing through the filter is evaporated and the residue represents the dissolved solids. Also see SPECIFIC CONDUCTANCE.

TOTAL DYNAMIC HEAD (TDH)

TOTAL DYNAMIC HEAD (TDH)

When a pump is lifting or pumping water, the vertical distance (in feet) from the elevation of the energy grade line on the suction side of the pump to the elevation of the energy grade line on the discharge side of the pump.

TOTAL ORGANIC CARBON (TOC)

TOTAL ORGANIC CARBON (TOC)

TOC measures the amount of organic carbon in water.

TOTAL RESIDUAL CHLORINE

TOTAL RESIDUAL CHLORINE

The amount of available chlorine remaining after a given contact time. The sum of the combined available residual chlorine and the free available residual chlorine. Also see RESIDUAL CHLORINE.

TOTALIZER

TOTALIZER

A device or meter that continuously measures and calculates (adds) a process rate variable in cumulative fashion; for example, total flows displayed in gallons, million gallons, cubic feet, or some other unit of volume measurement. Also called an INTEGRATOR.

TOXAPHENE (TOX-uh-FEEN)

TOXAPHENE

A chemical that causes adverse health effects in domestic water supplies and also is toxic to freshwater and marine aquatic life.

TOXIC (TOX-ick)

TOXIC

A substance which is poisonous to a living organism.

TRANSDUCER (trans-DUE-sir)

TRANSDUCER

A device that senses some varying condition measured by a primary sensor and converts it to an electrical or other signal for transmission to some other device (a receiver) for processing or decision making.

TRANSMISSION LINES

TRANSMISSION LINES

Pipelines that transport raw water from its source to a water treatment plant. After treatment, water is usually pumped into pipelines (transmission lines) that are connected to a distribution grid system.

TRANSMISSIVITY (TRANS-miss-SIV-it-tee)   TRANSMISSIVITY

A measure of the ability to transmit (as in the ability of an aquifer to transmit water).

TRANSPIRATION (TRAN-spur-RAY-shun)   TRANSPIRATION

The process by which water vapor is released to the atmosphere by living plants. This process is similar to people sweating. Also see EVAPOTRANSPIRATION.

TREMIE (TREH-me)   TREMIE

A device used to place concrete or grout under water.

TRICHLOROETHANE (TCE) (try-KLOR-o-ETH-hane)   TRICHLOROETHANE (TCE)

An organic chemical used as a cleaning solvent that causes adverse health effects in domestic water supplies.

TRIHALOMETHANES (THMs) (tri-HAL-o-METH-hanes)   TRIHALOMETHANES (THMs)

Derivatives of methane, CH_4, in which three halogen atoms (chlorine or bromine) are substituted for three of the hydrogen atoms. Often formed during chlorination by reactions with natural organic materials in the water. The resulting compounds (THMs) are suspected of causing cancer.

TRUE COLOR   TRUE COLOR

Color of the water from which turbidity has been removed. The turbidity may be removed by double filtering the sample through a Whatman No. 40 filter when using the visual comparison method.

TUBE SETTLER   TUBE SETTLER

A device that uses bundles of small-bore (2 to 3 inches or 50 to 75 mm) tubes installed on an incline as an aid to sedimentation. The tubes may come in a variety of shapes including circular and rectangular. As water rises within the tubes, settling solids fall to the tube surface. As the sludge (from the settled solids) in the tube gains weight, it moves down the tubes and settles to the bottom of the basin for removal by conventional sludge collection means. Tube settlers are sometimes installed in sedimentation basins and clarifiers to improve particle removal.

TUBERCLE (TOO-burr-cull)   TUBERCLE

A protective crust of corrosion products (rust) which builds up over a pit caused by the loss of metal due to corrosion.

TUBERCULATION (too-BURR-cue-LAY-shun)   TUBERCULATION

The development or formation of small mounds of corrosion products (rust) on the inside of iron pipe. These mounds (tubercles) increase the roughness of the inside of the pipe thus increasing resistance to water flow (decreases the C Factor).

TURBID   TURBID

Having a cloudy or muddy appearance.

TURBIDIMETER   TURBIDIMETER

See TURBIDITY METER.

TURBIDITY (ter-BID-it-tee)   TURBIDITY

The cloudy appearance of water caused by the presence of suspended and colloidal matter. In the waterworks field, a turbidity measurement is used to indicate the clarity of water. Technically, turbidity is an optical property of the water based on the amount of light reflected by suspended particles. Turbidity cannot be directly equated to suspended solids because white particles reflect more light than dark-colored particles and many small particles will reflect more light than an equivalent large particle.

TURBIDITY METER   TURBIDITY METER

An instrument for measuring and comparing the turbidity of liquids by passing light through them and determining how much light is reflected by the particles in the liquid. The normal measuring range is 0 to 100 and is expressed as Nephelometric Turbidity Units (NTUs).

TURBIDITY UNITS (TU)   TURBIDITY UNITS (TU)

Turbidity units are a measure of the cloudiness of water. If measured by a nephelometric (deflected light) instrumental procedure, turbidity units are expressed in nephelometric turbidity units (NTU) or simply TU. Those turbidity units obtained by visual methods are expressed in Jackson Turbidity Units (JTU) which are a measure of the cloudiness of water; they are used to indicate the clarity of water. There is no real connection between NTUs and JTUs. The Jackson turbidimeter is a visual method and the nephelometer is an instrumental method based on deflected light.

TURN-DOWN RATIO

TURN-DOWN RATIO

The ratio of the design range to the range of acceptable accuracy or precision of an instrument. Also see EFFECTIVE RANGE.

U

UNCONSOLIDATED FORMATION

UNCONSOLIDATED FORMATION

A sediment that is loosely arranged or unstratified (not in layers) or whose particles are not cemented together (soft rock); occurring either at the ground surface or at a depth below the surface. Also see CONSOLIDATED FORMATION.

UNIFORMITY COEFFICIENT (U.C.)

UNIFORMITY COEFFICIENT (U.C.)

The ratio of (1) the diameter of a grain (particle) of a size that is barely too large to pass through a sieve that allows 60 percent of the material (by weight) to pass through, to (2) the diameter of a grain (particle) of a size that is barely too large to pass through a sieve that allows 10 percent of the material (by weight) to pass through. The resulting ratio is a measure of the degree of uniformity in a granular material such as filter media.

$$\text{Uniformity Coefficient} = \frac{\text{Particle Diameter}_{60\%}}{\text{Particle Diameter}_{10\%}}$$

UPPER EXPLOSIVE LIMIT (UEL)

UPPER EXPLOSIVE LIMIT (UEL)

The point at which the concentration of a gas in air becomes too great to allow an explosion upon ignition due to insufficient oxygen present.

V

VARIABLE COSTS

VARIABLE COSTS

Costs that a utility must cover or pay that are associated with the production and delivery of water. The costs vary or fluctuate on the basis of the volume of water treated and delivered to customers (water production). Also see FIXED COSTS.

VARIABLE FREQUENCY DRIVE

VARIABLE FREQUENCY DRIVE

A control system that allows the frequency of the current applied to a motor to be varied. The motor is connected to a low-frequency source while standing still; the frequency is then increased gradually until the motor and pump (or other driven machine) are at the desired speed.

VARIABLE, MEASURED

VARIABLE, MEASURED

A factor (flow, temperature) that is sensed and quantified (reduced to a reading of some kind) by a primary element or sensor.

VARIABLE, PROCESS

VARIABLE, PROCESS

A physical or chemical quantity which is usually measured and controlled in the operation of a water treatment plant or an industrial plant.

VELOCITY HEAD

VELOCITY HEAD

The energy in flowing water as determined by a vertical height (in feet or meters) equal to the square of the velocity of flowing water divided by twice the acceleration due to gravity ($V^2/2g$).

VENTURI METER

VENTURI METER

A flow measuring device placed in a pipe. The device consists of a tube whose diameter gradually decreases to a throat and then gradually expands to the diameter of the pipe. The flow is determined on the basis of the difference in pressure (caused by different velocity heads) between the entrance and throat of the Venturi meter.

NOTE: Most Venturi meters have pressure sensing taps rather than a manometer to measure the pressure difference. The upstream tap is the high pressure tap or side of the manometer.

VENTURI METER

MANOMETER

VISCOSITY (vis-KOSS-uh-tee)   VISCOSITY

A property of water, or any other fluid, which resists efforts to change its shape or flow. Syrup is more viscous (has a higher viscosity) than water. The viscosity of water increases significantly as temperatures decrease. Motor oil is rated by how thick (viscous) it is; 20 weight oil is considered relatively thin while 50 weight oil is relatively thick or viscous.

VOID   VOID

A pore or open space in rock, soil or other granular material, not occupied by solid matter. The pore or open space may be occupied by air, water, or other gaseous or liquid material. Also called an INTERSTICE, PORE, or void space.

VOLATILE (VOL-uh-tull)   VOLATILE

(1) A volatile substance is one that is capable of being evaporated or changed to a vapor at relatively low temperatures. Volatile substances also can be partially removed by air stripping.

(2) In terms of solids analysis, volatile refers to materials lost (including most organic matter) upon ignition in a muffle furnace for 60 minutes at 550°C. Natural volatile materials are chemical substances usually of animal or plant origin. Manufactured or synthetic volatile materials such as ether, acetone, and carbon tetrachloride are highly volatile and not of plant or animal origin. Also see NONVOLATILE MATTER.

VOLATILE ACIDS   VOLATILE ACIDS

Fatty acids produced during digestion which are soluble in water and can be steam-distilled at atmospheric pressure. Also called organic acids. Volatile acids are commonly reported as equivalent to acetic acid.

VOLATILE LIQUIDS   VOLATILE LIQUIDS

Liquids which easily vaporize or evaporate at room temperature.

VOLATILE MATTER   VOLATILE MATTER

Matter in water, wastewater, or other liquids that is lost on ignition of the dry solids at 550°C.

VOLATILE SOLIDS   VOLATILE SOLIDS

Those solids in water or other liquids that are lost on ignition of the dry solids at 550°C.

VOLTAGE   VOLTAGE

The electrical pressure available to cause a flow of current (amperage) when an electric circuit is closed. Also called ELECTRO-MOTIVE FORCE (E.M.F.).

VOLUMETRIC   VOLUMETRIC

A measurement based on the volume of some factor. Volumetric titration is a means of measuring unknown concentrations of water quality indicators in a sample *BY DETERMINING THE VOLUME* of titrant or liquid reagent needed to complete particular reactions.

VOLUMETRIC FEEDER   VOLUMETRIC FEEDER

A dry chemical feeder which delivers a measured volume of chemical during a specific time period.

VORTEX   VORTEX

A revolving mass of water which forms a whirlpool. This whirlpool is caused by water flowing out of a small opening in the bottom of a basin or reservoir. A funnel-shaped opening is created downward from the water surface.

W

WARNING   WARNING

The word *WARNING* is used to indicate a hazard level between *CAUTION* and *DANGER*. Also see CAUTION, DANGER, and NOTICE.

WASTEWATER   WASTEWATER

A community's used water and water-carried solids (including used water from industrial processes) that flow to a treatment plant. Storm water, surface water, and groundwater infiltration also may be included in the wastewater that enters a wastewater treatment plant. The term "sewage" usually refers to household wastes, but this word is being replaced by the term "wastewater."

WATER AUDIT WATER AUDIT

A thorough examination of the accuracy of water agency records or accounts (volumes of water) and system control equipment. Water managers can use audits to determine their water distribution system efficiency. The overall goal is to identify and verify water and revenue losses in a water system.

WATER HAMMER WATER HAMMER

The sound like someone hammering on a pipe that occurs when a valve is opened or closed very rapidly. When a valve position is changed quickly, the water pressure in a pipe will increase and decrease back and forth very quickly. This rise and fall in pressures can cause serious damage to the system.

WATER PURVEYOR (purr-VAY-or) WATER PURVEYOR

An agency or person that supplies water (usually potable water).

WATER TABLE WATER TABLE

The upper surface of the zone of saturation of groundwater in an unconfined aquifer.

WATERSHED WATERSHED

The region or land area that contributes to the drainage or catchment area above a specific point on a stream or river.

WATT WATT

A unit of power equal to one joule per second. The power of a current of one ampere flowing across a potential difference of one volt.

WEIR (weer) WEIR

(1) A wall or plate placed in an open channel and used to measure the flow of water. The depth of the flow over the weir can be used to calculate the flow rate, or a chart or conversion table may be used to convert depth to flow.

(2) A wall or obstruction used to control flow (from settling tanks and clarifiers) to ensure a uniform flow rate and avoid short-circuiting.

WEIR (weer) DIAMETER WEIR DIAMETER

Many circular clarifiers have a circular weir within the outside edge of the clarifier. All the water leaving the clarifier flows over this weir. The diameter of the weir is the length of a line from one edge of a weir to the opposite edge and passing through the center of the circle formed by the weir.

WEIR LOADING WEIR LOADING

A guideline used to determine the length of weir needed on settling tanks and clarifiers in treatment plants. Used by operators to determine if weirs are hydraulically (flow) overloaded.

$$\text{Weir Loading, GPM/ft} = \frac{\text{Flow, GPM}}{\text{Length of Weir, ft}}$$

WELL ISOLATION ZONE WELL ISOLATION ZONE

The surface or zone surrounding a water well or well field, supplying a public water system, with restricted land uses to prevent contaminants from a not permitted land use to move toward and reach such water well or well field. Also see WELLHEAD PROTECTION AREA (WHPA).

WELL LOG WELL LOG

A record of the thickness and characteristics of the soil, rock and water-bearing formations encountered during the drilling (sinking) of a well.

WELLHEAD PROTECTION AREA (WHPA) WELLHEAD PROTECTION AREA (WHPA)

The surface and subsurface area surrounding a water well or well field, supplying a public water system, through which contaminants are reasonably likely to move toward and reach such water well or well field. Also see WELL ISOLATION ZONE.

WET CHEMISTRY WET CHEMISTRY

Laboratory procedures used to analyze a sample of water using liquid chemical solutions (wet) instead of, or in addition to, laboratory instruments.

WHOLESOME WATER

WHOLESOME WATER

A water that is safe and palatable for human consumption.

WIRE-TO-WATER EFFICIENCY

WIRE-TO-WATER EFFICIENCY

The combined efficiency of a pump and motor together. Also called the OVERALL EFFICIENCY.

WYE STRAINER

WYE STRAINER

A screen shaped like the letter Y. The water flows in at the top of the Y and the debris in the water is removed in the top part of the Y.

X

(NO LISTINGS)

Y

YIELD

YIELD

The quantity of water (expressed as a rate of flow — GPM, GPH, GPD, or total quantity per year) that can be collected for a given use from surface or groundwater sources. The yield may vary with the use proposed, with the plan of development, and also with economic considerations. Also see SAFE YIELD.

Z

ZEOLITE

ZEOLITE

A type of ion exchange material used to soften water. Natural zeolites are siliceous compounds (made of silica) which remove calcium and magnesium from hard water and replace them with sodium. Synthetic or organic zeolites are ion exchange materials which remove calcium or magnesium and replace them with either sodium or hydrogen. Manganese zeolites are used to remove iron and manganese from water.

ZETA POTENTIAL

ZETA POTENTIAL

In coagulation and flocculation procedures, the difference in the electrical charge between the dense layer of ions surrounding the particle and the charge of the bulk of the suspended fluid surrounding this particle. The zeta potential is usually measured in millivolts.

ZONE OF AERATION

ZONE OF AERATION

The comparatively dry soil or rock located between the ground surface and the top of the water table.

ZONE OF SATURATION

ZONE OF SATURATION

The soil or rock located below the top of the groundwater table. By definition, the zone of saturation is saturated with water. Also see WATER TABLE.

ZOOPLANKTON (ZOE-PLANK-ton)

ZOOPLANKTON

Small, usually microscopic animals (such as protozoans), found in lakes and reservoirs.

SUBJECT INDEX

A

ABC (Association of Boards of Certification), 579
Accident
  causes, 416
  prevention, 416, 443
  reports, 454, 455, 620, 622, 623
Accountable, 570
Accuracy, instrumentation, 366
Acetic acid (glacial), 417
Acid feed systems, 40, 174
Acids
  chemical handling, 417
  safety, 417
Action levels, lead and copper, 519
Activated carbon, 135, 137, 139, 430
Acute health effects, 437, 521, 526
Ad valorem taxes, 597
Additional reading, 22, 63, 116, 131, 140, 190, 220, 267, 342,
  403, 456, 531, 533, 630
Administration
  advertising positions, 575
  applications, 575
  backflow prevention, 608
  budgeting, 595
  capital improvements, 596
  certification, 578
  communication, 589
  compensation, 575, 578
  conducting meetings, 591
  confined space entry procedures, 617
  consumer complaints, 593
  consumer inquiries, 593
  contaminated water supply, 611
  contingency planning, 608
  continuing education, 579
  controlling, 568
  cross connection control program, 603-608
  directing, 568
  discipline problems, 582
  disposition of plant records, 630
  emergency response, 608-613
  employee complaints, 582
  equipment repair/replacement fund, 596
  evaluation, performance, 589
  financial assistance, 597
  financial management, 594-598
  financial stability, 594
  first aid, 616
  functions of manager, 568
  harassment, 583
  hazard communication, 616
  interviewing job applicants, 575, 576
  interviews, media, 592
  meetings, conducting, 591
  number of employees needed, 573
  operations and maintenance (O & M), 592, 599-608
  operator certification, 578
  oral communication, 589
  organizing, 570
  orientation, new employee, 578
  paper screening, 575
  performance evaluation, 579
  personnel records, 587
  planning, 570
  planning for emergencies, 608
  plant tours, 593
  policies and procedures, 578
  probationary period, 578
  procurement of materials, 628
  public relations, 592
  public speaking, 593
  qualifications profile, 574
  rates, water, 596
  recordkeeping, 627-630
  records, personnel, 573, 587
  repair/replacement fund, equipment, 596
  SCADA systems, 600-603
  safety program, 614-627
  selection process, 575
  sexual harassment, 583
  staffing, 573-587
  supervisor, training, 579
  telephone contacts, 593
  tours, plant, 593
  training, 578, 579
  unions, 587
  water rates, 596
  written communication, 589
Adsorption, 135, 137
Adverse effects
  hardness, 78
  iron and manganese, 6
Advertising, job openings, 575
Aeration
  iron and manganese, 12
  trihalomethanes, 135-137, 139
Affirmative action, 575
Air gap, 606, 607, 608
Air release assembly, 111
Air supply systems, 395, 396
Air temperatures, fluoridation, 32
Air-cooled engines, 332
Alarms
  fluoridation, 47
  instrumentation, 390, 391
  reverse osmosis, 174
Algae counts, 467
Alignment, pumps, 273, 289, 297-301
Alkalinity, softening, 79, 81, 91
Alternating current (A.C.), 241
Alum, 428
Alum sludge, 218
Aluminum, regulations, 536
Aluminum sulfate, 428
Amendments to SDWA, 512

Ammeter, 245, 246
Ammonia, 421
Amplitude, 241
Amps, 242
Analog, 366, 386, 387
Analysis
  Also see Laboratory test procedures
  iron and manganese, 7, 8
Annual report, 591, 596
Annunciator panels, 390
Antimony, 516
Applications, job, 575
Aquifer, 9
Arch, chemicals, 337, 417
Arithmetic assignment, 22, 63, 116, 140, 190, 342, 456
Arsenic, 514, 516
Asbestos, 516
Assessment bonds, 597
Assessment of system vulnerability, 608
Association of Boards of Certification (ABC), 579
Atmospheres, explosive, 451
Atomic absorption, 466
Audience, communications, 589, 590, 592
Audiovisuals, 590
Authority, 570
Autoclaves, 450
Automatic
  controller, 391
  valves, 325
Auxiliary electrical power, 256, 264

B

Back pressure, 603-608
Backflow, 603-608
Backsiphonage, 603-608
Backwash
  filters, 14
  ion exchange, 106, 109
  recovery ponds, 205, 207
  wastewater, 218
Bacteria
  iron and manganese, 6, 7, 21, 22
  regulations, 518, 523-531
Barium, 516
Bases
  chemical handling, 421
  safety, 421
Basket centrifuge, 213, 215
Batch systems, 40, 41
Batteries, 241, 265
Bearings, pump, 273, 278, 279, 289, 293
Beer's Law, 466
Belt drives, pumps, 294, 297
Belt filter presses, 202, 209, 212
Belts, compressors, 309
Bench-scale tests
  Information Collection Rule, 532
  iron and manganese, 9, 13
  trihalomethanes, 135, 139, 140
Benefits, employee, 575, 578
Benefits, softening, 79, 83
Benzene, 523
Beryllium, 516
Black water, 15
Blending, ion exchange, 114
Block grants, 597
Blown fuse, 245

Blue baby, 486, 517, 521
Bonds, 597
Booster shots, immunization, 450
Bourdon tube, 372, 373
Brackish water, 151, 152
Breakers, circuit, 242, 247, 250
Breakpoint chlorination, 15
Brine
  disposal, demineralization, 152
  disposal, process wastes, 202, 203, 213
  electrodialysis, 180
  ion exchange, 106, 107, 109
  reverse osmosis, 159, 174
Bromide, 129, 133, 134
Bubbler tube, 375, 377
Budgeting, 595
Buildings, maintenance, 341, 342
Butterfly valves, 312, 315
Bypass, ion exchange, 114, 115
By-products, disinfection, 514, 531, 532

C

CCR (Consumer Confidence Report), 514, 552
CPR (cardiopulmonary resuscitation), 417, 426, 428, 438, 440, 616
CT calculations, 688-696
CT values, 531
Cadmium, 519
Calcium carbonate equivalent, 79, 80
Calcium carbonate saturation test, 484
Calcium hydroxide, 422
Calcium test procedures, 468
Calculations
  chemical feeders, 339
  fluoridation, 59-63
  ion exchange softening, 112-114
  lime-soda ash softening, 83, 88, 94-99
  reverse osmosis, 156-164
  trihalomethanes, 132
Calibration
  chemical feeders, 337, 338
  curve, spectrophotometer, 467
  instrumentation, 366, 397
Call date, 597
Capital improvements, 596
Capital planning, 596
Carbon dioxide, 84, 91, 426
Carbon tetrachloride, 523
Carbonate hardness, 78, 84
Cardiopulmonary resuscitation (CPR), 417, 426, 428, 438, 440, 616
Cartridge filters, 174, 183, 185
Casing, pumps, 274, 278, 279
Cathodic protection, 341
Caustic soda, 422
Caustic soda softening, 85, 88
Cavitation, pumps, 276, 277
Cellulose acetate membranes, 155
Centrifugal pumps, 269, 277, 304
Centrifuges, 204, 209, 213, 214, 215
Certification, 578
Chain drives, pumps, 297
Charts
  circular, 387-390, 398, 400, 402
  fluoridation, 48-50
  strip, 387, 389, 390, 398, 400, 402
Check sampling, 540

Check valves, 289, 293, 316-325
Chemical feeders
  acid feed systems, 40
  batch systems, 40, 41
  calculating doses, 59-63, 86, 94-99
  calculations, 339
  calibration, 337, 338
  chemical storage, 336
  chlorinators, 340
  day tank, 41, 43
  diaphragm pumps, 33
  dose, 98, 339
  drainage, 336
  dry chemical, 337
  dry feeders, 33, 37-39, 57, 337
  electronic pumps, 33, 36, 48
  feed rate, 94-98, 339
  gas, 337
  gravimetric feeders, 34, 39
  instrumentation, 383
  liquid, 327
  maintenance, 19, 57, 337
  metering, 337
  operation, 48
  peristaltic pumps, 33, 35, 48
  positive displacement pumps, 33, 34
  saturators, 40, 41, 42, 57
  shutdown, 54
  solid, 337
  solution feeders, 33, 40
  solution preparation, 48
  start-up, 47
  storage, chemical, 336, 432
  volumetric feeders, 34, 37, 38, 40
Chemical flush system, 187
Chemical handling
  acetic acid (glacial), 417
  acids, 417
  activated carbon, 430
  alum, 428
  aluminum sulfate, 428
  ammonia, 421
  bases, 421
  calcium hydroxide, 422
  carbon dioxide, 426
  caustic soda, 422
  chlorine, 424
  CHLORINE MANUAL, 426
  drains, 432
  ferric chloride, 429
  ferric sulfate, 429
  ferrous sulfate, 429
  fluoride compounds, 429
  gas mask, 425-427
  gas-detection equipment, 437
  gases, 424
  hydrochloric acid, 420
  hydrofluoric acid, 420
  hydrofluosilicic acid, 418
  hypochlorite, 423
  muriatic acid, 420
  nitric acid, 420
  potassium permanganate, 430
  powdered activated carbon, 430
  powders, 430, 431
  safety, 417
  safety shower, 418, 419, 420
  salts, 428
  self-contained breathing apparatus, 425-427, 451

  sodium aluminate, 429
  sodium carbonate, 423
  sodium hydroxide, 422
  sodium silicate, 423
  storage, 336, 432
  sulfur dioxide, 426
  sulfuric acid, 420
Chemical metering pumps, 278, 337
Chemical reactions
  lime-soda ash softening, 84-86
  THM, 129, 133
Chemical storage, 336, 432
Chemicals
  labeling, 432
  laboratory, 449
Chemistry
  softening, 80
  trihalomethanes, 129, 133
CHEMTREC (800) 424-9300, 238, 454, 610
Chloramination, 531
Chloramines, 138, 139
Chloride
  regulations, 536
  test procedures, 469
Chlorination
  iron and manganese, 9-11, 13, 17, 20
  reverse osmosis, 174
Chlorinators, 9-11, 340
Chlorine, 129, 134, 137, 139, 424
Chlorine dioxide, 134, 135, 137, 139
CHLORINE MANUAL, 426
Chlorine residual substitution, 529
Chloroform, 129, 135
"Christmas Tree" arrangement, 164, 165, 174
Chromium, 519
Chronic health effects, 521
Circuit breakers, 242, 247, 250
Circuits, 241, 243
Circular charts, 387-390, 398, 400, 402
Civil rights, 575
Classification, fire protection, 433
Cleaning
  membranes, 178
  safety, 436
  stacks, 187
  tanks, 203, 206, 207
Coagulants, 91
Coagulation/sedimentation/filtration, 134, 137
Code requirements, fuel storage, 335
Coliform
  Colilert™ system (ONPG-MUG), 524
  Colisure test, 524
  community water system, 515, 525
  compliance, 526
  laboratory procedures, 524
  MCL, 518, 523
  membrane filter technique (MF), 524
  monitoring frequency, 524, 525
  multiple-tube fermentation (MTF), 524
  noncommunity water system, 525
  notification requirements, 526, 547, 548
  presence-absence (P-A), 523, 524
  reporting requirements, 526, 547, 548
  routine and repeat sampling, 524, 547
  rule, 523-527, 547
  sampling plan, 524
  sanitary survey, 524
Colilert™ system (ONPG-MUG), 524
Collecting samples, 7, 520, 540-542

Collection of sludges, 202
Collection systems, wastewater, 213, 218
Colloidal suspensions, 6
Colloids, 173
Color
  iron and manganese, 6
  regulations, 536
  removal, 91
  test procedures, 471
Colorimeter, 7, 8, 397
Communication, 589-591
Community water system, 515
Comparator, pocket, 466
Compensation, 578
Complaint procedure, 582
Complaints
  customer, 593
  employee, 582
Compliance schedule, 514
Compounds, fluoride, 32, 33, 57
Compressors
  belts, 309
  controls, 309
  drain, 309
  filter, 307
  fins, 308
  lubrication, 308
  maintenance, 307
  types, 307
  unloader, 308
  use, 307
  valves, 309
Concentration of sludges, 204
Concentration polarization, 159
Concrete tanks, 341
Conditioning of sludges, 203
Conducting meetings, 591
Conductivity, 489
Conductors, 243
Confined space entry permit, 439, 621
Confined space procedures, 371, 437-440, 617
Conservation, water, 592
Consumer complaints, 593
Consumer Confidence Report (CCR), 514, 552
Consumer inquiries, 593
Contaminants, unregulated, 514
Contaminated water supply
  contamination, 611-613
  countermeasures, 612
  Cryptosporidium, 612
  effective dosages, 611
  emergency treatment, 612, 613
  lethal dose 50 (LD 50), 611
  maximum allowable concentration (MAC), 611
  protective measures, 611
  response, 612
  toxicity, 611
  treatment, emergency, 612, 613
Contingency planning, 608
Continuing education, 579
Contract negotiations, 587
Control
  electrical, 302
  iron and manganese, 6, 9
  loop, 367
  panels, 447
  pumps, 293
  systems, 365-368, 391-395
  trihalomethanes, 131, 134, 138

Controllers, 366-368, 391
Controlling, 568
Cooling systems, engines, 332-334
Copper, 519, 536
Corrective maintenance, 599
Corrosion control, lead and copper, 519
Corrosivity, 519, 537
Couplings, 273, 298-301
Coverage ratio, 594, 595, 597
Cranes, 436
Crenothrix, 538
Criteria for avoiding filtration, 528
Cross connection, 285, 603-608
Cryptosporidium, 523, 528, 612
CT calculations, 688-696
CT values, 531
Current, electrical, 241, 243, 245, 250, 446, 447
Current imbalance, 245-248
Customer complaints, 593
Customer inquiries, 593
Cuvette, 466
Cyanide, 519
Cycle, electrical, 241

D

D/DBP (Disinfectants/Disinfection By-Products) Rule, 514, 523, 528, 531, 532
DO (dissolved oxygen)
  samples, 473, 475
  saturation table, 475
  test procedures, 472
Dall tube, 381
Dateometer, 294
Day tank, 41, 43
Debt service, 594
Decant, 205
Dechlorination, 13
Decibel, 440
Decision tree, coliform rule, 527
Delegation, 570
Demineralization
  Also see Electrodialysis and Reverse osmosis (RO)
  brackish water, 151, 152
  brine disposal, 152
  distillation, 152, 153
  electrodialysis, 152, 153, 180-190
  feedwater, 152
  freezing, 152, 153
  ion exchange, 152, 153
  mineralized waters, 151
  processes, 152, 153
  reverse osmosis, 152, 153
  salinity, 152
  seawater, 152
  total dissolved solids, 151, 152
Desiccant, 401
Desiccation, 395
Design review
  electrodialysis, 187
  fluoridation, 47
Detection lag, 368
Dewatering of sludges, 202, 203, 204, 208
Dial indicators, 300, 301
Diaphragm pumps, 33, 34
Diaphragm-operated valves, 325, 326
Diarrhea, "traveler's," 523
1,2-Dichloroethane, 523
1,1-Dichloroethylene, 522

Diesel
   engines, 329-333
   fuel storage, 335
Differential-pressure sensing, 366, 386-390
Digital, 366, 386-390
Direct current (D.C.), 241
Direct current, electrodialysis, 181, 182, 183, 187
Directing, 568
Dirty water
   iron and manganese, 6
   red water, 15, 21
Disciplinary problems, 582
Discriminatory hiring, 574, 575
Disinfectants/Disinfection By-Products (D/DBP) Rule, 514, 523, 528, 531, 532
Disinfection alternatives, 138
Disinfection by-products, 514, 518, 523, 528, 531, 532
Disinfection, CT values, 531, 688-696
Disposal of
   records, 630
   sludges, 202, 203, 204, 213
   spent brine, 107, 202, 213
Disposition of plant records, 630
Dissolved oxygen (DO)
   samples, 473, 475
   saturation table, 475
   test procedures, 472
Distillation, 152, 153
Divalent, 7, 78
Documentation, 573
Dose, chemical feeders, 98, 339
Downflow saturators, 41, 44
Drainage waters, plant, 220
Draining tanks, 203, 206, 207
Drains
   chemical feeders, 336
   chemical handling, 432
   compressors, 309
Drinking Water Contaminant Candidate List (DWCCL), 514
Drinking water regulations
   See Regulations, drinking water
Driving equipment, pumps, 302
Drowning, 453
Dry chemical feeders, 33, 37-39, 57, 337
Drying beds, 208, 210, 211, 218
Dust, fluoridation, 57
Dynamic types of pumps, 270

E

ESWTR (Enhanced Surface Water Treatment Rule), 514, 523, 528
E. coli, 523, 525, 526
Eccentric valves, 312-314
Effective range, 366
Effects of
   fluoride, 32
   iron and manganese, 6
   trihalomethanes, 129
Electric motors, 251-256, 294-296
Electrical equipment
   additional reading, 267
   alternating current (A.C.), 241
   ammeter, 245, 246
   amplitude, 241
   amps, 242
   auxiliary electrical power, 256, 264
   batteries, 241, 265
   blown fuse, 245
   breakers, 242, 247, 250
   circuit breakers, 242, 247, 250
   circuits, 241, 243
   conductors, 243
   control panels, 447
   controls, 302
   current, 241, 243, 245, 250, 446, 447
   cycle, 241
   direct current (D.C.), 241
   electric motors, 251-256, 294-296
   electromotive force (E.M.F.), 241
   emergency lighting, 264, 265
   fundamentals, 241
   fuse puller, 244
   fuses, 241, 242, 244, 245, 250
   ground, 250
   ground fault interrupter (G.F.I.), 447
   hazards, 240
   hertz, 241
   instrumentation, 368, 447
   insulation, motors, 255
   insulation resistance, 248
   insulators, 243
   kirk-key, 264
   lighting, emergency, 264, 265
   limitations, 240
   magnetic starters, 251-253
   maintenance, 236, 240, 294
   megger, 248
   megohm, 249
   meters, electrical, 243
   motor insulation, 255
   motor starters, 251, 446
   motors, 241, 251-256, 294-296
   nameplate, 255
   ohm, 242
   ohmmeters, 249
   Ohm's Law, 242
   overload relays, 250
   panels, control, 447
   phase, 241
   power requirements, 243, 303
   protection devices, 250
   recordkeeping, 236, 237, 255, 256
   safety, 238, 240, 267, 446
   standby power generation, 256, 264
   starters, 251, 446
   switch gear, 250, 266
   switches, 241, 243
   tag, warning, 239, 286
   testers, 243
   thermal overloads, 250
   transformers, 241, 247, 251, 266, 446
   transmission, 266
   troubleshooting, 256, 257-261
   voltage testing, 243, 245, 446
   volts, 241, 243, 266
   warning tag, 239, 286
   watts, 242
Electrical hazards, 240, 368
Electrode tab, 189
Electrodialysis
   Also see Demineralization and Reverse osmosis (RO)
   additional reading, 190
   advantages, 180
   arithmetic assignment, 190
   brine, 180
   cartridge filters, 183, 185
   chemical flush system, 187

Electrodialysis (continued)
   cleaning stacks, 187
   description, 180, 181
   design, 187
   direct current, 181, 182, 183, 187
   electrode tab, 189
   electrodialysis polarity reversal (EDR), 181, 183
   energy requirements, 180
   feedwater quality, 183
   flow diagram, 183, 185
   fouling, 181
   Langelier Index, 181
   log sheet, 187, 188
   membranes, 180-190
   multi-compartment units, 183, 184
   operation, 180, 187
   pH, 187
   piping, 183
   power supply, 183, 187
   pressures, 183
   pretreatment, 183
   principles, 181
   pumping equipment, 183
   recordkeeping, 187, 188
   safety, 189
   scaling, 181, 187
   specifications, 187
   stack, 181, 183, 187
   stages, 181
   temperature, 187
   three-cell unit, 181, 182
Electrodialysis polarity reversal (EDR), 181, 183
Electrolyte, 265
Electromedia process, 14
Electromotive force (E.M.F.), 241
Electronic chemical pumps, 33, 36, 48
Elements, instrumentation, 386
Emergencies
   administration, 608-613
   contaminated water supply, 611-613
   phone numbers, 238
   preparation for, 454, 570, 608-613
   procedures, 238, 454, 612
   response plan, 570, 608-613
   safety, 454
   team, 238
Emergency
   lighting, 264, 265
   maintenance, 599
   response plan, 570, 608-613
   treatment, 613
Employee
   benefits, 575, 578
   evaluation, 579-581
   orientation, 578
   pride, 578
   problems, 582, 587
Employee-management relationship, 587
Employees, number, 573
Employer policies, 578, 584
End bells, 251
Endemic, 32
Energy requirements, electrodialysis, 180
Enforcement, regulations, 512
Engines
   air cooled, 332
   cooling systems, 332-334
   diesel, 329-333
   fuel storage, 335

   fuel system, 329-332
   gasoline, 327
   governor, 331, 332
   lubrication, 327
   maintenance, 327, 332
   operation, diesel, 329
   problems, 327
   running, 327
   standby, 336
   starting, 327, 328, 332
   troubleshooting, 327, 332
   water cooled, 332
Enhanced Surface Water Treatment Rule (ESWTR), 514, 523, 528
Equipment
   gas detection, 437
   lab safety, 449
   records, 630
   repair/replacement fund, 596
   safety, operator, 451-454
   service card, 236, 237
Equivalent weight, 80
Establishment, regulations, 513-516
Evaluation, performance, 579-581
Explosive atmospheres, 451
Extinguishers, fire, 433-435
Eye protection, 452

F

Falls, injury, 371
Feasibility analysis process, 131
FEDERAL REGISTER, 129, 131, 139, 532
Feed rate, chemical, 94-98, 339
Feedback, instrumentation, 367
Feeders, chemical
   See Chemical feeders
Feedwater
   demineralization, 152
   electrodialysis, 183
   reverse osmosis, 174
Fees, user, 594, 595
Ferric chloride, 429
Ferric sulfate, 429
Ferrous sulfate, 429
Filter
   backwash recycling, 515
   backwash wastewater, 218
   compressor, 307
   presses, 204, 213, 216
Filtration, iron and manganese, 13, 14, 17-20
Financial assistance, 597
Financial management, 594-598
Financial stability, 594
Fins, compressors, 308
Fire prevention, 433
Fire protection
   classification, 433
   exits, 435
   extinguishers, 433-435
   flammable storage, 435
   hoses, 434
   prevention, 433
   storage, flammables, 435
First aid
   acetic acid, 418
   alum, 429
   aluminum sulfate, 429
   ammonia, 421

First aid (continued)
  calcium hydroxide, 422
  carbon dioxide, 426
  chlorine, 424-426
  equipment, 419
  ferric chloride, 429
  ferric sulfate, 429
  ferrous sulfate, 429
  fluoride, 58, 430
  hydrochloric acid, 420
  hydrofluosilicic acid, 418
  hydrogen fluoride, 420
  hypochlorite, 423
  lime, 422
  nitric acid, 420
  potassium permanganate, 430
  powdered activated carbon, 431
  safety program, 616
  sodium aluminate, 429
  sodium carbonate, 423
  sodium silicate, 423
  sulfur dioxide, 428
  sulfuric acid, 420
Flammable storage, 435
Flanges, pumps, 273
Floats, level, 372, 375, 376
Flow measurement
  Dall tube, 381
  differential-pressure sensing, 379, 381, 382
  magnetic, 379
  orifice, 381, 382
  positive displacement, 379
  propeller meter, 379-381
  rate of flow, 379
  rotameter, 378, 379, 383
  service meters, 379
  ultrasonic, 379
  velocity sensing, 379, 380
  Venturi, 381, 382
Fluoridation
  additional reading, 63
  air temperatures, 32
  alarms, 47
  arithmetic assignment, 63
  batch mix, 40, 41
  calculating doses, 59-63
  charts, 48-50
  chemical feeders, 33-46
    Also see Chemical feeders
  compounds, 32, 33, 57
  day tank, 41, 43
  downflow saturators, 41, 44
  dust, 57
  effects on teeth, 32, 519, 537
  first aid, fluoride, 58
  fluoride ion, 32
  formulas, 59
  hydrofluosilicic acid, 32, 33, 45, 46, 48, 49, 50
  importance, 32
  levels, 32
  log sheets, 48, 51, 53, 55
  maintenance, 57
  maximum contaminant level (MCL), 32
  operation, 48
  optimum level, 32
  overfeeding, 47, 54
  poisoning, fluoride, 58
  Primary Drinking Water Regulations, 32
  programs, 32

  public notification, 54
  records, 48, 51, 53, 55
  safety, 57
  safety equipment, 48, 57
  sanitary defects, 57
  saturator, 40, 41, 42, 57
  shutdown, 54
  sodium fluoride, 32, 33, 41
  sodium silicofluoride, 32, 33, 52
  solution preparation, 48
  specification review, 47
  start-up, 47
  systems, 33, 40
  training, 58
  treatment charts, 48-50
  underfeeding, 54
  upflow saturators, 41, 42, 44
Fluoride
  compounds, 32, 33, 57, 428
  fluorosis, 519, 537
  ion, 32
  levels, 32, 519, 537
  regulations, 519, 537
  test procedures, 475
Flux decline, 156
Flux, reverse osmosis, 155, 156
FmHA loans, 597
Foaming agents, 537
Foot protection, 452
Foot valves, 289, 316
Forklifts, 444, 445
Formation of THMs, 129, 133, 134, 137
Fouling, electrodialysis, 181
Freezing, demineralization, 152, 153
Frequency of sampling, 520, 524-526, 529, 530, 533, 536, 542
Fuel storage
  code requirements, 335
  diesel, 335
  gasoline, 335
  liquid petroleum gas (LPG), 335
  natural gas, 335
Fuel systems, engines, 329-332
Fueling vehicles, 443
Functions, of manager, 568
Fund, repair/replacement, 596
Fuse
  blown, 245
  puller, 244
Fuses, 241, 242, 244, 245, 250

G

G.F.I. (ground fault interrupter), 447
Gas, chemical feeders, 337
Gas detection equipment, 437
Gas masks, 425-427
Gases
  chemical handling, 424
  safety, 424
Gasoline
  engines, 327
  fuel storage, 335
Gate valves, 309, 310, 311
General obligation bonds, 597
Giardia, 523, 528-531
Glassware, laboratory safety, 449
Globe valves, 312, 323, 325, 326
Gloves, 452

Goals, utility, 570
Governor, engines, 331, 332
Grant programs, 597
Granular activated carbon, 137, 139
Gravimetric chemical feeders, 34, 39
Greensand, iron and manganese, 13, 17-20
Grievances, 582, 587
Gross alpha activity, 533
Gross beta activity, 533
Ground, electrical, 250
Ground fault interrupter (G.F.I.), 447
Ground Water Disinfection Rule (GWDR), 514, 523
Group 1 and 2 THM treatment techniques, 139
Groups, protected, 575

H

Hand protection, 452
Handling of chemicals
   See Chemical handling
Handling process wastes, 201, 202, 203
Harassment, 583, 584
Hard hat, 453
Hard water, 78
Hardness, 78-80, 83, 84, 484
   Also see Softening
Hardness leakage, 107
Hazard communication program, 616
Hazardous gases, 424, 437
Hazards
   drowning, 453
   electrical, 240, 368, 446
   gases, 424, 437
   instrumentation, 368-371
   laboratory, 449-451
   maintenance, 436
   mechanical, 370
Head protection, 453
Health effects
   bacteria, 523
   fluoride, 32, 519, 537
   iron and manganese, 6
   nitrate, 521
   primary contaminants, 517
   secondary contaminants, 535
   trihalomethanes, 129
Health regulations, 512, 515, 517, 535
Hertz, 241, 393
Heterotrophic bacteria, 524
Hiring procedures, 573-578
History of drinking water laws, 512
Hollow fine fiber, reverse osmosis, 169, 171, 173
Horizontal centrifugal pumps, 269, 270, 277, 304
Hoses, fire, 434
Hot plates, 450
Human factors, safety, 626
Hydrated lime, 84, 422
Hydrochloric acid, 420
Hydrofluosilicic acid, 32, 45, 46, 48, 49, 51, 418
Hydrogen fluoride, 420
Hydrogen sulfide, 538
Hydrolysis, 159, 163, 173
Hygroscopic, 336
Hypochlorite, 423

I

ICR (Information Collection Rule), 532
Immediate threats to health, 521, 523

Immunization, shots, 450
Impeller, pumps, 269, 271, 278, 279
Improvements, capital, 596
Improving system management, 569
Indicators, instruments, 386
Information Collection Rule (ICR), 532
Initial sampling, 540
Injury
   See Accident
Inorganic chemicals, regulations, 516-522
Inquiries, pre-employment, 576
Insoluble compounds, 6
Inspection of
   pumps, 306
   tanks, 341
Instrumentation
   accuracy, 366
   air supply systems, 395, 396
   alarms, 390, 391
   analog, 366, 386, 387
   annunciator panels, 390
   automatic controller, 391
   bubbler tube, 375, 377
   calibration, 366, 397
   categories, 386
   charts, strip and circular, 387-390, 398, 400, 402
   chemical feed, 383
   circular chart, 387-390, 398, 400, 402
   confined spaces, 371
   control loop, 367
   control systems, 365-368, 391-395
   controllers, 366-368, 391
   differential pressure sensing, 379, 381, 382
   digital, 366, 386-390
   effective range, 366
   electrical equipment, 447
   electrical hazards, 368
   elements, 386
   feedback, 367
   floats, 372, 375, 376
   flow, 379-383
   hazards, 368-371
   importance, 365
   indicators, 386
   integrator, 390
   laboratory, 397
   level sensing, 372, 375-377
   linearity, 366
   magnetic flow sensing, 379
   maintenance, 398, 401, 402
   measurement, 365, 371, 386, 399, 400
   mechanical hazards, 370
   motor control station, 367-370
   multimeter, 398
   ON/OFF controls, 391, 392
   operation, 398, 402
   panel, 366, 368, 369, 386
   pH, 383, 384, 397
   phone lines, 393, 394
   pneumatic systems, 383, 385, 389, 396, 401
   precision, 366
   pressure sensing, 372-374
   probes, 375, 376
   process control, 391
   proportional control, 391
   pump controllers, 391-395
   range, 366
   rate of flow, 379
   recorders, 386-390, 398, 400

Instrumentation (continued)
  records, 401
  rotameters, 378, 379, 383
  safety, 368, 447
  sensors, 371
  shutdown, 401
  signal transmitters, 383
  snubber, 372, 374
  standardization, 366
  start-up, 401
  strip chart, 387, 389, 390, 398, 400, 402
  surge protection, 372, 374
  symbols, 361-364
  telemetering, 383, 393, 396
  testing, 397
  total flow, 379
  totalizers, 390
  transducers, 380, 383
  transmitters, 371, 380, 383
  troubleshooting, 398-401
  turbidimeter, 383, 384, 397
  ultrasonic flow sensing, 379
  V-O-M (volt-ohm-milliammeter), 398, 399
  vaults, 371
  velocity sensing, 379, 380
  Venturi, 381, 382
Insulation, motors, 255
Insulation, resistance, 248
Insulators, 243
Integrator, instrument, 390
Interim regulations, 515
Internal combustion engines
  See Engines
Interview
  job, 575, 576
  media, 592
Inventory, 628
Ion exchange
  demineralization, 152, 153
  iron and manganese, 11
  softeners, 101-104
  trihalomethanes, 135, 137
  wastes, 218
Ion exchange resin, 11, 101, 104, 106, 135, 137
Ion exchange softening
  Also see Lime-soda ash softening and Softening
  air release assembly, 111
  backwash, 106, 109
  blending, 114
  brine, 106, 107, 109
  bypass, 114, 115
  calculations, 112-114
  description of process, 101-104
  disposal of spent brine, 107
  formulas, 112
  hardness leakage, 107
  iron and manganese problems, 107, 109
  limitations, 107
  maintenance, 108
  monitoring, 107
  operation, 104-107
  recordkeeping, 116
  resin, 101, 104, 106
  rinse, 105, 106, 110
  salt solution characteristics, 112
  sanitary defects, brine storage tanks, 109
  service, 104, 105, 109

  shutdown, 110
  split treatment, 114
  start-up, 110
  testing, 107
  troubleshooting, 109
  wastes, 218
  zeolite, 101
Iron and manganese
  additional reading, 22
  adverse effects, 6
  aeration, 12
  analysis, 7, 8
  arithmetic assignment, 22
  bacteria, 6, 7, 21, 22
  bench scale tests, 9, 13
  breakpoint chlorination, 15
  chlorination, 9-11, 13, 17, 20
  collecting samples, 7
  color, 6
  colorimetric testing, 7
  control, 6, 9
  dechlorination, 13
  dirty water, 6
  divalent, 7
  effects, 6
  electromedia process, 14
  ferrous ion, 7
  filtration, 13, 14, 17-20
  formulas, 16-18, 667
  greensand, 13, 17-20
  health effects, 6
  ion exchange, 11
  ion exchange problems, 107
  jar tests, 18
  limits, 6
  maintenance, 15, 19
  measurement, 6, 7, 16
  monitoring, 15, 20
  need to control, 6
  objections, 6
  occurrence, 6
  operation, 17-20
  oxidation, 12, 13
  permanganate, 13, 17-19
  pH, 12, 18, 19
  phosphate treatment, 9-11
  polyphosphate treatment, 9-11
  problems, ion exchange, 107
  proprietary processes, 14
  red water problems, 15, 21
  regulations, 537
  reservoirs, 6
  samples, 7
  sludge handling and disposal, 218
  stains, 6, 7
  tastes and odors, 6
  troubleshooting, 19, 20, 21
  zeolite, 13
Iron, regulations, 537
Iron (total), test procedures, 479

J

Jar tests, softening, 94-98
Job
  duties, 568, 572
  interview, 575, 576

Jogging, 157

K

Kemmerer-type sampler, 475, 476
Kirk-key, 264

L

LAS (Linear Alkylbenzene Sulfonate), 537
LPG (liquid petroleum gas), 335
Labeling chemicals, 432
Laboratory instrumentation, 397
Laboratory safety
   autoclaves, 450
   biological considerations, 450
   booster shots, 450
   chemicals, 449
   equipment, 450
   glassware, 449
   hazards, 449-451
   hot plates, 450
   immunization, 450
   pipet washers, 450
   radioactivity, 450
   shots, booster, 450
   sterilizers, 450
   water stills, 450
Laboratory test procedures
   algae counts, 467
   calcium, 468
   calcium carbonate saturation test, 484
   chloride, 469
   coliform, 524
   color, 471
   dissolved oxygen, 472
   fluoride, 475
   iron (total), 479
   manganese, 481
   marble test, 484
   metals, 485
   nitrate, 486
   odor, 492
   pH, 489
   specific conductance, 489
   sulfate, 490
   taste and odor, 492
   total dissolved solids, 497
   trihalomethanes, 496
Lagoons, process wastes, 205
Landfills, sanitary, 204, 213, 218, 219
Langelier Index, 81, 133, 181, 484
Lead, 519
Lead and Copper Rule, 514, 519-521
Leakage, hardness, 107
Legionella, 518, 528
Lethal dose 50 (LD 50), 611
Let's Build a Pump!, 269-276
Level controls, 302
Level sensing instruments, 372, 375-377
Library, maintenance, 236, 238
Lighting, emergency, 264, 265
Lime, 84, 87, 88, 89, 90
Lime sludge, 218
Lime-soda ash softening
   Also see Ion exchange softening and Softening
   alkalinity, 91
   application of lime, 90
   benefits, 83

   calculation of dosages, 86, 94-99
   carbon dioxide, 84, 91
   caustic soda softening, 85, 88
   chemical reactions, 84-86
   coagulants, 91
   color removal, 91
   formulas, 86
   handling lime, 90
   hardness removal, 84
   hydrated lime, 84
   jar tests, 94-98
   lime, 84, 90
   lime softening, 87, 88
   lime-soda ash softening, 83, 88
   limitations, 79, 83
   marble test, 92
   National Lime Association, 91
   partial lime softening, 87
   permanent hardness, 84
   polyphosphate, 87, 92
   quicklime, 84, 92
   recarbonation, 85, 86, 87, 88, 91
   recordkeeping, 93
   safety, 90, 92
   slake, 84, 92
   sludge, 93, 218
   split treatment, 87-90
   stability, 81, 85, 91
   storage of lime, 90
   supersaturated, 84
   temporary hardness, 84
Lime softening, 87, 88
Limitations
   ion exchange softening, 79
   lime-soda ash softening, 83
   softening, 79
Limits
   fluoride, 32
   iron and manganese, 6
Linear Alkylbenzene Sulfonate (LAS), 537
Linearity, 366
Liquid chemical feeders, 337
Liquid petroleum gas (LPG), 335
List, priority, 513
Listening skills, 589
Loan funding programs, 597
Location of sampling points, 540, 542
Lockout, safety, 238, 447, 448
Lockout/tagout procedure, 238, 447, 448
Log removals, 690
Log sheets
   electrodialysis, 187, 188
   fluoride, 48, 51, 53, 55
   reverse osmosis, 176, 177
Long-term capital improvements, 596
Lubrication
   compressors, 308
   engines, 327
   maintenance, 282-284
   mechanical equipment, 282-284
   pumps, 273, 282-284
   valves, 311

M

MBAS (methylene-blue-active substances), 537
MCLG (Maximum Contaminant Level Goal), 515
MCLs, 515, 516-534
MSDS (Material Safety Data Sheet), 617-619

Magnetic flow measurement, 379
Magnetic starters, 251-253
Maintenance
   administration, 592, 599-608
   buildings, 341, 342
   cathodic protection, 341
   chemical feeders, 19, 57, 337
   chlorinators, 340
   cleaning, 436
   compressors, 307
   concrete tanks, 341
   cooling systems, 332-335
   corrective, 599
   cranes, 436
   diesel engines, 329-333
   electrical equipment, 240, 294
   emergency, 599
   engines, 327, 329
   equipment service card, 236, 237
   fluoridation, 57
   gasoline engines, 327
   hazards, 436
   inspection, tanks, 341
   instrumentation, 398, 401, 402
   ion exchange softeners, 108
   iron and manganese, 15, 19
   library, 236, 238
   lubrication, 282-284
   manholes, 438
   manuals, 236
   manufacturers, 236, 237
   mechanical equipment, 269
   painting, 436
   power tools, 440
   predictive, 599
   preventive, 236, 285, 599
   program, 236
   pumps, 269, 285-301
   recordkeeping, 236, 628
   reservoirs, 341
   safety, 436-441, 446
   service record card, 236, 237
   steel tanks, 341
   tanks, 341
   tools, power, 440
   types, 599
   valves, 309, 311, 312, 325, 441
   vehicles, 441, 442
   welding, 441
Management questions, 569
Management, utility, 568
   Also see Administration
Manager's responsibilities, 568, 573, 599
Manganese
   Also see Iron and manganese
   aeration, 12
   greensand systems, 13, 17-20
   limits, 6
   manganous ion, 7
   oxidation, 13
   regulations, 538
   test procedures, 481
Manholes, 438
Manmade radioactivity, 533
Manuals, maintenance, 236
Manufacturers, 236
Marble test, 21, 92, 484
Mass media, 592

Material Safety Data Sheet (MSDS), 617-619
Maximum allowable concentration (MAC), 611
Maximum Contaminant Level Goal (MCLG), 515
Maximum Contaminant Level (MCL) (primary standards)
   chlorine residual substitution, 529
   development process, 513
   disinfection by-products, 514, 531, 532
   fluoride, 32, 519, 537
   inorganic chemicals, 513, 516-522
   manmade radioactivity, 518, 533, 550
   microbial contaminants, 513, 523-531
   natural radioactivity, 518, 533, 549
   organic chemicals, 512, 513, 522
   radiological contaminants, 513, 514, 533
   trihalomethanes, 129, 518, 531
   turbidity, 513, 518, 529
   types, 513
Measurement
   instrumentation, 365, 371, 386, 399, 400
   iron and manganese, 6, 7, 16
   safety, 625
Mechanical equipment
   centrifugal pumps, 269
   Let's Build a Pump!, 269-276
   lubrication, 282-284
   maintenance, 269
   pumps, 269
   repair shop, 269
Mechanical seals, 289
Media, news, 592
Meetings, conducting, 591
Megger, 248
Megohm, 249
Membrane filter, 524
Membranes
   electrodialysis, 180-190
   filter, 524
   performance, 155
   properties, 155
   reverse osmosis, 152, 155, 156, 172, 178
Mercury, 521
Metals, test procedures, 485
Metering chemical feeders, 337
Meters, electrical, 243
Methemoglobinemia, 486, 517, 521
Microbial contaminants, 513, 518, 523-531
Microbial organism fouling, 172, 173
Mineral rejection, 156, 157, 158
Mineralized waters, 151
Monitoring
   coliform frequency, 524-526
   ion exchange softening, 107
   iron and manganese, 15, 20
   process wastes, 201, 220
   regulations, 520, 524, 530, 532, 533, 536
   reverse osmosis, 172
   SWTR, 530
   secondary contaminants, 536
   trihalomethanes, 129, 133, 138, 531
   wastes, 201, 220
Motor
   control station, 367-370
   electrical, 240, 241, 251, 447
   insulation, 255
   pump, 251, 278
   safety, 447
   starters, 251, 446
Mottled teeth, 32

Multi-compartment units, electrodialysis, 183, 184
Multimeter, 398
Multiple-tube fermentation, 524
Muriatic acid, 420

N

NPDES Permit, 108, 201
NTU, 529
Nameplate, 255
Nanofiltration, reverse osmosis, 159
National Electrical Safety Code, 179
National Labor Relations Act, 616
National Lime Association, 91
National Safety Council, 624
National Secondary Drinking Water Regulations
    See Secondary Drinking Water Regulations
Natural gas, 335
Natural radioactivity, 533
Negotiations, contract, 587
Nephelometric turbidity unit (NTU), 529
Nessler tubes, 7, 466, 471
New employee orientation, 578
News media, 552, 592
Nitrate
    health effects, 517, 521
    regulations, 517, 521
    test procedures, 486
Nitric acid, 420
Nitrite, 521
Noise protection, 440
Noisy pump, 303
Noncarbonate hardness, 84, 85
Noncommunity water system, 515
Nontransient noncommunity water system, 515
Notification, 54, 514, 526, 543-551, 552
Number of employees needed, 573

O

Occupational Safety and Health Act (OSHA), 616
Odor
    regulations, 538
    test procedures, 492
Ohm, 242
Ohmmeter, 249
Ohm's Law, 242
Olfactory fatigue, 418
ON/OFF controls, 391, 392
ONPG-MUG test (coliforms), 524
Operating ratio, 594, 595, 597
Operation
    chemical feeders, 48
    diesel engines, 329
    electrodialysis, 180, 187
    fluoridation, 48
    greensand, 17-20
    instrumentation, 398, 402
    ion exchange softeners, 104-107
    iron and manganese, 17-20
    reverse osmosis, 172-179
    safety, 416, 444
    valves, 309, 311
Operations and maintenance (O & M), 599-608
Operator certification, 578
Operator protection
    atmospheres, explosive, 451
    drowning, 453
    equipment, safety, 419, 451

explosive atmospheres, 451
eye protection, 452
first-aid equipment, 616
foot protection, 452
gas-detection equipment, 437
gloves, 452
hand protection, 452
hard hat, 453
hazardous gases, 424, 437
head protection, 453
noise, 440
respiratory protection, 425-427, 451
safety equipment, 451
safety program, 614-627
self-contained breathing apparatus, 425-427, 451
traffic, 443
water safety, 453
Optimum level, fluoride, 32, 33
Oral communication, 589
Organic chemicals, regulations, 513, 517, 522
Organizational plan, 570, 571
Organizing, 568, 570
Orientation, new employee, 578
Orifice flow measurement, 381, 382
Osmosis, 152, 154
OUCH principle, 577
Overfeeding fluoride, 47, 54
Overload relays, 250
Oxidation
    iron and manganese, 12, 13
    trihalomethanes, 135, 137
Oxygen deficiency, 437, 451
Oxygen saturation table, 475
Ozone, 135, 137, 138, 139

P

Packing
    pumps, 275, 285, 287, 288, 290
    valves, 311
Painting, 436
Panels
    control, 447
    instrumentation, 366, 368, 369, 386
Paper screening, 575
Para-Dichlorobenzene, 523
Partial lime softening, 87
Parts, valves, 309
Payback time, 595, 597
Percentile, 90th, lead and copper, 521
Performance evaluation, 579-581
Peristaltic pumps, 33, 35, 48
Permanent hardness, 84
Permanganate, potassium
    See Potassium permanganate
Permeability constants, 156
Permeate, 156, 169
Permeate projections, computerized, 160, 161
Permit
    confined space entry, 619
    NPDES, 108, 201
Personnel records, 573, 587
Pesticides, 517
pH
    instrumentation, 383, 384, 397
    regulations, 538
    test procedures, 489
pH, effects on
    electrodialysis, 187

pH, effects on (continued)
  reverse osmosis, 159, 163, 173, 174
  softening, 81, 82
  trihalomethanes, 133
Phase, electrical, 241
Phone lines, 393, 394
Phosphate treatment, 9-11
picoCurie, 533
Pink water, 15, 19
Pipet washers, 450
Piston pumps, 277, 279
Plan, organizational, 570, 571
Planning
  administration, 568, 570
  emergencies, 570, 608
Plant
  drainage waters, 220
  maintenance, 436
  operations data, 627
  records, 627-630
  tours, 593
Pneumatic systems, 383, 385, 389, 396, 401
Pocket comparators, 466
Poisoning, fluoride, 58
Pole shader, 257
Policies and procedures, administration, 578
Policy statement, safety, 448, 615
Polyphosphate treatment
  iron and manganese, 9-11
  reverse osmosis, 173, 174
  softening, 87, 92
Ponds, process wastes, 205
Population decline, 570
Positive displacement flow measurement, 379
Positive displacement pumps, 33, 302
Potassium permanganate
  handling, 430
  iron and manganese, 13, 17-19
  safety, 430
  trihalomethanes, 134, 137, 139
Powdered activated carbon, 137, 139, 430
Powders, 430, 431
Power requirements, 243, 303
Power supply, electrodialysis, 183, 187
Power tools, 440
Precision, instrumentation, 366
Precursors, THM, 129, 133, 134, 137
Predictive maintenance, 599
Pre-employment inquiries, 576
Preparation for emergencies, 454, 608
Presence-absence (P-A), 523, 524
Pressure sensing instrumentation, 372-374
Pressures, electrodialysis, 183
Pretreatment
  electrodialysis, 183
  reverse osmosis, 172
Prevention of fires, 433
Preventive maintenance, 599
Pride, employee, 578
Primary Drinking Water Standards
  bacteria, 523
  disinfectants and disinfection by-products, 531
  establishment, 512-516
  inorganic chemicals, 516-522
  MCLs, 517-518
  microbial standards, 523-531
  organic chemicals, 522
  radioactivity, 533
  regulations, 32, 512

  treatment techniques, 516
Prime, pumps, 302, 304
Priority list, 513
Probationary period, 578
Probes, instrumentation, 375, 376
Problem employees, 582
Process control instrumentation, 391
Process variable, 371
Process wastes
  alum sludge, 218
  backwash recovery ponds, 205, 207
  backwash wastewater, 218
  basket centrifuge, 213, 215
  belt filter presses, 204, 209, 212
  brine, 202, 203, 213
  centrifuges, 204, 209, 213, 214, 215
  cleaning tanks, 203, 206, 207
  collection of sludges, 202
  collection systems, 213, 218
  concentration, 204
  conditioning, 203
  decant, 205
  dewatering of sludges, 202, 203, 204, 208
  disposal of sludges and brines, 202, 203, 204, 213
  draining tanks, 203, 206, 207
  drying beds, 208, 210, 211, 218
  filter backwash wastewater, 218
  filter presses, 204, 213, 216
  handling, 201, 202, 203
  ion exchange wastes, 218
  iron sludge, 218
  lagoons, 205
  landfills, 204, 213, 218, 219
  lime sludge, 218
  monitoring, 201, 220
  NPDES Permit, 108, 201
  need for handling and disposal, 201
  ponds, 205
  processing alternatives, 203, 204
  Public Law 92-500, 201
  reporting, 220
  sand drying beds, 208, 210, 211, 218
  sand filter, 218
  sanitary landfills, 204, 213, 218, 219
  scroll centrifuge, 213, 214
  septic wastes, 220
  sewers, 213, 218
  sludge pumps, 220
  sludge volumes, 202
  solar lagoons, 204, 205, 208
  sources, 201, 202, 204
  supernatant, 208
  tanks, draining and cleaning, 203, 206, 207
  temperature effects, 202
  thickening, 203, 204
  vacuum filters, 204, 213, 217
  vacuum tank truck, 207, 208, 218
  volumes of sludges, 202
  wastewater collection system, 213, 218
  Water Pollution Control Act, 201
  Winklepress, 212
Procurement of materials, 628, 629
Procurement records, 628
Productive meetings, 591
Profile, qualifications, 574
Program, maintenance, 236
Progressive cavity pumps, 277, 278, 280, 293
Propeller meter, 379-381
Propeller pumps, 293

Property taxes, 597
Proportional control instrumentation, 391
Proprietary processes, iron and manganese, 14
Protected groups, 575
Protection devices, electrical equipment, 250
Protective measures, water supply, 611
Prussian blue, 311
Public Law 92-500, 201
Public
   notification, fluoride, 54
   relations, 592-594
   speaking, 593
   water systems, 515
Pump controllers, instrumentation, 391-395
Pump maintenance
   alignment, 273, 289, 297-301
   bearings, 289, 293
   belt drives, 294, 297
   chain drives, 297
   check valves, 289, 293, 316-325
   controls, 293
   couplings, 298-301
   dial indicators, 300, 301
   electric motors, 251-256, 294-296
   foot valves, 289, 316
   mechanical seals, 289
   packing, 275, 285, 288, 290
   preventive maintenance, 285
   progressive cavity pumps, 293
   propeller pumps, 293
   reciprocating pumps, 292
   shear pin, 292, 300
   shutdown, 289, 302
   variable speed belt drives, 298
   wearing rings, 289
Pump operation
   centrifugal pumps, 304-306
   discharge, 303
   driving equipment, 302
   electrical controls, 302
   inspection, 306
   level controls, 302
   noisy pump, 303
   positive displacement pumps, 33, 306
   power requirements, 303
   prime, 302, 304
   rotation, 303
   shutdown, 302, 304
   starting, 302-306
   troubleshooting, 303
Pumping equipment, electrodialysis, 183
Pumps
   alignment, 273, 289, 297-301
   bearings, 273, 278, 279, 289, 293
   casing, 274, 278, 279
   cavitation, 276, 277
   centrifugal pumps, 269, 277, 304
   chemical metering, 278, 337
   couplings, 273, 298-301
   displacement, 270
   dynamic types, 270
   flanges, 273
   horizontal centrifugal pumps, 269, 270, 277, 304
   impeller, 269, 271, 278, 279
   Let's Build a Pump!, 269-276
   lubrication, 273, 282-284
   maintenance
      See Pump maintenance
   motors, 240-264
   packing, 275, 285, 288, 290
   piston type, 277, 279
   progressive cavity, 277, 278, 280, 293
   reciprocating, 277, 279, 292
   rings, wearing, 274, 275
   screw flow, 278, 280
   seal, 275
   shaft, 271, 273, 278, 279
   sleeves, 271, 273, 278, 279
   stuffing boxes, 275
   suction, 273, 274, 276
   vertical centrifugal pumps, 277
   wearing rings, 274, 275
Purchase order, 595, 628, 629

Q

Qualifications profile, 574
Questions
   management, 569
   pre-employment, 576
Quicklime, 84, 92, 422

R

Radio, 552, 592
Radioactivity, 533
Radiological contaminants, 513, 514, 518, 533
Radon, 514, 533
Range, instrumentation, 366
Rate of flow instrumentation, 379
Rates, water, 596
Recarbonation, 85, 86, 87, 88, 91
Reciprocating pumps, 277, 279, 292
Recognition, employee, 578
Recorders, instruments, 386-390, 398, 400
Recordkeeping
   accident reports, 620
   bacteriological, 552
   chemical, 552
   disposition of records, 630
   electrical equipment, 236, 237, 255, 256
   electrodialysis, 187, 188
   equipment, 630
   fluoridation, 48, 51, 53, 55
   Information Collection Rule (ICR), 532
   instrumentation, 401
   inventory, 628
   ion exchange softening, 116
   lime-soda ash softening, 93
   maintenance, 628
   operations data, 627
   personnel, 573, 587
   plant, 627-630
   process wastes, 220
   procurement, 628
   purchase order, 595, 628, 629
   purpose, 627
   requisition, 595, 628, 629
   retention of records, 552, 630
   reverse osmosis, 174, 176, 177
   safety, 620
   sanitary survey, 552
   softening, 93
   types of records, 627
   variance and exemptions, 552
Recovery, reverse osmosis, 159, 174

Red water problems, 15, 21
Regulations, drinking water
   arsenic, 514, 516
   bacteria, 518, 523-531
   barium, 516
   cadmium, 519
   check sampling, 540
   chloride, 536
   chlorine residual substitution, 529
   chromium, 519
   coliforms, 518, 523-531
   color, 536
   community water system, 515
   copper, 519, 536
   establishment, 513-516
   filtration, 528-531
   fluoride, 19, 537
   foaming agents, 537
   Giardia lamblia, 523, 528-531
   health, 512, 515, 516, 517-518, 535
   immediate threats to health, 521, 523
   initial sampling, 540
   inorganic chemicals, 516-522
   iron, 537
   lead, 519
   MCLs, 513, 516-534
   maximum contaminant levels, 513, 516-534
   membrane filter, 524
   mercury, 521
   microbiological contaminants, 513, 518, 523-531
   monitoring, 520, 524, 530, 532, 533, 536
   multiple-tube fermentation, 524
   natural radioactivity, 533
   nitrate, 517, 521
   nontransient noncommunity water system, 515
   notification, 526, 543-551, 552
   odor, 538
   organic chemicals, 513, 517, 522
   pH, 538
   Primary Drinking Water Standards, 516-534
   radioactivity, 533
   radiological contaminants, 513, 514, 518, 583
   reporting procedures, 526, 542, 543-551
   required sampling, 520, 524, 525, 530, 533, 536, 540-542
   routine sampling, 540
   Safe Drinking Water Act, 540
   sampling points, 540
   sampling procedures, 540-542
   Secondary Drinking Water Regulations, 535-539
   selenium, 522
   setting standards, 512
   silver, 539
   solvents, 522
   sulfate, 514, 539
   total dissolved solids (TDS), 539
   treatment techniques, 516
   trihalomethanes, 129, 139, 531
   turbidity, 513, 515, 529
   zinc, 539
Regulatory agencies, safety, 614
Regulatory negotiation, 532
Rejection, mineral, 156, 157, 158
Repair shop, 269
Repair/replacement fund, 596
Replacement cost, 596
Report writing, 589-591
Reporting
   procedures, 526, 542, 543-551
   safety, 454, 455, 620

   waste disposal, 220
Representative sample, 131
Required sampling, 520, 524, 525, 530, 533, 536, 540-542
Requisition system, 595, 628, 629
Reservoirs, 6, 341
Resin, ion exchange, 11, 101, 104, 106, 135, 137
Respiratory protection, 425-427, 451
Responsibilities, manager, 568, 573
Responsibilities, safety, 416, 614
Retaliation, 586
Revenue bonds, 597
Reverse osmosis (RO)
   Also see Demineralization and Electrodialysis
   acid feed system, 174
   additional reading, 190
   alarms, 174
   arithmetic assignment, 190
   brine, 159, 174
   calculations, 156-164
   cartridge filters, 174
   chlorination, 174
   "Christmas Tree" arrangement, 164, 165, 174
   cleaning membrane, 178
   colloids, 173
   concentration polarization, 159
   definition, 152
   feed, 174
   flow diagram, 154, 175
   flux, 155, 156
   flux decline, 156
   hollow fine fiber, 169, 171, 173
   hydrolysis, 159, 163, 173
   layout, 165, 168
   log sheet, 176, 177
   membrane, 152, 155, 156, 169, 172, 178
   microbial organisms, 172, 173
   mineral rejection, 156, 157, 158
   monitoring, 172
   operation, 172-179
   osmosis, 152, 154
   permeate, 156, 169
   pH effects, 159, 163, 173, 174
   polyphosphate treatment, 173, 174
   pretreatment, 172
   pumps, 166
   recordkeeping, 174, 176, 177
   recovery, 159, 174
   rejection, mineral, 156, 157, 158
   safety, 179
   scalants, 173
   spiral wound, 169, 170
   suspended solids, 173
   temperature effects, 159, 162, 163, 173
   threshold treatment, 173
   troubleshooting, 178
   tubular, 169, 172
   turbidity, 173
   types of plants, 169
Right-To-Know (RTK) Laws, 432, 616
Rings, wearing, 274, 275
Rinse, ion exchange softening, 105, 106, 110
Rodenticide, 401
Rotameter, 378, 379, 383
Rotation of pump operation, 303
Rotor, 251
Route, sampling, 542
Routine sampling, 520, 524, 540
Rules
   coliform, 523-527

Rules (continued)
  copper, 519
  lead, 519
  surface water treatment, 528-531

S

SCADA (Supervisory Control and Data Acquisition) systems
  communications, 601
  description, 600
  distribution systems, 601-603
  treatment plants, 601-603
SDWA (Safe Drinking Water Act), 512, 514, 539, 542
SRF (State Revolving Fund), 597
SWTR (Surface Water Treatment Rule), 528-531
Safe Drinking Water Act (SDWA), 512, 514, 539, 542
Safe Drinking Water Regulations
  sampling points, 540
  schedule, 540
Safety
  accident
    causes, 416, 614
    prevention, 416, 443
    reports, 454, 455, 620, 622, 623
  acetic acid (glacial), 417
  acids, 417
  activated carbon, 430
  additional reading, 456
  alum, 428
  aluminum sulfate, 428
  ammonia, 421
  atmospheres, explosive, 451
  autoclaves, 450
  bases, 421
  biological considerations, 450
  booster shots, 450
  calcium hydroxide, 422
  carbon dioxide, 426
  caustic soda, 422
  chemical handling, 179, 417
  chemical storage drains, 432
  chemicals, laboratory, 449
  CHEMTREC (800) 424-9300, 454
  chlorine, 424
  CHLORINE MANUAL, 426
  classification, fires, 433
  cleaning, 436
  confined spaces, 371, 437-440, 617, 621
  control panels, 447
  costs, 625
  cranes, 436
  current, 446, 447
  dangerous air, 437
  definition, 416
  drains, 432
  drowning, 453
  education, 620
  electrical equipment, 179, 238, 240, 267, 446
  electrodialysis, 189
  emergencies, 454, 616
  equipment, laboratory, 450
  exits, 435
  explosive atmospheres, 451
  extinguishers, fire, 433-435
  eye protection, 452
  falls, injury, 371
  ferric chloride, 429
  ferric sulfate, 429
  ferrous sulfate, 429

  fire protection, 433
  first aid, 58, 616
  flammable storage, 435
  fluoridation, 57
  fluoride compounds, 429
  foot protection, 452
  forklifts, 444, 445
  fueling vehicles, 443
  gas masks, 425-427
  gas-detection equipment, 437
  gases, 424
  glassware, 449
  gloves, 452
  ground fault interrupter, 447
  hand protection, 452
  handling chemicals, 417
  hard hat, 453
  hazard communication program, 616
  hazardous gases, 424, 437
  hazards, laboratory, 449-451
  hazards, maintenance, 436
  head protection, 453
  hot plates, 450
  human factors, 626
  hydrated lime, 422
  hydraulic equipment, 179
  hydrochloric acid, 420
  hydrofluosilicic acid, 418
  hydrogen fluoride, 420
  hypochlorite, 423
  immunization, 450
  injury, falls, 371
  injury frequency rate, 625
  injury severity rate, 626
  instrumentation, 368, 447
  laboratory, 449-451
  lime-soda ash softening, 90, 92
  lockout/tagout procedure, 238, 447, 448
  maintenance, 436-441, 446
  manholes, 438
  Material Safety Data Sheet (MSDS), 617-619
  measuring, 625
  motors, 447
  muriatic acid, 420
  National Safety Council, 624
  nitric acid, 420
  noise, 440
  OSHA, 616, 617
  officer, 620
  olfactory fatigue, 418
  operator, 416, 450, 451-454, 616
  oxygen deficiency, 437
  painting, 436
  panels, control, 447
  permit, confined space, 439, 617, 621
  permit-required confined space, 438
  pipet washers, 450
  plant maintenance, 436
  policy statement, 448, 614, 615
  potassium permanganate, 430
  powdered activated carbon, 430
  powders, 430, 431
  power tools, 440
  program, 614-627
  quicklime, 84, 92, 422
  radioactivity, 450
  regulatory agencies, 614
  reporting, 454, 455, 620, 622, 623
  respiratory protection, 425-427, 451

Safety (continued)
  responsibilities, 416, 614
  reverse osmosis, 179
  safety check, vehicles, 441, 442
  safety shower, 418, 419, 420
  salts, 428
  seat belts, 443
  self-contained breathing apparatus, 425-427, 451
  shots, booster, 450
  shower, safety, 418, 419, 420
  sodium aluminate, 429
  sodium carbonate, 423
  sodium hydroxide, 422
  sodium silicate, 423
  softening, 90, 92
  standard operating procedures (SOPs), 438, 447, 448, 616
  starters, 446
  statistics, 625
  sterilizers, 450
  stills, water, 450
  storage, chemicals, 432
  storage, flammables, 435
  sulfur dioxide, 426
  sulfuric acid, 420
  supervisors, 614, 615, 622, 624
  tailgate training, 417, 624
  tools, power, 440
  traffic, 443
  training, 578, 620
  transformers, 446
  underwater inspection, 454
  unsafe acts, 616
  valves, 441
  vehicles, 441
  voltage, 446
  water, 453
  water stills, 450
  welding, 441
  Worker Right-To-Know (RTK) Laws, 616
Safety check, vehicles, 441, 442
Safety equipment
  fluoridation, 48, 57
  operator protection, 416, 450, 451-454, 616
  shower, 418, 419, 420
Safety shower, 418, 419, 420
Salinity, 152
Salt solution characteristics, 12
Salts
  handling, 428
  safety, 428
Sampling
  coliform, 524
  iron and manganese, 7
  lead and copper, 520
  points, 540
  procedures, 540-542
  trihalomethanes, 131
Sampling procedures
  check sampling, 540
  collection, 520, 540-542
  frequency, 520, 524-526, 529, 530, 533, 536, 540-542
  how often, 520, 524-526, 529, 530, 533, 536, 540-542
  initial sampling, 540
  lead and copper, 520
  location, 540, 542
  number of samples, coliform, 524
  plan, 524
  required sampling, 520, 524, 540, 541
  route, 542

routine sampling, 540
Sand drying beds, 208, 210, 211, 218
Sand filter, 218
Sanitary defects
  brine storage tanks, 109
  fluoridation, 57
Sanitary landfills, 204, 213, 218, 219
Sanitary survey, 524, 552
Saturators, fluoridation, 40, 41, 42, 57
Scaling
  electrodialysis, 181, 187
  reverse osmosis, 172, 173
Schedule
  compliance, 514
  SDWA, 514
  sampling, 542
Screw flow pumps, 278, 280
Scroll centrifuge, 213, 214
Seal, pump, 275
Seat belts, 443
Seats, valves, 311
Seawater, 152
Secondary Drinking Water Regulations
  aluminum, 536
  chloride, 536
  color, 536
  copper, 536
  enforcement, 535
  fluoride, 537
  foaming agents, 537
  hydrogen sulfide, 538
  iron, 537
  iron and manganese, 537
  manganese, 537
  maximum contaminant levels (MCLs), 535
  monitoring, 536
  odor, 538
  pH, 538
  silver, 539
  sulfate, 514, 539
  total dissolved solids (TDS), 539
  zinc, 539
Selection, employees, 575
Selenium, 522
Self-contained breathing apparatus, 425-427, 451
Sensors, instrumentation, 371
Septic wastes, 220
Service, ion exchange softeners, 104, 105, 109
Service line replacement, 521
Service meters, 379
Service record card, 236, 237
Set point, 368
Sewers, 213, 218
Sexual harassment, 583, 584
Shaft, pump, 271, 273, 278, 279
Shear pin, 292, 300
Shop steward, 587
Shots, booster, 450
Shower, safety, 418, 419, 420
Shutdown
  chemical feeders, 54
  fluoridation, 54
  instrumentation, 401
  ion exchange softeners, 110
  pumps, 289, 302, 304
Signal transmitters, 383, 600
Silver, 539
Slake, 84, 92
Sleeves, pump, 271, 273, 278, 279

Sludge pumps, 220
Sludge, softening, 93
Sludge volumes, 202
Snubber, 372, 374
Sodium
  aluminate, 429
  carbonate, 423
  fluoride, 32, 33, 41
  hydroxide, 422
  silicate, 423
  silicofluoride, 32, 33, 52
Softening
  Also see Ion exchange softening and Lime-soda ash soft-
    ening
  additional reading, 116
  alkalinity, 79, 81, 91
  arithmetic assignment, 116
  basic methods, 83
  benefits, 79, 83
  calcium carbonate equivalent, 79, 80
  carbonate hardness, 78, 84
  chemical reactions, 84-87
  chemistry, 80
  hard water, 78
  hardness, 78, 83, 85
  importance, 79
  ion exchange softening, 101
  jar tests, 94-98
  Langelier Index, 81
  lime-soda ash softening, 83, 88
  limitations, 79, 83
  need, 79
  noncarbonate hardness, 84, 85
  permanent hardness, 84
  pH, 81, 82
  recordkeeping, 93
  safety, 90, 92
  sludge, 93
  stability, 81, 85, 91
  temporary hardness, 84
  total hardness, 78
  zeolite, 101
Softening membrane, RO, 159
Solar lagoons, 204, 205, 208
Solid chemical feeders, 337
Solution feeders, 33, 40
Solution preparation, fluoridation, 48
Solvents, 522
Special assessment bonds, 597
Specific conductance test procedures, 489
Specification review
  electrodialysis, 187
  fluoridation, 47
Spectrophotometer
  absorbance, 466
  calibration, 466
  description, 466
  iron and manganese analysis, 7
  percent transmittance, 466
  standards, 467
  transmittance, 466
  units, 466
Spiral wound membrane, 169, 170
Split treatment
  ion exchange softening, 114
  lime-soda ash softening, 87-90
Stability, water, 81, 85, 91
Stack, electrodialysis, 181, 183, 187

Staffing
  advertising positions, 575
  applications, job, 575
  certification, 578
  compensation, 575, 578
  disciplinary problems, 582
  employee orientation, 578
  employee problems, 582, 587
  employee-management relationship, 587
  employees, 573
  employer policies, 578, 584
  evaluation, performance, 579-581
  grievances, 582, 587
  groups, protected, 575
  harassment, 583, 584
  hiring procedures, 573-578
  interview questions, 576
  interviewing, 575
  manager's responsibilities, 568, 573
  National Labor Relations Act, 587
  new employee orientation, 578
  number of employees, 573
  orientation, new employees, 578
  paper screening, 575
  performance evaluation, 579-581
  personnel records, 587
  policies, employer, 578, 584
  probationary period, 578
  problem employees, 582
  profile, qualifications, 574
  protected groups, 575
  qualifications profile, 574
  retaliation, 586
  selection process, 575
  sexual harassment, 583, 584
  training, 578
  unions, 587
Stages, electrodialysis, 181
Standard deviation, 495
Standard operating procedures (SOPs), 437, 438, 447, 448,
  616
Standardization, instrumentation, 366
Standards, drinking water, 512, 535
Standby engines, 336
Standby power generation, 256, 264
Starters, electrical, 251, 446
Start-up
  chemical feeders, 47
  engines, 327, 328, 332
  fluoridation, 47
  instrumentation, 401
  ion exchange softeners, 110
  pumps, 302-306
State Revolving Fund (SRF), 597
Stator, 251
Steel tanks, 341
Sterilizers, 450
Stethoscope, 294
Steward, shop, 587
Stills, water, 450
Storage of
  chemicals, 336, 432
  flammables, 435
  fuel, 335
  lime, 90
Strip chart, 387, 389, 390, 398, 400, 402
Stuffing boxes, pumps, 275
Suction, pumps, 273, 274, 276

Sulfate
  regulations, 514, 539
  test procedures, 490
Sulfur dioxide, 426
Sulfuric acid, 420
Supernatant, 208
Supersaturated, 84
Supervision, 579
Supervisors, safety, 614, 615, 622, 624
Surface Water Treatment Rule (SWTR), 528-531
Surfactant, 537
Surge protection, 372, 374
Switch gear, electrical, 250, 266
Switches, electrical, 241, 243
Symbols, instrumentation, 361-364
Synthetic organic chemicals, 522
Synthetic resins, 135, 137

T

TCE (trichloroethylene), 522
TON (Threshold Odor Number), 492-496, 538
Tag, warning, 239, 286
Tagout/lockout procedure, 238, 447, 448
Tailgate training, 417, 624
Tanks
  draining and cleaning, 203, 206, 207
  steel, maintenance, 341
Target audience, 589, 590, 592
Taste rating scale, 494
Tastes and odors
  iron and manganese, 6
  test procedures, 492
Teeth, mottling and cavities, 32, 519, 537
Telemetering, instrumentation, 383, 393, 396, 600
Telephone contacts, 593
Television, 552, 592
Temperature effects
  electrodialysis, 187
  process wastes, 202
  reverse osmosis, 159, 162, 163, 173
  THM formation, 133
Temporary hardness, 84
Test procedures
  See Laboratory test procedures
Testers, electrical, 243
Testing, instrumentation, 397
Testing ion exchange softeners, 107
Thallium, 522
Thermal overloads, 250
Thickening wastes, 203, 204
Thin film composite membrane, 155
Threshold Odor Number (TON), 492-496, 538
Threshold treatment, 173
Tier 1 and 2 violations, 526, 552
Titrate, 80
Tools, power, 440
Total Coliform Rule, 523-527
Total dissolved solids (TDS), 152, 153, 497, 539
Total flow, instrumentation, 390
Total hardness, 78
Total trihalomethanes, 129, 131, 133, 139, 531
Totalizers, instrumentation, 390
Tours, plant, 593
Toxicity, 611
Traffic, 443

Training
  administration, 578
  fluoridation, 58
  safety, 578, 620
Transducers, 380, 383
Transformers, 241, 247, 251, 266, 446
Transient noncommunity water system, 516
Transmission, electrical, 266
Transmitters, 371, 380, 383
"Traveler's" diarrhea, 523
Treatment charts, fluoridation, 48-50
Treatment, emergency, 612, 613
Treatment techniques, 516
1,1,1-Trichloroethane, 522
Trichloroethylene (TCE), 522
Trihalomethanes
  activated carbon, 135, 137, 139
  additional reading, 131, 140
  adsorption, 135, 137
  aeration, 135-137, 139
  arithmetic assignment, 140
  bench-scale studies, 135, 139, 140
  bromide, 129, 133, 134
  calculations, 132
  chemical reactions, 129, 133
  chloramines, 138, 139
  chlorine, 129, 134, 137, 139
  coagulation/sedimentation/filtration, 134, 137
  control strategies, 131, 134, 138
  disinfection alternatives, 138
  existing treatment processes, 134
  feasibility analysis process, 131
  FEDERAL REGISTER, 129, 131, 139
  formation, 129, 133, 134, 137
  formulas, 132, 673, 684
  Group 1 and 2 treatment techniques, 139
  health effects, 129
  ion exchange resins, 135, 137
  maximum contaminant level (MCL), 129, 139, 531
  monitoring, 129, 133, 138
  options for control, 134
  oxidation, 135, 137
  ozone, 135, 137, 138, 139
  pH, THM formation, 133
  potassium permanganate, 134, 137, 139
  precursors, THM, 129, 133, 134, 137
  problem, 129, 131
  regulations, 129, 139, 531
  resins, synthetic, 135, 137
  sampling, 131
  sources of water, 134
  synthetic resins, 135, 137
  temperature, THM formation, 133
  test procedures, 496
  total trihalomethanes, TTHMs, 129, 131, 133, 139
  ultraviolet light, 135, 137
  variance, 139
Troubleshooting
  electrical equipment, 256, 257-261
  engines, 327, 332
  instrumentation, 398-401
  ion exchange softeners, 109
  iron and manganese, 19, 20, 21
  pumps, 303
  reverse osmosis, 178
Tubular membranes, 169, 172

Turbidimeter, 383, 384, 397
Turbidity regulations, 513, 515, 518, 529, 545, 546

U

Ultrasonic flow measurement, 379
Ultraviolet light, 135, 137
Unaccounted for water, 569
Unbalanced current, 245-248
Underfeeding, fluoridation, 54
Underwater inspection, 454
Unions, 587
Unity of command, 570
Unloader, compressor, 308
Unregulated contaminants, 514, 515
Unsafe acts, 616
Upflow saturators, 41, 42, 44
Uranium, 514, 533
User fees, 594, 595
Utility management, 568

V

VOCs (Volatile organic chemicals), 517, 522
V-O-M (volt-ohm-milliammeter), 398, 399
Vacuum breakers, 608, 609
Vacuum filters, 204, 213, 217
Vacuum tank truck, 207, 208, 218
Valves
   automatic, 325
   butterfly, 312, 315
   check, 289, 293, 316-325
   compressor, 309
   diaphragm-operated, 325, 326
   eccentric, 312-314
   foot, 289, 316
   gate, 309, 310, 311
   globe, 312, 323, 325, 326
   lubrication, 311
   maintenance, 309, 311, 312, 325
   operation, 309, 311
   packing, 311
   parts, 309
   safety, 441
   seats, 311
   types, 317
   use, 309, 316
   wafer check valve, 316, 317, 322
Variable speed belt drives, 298
Variance and exemptions, 139, 552
Variance, THM, 139
Vaults, instrumentation, 371
Vehicles
   accident prevention, 443
   forklifts, 444, 445
   fueling, 443
   maintenance, 441

   operation, 441-444
   safety check, 441, 442
   seat belts, 443
   types, 441
Velocity sensing flow measurement, 379, 380
Venturi, 381, 382
Vertical centrifugal pumps, 277
Vinyl chloride, 522
Violations, tier 1 and 2, 552
Violence, 582
Viscosity, 283
Volatile, 135
Volatile organic chemicals (VOCs), 517, 522
Voltage testing, 243, 245, 446
Volt-ohm-milliammeter (V-O-M), 398, 399
Volts, 241, 243, 266
Volumes of sludges, 202
Volumetric feeders, 34, 37, 38, 40
Vulnerability assessment, 608

W

Wafer check valve, 316, 317, 322
Warning tag, 239, 286
Wastewater collection system, 213, 218
Water
   conservation, 592
   cooled engines, 332
   hammer, 304
   Pollution Control Act, 201
   rates, 596
   safety, 453
   stills, 450
Watts, 242
Wearing rings, pumps, 274, 275
Welding, 441
Wilson's disease, 519
Winklepress, 212
Worker Right-To-Know (RTK) Laws, 432, 616
Working conditions, 575
Written communication, 589-591

X

(NO LISTINGS)

Y

(NO LISTINGS)

Z

Zeolite
   iron and manganese, 13
   softening, 101
Zinc, 539

NOTES

NOTES

NOTES